Periodic Table of the Elements

Metals (main-group)
Metals (transition)
Metals (inner transition)
Metalloids
Nonmetals

MAIN–GROUP ELEMENTS (1A–2A; 3A–8A) — TRANSITION ELEMENTS (3B–2B)

Period	1A (1)	2A (2)	3B (3)	4B (4)	5B (5)	6B (6)	7B (7)	8B (8)	8B (9)	8B (10)	1B (11)	2B (12)	3A (13)	4A (14)	5A (15)	6A (16)	7A (17)	8A (18)
1	1 **H** 1.008																	2 **He** 4.003
2	3 **Li** 6.941	4 **Be** 9.012											5 **B** 10.81	6 **C** 12.01	7 **N** 14.01	8 **O** 16.00	9 **F** 19.00	10 **Ne** 20.18
3	11 **Na** 22.99	12 **Mg** 24.31											13 **Al** 26.98	14 **Si** 28.09	15 **P** 30.97	16 **S** 32.07	17 **Cl** 35.45	18 **Ar** 39.95
4	19 **K** 39.10	20 **Ca** 40.08	21 **Sc** 44.96	22 **Ti** 47.88	23 **V** 50.94	24 **Cr** 52.00	25 **Mn** 54.94	26 **Fe** 55.85	27 **Co** 58.93	28 **Ni** 58.69	29 **Cu** 63.55	30 **Zn** 65.41	31 **Ga** 69.72	32 **Ge** 72.61	33 **As** 74.92	34 **Se** 78.96	35 **Br** 79.90	36 **Kr** 83.80
5	37 **Rb** 85.47	38 **Sr** 87.62	39 **Y** 88.91	40 **Zr** 91.22	41 **Nb** 92.91	42 **Mo** 95.94	43 **Tc** (98)	44 **Ru** 101.1	45 **Rh** 102.9	46 **Pd** 106.4	47 **Ag** 107.9	48 **Cd** 112.4	49 **In** 114.8	50 **Sn** 118.7	51 **Sb** 121.8	52 **Te** 127.6	53 **I** 126.9	54 **Xe** 131.3
6	55 **Cs** 132.9	56 **Ba** 137.3	57 **La** 138.9	72 **Hf** 178.5	73 **Ta** 180.9	74 **W** 183.9	75 **Re** 186.2	76 **Os** 190.2	77 **Ir** 192.2	78 **Pt** 195.1	79 **Au** 197.0	80 **Hg** 200.6	81 **Tl** 204.4	82 **Pb** 207.2	83 **Bi** 209.0	84 **Po** (209)	85 **At** (210)	86 **Rn** (222)
7	87 **Fr** (223)	88 **Ra** (226)	89 **Ac** (227)	104 **Rf** (263)	105 **Db** (262)	106 **Sg** (266)	107 **Bh** (267)	108 **Hs** (277)	109 **Mt** (268)	110 **Ds** (281)	111 **Rg** (272)	112 **Cn** (285)	113 (284)	114 (289)	115 (288)	116 (292)		118 (294)

As of late 2010, elements 113 through 116 and 118 had not been named.

INNER TRANSITION ELEMENTS

6	Lanthanides	58 **Ce** 140.1	59 **Pr** 140.9	60 **Nd** 144.2	61 **Pm** (145)	62 **Sm** 150.4	63 **Eu** 152.0	64 **Gd** 157.3	65 **Tb** 158.9	66 **Dy** 162.5	67 **Ho** 164.9	68 **Er** 167.3	69 **Tm** 168.9	70 **Yb** 173.0	71 **Lu** 175.0
7	Actinides	90 **Th** 232.0	91 **Pa** (231)	92 **U** 238.0	93 **Np** (237)	94 **Pu** (242)	95 **Am** (243)	96 **Cm** (247)	97 **Bk** (247)	98 **Cf** (251)	99 **Es** (252)	100 **Fm** (257)	101 **Md** (258)	102 **No** (259)	103 **Lr** (260)

The Elements

Name	Symbol	Atomic Number	Atomic Mass*
Actinium	Ac	89	(227)
Aluminum	Al	13	26.98
Americium	Am	95	(243)
Antimony	Sb	51	121.8
Argon	Ar	18	39.95
Arsenic	As	33	74.92
Astatine	At	85	(210)
Barium	Ba	56	137.3
Berkelium	Bk	97	(247)
Beryllium	Be	4	9.012
Bismuth	Bi	83	209.0
Bohrium	Bh	107	(267)
Boron	B	5	10.81
Bromine	Br	35	79.90
Cadmium	Cd	48	112.4
Calcium	Ca	20	40.08
Californium	Cf	98	(249)
Carbon	C	6	12.01
Cerium	Ce	58	140.1
Cesium	Cs	55	132.9
Chlorine	Cl	17	35.45
Chromium	Cr	24	52.00
Cobalt	Co	27	58.93
Copernicium	Cn	112	(285)
Copper	Cu	29	63.55
Curium	Cm	96	(247)
Darmstadtium	Ds	110	(281)
Dubnium	Db	105	(262)
Dysprosium	Dy	66	162.5
Einsteinium	Es	99	(254)
Erbium	Er	68	167.3
Europium	Eu	63	152.0
Fermium	Fm	100	(253)
Fluorine	F	9	19.00
Francium	Fr	87	(223)
Gadolinium	Gd	64	157.3
Gallium	Ga	31	69.72
Germanium	Ge	32	72.61
Gold	Au	79	197.0
Hafnium	Hf	72	178.5
Hassium	Hs	108	(277)
Helium	He	2	4.003
Holmium	Ho	67	164.9
Hydrogen	H	1	1.008
Indium	In	49	114.8
Iodine	I	53	126.9
Iridium	Ir	77	192.2
Iron	Fe	26	55.85
Krypton	Kr	36	83.80
Lanthanum	La	57	138.9
Lawrencium	Lr	103	(257)
Lead	Pb	82	207.2
Lithium	Li	3	6.941
Lutetium	Lu	71	175.0
Magnesium	Mg	12	24.31
Manganese	Mn	25	54.94
Meitnerium	Mt	109	(268)
Mendelevium	Md	101	(256)

Name	Symbol	Atomic Number	Atomic Mass*
Mercury	Hg	80	200.6
Molybdenum	Mo	42	95.94
Neodymium	Nd	60	144.2
Neon	Ne	10	20.18
Neptunium	Np	93	(244)
Nickel	Ni	28	58.70
Niobium	Nb	41	92.91
Nitrogen	N	7	14.01
Nobelium	No	102	(253)
Osmium	Os	76	190.2
Oxygen	O	8	16.00
Palladium	Pd	46	106.4
Phosphorus	P	15	30.97
Platinum	Pt	78	195.1
Plutonium	Pu	94	(242)
Polonium	Po	84	(209)
Potassium	K	19	39.10
Praseodymium	Pr	59	140.9
Promethium	Pm	61	(145)
Protactinium	Pa	91	(231)
Radium	Ra	88	(226)
Radon	Rn	86	(222)
Rhenium	Re	75	186.2
Rhodium	Rh	45	102.9
Roentgenium	Rg	111	(272)
Rubidium	Rb	37	85.47
Ruthenium	Ru	44	101.1
Rutherfordium	Rf	104	(263)
Samarium	Sm	62	150.4
Scandium	Sc	21	44.96
Seaborgium	Sg	106	(266)
Selenium	Se	34	78.96
Silicon	Si	14	28.09
Silver	Ag	47	107.9
Sodium	Na	11	22.99
Strontium	Sr	38	87.62
Sulfur	S	16	32.07
Tantalum	Ta	73	180.9
Technetium	Tc	43	(98)
Tellurium	Te	52	127.6
Terbium	Tb	65	158.9
Thallium	Tl	81	204.4
Thorium	Th	90	232.0
Thulium	Tm	69	168.9
Tin	Sn	50	118.7
Titanium	Ti	22	47.88
Tungsten	W	74	183.9
Uranium	U	92	238.0
Vanadium	V	23	50.94
Xenon	Xe	54	131.3
Ytterbium	Yb	70	173.0
Yttrium	Y	39	88.91
Zinc	Zn	30	65.41
Zirconium	Zr	40	91.22
		113**	(284)
		114	(289)
		115	(288)
		116	(292)
		118	(294)

*All atomic masses are given to four significant figures. Values in parentheses represent the mass number of the most stable isotope.

**The names and symbols for elements 113 through 116 and 118 have not yet been chosen.

SELECTED MATERIALS FROM

CHEMISTRY

The Molecular Nature of Matter and Change

SIXTH EDITION

MARTIN S. SILBERBERG

CHEMISTRY 121
WORCESTER STATE COLLEGE
CHEMISTRY 2

McGraw Hill Learning Solutions

Boston Burr Ridge, IL Dubuque, IA New York San Francisco St. Louis
Bangkok Bogotá Caracas Lisbon London Madrid
Mexico City Milan New Delhi Seoul Singapore Sydney Taipei Toronto

Selected Materials from
Chemistry: The Molecular Nature of Matter and Change, Sixth Edition
Chemistry 121
Worcester State College
Chemistry 2

This book is a McGraw-Hill Learning Solutions textbook and contains select material from *Chemistry: The Molecular Nature of Matter and Change*, Sixth Edition by Martin S. Silberberg. Copyright © 2012 by The McGraw-Hill Companies, Inc. Reprinted with permission of the publisher. Many custom published texts are modified versions or adaptations of our best-selling textbooks. Some adaptations are printed in black and white to keep prices at a minimum, while others are in color.

1 2 3 4 5 6 7 8 9 0 DIG DIG 13 12 11

ISBN-13: 978-0-07-755697-6
ISBN-10: 0-07-755697-6

Learning Solutions Specialist: Stephen Tomecek
Production Editor: Jolynn Kilburg
Printer/Binder: Digital Impressions

To Ruth and Daniel, with all my love,
and
In Memory of my Mother,
Gert Mazur,
Whose unfailing belief in me, I have finally come to realize,
has been a driving force in my life.

BRIEF CONTENTS

DETAILED CONTENTS

CHAPTER 11 • Theories of Covalent Bonding 394

CHAPTER 5 • Gases and the Kinetic-Molecular Theory 180

CHAPTER 12 • Intermolecular Forces: Liquids, Solids, and Phase Changes 418

CHAPTER 13 • The Properties of Mixtures: Solutions and Colloids 476

CHAPTER 16 • Kinetics: Rates and Mechanisms of Chemical Reactions 626

CHAPTER 17 • Equilibrium: The Extent of Chemical Reactions 676

CHAPTER 18 • Acid-Base Equilibria 718

CHAPTER 19 • Ionic Equilibria in Aqueous Systems 764

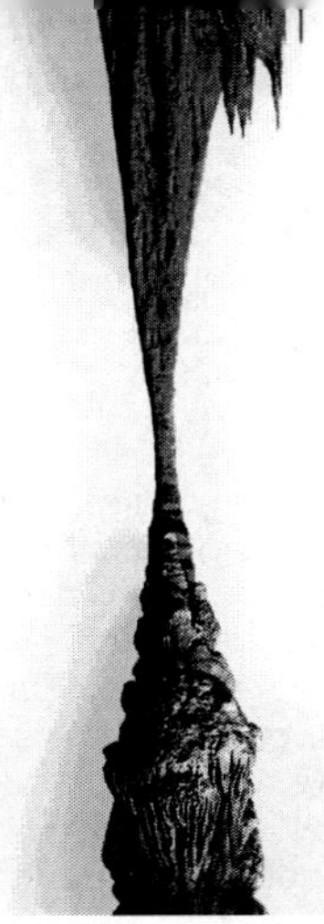

LIST OF SAMPLE PROBLEMS (Molecular-scene problems are shown in color.)

About the Author

Martin S. Silberberg received a B.S. in Chemistry from the City University of New York and a Ph.D. in Chemistry from the University of Oklahoma. He then accepted a position as research associate in analytical biochemistry at the Albert Einstein College of Medicine in New York City, where he developed methods to study neurotransmitter metabolism in Parkinson's disease and other neurological disorders. Following six years as research associate, Dr. Silberberg joined the faculty of Bard College at Simon's Rock, a liberal arts college known for its excellence in teaching small classes of highly motivated students. As head of the Natural Sciences Major and Director of Premedical Studies, he taught courses in general chemistry, organic chemistry, biochemistry, and liberal-arts chemistry. The small class size and close student contact afforded him insights into how students learn chemistry, where they have difficulties, and what strategies can help them succeed. Dr. Silberberg decided to apply these insights in a broader context and established a textbook writing, editing, and consulting company. Before writing his own texts, he worked as a consulting and development editor on chemistry, biochemistry, and physics texts for several major college publishers. He resides with his wife Ruth and son in the Pioneer Valley near Amherst, Massachusetts, where he enjoys the rich cultural and academic life of the area and relaxes by cooking and singing.

Preface

At the core of natural science, chemistry is so crucial to an understanding of medicine, molecular biology, genetics, pharmacology, ecology, atmospheric science, engineering, nuclear studies, materials science, and many other fields that it has become a central requirement for an increasing number of academic majors. Furthermore, chemical principles are at the core of many key societal issues, including climate change, energy options, materials recycling, diet and nutrition, and medicine and disease. Clearly, the study of chemistry plays an essential role in our world.

WHAT SETS THIS BOOK APART

For five editions, *Chemistry: The Molecular Nature of Matter and Change* has been recognized for setting the standard among general chemistry textbooks. This sixth edition maintains that unparalleled reputation by keeping pace with the evolution of student learning. The text still contains the most accurate macroscopic-to-molecular illustrations, consistent step-by-step worked problems, and an extensive collection of end-of-chapter problems, with a wide range of difficulties and applications targeting student interests in engineering, medicine, materials, and environmental studies. Changes throughout the text have made it more succinct, the artwork more teachable and modern, and the design more open and inviting. And, while the content has certainly been updated to reflect chemistry's growing impact in the world, the mechanisms of the text—the teaching approaches that are so admired and emulated—have remained the same. Three hallmarks make this text a market leader.

Visualizing Chemical Models—Macroscopic to Molecular

Chemistry deals with observable changes caused by unobservable atomic-scale events, requiring an understanding of a size gap of mind-boggling proportions. One of the text's goals coincides with that of so many instructors: to help the student visualize chemical events on the molecular scale. Thus, concepts are explained first at the macroscopic level and then from a molecular point of view, with the text's groundbreaking illustrations always placed next to the discussion to bring the point home for today's visually oriented students.

Thinking Logically to Solve Problems

The problem-solving approach, based on the four-step method widely accepted by experts in chemical education, is introduced in Chapter 1 and employed *consistently* throughout the text. It encourages students to *plan* a logical approach to a problem, and only then proceed to *solve* it. Each sample problem includes a *check,* which fosters the habit of "taking a breath" to assess the reasonableness and magnitude of the answer. Finally, for *practice* and reinforcement, each sample problem is followed immediately by a similar follow-up problem, for which an abbreviated solution, not merely a numerical answer, is given at the end of the chapter. In this edition, solving problems and visualizing models have been married through an increasing number of molecular-scene problems in both worked examples and homework sets.

Applying Ideas to the Real World

An understanding of modern chemistry influences attitudes about climate change and health care, while also explaining the spring in a running shoe and the display of a laptop screen. Today's students may enter one of the emerging chemistry-related hybrid fields—biomaterials science or planetary geochemistry, for example—and their text should point out the relevance of chemical concepts to such career directions. The *Chemical Connections* and *Tools of the Laboratory* boxed essays (which now include problems to reinforce learning), the fewer but more pedagogic margin notes, and the many applications woven into the chapter content are up-to-date, student-friendly features that complement the text content.

REFINING THE STANDARD: AN EVOLVING LEARNING SYSTEM

Just as the field of chemistry is addressing major changes in the world, the student learning experience is changing as well—different math and reading preparation, less time for traditional studying, electronic media as part of daily lectures and homework, new challenges and options in career choices, and so on. To address these dynamic times, a modern general chemistry text supported by a suite of robust electronic tools for professor and student must continue to evolve, as this text has through all previous editions. From first to second edition, a major emphasis was placed on creating more molecular art to help students visualize chemistry at that level. The third edition incorporated many revised sample problems and a plethora of new end-of-chapter problems. The fourth edition gave birth to molecular-scene sample problems to help students understand concepts through simple molecular depictions. Molecular scenes became so popular that the fifth edition tripled the number of sample problems and doubled the number of end-of-chapter problems using them. During these revisions, major content improvements took place in limiting-reactant stoichiometry, green chemistry, biomolecular structure, kinetics and equilibrium, entropy and free energy, and nuclear chemistry, among many other areas.

With each edition, students and instructors alike have been involved in refining the text. Especially in preparation for the sixth edition, the author, together with key members of the editorial, sales, and marketing teams, consulted extensively with student and faculty users. From chapter reviews, focus groups, symposia, class tests, and one-on-one interviews with instructors, we were gratified to learn that everyone loved the pioneering, and still the most accurate, molecular art; the stepwise problem-solving approach, time-honored and consistent with decades of education research; the abundant mix of qualitative, basic quantitative, and applied end-of-chapter problems; and the thorough, student-friendly coverage of mainstream topics.

Based on this feedback, our revision for this edition focuses on "refining the standard" set earlier: distilling the writing to be concise and direct, opening up the overall appearance of pages, and improving illustrations by shortening legends and adding explanations into the art. We are delighted to introduce the sixth edition of *Chemistry: The Molecular Nature of Matter and Change,* which moves further toward perfecting content and approach in these ways:

Chapter openings, simplified. A familiar application and photo engage the student, followed by a bulleted list of main topics covered in the chapter.

Writing style and content presentation. Every line of every discussion has been revised to optimize clarity, readability, and a more direct presentation of ideas. The use of additional subheads, numbered (and titled) paragraphs, and bulleted (and titled) lists has eliminated long unbroken paragraphs. Main ideas are delineated and highlighted, making for more efficient study and lectures. As a result, the text is over 70 pages shorter, yet no key topics have been removed.

Problem-solving format. The much admired and duplicated four-part (plan, solution, check, practice) *Sample Problems* are displayed cleanly. Both data-based and molecular-scene problems occur throughout, and, to deepen understanding, most *Follow-Up Problems* have worked-out solutions at the back of each chapter, with a road map when appropriate, effectively doubling the number of worked problems. This edition has 15 more sample problems—many in the earlier chapters, where students need the most practice and confidence.

Art and figure legends. The innovative art that raised the bar in chemistry textbooks is still present, with many figures made more realistic and modern. Moreover, figure legends have been greatly shortened and their explanations added to neighboring text and the figures themselves for greater comprehension and less redundancy.

Page design and layout. A more open look invites the reader with cleaner margins and more white space, yet with the same attention to keeping text, figures, and tables near each other for easier viewing and studying.

Incorporating relevance. Applications make chemistry meaningful, so many exciting ideas from the margin notes and galleries of the fifth edition have been incorporated directly into the text, where they are more likely to be read. The boxed essays—*Chemical Connections* and *Tools of the Laboratory*—are more concise and are now accompanied by several homework problems to make them more useful for student and teacher.

Section Summaries. This universally approved feature is even easier to use in its new bulleted format.

Chapter review. Our unique *Chapter Review Guide* aids study by presenting concepts to understand and skills to master, key terms, key equations, and the multistep *Brief Solutions to Follow-Up Problems* (rather than simple numerical answers).

End-of-chapter problem sets. With an enhanced design to improve readability and traditional and molecular-scene problems updated and revised, these problem sets, more extensive than in most other texts, provide students and teachers with abundant choices in a wide range of difficulty and set in real-life scenarios.

Content Changes to Individual Chapters

- Chapter 2 presents a new figure and table on molecular modeling.
- Discussion of empirical formulas has been moved from Chapter 2 to Chapter 3 so it appears just before molecular formulas.
- Within Chapter 3, some sample problems have been segmented and seven new sample problems introduced to better focus problem-solving on distinct concepts.
- Chapter 3 contains more extensive use of stoichiometry reaction tables in limiting-reactant problems.
- Chapter 4 presents a new molecular-scene sample problem on depicting an ionic compound in aqueous solution.
- Chapter 5 includes a new subsection on how gas laws apply to breathing.
- Chapter 5 also contains new short discussions on the relevance of gas density.
- Also in Chapter 5, coverage of reaction stoichiometry has been more logically grouped with other rearrangements of the ideal gas law.
- Chapter 5 contains new illustrations of diffusion and origin of pressure.
- In Chapter 5, *Chemical Connections to Atmospheric Science* uses the gas laws to explain why the troposphere has a uniform composition.
- Chapter 7 includes a new sample problem on using the Rydberg equation.
- Chapter 8 contains a new subsection covering electron configuration, chemical reactivity, and redox behavior.

- In Chapter 9, *Tools of the Laboratory: Infrared Spectroscopy* contains a new discussion of carbon dioxide in global warming.
- Chapter 11 includes a new discussion of limitations to *d*-orbital hybridization.
- Chapter 12 presents new short discussions of everyday applications of surface tension, capillarity, and viscosity.
- Chapter 13 presents everyday applications of freezing point depression and osmotic pressure.
- The fifth edition's *Interchapter* has been deleted, but key figures have been placed in relevant locations within other chapters.
- Chapter 14 provides a thorough, focused survey of main-group descriptive chemistry.
- Chapter 15 contains new art for the molecular biology of protein synthesis and DNA replication.
- Chapter 16 incorporates two of the fifth edition's boxed features—on measuring reaction rates and on enzymes—into the chapter text.
- Chapter 17 makes consistent use of benchmarks for determining when an assumption is valid.
- Chapter 17 incorporates the fifth edition's boxed feature on ammonia production into the chapter text.
- Chapter 19 incorporates the fifth edition's boxed feature on cave formation into the chapter text.

Flexibility in Topic and Chapter Presentation

Chemistry: The Molecular Nature of Matter and Change has been revised to keep the mainstream topic sequence working optimally for teacher and student. But every course is unique, so flexibility has been built in: many section and subsection breaks allow topics to be rearranged with minimal loss of continuity. For example, redox balancing can be covered in Chapter 4, in Chapter 21, or, as done in the text, in both Chapter 4 (oxidation-number method) *and* Chapter 21 (half-reaction method, in preparation for electrochemistry). Likewise, several chapters can be taught in different orders. For instance, gases (Chapter 5) can be covered in sequence to explore the mathematical modeling of physical behavior or, with no loss of continuity, just before liquids and solids (Chapter 12) to show the effects of intermolecular forces on the three states of matter. In fact, feedback has indicated that many instructors move chapters, sections, and topics around, for example, covering descriptive chemistry (Chapter 14) and organic chemistry (Chapter 15) in the more traditional placement at the end of the course. Because the topic sequence is so flexible, any instructor can feel comfortable making such changes to suit his or her course.

KEEPING PACE WITH THE EVOLUTION OF STUDENT LEARNING

Many of us don't have the same cell phones, computers, or cars that we did just a few years ago—because technology is improving. In much the same way, the Silberberg Learning System has also been improving. The fifth edition of this text was accompanied by an online homework program called ARIS. Through careful observation of students and collaboration with instructors, the online homework tool has evolved into an online learning and engagement tool: **Connect:™ Chemistry.** The goal of Connect: Chemistry is to usher in a new era of meaningful online learning that balances the conceptual and quantitative aspect of this most vital discipline.

With this sixth edition, McGraw-Hill is offering students and instructors a greatly enhanced digital homework experience through Connect: Chemistry. Each problem formerly in the ARIS system has been carefully converted into the new program. Within Connect: Chemistry, each problem retains Silberberg's problem-solving methodology and is enhanced with specific hints, as well as feedback for common incorrect answers—all authored and accuracy-checked by teams of dedicated chemistry professors with many years of classroom experience. Several rounds of editorial revising and more expert checking, in addition to numerous instructor and student tests of all problems, ensure the accuracy and pedagogic soundness of all content.

In addition to the specific hints and feedback, many problems offer students the opportunity to engage in chemical drawing that can be assessed directly within their homework. To provide this important pedagogic experience, Connect: Chemistry has partnered with CambridgeSoft's® ChemDraw, widely considered the "gold standard" of scientific drawing programs and *the* cornerstone application for drawing and annotating molecules, reactions, and pathways. This collaboration of Connect: Chemistry and ChemDraw features an easy-to-use, intuitive, and comprehensive course management and homework system with professional-grade drawing capabilities.

THE SILBERBERG LEARNING SYSTEM

Many pedagogic tools are woven throughout the chapters to guide students on their learning journey.

Chapter Openers

Each chapter introduces a familiar application and photo relating to the main topic of the chapter, followed by a bulleted list of main topics. The chapter outline shows the sequence of topics and subtopics. At the top of the opposite page, *Concepts and Skills to Review* lists key material from earlier chapters that students should understand before starting to read the current one.

Three Major Classes of Chemical Reactions

4.1 **The Role of Water as a Solvent**
Polar Nature of Water
Ionic Compounds in Water
Covalent Compounds in Water

4.2 **Writing Equations for Aqueous Ionic Reactions**

4.3 **Precipitation Reactions**
The Key Event: Formation of a Solid
Predicting Whether a Precipitate Will Form

4.4 **Acid-Base Reactions**
The Key Event: Formation of Water
Proton Transfer in Acid-Base Reactions
Acid-Base Titrations

4.5 **Oxidation-Reduction (Redox) Reactions**
The Key Event: Movement of Electrons
Redox Terminology
Oxidation Numbers
Balancing Redox Equations
Redox Titrations

4.6 **Elements in Redox Reactions**
Combination Reactions
Decomposition Reactions
Displacement Reactions and Activity Series
Combustion Reactions

4.7 **The Reversibility of Reactions and the Equilibrium State**

Concepts and skills to review before you study this chapter

- names and formulas of compounds (Section 2.8)
- nature of ionic and covalent bonding (Section 2.7)
- amount-mass-number conversions (Section 3.1)
- molarity and amount-mass-number conversions in solution (Section 3.5)
- balancing chemical equations (Section 3.3)
- calculating quantities of reactants and products (Section 3.4)

4

Rapid chemical changes occur among gas molecules as sunlight bathes the atmosphere or lightning rips through a stormy sky and strikes the sea. Aqueous reactions occur unceasingly in the gigantic containers we know as oceans. And, in every cell of your body, thousands of reactions taking place right now enable you to function. Indeed, the amazing variety in nature is largely a consequence of the amazing variety of chemical reactions. With millions of reactions occurring in and around you, it would be impossible to describe them all. Fortunately, it isn't necessary because, when we survey even a small percentage of reactions, especially those in aqueous solution, a few major classes emerge.

IN THIS CHAPTER . . . We examine the underlying nature of three classes of reactions and the complex part that water plays in aqueous chemistry.

- We visualize the molecular structure of water to learn its role as solvent, how it interacts with ionic and covalent compounds, and the nature of electrolytes.
- We write ionic equations that represent the species in solution and the actual change that occurs when ionic compounds dissolve and react in water.
- We describe precipitation reactions and learn how to predict when they will occur.
- We see how acids and bases act as electrolytes and how they neutralize each other. We view acid-base reactions as proton-transfer processes and discuss how to quantify these reactions through titration.
- We examine oxidation-reduction (redox) reactions in the formation of ionic and covalent substances. We learn how to determine oxidation numbers and use them to balance redox equations and how to quantify these reactions through titration. We describe several important types of redox reactions, one of which is used to predict the relative reactivity of metals.
- An introduction to the reversible nature of all chemical change and the nature of equilibrium previews coverage of this central topic in later chapters.

4.1 • THE ROLE OF WATER AS A SOLVENT

For any reaction in solution, the solvent plays a key role that depends on its chemical nature. Some solvents passively disperse the substances into individual molecules. But water is much more active, interacting strongly with the substances and even reacting with them in some cases. Let's focus on how the water molecule interacts with both ionic and covalent solutes.

The Polar Nature of Water

On the atomic scale, water's great solvent power arises from the *uneven distribution of electron charge* and its *bent molecular shape*, which create a *polar molecule:*

1. *Uneven charge distribution.* Recall from Section 2.7 that the electrons in a covalent bond are shared between the atoms. In a bond between identical atoms—as in H_2, Cl_2, O_2—the sharing is equal and electron charge is distributed evenly between the two nuclei (symmetrical shading in the space-filling model of Figure 4.1A on the next page). In covalent bonds between different atoms, the sharing is uneven because one atom attracts the electron pair more strongly than the other atom does.

135

Problem Solving

A worked-out *Sample Problem* appears whenever an important new concept or skill is introduced. The problem-solving step helps students think through chemistry problems logically and systematically. The universally accepted four-step approach of plan, solve, check, and practice is used consistently for every sample problem in the text. The steps are:

- **Plan** analyzes the problem so that students can use what is known to find what is unknown. This step develops the habit of thinking through the solution before performing calculations. Most quantitative problems are accompanied in the margin by a *Road Map*, a block diagram that is specific to the problem and leads students visually through the planned steps.
- **Solution** presents the calculation steps *in the same order* as they appear in the plan and in the road map.
- **Check** fosters the habit of going over one's work with a rough calculation to make sure the answer is both chemically and mathematically reasonable—a great way to avoid careless errors. In many cases, this step is followed by a *Comment* that identifies an additional insight, alternative approach, or common mistake to avoid.
- **Follow-Up Problem** presents a similar problem to provide immediate practice, with an abbreviated multistep solution appearing at the end of the chapter. Where appropriate in the first several chapters, students are asked to draw their own road map to solve the follow-up problem.

Sample Problem 3.13 **Balancing an Equation from a Molecular Scene**

Problem The following molecular scenes depict an important reaction in nitrogen chemistry (nitrogen is blue; oxygen is red):

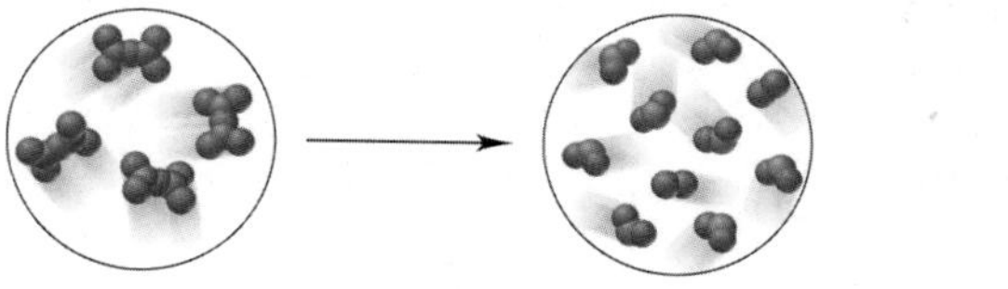

Write a balanced equation for this reaction.

Plan To write a balanced equation, we first have to determine the formulas of the molecules and obtain coefficients by counting the number of each molecule. Then, we arrange this information in the correct equation format, using the smallest whole-number coefficients and including states of matter.

Solution The reactant circle shows only one type of molecule. It has two N and five O atoms, so the formula is N_2O_5; there are four of these molecules. The product circle shows two different molecules, one with one N and two O atoms, and the other with two O atoms; there are eight NO_2 and two O_2. Thus, we have:

$$4N_2O_5 \longrightarrow 8NO_2 + 2O_2$$

Writing the balanced equation with the smallest whole-number coefficients and all substances as gases:

$$2N_2O_5(g) \longrightarrow 4NO_2(g) + O_2(g)$$

Check Reactant (4 N, 10 O) ⟶ products (4 N, 8 + 2 = 10 O)

Follow-Up Problem 3.13 Write a balanced equation for the important atmospheric reaction depicted below (carbon is black; oxygen is red):

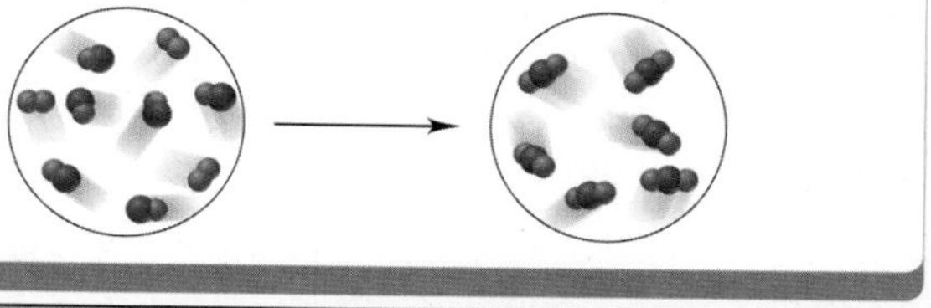

Three-Level Illustrations

As the art that set the standard for chemistry textbooks, these illustrations connect the macroscopic and molecular levels of reality with the symbolic level in the form of a chemical equation.

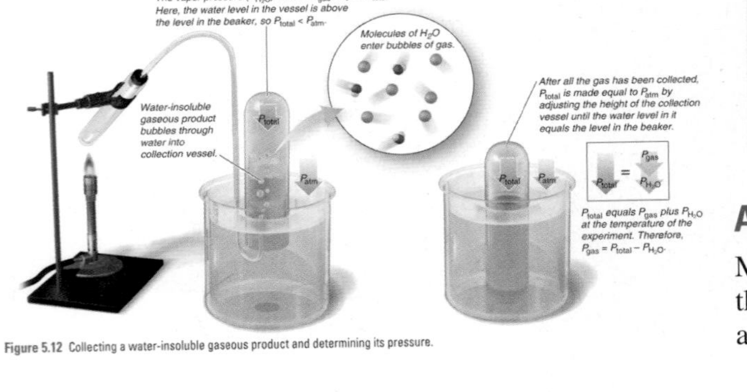

Figure 5.12 Collecting a water-insoluble gaseous product and determining its pressure.

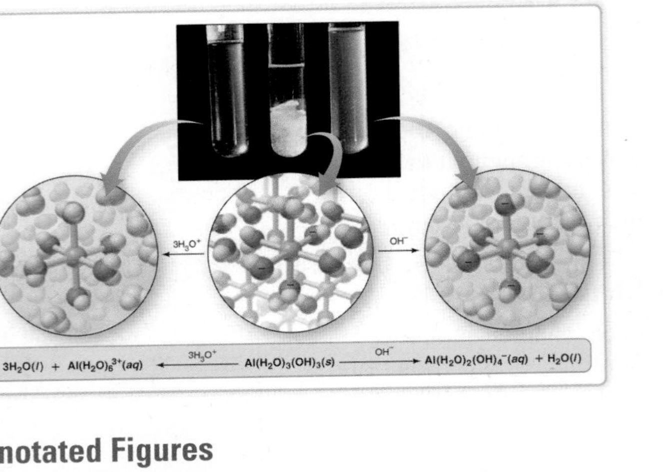

Annotated Figures

Modern, explanatory figures describe chemical processes through instructional labeling and realistic, three-dimensional art.

Optimized Presentation

Text paragraphs have been made more concise, with presentation of content optimized through the use of subheads, numbered paragraphs, and lists. Main ideas are delineated, resulting in a more student-friendly study format.

Converting Between Amount, Mass, and Number of Chemical Entities

One of the most common skills in the lab—and on exams—is converting between amount (mol), mass (g), and number of entities of a substance.

1. *Converting between amount and mass.* If you know the amount of a substance, you can find its mass, and vice versa. The molar mass ($\mathcal{M}$), which expresses the equivalence between 1 mole of a substance and its mass in grams, is the conversion factor.
   - *From amount (mol) to mass (g),* multiply by the molar mass:

$$\text{Mass (g)} = \text{amount (mol)} \times \frac{\text{no. of grams}}{\text{1 mol}} \quad (3.2)$$

   - *From mass (g) to amount (mol),* divide by the molar mass (multiply by $1/\mathcal{M}$):

$$\text{Amount (mol)} = \text{mass (g)} \times \frac{\text{1 mol}}{\text{no. of grams}} \quad (3.3)$$

2. *Converting between amount and number.* Similarly, if you know the amount (mol), you can find the number of entities, and vice versa. Avogadro's number, which expresses the equivalence between 1 mole of a substance and the number of entities it contains, is the conversion factor.
   - *From amount (mol) to number of entities,* multiply by Avogadro's number:

$$\text{No. of entities} = \text{amount (mol)} \times \frac{6.022\times10^{23}\ \text{entities}}{\text{1 mol}} \quad (3.4)$$

   - *From number of entities to amount (mol),* divide by Avogadro's number:

$$\text{Amount (mol)} = \text{no. of entities} \times \frac{\text{1 mol}}{6.022\times10^{23}\ \text{entities}} \quad (3.5)$$

Applications

Chemical Connections essays show the interdisciplinary nature of chemistry by applying chemical principles directly to related scientific fields, including physiology, geology, biochemistry, engineering, and environmental science. *Tools of the Laboratory* essays describe the key instruments and techniques that chemists use in modern practice to obtain the data that underlie their theories. Both essay features now include several problems to enhance learning and relevance.

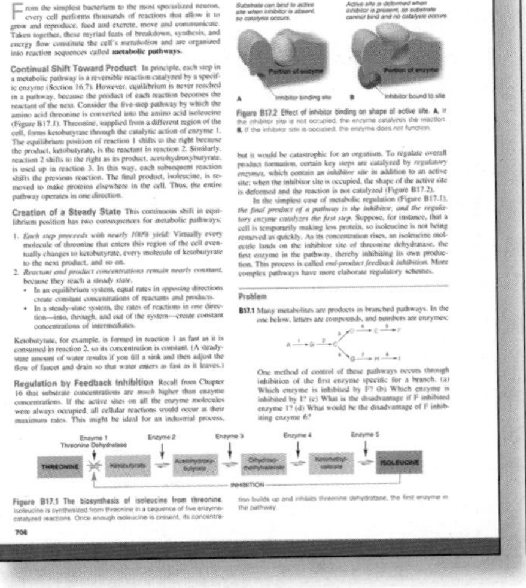

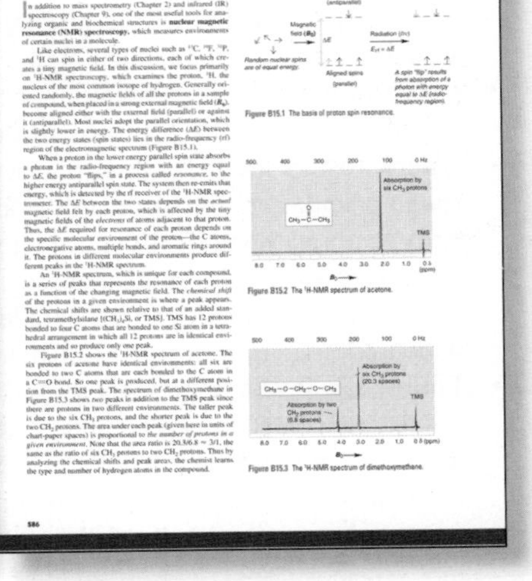

Section Summaries

Concise, bulleted summary lists conclude each section, restating the major ideas just covered.

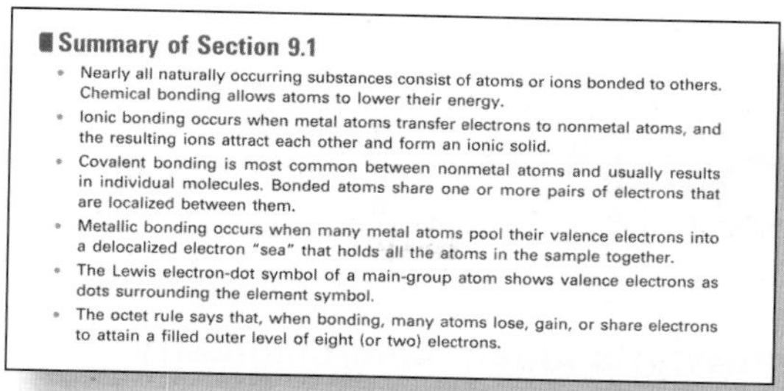

Summary of Section 9.1

- Nearly all naturally occurring substances consist of atoms or ions bonded to others. Chemical bonding allows atoms to lower their energy.
- Ionic bonding occurs when metal atoms transfer electrons to nonmetal atoms, and the resulting ions attract each other and form an ionic solid.
- Covalent bonding is most common between nonmetal atoms and usually results in individual molecules. Bonded atoms share one or more pairs of electrons that are localized between them.
- Metallic bonding occurs when many metal atoms pool their valence electrons into a delocalized electron "sea" that holds all the atoms in the sample together.
- The Lewis electron-dot symbol of a main-group atom shows valence electrons as dots surrounding the element symbol.
- The octet rule says that, when bonding, many atoms lose, gain, or share electrons to attain a filled outer level of eight (or two) electrons.

Chapter Review Guide

A rich catalog of study aids ends each chapter to help students review its content.

- **Learning Objectives,** with section and/or sample problem numbers, focus on key concepts and skills.
- **Key Terms** are boldfaced and defined within the chapter and listed here by section (with page numbers), as well as being defined again in the *Glossary*.
- **Key Equations and Relationships** are screened and numbered within the chapter and listed here with page numbers.
- **Brief Solutions to Follow-Up Problems** double the number of worked problems by providing multistep calculations at the ends of the chapters, rather than just a numerical answer at the back of the book. Road maps are supplied for those follow-up problems that ask students to prepare one in planning their solution.

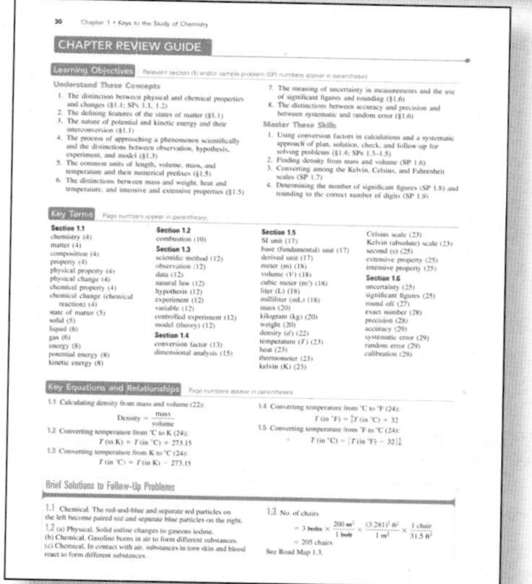

CHAPTER REVIEW GUIDE

Learning Objectives

Key Terms

Key Equations and Relationships

Brief Solutions to Follow-Up Problems

End-of-Chapter Problems

An exceptionally large number of qualitative, quantitative, and molecular-scene homework problems end each chapter. Three types of problems are keyed by chapter section, with comprehensive problems following:

- **Concept Review Questions** test students' qualitative understanding of key ideas.
- **Skill-Building Exercises** are grouped in pairs that cover a similar idea, with one of each pair answered in the back of the book. These exercises begin with simple questions and increase in difficulty, gradually eliminating students' need for multistep directions.
- **Problems in Context** apply the skills learned in the skill-building exercises to interesting scenarios, including examples from industry, medicine, and the environment.
- **Comprehensive Problems,** most based on realistic applications, are more challenging and rely on concepts and skills from any section of the current chapter or from previous chapters.

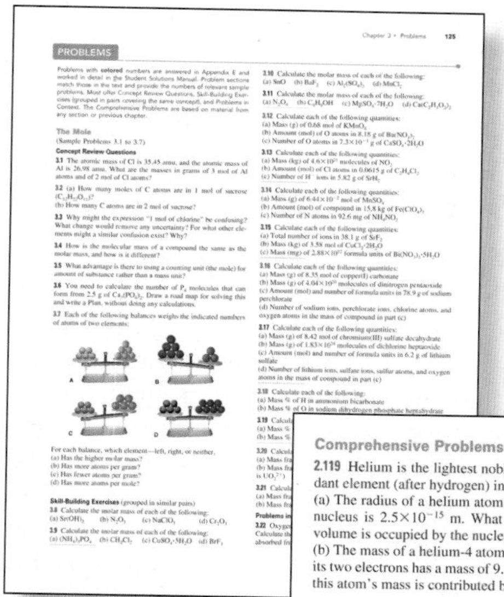

PROBLEMS

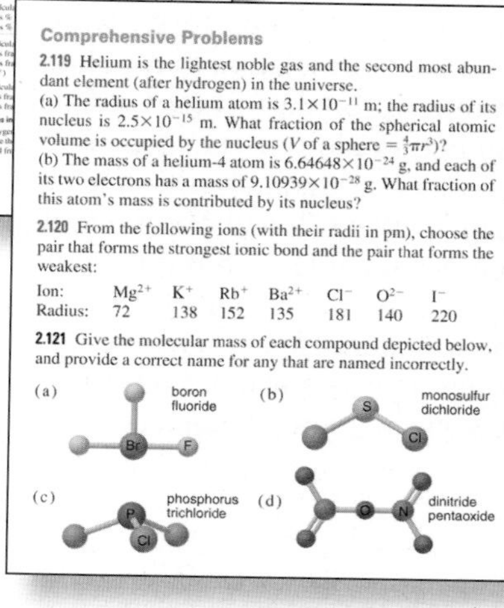

Comprehensive Problems

2.119 Helium is the lightest noble gas and the second most abundant element (after hydrogen) in the universe.
(a) The radius of a helium atom is 3.1×10^{-11} m; the radius of its nucleus is 2.5×10^{-15} m. What fraction of the spherical atomic volume is occupied by the nucleus (V of a sphere $= \frac{4}{3}\pi r^3$)?
(b) The mass of a helium-4 atom is 6.64648×10^{-24} g, and each of its two electrons has a mass of 9.10939×10^{-28} g. What fraction of this atom's mass is contributed by its nucleus?

2.120 From the following ions (with their radii in pm), choose the pair that forms the strongest ionic bond and the pair that forms the weakest:

Ion:	Mg^{2+}	K^+	Rb^+	Ba^{2+}	Cl^-	O^{2-}	I^-
Radius:	72	138	152	135	181	140	220

2.121 Give the molecular mass of each compound depicted below, and provide a correct name for any that are named incorrectly.

LEARNING SYSTEM RESOURCES FOR INSTRUCTORS

Mc Graw Hill connect™ | CHEMISTRY

www.mcgrawhillconnect.com/chemistry

McGraw-Hill Connect is a web-based, interactive assignment and assessment platform that incorporates cognitive science principles to customize the learning process. The chemical drawing tool found within Connect: Chemistry is CambridgeSoft's ChemDraw, which is widely considered the "gold standard" of scientific drawing programs and the cornerstone application for drawing and annotating molecules, reactions, and pathways. This combination of Connect and ChemDraw is an easy-to-use, intuitive, and comprehensive course management and homework system with professional-grade drawing capabilities.

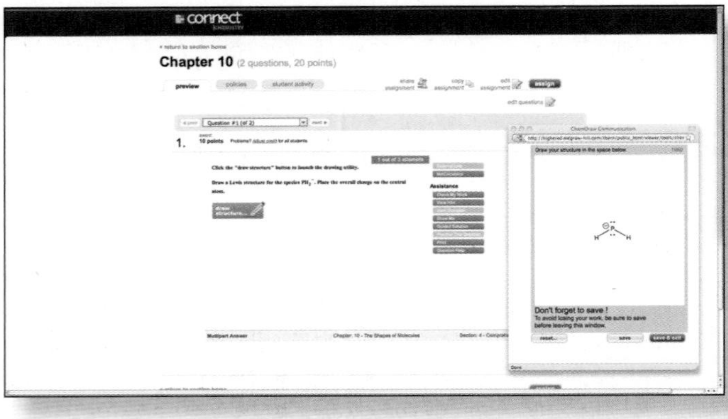

End-of-chapter problems from this textbook are available in Connect: Chemistry for instructors to build assignments that are automatically graded and tracked through reports that export easily to Excel. Instructors can edit existing problems and write entirely new problems; track individual student performance—by problem, assignment, concept, or in relation to the class overall—with automatic grading; provide instant feedback to students; and store detailed grade reports securely online. Grade reports can be easily integrated with learning management systems such as WebCT and Blackboard. Single sign-on integration is available with the Blackboard course management system. Within Connect, instructors can also create and share materials with colleagues. Ask your McGraw-Hill representative for more information, and then check it out at www.mcgrawhillconnect.com/chemistry.

Blackboard Course Management Integration with McGraw-Hill Content

Mc Graw Hill Bb Blackboard Do More

McGraw-Hill Higher Education and Blackboard, the Web-based course-management system, have teamed up to allow students and faculty to easily use online materials and activities to complement face-to-face teaching. Blackboard features exciting social learning and teaching tools that foster more logical, visually impactful, and active learning opportunities for students. This partnership transforms closed-door classrooms into communities where students remain connected to their educational experience 24 hours a day.

This partnership allows instructors and students access to McGraw-Hill's Connect™ and Create™ from within Blackboard—with a single sign-on.

Instructors also get deep integration of McGraw-Hill content and content engines into Blackboard. Whether choosing a book for your course or building Connect™ assignments, all the tools you need are right where you want them—inside Blackboard.

Gradebooks are now seamless. When a student completes an integrated Connect™ assignment, the grade for that assignment is automatically (and instantly) fed to the Blackboard grade center.

McGraw-Hill and Blackboard now offer easy access to industry-leading technology and content, whether your campus hosts it, or we do. Be sure to ask your local McGraw-Hill representative for details.

Presentation Center Accessed from your textbook's Connect website, Presentation Center is an online digital library containing McGraw-Hill owned photos, artwork, animations, and other types of media that can be used to create customized lectures, visually enhanced tests and quizzes, compelling course websites, or attractive printed support materials for classroom purposes. The visual resources in this collection include the following:

- **Art** Full-color digital files of all illustrations in the book can be readily incorporated into lecture presentations, exams, or custom-made classroom materials. In addition, all files have been inserted into PowerPoint slides for ease of lecture preparation.
- **Photos** The photo collection contains digital files of photographs from the text, which can be reproduced for multiple classroom uses.
- **Tables** Every table that appears in the text has been saved in electronic form for use in classroom presentations and/or classroom materials.

- **Animations** Numerous full-color animations illustrating important processes are also provided. Harness the visual impact of concepts in motion by importing these files into classroom presentations or online course materials.

PowerPoint materials can also be accessed through your textbook's Connect website:

- **PowerPoint Lecture Outlines** Ready-made presentations that combine art and lecture notes are provided for each chapter of the text.
- **PowerPoint Slides** For instructors who prefer to create their lectures from scratch, all illustrations, photos, sample problems, and tables have been inserted into blank PowerPoint slides, arranged by chapter.

The Presentation Center library includes thousands of assets from many McGraw-Hill titles. This ever-growing resource gives instructors the power to utilize assets specific to an adopted textbook as well as content from all other books in the library. Accessed through the instructor side of your textbook's Connect website, Presentation Center's dynamic search engine allows you to explore by discipline, course, textbook chapter, asset type, or keyword. Simply browse, select, and download the files you need to build engaging course materials. To access Connect, request registration information from your McGraw-Hill sales representative.

McGraw-Hill Tegrity campus

Digital Lecture Capture: Tegrity McGraw-Hill *Tegrity Campus* records and distributes your lecture with just a click of a button. Students can view anytime/anywhere via computer, iPod, or mobile device. *Tegrity* indexes as it records your slideshow presentations and anything shown on your computer, so students can use keywords to find exactly what they want to study.

Computerized Test Bank Prepared by Walter Orchard, Professor Emeritus of Tacoma Community College, over 2300 test questions to accompany *Chemistry: The Molecular Nature of Matter and Change* are available utilizing Brownstone's Diploma testing software. *Diploma's* software allows you to quickly create a customized test using McGraw-Hill's supplied questions or by authoring your own. *Diploma* allows you to create your tests without an Internet connection—just download the software and question files directly to your computer.

Instructor's Solutions Manual This supplement, prepared by Patricia Amateis of Virginia Tech, contains complete, worked-out solutions for *all* the end-of-chapter problems in the text. It can be found within the Instructors Resources, on the Connect: Chemistry site.

Content Delivery Flexibility *Chemistry: The Molecular Nature of Matter and Change,* by Martin Silberberg, is available in other formats in addition to the traditional textbook, giving instructors and students more choices for the format of their chemistry text.

McGraw-Hill create

- **Customizable Textbooks: Create** McGraw-Hill Create™ is a new, self-service website that allows you to create custom course materials—print or eBook—by drawing on McGraw-Hill's comprehensive, cross-disciplinary content. Add your own content quickly and easily. Tap into other rights-secured third-party sources as well. Then, arrange the content in a way that makes the most sense for your course. Even personalize your book with your course name and information. Choose the best format for your course: color print, black-and-white print, or ebook (which is viewable on an iPad). And when you are finished customizing, you will receive a free PDF review copy in just minutes. Visit McGraw-Hill Create at www.mcgrawhillcreate.com today and begin building your perfect book.
- **ConnectPlus eBook** McGraw-Hill's ConnectPlus eBook takes digital texts beyond a simple PDF. With the same content as the printed book, but optimized for the screen, the ConnectPlus eBook has embedded media, including animations and videos, which bring concepts to life and provide "just in time" learning for students. Additionally, fully integrated homework problems allow students to interact with the problems to determine if they're gaining mastery of the content, and the problems can also be assigned by the instructor.

Cooperative Chemistry Laboratory Manual Prepared by Melanie Cooper of Clemson University, this innovative manual features open-ended problems designed to simulate experience in a research lab. Working in groups, students investigate one problem over a period of several weeks, so they might complete three or four projects during the semester, rather than one preprogrammed experiment per class. The emphasis is on experimental design, analytic problem solving, and communication.

LEARNING SYSTEM RESOURCES FOR STUDENTS

Student Study Guide This valuable study guide, prepared by Libby Bent Weberg, is designed to help you recognize your learning style; understand how to read, classify, and create a plan for solving a problem; and practice your problem-solving skills. For each section of each chapter, the guide provides study objectives and a summary of the corresponding text. Following the summary are sample problems with detailed solutions. Each chapter has true-false questions and a self-test, with all answers provided at the end of the chapter.

Student Solutions Manual This supplement, prepared by Patricia Amateis of Virginia Tech, contains detailed solutions and explanations for all problems in the main text that have colored numbers.

Mc Graw Hill connect™ CHEMISTRY

Connect: Chemistry With Connect: Chemistry, you can practice solving assigned homework problems using the Silberberg problem-solving methodology applied in the textbook. Algorithmic problems serve up multiple versions of similar problems for mastery of content, with hints and feedback for common incorrect answers to help you stay on track. Where appropriate, you engage in accurate, professional-grade chemical drawing through the use of CambridgeSoft's ChemDraw tool, which is implemented directly into homework problems. Check it out at www.mcgraw-hillconnect.com/chemistry.

Mc Graw Hill LearnSmart™

LearnSmart™ This adaptive diagnostic learning system, powered by Connect: Chemistry and based on artificial intelligence, constantly assesses your knowledge of the course material. As you work within the system, LearnSmart develops a personal learning path adapted to what you have actively learned and retained. This innovative study tool also has features to allow your instructor to see exactly what you have accomplished, with a built-in assessment tool for graded assignments. You can access LearnSmart for general chemistry by going to www.mcgraw-hillconnect.com/chemistry.

Animations for MP3/iPod A number of animations are available for download to your MP3/iPod through the textbook's Connect website.

Acknowledgments

The sixth edition and its associated learning system are the culmination of numerous chapter reviews, insightful suggestions, brainstorming sessions, focus groups, interviews, and class tests. Each person involved played an important part in the revision of the text and its ancillaries.

I feel very fortunate to have a relationship with my publisher based on mutual respect, shared goals, and warm friendship. Heading the McGraw-Hill Higher Education team with their advice and support were Publisher Ryan Blankenship and Executive Editor Jeff Huettman, Developmental Editor Donna Nemmers, Director of Digital Content David Spurgeon, Digital Project Manager Daryl Bruflodt, Project Manager Peggy Selle, Designer David Hash, and Marketing Manager Tami Hodge.

Patricia Amateis, Virginia Tech, helped revise several chapters and prepared Appendix E as well as the Instructor's and Student Solutions Manuals. Krishnan Rajeshwar, University of Texas–Arlington, updated the discussion of the future of energy use.

I am very grateful to the Board of Advisors, who helped me make this text the optimum teaching tool: Debra Feakes, Texas State University–San Marcos, Derek Gragson, California Polytechnic State University–San Luis Obispo, and James Reeves, University of North Carolina–Wilmington. Also, my deepest gratitude extends to the following individuals, who attended focus groups or symposia, provided content reviews, and class-tested materials in preparation for the Sixth Edition and its associated learning system:

Patricia Amateis, *Virginia Tech*
Margaret Asirvatham, *University of Colorado—Boulder*
Yiyan Bai, *Houston Community College–Central*
Laurance Beauvais, *San Diego State University*
Thomas Bertolini, *University of Southern California*
Fereshteh Billiot, *Texas A&M University–Corpus Christi*
Deborah Booth, *University of Southern Mississippi*
Simon Bott, *University of Houston*
Stacey Lowery Bretz, *Miami University of Ohio*
Karen Brewer, *Virginia Tech*
Les Butler, *Louisiana State University*
Bindu Chakravarty, *Houston Community College–Northeast Campus*
Chris Cheatum, *University of Iowa*
Liwei Chen, *Ohio University*
Tom Clausen, *University of Alaska–Fairbanks*
Erin Dahlke, *Loras College*
Michelle Driessen, *University of Minnesota*
Jack Duff, *Southern Polytechnic State University*
Bill Durham, *University of Arkansas*
Emmanuel Ewane, *Houston Community College–Northwest*
Deborah Exton, *University of Oregon*
Paul Fazen, *Villanova University*
David Frank, *California State University–Fresno*
John Gelder, *Oklahoma State University*
Greg Gellene, *Texas Tech University*
Dimitri Giarikos, *Nova Southeastern University*
Michael Greenlief, *University of Missouri–Columbia*
Todor Gounev, *University of Missouri–Kansas City*
John Hagen, *California Polytechnic State University–San Luis Obispo*
Michael Hailu, *Columbus State Community College*
John Halpin, *New York University*
Narayan Hosmane, *Northern Illinois University*
Larry Houk, *University of Memphis*
Eihab Jaber, *Worcester State University*
Heiko Jacobsen, *Tulane University*
Richard Jarman, *College of DuPage*
Steve Keller, *University of Missouri*
San Kim, *Northern Virginia Community College*
Chuck Kirkpatrick, *St. Louis University*
Marina Koether, *Kennesaw State University*
Patric Kolniak, *Louisiana State University*
Pamela Kraemer, *Northern Virginia Community College*
Jothi Kumar, *North Carolina A&T State University*
Dorothy B. Kurland, *Emeritus, West Virginia Institute of Technology*
Anna Larsen, *Ithaca College*
Allison Long, *Georgia Southern University*
Jeanette Madea, *Broward Community College*
Diana Malone, *Clarke University*
Lisa McGaw, *University of Central Oklahoma*
Thomas McGrath, *Baylor University*
Danny McGuire, *Cameron University*
Bill McLaughlin, *Montana State University*
Lauren McMills, *Ohio University*
Joyce Miller, *San Jacinto College–South*
Kristine Miller, *Anne Arundel Community College*
Jeremy Mitchell-Koch, *Emporia State University*
Debbie Mohler, *James Madison University*
Kereen Monteyne, *University of Northern Kentucky*
Mahesh Narayan, *University of Texas–El Paso*
Jessica Orvis, *Georgia Southern University*
Jason Overby, *College of Charleston*
Richard Paselk, *Humboldt State University*
Louis Pignolet, *Emeritus, University of Minnesota*
John Pollard, *The University of Arizona*
Bernard Powell, *University of Texas–San Antonio*
William Quintana, *New Mexico State University*
Edward Quitevis, *Texas Tech University*
Jeff Rack, *Ohio University*
Lisa Reece, *Ozarks Technical Community College*
Michelle Richards-Babb, *West Virginia University*
Dawn Rickey, *Colorado State University*
Thomas Ridgway, *University of Cincinnati*
Steven Rowley, *Middlesex County College*
Raymond Sadeghi, *University of Texas–San Antonio*
Issa Salame, *The City College of New York*
Jim Satterlee, *Washington State University*
Colleen Scott, *Southern Illinois University–Carbondale*
Thomas Selegue, *Pima Community College*
Steve Shore, *Oklahoma City Community College*
Michael Sommer, *University of Wyoming*
Jie Song, *University of Michigan–Flint*

David Speckhard, *Loras College*
Rick Spinney, *Ohio State University*
Emelyn S. Q. Tan, *National University of Singapore*
Kimberly Trick, *University of Dayton*
Cyriacus Uzomba, *Austin Community College*
Debbie Warnaar, *James Madison University*
Lyle Wescott, *University of Mississippi*
Wayne Wesolowski, *The University of Arizona*
Daniel Williams, *Kennesaw State University*
Stephanie Wunder, *Temple University*
Timothy Zauche, *University of Wisconsin–Platteville*
Lin Zhu, *IUPUI*

Connect: Chemistry has been greatly enhanced by the efforts of Kereen Monteyne, University of Northern Kentucky; MaryKay Orgill, University of Nevada–Las Vegas; and Yasmin Patell, Kansas State University; who did a masterful job of authoring hints and feedback to augment all of the system's homework problems. The following individuals helped write and review learning goal–oriented content for **LearnSmart for General Chemistry:** Margaret Asirvatham, University of Colorado–Boulder; William Burns, Arkansas State University; Cabot-Ann Christofferson, South Dakota School of Mines; Christina Johnson, University of California–San Diego; Adam I. Keller, Columbus State Community College; Willem R. Leenstra, University of Vermont; Margaret Ruth Leslie, Kent State University; Benjamin R. Martin, Texas State University–San Marcos; Kathy Thrush Shaginaw, Particular Solutions, Inc.; and Erin Whitteck.

Several expert freelancers contributed as well. As always, Jane Hoover did an excellent copyediting of the textbook, and Francine Banwarth and Rose Kramer followed with meticulous proofreading. John Murdzek and LaurelTech exercised careful skill in accuracy-checking content within Connect: Chemistry.

Over the years and editions, I've always had the great benefit of the expertise of my "in-home" team. This time around, my son, Daniel, offered his keen artist's eye to the figures revised, the photos selected, and the cover devised. And my wife, Ruth, made this text come to fruition—literally. She worked closely with the McGraw-Hill production team and provided indispensable, detailed input to the compositor, copy editor, and proof readers. And, of course, they both kept the author going with their love and support.

Theories of Covalent Bonding

11

Concepts and skills to review before you study this chapter

- atomic orbital shapes (Section 7.4)
- exclusion principle (Section 8.1)
- Hund's rule (Section 8.2)
- Lewis structures (Section 10.1)
- resonance in covalent bonding (Section 10.1)
- molecular shapes (Section 10.2)
- molecular polarity (Section 10.3)

All scientific models have limitations because they are simplifications of reality. The VSEPR theory, covered in Chapter 10, accounts for molecular shapes, but it doesn't explain how they arise from interactions of atomic orbitals. After all, the orbitals described in Chapter 7 aren't oriented toward the corners of, say, an octahedron, like the ones shown at left for the sulfur in SF_6. Moreover, knowing the shape doesn't help us explain the magnetic and spectral properties of molecules; only an understanding of their orbitals and energy levels can.

The two theories presented in this chapter focus on different questions and complement each other. Don't be concerned if we need several models to explain a complex phenomenon like bonding. In every science, one model may account for some aspect of a topic better than another, and several are employed to explain a wider range of phenomena.

IN THIS CHAPTER . . . We introduce two theories of bonding in molecules based on the interactions of the orbitals of their atoms.

- We discuss valence bond (VB) theory, which rationalizes molecular shapes through interactions of atomic orbitals during bonding to form hybrid orbitals.
- We apply VB theory to sigma and pi bonds, the two types of covalent bonds.
- We see why parts of molecules don't rotate freely around multiple bonds, which has major effects on reactivity, physical properties, and biological behavior.
- We discuss molecular orbital (MO) theory, which explains molecular energy levels and properties through formation of orbitals that spread over the whole molecule.
- We apply MO theory to understand key properties of some diatomic and simple polyatomic molecules.

11.1 • VALENCE BOND (VB) THEORY AND ORBITAL HYBRIDIZATION

What *is* a covalent bond, and what characteristic gives it strength? And how can we explain *molecular* shapes based on the interactions of *atomic* orbitals? The most useful approach for answering these questions is based on quantum mechanics (Chapter 7) and called **valence bond (VB) theory.**

The Central Themes of VB Theory

The basic principle of VB theory is that *a covalent bond forms when orbitals of two atoms overlap and a pair of electrons occupy the overlap region.* In the terminology of quantum mechanics, overlap of the two orbitals means their wave functions are *in phase* (constructive interference), so the amplitude between the nuclei increases (see Figure 7.5, p. 265). The central themes of VB theory derive from this principle:

1. *Opposing spins of the electron pair.* As the exclusion principle (Section 8.1) prescribes, the space formed by the overlapping orbitals *has a maximum capacity for two electrons that have opposite (paired) spins.* In the simplest case, a molecule of H_2 forms when the 1*s* orbitals of two H atoms overlap, and the electrons, with their spins paired, spend more time in the overlap region (up and down arrows in Figure 11.1).

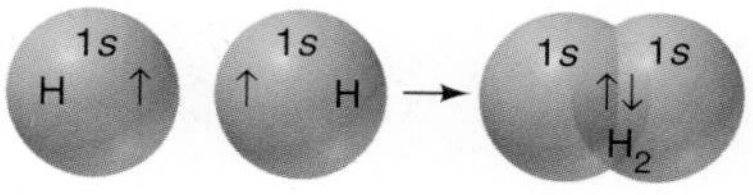

Figure 11.1 Orbital overlap and spin pairing in H_2.

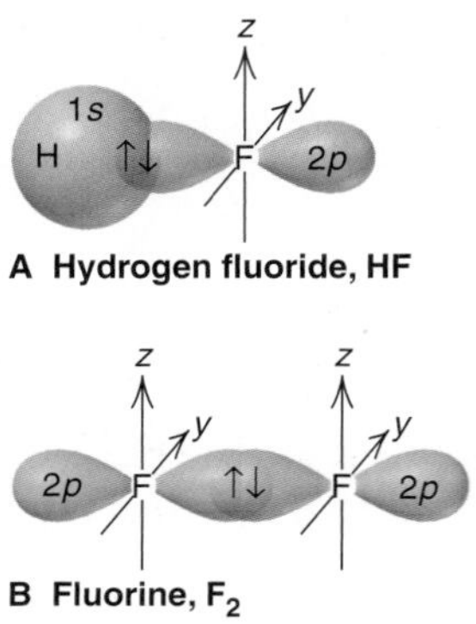

Figure 11.2 Orbital orientation and maximum overlap. (The $2p_x$ orbital is shown bonding; the other two 2*p* orbitals of F are omitted for clarity.)

2. *Maximum overlap of bonding orbitals.* Bond strength depends on the attraction between nuclei and shared electrons, so *the greater the orbital overlap, the stronger the bond.* Extent of overlap depends on orbital shape and direction. An *s* orbital is spherical, so its orientation is the same in any direction, but *p* and *d* orbitals have specified directions. Thus, a *p* or *d* orbital involved in a bond is oriented so as to maximize overlap. In HF, for example, the 1*s* orbital of H overlaps a half-filled 2*p* orbital of F *along its long axis* (Figure 11.2A). In F_2, the two half-filled 2*p* orbitals interact end to end, that is, *along the long axes* of the orbitals (Figure 11.2B).

3. *Hybridization of atomic orbitals.* To account for the bonding in diatomic molecules, we picture direct overlap of *s* and/or *p* orbitals of isolated atoms. But how can we account for the shape of a molecule like methane from the shapes and orientations of C and H atomic orbitals? A C atom ([He] $2s^22p^2$) has two valence electrons in the spherical 2*s* orbital and one each in two of the three mutually perpendicular 2*p* orbitals. If the half-filled *p* orbitals overlap the 1*s* orbitals of two H atoms, *two* C—H bonds would form with a 90° H—C—H bond angle. But methane has the formula CH_4, not CH_2, and its bond angle is 109.5°.

To explain such facts, Linus Pauling proposed that, during bonding, *the valence atomic orbitals in the isolated atoms become* ***different*** *when they are in the molecule.* Quantum-mechanical calculations show that if we mathematically "mix" certain combinations of orbitals, we form new ones whose spatial orientations *do* match the observed molecular shapes. The process of orbital mixing is called **hybridization,** and the new atomic orbitals are called **hybrid orbitals.**

4. *Features of hybrid orbitals.* Here are some central points about hybrid orbitals that arise during bonding:

- The *number* of hybrid orbitals formed *equals* the number of atomic orbitals mixed.
- The *type* of hybrid orbitals formed *varies* with the types of atomic orbitals mixed.
- The *shape* and *orientation* of a hybrid orbital *maximizes* overlap with the orbital of the other atom in the bond.

You can think of hybridization as a process in which atomic orbitals mix, hybrid orbitals form, they overlap other orbitals, and electrons enter the overlap region with opposing spins, thus forming stable bonds. In truth, hybridization is a concept to explain the results we calculate that predict the molecular shapes we observe.

Types of Hybrid Orbitals

We postulate the type of hybrid orbitals in a molecule *after* we observe its shape. Note that the orientations of the five types of hybrid orbitals we discuss next correspond to the five electron-group arrangements in VSEPR theory.

***sp* Hybridization** When two electron groups surround the central atom, we observe a linear shape, which means the bonding orbitals must have a linear orientation.

1. *Orbitals mixed and orbitals formed.* VB theory proposes two *nonequivalent* orbitals of a central atom, one *s* and one *p*, mix and form two *equivalent* ***sp*** **hybrid orbitals** that are oriented 180° apart (Figure 11.3A). The shape of these hybrid orbitals, with one large and one small lobe, differs markedly from the shapes of the atomic orbitals. The orbital orientations increase electron density *in the bonding direction.*

2. *Overlap of orbitals from central and surrounding atoms: $BeCl_2$.* In beryllium chloride, the Be atom is *sp* hybridized. Figure 11.3B depicts the hybridization of Be in an orbital box diagram, and part C shows an orbital box diagram with shaded contours instead of arrows. Bond formation with Cl is shown in part D. The filled 2*s* and one of the three empty 2*p* orbitals of Be mix and form two half-filled *sp* orbitals. Two empty unhybridized 2*p* orbitals of Be lie perpendicular to each other and to the *sp* hybrids. The hybrid orbitals overlap the half-filled 3*p* orbital in each of two Cl atoms. The four electrons—two from Be and one from each Cl—appear as pairs with opposite spins in the two overlap regions. (The 3*p* and *sp* hybrid orbitals that are partially colored on the left become fully colored on the right, after the bonds form and each orbital is filled with two electrons.)

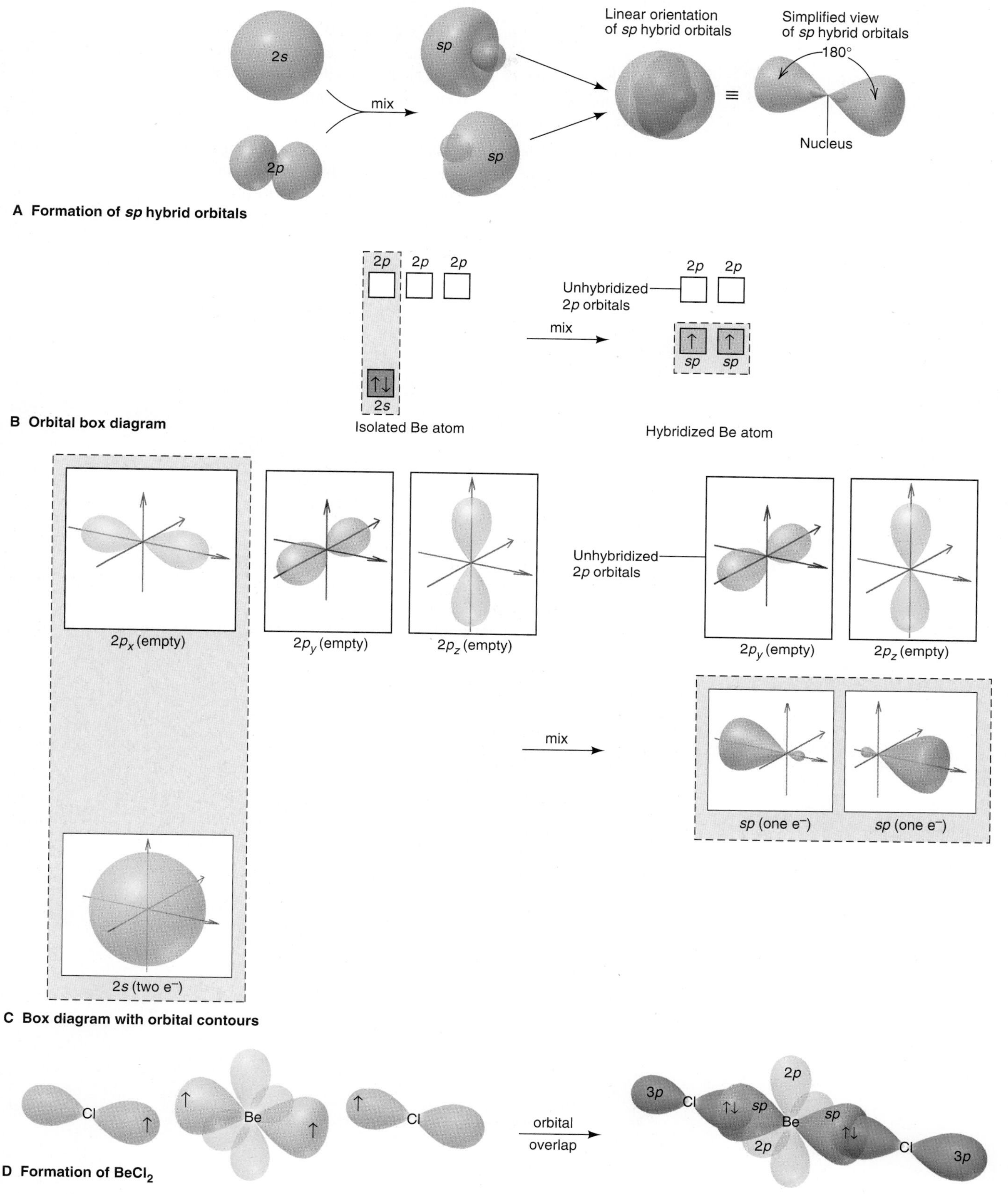

Figure 11.3 Formation and orientation of *sp* hybrid orbitals and the bonding in $BeCl_2$. **A,** One 2*s* and one 2*p* atomic orbital mix to form two *sp* hybrid orbitals. (The simplified hybrid orbitals at far right are used elsewhere, often even without the small lobe.) **B,** The orbital box diagram for hybridization of Be, drawn vertically. **C,** The orbital box diagram with orbital contours. **D,** Overlap of Be and Cl orbitals to form $BeCl_2$. (Only the Cl 3*p* orbital involved in bonding is shown.)

sp^2 Hybridization We use this type of hybridization to rationalize the two shapes possible for the trigonal planar electron-group arrangement.

1. *Orbitals mixed and orbitals formed.* Mixing one *s* and two *p* orbitals gives three **sp^2 hybrid orbitals** that point to the corners of an equilateral triangle, their axes 120° apart. (In hybrid orbitals, unlike in electron configurations, superscripts refer to the number of *atomic orbitals* of a given type, *not* the number of *electrons* in the orbital: thus, one *s* and two *p* orbitals give s^1p^2, or sp^2.) The third 2*p* orbital remains unhybridized.

2. *Overlap of orbitals from central and surrounding atoms: BF_3.* The central B atom in BF_3 is sp^2 hybridized, with the three sp^2 orbitals in a trigonal plane and the third 2*p* orbital unhybridized and perpendicular to this plane (Figure 11.4). Each half-filled sp^2 orbital overlaps the half-filled 2*p* orbital of an F atom, and the six valence electrons—three from B and one from each of the three F atoms—form three bonding pairs.

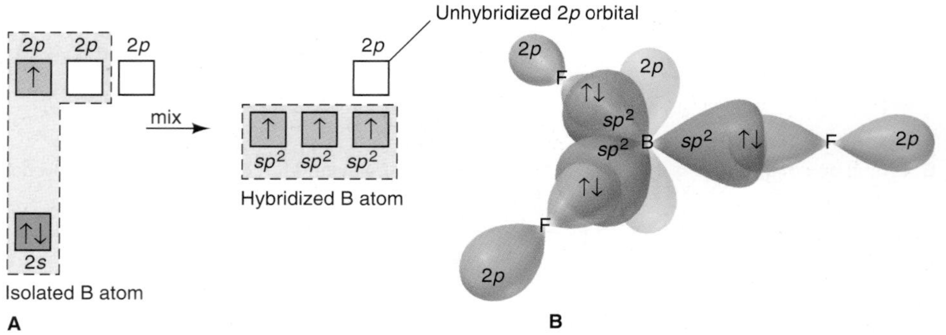

Figure 11.4 The sp^2 hybrid orbitals in BF_3. **A,** The orbital box diagram shows the formation of three sp^2 hybrid orbitals. One 2*p* orbital is unhybridized and empty. **B,** Contour depiction of BF_3.

3. *Placement of lone pairs.* To account for other molecular shapes within a given electron-group arrangement, one or more hybrid orbitals contains a lone pair. In ozone (O_3), for example, the central O is sp^2 hybridized and a lone pair fills one of the three sp^2 orbitals.

sp^3 Hybridization The type of hybridization that accounts for the shape of methane applies to any species with a tetrahedral electron-group arrangement.

1. *Orbitals mixed and orbitals formed.* Mixing one *s* and three *p* orbitals gives four **sp^3 hybrid orbitals** that point to the corners of a tetrahedron.

2. *Overlap of orbitals from central and surrounding atoms: CH_4.* The C atom in methane is sp^3 hybridized. Its four valence electrons half-fill the four sp^3 hybrids, which overlap the half-filled 1*s* orbitals of four H atoms to form four C—H bonds (Figure 11.5).

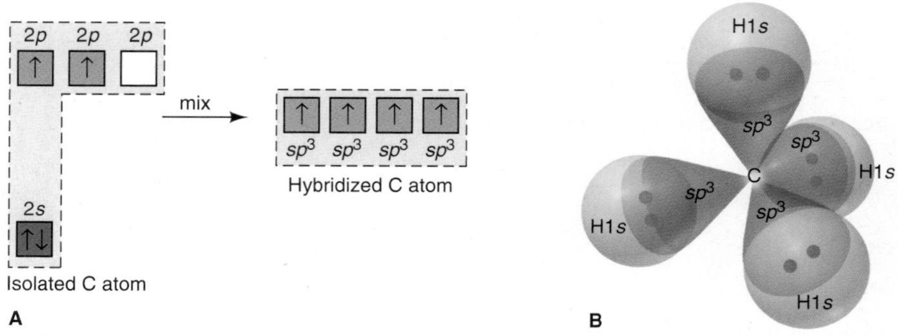

Figure 11.5 The sp^3 hybrid orbitals in CH_4. **A,** The orbital box diagram shows formation of four sp^3 hybrids. **B,** Contour depiction of CH_4, with electron pairs shown as dots.

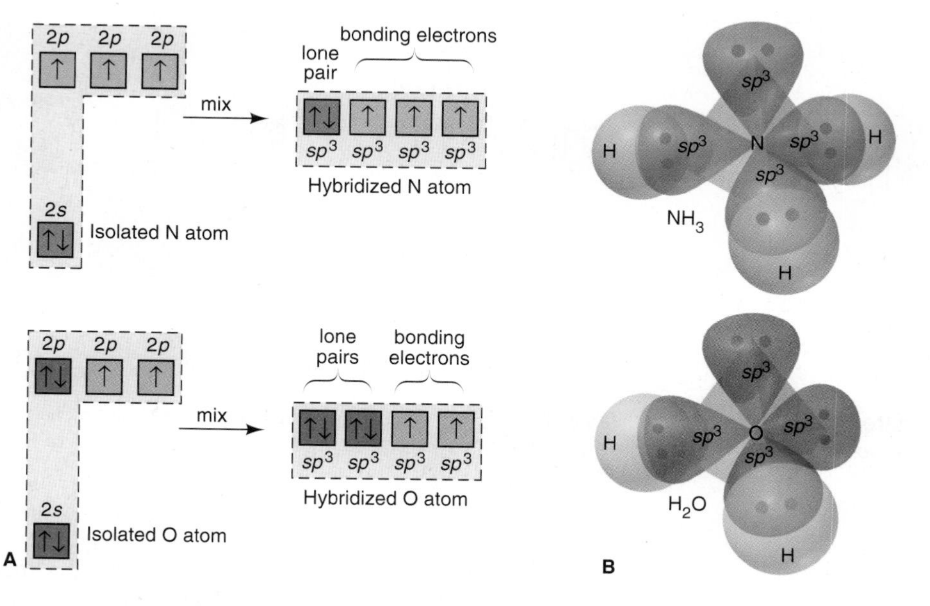

Figure 11.6 The sp^3 hybrid orbitals in NH_3 and H_2O. **A,** The orbital box diagrams show sp^3 hybridization, with lone pairs filling one (NH_3) or two (H_2O) hybrid orbitals. **B,** Contour depictions.

3. *Placement of lone pairs.* The trigonal pyramidal shape of NH_3 arises when a lone pair fills any one of the four sp^3 orbitals of N, and the bent shape of H_2O arises when lone pairs fill any two of the sp^3 orbitals of O (Figure 11.6).

sp^3d Hybridization Molecules with shapes due to the trigonal bipyramidal electron-group arrangement have central atoms from Period 3 or higher. VB theory proposes that *d* orbitals, as well as *s* and *p* orbitals, are mixed to form hybrid orbitals.

1. *Orbitals mixed and orbitals formed.* Mixing one 3*s*, the three 3*p*, and one of the five 3*d* orbitals gives five ***sp^3d* hybrid orbitals,** which point to the corners of a trigonal bipyramid.

2. *Overlap of orbitals from central and surrounding atoms: PCl_5.* The P atom in PCl_5 is sp^3d hybridized. Each hybrid orbital overlaps a 3*p* orbital of a Cl atom, and ten valence electrons—five from P and one from each of the five Cl atoms—form five P—Cl bonds (Figure 11.7).

3. *Placement of lone pairs.* Seesaw, T-shaped, and linear molecules have lone pairs in, respectively, one, two, or three of the central atom's sp^3d orbitals.

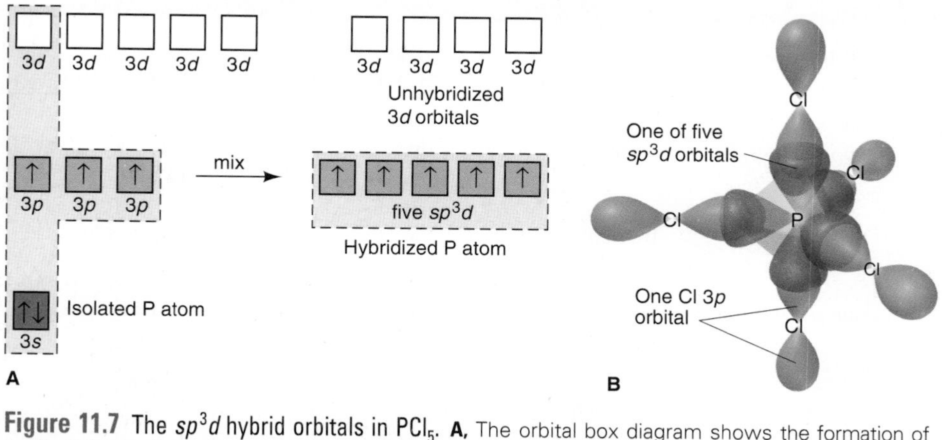

Figure 11.7 The sp^3d hybrid orbitals in PCl_5. **A,** The orbital box diagram shows the formation of five half-filled sp^3d orbitals. Four 3*d* orbitals are unhybridized and empty. **B,** Contour depiction of PCl_5. (For clarity, unhybridized 3*d* orbitals, the other two Cl 3*p* orbitals, and the five bonding P—Cl pairs are not shown.)

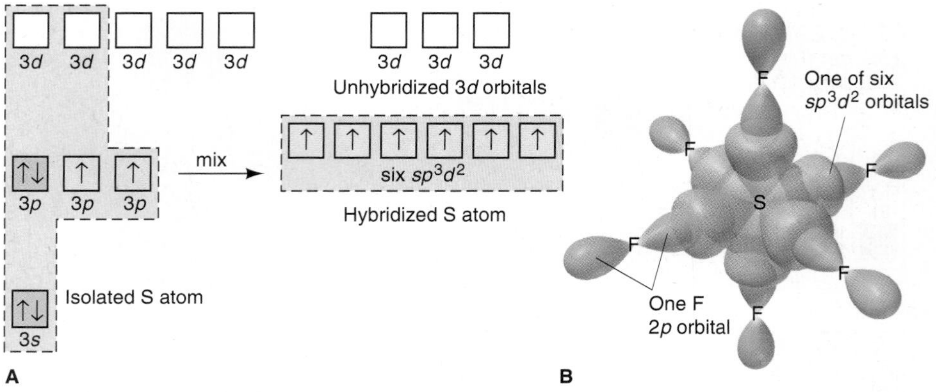

Figure 11.8 The sp^3d^2 hybrid orbitals in SF_6. **A,** The orbital box diagram shows formation of six half-filled sp^3d^2 orbitals; three 3*d* orbitals remain unhybridized and empty. **B,** Contour depiction of SF_6.

sp^3d^2 Hybridization The VB model proposes that molecules with shapes having the octahedral electron-group arrangement also use *d* orbitals to form hybrids.

1. *Orbitals mixed and orbitals formed.* Mixing one 3*s*, the three 3*p*, and two 3*d* orbitals gives six **sp^3d^2 hybrid orbitals,** which point to the corners of an octahedron.

2. *Overlap of orbitals from central and surrounding atoms: SF_6.* The S atom in SF_6 is sp^3d^2 hybridized. Each half-filled hybrid orbital overlaps a half-filled 2*p* orbital of an F atom, and 12 valence electrons—six from S and one from each of the six F atoms—form six S—F bonds (Figure 11.8).

3. *Placement of lone pairs.* Square pyramidal and square planar molecules have lone pairs in one and two of the central atom's sp^3d^2 orbitals, respectively.

Table 11.1 summarizes the numbers and types of atomic orbitals that mix to form the five types of hybrid orbitals. Figure 11.9 shows three conceptual steps from a molecular formula to the hybrid orbitals in the molecule, and Sample Problem 11.1 focuses on the last step of that process.

Table 11.1 Composition and Orientation of Hybrid Orbitals

	Linear	Trigonal Planar	Tetrahedral	Trigonal Bipyramidal	Octahedral
Atomic orbitals mixed	one *s* one *p*	one *s* two *p*	one *s* three *p*	one *s* three *p* one *d*	one *s* three *p* two *d*
Hybrid orbitals formed	two *p*	three sp^2	four sp^3	five sp^3d	six sp^3d^2
Unhybridized orbitals remaining	two *p*	one *p*	none	four *d*	three *d*
Orientation			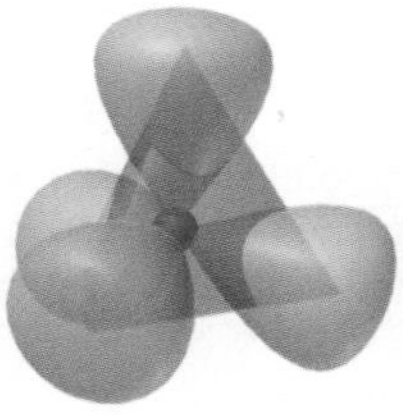	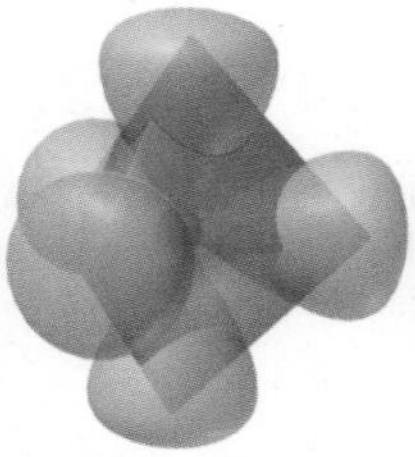	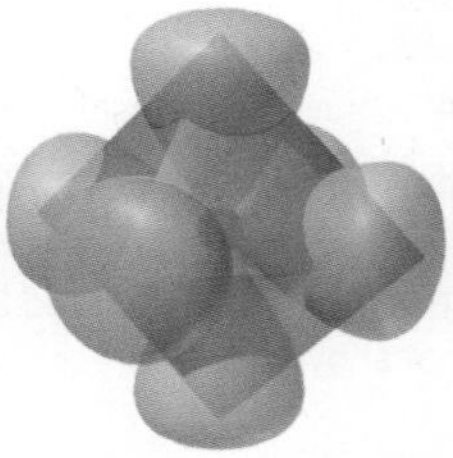

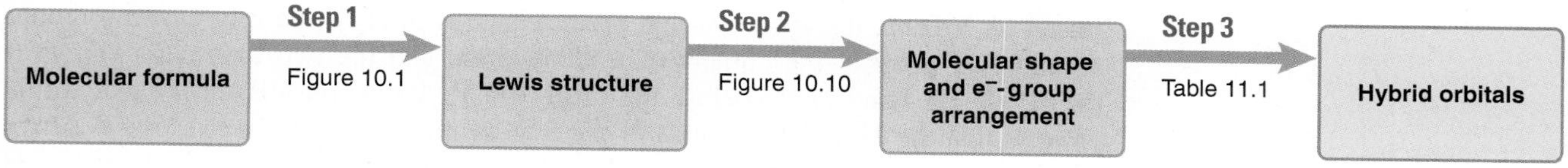

Figure 11.9 **From molecular formula to hybrid orbitals.** (See Figures 10.1, p. 364, and 10.10, p. 379.)

Sample Problem 11.1 Postulating Hybrid Orbitals in a Molecule

Problem Use partial orbital diagrams to describe how mixing the atomic orbitals of the central atom(s) leads to the hybrid orbitals in each of the following:
(a) Methanol, CH_3OH **(b)** Sulfur tetrafluoride, SF_4

Plan Prior to the Solution steps below, we have used the molecular formula to draw the Lewis structure and determined the electron-group arrangement of each central atom. Then, starting from there, we use Table 11.1 to postulate the type of hybrid orbitals. We write the partial orbital diagram for each central atom before and after the orbitals are hybridized.

Solution **(a)** For CH_3OH. The electron-group arrangement is tetrahedral around both the C and the O atom, so each mixed one 2*s* and three 2*p* to become sp^3 hybridized. The C atom has four half-filled sp^3 orbitals:

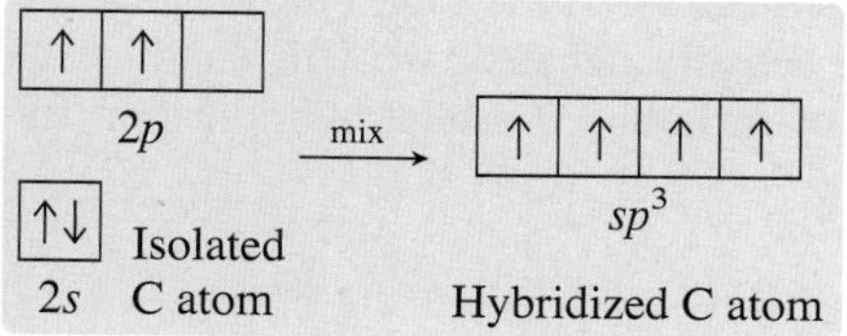

The O atom has two half-filled sp^3 orbitals and two filled with lone pairs:

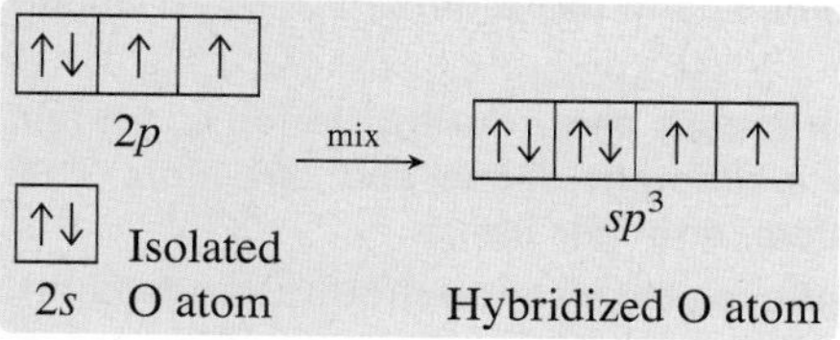

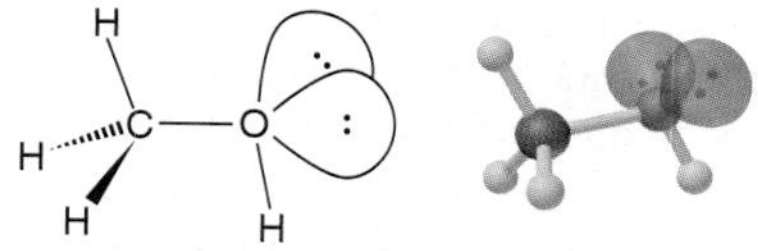

(b) For SF_4. The electron-group arrangement is trigonal bipyramidal, so the central S atom is sp^3d hybridized, which means one 3*s*, three 3*p*, and one 3*d* orbital are mixed. One hybrid orbital is filled with a lone pair, and four are half-filled. Four unhybridized 3*d* orbitals remain empty:

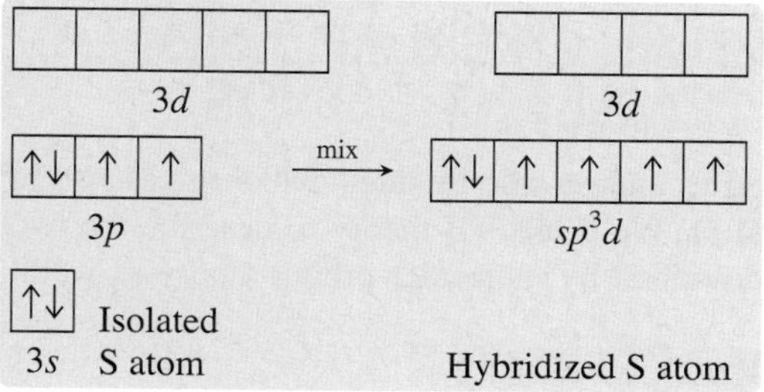

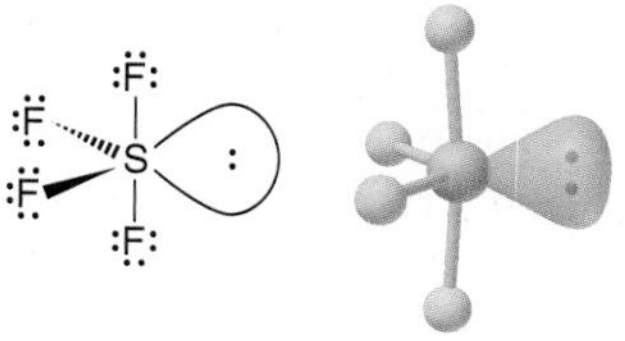

Follow-Up Problem 11.1 Use partial orbital diagrams to show how the atomic orbitals of the central atom mix to form hybrid orbitals in **(a)** beryllium fluoride, BeF_2; **(b)** silicon tetrachloride, $SiCl_4$; **(c)** xenon tetrafluoride, XeF_4.

Limitations to the Concept of Hybridization We rely on the VSEPR and VB theories to rationalize an observed molecular shape. In some cases, however, the theories may not be consistent with other findings.

1. *Hybridization does not apply: large nonmetal hydrides.* Consider the Lewis structure and bond angle of H_2S:

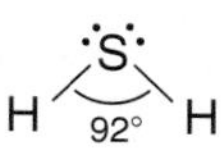

Based on VSEPR theory, we would predict that, as in H_2O, the four electron groups around H_2S point to the corners of a tetrahedron, and the two lone pairs compress the H—S—H bond angle below the ideal 109.5°. Based on VB theory, we would propose that the 3*s* and 3*p* orbitals of the S atom mix and form four sp^3 hybrids, two of which are filled with lone pairs, while the other two overlap 1*s* orbitals of two H atoms and are filled with bonding pairs.

But observation does *not* support these arguments. The bond angle of 92° is close to the 90° angle between *unhybridized p* orbitals. Similar angles occur in the hydrides of other large nonmetals of Groups 5A(15) and 6A(16). Why apply a theory if the facts don't warrant it? Real factors—bond length, atomic size, and electrostatic repulsions—influence shape. Larger atoms form longer bonds to H, which decreases repulsions; thus, overlap of *unhybridized* orbitals explains these shapes.

2. *d-Orbital hybridization is less important: rationalizing shapes with expanded valence shells.* Quantum-mechanical calculations show that *d*-orbitals have such high energies that they do not hybridize effectively with the *much* more stable *s* and *p* orbitals of a given *n* value. Thus, for example, some have proposed that SF_6 is most stable when the bonding orbitals of the central S use a combination of *sp*-hybrid orbitals and unhybridized 3*p*-orbitals instead of sp^3d^2 hybrid orbitals. Others prefer explanations that involve molecular orbitals or even ionic structures. These topics are beyond the scope of this text, and while they are being actively debated, we will continue to use the traditional, though limited, approach of including *d*-orbital hybridization for molecules with expanded valence shells.

Summary of Section 11.1

- VB theory explains that a covalent bond forms when two atomic orbitals overlap and two electrons with paired (opposite) spins spend more time in the overlapped regions.
- To explain molecular shape, the theory proposes that, during bonding, atomic orbitals mix to form hybrid orbitals with a different shape and direction. This process gives rise to greater overlap and, thus, stronger bonds.
- Based on the observed molecular shape (and the related electron-group arrangement), we postulate the type of hybrid orbital that accounts for the shape. In many cases, especially molecules with larger central atoms, the concept of hybridization has major limitations.

11.2 • MODES OF ORBITAL OVERLAP AND THE TYPES OF COVALENT BONDS

Orbitals can overlap by two *modes*—end to end or side to side—which gives rise to two types of covalent bonds—*sigma* and *pi*. We'll use VB theory to describe the two types here and, as you'll see, they are described by molecular orbital theory as well.

Orbital Overlap in Single and Multiple Bonds

Ethane (C_2H_6), ethylene (C_2H_4), and acetylene (C_2H_2) have different shapes. Ethane is tetrahedral at both carbons with bond angles near the ideal 109.5°. Ethylene is trigonal planar at both carbons with bond angles near the ideal 120°. Acetylene is linear with bond angles of 180°:

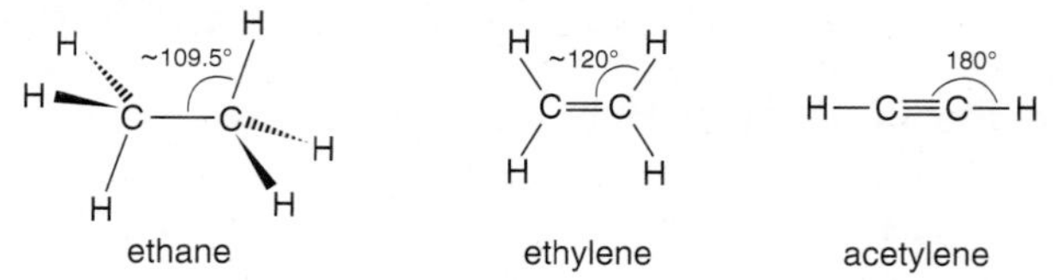

In these molecules, two modes of orbital overlap result in two types of bonds.

End-to-End Overlap and Sigma (σ) Bonding Both C atoms of ethane are sp^3 hybridized (Figure 11.10). The C—C bond arises from overlap of the end of one sp^3 orbital with the end of the other. *End-to-end* overlap forms a **sigma (σ) bond,** which has its *highest electron density along the bond axis* and is shaped like an ellipse rotated

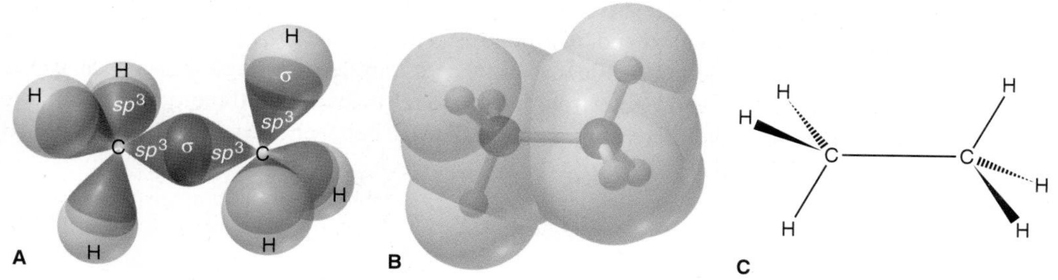

Figure 11.10 The σ bonds in ethane (C_2H_6). **A,** Depiction using atomic contours. **B,** An electron density model shows very slightly positive (*blue*) and negative (*red*) regions. **C,** Wedge-bond perspective drawing.

about its long axis (like a football). *All single bonds are σ bonds,* including the six C—H bonds in ethane.

Side-to-Side Overlap and Pi (π) Bonding For this type of bonding, we'll examine ethylene and acetylene:

1. *In ethylene,* each C atom is sp^2 hybridized. The four valence electrons of C half-fill the three sp^2 orbitals *and* the unhybridized 2*p* orbital, which lies perpendicular to the sp^2 plane (Figure 11.11). Two sp^2 orbitals of each C form C—H σ bonds. The third sp^2 orbital forms a σ bond with the other C. With the σ-bonded C atoms near each other, their half-filled 2*p* orbitals overlap *side to side,* which forms a **pi (π) bond.** It has *two regions (lobes) of electron density,* one above and one below the σ-bond axis. *The two electrons in one π bond occupy both lobes. A double bond consists of one σ bond and one π bond,* which increases electron density between the nuclei (Figure 11.11D). The two electron pairs act as one electron group because each pair occupies a different orbital, which reduces repulsions.

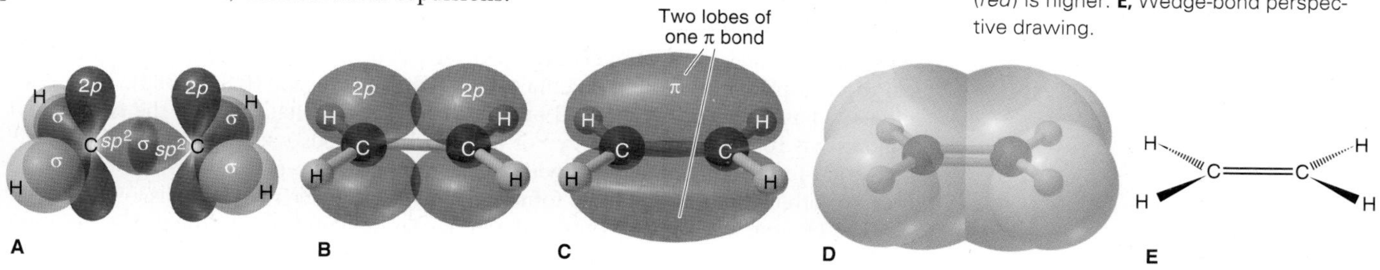

Figure 11.11 The σ and π bonds in ethylene (C_2H_4). **A,** The C—C σ bond and the four C—H σ bonds are shown with the unhybridized 2*p* orbitals. **B,** An accurate depiction of the 2*p* orbitals shows the side-to-side overlap; σ bonds are shown in ball-and-stick form. **C,** Two overlapping regions comprise *one* π bond, which is occupied by two electrons. **D,** With four electrons (one σ bond and one π bond) between the C atoms, electron density (*red*) is higher. **E,** Wedge-bond perspective drawing.

2. *In acetylene,* each C atom is *sp* hybridized, and its four valence electrons half-fill the two *sp* hybrids *and* the two unhybridized 2*p* orbitals (Figure 11.12). Each C forms a C—H σ bond with one *sp* orbital and a C—C σ bond with the other. Side-to-side overlap of one pair of 2*p* orbitals gives one π bond, with electron density above and below the σ bond. Side-to-side overlap of the other pair of 2*p* orbitals gives another π bond, 90° away from the first, with electron density in front and back of the σ bond. The result is a *cylindrically symmetrical* H—C≡C—H molecule. Note the greater electron density between the C atoms created by the six bonding electrons. Any triple bond *consists of one σ and two π bonds.*

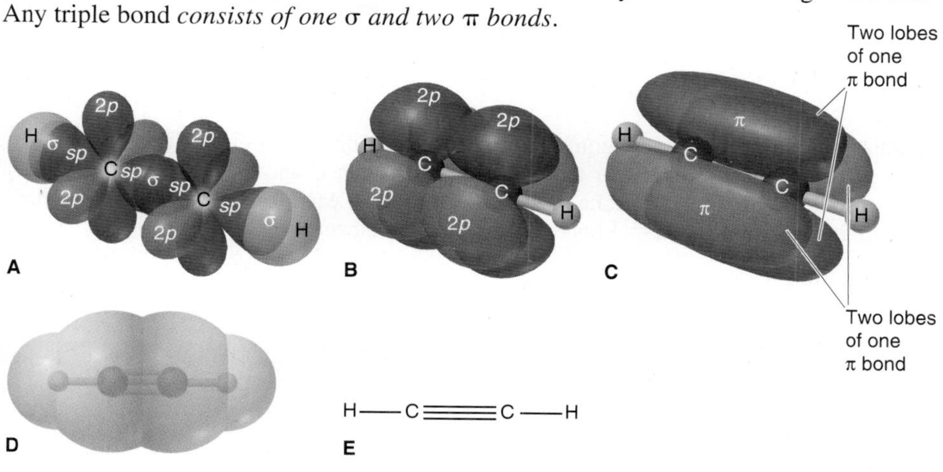

Figure 11.12 The σ bonds and π bonds in acetylene (C_2H_2). **A,** A contour depiction shows the C—C σ bond, the two C—H σ bonds, and two unhybridized 2*p* orbitals (one pair is in *red* for clarity). **B,** The 2*p* orbitals (accurate form) overlap side to side; σ bonds are shown by a ball-and-stick model. **C,** Overlapping regions of two π bonds, one black and the other red. **D,** The molecule has cylindrical symmetry. Six electrons (one σ bond and two π bonds) create even higher electron density (*red*) between the C atoms. **E,** Bond-line drawing.

Mode of Overlap, Bond Strength, and Bond Order Because orbitals overlap less side to side than end to end, a π bond is weaker than a σ bond; thus, for carbon-carbon bonds, a double bond is less than twice as strong as a single bond (Table 9.2, p. 340). Figure 11.13 shows electron density relief maps of the three types of carbon-carbon bonds; note the increasing electron density between the nuclei from single to double to triple bond.

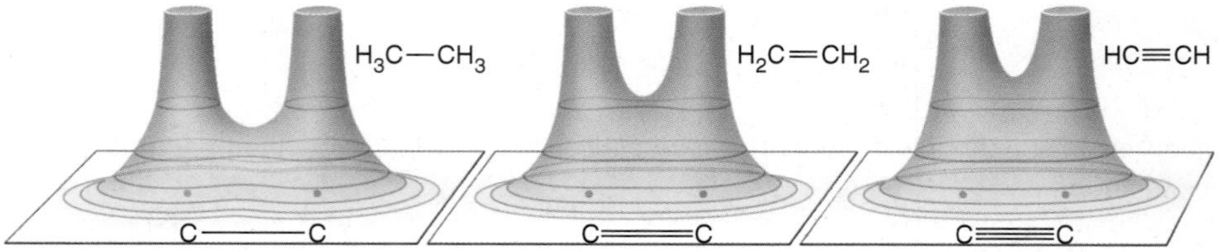

Figure 11.13 Electron density and bond order in ethane, ethylene, and acetylene.

Lone-pair repulsions, bond polarities, and other factors affect overlap between other pairs of atoms. Nevertheless, as a rough approximation, in terms of bond order (BO), a double bond (BO = 2) is about twice as strong as a single bond (BO = 1), and a triple bond (BO = 3) is about three times as strong.

Sample Problem 11.2 Describing the Types of Bonds in Molecules

Problem Describe the types of bonds and orbitals in acetone, $(CH_3)_2CO$.

Plan We use the shape around each central atom to postulate the hybrid orbitals used and use unhybridized orbitals to form the C=O bond.

Solution The shapes are tetrahedral around each C of the two CH_3 (methyl) groups and trigonal planar around the middle C (see Sample Problem 10.8, p. 382). Thus, the middle C has three sp^2 orbitals and one unhybridized p orbital. Each of the two methyl C atoms has four sp^3 orbitals. Three of these form σ bonds with the 1s orbitals of H atoms; the fourth forms a σ bond with an sp^2 orbital of the middle C. Thus, two of the three sp^2 orbitals of the middle C form σ bonds to the other two C atoms.

The O atom is also sp^2 hybridized and has an unhybridized p orbital that can form a π bond. Two of the O atom's sp^2 orbitals hold lone pairs, and the third forms a σ bond with the third sp^2 orbital of the middle C atom. The unhybridized, half-filled 2p orbitals of C and O form a π bond. The σ and π bonds constitute the C=O bond:

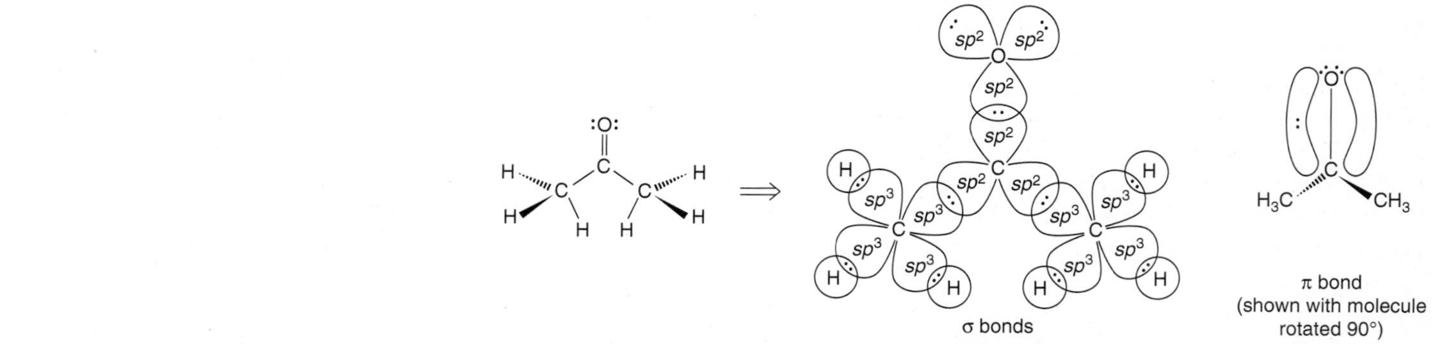

Comment Why would the O atom in acetone be hybridized? After all, it could use two perpendicular p orbitals for the σ and π bonds with C and leave the other p and the s orbital to hold the two lone pairs. Instead, having each lone pair in an sp^2 orbital oriented away from the C=O bond lowers electron-electron repulsions.

Follow-Up Problem 11.2 Describe the types of bonds and orbitals in **(a)** hydrogen cyanide, HCN, and **(b)** carbon dioxide, CO_2.

Orbital Overlap and Molecular Rotation

The type of overlap—end-to-end or side-to-side—affects rotation around the bond:

- *Sigma bond.* A *σ bond allows free rotation* because the extent of overlap is not affected. If you could hold one CH_3 group of ethane, the other CH_3 could spin without affecting the overlap of the C—C σ bond (see Figure 11.10).
- *Pi bond.* A *π bond restricts rotation* because *p* orbitals must be parallel to each other to overlap most effectively. Holding one CH_2 group in ethylene and trying to spin the other decreases the side-to-side overlap and breaks the π bond. For this reason, distinct *cis* and *trans* structures exist for compounds such as 1,2-dichloroethylene (Section 10.3). As Figure 11.14 shows, the π bond allows two *different* arrangements of atoms around the C atoms, which has a major effect on molecular polarity (see p. 385). Rotation around a triple bond is not meaningful: each triple-bonded C atom is bonded to one other group in a linear arrangement, so there can be no difference in the relative positions of attached groups.

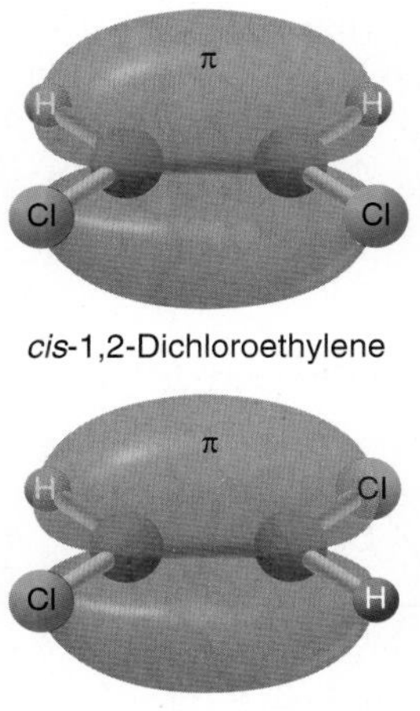

Figure 11.14 Restricted rotation around a π bond. *Cis-* and *trans-*1,2-dichloroethylene are different molecules because the π bond restricts rotation.

Summary of Section 11.2

- End-to-end overlap of atomic orbitals forms a σ bond, which allows free rotation of the bonded parts of the molecule.
- Side-to-side overlap forms a π bond, which restricts rotation.
- A multiple bond consists of a σ bond and either one π bond (double bond) or two (triple bond). Multiple bonds have greater electron density between the nuclei than single bonds do and, thus, higher bond energies.

11.3 • MOLECULAR ORBITAL (MO) THEORY AND ELECTRON DELOCALIZATION

Scientists choose the model that best answers a question: VSEPR for one about molecular shape and VB theory for one about orbital overlap. But neither adequately explains magnetic and spectral properties, and both understate the importance of electron delocalization. To deal with phenomena like these, which involve molecular energy levels, chemists choose **molecular orbital (MO) theory.** The MO model is a quantum-mechanical treatment for molecules similar to the one for atoms (Chapter 8): just as an atom has atomic orbitals (AOs) of given energies and shapes that are occupied by the atom's electrons, a molecule has **molecular orbitals (MOs)** of given energies and shapes that are occupied by the molecule's electrons.

There is a key distinction between VB and MO theories:

- VB theory pictures a molecule as a group of atoms bonded through *localized* overlapping of valence-shell atomic and/or hybrid orbitals occupied by electrons.
- MO theory pictures a molecule as a collection of nuclei with orbitals *delocalized* over the whole molecule and occupied by electrons.

Despite its usefulness, MO theory has a drawback in that MOs are more difficult to visualize than the shapes of VSEPR theory or the hybrid orbitals of VB theory.

The Central Themes of MO Theory

Several key ideas of MO theory appear in its description of H_2 and other simple species: how MOs form, what their energies and shapes are, and how they fill with electrons.

Formation of Molecular Orbitals Just as we need approximations to solve the Schrödinger equation for any atom with more than one electron, we need an approximation to determine the MOs of even the simplest molecule, H_2. The approximation is

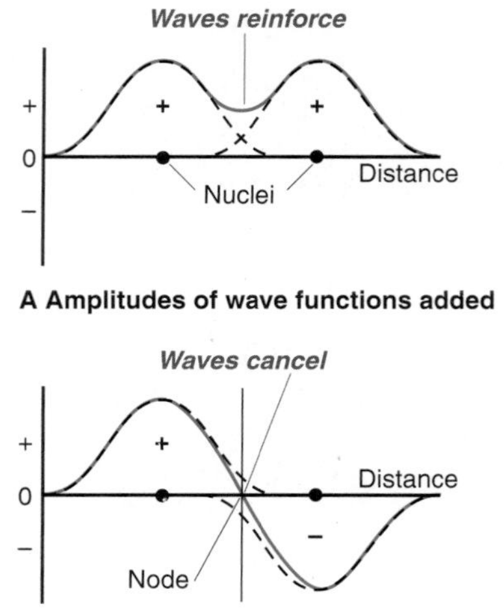

Figure 11.15 An analogy between light waves and atomic wave functions.

to mathematically *combine* (add or subtract) AOs (atomic wave functions) of nearby atoms to form MOs (molecular wave functions). Thus, when two H nuclei lie near each other, their AOs overlap and combine in two ways:

- *Adding the wave functions together.* This combination forms a **bonding MO,** which has *a region of high electron density between the nuclei.* Additive overlap is analogous to light waves reinforcing each other, which makes the amplitude higher and the light brighter. For electron waves, the overlap *increases* the probability that the electrons are between the nuclei (Figure 11.15A).
- *Subtracting the wave functions from each other.* This combination forms an **antibonding MO,** which has *a node, a region of zero electron density, between the nuclei* (Figure 11.15B). Subtractive overlap is analogous to light waves canceling each other, causing the light to disappear. With electron waves, the probability that the electrons lie between the nuclei *decreases* to zero.

The two possible combinations for hydrogen atoms H_A and H_B are

AO of H_A + AO of H_B = bonding MO of H_2 (more e^- density between nuclei)

AO of H_A − AO of H_B = antibonding MO of H_2 (less e^- density between nuclei)

Notice that *the number of AOs combined always equals the number of MOs formed:* two H atomic orbitals combine to form two H_2 molecular orbitals.

Shape and Energy of H_2 Molecular Orbitals Bonding and antibonding MOs have different shapes and energies. Figure 11.16 shows these orbitals for H_2:

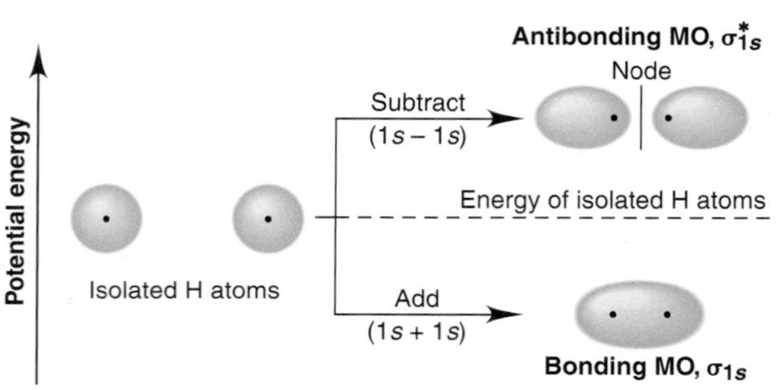

Figure 11.16 Contours and energies of H_2 bonding and antibonding MOs.

- *Bonding MO.* A bonding MO is *lower in energy* than the AOs that form it. Because it is spread mostly *between* the nuclei, nuclear repulsions decrease while nucleus-electron attractions increase. Moreover, two electrons in this MO can delocalize their charges over a larger volume than in nearby, separate AOs, which lowers electron repulsions. Because of these electrostatic effects, when electrons occupy this orbital, the H_2 molecule is *more stable* than the separate H atoms.
- *Antibonding MO.* An antibonding MO is *higher in energy* than the AOs that form it. With most of its electron density *outside* the internuclear region, it has a node between the nuclei, and nuclear repulsions increase. Therefore, when electrons occupy this orbital, the H_2 molecule is *less stable* than the separate H atoms.

Both the bonding and antibonding MOs of H_2 are **sigma (σ) MOs** because they are cylindrically symmetrical about an imaginary line between the nuclei. The bonding MO is denoted by σ_{1s}; that is, a σ MO derived from 1*s* AOs. Antibonding orbitals are denoted with a superscript star: the antibonding MO derived from 1*s* AOs is σ^*_{1s} (spoken "sigma, one ess, star").

For AOs to interact enough to form MOs, they must be similar in *energy* and *orientation.* The 1*s* orbitals of two H atoms have identical energy and orientation, so they interact strongly. We'll revisit this requirement for molecules composed of many-electron atoms.

Electrons in Molecular Orbitals Several aspects of MO theory—filling of MOs, energy-level diagrams, electron configuration, and bond order—relate to earlier ideas:

1. *Filling MOs with electrons.* Electrons enter MOs just as they do AOs:

- MOs are filled in order of increasing energy (aufbau principle).
- An MO can hold a maximum of two electrons with opposite spins (exclusion principle).
- Orbitals of equal energy are half-filled, with spins parallel, before any of them are filled (Hund's rule).

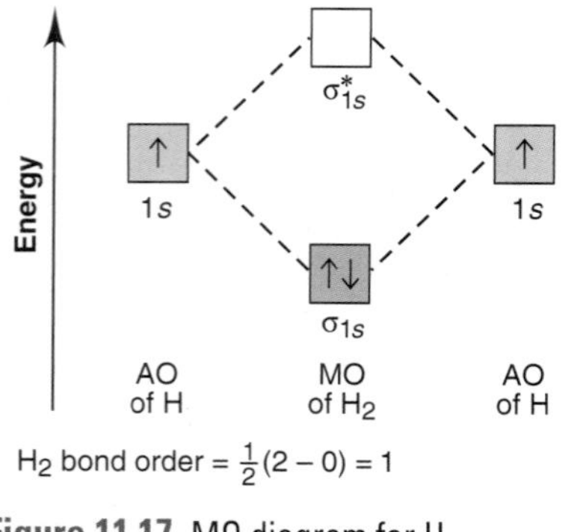

Figure 11.17 MO diagram for H_2.
The vertical placement of the boxes indicates relative energies. Orbital occupancy is shown with arrows and color (dark = full, pale = half-filled, none = empty).

2. *MO energy-level diagrams.* A **molecular orbital (MO) diagram** shows the relative energy and number of electrons in each MO, as well as the AOs from which they formed. In the MO diagram for H_2 (Figure 11.17), two electrons, one from the AO of each H, fill the H_2 bonding MO, while the antibonding MO remains empty.

3. *Electron configuration.* Just as we write an electron configuration for an atom, we can write one for a molecule. The symbol of each occupied MO is written in parentheses, with the number of electrons in it as a superscript outside: the electron configuration of H_2 is $(\sigma_{1s})^2$.

4. *Bond order.* In a Lewis structure, bond order is the number of electron pairs per atom-to-atom linkage. The **MO bond order** is the number of electrons in bonding MOs minus the number in antibonding MOs, divided by two:

$$\text{Bond order} = \tfrac{1}{2}[(\text{no. of e}^- \text{ in bonding MO}) - (\text{no. of e}^- \text{ in antibonding MO})] \quad (11.1)$$

Here are three key points about MO bond order:

- Bond order > 0: the molecule is more stable than the separate atoms, so it *will* form. For H_2, the bond order is $\frac{1}{2}(2 - 0) = 1$.
- Bond order $= 0$: the molecule is as stable as the separate atoms, so it will *not* form (occurs when equal numbers of electrons occupy bonding and antibonding MOs).
- In general, the *higher* the bond order, the *stronger* the bond is.

Do He_2^+ and He_2 Exist? One of the early triumphs of MO theory was its ability to *predict* the existence of He_2^+, the helium molecule-ion, which consists of two He nuclei and three electrons. Let's use MO diagrams to see why He_2^+ exists but He_2 doesn't:

- In He_2^+, the 1*s* AOs form MOs (Figure 11.18A). The three electrons are distributed as a pair in the σ_{1s} MO and a lone electron in the σ^*_{1s} MO. The bond order is $\frac{1}{2}(2 - 1) = \frac{1}{2}$. Thus, He_2^+ has a relatively weak bond, but it should exist. Indeed, this species has been observed frequently when He atoms collide with He^+ ions. Its electron configuration is $(\sigma_{1s})^2(\sigma^*_{1s})^1$.
- In He_2, with four electrons in the σ_{1s} and σ^*_{1s} MOs, both the bonding and antibonding orbitals are filled (Figure 11.18B). Stabilization from the electron pair in the bonding MO is canceled by destabilization from the electron pair in the antibonding MO. With a zero bond order $[\frac{1}{2}(2 - 2) = 0]$, we predict, and experiment has so far confirmed, that a covalent He_2 molecule does not exist.

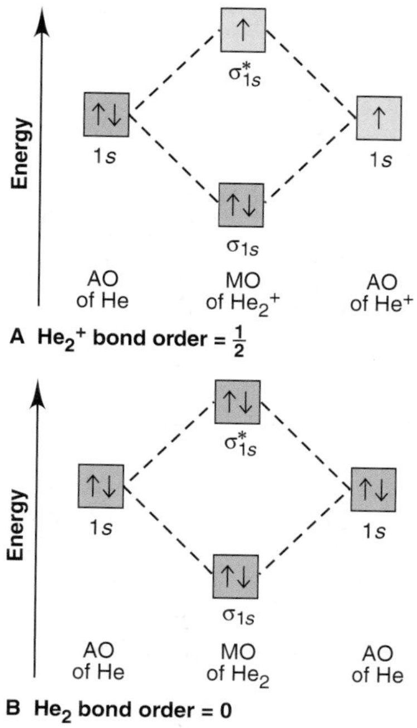

Figure 11.18 MO diagrams for He_2^+ and He_2.

Sample Problem 11.3 Predicting Stability of Species Using MO Diagrams

Problem Use MO diagrams to find bond orders and predict whether H_2^+ and H_2^- exist. If either exists, write its electron configuration.

Plan Since the 1*s* AOs form the MOs, the MO diagrams are similar to the one for H_2. We find the number of electrons in each species and distribute them one at a time to the MOs in order of increasing energy. We obtain the bond order with Equation 11.1 and write the electron configuration as described in the text.

Solution For H_2^+. H_2 has two e^-, so H_2^+ has only one, which enters the bonding MO (*see diagram, below left*). The bond order is $\frac{1}{2}(1 - 0) = \frac{1}{2}$, so we predict that H_2^+ exists. The electron configuration is $(\sigma_{1s})^1$.

For H_2^-. H_2 has two e^-, so H_2^- has three. We place two paired e^- in the bonding MO and one unpaired e^- in the antibonding MO (*see diagram, below right*). The bond order is $\frac{1}{2}(2 - 1) = \frac{1}{2}$, so we predict that H_2^- exists. The electron configuration is $(\sigma_{1s})^2(\sigma^*_{1s})^1$.

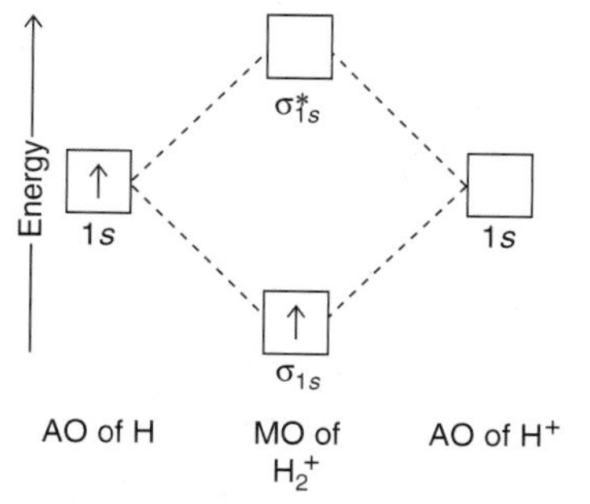

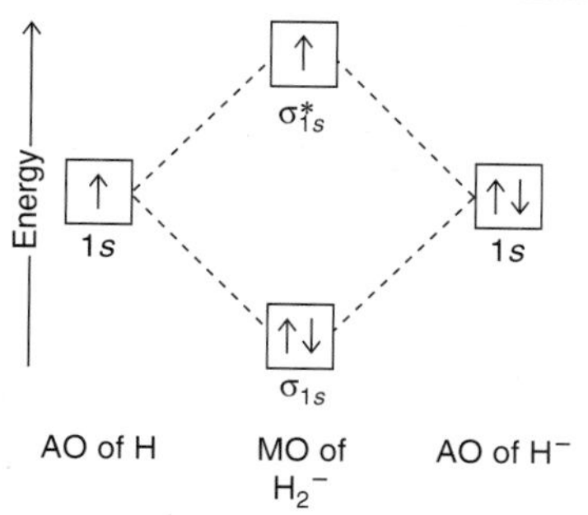

Check The number of electrons in the MOs equals the number of electrons in the AOs.

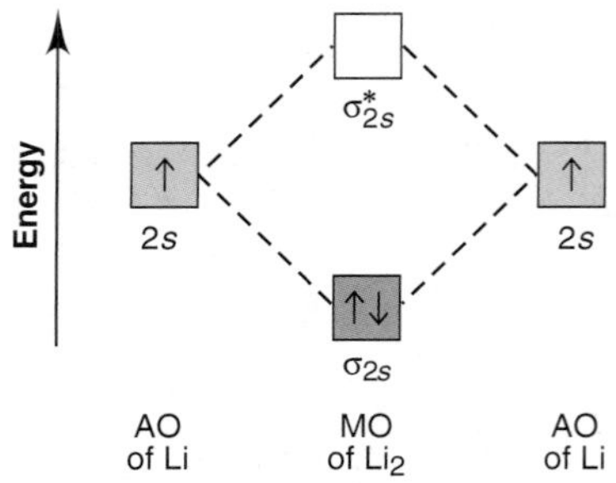

A Li_2 **bond order = 1**

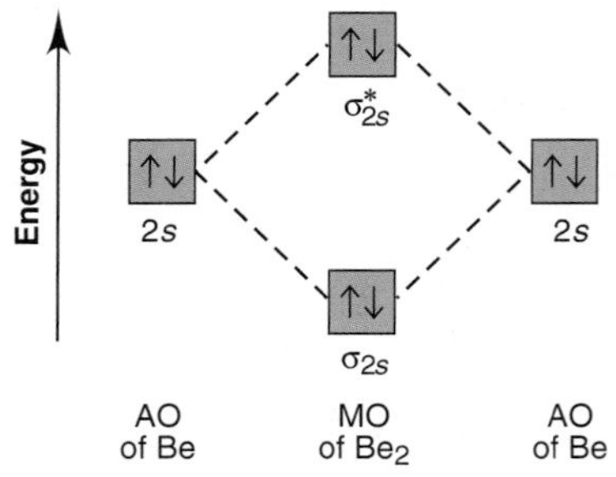

B Be_2 **bond order = 0**

Figure 11.19 Bonding in *s*-block homonuclear diatomic molecules. Only outer (valence) AOs interact enough to form MOs.

Comment Both species have been detected spectroscopically, H_2^+ in the material around stars and H_2^- in the laboratory.

Follow-Up Problem 11.3 Use an MO diagram to find the bond order and predict whether two H^- ions could form H_2^{2-}. If it does exist, write its electron configuration.

Homonuclear Diatomic Molecules of Period 2 Elements

Homonuclear diatomic molecules are composed of two identical atoms. In addition to H_2 from Period 1, you're familiar with N_2, O_2, and F_2 from Period 2 as the elemental forms under standard conditions. Others in Period 2—Li_2, Be_2, B_2, C_2, and Ne_2—are observed, if at all, at high temperatures. We'll divide them into molecules from the *s* block, Groups 1A(1) and 2A(2), and the *p* block, Groups 3A(13) through 8A(18).

Bonding in the *s*-Block Homonuclear Diatomic Molecules Both Li and Be occur as metals under normal conditions, but MO theory can examine their stability as diatomic gases, dilithium (Li_2) and diberyllium (Be_2).

These atoms have electrons in inner (1*s*) and outer (2*s*) AOs, but we ignore the inner ones because, in general, *only outer (valence) AOs interact enough to form MOs.* Like those formed from 1*s* AOs, these 2*s* AOs form σ MOs, cylindrically symmetrical around the internuclear axis.

- In Li_2, the two valence electrons fill the bonding (σ_{2s}) MO, with opposing spins, leaving the antibonding (σ^*_{2s}) MO empty (Figure 11.19A). The bond order is $\frac{1}{2}(2 - 0) = 1$. In fact, Li_2 *has* been observed; the electron configuration is $(\sigma_{2s})^2$.
- In Be_2, the four valence electrons fill the σ_{2s} and σ^*_{2s} MOs (Figure 11.19B), giving an orbital occupancy similar to that in He_2. The bond order is $\frac{1}{2}(2 - 2) = 0$, and the ground state of Be_2 has never been observed.

Shape and Energy of MOs from Atomic *p*-Orbital Combinations As we move to boron, atomic 2*p* orbitals are occupied. Recall that *p* orbitals can overlap by two modes, which correspond to two ways their wave functions combine (Figure 11.20):

- End-to-end combination gives a pair of σ MOs, the σ_{2p} and σ^*_{2p}.
- Side-to-side combination gives a pair of **pi (π) MOs,** π_{2p} and π^*_{2p}.

Despite the different shapes, MOs derived from *p* orbitals are like those from *s* orbitals. Bonding MOs have most of the electron density *between* the nuclei, and antibonding MOs have most *outside* the internuclear region, with a node between the nuclei.

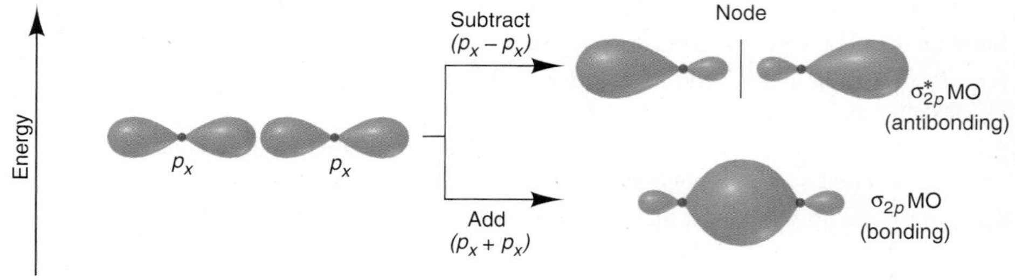

A

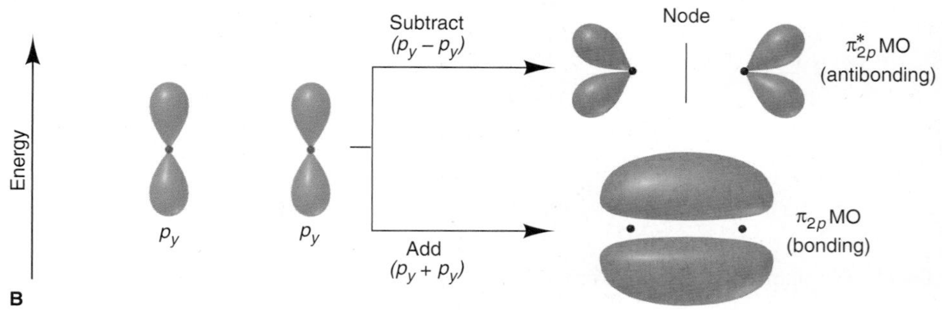

B

Figure 11.20 Shapes and energies of σ and π MOs from combinations of 2*p* atomic orbitals. A, The *p* orbitals lying along the internuclear axis (designated p_x) overlap end to end and form σ_{2p} and σ^*_{2p} MOs. **B,** The *p* orbitals perpendicular to the internuclear axis overlap side to side and form two π MOs. (The p_y interactions, shown here, are the same as for the p_z, for a total of four π MOs.)

The order of energy levels for MOs, whether bonding or antibonding, is based on the order of AO energy levels *and* on the mode of the *p*-orbital overlap:

- MOs formed from 2*s* orbitals are *lower in energy* than MOs formed from 2*p* orbitals because 2*s* AOs are lower in energy than 2*p* AOs.
- Bonding MOs are *lower in energy* than antibonding MOs: σ_{2p} is lower in energy than σ^*_{2p} and π_{2p} is lower than π^*_{2p}.
- Atomic *p* orbitals overlap more extensively end to end than side to side. Thus, the σ_{2p} MO is usually lower in energy than the π_{2p} MO. We also find that the destabilizing effect of the σ^*_{2p} MO is greater than that of the π^*_{2p} MO.

Thus, the energy order for MOs derived from 2*p* orbitals is typically

$$\sigma_{2p} < \pi_{2p} < \pi^*_{2p} < \sigma^*_{2p}$$

Each atom has three mutually perpendicular 2*p* orbitals. When the six *p* orbitals in two atoms combine, the two that interact end to end form one σ and one σ* MO, and the two pairs of orbitals that interact side to side form two π MOs and two π* MOs. Placing these orientations within the energy order gives the *expected* MO diagram for the *p*-block Period 2 homonuclear diatomic molecules (Figure 11.21A).

Recall that only AOs of similar energy interact enough to form MOs. This fact leads to two energy orders:

1. ***Without** s and p orbital mixing: O_2, F_2, and Ne_2.* The order in Figure 11.21A assumes that *s* and *p* AOs are so different in energy that they do not interact; we say the orbitals do not *mix*. Lying at the right of Period 2, O, F, and Ne are relatively small. Thus, as electrons start to pair up in the half-filled 2*p* orbitals, strong repulsions raise the energy of the 2*p* orbitals high enough above the 2*s* orbitals to prevent orbital mixing.

2. ***With** s and p orbital mixing: B_2, C_2, and N_2.* B, C, and N atoms are relatively large, with 2*p* AOs only half-filled, so repulsions are weaker. As a result, orbital energies are close enough for some mixing to occur between the 2*s* of one atom and the end-on 2*p* of the other. The effect is to *lower* the energy of the σ_{2s} and σ^*_{2s} MOs and *raise* the energy of the σ_{2p} and σ^*_{2p} MOs; the π MOs are not affected. The MO diagram for B_2, C_2, and N_2 reflects this mixing (Figure 11.21B). The only difference from the MO diagram for O_2, F_2, and Ne_2 is the *reverse in energy order* of the σ_{2p} and π_{2p} MOs.

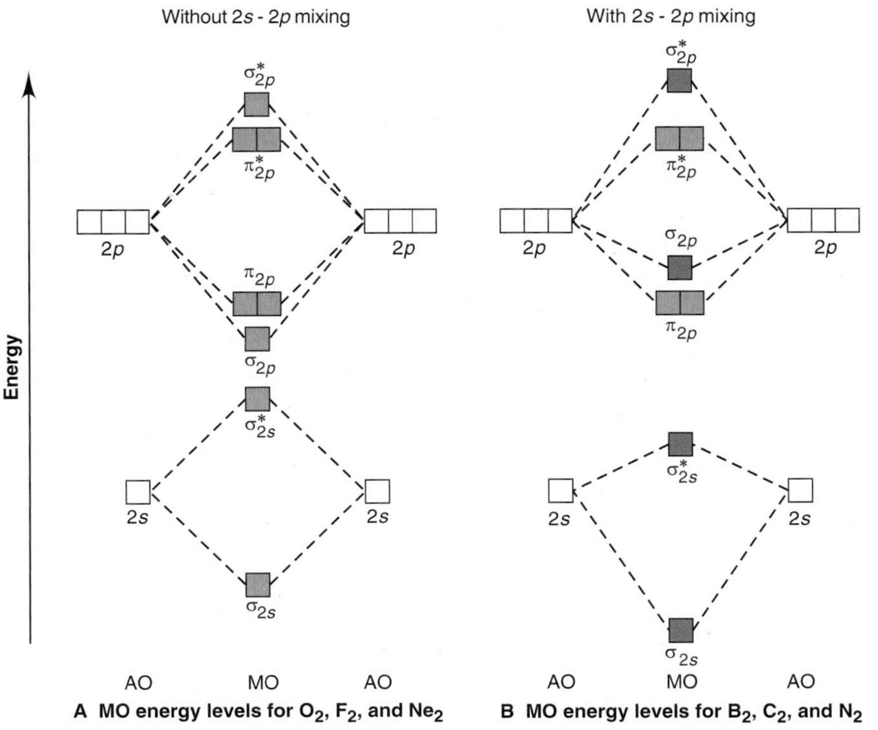

Figure 11.21 Relative MO energy levels for Period 2 homonuclear diatomic molecules. (For clarity, the MOs affected by mixing are shown in *purple*.)

Figure 11.22 MO occupancy and some properties of B_2 through Ne_2. Energy order and occupancy of MOs are above bar graphs of bond energy and length, bond order, magnetic properties, and outer (valence) electron configuration.

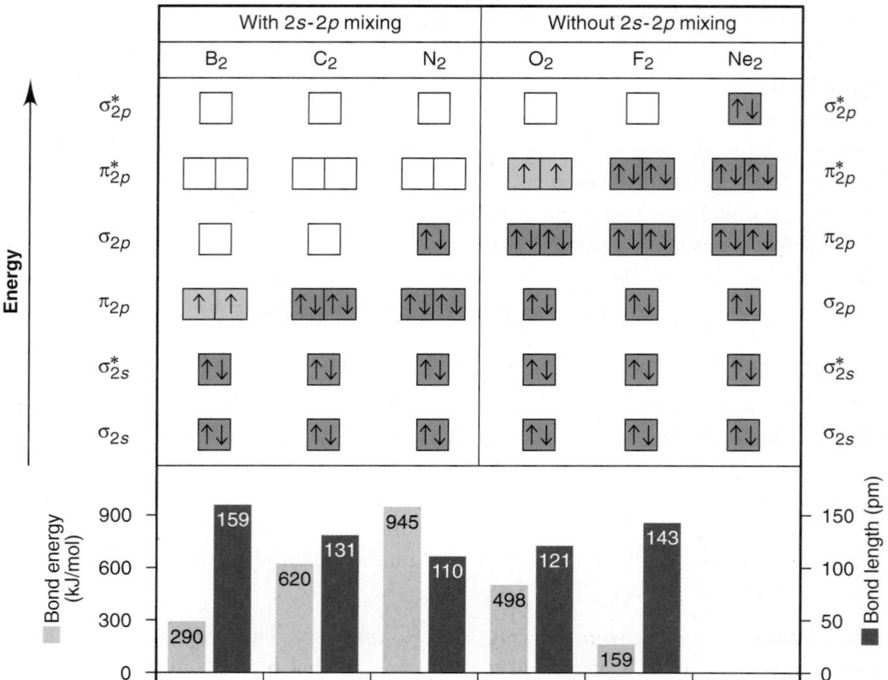

	B_2	C_2	N_2	O_2	F_2	Ne_2
Bond order	1	2	3	2	1	0
Magnetic properties	Paramagnetic	Diamagnetic	Diamagnetic	Paramagnetic	Diamagnetic	—
Valence electron configuration	$(\sigma_{2s})^2(\sigma^*_{2s})^2(\pi_{2p})^2$	$(\sigma_{2s})^2(\sigma^*_{2s})^2(\pi_{2p})^4$	$(\sigma_{2s})^2(\sigma^*_{2s})^2(\pi_{2p})^4(\sigma_{2p})^2$	$(\sigma_{2s})^2(\sigma^*_{2s})^2(\sigma_{2p})^2(\pi_{2p})^4(\pi^*_{2p})^2$	$(\sigma_{2s})^2(\sigma^*_{2s})^2(\sigma_{2p})^2(\pi_{2p})^4(\pi^*_{2p})^4$	$(\sigma_{2s})^2(\sigma^*_{2s})^2(\sigma_{2p})^2(\pi_{2p})^4(\pi^*_{2p})^4(\sigma^*_{2p})^2$

Bonding in the *p*-Block Homonuclear Diatomic Molecules Figure 11.22 shows the MOs, electron occupancy, and some properties of B_2 through Ne_2. Note that

1. *Higher* bond order correlates with *greater* bond energy and *shorter* bond length.

2. Orbital occupancy correlates with magnetic properties. Recall from Chapter 8 that if a substance has unpaired electrons, it is *paramagnetic,* and if all electrons are paired, the substance is *diamagnetic;* the same applies to molecules. Let's examine the MO occupancy and some properties of these molecules:

- *B_2*. The B_2 molecule has six outer electrons: four fill the σ_{2s} and σ^*_{2s} MOs. The remaining two electrons occupy the two π_{2p} MOs, one in each orbital, in keeping with Hund's rule. With four electrons in bonding MOs and two in antibonding MOs, the bond order of B_2 is $\frac{1}{2}(4 - 2) = 1$. As expected from the two lone electrons, B_2 is paramagnetic.
- *C_2*. Two additional electrons in C_2 fill the two π_{2p} MOs. With two more bonding electrons than B_2, the bond order of C_2 is 2 and the bond is stronger and shorter. But with all the electrons paired, C_2 is diamagnetic.
- *N_2*. Two more electrons in N_2 fill the σ_{2p} MO, so the molecule is also diamagnetic. The bond order of 3 is consistent with the triple bond in the Lewis structure and with a stronger, shorter bond.
- *O_2*. With this molecule, we see the power of MO theory over VB theory and others based on electrons in localized orbitals. It is impossible to write one Lewis structure consistent with the fact that O_2 is double bonded and paramagnetic. We can write one with a double bond and paired electrons, and another with a single bond and two unpaired electrons:

  $$\ddot{\underset{..}{O}}{=}\ddot{\underset{..}{O}} \quad \text{or} \quad :\dot{\underset{..}{O}}{-}\dot{\underset{..}{O}}:$$

  MO theory resolves this paradox beautifully: with eight electrons in bonding MOs and four in antibonding MOs, the bond order is $\frac{1}{2}(8 - 4) = 2$, and it is paramagnetic because *one* electron occupies each of *two* π^*_{2p} MOs with unpaired (parallel) spins. A thin stream of liquid O_2 will remain suspended between the poles of a powerful magnet (Figure 11.23). As expected, the bond is weaker and longer than the one in N_2.

- F_2. Two more electrons in F_2 fill the π^*_{2p} orbitals, so it is diamagnetic. The bond has an order of 1 and is weaker and longer than the one in O_2. Note that this bond is shorter, yet about half as strong as the single bond in B_2. We might have expected it to be stronger because F is smaller than B. But 18 electrons in the smaller volume of F_2 cause greater repulsions than the 10 in B_2, so the F_2 bond is weaker.
- Ne_2. The final member of the Period 2 series doesn't exist for the same reason He_2 doesn't: all the MOs are filled, which gives a bond order of zero.

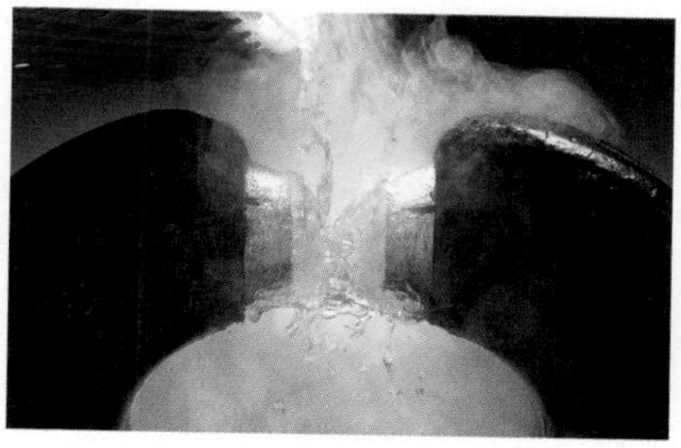

Figure 11.23 The paramagnetic properties of O_2.

Sample Problem 11.4 Using MO Theory to Explain Bond Properties

Problem Explain the following data with diagrams showing the occupancy of MOs:

	N_2	N_2^+	O_2	O_2^+
Bond energy (kJ/mol)	945	841	498	623
Bond length (pm)	110	112	121	112

Plan The data show that removing an electron from each parent molecule has opposite effects: N_2^+ has a weaker, longer bond than N_2, but O_2^+ has a stronger, shorter bond than O_2. We determine the valence electrons in each species, draw the sequence of MO energy levels (showing orbital mixing in N_2 but not in O_2), and fill them with electrons. To explain the data, we calculate bond orders, which relate directly to bond energy and inversely to bond length.

Solution Determining the valence electrons:

N has 5 valence e^-, so N_2 has 10 and N_2^+ has 9

O has 6 valence e^-, so O_2 has 12 and O_2^+ has 11

Drawing and filling the MO diagrams:

N_2		N_2^+	O_2		O_2^+
[ ]	σ^*_{2p}	[ ]	[ ]	σ^*_{2p}	[ ]
[ ][ ]	π^*_{2p}	[ ][ ]	[↑][↑]	π^*_{2p}	[↑][ ]
[↑↓]	σ_{2p}	[↑]	[↑↓][↑↓]	π_{2p}	[↑↓][↑↓]
[↑↓][↑↓]	π_{2p}	[↑↓][↑↓]	[↑↓]	σ_{2p}	[↑↓]
[↑↓]	σ^*_{2s}	[↑↓]	[↑↓]	σ^*_{2s}	[↑↓]
[↑↓]	σ_{2s}	[↑↓]	[↑↓]	σ_{2s}	[↑↓]

Calculating bond orders:

$\frac{1}{2}(8-2)=3$ $\quad \frac{1}{2}(7-2)=2.5$ $\quad \frac{1}{2}(8-4)=2$ $\quad \frac{1}{2}(8-3)=2.5$

Explaining the data:

1. When N_2 becomes N_2^+, a *bonding* electron is removed, so the bond order decreases. Thus, N_2^+ has a weaker, longer bond than N_2.
2. When O_2 becomes O_2^+, an *antibonding* electron is removed, so the bond order increases. Thus, O_2^+ has a stronger, shorter bond than O_2.

Check The answers make sense in terms of bond order, bond energy, and bond length. Check that the total number of bonding and antibonding electrons equals the number of valence electrons calculated.

Follow-Up Problem 11.4 Determine the bond orders for the following species: F_2^{2-}, F_2^-, F_2, F_2^+, F_2^{2+}. List the species in order of increasing bond energy and in order of increasing bond length.

Two Heteronuclear Diatomic Molecules: HF and NO

Heteronuclear diatomic molecules have asymmetric MO diagrams because the AOs of the *different* atoms have unequal energies. Atoms with greater effective nuclear charge (Z_{eff}) pull their electrons closer, so they have more stable (lower energy) AOs (Section 8.1) and higher EN values (Section 9.5). Let's examine the bonding in HF and NO.

Bonding in HF To form the MOs in HF, we decide which AOs will combine. The high Z_{eff} of F holds its electrons so tightly that the 1*s*, 2*s*, and 2*p* orbitals of F have lower energy than the 1*s* of H. The half-filled F 2*p* orbital interacts with the H 1*s* through end-on overlap, which forms σ and σ* MOs. The two filled 2*p* orbitals of F are called **nonbonding MOs.** Because they are not involved in bonding, they have the same energy as the isolated AOs (Figure 11.24A).

The bonding MO is closer in energy to the AOs of F, so the F 2*p* orbital contributes more to the HF bond than the H 1*s* does. In polar covalent molecules, *bonding MOs are closer in energy to the AOs of the more electronegative atom.* In effect, fluorine's greater electronegativity lowers the energy of the bonding MO and draws the bonding electrons closer.

Bonding in NO Nitrogen monoxide (nitric oxide) is highly reactive because of its lone electron. Two possible Lewis structures for NO, with formal charges (Section 10.1), are

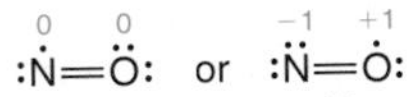

I II

Both structures show a double bond, but the *measured* bond energy suggests a bond order *higher* than 2. Moreover, it is not clear where the lone electron resides, although the lower formal charges for structure I suggest that it is on the N.

The MO diagram is asymmetric, with the AOs of the more electronegative O lower in energy (Figure 11.24B). When the 11 valence electrons fill the MOs of NO, the lone electron occupies one of the π^*_{2p} orbitals. Eight bonding and three antibonding electrons give a bond order of $\frac{1}{2}(8 - 3) = 2.5$, more in keeping with the data than either Lewis structure. Bonding electrons lie in MOs closer in energy to the AOs of the O atom. The 2*p* orbitals of N contribute more to the orbital that holds the lone electron, so it spends more time closer to N. (This diagram shows the energy order *with* 2*s*–2*p* mixing, as in Figure 11.21, but the result is the same as the order without mixing.)

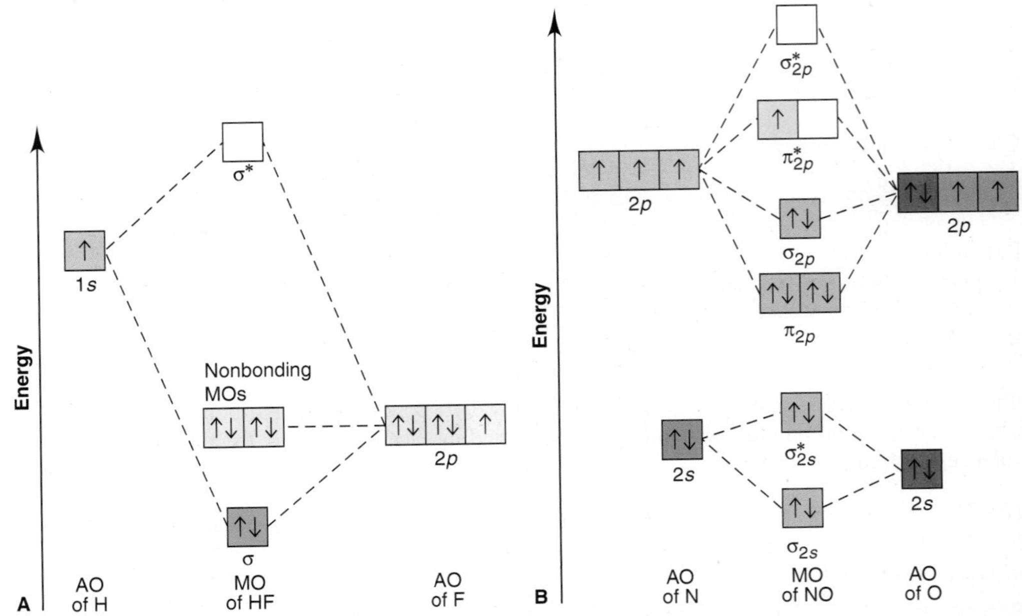

Figure 11.24 The MO diagrams for HF and NO. **A,** In HF, the bonding MO is closer in energy to the 2*p* orbital of F. (The 2*s* AO of F is not shown.) **B,** In NO, the lone electron occupies an MO closer in energy to the 2*p* of N.

Two Polyatomic Molecules: Benzene and Ozone

The orbital shapes and MO diagrams for polyatomic molecules are too complex for a detailed treatment here. But we'll briefly discuss how the model eliminates the need for resonance forms and helps explain the effects of the absorption of energy.

Recall that we cannot draw one Lewis structure for either benzene or ozone, so we draw separate forms of a resonance hybrid. The VB model also uses resonance because it relies on *localized* bonds. In contrast, MO theory pictures a structure of delocalized σ and π MOs. Figure 11.25 shows the lowest energy π-bonding MOs in benzene and ozone. The extended areas of electron density allow delocalization of one π-bonding electron pair over the entire molecule, thus eliminating the need for separate resonance forms:

- *In benzene*, the upper and lower hexagonal lobes of this MO lie above and below the σ plane of the six C nuclei.
- *In ozone*, the two lobes of this MO extend over and under the three O nuclei.

The full MO diagrams for these molecules help us rationalize how bonding electrons in O_3 become excited and occupy empty antibonding orbitals when the molecule absorbs UV radiation in the stratosphere, and why the UV spectrum of benzene has its characteristic absorption bands.

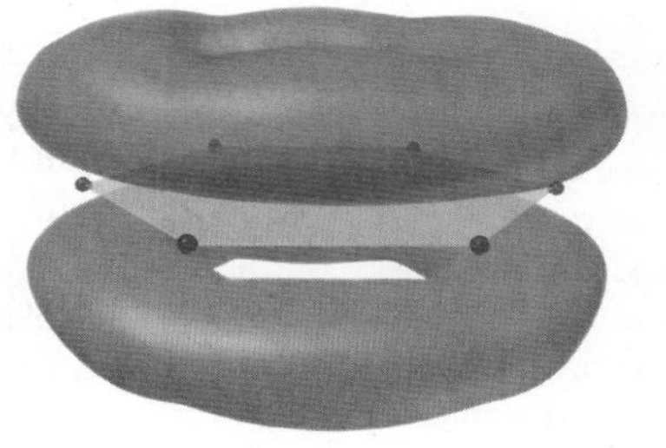
Benzene, C_6H_6

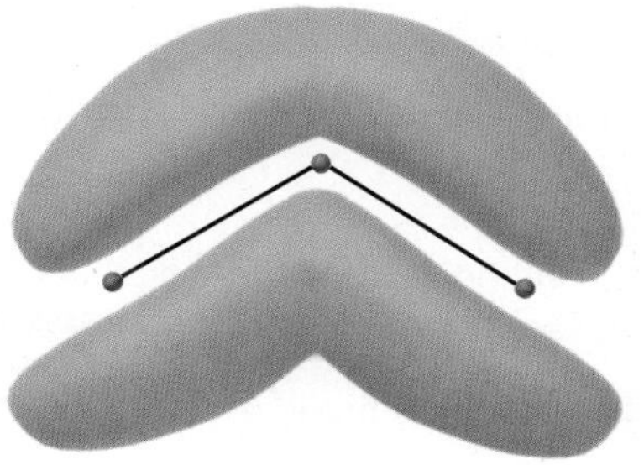
Ozone, O_3

Figure 11.25 The lowest energy π-bonding MOs in benzene and ozone.

Summary of Section 11.3

- Molecular orbital (MO) theory treats a molecule as a collection of nuclei with MOs delocalized over the entire structure.
- Atomic orbitals of comparable energy can be added or subtracted to obtain bonding or antibonding MOs, respectively.
- Bonding MOs, whether σ or π, have most of the electron density between the nuclei and are lower in energy than the AOs; most of the electron density in antibonding MOs does not lie between the nuclei, so these MOs are higher in energy.
- MOs are filled in order of their energy with paired electrons having opposite spins.
- MO diagrams show energy levels and orbital occupancy. Diagrams for the Period 2 homonuclear diatomic molecules explain bond energy, bond length, and magnetic behavior.
- In heteronuclear diatomic molecules, the more electronegative atom contributes more to the bonding MOs.
- MO theory eliminates the need for resonance forms to depict larger molecules.

CHAPTER REVIEW GUIDE

Learning Objectives

Relevant section (§) and/or sample problem (SP) numbers appear in parentheses.

Understand These Concepts

1. The main ideas of valence bond theory—orbital overlap, opposing electron spins, and hybridization—as a means of rationalizing molecular shapes (§11.1)
2. How orbitals mix to form hybrid orbitals with different spatial orientations (§11.1)
3. The distinction between end-to-end and side-to-side overlap and the origin of sigma (σ) and pi (π) bonds in simple molecules (§11.2)
4. How these two modes of orbital overlap lead to single, double, and triple bonds (§11.2)
5. Why π bonding restricts rotation around double bonds (§11.2)
6. The distinction between the localized bonding of VB theory and the delocalized bonding of MO theory (§11.3)
7. How addition or subtraction of AOs forms bonding or antibonding MOs (§11.3)
8. The shapes of MOs formed from combinations of two *s* orbitals and combinations of two *p* orbitals (§11.3)
9. How MO bond order predicts the stability of molecular species (§11.3)
10. How MO theory explains the bonding and magnetic properties of homonuclear and heteronuclear diatomic molecules of Period 2 elements (§11.3)

Master These Skills

1. Using molecular shape to postulate the hybrid orbitals used by a central atom (SP 11.1)
2. Describing the types of orbitals and bonds in a molecule (SP 11.2)
3. Drawing MO diagrams, writing electron configurations, and calculating bond orders of molecular species (SP 11.3)
4. Explaining bond and magnetic properties with MO theory (SP 11.4)

Key Terms

Page numbers appear in parentheses.

Section 11.1
valence bond (VB) theory (395)
hybridization (396)
hybrid orbital (396)
sp hybrid orbital (396)
sp^2 hybrid orbital (398)
sp^3 hybrid orbital (398)
sp^3d hybrid orbital (399)
sp^3d^2 hybrid orbital (400)

Section 11.2
sigma (σ) bond (402)
pi (π) bond (403)

Section 11.3
molecular orbital (MO) theory (405)
molecular orbital (MO) (405)
bonding MO (406)
antibonding MO (406)
sigma (σ) MO (406)
molecular orbital (MO) diagram (406)
MO bond order (407)
homonuclear diatomic molecule (408)
pi (π) MO (408)
nonbonding MO (412)

Key Equations and Relationships

Page numbers appear in parentheses.

11.1 Calculating the MO bond order (407): Bond order $= \frac{1}{2}[(\text{no. of } e^- \text{ in bonding MO}) - (\text{no. of } e^- \text{ in antibonding MO})]$

Brief Solutions to Follow-Up Problems

11.1 (a) Shape is linear, so Be is *sp* hybridized.

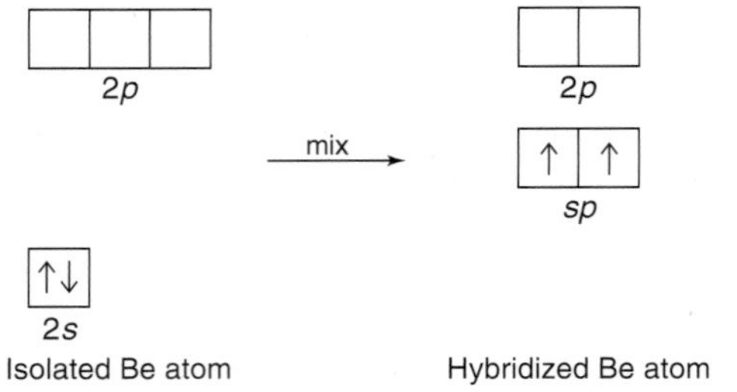

(b) Shape is tetrahedral, so Si is sp^3 hybridized.

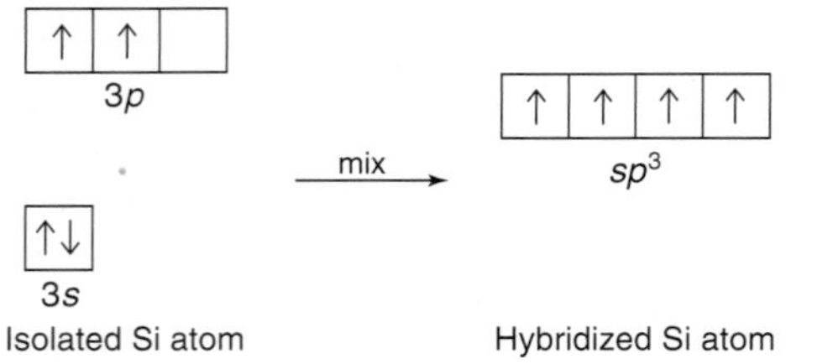

(c) Shape is square planar, so Xe is sp^3d^2 hybridized.

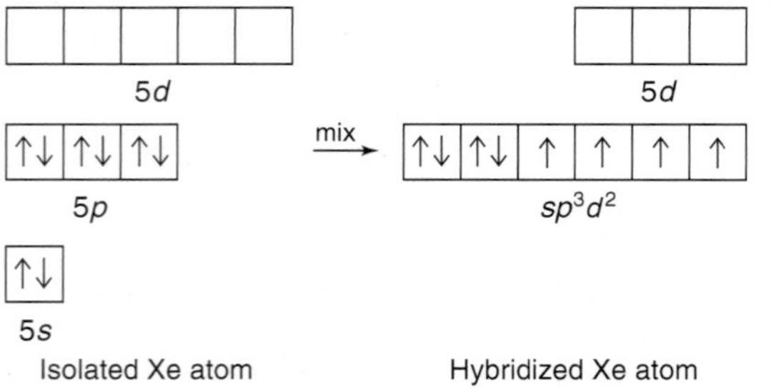

11.2 (a) H—C≡N:

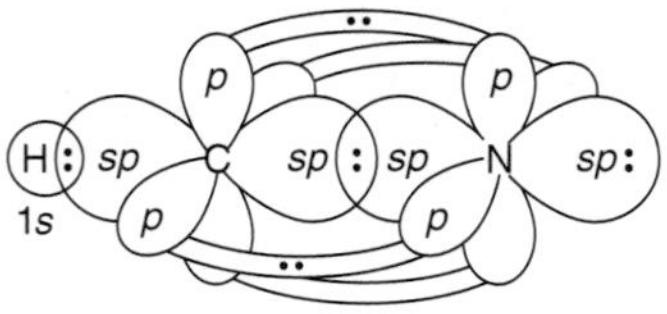

HCN is linear, so C is *sp* hybridized. N is also *sp* hybridized. One *sp* of C overlaps the 1*s* of H to form a σ bond. The other *sp* of C overlaps one *sp* of N to form a σ bond. The other *sp* of N holds a lone pair. Two unhybridized *p* orbitals of N and two of C overlap to form two π bonds.

(b) Ö=C=Ö

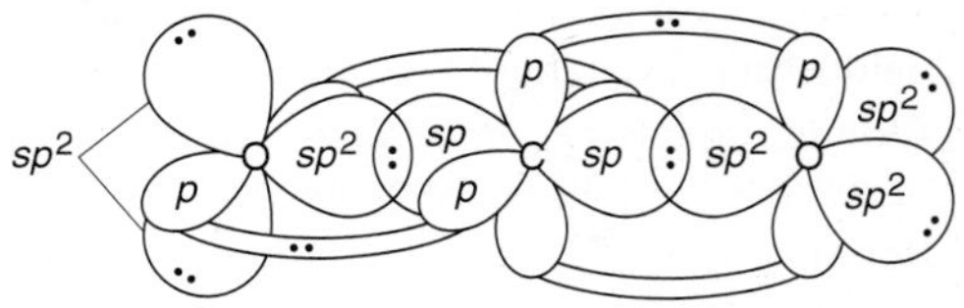

CO_2 is linear, so C is *sp* hybridized. Both O atoms are sp^2 hybridized. Each *sp* of C overlaps one sp^2 of an O to form two σ bonds. Each of the two unhybridized *p* orbitals of C forms a π bond with the unhybridized *p* of one of the two O atoms. Two sp^2 of each O hold lone pairs.

11.3

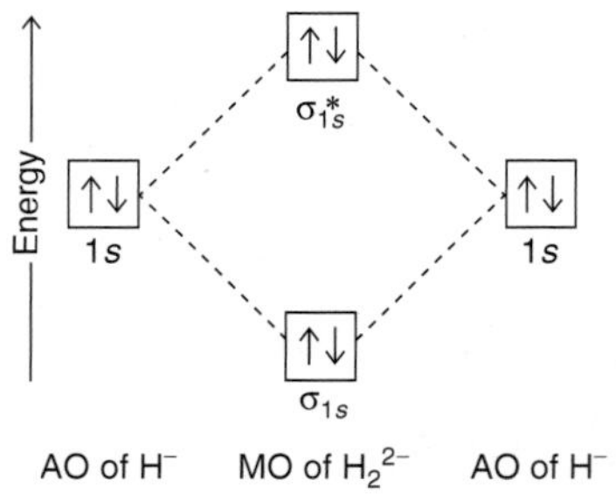

Does not exist: bond order $= \frac{1}{2}(2 - 2) = 0$.

11.4 Bond orders: $F_2^{2-} = 0$; $F_2^- = \frac{1}{2}$; $F_2 = 1$; $F_2^+ = 1\frac{1}{2}$; $F_2^{2+} = 2$

Bond energy: $F_2^{2-} < F_2^- < F_2 < F_2^+ < F_2^{2+}$

Bond length: $F_2^{2+} < F_2^+ < F_2 < F_2^-$; F_2^{2-} does not exist

PROBLEMS

Problems with **colored** numbers are answered in Appendix E and worked in detail in the Student Solutions Manual. Problem sections match those in the text and provide the numbers of relevant sample problems. Most offer Concept Review Questions, Skill-Building Exercises (grouped in pairs covering the same concept), and Problems in Context. The Comprehensive Problems are based on material from any section or previous chapter.

Valence Bond (VB) Theory and Orbital Hybridization

(Sample Problem 11.1)

Concept Review Questions

11.1 What type of central-atom orbital hybridization corresponds to each electron-group arrangement: (a) trigonal planar; (b) octahedral; (c) linear; (d) tetrahedral; (e) trigonal bipyramidal?

11.2 What is the orbital hybridization of a central atom that has one lone pair and bonds to: (a) two other atoms; (b) three other atoms; (c) four other atoms; (d) five other atoms?

11.3 How do carbon and silicon differ with regard to the *types* of orbitals available for hybridization? Explain.

11.4 How many hybrid orbitals form when four atomic orbitals of a central atom mix? Explain.

Skill-Building Exercises (grouped in similar pairs)

11.5 Give the number and type of hybrid orbital that forms when each set of atomic orbitals mixes:
(a) two *d*, one *s*, and three *p* (b) three *p* and one *s*

11.6 Give the number and type of hybrid orbital that forms when each set of atomic orbitals mixes:
(a) one *p* and one *s* (b) three *p*, one *d*, and one *s*

11.7 What is the hybridization of nitrogen in each of the following: (a) NO; (b) NO_2; (c) NO_2^-?

11.8 What is the hybridization of carbon in each of the following: (a) CO_3^{2-}; (b) $C_2O_4^{2-}$; (c) NCO^-?

11.9 What is the hybridization of chlorine in each of the following: (a) ClO_2; (b) ClO_3^-; (c) ClO_4^-?

11.10 What is the hybridization of bromine in each of the following: (a) BrF_3; (b) BrO_2^-; (c) BrF_5?

11.11 Which types of atomic orbitals of the central atom mix to form hybrid orbitals in (a) $SiClH_3$; (b) CS_2; (c) SCl_3F; (d) NF_3?

11.12 Which types of atomic orbitals of the central atom mix to form hybrid orbitals in (a) Cl_2O; (b) $BrCl_3$; (c) PF_5; (d) SO_3^{2-}?

11.13 Phosphine (PH_3) reacts with borane (BH_3) as follows:

$$PH_3 + BH_3 \longrightarrow H_3P—BH_3$$

(a) Which of the illustrations below depicts the change, if any, in the orbital hybridization of P during this reaction? (b) Which depicts the change, if any, in the orbital hybridization of B?

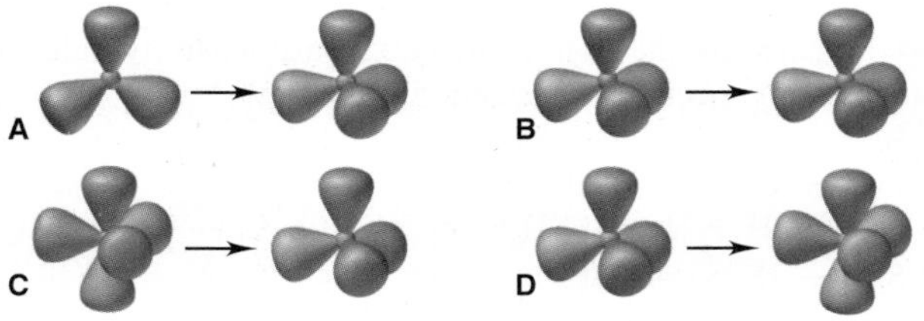

11.14 The illustrations below depict differences in orbital hybridization of some tellurium (Te) fluorides. (a) Which depicts the difference, if any, between TeF_6 (*left*) and TeF_5^- (*right*)? (b) Which depicts the difference, if any, between TeF_4 (*left*) and TeF_6 (*right*)?

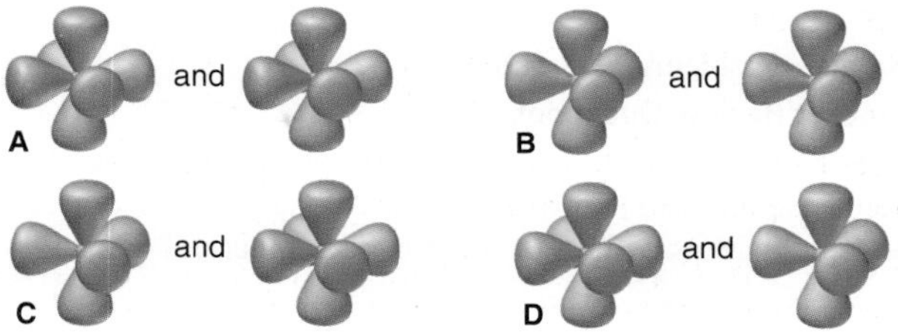

11.15 Use partial orbital diagrams to show how the atomic orbitals of the central atom lead to hybrid orbitals in (a) $GeCl_4$; (b) BCl_3; (c) CH_3^+.

11.16 Use partial orbital diagrams to show how the atomic orbitals of the central atom lead to hybrid orbitals in (a) BF_4^-; (b) PO_4^{3-}; (c) SO_3.

11.17 Use partial orbital diagrams to show how the atomic orbitals of the central atom lead to hybrid orbitals in (a) $SeCl_2$; (b) H_3O^+; (c) IF_4^-.

11.18 Use partial orbital diagrams to show how the atomic orbitals of the central atom lead to hybrid orbitals in (a) $AsCl_3$; (b) $SnCl_2$; (c) PF_6^-.

Problems in Context

11.19 Methyl isocyanate, $CH_3—\ddot{N}=C=\ddot{O}:$, is an intermediate in the manufacture of many pesticides. In 1984 a leak from a manufacturing plant resulted in the death of more than 2000 people in Bhopal, India. What are the hybridizations of the N atom and the two C atoms in methyl isocyanate? Sketch the molecular shape.

Modes of Orbital Overlap and the Types of Covalent Bonds

(Sample Problem 11.2)

Concept Review Questions

11.20 Are these statements true or false? Correct any false ones.
(a) Two σ bonds comprise a double bond.
(b) A triple bond consists of one π bond and two σ bonds.
(c) Bonds formed from atomic *s* orbitals are always σ bonds.
(d) A π bond restricts rotation about the σ-bond axis.
(e) A π bond consists of two pairs of electrons.
(f) End-to-end overlap results in a bond with electron density above and below the bond axis.

Skill-Building Exercises (grouped in similar pairs)

11.21 Describe the hybrid orbitals used by the central atom and the type(s) of bonds formed in (a) NO_3^-; (b) CS_2; (c) CH_2O.

11.22 Describe the hybrid orbitals used by the central atom and the type(s) of bonds formed in (a) O_3; (b) I_3^-; (c) $COCl_2$ (C is central).

11.23 Describe the hybrid orbitals used by the central atom(s) and the type(s) of bonds formed in (a) FNO; (b) C_2F_4; (c) $(CN)_2$.

11.24 Describe the hybrid orbitals used by the central atom(s) and the type(s) of bonds formed in (a) BrF_3; (b) $CH_3C\equiv CH$; (c) SO_2.

Problem in Context

11.25 2-Butene ($CH_3CH{=}CHCH_3$) is a starting material in the manufacture of lubricating oils and many other compounds. Draw two different structures for 2-butene, indicating the σ and π bonds in each.

Molecular Orbital (MO) Theory and Electron Delocalization

(Sample Problems 11.3 and 11.4)

Concept Review Questions

11.26 Two *p* orbitals from one atom and two *p* orbitals from another atom are combined to form molecular orbitals for the joined atoms. How many MOs will result from this combination? Explain.

11.27 Certain atomic orbitals on two atoms were combined to form the following MOs. Name the atomic orbitals used and the MOs formed, and explain which MO has higher energy:

11.28 How do the bonding and antibonding MOs formed from a given pair of AOs compare to each other with respect to (a) energy; (b) presence of nodes; (c) internuclear electron density?

11.29 Antibonding MOs always have at least one node. Can a bonding MO have a node? If so, draw an example.

Skill-Building Exercises (grouped in similar pairs)

11.30 How many electrons does it take to fill (a) a σ bonding MO; (b) a π antibonding MO; (c) the MOs formed from combination of the 1*s* orbitals of two atoms?

11.31 How many electrons does it take to fill (a) the MOs formed from combination of the 2*p* orbitals of two atoms; (b) a σ^*_{2p} MO; (c) the MOs formed from combination of the 2*s* orbitals of two atoms?

11.32 The molecular orbitals depicted below are derived from 2*p* atomic orbitals in F_2^+. (a) Give the orbital designations. (b) Which is occupied by at least one electron in F_2^+? (c) Which is occupied by only one electron in F_2^+?

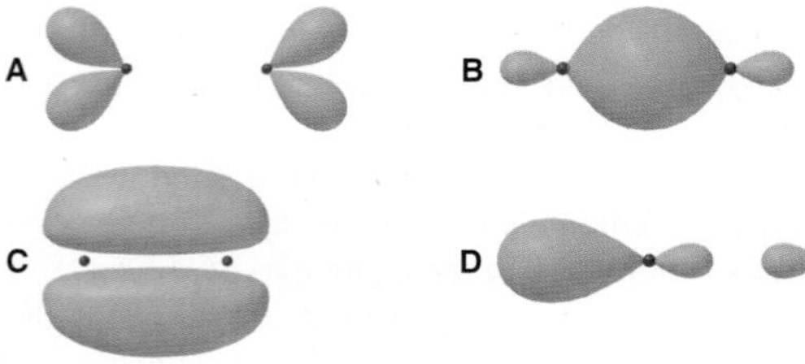

11.33 The molecular orbitals depicted below are derived from $n = 2$ atomic orbitals. (a) Give the orbital designations. (b) Which is highest in energy? (c) Lowest in energy? (d) Rank the MOs in order of increasing energy for B_2.

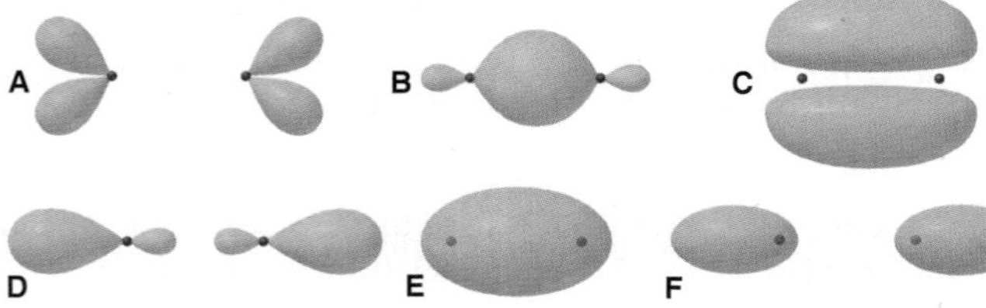

11.34 Use MO diagrams and the bond orders you obtain from them to answer: (a) Is Be_2^+ stable? (b) Is Be_2^+ diamagnetic? (c) What is the outer (valence) electron configuration of Be_2^+?

11.35 Use MO diagrams and the bond orders you obtain from them to answer: (a) Is O_2^- stable? (b) Is O_2^- paramagnetic? (c) What is the outer (valence) electron configuration of O_2^-?

11.36 Use MO diagrams to place C_2^-, C_2, and C_2^+ in order of (a) increasing bond energy; (b) increasing bond length.

11.37 Use MO diagrams to place B_2^+, B_2, and B_2^- in order of (a) decreasing bond energy; (b) decreasing bond length.

Comprehensive Problems

11.38 Predict the shape, state the hybridization of the central atom, and give the ideal bond angle(s) and any expected deviations for:
(a) BrO_3^- (b) $AsCl_4^-$ (c) SeO_4^{2-} (d) BiF_5^{2-}
(e) SbF_4^+ (f) AlF_6^{3-} (g) IF_4^+

11.39 Butadiene (*right*) is a colorless gas used to make synthetic rubber and many other compounds. (a) How many σ bonds and π bonds does the molecule have? (b) Are *cis-trans* arrangements about the double bonds possible? Explain.

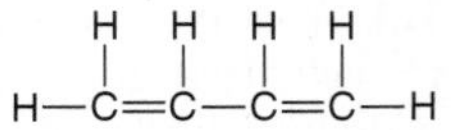

11.40 Epinephrine (or adrenaline; *below*) is a naturally occurring hormone that is also manufactured commercially for use as a heart stimulant, a nasal decongestant, and a glaucoma treatment.

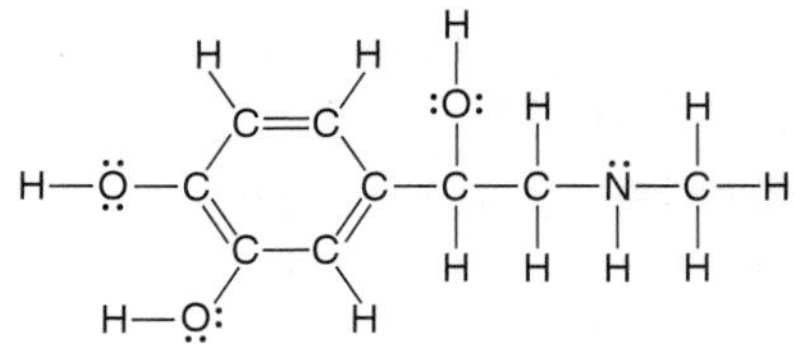

(a) What is the hybridization of each C, O, and N atom? (b) How many σ bonds does the molecule have? (c) How many π electrons are delocalized in the ring?

11.41 Use partial orbital diagrams to show how the atomic orbitals of the central atom lead to the hybrid orbitals in:
(a) IF_2^- (b) ICl_3 (c) $XeOF_4$ (d) BHF_2

11.42 Isoniazid (*below*) is an antibacterial agent that is very useful against many common strains of tuberculosis. (a) How many σ bonds are in the molecule? (b) What is the hybridization of each C and N atom?

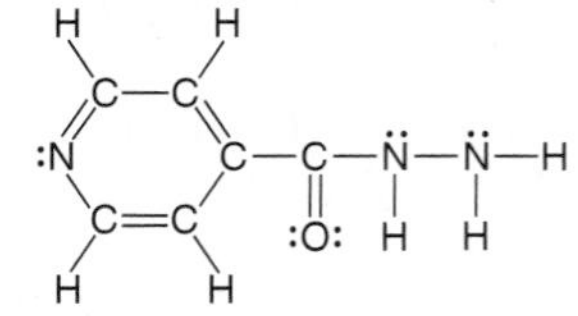

11.43 Hydrazine, N_2H_4, and carbon disulfide, CS_2, form a cyclic molecule (*below*). (a) Draw Lewis structures for N_2H_4 and CS_2. (b) How do electron-group arrangement, molecular shape, and hybridization of N change when N_2H_4 reacts to form the product? (c) How do electron-group arrangement, molecular shape, and hybridization of C change when CS_2 reacts to form the product?

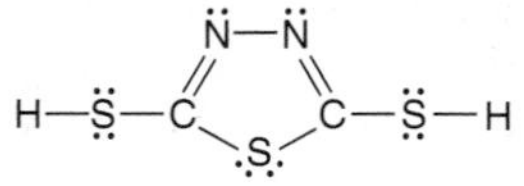

11.44 In each of the following equations, what hybridization change, if any, occurs for the underlined atom?
(a) $\underline{B}F_3 + NaF \longrightarrow Na^+BF_4^-$
(b) $\underline{P}Cl_3 + Cl_2 \longrightarrow PCl_5$
(c) $H\underline{C}{\equiv}CH + H_2 \longrightarrow H_2C{=}CH_2$
(d) $\underline{Si}F_4 + 2F^- \longrightarrow SiF_6^{2-}$
(e) $\underline{S}O_2 + \frac{1}{2}O_2 \rightarrow SO_3$

11.45 The ionosphere lies about 100 km above Earth's surface. This layer consists mostly of NO, O_2, and N_2, and photoionization creates NO^+, O_2^+, and N_2^+. (a) Use MO theory to compare the bond orders of the molecules and ions. (b) Does the magnetic behavior of each species change when its ion forms?

11.46 Glyphosate (*below*) is a common herbicide that is relatively harmless to animals but deadly to most plants. Describe the shape around and the hybridization of the P, N, and three numbered C atoms.

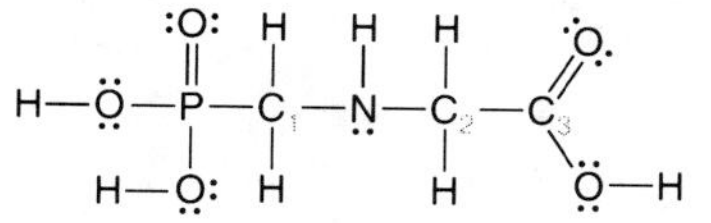

11.47 Tryptophan is one of the amino acids found in proteins:

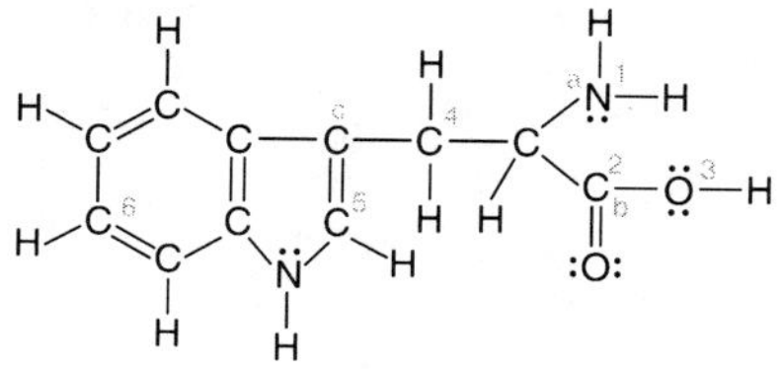

(a) What is the hybridization of each of the numbered C, N, and O atoms? (b) How many σ bonds are present in tryptophan? (c) Predict the bond angles at points a, b, and c.

11.48 Some species with two oxygen atoms only are the oxygen molecule, O_2, the peroxide ion, O_2^{2-}, the superoxide ion, O_2^-, and the dioxygenyl ion, O_2^+. Draw an MO diagram for each, rank them in order of increasing bond length, and find the number of unpaired electrons in each.

11.49 Molecular nitrogen, carbon monoxide, and cyanide ion are isoelectronic. (a) Draw an MO diagram for each. (b) CO and CN^- are toxic. What property may explain why N_2 isn't?

11.50 There is concern in health-related government agencies that the American diet contains too much meat, and numerous recommendations have been made urging people to consume more fruit and vegetables. One of the richest sources of vegetable protein is soy, available in many forms. Among these is soybean curd, or tofu, which is a staple of many Asian diets. Chemists have isolated an anticancer agent called *genistein* from tofu, which may explain the much lower incidence of cancer among people in the Far East. A valid Lewis structure for genistein is

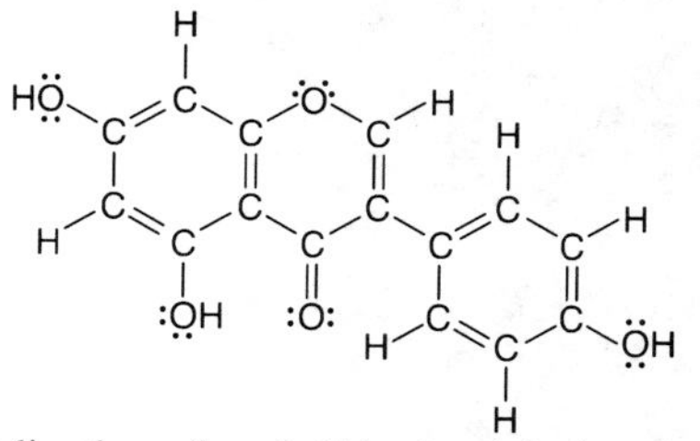

(a) Is the hybridization of each C in the right-hand ring the same? Explain. (b) Is the hybridization of the O atom in the center ring the same as that of the O atoms in OH groups? Explain. (c) How many carbon-oxygen σ bonds are there? How many carbon-oxygen π bonds? (d) Do all the lone pairs on oxygens occupy the same type of hybrid orbital? Explain.

11.51 An organic chemist synthesizes the molecule below:

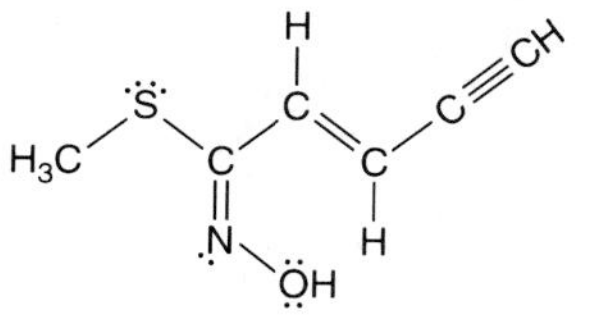

(a) Which of the orientations of hybrid orbitals shown below are present in the molecule? (b) Are there any present that are not shown below? If so, what are they? (c) How many of each type of hybrid orbital are present?

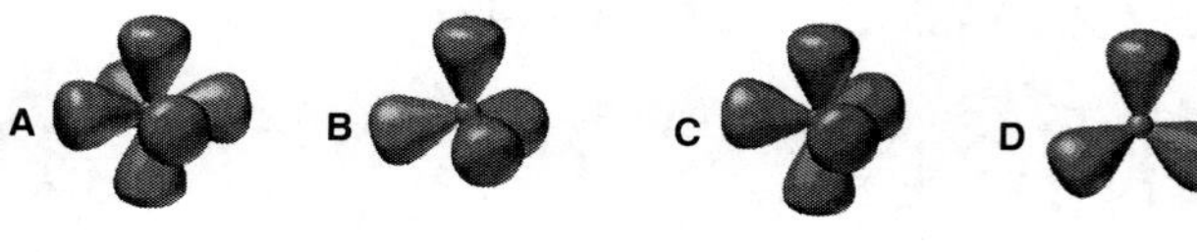

11.52 Simple proteins consist of amino acids linked together in a long chain; a small portion of such a chain is

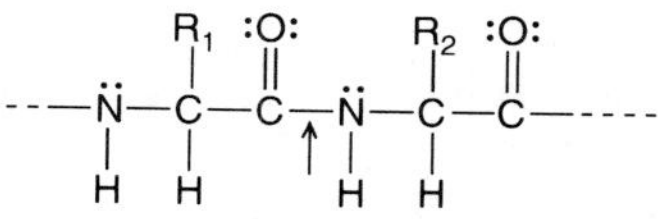

Experiment shows that rotation about the C—N bond (indicated by the arrow) is somewhat restricted. Explain with resonance structures, and show the types of bonding involved.

11.53 Sulfur forms oxides, oxoanions, and halides. What is the hybridization of the central S in SO_2, SO_3, SO_3^{2-}, SCl_4, SCl_6, and S_2Cl_2 (atom sequence Cl—S—S—Cl)?

11.54 The compound 2,6-dimethylpyrazine (*below*) gives chocolate its odor and is used in flavorings. (a) Which atomic orbitals mix to form the hybrid orbitals of N? (b) In what type of hybrid orbital do the lone pairs of N reside? (c) Is C in CH_3 hybridized the same as any C in the ring? Explain.

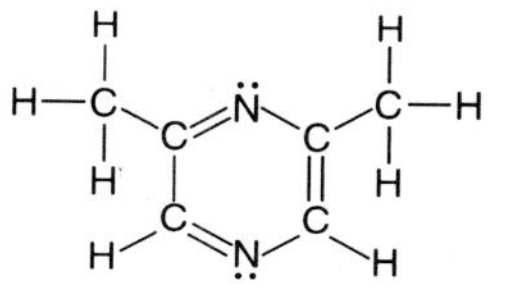

11.55 Acetylsalicylic acid (aspirin), the most widely used medicine in the world, has the Lewis structure shown below. (a) What is the hybridization of each C and each O atom? (b) How many localized π bonds are present? (c) How many C atoms have a trigonal planar shape around them? A tetrahedral shape?

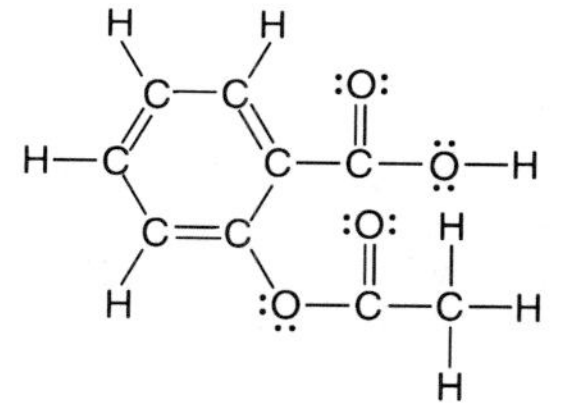

11.56 Linoleic acid is an essential fatty acid found in many vegetable oils, such as soy, peanut, and cottonseed. A key structural feature of the molecule is the *cis* orientation around its two double bonds, where R_1 and R_2 represent two different groups that form the rest of the molecule.

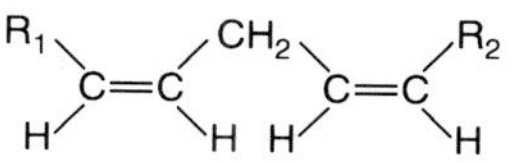

(a) How many different compounds are possible, changing only the *cis-trans* arrangements around these two double bonds?
(b) How many are possible for a similar compound with three double bonds?

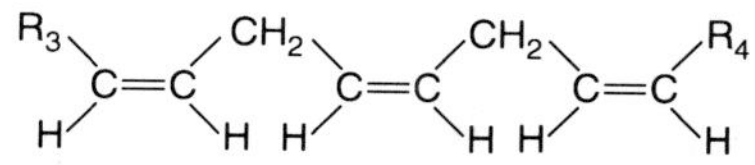

Gases and the Kinetic-Molecular Theory

Concepts and skills to review before you study this chapter

- physical states of matter (Section 1.1)
- SI unit conversions (Section 1.5)
- mole-mass-number conversions (Section 3.1)

5

Amazing as it may seem, what actually occurs when you drink through a straw is that you suck the air out of the straw and the weight of Earth's atmosphere pushes down on the liquid and forces it into your mouth! Other remarkable properties of gases are at work in the rising of a loaf of bread, the operation of a car engine, and, as we'll discuss later in the chapter, even in the act of breathing. People have been studying the behavior of gases and the other states of matter throughout history; in fact, three of the four "elements" of the ancient Greeks were air (gas), water (liquid), and earth (solid). Yet, despite millennia of observations, many questions remain. In this chapter and its companion, Chapter 12, we examine the physical states and their interrelations. Here, we highlight the gaseous state, the one we understand best.

Gases are everywhere. Our atmosphere is a colorless, odorless mixture of 18 gases, some of which—O_2, N_2, H_2O vapor, and CO_2—take part in life-sustaining cycles of redox reactions throughout the environment. And several other gases, such as chlorine and ammonia, have essential roles in industry. Yet, in this chapter, we put aside the *chemical* behavior unique to any particular gas and focus instead *on the* ***physical*** *behavior common to all gases.*

IN THIS CHAPTER . . . We explore the physical behavior of gases and the theory that explains it. In the process, we see how scientists use mathematics to model nature.

- We compare the behaviors of gases, liquids, and solids.
- We discuss laboratory methods for measuring gas pressure.
- We consider laws that describe the behavior of a gas in terms of how its volume changes with a change in (1) pressure, (2) temperature, or (3) amount. We focus on the ideal gas law, which encompasses these three laws, and apply it to solve gas law problems.
- We rearrange the ideal gas law to determine the density and molar mass of an unknown gas, the partial pressure of any gas in a mixture, and the amounts of gaseous reactants and products in a chemical change.
- We see how the kinetic-molecular theory explains the gas laws and accounts for other important behaviors of gas particles.
- We apply key ideas about gas behavior to Earth's atmosphere.
- We find that the behavior of real, not ideal, gases, especially under extreme conditions, requires refinements of the ideal gas law and the kinetic-molecular theory.

5.1 • AN OVERVIEW OF THE PHYSICAL STATES OF MATTER

Most substances can exist as a solid, a liquid, or a gas under appropriate conditions of pressure and temperature. In Chapter 1, we used the relative position and motion of the particles of a substance to distinguish how each state fills a container (see Figure 1.2, p. 6):

Figure 5.1 The three states of matter. Many pure substances, such as bromine (Br_2), can exist under appropriate conditions of pressure and temperature as a gas, liquid, or solid.

- A gas adopts the container shape and fills it, because its particles are far apart and move randomly.
- A liquid adopts the container shape to the extent of its volume, because its particles are close together but free to move around each other.
- A solid has a fixed shape regardless of the container shape, because its particles are close together and held rigidly in place.

Figure 5.1 focuses on the three states of bromine.

Several other aspects of their behaviors distinguish gases from liquids and solids:

1. *Gas volume changes significantly with pressure.* When a sample of gas is confined to a container of variable volume, such as a cylinder with a piston, *increasing* the force on the piston *decreases* the gas volume. Removing the external force allows the volume to increase again. Gases under pressure can do a lot of work: rapidly expanding compressed air in a jackhammer breaks rock and cement; compressed air in tires lifts the weight of a car. In contrast, the volume of a liquid or a solid does not change significantly under pressure.
2. *Gas volume changes significantly with temperature.* When a sample of gas is heated, it expands; when it is cooled, it shrinks. This volume change is 50 to 100 times greater for gases than for liquids or solids. The expansion that occurs when gases are rapidly heated can have dramatic effects, like lifting a rocket into space, and everyday ones, like popping corn.
3. *Gases flow very freely.* Gases flow much more freely than liquids and solids. This behavior allows gases to be transported more easily through pipes, but it also means they leak more rapidly out of small holes and cracks.
4. *Gases have relatively low densities.* Gas density is usually measured in units of grams per liter (g/L), whereas liquid and solid densities are in grams per milliliter (g/mL), about 1000 times as dense (see Table 1.5, p. 22). For example, at 20°C and normal atmospheric pressure, the density of $O_2(g)$ is 1.3 g/**L**, whereas the density of $H_2O(l)$ is 1.0 g/**mL** and the density of NaCl(s) is 2.2 g/**mL**. When a gas cools, its density *increases* because its volume *decreases:* on cooling from 20°C to 0°C, the density of $O_2(g)$ increases from 1.3 to 1.4 g/L.

5. *Gases form a solution in any proportions.* Air is a solution of 18 gases. Two liquids, however, may or may not form a solution: water and ethanol do, but water and gasoline do not. Two solids generally do not form a solution unless they are melted and mixed while liquids, then allowed to solidify (as is done to make the alloy bronze from copper and tin).

Like the way a gas completely fills a container, these macroscopic properties—changing volume with pressure or temperature, great ability to flow, low density, and ability to form solutions—arise because the particles in a gas are much farther apart than those in either a liquid or a solid.

Summary of Section 5.1

- The volume of a gas can be altered significantly by changing the applied force or the temperature. Corresponding changes for liquids and solids are *much* smaller.
- Gases flow more freely and have much lower densities than liquids and solids.
- Gases mix in any proportions to form solutions; liquids and solids generally do not.
- Differences in the physical states are due to the greater average distance between particles in a gas than in a liquid or a solid.

5.2 • GAS PRESSURE AND ITS MEASUREMENT

You can blow up a balloon or pump up a tire because *a gas exerts pressure on the walls of its container.* **Pressure (*P*)** is defined as the force exerted per unit of surface area:

$$\text{Pressure} = \frac{\text{force}}{\text{area}}$$

Earth's gravity attracts the atmospheric gases, and they exert a force uniformly on *all* surfaces. The force, or *weight,* of these gases creates a pressure of about 14.7 pounds per square inch (lb/in^2; psi) of surface. Thus, a pressure of 14.7 lb/in^2 exists on the outside of your room (or your body), and it equals the pressure on the inside. What would happen if the pressures were *not* equal? Consider the empty can attached to a vacuum pump in Figure 5.2. With the pump off (*left*) the can maintains its shape because the pressure on the outside is equal to the pressure on the inside. With the pump on (*right*), much of the air inside is removed, decreasing the internal pressure greatly, and the pressure of the atmosphere easily crushes the can. The vacuum-filtration flasks and tubing that you may have used in the lab have thick walls that withstand the relatively higher external pressure.

Laboratory Devices for Measuring Gas Pressure

The **barometer** is used to measure atmospheric pressure. The device is still essentially the same as it was when invented in 1643 by the Italian physicist Evangelista Torricelli:

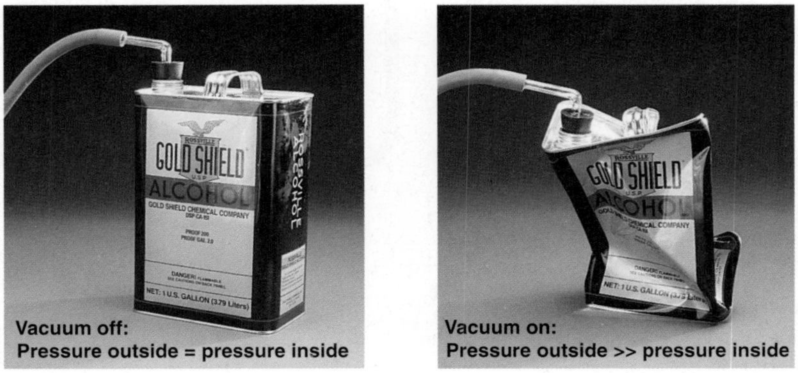

Figure 5.2 Effect of atmospheric pressure on a familiar object.

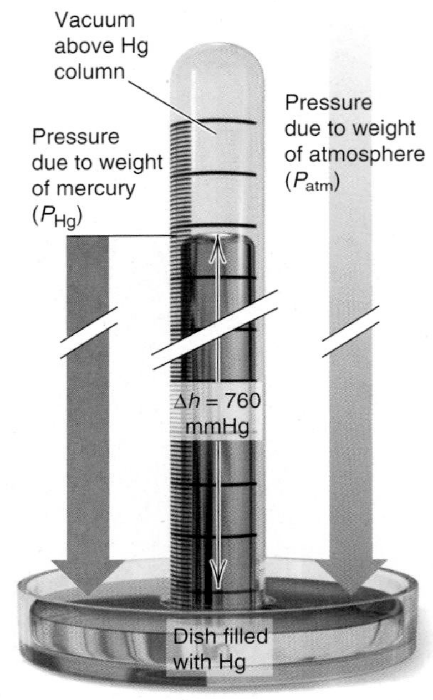

Figure 5.3 A mercury barometer. The pressure of the atmosphere, P_{atm}, balances the pressure of the mercury column, P_{Hg}.

a tube about 1 m long, closed at one end, filled with mercury (atomic symbol, Hg), and inverted into a dish containing more mercury. When the tube is inverted, some of the mercury flows out into the dish, and a vacuum forms above the mercury remaining in the tube (Figure 5.3). At sea level, under ordinary atmospheric conditions, the mercury stops flowing out when the surface of the mercury in the tube is about 760 mm above the surface of the mercury in the dish. At that height, the column of mercury exerts the same pressure (weight/area) on the mercury surface in the dish as the atmosphere does: $P_{Hg} = P_{atm}$. Likewise, if you evacuate a closed tube and invert it into a dish of mercury, the atmosphere pushes the mercury up to a height of about 760 mm.

Notice that we did not specify the diameter of the barometer tube. If the mercury in a 1-cm diameter tube rises to a height of 760 mm, the mercury in a 2-cm diameter tube will rise to that height also. The *weight* of mercury is greater in the wider tube, but so is the area; thus, the *pressure,* the *ratio* of weight to area, is the same.

Because the pressure of the mercury column is directly proportional to its height, a unit commonly used for pressure is millimeters of mercury (mmHg). We discuss other units of pressure shortly. *At sea level and 0°C, normal atmospheric pressure is 760 mmHg;* at the top of Mt. Everest (elevation 29,028 ft, or 8848 m), the atmospheric pressure is only about 270 mmHg. Thus, *pressure decreases with altitude:* the column of air above the sea is taller, so it weighs more than the column of air above Mt. Everest.

Laboratory barometers contain mercury because its high density allows a barometer to be a convenient size. If a barometer contained water instead, it would have to be more than 34 ft high, because the pressure of the atmosphere equals the pressure of a column of water about 10,300 mm (almost 34 ft) high. For a given pressure, the ratio of heights (h) of the liquid columns is inversely related to the ratio of the densities (d) of the liquids:

$$\frac{h_{H_2O}}{h_{Hg}} = \frac{d_{Hg}}{d_{H_2O}}$$

Interestingly, several centuries ago, people thought a vacuum had mysterious "suction" powers, and they didn't understand why a suction pump could remove water from a well only to a depth of 34 feet. We know now, as the great 17th-century scientist Galileo explained, that a vacuum does not suck mercury up into a barometer tube, a suction pump does not suck water up from a well, the vacuum pump in Figure 5.2 does not suck in the walls of the crushed can, and the vacuum you create in a straw does not suck the drink into your mouth. Only matter—in this case, the atmospheric gases—can exert a force.

Manometers are devices used to measure the pressure of a gas in an experiment. Figure 5.4 shows two types of manometer. In the *closed-end manometer (left side),* a

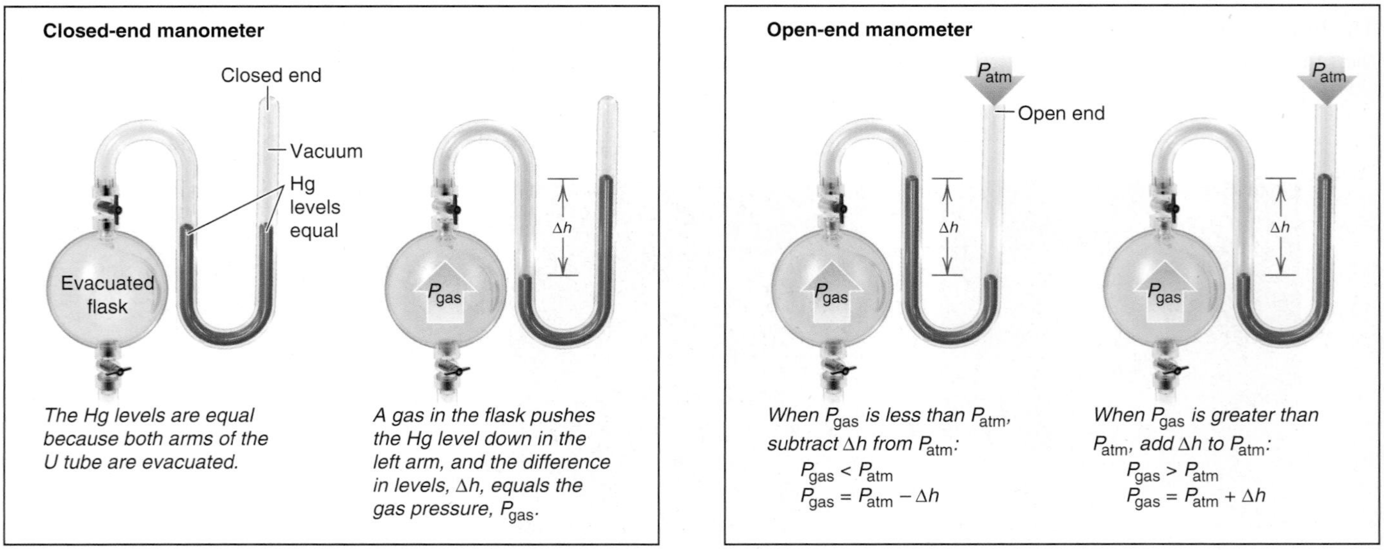

Figure 5.4 Two types of manometer.

mercury-filled, curved tube is *closed* at one end and attached to a flask at the other. When the flask is evacuated, the mercury levels in the two arms of the tube are the same because no gas exerts pressure on either mercury surface. When a gas is in the flask, it pushes down the mercury level in the near arm, causing the level to rise in the far arm. The *difference* in column heights (Δh) equals the gas pressure.

The *open-end manometer* (*right side* of Figure 5.4) also consists of a curved tube filled with mercury, but one end of the tube is *open* to the atmosphere and the other is connected to the gas sample. The atmosphere pushes on one mercury surface, and the gas pushes on the other. Again, Δh equals the difference between two pressures. But, when using this type of manometer, we must measure the atmospheric pressure with a barometer and either add or subtract Δh from that value.

Units of Pressure

Pressure results from a force exerted on an area. The SI unit of force is the newton (N): $1\ \text{N} = 1\ \text{kg}\cdot\text{m/s}^2$ (about the weight of an apple). The SI unit of pressure is the **pascal (Pa),** which equals a force of one newton exerted on an area of one square meter:

$$1\ \text{Pa} = 1\ \text{N/m}^2$$

A much larger unit is the **standard atmosphere (atm),** the average atmospheric pressure measured at sea level and 0°C. It is defined in terms of the pascal:

$$1\ \text{atm} = 101.325\ \text{kilopascals (kPa)} = 1.01325\times10^5\ \text{Pa}$$

Another common unit is the **millimeter of mercury (mmHg),** mentioned earlier; in honor of Torricelli, this unit has been renamed the **torr:**

$$1\ \text{torr} = 1\ \text{mmHg} = \frac{1}{760}\ \text{atm} = \frac{101.325}{760}\ \text{kPa} = 133.322\ \text{Pa}$$

The *bar* is coming into more common use in chemistry:

$$1\ \text{bar} = 1\times10^2\ \text{kPa} = 1\times10^5\ \text{Pa}$$

Despite a gradual change to SI units, many chemists still express pressure in torrs and atmospheres, so those units are used in this book, with reference to pascals and bars. Table 5.1 lists some important pressure units with the corresponding values for normal atmospheric pressure.

Table 5.1 Common Units of Pressure

Unit	Normal Atmospheric Pressure at Sea Level and 0°C
pascal (Pa); kilopascal (kPa)	1.01325×10^5 Pa; 101.325 kPa
atmosphere (atm)	1 atm*
millimeters of mercury (mmHg)	760 mmHg*
torr	760 torr*
pounds per square inch (lb/in^2 or psi)	14.7 lb/in^2
bar	1.01325 bar

*This is an exact quantity; in calculations, we use as many significant figures as necessary.

Sample Problem 5.1 Converting Units of Pressure

Problem A geochemist heats a limestone ($CaCO_3$) sample and collects the CO_2 released in an evacuated flask attached to a closed-end manometer. After the system comes to room temperature, $\Delta h = 291.4$ mmHg. Calculate the CO_2 pressure in torrs, atmospheres, and kilopascals.

Plan The CO_2 pressure is given in units of mmHg, so we construct conversion factors from Table 5.1 to find the pressure in the other units.

Solution Converting from mmHg to torr:

$$P_{CO_2}\text{ (torr)} = 291.4\ \cancel{\text{mmHg}} \times \frac{1\text{ torr}}{1\ \cancel{\text{mmHg}}} = 291.4\text{ torr}$$

Converting from torr to atm:

$$P_{CO_2}\text{ (atm)} = 291.4\ \cancel{\text{torr}} \times \frac{1\text{ atm}}{760\ \cancel{\text{torr}}} = 0.3834\text{ atm}$$

Converting from atm to kPa:

$$P_{CO_2}\text{ (kPa)} = 0.3834\ \cancel{\text{atm}} \times \frac{101.325\text{ kPa}}{1\ \cancel{\text{atm}}} = 38.85\text{ kPa}$$

Check There are 760 torr in 1 atm, so ~300 torr should be <0.5 atm. There are ~100 kPa in 1 atm, so <0.5 atm should be <50 kPa.

Comment 1. In the conversion from torr to atm, we retained four significant figures because this unit conversion factor involves *exact* numbers; that is, 760 torr has as many significant figures as the calculation requires (see the footnote on Table 5.1).
2. From here on, except in particularly complex situations, *unit canceling will no longer be shown.*

Follow-Up Problem 5.1 The CO_2 released from another mineral sample was collected in an evacuated flask connected to an open-end manometer. If the barometer reading is 753.6 mmHg and P_{gas} is less than P_{atm} to give a Δh of 174.0 mmHg, calculate P_{CO_2} in torrs, pascals, and lb/in^2.

Summary of Section 5.2

- Gases exert pressure (force/area) on all surfaces they contact.
- A barometer measures atmospheric pressure based on the height of a mercury column that the atmosphere can support (760 mmHg at sea level and 0°C).
- Closed-end and open-end manometers are used to measure the pressure of a gas sample.
- Pressure units include the atmosphere (atm), torr (identical to mmHg), and pascal (Pa, the SI unit).

5.3 • THE GAS LAWS AND THEIR EXPERIMENTAL FOUNDATIONS

The physical behavior of a sample of gas can be described completely by four variables: pressure (P), volume (V), temperature (T), and amount (number of moles, n). The variables are interdependent, which means that *any one of them can be determined by measuring the other three.* Three key relationships exist among the four gas variables—Boyle's, Charles's, and Avogadro's laws. Each of these *gas laws expresses the effect of one variable on another, with the remaining two variables held constant.* Because gas volume is so easy to measure, the laws are expressed as the effect on gas volume of a change in the pressure, temperature, or amount of the gas.

The individual gas laws are special cases of a unifying relationship called the *ideal gas law,* which quantitatively describes the behavior of an **ideal gas,** one that exhibits linear relationships among volume, pressure, temperature, and amount. Although *no ideal gas actually exists,* most simple gases, such as N_2, O_2, H_2, and the noble gases, behave nearly ideally at ordinary temperatures and pressures. We discuss the ideal gas law after the three individual laws.

The Relationship Between Volume and Pressure: Boyle's Law

Following Torricelli's invention of the barometer, the great 17th-century English chemist Robert Boyle studied the effect of pressure on the volume of a sample of gas.

1. *The experiment.* Figure 5.5 illustrates the setup Boyle might have used in his experiments (parts A and B), the data he might have collected (part C), and graphs of

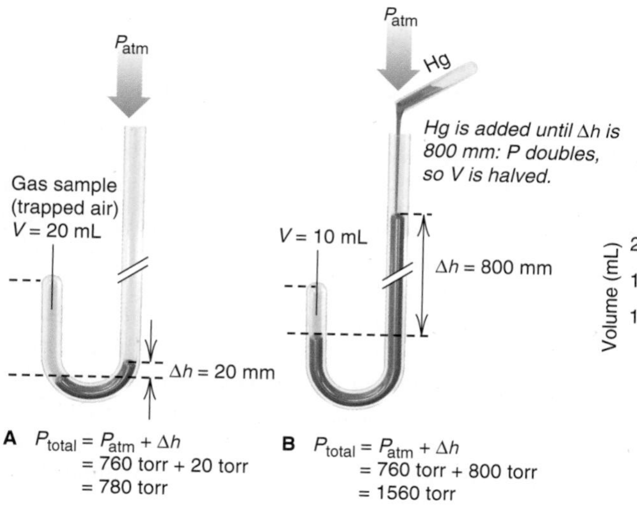

C

V (mL)	P (torr) Δh	+ P_{atm}	= P_{total}	$\frac{1}{P_{total}}$	PV (torr•mL)
20.0	20.0	760	780	0.00128	1.56×10^4
15.0	278	760	1038	0.000963	1.56×10^4
10.0	800	760	1560	0.000641	1.56×10^4
5.0	2352	760	3112	0.000321	1.56×10^4

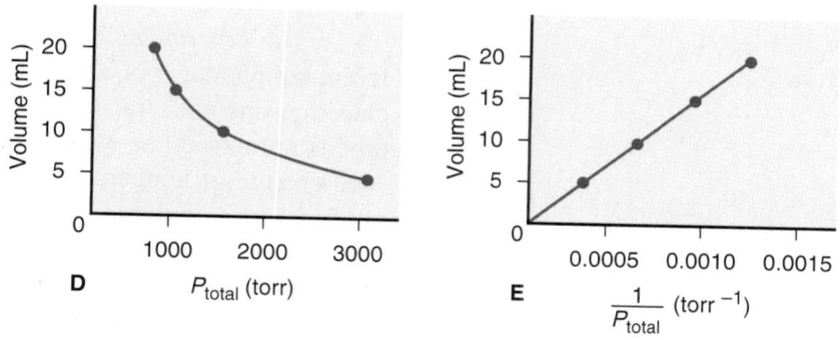

Figure 5.5 Boyle's law, the relationship between the volume and pressure of a gas.

the data (parts D and E). Boyle sealed the shorter leg of a J-shaped glass tube and poured mercury into the longer open leg, thereby trapping some air (the gas in the experiment) in the shorter leg. He calculated the gas volume (V_{gas}) from the height of the trapped air and the diameter of the tube. The total pressure, P_{total}, applied to the trapped gas is the pressure of the atmosphere, P_{atm} (760 mm, measured with a barometer), plus the difference in the heights of the mercury columns (Δh) in the two legs of the J tube, 20 mm (Figure 5.5A); thus, P_{total} is 780 torr. By adding mercury, Boyle increased P_{total}, and the gas volume decreased. In Figure 5.5B, more mercury has been added to the original Δh of 20 mm, so P_{total} doubles to 1560 torr; note that V_{gas} is halved from 20 mL to 10 mL. In this way, by keeping the temperature and amount of gas constant, Boyle was able to measure the effect of the applied pressure on gas volume.

Note the following results in Figure 5.5:

- The product of corresponding P and V values is a constant (part C, rightmost column).
- V is *inversely* proportional to P (part D).
- V is *directly* proportional to $1/P$ (part E), and a plot of V versus $1/P$ is linear. This *linear relationship between two gas variables* is a hallmark of ideal gas behavior.

2. *Conclusion and statement of the law.* The generalization of Boyle's observations is known as **Boyle's law:** *at constant temperature, the volume occupied by a fixed amount of gas is* ***inversely*** *proportional to the applied (external) pressure,* or

$$V \propto \frac{1}{P} \qquad [T \text{ and } n \text{ fixed}] \tag{5.1}$$

This relationship can also be expressed as

$$PV = \text{constant} \qquad \text{or} \qquad V = \frac{\text{constant}}{P} \qquad [T \text{ and } n \text{ fixed}]$$

That is, at fixed T and n, $\quad P\uparrow, V\downarrow \quad$ and $\quad P\downarrow, V\uparrow$

The constant is the same for most simple gases under ordinary conditions. Thus, tripling the external pressure reduces the volume of a gas to a third of its initial value; halving the pressure doubles the volume; and so forth.

The wording of Boyle's law focuses on *external* pressure. But, notice that the mercury level rises as mercury is added, until the pressure of the trapped gas *on* the mercury increases enough to stop its rise. At that point, the pressure exerted *on* the gas equals the pressure exerted *by* the gas (P_{gas}). Thus, in general, if V_{gas} increases, P_{gas} decreases, and vice versa.

The Relationship Between Volume and Temperature: Charles's Law

Boyle's work showed that the pressure-volume relationship holds only at constant temperature, but why should that be so? It would take more than a century, until the work of French scientists J. A. C. Charles and J. L. Gay-Lussac, for the relationship between gas volume and temperature to be understood.

1. *The experiment.* Let's examine this relationship by measuring the volume at different temperatures of a fixed amount of a gas under constant pressure. A straight tube, closed at one end, traps a fixed amount of gas (air) under a small mercury plug. The tube is immersed in a water bath that is warmed with a heater or cooled with ice. After each change of temperature, we measure the length of the gas column, which is proportional to its volume. The total pressure exerted on the gas is constant because the mercury plug and the atmospheric pressure do not change (Figure 5.6, parts A and B).

Figure 5.6C shows some typical data. Consider the red line, which shows how the volume of 0.04 mol of gas at 1 atm pressure changes with temperature. Extrapolating that line to lower temperatures (dashed portion) shows that, in theory, the gas occupies zero volume at −273.15°C (the intercept on the temperature axis). Plots for a different amount of gas (green) or a different gas pressure (blue) have different slopes, but they all converge at −273.15°C. William Thomson (Lord Kelvin) later used this linear relation between gas volume and temperature to devise the absolute temperature scale (Section 1.5).

2. *Conclusion and statement of the law.* Above all, note that *the volume-temperature relationship is linear,* but, unlike volume and pressure, volume and temperature are *directly* proportional. This behavior is incorporated into the modern statement of the volume-temperature relationship, which is known as **Charles's law:** *at constant pressure, the volume occupied by a fixed amount of gas is* ***directly*** *proportional to its absolute (Kelvin) temperature,* or

$$V \propto T \qquad [P \text{ and } n \text{ fixed}] \tag{5.2}$$

This relationship can also be expressed as

$$\frac{V}{T} = \text{constant} \qquad \text{or} \qquad V = \text{constant} \times T \qquad [P \text{ and } n \text{ fixed}]$$

That is, at fixed P and n, $T\uparrow, V\uparrow$ and $T\downarrow, V\downarrow$

If T increases, V increases, and vice versa. Once again, for any given P and n, the constant is the same for most simple gases under ordinary conditions.

Figure 5.6 Charles's law, the relationship between the volume and temperature of a gas.

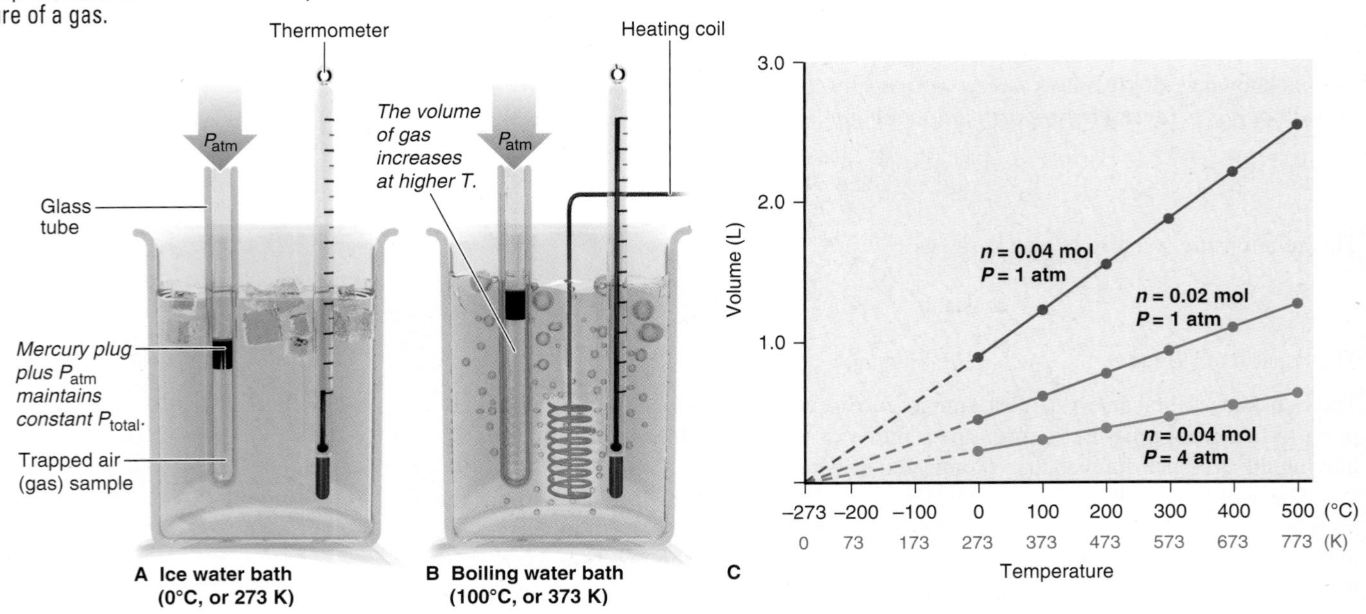

Absolute zero (0 K or −273.15°C) is the temperature at which an ideal gas would have zero volume. (Absolute zero has never been reached, but physicists have attained 10^{-9} K.) In reality, no sample of matter can have zero volume, and every real gas condenses to a liquid at some temperature higher than 0 K. Nevertheless, the linear dependence of volume on absolute temperature holds for most common gases over a wide temperature range. This dependence of gas volume on the *absolute* temperature adds a practical requirement for chemists (and chemistry students): *the Kelvin scale must be used in gas law calculations.* For instance, if the temperature changes from 200 K to 400 K, the volume of gas doubles. But, if the temperature changes from 200°C to 400°C, the volume increases by a factor of 1.42; that is,

$$\left(\frac{400°\text{C} + 273.15}{200°\text{C} + 273.15}\right) = \frac{673}{473} = 1.42$$

Other Relationships Based on Boyle's and Charles's Laws Two other important relationships arise from Boyle's and Charles's laws:

1. *The pressure-temperature relationship.* Charles's law is expressed as the effect of temperature on gas *volume* at constant pressure. But volume and pressure are interdependent, so a similar relationship can be expressed for the effect of temperature on pressure (sometimes referred to as *Amontons's law*). Measure the pressure in your car or bike tires before and after a long ride, and you'll find that it increases. Heating due to friction between the tires and the road increases the air temperature inside the tires, but since a tire's volume can't increase very much, the air pressure does. Thus, *at constant volume, the pressure exerted by a fixed amount of gas is directly proportional to the absolute temperature:*

$$P \propto T \qquad [V \text{ and } n \text{ fixed}] \tag{5.3}$$

or

$$\frac{P}{T} = \text{constant} \qquad \text{or} \qquad P = \text{constant} \times T$$

That is, at fixed V and n, $T\uparrow, P\uparrow$ and $T\downarrow, P\downarrow$

2. *The combined gas law.* Combining Boyle's and Charles's laws gives the *combined gas law,* which applies to cases when changes in *two* of the three variables (V, P, T) affect the third:

$$V \propto \frac{T}{P} \qquad \text{or} \qquad V = \text{constant} \times \frac{T}{P} \qquad \text{or} \qquad \frac{PV}{T} = \text{constant}$$

The Relationship Between Volume and Amount: Avogadro's Law

Let's see why both Boyle's and Charles's laws specify a fixed amount of gas.

1. *The experiment.* Figure 5.7 shows an experiment that involves two small test tubes, each fitted to a much larger piston-cylinder assembly. We add 0.10 mol (4.4 g) of dry ice (solid CO_2) to the first tube (A) and 0.20 mol (8.8 g) to the second tube (B). As the solid CO_2 warms to room temperature, it changes to gaseous CO_2, and the volume increases until $P_{gas} = P_{atm}$. At constant temperature, when all the solid has changed to gas, cylinder B has twice the volume of cylinder A.

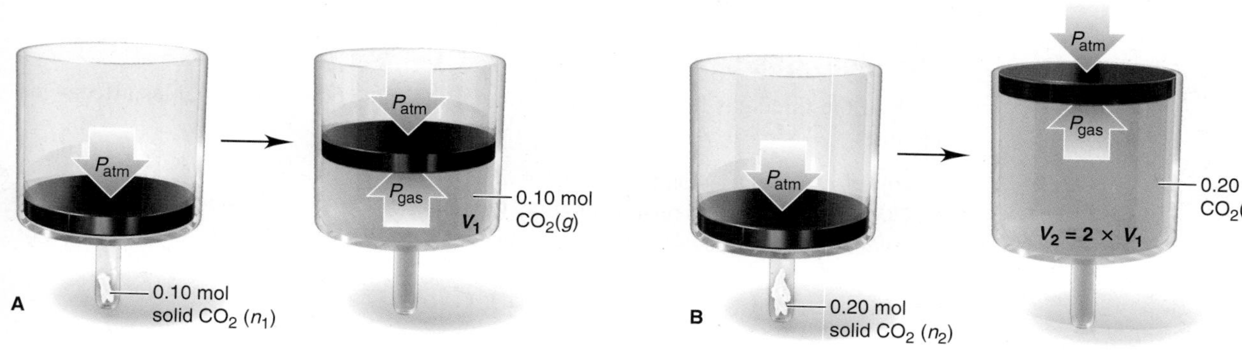

Figure 5.7 The relationship between the volume and amount of a gas.

2. *Conclusion and statement of the law.* Thus, *at fixed temperature and pressure, the volume occupied by a gas is directly proportional to the amount (mol) of gas:*

$$V \propto n \qquad [P \text{ and } T \text{ fixed}] \tag{5.4}$$

That is, as n increases, V increases, and vice versa. This relationship is also expressed as

$$\frac{V}{n} = \text{constant} \qquad \text{or} \qquad V = \text{constant} \times n$$

That is, at fixed P and T, $\quad n\uparrow, V\uparrow \quad$ and $\quad n\downarrow, V\downarrow$

The constant is the same for all simple gases at ordinary temperature and pressure. This relationship is another way of expressing **Avogadro's law,** which states that *at fixed temperature and pressure, equal volumes of* ***any*** *ideal gas contain equal numbers of particles (or moles).*

Familiar Applications of the Gas Laws The gas laws apply to countless familiar phenomena. In a car engine, a reaction occurs in which fewer moles of gasoline and O_2 form more moles of CO_2 and H_2O vapor, and heat is released. The increase in n (Avogadro's law) and T (Charles's law) increases V, and the piston is pushed back. Dynamite is a solid that forms more moles of hot gases very rapidly when it reacts (Avogadro's and Charles's laws). Dough rises because yeast digests sugar, which creates bubbles of CO_2 (Avogadro's law); the dough expands more as the bread bakes in a hot oven (Charles's law).

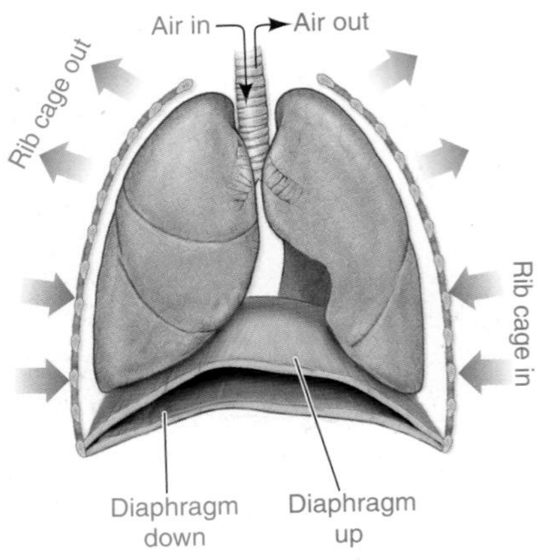

Figure 5.8 The process of breathing applies the gas laws.

No application of the gas laws can be more vital or familiar than breathing (Figure 5.8). When you inhale, muscles move your diaphragm down and your rib cage out (*blue*). This coordinated movement increases the volume of your lungs, which decreases the air pressure inside them (Boyle's law). The inside pressure is 1–3 torr *less* than atmospheric pressure, so air rushes in. The greater amount of air stretches the elastic tissue of the lungs and expands the volume further (Avogadro's law). The air also expands as it warms from the external temperature to your body temperature (Charles's law). When you exhale, the diaphragm moves up and the rib cage moves in, so your lung volume decreases (*red*). The inside pressure becomes 1–3 torr *more* than the outside pressure (Boyle's law), so air rushes out.

Gas Behavior at Standard Conditions

To better understand the factors that influence gas behavior, chemists have assigned a baseline set of *standard conditions* called **standard temperature and pressure (STP):**

$$\text{STP:} \quad 0°\text{C (273.15 K) and 1 atm (760 torr)} \tag{5.5}$$

Under these conditions, the volume of 1 mol of an ideal gas is called the **standard molar volume:**

$$\text{Standard molar volume} = 22.4141 \text{ L or } 22.4 \text{ L [to 3 sf]} \tag{5.6}$$

At STP, helium (He), nitrogen (N_2), oxygen (O_2), and other simple gases behave nearly ideally (Figure 5.9). Note that the mass, and thus the density (d), depend on the specific gas, but 1 mol of any of them occupies 22.4 L at STP. Figure 5.10 compares the volumes of some familiar objects with the standard molar volume of an ideal gas.

The Ideal Gas Law

Each of the three gas laws shows how one of the three other gas variables affects gas volume:

- Boyle's law focuses on pressure ($V \propto 1/P$).
- Charles's law focuses on temperature ($V \propto T$).
- Avogadro's law focuses on amount (mol) of gas ($V \propto n$).

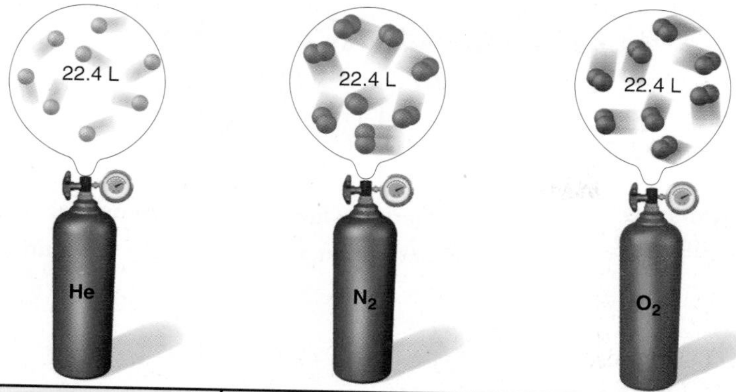

n = 1 mol	n = 1 mol	n = 1 mol
P = 1 atm (760 torr)	P = 1 atm (760 torr)	P = 1 atm (760 torr)
T = 0°C (273 K)	T = 0°C (273 K)	T = 0°C (273 K)
V = 22.4 L	V = 22.4 L	V = 22.4 L
Number of gas particles = 6.022×10^{23}	Number of gas particles = 6.022×10^{23}	Number of gas particles = 6.022×10^{23}
Mass = 4.003 g	Mass = 28.02 g	Mass = 32.00 g
d = 0.179 g/L	d = 1.25 g/L	d = 1.43 g/L

Figure 5.9 **Standard molar volume.** One mole of an ideal gas occupies 22.4 L at STP (0°C and 1 atm).

Figure 5.10 The volumes of 1 mol (22.4 L) of an ideal gas and of some familiar objects: 1 gal of milk (3.79 L), a basketball (7.50 L), and 2.00 L of a carbonated drink.

By combining these individual effects, we obtain the **ideal gas law** (or *ideal gas equation*):

$$V \propto \frac{nT}{P} \qquad \text{or} \qquad PV \propto nT \qquad \text{or} \qquad \frac{PV}{nT} = R$$

where R is a proportionality constant known as the **universal gas constant.** Rearranging gives the most common form of the ideal gas law:

$$PV = nRT \tag{5.7}$$

We obtain a value of R by measuring the volume, temperature, and pressure of a given amount of gas and substituting the values into the ideal gas law. For example, using standard conditions for the gas variables and 1 mol of gas, we have

$$R = \frac{PV}{nT} = \frac{1 \text{ atm} \times 22.4141 \text{ L}}{1 \text{ mol} \times 273.15 \text{ K}} = 0.082058 \frac{\text{atm}\cdot\text{L}}{\text{mol}\cdot\text{K}} = 0.0821 \frac{\text{atm}\cdot\text{L}}{\text{mol}\cdot\text{K}} \text{ [3 sf]} \tag{5.8}$$

This numerical value of R corresponds to P, V, and T expressed *in these units; R has a different numerical value when different units are used.* For example, on p. 209, R has the value 8.314 J/mol·K (J stands for joule, the SI unit of energy).

Figure 5.11 on the next page makes a central point: the ideal gas law *becomes* one of the individual gas laws when two of the four variables are kept constant. When initial conditions (subscript 1) change to final conditions (subscript 2), we have

$$P_1V_1 = n_1RT_1 \quad \text{and} \quad P_2V_2 = n_2RT_2$$

Thus,

$$\frac{P_1V_1}{n_1T_1} = R \quad \text{and} \quad \frac{P_2V_2}{n_2T_2} = R, \quad \text{so} \quad \frac{P_1V_1}{n_1T_1} = \frac{P_2V_2}{n_2T_2}$$

Notice that if, for example, the two variables P and T remain constant, then $P_1 = P_2$ and $T_1 = T_2$, and we obtain an expression for Avogadro's law:

$$\frac{\cancel{P_1}V_1}{n_1\cancel{T_1}} = \frac{\cancel{P_2}V_2}{n_2\cancel{T_2}} \qquad \text{or} \qquad \frac{V_1}{n_1} = \frac{V_2}{n_2}$$

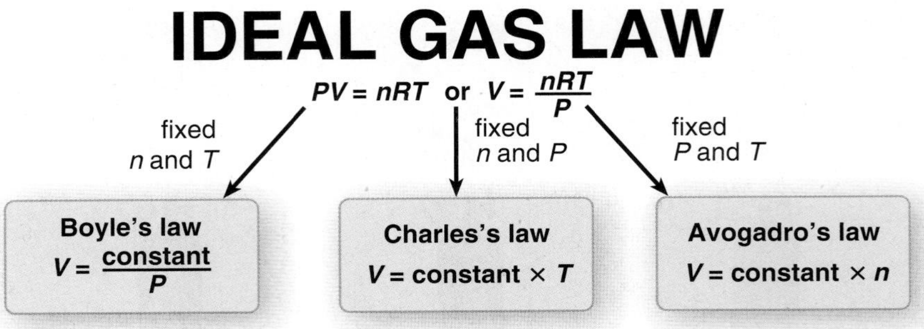

Figure 5.11 The individual gas laws as special cases of the ideal gas law.

As you'll see next, you can use a similar approach to solve gas law problems. Thus, by keeping track of the initial and final values of the gas variables, you avoid the need to memorize the three individual gas laws.

Solving Gas Law Problems

Gas law problems are phrased in many ways but can usually be grouped into two types:

1. *A change in one of the four variables causes a change in another, while the two other variables remain constant.* In this type, the ideal gas law reduces to one of the individual gas laws, and you solve for the new value of the affected variable. Units must be consistent and T must always be in kelvins, but R is not involved. Sample Problems 5.2 to 5.4 and 5.6 are of this type. [A variation on this type involves the combined gas law (p. 189) when simultaneous changes in two of the variables cause a change in a third.]

2. *One variable is unknown, but the other three are known and no change occurs.* In this type, exemplified by Sample Problem 5.5, you apply the ideal gas law directly to find the unknown, and the units must conform to those in R.

Solving these problems requires a systematic approach:

- Summarize the changing gas variables—knowns and unknown—and those held constant.
- Convert units, if necessary.
- Rearrange the ideal gas law to obtain the needed relationship of variables, and solve for the unknown.

Road Map

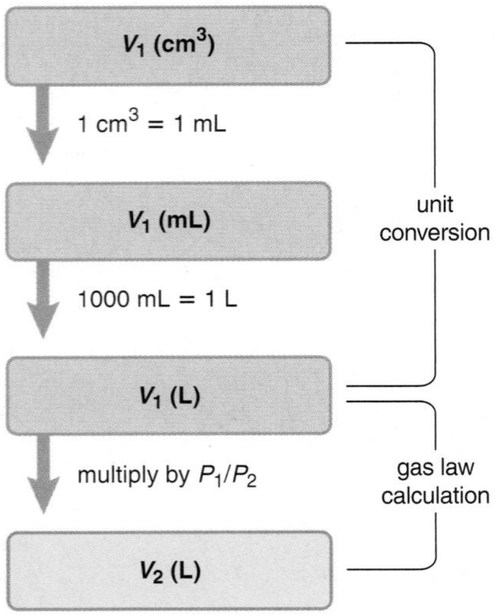

Sample Problem 5.2 Applying the Volume-Pressure Relationship

Problem Boyle's apprentice finds that the air trapped in a J tube occupies 24.8 cm^3 at 1.12 atm. By adding mercury to the tube, he increases the pressure on the trapped air to 2.64 atm. Assuming constant temperature, what is the new volume of air (in L)?

Plan We must find the final volume (V_2) in liters, given the initial volume (V_1), initial pressure (P_1), and final pressure (P_2). The temperature and amount of gas are fixed. We convert the units of V_1 from cm^3 to mL and then to L, rearrange the ideal gas law to the appropriate form, and solve for V_2. (Note that the road map has two parts.)

Solution Summarizing the gas variables:

$P_1 = 1.12$ atm $\quad P_2 = 2.64$ atm

$V_1 = 24.8$ cm^3 (convert to L) $\quad V_2 =$ unknown $\quad$ T and n remain constant

Converting V_1 from cm^3 to L:

$$V_1 = 24.8\ \text{cm}^3 \times \frac{1\ \text{mL}}{1\ \text{cm}^3} \times \frac{1\ \text{L}}{1000\ \text{mL}} = 0.0248\ \text{L}$$

Rearranging the ideal gas law and solving for V_2: At fixed n and T, we have

$$\frac{P_1V_1}{\cancel{n_1}\cancel{T_1}} = \frac{P_2V_2}{\cancel{n_2}\cancel{T_2}} \quad \text{or} \quad P_1V_1 = P_2V_2$$

$$V_2 = V_1 \times \frac{P_1}{P_2} = 0.0248\ \text{L} \times \frac{1.12\ \text{atm}}{2.64\ \text{atm}} = 0.0105\ \text{L}$$

Check The relative values of P and V can help us check the math: P more than doubled, so V_2 should be less than $\frac{1}{2}V_1$ ($0.0105/0.0248 < \frac{1}{2}$).

Comment Predicting the direction of the change provides another check on the problem setup: Since P increases, V will decrease; thus, V_2 should be less than V_1. To make $V_2 < V_1$, we must multiply V_1 by a number *less than* 1. This means the ratio of pressures must be *less than* 1, so the larger pressure (P_2) must be in the denominator, or P_1/P_2.

Follow-Up Problem 5.2 A sample of argon gas occupies 105 mL at 0.871 atm. If the temperature remains constant, what is the volume (in L) at 26.3 kPa?

Sample Problem 5.3 Applying the Pressure-Temperature Relationship

Problem A steel tank used for fuel delivery is fitted with a safety valve that opens if the internal pressure exceeds 1.00×10^3 torr. It is filled with methane at 23°C and 0.991 atm and placed in boiling water 100.°C. Will the safety valve open?

Plan The question "Will the safety valve open?" translates to "Is P_2 greater than 1.00×10^3 torr at T_2?" Thus, P_2 is the unknown, and T_1, T_2, and P_1 are given, with V (steel tank) and n fixed. We convert both T values to kelvins and P_1 to torrs in order to compare P_2 with the safety-limit pressure. We rearrange the ideal gas law and solve for P_2.

Road Map

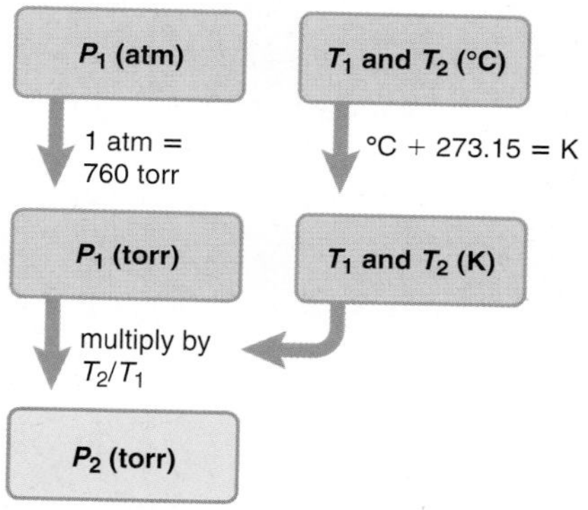

Solution Summarizing the gas variables:

$P_1 = 0.991$ atm (convert to torr) $\quad P_2 =$ unknown

$T_1 = 23°\text{C}$ (convert to K) $\quad T_2 = 100.°\text{C}$ (convert to K)

V and n remain constant

Converting T from °C to K:

$$T_1\ (\text{K}) = 23°\text{C} + 273.15 = 296\ \text{K} \qquad T_2\ (\text{K}) = 100.°\text{C} + 273.15 = 373\ \text{K}$$

Converting P from atm to torr:

$$P_1\ (\text{torr}) = 0.991\ \text{atm} \times \frac{760\ \text{torr}}{1\ \text{atm}} = 753\ \text{torr}$$

Rearranging the ideal gas law and solving for P_2: At fixed n and V, we have

$$\frac{P_1\cancel{V_1}}{\cancel{n_1}T_1} = \frac{P_2\cancel{V_2}}{\cancel{n_2}T_2} \quad \text{or} \quad \frac{P_1}{T_1} = \frac{P_2}{T_2}$$

$$P_2 = P_1 \times \frac{T_2}{T_1} = 753\ \text{torr} \times \frac{373\ \text{K}}{296\ \text{K}} = 949\ \text{torr}$$

P_2 is less than 1.00×10^3 torr, so the valve will *not* open.

Check Let's predict the change to check the math: Because $T_2 > T_1$, we expect $P_2 > P_1$. Thus, the temperature ratio should be >1 (T_2 in the numerator). The T ratio is about 1.25 (373/296), so the P ratio should also be about 1.25 ($950/750 \approx 1.25$).

Follow-Up Problem 5.3 An engineer pumps air at 0°C into a newly designed piston-cylinder assembly. The volume measures 6.83 cm^3. At what temperature (in K) will the volume be 9.75 cm^3?

Sample Problem 5.4 Applying the Volume-Amount Relationship

Problem A scale model of a blimp rises when it is filled with helium to a volume of 55.0 dm^3. When 1.10 mol of He is added to the blimp, the volume is 26.2 dm^3. How many more grams of He must be added to make it rise? Assume constant T and P.

Plan We are given the initial amount of helium (n_1), the initial volume of the blimp (V_1), and the volume needed for it to rise (V_2), and we need the additional mass of helium to make it rise. So we first need to find n_2. We rearrange the ideal gas law to the appropriate form, solve for n_2, subtract n_1 to find the additional amount ($n_{\text{add'l}}$), and then convert moles to grams.

Road Map

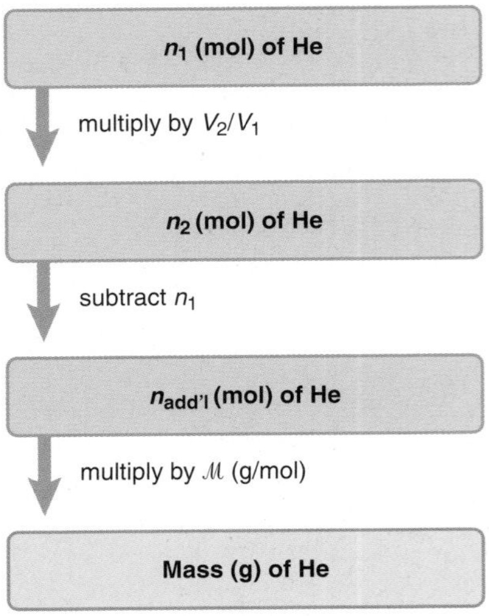

Solution Summarizing the gas variables:

$$n_1 = 1.10 \text{ mol} \qquad n_2 = \text{unknown (find, and then subtract } n_1)$$
$$V_1 = 26.2 \text{ dm}^3 \qquad V_2 = 55.0 \text{ dm}^3$$
P and T remain constant

Rearranging the ideal gas law and solving for n_2: At fixed P and T, we have

$$\frac{\cancel{P_1}V_1}{n_1\cancel{T_1}} = \frac{\cancel{P_2}V_2}{n_2\cancel{T_2}} \quad \text{or} \quad \frac{V_1}{n_1} = \frac{V_2}{n_2}$$

$$n_2 = n_1 \times \frac{V_2}{V_1} = 1.10 \text{ mol He} \times \frac{55.0 \text{ dm}^3}{26.2 \text{ dm}^3}$$
$$= 2.31 \text{ mol He}$$

Finding the additional amount of He:

$$n_{\text{add'l}} = n_2 - n_1 = 2.31 \text{ mol He} - 1.10 \text{ mol He}$$
$$= 1.21 \text{ mol He}$$

Converting amount (mol) of He to mass (g):

$$\text{Mass (g) of He} = 1.21 \text{ mol He} \times \frac{4.003 \text{ g He}}{1 \text{ mol He}}$$
$$= 4.84 \text{ g He}$$

Check We predict that $n_2 > n_1$ because $V_2 > V_1$: since V_2 is about twice V_1 ($55/26 \approx 2$), n_2 should be about twice n_1 ($2.3/1.1 \approx 2$). Since $n_2 > n_1$, we were right to multiply n_1 by a number >1 (that is, V_2/V_1). About 1.2 mol $\times$ 4 g/mol $\approx$ 4.8 g.

Comment **1.** A different sequence of steps will give you the same answer: first find the additional volume ($V_{\text{add'l}} = V_2 - V_1$), and then solve directly for $n_{\text{add'l}}$. Try it for yourself.
2. You saw that Charles's law ($V \propto T$ at fixed P and n) becomes a similar relationship between P and T at fixed V and n. The follow-up problem demonstrates that Avogadro's law ($V \propto n$ at fixed P and T) becomes a similar relationship at fixed V and T.

Follow-Up Problem 5.4 A rigid plastic container holds 35.0 g of ethylene gas (C_2H_4) at a pressure of 793 torr. What is the pressure if 5.0 g of ethylene is removed at constant temperature?

Sample Problem 5.5 Solving for an Unknown Gas Variable at Fixed Conditions

Problem A steel tank has a volume of 438 L and is filled with 0.885 kg of O_2. Calculate the pressure of O_2 at 21°C.

Plan We are given V, T, and the mass of O_2, and we must find P. Since conditions are not changing, we apply the ideal gas law without rearranging it. We use the given V in liters, convert T to kelvins and mass (kg) of O_2 to amount (mol), and solve for P.

Solution Summarizing the gas variables:

$V = 438$ L $\quad$ $T = 21°C$ (convert to K)
$n = 0.885$ kg O_2 (convert to mol) $\quad$ $P =$ unknown

Converting T from °C to K:

$$T\,(\text{K}) = 21°\text{C} + 273.15 = 294\ \text{K}$$

Converting from mass (g) of O_2 to amount (mol):

$$n = \text{mol of } O_2 = 0.885\ \text{kg } O_2 \times \frac{1000\ \text{g}}{1\ \text{kg}} \times \frac{1\ \text{mol } O_2}{32.00\ \text{g } O_2} = 27.7\ \text{mol } O_2$$

Solving for P (note the unit canceling here):

$$P = \frac{nRT}{V} = \frac{27.7\ \cancel{\text{mol}} \times 0.0821\ \dfrac{\text{atm}\cdot\cancel{\text{L}}}{\cancel{\text{mol}}\cdot\cancel{\text{K}}} \times 294\ \cancel{\text{K}}}{438\ \cancel{\text{L}}}$$
$$= 1.53\ \text{atm}$$

Check The amount of O_2 seems correct: ~900 g/(30 g/mol) = 30 mol. To check the approximate size of the final calculation, round off the values, including that for R:

$$P = \frac{30\ \text{mol } O_2 \times 0.1\ \dfrac{\text{atm}\cdot\text{L}}{\text{mol}\cdot\text{K}} \times 300\ \text{K}}{450\ \text{L}} = 2\ \text{atm}$$

which is reasonably close to 1.53 atm.

Follow-Up Problem 5.5 The tank in the sample problem develops a slow leak that is discovered and sealed. The new pressure is 1.37 atm. How many grams of O_2 remain?

Finally, in a picture problem, we apply the gas laws to determine the balanced equation for a gaseous reaction.

Sample Problem 5.6 Using Gas Laws to Determine a Balanced Equation

Problem The piston-cylinder below is depicted before and after a gaseous reaction that is carried out in it at constant pressure: the temperature is 150 K before and 300 K after the reaction. (Assume the cylinder is insulated.)

Which of the following balanced equations describes the reaction?

(1) $A_2(g) + B_2(g) \longrightarrow 2AB(g)$ $\quad$ (2) $2AB(g) + B_2(g) \longrightarrow 2AB_2(g)$
(3) $A(g) + B_2(g) \longrightarrow AB_2(g)$ $\quad$ (4) $2AB_2(g) \longrightarrow A_2(g) + 2B_2(g)$

Plan We are shown a depiction of the volume and temperature of a gas mixture before and after a reaction and must deduce the balanced equation. The problem says that P is constant, and the picture shows that, when T doubles, V stays the same. If n were also constant, Charles's law tells us that V should double when T doubles. But, since V does not change, n cannot be constant. From Avogadro's law, the only way to maintain V constant, with P constant and T doubling, is for n to be halved. So we examine the four balanced equations and count the number of moles on each side to see in which equation n is halved.

Solution In equation (1), n does not change, so doubling T would double V.
In equation (2), n decreases from 3 mol to 2 mol, so doubling T would increase V by one-third.
In equation (3), n decreases from 2 mol to 1 mol. Doubling T would exactly balance the decrease from halving n, so V would stay the same.
In equation (4), n increases, so doubling T would more than double V.
Therefore, equation (3) is correct:

$$A(g) + B_2(g) \longrightarrow AB_2(g)$$

Follow-Up Problem 5.6 The piston-cylinder below shows the volumes of a gaseous reaction mixture before and after a reaction that takes place at constant pressure and an initial temperature of −73°C.

If the *unbalanced* equation is $CD(g) \longrightarrow C_2(g) + D_2(g)$, what is the final temperature (in °C)?

Summary of Section 5.3

- Four interdependent variables define the physical behavior of an ideal gas: volume (V), pressure (P), temperature (T), and amount (number of moles, n).
- Most simple gases display nearly ideal behavior at ordinary temperatures and pressures.
- Boyle's, Charles's, and Avogadro's laws refer to the linear relationships between the volume of a gas and the pressure, temperature, and amount of gas, respectively.
- At STP (0°C and 1 atm), 1 mol of an ideal gas occupies 22.4 L.
- The ideal gas law incorporates the individual gas laws into one equation: $PV = nRT$, where R is the universal gas constant.

5.4 • REARRANGEMENTS OF THE IDEAL GAS LAW

In this section, we mathematically rearrange the ideal gas law to find gas density, molar mass, the partial pressure of each gas in a mixture, and the amount of gaseous reactant or product in a reaction.

The Density of a Gas

One mole of any gas behaving ideally occupies the same volume at a given temperature and pressure, so differences in gas density ($d = m/V$) depend on differences in molar mass (see Figure 5.9, p. 191). For example, at STP, 1 mol of O_2 occupies the same volume as 1 mol of N_2; however, O_2 is denser because each O_2 molecule has a greater mass (32.00 amu) than each N_2 molecule (28.02 amu). Thus, d of O_2 is $\frac{32.00}{28.02} \times d$ of N_2.

We can rearrange the ideal gas law to calculate the density of a gas from its molar mass. Recall that the number of moles (n) is the mass (m) divided by the molar mass ($\mathcal{M}$), $n = m/\mathcal{M}$. Substituting for n in the ideal gas law gives

$$PV = \frac{m}{\mathcal{M}}RT$$

Rearranging to isolate m/V gives

$$\frac{m}{V} = d = \frac{\mathcal{M} \times P}{RT} \qquad (5.9)$$

Two important ideas are expressed by Equation 5.9:

- *The density of a gas is directly proportional to its molar mass.* The volume of a given amount of a heavier gas equals the volume of the same amount of a lighter gas (Avogadro's law), so the density of the heavier gas is higher (as you just saw for O_2 and N_2).
- *The density of a gas is inversely proportional to the temperature.* As the volume of a gas increases with temperature (Charles's law), the same mass occupies more space, so the density of the gas is lower.

We use Equation 5.9 to find the density of a gas at any temperature and pressure near standard conditions.

Sample Problem 5.7 Calculating Gas Density

Problem To apply a green chemistry approach, a chemical engineer uses waste CO_2 from a manufacturing process, instead of chlorofluorocarbons, as a "blowing agent" in the production of polystyrene. Find the density (in g/L) of CO_2 and the number of molecules per liter **(a)** at STP (0°C and 1 atm) and **(b)** at room conditions (20.°C and 1.00 atm).

Plan We must find the density (d) and the number of molecules of CO_2, given two sets of P and T data. We find $\mathcal{M}$, convert T to kelvins, and calculate d with Equation 5.9. Then we convert the mass per liter to molecules per liter with Avogadro's number.

Solution **(a)** Density and molecules per liter of CO_2 at STP. Summary of gas properties:

$$T = 0°\text{C} + 273.15 = 273\ \text{K} \qquad P = 1\ \text{atm} \qquad \mathcal{M}\ \text{of}\ CO_2 = 44.01\ \text{g/mol}$$

Calculating density (note the unit canceling here):

$$d = \frac{\mathcal{M} \times P}{RT} = \frac{44.01\ \text{g}/\cancel{\text{mol}} \times 1.00\ \cancel{\text{atm}}}{0.0821\ \dfrac{\cancel{\text{atm}}\cdot\text{L}}{\cancel{\text{mol}}\cdot\cancel{\text{K}}} \times 273\ \cancel{\text{K}}} = \boxed{1.96\ \text{g/L}}$$

Converting from mass/L to molecules/L:

$$\text{Molecules}\ CO_2/\text{L} = \frac{1.96\ \text{g}\ CO_2}{1\ \text{L}} \times \frac{1\ \text{mol}\ CO_2}{44.01\ \text{g}\ CO_2} \times \frac{6.022{\times}10^{23}\ \text{molecules}\ CO_2}{1\ \text{mol}\ CO_2}$$

$$= \boxed{2.68{\times}10^{22}\ \text{molecules}\ CO_2/\text{L}}$$

(b) Density and molecules of CO_2 per liter at room conditions. Summary of gas properties:

$$T = 20.°\text{C} + 273.15 = 293\ \text{K} \qquad P = 1.00\ \text{atm} \qquad \mathcal{M}\ \text{of}\ CO_2 = 44.01\ \text{g/mol}$$

Calculating density:

$$d = \frac{\mathcal{M} \times P}{RT} = \frac{44.01\ \text{g/mol} \times 1.00\ \text{atm}}{0.0821\ \dfrac{\text{atm}\cdot\text{L}}{\text{mol}\cdot\text{K}} \times 293\ \text{K}} = \boxed{1.83\ \text{g/L}}$$

Converting from mass/L to molecules/L:

$$\text{Molecules}\ CO_2/\text{L} = \frac{1.83\ \text{g}\ CO_2}{1\ \text{L}} \times \frac{1\ \text{mol}\ CO_2}{44.01\ \text{g}\ CO_2} \times \frac{6.022{\times}10^{23}\ \text{molecules}\ CO_2}{1\ \text{mol}\ CO_2}$$

$$= \boxed{2.50{\times}10^{22}\ \text{molecules}\ CO_2/\text{L}}$$

Check Round off to check the density values; for example, in (a), at STP:

$$\frac{50\ \text{g/mol} \times 1\ \text{atm}}{0.1\ \dfrac{\text{atm}\cdot\text{L}}{\text{mol}\cdot\text{K}} \times 250\ \text{K}} = 2\ \text{g/L} \approx 1.96\ \text{g/L}$$

At the higher temperature in (b), the density should decrease, which can happen only if there are fewer molecules per liter, so the answer is reasonable.

Comment 1. An *alternative approach* for finding the density of most simple gases, but *at STP only,* is to divide the molar mass by the standard molar volume, 22.4 L:

$$d = \frac{\mathcal{M}}{V} = \frac{44.01\ \text{g/mol}}{22.4\ \text{L/mol}} = 1.96\ \text{g/L}$$

Once you know the density at one temperature (0°C), you can find it at any other temperature with the following relationship: $d_1/d_2 = T_2/T_1$.

2. Note that we have different numbers of significant figures for the pressure values. In (a), "1 atm" is part of the definition of STP, so it is an exact number. In (b), we specified "1.00 atm" to allow three significant figures in the answer.

Follow-Up Problem 5.7 Compare the density of CO_2 at 0°C and 380. torr with its density at STP.

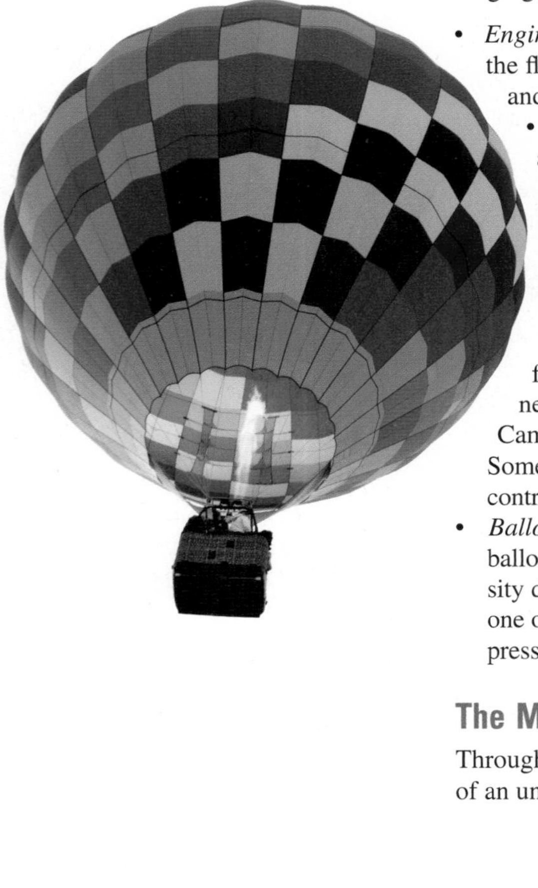

Gas Density and the Human Condition A few applications demonstrate the wide-ranging relevance of gas density:

- *Engineering.* Architectural designers and heating engineers place heating ducts near the floor so that the warmer, and thus less dense, air coming from the ducts will rise and mix with the cooler room air.
- *Safety and air pollution.* In the absence of mixing, a less dense gas will lie above a more dense one. Fire extinguishers that release CO_2 are effective because this gas is heavier than air: it sinks onto the fire and keeps more O_2 from reaching the fuel. The dense gases in smog that blankets urban centers, such as Mexico City, Los Angeles, and Beijing, contribute to respiratory illnesses.
- *Toxic releases.* During World War I, poisonous phosgene gas ($COCl_2$) was used against ground troops because it was dense enough to sink into their trenches. In 1984, the accidental release of poisonous methylisocyanate gas from a Union Carbide plant in India killed thousands of people as it blanketed nearby neighborhoods. In 1986, CO_2 released naturally from Lake Nyos in Cameroon suffocated thousands of people as it flowed down valleys into villages. Some paleontologists suggest that the release of CO_2 from volcanic lakes may have contributed to widespread dying off of dinosaurs.
- *Ballooning.* When the gas in a hot-air balloon is heated, its volume increases and the balloon inflates. Further heating causes some of the gas to escape. Thus, the gas density decreases and the balloon rises. In 1783, Jacques Charles (of Charles's law) made one of the first balloon flights, and 20 years later, Joseph Gay-Lussac (who studied the pressure-temperature relationship) set a solo altitude record that held for 50 years.

The Molar Mass of a Gas

Through another rearrangement of the ideal gas law, we can determine the molar mass of an unknown gas or a volatile liquid (one that is easily vaporized):

$$n = \frac{m}{\mathcal{M}} = \frac{PV}{RT} \quad \text{so} \quad \mathcal{M} = \frac{mRT}{PV} \qquad (5.10)$$

Notice that this equation is just a rearrangement of Equation 5.9.

Sample Problem 5.8 Finding the Molar Mass of a Volatile Liquid

Problem An organic chemist isolates a colorless liquid from a petroleum sample. She places the liquid in a preweighed flask and puts the flask in boiling water, which vaporizes the liquid and fills the flask with gas. She closes the flask and reweighs it. She obtains the following data:

Volume (V) of flask = 213 mL T = 100.0°C P = 754 torr

Mass of flask + gas = 78.416 g   Mass of flask = 77.834 g

Calculate the molar mass of the liquid.

Plan We are given V, T, P, and mass data and must find the molar mass ($\mathcal{M}$) of the liquid. We convert V to liters, T to kelvins, and P to atmospheres, find the mass of gas by subtracting the mass of the flask from the mass of the flask plus gas, and use Equation 5.10 to calculate $\mathcal{M}$.

Solution Summarizing and converting the gas variables:

$$V\ (\text{L}) = 213\ \text{mL} \times \frac{1\ \text{L}}{1000\ \text{mL}} = 0.213\ \text{L} \qquad T\ (\text{K}) = 100.0°\text{C} + 273.15 = 373.2\ \text{K}$$

$$P\ (\text{atm}) = 754\ \text{torr} \times \frac{1\ \text{atm}}{760\ \text{torr}} = 0.992\ \text{atm} \qquad m = 78.416\ \text{g} - 77.834\ \text{g} = 0.582\ \text{g}$$

Calculating $\mathcal{M}$:

$$\mathcal{M} = \frac{mRT}{PV} = \frac{0.582\ \text{g} \times 0.0821\ \dfrac{\text{atm}\cdot\text{L}}{\text{mol}\cdot\text{K}} \times 373.2\ \text{K}}{0.992\ \text{atm} \times 0.213\ \text{L}} = 84.4\ \text{g/mol}$$

Check Rounding to check the arithmetic, we have

$$\frac{0.6\ \text{g} \times 0.08\ \dfrac{\text{atm}\cdot\text{L}}{\text{mol}\cdot\text{K}} \times 375\ \text{K}}{1\ \text{atm} \times 0.2\ \text{L}} = 90\ \text{g/mol} \qquad \text{(which is close to 84.4 g/mol)}$$

Follow-Up Problem 5.8 An empty 149-mL flask weighs 68.322 g before a sample of volatile liquid is added. The flask is then placed in a hot (95.0°C) water bath; the barometric pressure is 740. torr. The liquid vaporizes and the gas fills the flask. After cooling, flask and condensed liquid together weigh 68.697 g. What is the molar mass of the liquid?

The Partial Pressure of Each Gas in a Mixture of Gases

The gas behaviors we've discussed so far were observed in experiments with air, which is a mixture of gases; thus, the ideal gas law holds for virtually any gas at ordinary conditions, whether pure or a mixture, because

- Gases mix homogeneously (form a solution) in any proportions.
- Each gas in a mixture behaves as if it were the only gas present (assuming no chemical interactions).

Dalton's Law of Partial Pressures The second point above was discovered by John Dalton during his lifelong study of humidity. He observed that when water vapor is added to dry air, the total air pressure increases by the pressure of the water vapor:

$$P_{\text{humid air}} = P_{\text{dry air}} + P_{\text{added water vapor}}$$

He concluded that each gas in the mixture exerts a **partial pressure** equal to the pressure it would exert *by itself.* Stated as **Dalton's law of partial pressures,** his discovery was that *in a mixture of unreacting gases, the total pressure is the sum of the partial pressures of the individual gases:*

$$P_{\text{total}} = P_1 + P_2 + P_3 + \cdots \qquad (5.11)$$

As an example, suppose we have a tank of fixed volume that contains nitrogen gas at a certain pressure, and we introduce a sample of hydrogen gas into the tank. Each gas behaves independently, so we can write an ideal gas law expression for each:

$$P_{N_2} = \frac{n_{N_2}RT}{V} \qquad \text{and} \qquad P_{H_2} = \frac{n_{H_2}RT}{V}$$

Because each gas occupies the same total volume and is at the same temperature, the pressure of each gas depends only on its amount, n. Thus, the total pressure is

$$P_{\text{total}} = P_{N_2} + P_{H_2} = \frac{n_{N_2}RT}{V} + \frac{n_{H_2}RT}{V} = \frac{(n_{N_2} + n_{H_2})RT}{V} = \frac{n_{\text{total}}RT}{V}$$

where $n_{\text{total}} = n_{N_2} + n_{H_2}$.

Each component in a mixture contributes a fraction of the total number of moles in the mixture; this portion is the **mole fraction (*X*)** of that component. Multiplying *X* by 100 gives the mole percent. The sum of the mole fractions of all components must be 1, and the sum of the mole percents must be 100%. For N_2 in our mixture, the mole fraction is

$$X_{N_2} = \frac{n_{N_2}}{n_{total}} = \frac{n_{N_2}}{n_{N_2} + n_{H_2}}$$

If the total pressure is due to the total number of moles, the partial pressure of gas A is the total pressure multiplied by the mole fraction of A, X_A:

$$P_A = X_A \times P_{total} \qquad (5.12)$$

Equation 5.12 is a very useful result. To see that it is valid for the mixture of N_2 and H_2, we recall that $X_{N_2} + X_{H_2} = 1$; then we obtain

$$P_{total} = P_{N_2} + P_{H_2} = (X_{N_2} \times P_{total}) + (X_{H_2} \times P_{total}) = (X_{N_2} + X_{H_2})P_{total} = 1 \times P_{total}$$

Sample Problem 5.9 Applying Dalton's Law of Partial Pressures

Problem In a study of O_2 uptake by muscle at high altitude, a physiologist prepares an atmosphere consisting of 79 mole % N_2, 17 mole % $^{16}O_2$, and 4.0 mole % $^{18}O_2$. (The isotope ^{18}O will be measured to determine O_2 uptake.) The total pressure is 0.75 atm to simulate high altitude. Calculate the mole fraction and partial pressure of $^{18}O_2$ in the mixture.

Plan We must find $X_{^{18}O_2}$ and $P_{^{18}O_2}$ from P_{total} (0.75 atm) and the mole % of $^{18}O_2$ (4.0). Dividing the mole % by 100 gives the mole fraction, $X_{^{18}O_2}$. Then, using Equation 5.12, we multiply $X_{^{18}O_2}$ by P_{total} to find $P_{^{18}O_2}$.

Road Map

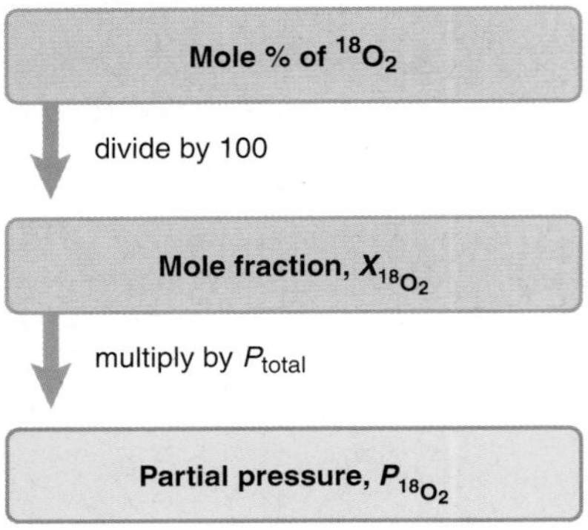

Solution Calculating the mole fraction of $^{18}O_2$:

$$X_{^{18}O_2} = \frac{4.0 \text{ mol \% } ^{18}O_2}{100} = 0.040$$

Solving for the partial pressure of $^{18}O_2$:

$$P_{^{18}O_2} = X_{^{18}O_2} \times P_{total} = 0.040 \times 0.75 \text{ atm} = 0.030 \text{ atm}$$

Check $X_{^{18}O_2}$ is small because the mole % is small, so $P_{^{18}O_2}$ should be small also.

Comment At high altitudes, specialized brain cells that are sensitive to O_2 and CO_2 levels in the blood trigger an increase in rate and depth of breathing for several days, until a person becomes acclimated.

Follow-Up Problem 5.9 To prevent the presence of air, noble gases are placed over highly reactive chemicals to act as inert "blanketing" gases. A chemical engineer places a mixture of noble gases consisting of 5.50 g of He, 15.0 g of Ne, and 35.0 g of Kr in a piston-cylinder assembly at STP. Calculate the partial pressure of each gas.

Table 5.2 Vapor Pressure of Water (P_{H_2O}) at Different *T*

T (°C)	P_{H_2O} (torr)	*T* (°C)	P_{H_2O} (torr)
0	4.6	40	55.3
5	6.5	45	71.9
10	9.2	50	92.5
12	10.5	55	118.0
14	12.0	60	149.4
16	13.6	65	187.5
18	15.5	70	233.7
20	17.5	75	289.1
22	19.8	80	355.1
24	22.4	85	433.6
26	25.2	90	525.8
28	28.3	95	633.9
30	31.8	100	760.0
35	42.2		

Collecting a Gas over Water Whenever a gas is in contact with water, some of the water vaporizes into the gas. The water vapor that mixes with the gas contributes the *vapor pressure,* a portion of the total pressure that depends only on the water temperature (Table 5.2). A common use of the law of partial pressures is to determine the yield of a water-insoluble gas formed in a reaction: the gaseous product bubbles through water, some water vaporizes into the bubbles, and the mixture of product gas and water vapor is collected into an inverted container (Figure 5.12).

To determine the yield, we look up the vapor pressure (P_{H_2O}) at the temperature of the experiment in Table 5.2 and subtract it from the total gas pressure (P_{total}, corrected for barometric pressure) to get the partial pressure of the gaseous product (P_{gas}). With *V* and *T* known, we can calculate the amount of product.

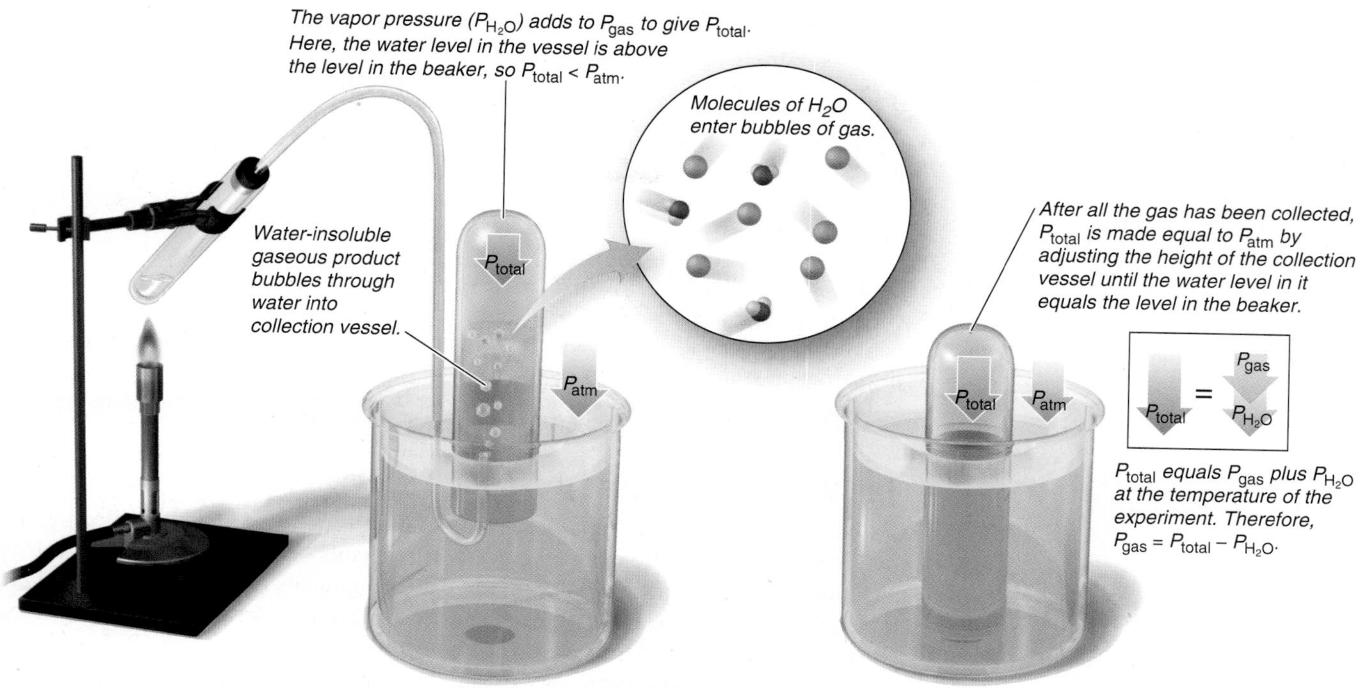

Figure 5.12 Collecting a water-insoluble gaseous product and determining its pressure.

Sample Problem 5.10 Calculating the Amount of Gas Collected over Water

Problem Acetylene (C_2H_2), an important fuel in welding, is produced in the laboratory when calcium carbide (CaC_2) reacts with water:

$$CaC_2(s) + 2H_2O(l) \longrightarrow C_2H_2(g) + Ca(OH)_2(aq)$$

For a sample of acetylene collected over water, total gas pressure (adjusted to barometric pressure) is 738 torr and the volume is 523 mL. At the temperature of the gas (23°C), the vapor pressure of water is 21 torr. How many grams of acetylene are collected?

Plan In order to find the mass of C_2H_2, we first need to find the number of moles of C_2H_2, $n_{C_2H_2}$, which we can obtain from the ideal gas law by calculating $P_{C_2H_2}$. The barometer reading gives us P_{total}, which is the sum of $P_{C_2H_2}$ and P_{H_2O}, and we are given P_{H_2O}, so we subtract to find $P_{C_2H_2}$. We are also given V and T, so we convert to consistent units, and find $n_{C_2H_2}$ from the ideal gas law. Then we convert moles to grams using the molar mass from the formula, as shown in the road map.

Road Map

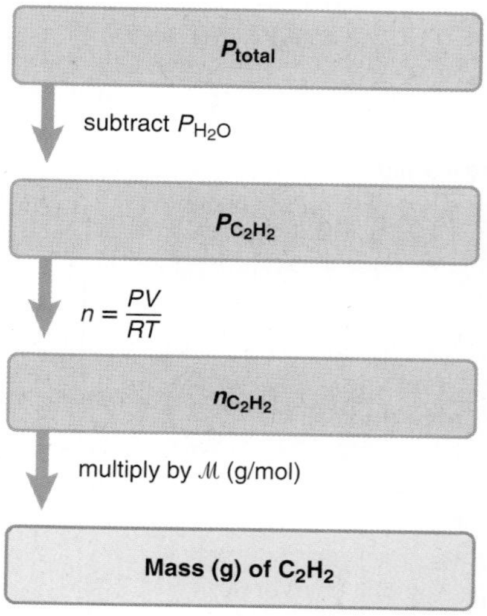

Solution Summarizing and converting the gas variables:

$$P_{C_2H_2}\text{ (torr)} = P_{total} - P_{H_2O} = 738\text{ torr} - 21\text{ torr} = 717\text{ torr}$$

$$P_{C_2H_2}\text{ (atm)} = 717\text{ torr} \times \frac{1\text{ atm}}{760\text{ torr}} = 0.943\text{ atm}$$

$$V\text{ (L)} = 523\text{ mL} \times \frac{1\text{ L}}{1000\text{ mL}} = 0.523\text{ L}$$

$$T\text{ (K)} = 23°\text{C} + 273.15 = 296\text{ K}$$

$$n_{C_2H_2} = \text{unknown}$$

Solving for $n_{C_2H_2}$:

$$n_{C_2H_2} = \frac{PV}{RT} = \frac{0.943\text{ atm} \times 0.523\text{ L}}{0.0821\,\frac{\text{atm·L}}{\text{mol·K}} \times 296\text{ K}} = 0.0203\text{ mol}$$

Converting $n_{C_2H_2}$ to mass (g):

$$\text{Mass (g) of } C_2H_2 = 0.0203\text{ mol } C_2H_2 \times \frac{26.04\text{ g } C_2H_2}{1\text{ mol } C_2H_2}$$

$$= 0.529\text{ g } C_2H_2$$

Check Rounding to one significant figure, a quick arithmetic check for n gives

$$n \approx \frac{1 \text{ atm} \times 0.5 \text{ L}}{0.08 \dfrac{\text{atm}\cdot\text{L}}{\text{mol}\cdot\text{K}} \times 300 \text{ K}} = 0.02 \text{ mol} \approx 0.0203 \text{ mol}$$

Comment The C_2^{2-} ion (called the *carbide,* or *acetylide, ion*) is an interesting anion. It is simply $^-C{\equiv}C^-$, which acts as a base in water, removing an H^+ ion from two H_2O molecules to form acetylene, $H{-}C{\equiv}C{-}H$.

Follow-Up Problem 5.10 A small piece of zinc reacts with dilute HCl to form H_2, which is collected over water at 16°C into a large flask. The total pressure is adjusted to barometric pressure (752 torr), and the volume is 1495 mL. Use Table 5.2 to help calculate the partial pressure and mass of H_2.

The Ideal Gas Law and Reaction Stoichiometry

As you saw in Chapters 3 and 4, and in the preceding discussion of collecting a gas over water, many reactions involve gases as reactants or products. From the balanced equation for such a reaction, you can calculate the amounts (mol) of reactants and products and convert these quantities into masses or numbers of molecules. Figure 5.13 shows how you use the ideal gas law to convert between gas variables (P, T, and V) and amounts (mol) of gaseous reactants and products. In effect, you combine a gas law problem with a stoichiometry problem, as you'll see in Sample Problems 5.11 and 5.12.

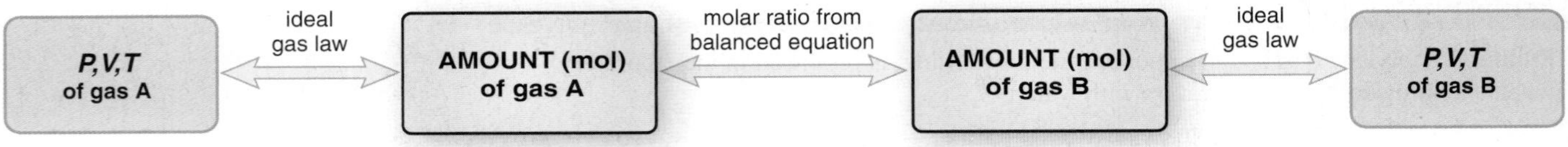

Figure 5.13 The relationships among the amount (mol, n) of gaseous reactant (or product) and the gas pressure (P), volume (V), and temperature (T).

Sample Problem 5.11 Using Gas Variables to Find Amounts of Reactants or Products I

Problem Engineers use copper in absorbent beds to react with and remove oxygen impurities in ethylene used to make polyethylene. The beds are regenerated when hot H_2 reduces the copper(II) oxide, forming the pure metal and H_2O. On a laboratory scale, what volume of H_2 at 765 torr and 225°C is needed to reduce 35.5 g of copper(II) oxide?

Plan This is a stoichiometry *and* gas law problem. To find V_{H_2}, we first need n_{H_2}. We write and balance the equation. Next, we convert the given mass (35.5 g) of copper(II) oxide, CuO, to amount (mol) and use the molar ratio to find amount (mol) of H_2 needed (stoichiometry portion). Then, we use the ideal gas law to convert moles of H_2 to liters (gas law portion). A road map is shown, but you are familiar with all the steps.

Road Map

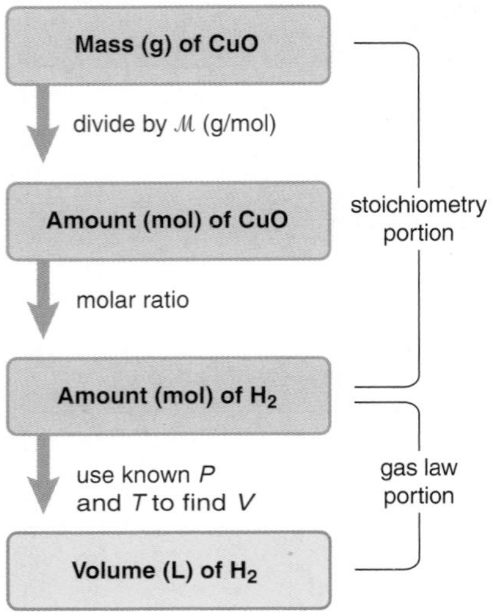

Solution Writing the balanced equation:

$$CuO(s) + H_2(g) \longrightarrow Cu(s) + H_2O(g)$$

Calculating n_{H_2}:

$$n_{H_2} = 35.5 \text{ g CuO} \times \frac{1 \text{ mol CuO}}{79.55 \text{ g CuO}} \times \frac{1 \text{ mol } H_2}{1 \text{ mol CuO}} = 0.446 \text{ mol } H_2$$

Summarizing and converting other gas variables:

$$V = \text{unknown} \qquad P \text{ (atm)} = 765 \text{ torr} \times \frac{1 \text{ atm}}{760 \text{ torr}} = 1.01 \text{ atm}$$

$$T \text{ (K)} = 225°\text{C} + 273.15 = 498 \text{ K}$$

Solving for V_{H_2}:

$$V = \frac{nRT}{P} = \frac{0.446 \text{ mol} \times 0.0821 \frac{\text{atm·L}}{\text{mol·K}} \times 498 \text{ K}}{1.01 \text{ atm}} = \boxed{18.1 \text{ L}}$$

Check One way to check the answer is to compare it with the molar volume of an ideal gas at STP (22.4 L at 273.15 K and 1 atm). One mole of H_2 at STP occupies about 22 L, so less than 0.5 mol occupies less than 11 L. T is less than twice 273 K, so V should be less than twice 11 L.

Comment The main point here is that the stoichiometry provides one gas variable (n), two more are given, and the ideal gas law is used to find the fourth.

Follow-Up Problem 5.11 Sulfuric acid reacts with sodium chloride to form aqueous sodium sulfate and hydrogen chloride gas. How many milliliters of gas form at STP when 0.117 kg of sodium chloride reacts with excess sulfuric acid?

Sample Problem 5.12 Using Gas Variables to Find Amounts of Reactants or Products II

Problem The alkali metals [Group 1A(1)] react with the halogens [Group 7A(17)] to form ionic metal halides. What mass of potassium chloride forms when 5.25 L of chlorine gas at 0.950 atm and 293 K reacts with 17.0 g of potassium (*see photo*)?

Chlorine gas reacting with potassium.

Plan The amounts of two reactants are given, so this is a limiting-reactant problem. The only difference between this and previous limiting-reactant problems (see Sample Problem 3.20, p. 111) is that here we use the ideal gas law to find the amount (n) of gaseous reactant from the known V, P, and T. We first write the balanced equation and then use it to find the limiting reactant and the amount and mass of product.

Solution Writing the balanced equation:

$$2K(s) + Cl_2(g) \longrightarrow 2KCl(s)$$

Summarizing the gas variables:

$P = 0.950$ atm $V = 5.25$ L
$T = 293$ K $n =$ unknown

Solving for n_{Cl_2}:

$$n_{Cl_2} = \frac{PV}{RT} = \frac{0.950 \text{ atm} \times 5.25 \text{ L}}{0.0821 \frac{\text{atm·L}}{\text{mol·K}} \times 293 \text{ K}} = 0.207 \text{ mol}$$

Converting from mass (g) of potassium (K) to amount (mol):

$$\text{Amount (mol) of K} = 17.0 \text{ g K} \times \frac{1 \text{ mol K}}{39.10 \text{ g K}} = 0.435 \text{ mol K}$$

Determining the limiting reactant: If Cl_2 is limiting,

$$\text{Amount (mol) of KCl} = 0.207 \text{ mol } Cl_2 \times \frac{2 \text{ mol KCl}}{1 \text{ mol } Cl_2} = 0.414 \text{ mol KCl}$$

If K is limiting,

$$\text{Amount (mol) of KCl} = 0.435 \text{ mol K} \times \frac{2 \text{ mol KCl}}{2 \text{ mol K}} = 0.435 \text{ mol KCl}$$

Cl_2 is the limiting reactant because it forms less KCl.
Converting from amount (mol) of KCl to mass (g):

$$\text{Mass (g) of KCl} = 0.414 \text{ mol KCl} \times \frac{74.55 \text{ g KCl}}{1 \text{ mol KCl}} = \boxed{30.9 \text{ g KCl}}$$

Check The gas law calculation seems correct. At STP, 22 L of Cl_2 gas contains about 1 mol, so a 5-L volume will contain a bit less than 0.25 mol of Cl_2. Moreover, since P (in numerator) is slightly lower than STP, and T (in denominator) is slightly higher than STP, these should lower the calculated n further below the ideal value. The mass of KCl seems correct: less than 0.5 mol of KCl gives $<0.5 \text{ mol} \times \mathcal{M}$ (~75 g/mol), and 30.9 g < 0.5 mol × 75 g/mol.

Follow-Up Problem 5.12 Ammonia and hydrogen chloride gases react to form solid ammonium chloride. A 10.0-L reaction flask contains ammonia at 0.452 atm and 22°C, and 155 mL of hydrogen chloride gas at 7.50 atm and 271 K is introduced. After the reaction occurs and the temperature returns to 22°C, what is the pressure inside the flask? (Neglect the volume of the solid product.)

Summary of Section 5.4

- Gas density is inversely related to temperature: higher T causes lower d, and vice versa. At the same P and T, gases with larger $\mathcal{M}$ have higher d.
- In a mixture of gases, each component contributes its partial pressure to the total pressure (Dalton's law of partial pressures). The mole fraction of each component is the ratio of its partial pressure to the total pressure.
- When a gaseous reaction product is collected by bubbling it through water, the total pressure is the sum of the gas pressure and the vapor pressure of water at the given temperature.
- By converting the variables P, V, and T for a gaseous reactant (or product) to amount (n, mol), we can solve stoichiometry problems for gaseous reactions.

5.5 • THE KINETIC-MOLECULAR THEORY: A MODEL FOR GAS BEHAVIOR

The **kinetic-molecular theory** is the model that accounts for macroscopic gas behavior at the level of individual particles (atoms or molecules). Developed by some of the great scientists of the 19th century, most notably James Clerk Maxwell and Ludwig Boltzmann, the theory was able to explain the gas laws that some of the great scientists of the 18th century had arrived at empirically. The theory draws quantitative conclusions based on a few postulates (assumptions), but our discussion will be largely qualitative.

How the Kinetic-Molecular Theory Explains the Gas Laws

Let's address some questions the theory must answer, then state the postulates, and draw conclusions that explain the gas laws and related phenomena.

Questions Concerning Gas Behavior Observing gas behavior at the macroscopic level, we must derive a molecular model that explains it:

1. *Origin of pressure.* Pressure is a measure of the force a gas exerts on a surface. How do individual gas particles create this force?
2. *Boyle's law* ($V \propto 1/P$). A change in gas pressure in one direction causes a change in gas volume in the other. What happens to the particles when external pressure compresses the gas volume? And why aren't liquids and solids compressible?
3. *Dalton's law* ($P_{total} = P_1 + P_2 + P_3 + \cdots$). The pressure of a gas mixture is the sum of the pressures of the individual gases. Why does each gas contribute to the total pressure in proportion to its number of particles?
4. *Charles's law* ($V \propto T$). A change in temperature causes a corresponding change in volume. What effect does higher temperature have on gas particles that increases gas volume? This question raises a more fundamental one: what does temperature measure on the molecular scale?
5. *Avogadro's law* ($V \propto n$). Gas volume depends on the number of moles present, not on the chemical nature of the gas. But shouldn't 1 mol of heavier particles exert more pressure, and thus take up more space, than 1 mol of lighter ones?

Postulates of the Kinetic-Molecular Theory The theory is based on three postulates:

Postulate 1. *Particle volume.* A gas consists of a large collection of individual particles with empty space between them. The volume of each particle is so small compared with the volume of the whole sample that it is assumed to be zero; each particle is essentially a point of mass.

Postulate 2. *Particle motion.* The particles are in constant, random, straight-line motion, except when they collide with the container walls or with each other.

Postulate 3. *Particle collisions.* The collisions are *elastic,* which means that, like minute billiard balls, the colliding molecules exchange energy but do not lose any energy through friction. Thus, *their total kinetic energy (E_k) is constant.* Between collisions, the molecules do not influence each other by attractive or repulsive forces.

Imagine what a sample of gas in a container looks like. Countless minute particles move in every direction, smashing into the container walls and each other. Any given particle changes its speed often—at one moment standing still from a head-on collision and the next moment zooming away from a smash on the side.

In the sample as a whole, *each particle has a molecular speed (u); most are moving near the most probable speed, but some are much faster and others much slower.* Figure 5.14 depicts this distribution of molecular speeds for N_2 gas at three temperatures.

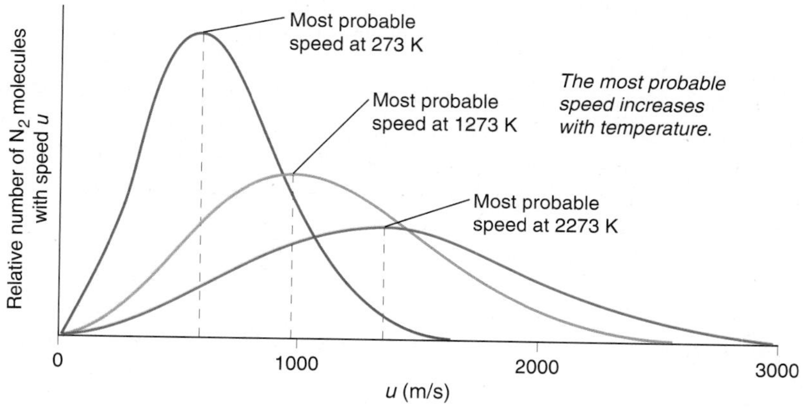

Figure 5.14 Distribution of molecular speeds for N_2 at three temperatures.

Note that the curves flatten and spread at higher temperatures and that the *most probable speed (the peak of each curve) increases as the temperature increases.* This increase occurs because the average kinetic energy of the molecules, which is related to the most probable speed, is proportional to the absolute temperature: $\overline{E_k} \propto T$, or $\overline{E_k} = c \times T$, where $\overline{E_k}$ is the average kinetic energy of the molecules (an overbar indicates the average value of a quantity) and c is a constant that is the same for any gas. (We'll return to this equation shortly.) Thus, a major conclusion based on the distribution of speeds, which arises directly from postulate 3, is that *at a given temperature, all gases have the same average kinetic energy.*

A Molecular View of the Gas Laws Let's keep visualizing gas particles in a container to see how the theory explains the macroscopic behavior of gases and answers the questions we posed above:

1. *Origin of pressure* (Figure 5.15). From postulates 1 and 2, each gas particle (point of mass) colliding with the container walls (and bottom of piston) exerts a force. Countless collisions over the inner surface of the container result in a pressure. The greater the number of particles, the more frequently they collide with the container, and so the greater the pressure.

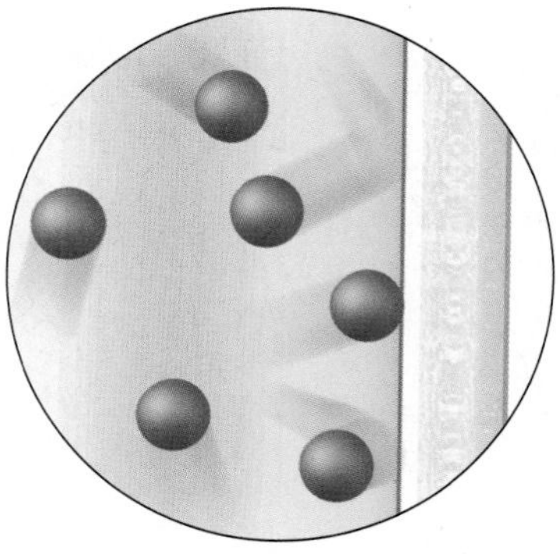

Figure 5.15 Pressure arises from countless collisions between gas particles and walls.

2. *Boyle's law* ($V \propto 1/P$) (Figure 5.16). The particles in a gas are points of mass with empty space between them (postulate 1). Before any change in pressure, the pressure exerted *by* the gas (P_{gas}) equals the pressure exerted *on* the gas (P_{ext}), and there is some average distance (d_1) between the particles and the container walls. As P_{ext} increases at constant temperature, the average distance (d_2) between the particles and the walls decreases (that is, $d_2 < d_1$), and so the sample volume decreases. Collisions of the particles with the walls become more frequent over the shorter average distance, which causes P_{gas} to increase until it again equals P_{ext}. The fact that liquids and solids cannot be compressed implies there is little, if any, free space between their particles.

Figure 5.16 A molecular view of Boyle's law.

3. *Dalton's law of partial pressures* ($P_{total} = P_A + P_B$) (Figure 5.17). Adding a given amount (mol) of gas A to a given amount of gas B causes an increase in the total number of particles, in proportion to the particles of A added. This increase causes a corresponding increase in the total number of collisions with the walls per second (postulate 2), which causes a corresponding increase in the total pressure of the gas mixture (P_{total}). Each gas exerts a fraction of P_{total} in proportion to its fraction of the total number of particles (or equivalently, its fraction of the total number of moles, that is, the mole fraction).

Figure 5.17 A molecular view of Dalton's law.

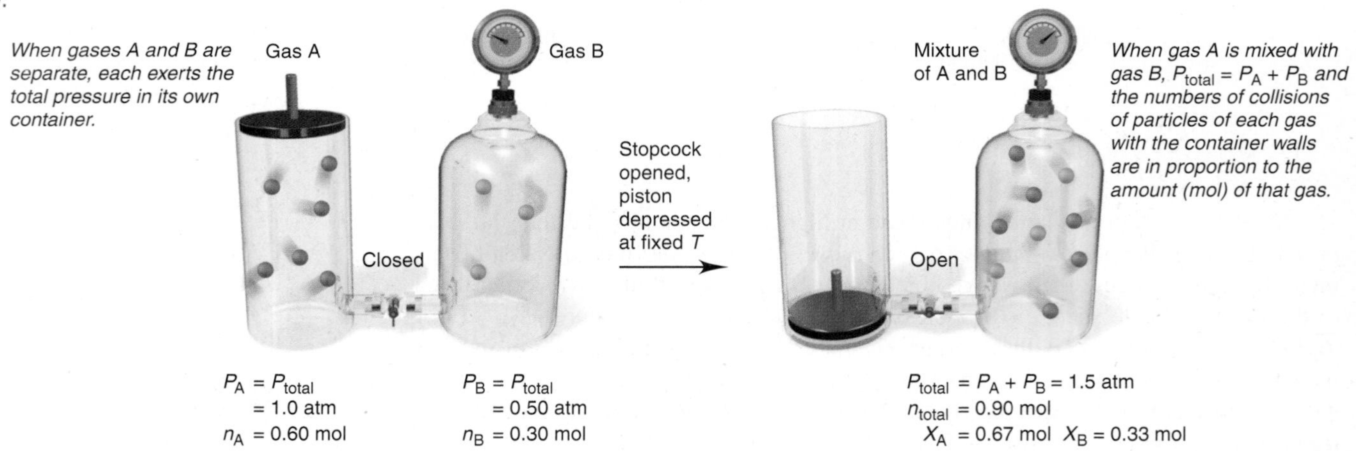

4. *Charles's law* ($V \propto T$) (Figure 5.18). At some starting temperature, T_1, the external (atmospheric) pressure (P_{atm}) equals the pressure of the gas (P_{gas}). When the gas is heated and the temperature increases to T_2, the most probable molecular speed and the average kinetic energy increase (postulate 3). Thus, the particles hit the walls more frequently *and* more energetically. This change temporarily increases P_{gas}. As a result, the piston moves up, which increases the volume and lowers the collision frequency until P_{atm} and P_{gas} are again equal.

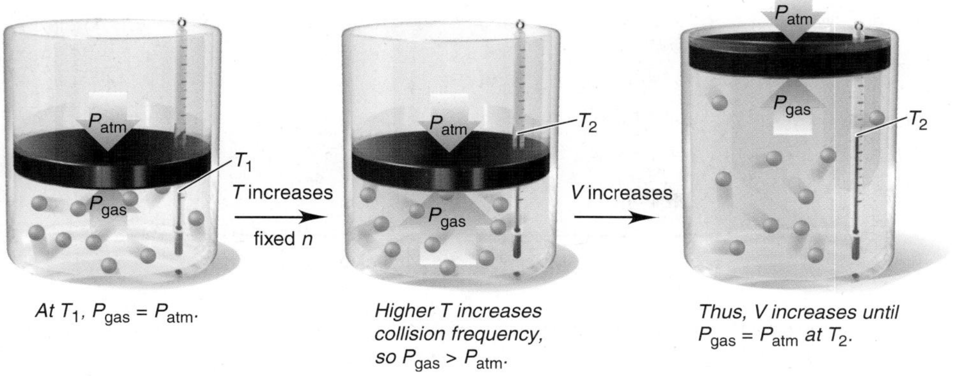

Figure 5.18 A molecular view of Charles's law.

5. *Avogadro's law* ($V \propto n$) (Figure 5.19). At some starting amount, n_1, of gas, P_{atm} equals P_{gas}. When more gas is added from the attached tank, the amount increases to n_2. Thus, more particles hit the walls more frequently, which temporarily increases P_{gas}. As a result, the piston moves up, which increases the volume and lowers the collision frequency until P_{atm} and P_{gas} are again equal.

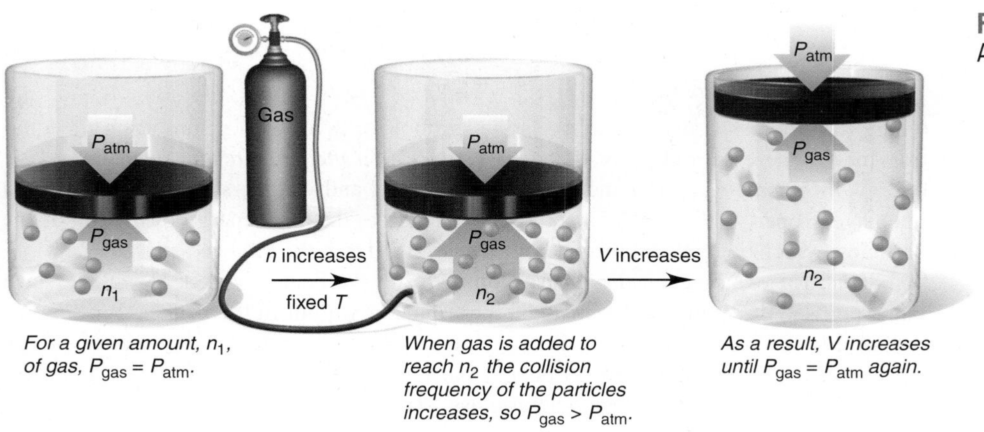

Figure 5.19 A molecular view of Avogadro's law.

The Central Importance of Kinetic Energy Recall from Chapter 1 that the kinetic energy of an object is the energy associated with its motion. It is key to explaining some implications of Avogadro's law and, most importantly, the meaning of temperature.

1. *Implications of Avogadro's law.* As we just saw, Avogadro's law says that, at any given *T* and *P*, the volume of a gas depends only on the number of moles—that is, number of particles—in the sample. The law doesn't mention the chemical nature of the gas, so equal numbers of particles of any two gases, say O_2 and H_2, should occupy the same volume. But, why don't the heavier O_2 molecules exert more pressure on the container walls, and thus take up more volume, than the lighter H_2 molecules? To answer this, we'll show one way to express kinetic energy mathematically:

$$E_k = \tfrac{1}{2}\text{mass} \times \text{speed}^2$$

This equation says that, for a given E_k, an object's mass and speed are inversely related, which means that *a heavier object moving slower can have the same kinetic energy as a lighter object moving faster.* Figure 5.20 on the next page shows that, for several gases, *the most probable speed (top of each curve) increases as the molar mass (number in parentheses) decreases.*

As we saw earlier, postulate 3 of the kinetic-molecular theory directly implies that, at a given *T*, all gases have the same average kinetic energy. From Figure 5.20, we see

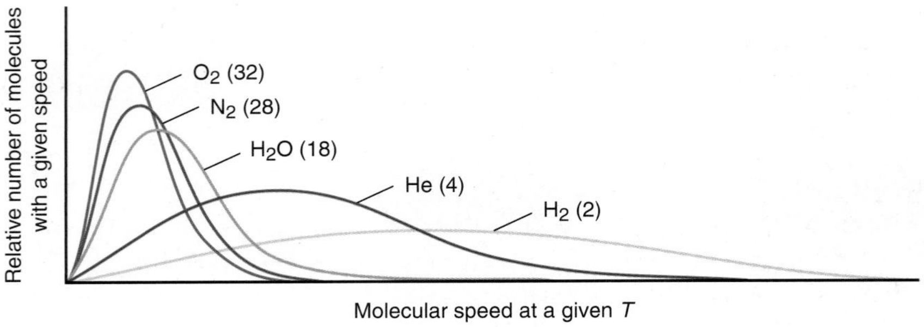

Figure 5.20 The relationship between molar mass and molecular speed. At a given temperature, gases with lower molar masses (numbers in parentheses) have higher most probable speeds (peak of each curve).

that O_2 molecules move more slowly, on average, than H_2 molecules. With their higher most probable speed, H_2 molecules collide with the walls of a container more often than O_2 molecules do, but their lower mass means that each collision has less force. Therefore, at a given T, equimolar samples of H_2 and O_2 (or any other gas) exert the same pressure and, thus, occupy the same volume because, on average, *their molecules hit the walls with the same kinetic energy*.

2. *The meaning of temperature.* Closely related to these ideas is the central relation between kinetic energy and temperature. Earlier we said that the average kinetic energy of the particles ($\overline{E_k}$) equals the absolute temperature times a constant; that is, $\overline{E_k} = c \times T$. Using definitions of velocity, momentum, force, and pressure, we can also express this relationship by the following equation:

$$\overline{E_k} = \frac{3}{2}\left(\frac{R}{N_A}\right)T$$

where R is the gas constant and N_A is the symbol for Avogadro's number. This equation makes the essential point that *temperature is a* ***measure*** *of the average kinetic energy of the particles:* as T increases, $\overline{E_k}$ increases, and vice versa. Temperature is an intensive property (Section 1.5), so it is not related to the *total* energy of motion of the particles, which depends on the size of the sample, but to the *average* energy.

Thus, for example, in the macroscopic world, we heat a beaker of water over a flame and see the mercury rise inside a thermometer we put in the beaker. We see this because, in the molecular world, kinetic energy transfers, in turn, from higher energy gas particles in the flame to lower energy particles in the beaker glass, the water molecules, the particles in the thermometer glass, and the atoms of mercury.

Root-Mean-Square Speed Finally, let's derive an expression for the speed of a gas particle that has the average kinetic energy of the particles in a sample. From the general expression for kinetic energy of an object,

$$E_k = \tfrac{1}{2}\text{mass} \times \text{speed}^2$$

the average kinetic energy of each particle in a large population is

$$\overline{E_k} = \tfrac{1}{2}m\overline{u^2}$$

where m is the particle's mass (atomic or molecular) and $\overline{u^2}$ is the average of the squares of the molecular speeds. Setting this expression for average kinetic energy equal to the earlier one gives

$$\tfrac{1}{2}m\overline{u^2} = \frac{3}{2}\left(\frac{R}{N_A}\right)T$$

Multiplying through by Avogadro's number, N_A, gives the average kinetic energy for a mole of gas particles:

$$\tfrac{1}{2}N_A\, m\overline{u^2} = \tfrac{3}{2}RT$$

Avogadro's number times the molecular mass, $N_A \times m$, is the molar mass, $\mathcal{M}$, and solving for $\overline{u^2}$, we have

$$\overline{u^2} = \frac{3RT}{\mathcal{M}}$$

The square root of $\overline{u^2}$ is the root-mean-square speed, or **rms speed (u_{rms})**: *a particle moving at this speed has the average kinetic energy.** That is, taking the square root of both sides of the previous equation gives

$$u_{rms} = \sqrt{\frac{3RT}{\mathcal{M}}} \quad (5.13)$$

where R is the gas constant, T is the absolute temperature, and $\mathcal{M}$ is the molar mass. (Because we want u in m/s and R includes the joule, which has units of kg·m²/s², we use the value 8.314 J/mol·K for R and express $\mathcal{M}$ in kg/mol.)

Thus, as an example, the root-mean-square speed of an O_2 molecule ($\mathcal{M} = 3.200\times10^{-2}$ kg/mol) at room temperature (20°C, or 293 K) in the air you're breathing right now is

$$u_{rms} = \sqrt{\frac{3RT}{\mathcal{M}}} = \sqrt{\frac{3(8.314\ \text{J/mol·K})(293\ \text{K})}{3.200\times10^{-2}\ \text{kg/mol}}}$$

$$= \sqrt{\frac{3(8.314\ \cancel{\text{kg}}\cdot\text{m}^2/\text{s}^2/\cancel{\text{mol}}\cdot\cancel{\text{K}})(293\ \cancel{\text{K}})}{3.200\times10^{-2}\ \cancel{\text{kg}}/\cancel{\text{mol}}}}$$

$$= 478\ \text{m/s (about 1070 mi/hr)}$$

Effusion and Diffusion

The movement of a gas into a vacuum and the movement of gases through one another are phenomena with some vital applications.

The Process of Effusion One of the early triumphs of the kinetic-molecular theory was an explanation of **effusion,** the process by which a gas escapes through a tiny hole in its container into an evacuated space. In 1846, Thomas Graham studied the effusion rate of a gas, the number of molecules escaping per unit time, and found that it was inversely proportional to the square root of the gas density. But, density is directly related to molar mass, so **Graham's law of effusion** is stated as follows: *the rate of effusion of a gas is inversely proportional to the square root of its molar mass,* or

$$\text{Rate of effusion} \propto \frac{1}{\sqrt{\mathcal{M}}}$$

Argon (Ar) is lighter than krypton (Kr), so it effuses faster, assuming equal pressures of the two gases (Figure 5.21). Thus, the ratio of the rates is

$$\frac{\text{Rate}_{Ar}}{\text{Rate}_{Kr}} = \frac{\sqrt{\mathcal{M}_{Kr}}}{\sqrt{\mathcal{M}_{Ar}}} \quad \text{or, in general,} \quad \frac{\text{Rate}_A}{\text{Rate}_B} = \frac{\sqrt{\mathcal{M}_B}}{\sqrt{\mathcal{M}_A}} = \sqrt{\frac{\mathcal{M}_B}{\mathcal{M}_A}} \quad (5.14)$$

The kinetic-molecular theory explains that, at a given temperature and pressure, *the gas with the lower molar mass effuses faster because the rms speed of its molecules is higher; therefore, more molecules reach the hole and escape per unit time.*

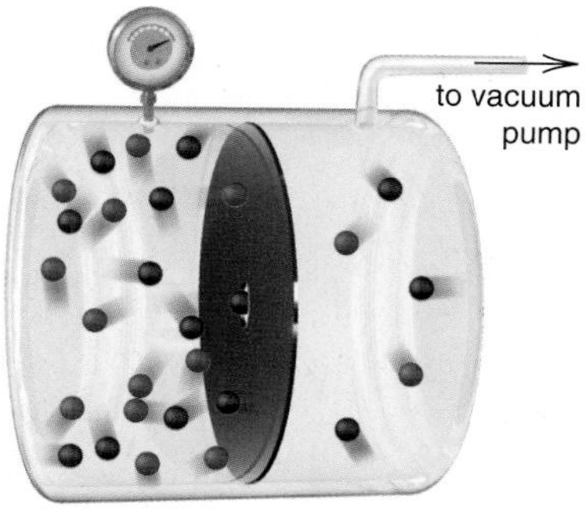

Figure 5.21 Effusion. Lighter (*black*) particles effuse faster than heavier (*red*) particles.

Sample Problem 5.13 Applying Graham's Law of Effusion

Problem A mixture of helium (He) and methane (CH_4) is placed in an effusion apparatus. Calculate the ratio of their effusion rates.

Plan The effusion rate is inversely proportional to $\sqrt{\mathcal{M}}$, so we find the molar mass of each substance from the formula and take its square root. The inverse of the ratio of the square roots is the ratio of the effusion rates.

Solution

$$\mathcal{M}\ \text{of}\ CH_4 = 16.04\ \text{g/mol} \qquad \mathcal{M}\ \text{of He} = 4.003\ \text{g/mol}$$

*The rms speed, u_{rms}, is proportional to, but slightly higher than, the most probable speed; for an ideal gas, $u_{rms} = 1.09 \times$ average speed.

Calculating the ratio of the effusion rates:

$$\frac{\text{Rate}_{\text{He}}}{\text{Rate}_{\text{CH}_4}} = \sqrt{\frac{\mathcal{M}_{\text{CH}_4}}{\mathcal{M}_{\text{He}}}} = \sqrt{\frac{16.04\ \text{g/mol}}{4.003\ \text{g/mol}}} = \sqrt{4.007} = 2.002$$

Check A ratio >1 makes sense because the lighter He should effuse faster than the heavier CH_4. Because the molar mass of CH_4 is about four times the molar mass of He, He should effuse about twice as fast as CH_4 ($\sqrt{4}$).

Follow-Up Problem 5.13 If it takes 1.25 min for 0.010 mol of He to effuse, how long will it take for the same amount of ethane (C_2H_6) to effuse?

Applications of Effusion The process of effusion has two important uses.

1. *Determination of molar mass.* We can also use Graham's law to *determine the molar mass of an unknown gas.* By comparing the effusion rate of gas X with that of a known gas, such as He, we can solve for the molar mass of X:

$$\frac{\text{Rate}_{\text{X}}}{\text{Rate}_{\text{He}}} = \sqrt{\frac{\mathcal{M}_{\text{He}}}{\mathcal{M}_{\text{X}}}}$$

Squaring both sides and solving for the molar mass of X gives

$$\mathcal{M}_{\text{X}} = \mathcal{M}_{\text{He}} \times \left(\frac{\text{rate}_{\text{He}}}{\text{rate}_{\text{X}}}\right)^2$$

2. *Preparation of nuclear fuel.* By far the most important application of Graham's law is in the preparation of fuel for nuclear energy reactors. The process of *isotope enrichment* increases the proportion of fissionable, but rarer, ^{235}U (only 0.7% by mass of naturally occurring uranium) to the nonfissionable, more abundant ^{238}U (99.3% by mass). Because the two isotopes have identical chemical properties, they are extremely difficult to separate chemically. But, one way to separate them takes advantage of a difference in a physical property—the effusion rate of gaseous compounds. Uranium ore is treated with fluorine to yield a gaseous mixture of $^{238}UF_6$ and $^{235}UF_6$ that is pumped through a series of chambers separated by porous barriers. Molecules of $^{235}UF_6$ are slightly lighter ($\mathcal{M}$ = 349.03) than molecules of $^{238}UF_6$ ($\mathcal{M}$ = 352.04), so they move slightly faster and effuse through each barrier 1.0043 times faster. Many passes must be made, each one increasing the fraction of $^{235}UF_6$, until the mixture obtained is 3–5% by mass $^{235}UF_6$. This process was developed during the latter years of World War II and produced enough ^{235}U for two of the world's first atomic bombs. Today, a less expensive centrifuge process is used more often. The ability to enrich uranium has become a key international concern, as more countries aspire to develop nuclear energy and nuclear arms.

The Process of Diffusion Closely related to effusion is the process of gaseous **diffusion,** the movement of one gas through another. Diffusion rates are also described generally by Graham's law:

$$\text{Rate of diffusion} \propto \frac{1}{\sqrt{\mathcal{M}}}$$

For two gases at equal pressures, such as NH_3 and HCl, moving through another gas or a mixture of gases, such as air, we find

$$\frac{\text{Rate}_{\text{NH}_3}}{\text{Rate}_{\text{HCl}}} = \sqrt{\frac{\mathcal{M}_{\text{HCl}}}{\mathcal{M}_{\text{NH}_3}}}$$

The reason for this dependence on molar mass is the same as for effusion rates: *lighter molecules have higher average speeds than heavier molecules, so they move farther in a given time.*

If gas molecules move at hundreds of meters per second (see Figure 5.14), why does it take a second or two after you open a bottle of perfume to smell it? Although convection plays an important role in this process, another reason for the time lag is

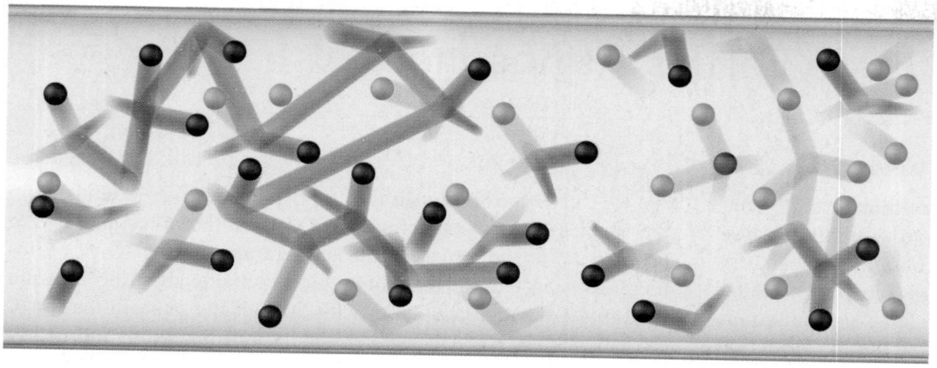

Figure 5.22 Diffusion of gases. When different gases (*black*, from the left, and *green,* from the right) move through each other, they mix. For simplicity, the complex path of only one black particle is shown (in *red*). In reality, all the particles have similar paths.

that a gas particle does not travel very far before it collides with another particle (Figure 5.22). Thus, a perfume molecule travels slowly because it collides with countless molecules in the air. The presence of so many other particles means that *diffusion rates are much lower than effusion rates.* Imagine how much quicker you can walk through an empty room than through a room crowded with other moving people.

Diffusion also occurs when a gas enters a liquid (and even to a small extent a solid). However, the average distances between molecules are so much shorter in a liquid that collisions are much more frequent; thus, diffusion of a gas through a liquid is *much* slower than through a gas. Nevertheless, this type of diffusion is a vital process in biological systems, for example, in the movement of O_2 from lungs to blood.

The Chaotic World of Gases: Mean Free Path and Collision Frequency

Refinements of the basic kinetic-molecular theory provide a view into the chaotic molecular world of gases. Try to visualize an "average" N_2 molecule in the room you are in now. It is continually changing speed as it collides with other molecules—at one instant, going 2500 mi/h, and at another, standing still. But these extreme speeds are *much* less likely than the most probable one and those near it (see Figure 5.14). At 20°C and 1 atm pressure, the N_2 molecule is hurtling at an average speed of 470 m/s (rms speed = 510 m/s), or nearly 1100 mi/h!

Mean Free Path From a particle's diameter, we can obtain the **mean free path,** the average distance it travels between collisions at a given temperature and pressure. An N_2 molecule (3.7×10^{-10} m in diameter) has a mean free path of 6.6×10^{-8} m, which means it travels an average of 180 molecular diameters before smashing into a fellow traveler. (An N_2 molecule the size of a billiard ball would travel an average of about 30 ft before hitting another.) Therefore, even though gas molecules are *not* points of mass, it is still valid to assume that a gas sample *is* nearly all empty space. Mean free path is a key factor in the rate of diffusion and the rate of heat flow through a gas.

Collision Frequency Divide the most probable speed (meters per second) by the mean free path (meters per collision) and you obtain the **collision frequency,** the average number of collisions per second that each particle undergoes. As you can see, the N_2 molecule experiences, on average, an enormous number of collisions every second: ●

$$\text{Collision frequency} = \frac{4.7\times10^2 \text{ m/s}}{6.6\times10^{-8} \text{ m/collision}} = 7.0\times10^9 \text{ collision/s}$$

Distribution of speed (and kinetic energy) and collision frequency are essential ideas for understanding the speed of a reaction, as you'll see in Chapter 16. As the Chemical Connections essay shows, many of the concepts we've discussed so far apply directly to our planet's atmosphere.

● **Danger in a Molecular Amusement Park** To really appreciate the astounding events in the molecular world, let's use a two-dimensional analogy to compare the moving N_2 molecule with a bumper car you are driving in an enormous amusement park ride. To match the collision frequency of the N_2 molecule, you would need to be traveling 2.8 billion mi/s (4.5 billion km/s, much faster than the speed of light!) and would smash into another bumper car every 700 yd (640 m).

CHEMICAL CONNECTIONS TO ATMOSPHERIC SCIENCE | How Do the Gas Laws Apply to Earth's Atmosphere?

An **atmosphere** is the envelope of gases that extends continuously from a planet's surface outward, thinning gradually until it is identical with outer space. A sample of clean, dry air at sea level on Earth contains 18 gases (Table B5.1). Under standard conditions, they behave nearly ideally, so volume percent equals mole percent (Avogadro's law), and the mole fraction of a component relates directly to its partial pressure (Dalton's law). Let's see how the gas laws and kinetic-molecular theory apply to our atmosphere, first with regard to variations in pressure and temperature, and then as explanations of some very familiar phenomena.

Table B5.1 Composition of Clean, Dry Air at Sea Level

Component	Mole Fraction
Nitrogen (N_2)	0.78084
Oxygen (O_2)	0.20946
Argon (Ar)	0.00934
Carbon dioxide (CO_2)	0.00933
Neon (Ne)	1.818×10^{-5}
Helium (He)	5.24×10^{-6}
Methane (CH_4)	2×10^{-6}
Krypton (Kr)	1.14×10^{-6}
Hydrogen (H_2)	5×10^{-7}
Dinitrogen monoxide (N_2O)	5×10^{-7}
Carbon monoxide (CO)	1×10^{-7}
Xenon (Xe)	8×10^{-8}
Ozone (O_3)	2×10^{-8}
Ammonia (NH_3)	6×10^{-9}
Nitrogen dioxide (NO_2)	6×10^{-9}
Nitrogen monoxide (NO)	6×10^{-10}
Sulfur dioxide (SO_2)	2×10^{-10}
Hydrogen sulfide (H_2S)	2×10^{-10}

The Smooth Variation in Pressure with Altitude

Because gases are compressible (Boyle's law), the pressure of the atmosphere *increases* smoothly as we approach Earth's surface, with a more rapid increase at lower altitudes (Figure B5.1, *left*). No boundary delineates the beginning of the atmosphere from the end of outer space, but the densities and compositions are identical at an altitude of about 10,000 km (6000 mi). Yet, about 99% of the atmosphere's mass lies within 30 km (almost 19 mi) of the surface, and 75% lies within the lowest 11 km (almost 7 mi).

The Zig-Zag Variation in Temperature with Altitude

Unlike pressure, temperature does *not* change smoothly with altitude above Earth's surface. The atmosphere is classified into regions based on the direction of temperature change, and we'll start at the surface (Figure B5.1, *right*).

1. *The troposphere.* In the troposphere, which extends from the surface to between 7 km (23,000 ft) at the poles and 17 km (60,000 ft) at the equator, the temperature *drops* 7°C per kilometer to −55°C (218 K). This region contains about 80% of the total mass of the atmosphere, with 50% of the mass in the lower 5.6 km (18,500 ft). All weather occurs in this region, and nearly all, except supersonic, aircraft fly here.

2. *The stratosphere and the ozone layer.* In the stratosphere, the temperature *rises* from −55°C to about 7°C (280 K) at 50 km. This rise is due to a variety of complex reactions, mostly involving ozone, and is caused by the absorption of solar radiation. Most high-energy radiation is absorbed by upper levels of the atmosphere, but some that reaches the stratosphere breaks O_2 into O atoms. The energetic O atoms collide with more O_2 to form ozone (O_3), another molecular form of oxygen:

$$O_2(g) \xrightarrow{\text{high-energy radiation}} 2O(g)$$

$$M + O(g) + O_2(g) \longrightarrow O_3(g) + M + \textit{heat}$$

where M is any particle that can carry away excess energy. This reaction releases heat, which is why stratospheric temperatures increase with altitude. Over 90% of atmospheric ozone remains in a thin layer within the stratosphere, its thickness varying both geographically (greatest at the poles) and seasonally (greatest in spring in the Northern Hemisphere and in fall in the Southern). Stratospheric ozone is vital to life because it absorbs over 95% of the harmful ultraviolet (UV) solar radiation that would otherwise reach the surface. In Chapter 16, we'll discuss the destructive effect of certain industrial chemicals on the ozone layer.

3. *The mesosphere.* In the mesosphere, the temperature *drops* again to −93°C (180 K) at around 80 km.

4. *The outer atmosphere.* Within the *thermosphere,* which extends to around 500 km, the temperature *rises* again, but varies between 700 and 2000 K, depending on the intensity of solar radiation and sunspot activity. The *exosphere,* the outermost region, maintains these temperatures and merges with outer space.

What does it actually mean to have a temperature of 2000 K at 500 km (300 mi) above Earth's surface? Would a piece of iron (melting point = 1808 K) glow red-hot within a minute or so and melt in the thermosphere, as it does if heated to 2000 K in the troposphere? The answer involves the relation between temperature and the time it takes to transfer kinetic energy. Our use of the words "hot" and "cold" refers to measurements near the surface. There, the collision frequency of gas particles with a thermometer is enormous, and so the transfer of their kinetic energy is very fast. But, at an altitude of 500 km, where the density of gas particles is a million times *less,* collision frequency is extremely low, and a thermometer, or any object, experiences *very slow transfer of kinetic energy.* Thus, the object would not become "hot" in the usual sense in any reasonable time. But the high-energy solar radiation that *is* transferred to the few particles present in these regions makes their average kinetic energy extremely high, as indicated by the high absolute temperature.

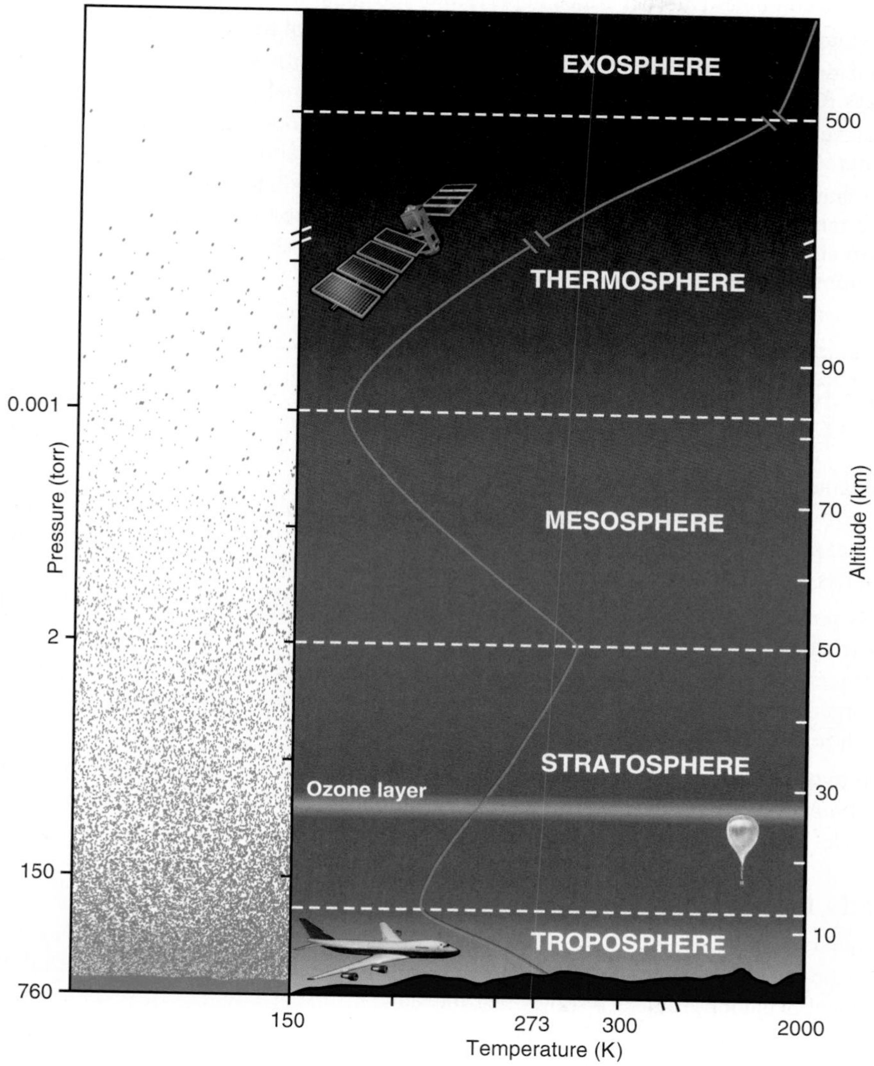

Figure B5.1 Variations in pressure and temperature with altitude in Earth's atmosphere.

Convection in the Lower Atmosphere

Why must you take more breaths per minute on a high mountaintop than at sea level? Because at the higher elevation, there is a smaller *amount* of O_2 in each breath. However, the *proportion* (mole percent) of O_2 throughout the lower atmosphere remains about 21%. This uniform composition arises from *vertical (convective) mixing,* and the gas laws explain how it occurs.

Let's follow an air mass from ground level, as solar heating of Earth's surface warms it. The warmer air mass expands (Charles's law), which makes it less dense, so it rises. As it does so, the pressure on it decreases, making it expand further (Boyle's law). Pushing against the surrounding air requires energy, so the temperature of the air mass decreases and thus the air mass shrinks slightly (Charles's law). But, as its temperature drops, its water vapor condenses (or solidifies), and these changes of state release heat; therefore, the air mass becomes warmer and rises further. Meanwhile, the cooler, and thus denser, air that was above it sinks, becomes warmer through contact with the surface, and goes through the same process as the first air mass. As a result of this vertical mixing, the composition of the lower atmosphere remains uniform.

Warm air rising from the ground, called a *thermal,* is used by soaring birds and glider pilots to stay aloft. Convection helps clean the air in urban areas, because the rising air carries up pollutants, which are dispersed by winds. Under certain conditions, however, a warm air mass remains stationary over a cool one. The resulting *temperature inversion* blocks normal convection, and harmful pollutants build up, causing severe health problems.

Problems

B5.1 Suggest a reason why supersonic aircraft are kept well below their maximum speeds until they reach their highest altitudes.

B5.2 Gases behave nearly ideally under Earth's conditions. Elsewhere in the Solar System, however, conditions are very different. On which would you expect atmospheric gases to deviate most from ideal behavior, Saturn (4×10^6 atm and 130 K) or Venus (90 atm and 730 K)? Explain.

B5.3 What is the volume percent and partial pressure (in torr) of argon in a sample of dry air at sea level?

B5.4 Earth's atmosphere is estimated to have a mass of 5.14×10^{15} t (1 t = 1000 kg).
(a) If the average molar mass of air is 28.8 g/mol, how many moles of gas are in the atmosphere?
(b) How many liters would the atmosphere occupy at 25°C and 1 atm?

Summary of Section 5.5

- The kinetic-molecular theory postulates that gas particles have no volume, move in straight-line paths between elastic (energy-conserving) collisions, and have average kinetic energies proportional to the absolute temperature of the gas.
- This theory explains the gas laws in terms of changes in distances between particles and the container walls, changes in molecular speed, and the energy of collisions.
- Temperature is a measure of the average kinetic energy of the particles.
- Effusion and diffusion rates are *inversely* proportional to the square root of the molar mass (Graham's law) because they are *directly* proportional to molecular speed.
- Molecular motion is characterized by a temperature-dependent, most probable speed (within a range of speeds), which affects mean free path and collision frequency.
- The atmosphere is a complex mixture of gases that exhibits variations in pressure and temperature with altitude. High temperatures in the upper atmosphere result from absorption of high-energy solar radiation. The lower atmosphere has a uniform composition as a result of convective mixing.

5.6 • REAL GASES: DEVIATIONS FROM IDEAL BEHAVIOR

A fundamental principle of science is that simpler models are more useful than complex ones, as long as they explain the data. With only a few postulates, the kinetic-molecular theory explains the behavior of most gases under ordinary conditions. But, two of the postulates are useful approximations that do not reflect reality:

1. *Gas particles are* ***not*** *points of mass* but have volumes determined by the sizes of their atoms and the lengths and directions of their bonds.
2. *Attractive and repulsive forces* ***do*** *exist among gas particles* because atoms contain charged subatomic particles and many bonds are polar. (As you'll see in Chapter 12, such forces lead to changes of physical state.)

These two features cause deviations from ideal behavior under *extreme conditions of low temperature and high pressure.* These deviations mean that we must alter the simple model and the ideal gas law to predict the behavior of real gases.

Effects of Extreme Conditions on Gas Behavior

Table 5.3 Molar Volume of Some Common Gases at STP (0°C and 1 atm)

Gas	Molar Volume (L/mol)	Boiling Point (°C)
He	22.435	−268.9
H_2	22.432	−252.8
Ne	22.422	−246.1
Ideal gas	**22.414**	—
Ar	22.397	−185.9
N_2	22.396	−195.8
O_2	22.390	−183.0
CO	22.388	−191.5
Cl_2	22.184	−34.0
NH_3	22.079	−33.4

At ordinary conditions—relatively high temperatures and low pressures—most real gases exhibit nearly ideal behavior. Yet, even at STP (0°C and 1 atm), gases deviate *slightly* from ideal behavior. Table 5.3 shows that the standard molar volumes of several gases, when measured to five significant figures, do not equal the ideal value. Note that the deviations increase as the boiling point rises.

The phenomena that cause slight deviations under standard conditions exert more influence as temperature decreases and pressure increases. Figure 5.23 shows a plot of PV/RT versus external pressure (P_{ext}) for 1 mol of several real gases and an ideal gas. The PV/RT values range from normal (at $P_{ext} = 1$ atm, $PV/RT = 1$) to very high (at $P_{ext} \approx 1000$ atm, $PV/RT \approx 1.6$ to 2.3). For the *ideal* gas, PV/RT is 1 at any P_{ext}.

The PV/RT curve for methane (CH_4) is typical of most gases: it decreases *below* the ideal value at moderately high P_{ext} and then rises *above* the ideal value as P_{ext} increases to very high values. This shape arises from two overlapping effects:

- At moderately high P_{ext}, PV/RT values are lower than ideal values (less than 1) because of *interparticle attractions.*
- At very high P_{ext}, PV/RT values are greater than ideal values (more than 1) because of *particle volume.*

Let's examine these effects on the molecular level:

1. *Effect of interparticle attractions.* Interparticle attractions occur between separate atoms or molecules and are caused by imbalances in electron distributions. They are important only over *very* short distances and are *much* weaker than the covalent bonding forces that hold a molecule together. At normal P_{ext}, the spaces between the particles are so large that attractions are negligible and the gas behaves nearly ideally.

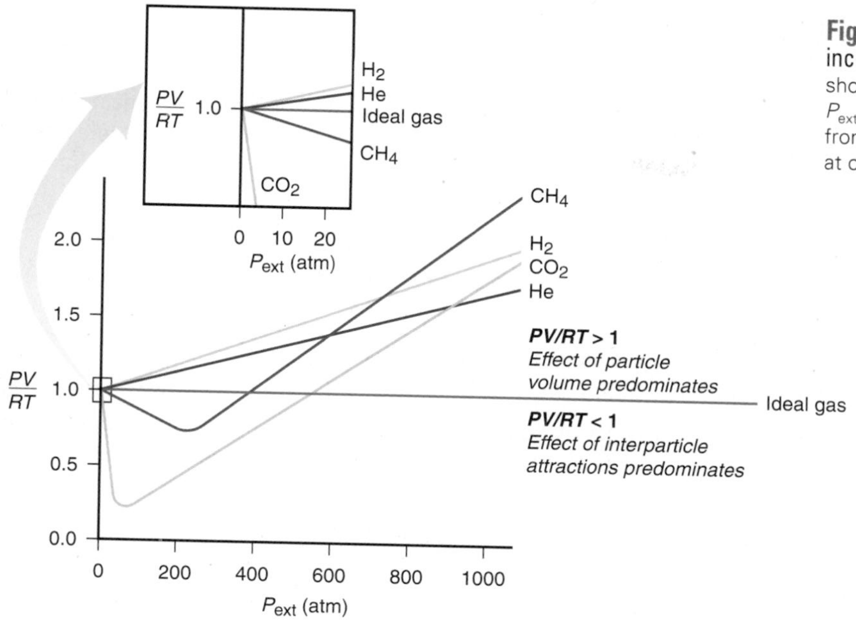

Figure 5.23 Deviations from ideal behavior with increasing external pressure. The horizontal line shows that, for 1 mol of ideal gas, $PV/RT = 1$ at all P_{ext}. At very high P_{ext}, real gases deviate significantly from ideal behavior, but small deviations appear even at ordinary pressures (expanded portion).

As P_{ext} rises, the volume of the sample decreases and the particles get closer together, so interparticle attractions have a greater effect. As a particle approaches the container wall under these higher pressures, nearby particles attract it, which lessens the force of its impact (Figure 5.24). *Repeated throughout the sample, this effect results in decreased gas pressure and, thus, a smaller numerator in PV/RT.* Similarly, lowering the temperature slows the particles, so they attract each other for a longer time.

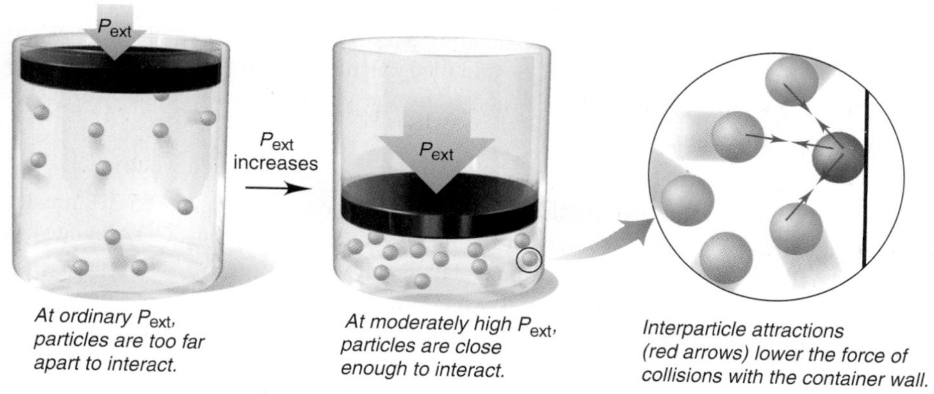

Figure 5.24 The effect of interparticle attractions on measured gas pressure.

2. *Effect of particle volume.* At normal P_{ext}, the space between particles (free volume) is enormous compared with the volume of the particles *themselves* (particle volume); thus, the free volume is essentially equal to V, the container volume in PV/RT. At *moderately* high P_{ext} and as free volume decreases, the particle volume makes up an increasing proportion of the container volume (Figure 5.25). At *extremely* high pressures, the space taken up by the particles themselves makes the free volume significantly *less* than the container volume. Nevertheless, we continue to use the container volume for V in PV/RT, which causes the numerator, and thus the ratio, to become

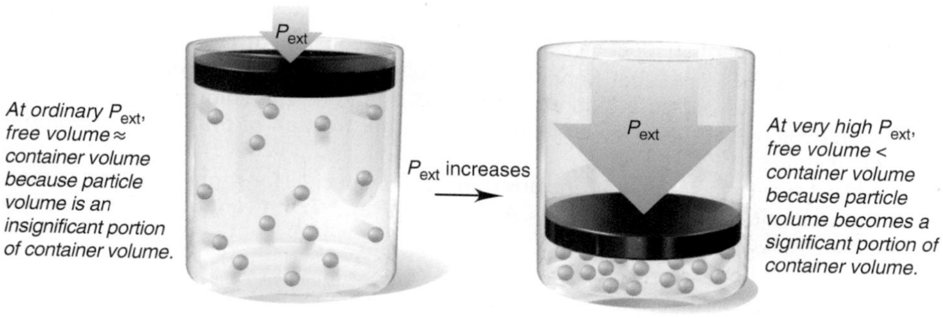

Figure 5.25 The effect of particle volume on measured gas volume.

artificially high. This particle volume effect increases as P_{ext} increases, eventually outweighing the effect of interparticle attractions and causing PV/RT to rise above the ideal value.

In Figure 5.23, note that the H_2 and He curves do not show the typical dip at moderate pressures. These gases consist of particles with such weak interparticle attractions that the particle volume effect predominates at all pressures.

The van der Waals Equation: Adjusting the Ideal Gas Law

To describe real gas behavior more accurately, we need to adjust the ideal gas equation in two ways:

1. Adjust *P up* by adding a factor that accounts for interparticle attractions.
2. Adjust *V down* by subtracting a factor that accounts for particle volume.

In 1873, Johannes van der Waals revised the ideal gas equation to account for the behavior of real gases. The **van der Waals equation** for *n* moles of a real gas is

$$\underbrace{\left(P + \frac{n^2a}{V^2}\right)}_{\text{adjusts } P \text{ up}}\underbrace{(V - nb)}_{\text{adjusts } V \text{ down}} = nRT \qquad (5.15)$$

where *P* is the measured pressure, *V* is the known container volume, *n* and *T* have their usual meanings, and *a* and *b* are **van der Waals constants,** experimentally determined and specific for a given gas (Table 5.4). The constant *a* depends on the number and distribution of electrons, which relates to the complexity of a particle and the strength of its interparticle attractions. The constant *b* relates to particle volume. For instance, CO_2 is both more complex and larger than H_2, and the values of their constants reflect this.

Table 5.4 Van der Waals Constants for Some Common Gases

Gas	$a\left(\frac{\text{atm}\cdot\text{L}^2}{\text{mol}^2}\right)$	$b\left(\frac{\text{L}}{\text{mol}}\right)$
He	0.034	0.0237
Ne	0.211	0.0171
Ar	1.35	0.0322
Kr	2.32	0.0398
Xe	4.19	0.0511
H_2	0.244	0.0266
N_2	1.39	0.0391
O_2	1.36	0.0318
Cl_2	6.49	0.0562
CH_4	2.25	0.0428
CO	1.45	0.0395
CO_2	3.59	0.0427
NH_3	4.17	0.0371
H_2O	5.46	0.0305

Here is a typical application of the van der Waals equation. A 1.98-L vessel contains 215 g (4.89 mol) of dry ice. After standing at 26°C (299 K), the $CO_2(s)$ changes to $CO_2(g)$. The pressure is measured (P_{real}) and then calculated by the ideal gas law (P_{IGL}) and, using the appropriate values of *a* and *b*, by the van der Waals equation (P_{VDW}). The results are revealing:

$$P_{real} = 44.8 \text{ atm} \qquad P_{IGL} = 60.6 \text{ atm} \qquad P_{VDW} = 45.9 \text{ atm}$$

Comparing the real value with each calculated value shows that P_{IGL} is 35.3% greater than P_{real}, but P_{VDW} is only 2.5% greater than P_{real}. At these conditions, CO_2 deviates so much from ideal behavior that the ideal gas law is not very useful.

A key point to realize: According to kinetic-molecular theory, the constants *a* and *b* are zero for an ideal gas because the gas particles do not attract each other and have no volume. Yet, even in a real gas at ordinary pressures, the particles are very far apart. This large average interparticle distance has two consequences:

- Attractive forces are miniscule, so $P + \frac{n^2a}{V^2} \approx P$.
- The particle volume is a minute fraction of the container volume, so $V - nb \approx V$.

Therefore, *at ordinary conditions, the van der Waals equation* ***becomes*** *the ideal gas equation.*

Summary of Section 5.6

- At very high *P* or low *T*, all gases deviate significantly from ideal behavior.
- As external pressure increases, most real gases exhibit first a lower and then a higher *PV/RT*; for 1 mol of an ideal gas, this ratio remains constant at 1.
- The deviations from ideal behavior are due to (1) attractions between particles, which lower the pressure (and decrease *PV/RT*), and (2) the volume of the particles themselves, which takes up an increasingly larger fraction of the container volume (and increases *PV/RT*).
- The van der Waals equation includes constants specific for a given gas to correct for deviations from ideal behavior. At ordinary *P* and *T*, the van der Waals equation reduces to the ideal gas equation.

CHAPTER REVIEW GUIDE

Learning Objectives

Relevant section (§) and/or sample problem (SP) numbers appear in parentheses.

Understand These Concepts

1. How gases differ in their macroscopic properties from liquids and solids (§5.1)
2. The meaning of pressure and the operation of a barometer and a manometer (§5.2)
3. The relations among gas variables expressed by Boyle's, Charles's, and Avogadro's laws (§5.3)
4. How the individual gas laws are incorporated into the ideal gas law (§5.3)
5. How the ideal gas law can be used to study gas density, molar mass, and amounts of gases in reactions (§5.4)
6. The relation between the density and the temperature of a gas (§5.4)
7. The meaning of Dalton's law and the relation between partial pressure and mole fraction of a gas; how Dalton's law applies to collecting a gas over water (§5.4)
8. How the postulates of the kinetic-molecular theory are applied to explain the origin of pressure and the gas laws (§5.5)
9. The relations among molecular speed, average kinetic energy, and temperature (§5.5)
10. The meanings of *effusion* and *diffusion* and how their rates are related to molar mass (§5.5)
11. The relations among mean free path, molecular speed, and collision frequency (§5.5)
12. Why intermolecular attractions and molecular volume cause gases to deviate from ideal behavior at low temperatures and high pressures (§5.6)
13. How the van der Waals equation corrects the ideal gas law for extreme conditions (§5.6)

Master These Skills

1. Interconverting among the units of pressure (atm, mmHg, torr, pascal, lb/in^2) (SP 5.1)
2. Reducing the ideal gas law to the individual gas laws (SPs 5.2–5.5)
3. Applying gas laws to choose the correct chemical equation (SP 5.6)
4. Rearranging the ideal gas law to calculate gas density (SP 5.7) and molar mass of a volatile liquid (SP 5.8)
5. Calculating the mole fraction and the partial pressure of a gas (SP 5.9)
6. Using the vapor pressure of water to correct for the amount of a gas collected over water (SP 5.10)
7. Applying stoichiometry and gas laws to calculate amounts of reactants and products (SPs 5.11, 5.12)
8. Using Graham's law to solve problems of gaseous effusion (SP 5.13)

Key Terms

Page numbers appear in parentheses.

Section 5.2
pressure (P) (183)
barometer (183)
manometer (184)
pascal (Pa) (185)
standard atmosphere (atm) (185)
millimeter of mercury (mmHg) (185)
torr (185)

Section 5.3
ideal gas (186)
Boyle's law (187)
Charles's law (188)
Avogadro's law (190)
standard temperature and pressure (STP) (190)
standard molar volume (190)
ideal gas law (191)
universal gas constant (R) (191)

Section 5.4
partial pressure (199)
Dalton's law of partial pressures (199)
mole fraction (X) (200)

Section 5.5
kinetic-molecular theory (204)
rms speed (u_{rms}) (209)
effusion (209)
Graham's law of effusion (209)
diffusion (210)
mean free path (211)
collision frequency (211)
atmosphere (212)

Section 5.6
van der Waals equation (216)
van der Waals constants (216)

Key Equations and Relationships

Page numbers appear in parentheses.

5.1 Expressing the volume-pressure relationship (Boyle's law) (187):

$$V \propto \frac{1}{P} \quad \text{or} \quad PV = \text{constant} \quad [T \text{ and } n \text{ fixed}]$$

5.2 Expressing the volume-temperature relationship (Charles's law) (188):

$$V \propto T \quad \text{or} \quad \frac{V}{T} = \text{constant} \quad [P \text{ and } n \text{ fixed}]$$

5.3 Expressing the pressure-temperature relationship (Amontons's law) (189):

$$P \propto T \quad \text{or} \quad \frac{P}{T} = \text{constant} \quad [V \text{ and } n \text{ fixed}]$$

5.4 Expressing the volume-amount relationship (Avogadro's law) (190):

$$V \propto n \quad \text{or} \quad \frac{V}{n} = \text{constant} \quad [P \text{ and } T \text{ fixed}]$$

5.5 Defining standard temperature and pressure (190):

STP: 0°C (273.15 K) and 1 atm (760 torr)

5.6 Defining the volume of 1 mol of an ideal gas at STP (190):

Standard molar volume = 22.4141 L = 22.4 L [3 sf]

5.7 Relating volume to pressure, temperature, and amount (ideal gas law) (191):

$$PV = nRT \quad \text{and} \quad \frac{P_1V_1}{n_1T_1} = \frac{P_2V_2}{n_2T_2}$$

5.8 Calculating the value of R (191):

$$R = \frac{PV}{nT} = \frac{1\ \text{atm} \times 22.4141\ \text{L}}{1\ \text{mol} \times 273.15\ \text{K}}$$

$$= 0.082058\ \frac{\text{atm·L}}{\text{mol·K}} = 0.0821\ \frac{\text{atm·L}}{\text{mol·K}} \quad [3\ \text{sf}]$$

5.9 Rearranging the ideal gas law to find gas density (196):

$$PV = \frac{m}{\mathcal{M}}RT$$

so $$\frac{m}{V} = d = \frac{\mathcal{M} \times P}{RT}$$

5.10 Rearranging the ideal gas law to find molar mass (198):

$$n = \frac{m}{\mathcal{M}} = \frac{PV}{RT} \quad \text{so} \quad \mathcal{M} = \frac{mRT}{PV}$$

5.11 Relating the total pressure of a gas mixture to the partial pressures of the components (Dalton's law of partial pressures) (199):

$$P_{\text{total}} = P_1 + P_2 + P_3 + \cdots$$

5.12 Relating partial pressure to mole fraction (200):

$$P_A = X_A \times P_{\text{total}}$$

5.13 Defining rms speed as a function of molar mass and temperature (209):

$$u_{\text{rms}} = \sqrt{\frac{3RT}{\mathcal{M}}}$$

5.14 Applying Graham's law of effusion (209):

$$\frac{\text{Rate}_A}{\text{Rate}_B} = \frac{\sqrt{\mathcal{M}_B}}{\sqrt{\mathcal{M}_A}} = \sqrt{\frac{\mathcal{M}_B}{\mathcal{M}_A}}$$

5.15 Applying the van der Waals equation to find the pressure or volume of a gas under extreme conditions (216):

$$\left(P + \frac{n^2a}{V^2}\right)(V - nb) = nRT$$

Brief Solutions to Follow-Up Problems

5.1 $$P_{CO_2}\ (\text{torr}) = (753.6\ \text{mmHg} - 174.0\ \text{mmHg}) \times \frac{1\ \text{torr}}{1\ \text{mmHg}} = 579.6\ \text{torr}$$

$$P_{CO_2}\ (\text{Pa}) = 579.6\ \text{torr} \times \frac{1\ \text{atm}}{760\ \text{torr}} \times \frac{1.01325\times10^5\ \text{Pa}}{1\ \text{atm}} = 7.727\times10^4\ \text{Pa}$$

$$P_{CO_2}\ (\text{lb/in}^2) = 579.6\ \text{torr} \times \frac{1\ \text{atm}}{760\ \text{torr}} \times \frac{14.7\ \text{lb/in}^2}{1\ \text{atm}} = 11.2\ \text{lb/in}^2$$

5.2 $$P_2\ (\text{atm}) = 26.3\ \text{kPa} \times \frac{1\ \text{atm}}{101.325\ \text{kPa}} = 0.260\ \text{atm}$$

$$V_2\ (\text{L}) = 105\ \text{mL} \times \frac{1\ \text{L}}{1000\ \text{mL}} \times \frac{0.871\ \text{atm}}{0.260\ \text{atm}} = 0.352\ \text{L}$$

5.3 $$T_2\ (\text{K}) = 273\ \text{K} \times \frac{9.75\ \text{cm}^3}{6.83\ \text{cm}^3} = 390.\ \text{K}$$

5.4 $$P_2\ (\text{torr}) = 793\ \text{torr} \times \frac{35.0\ \text{g} - 5.0\ \text{g}}{35.0\ \text{g}} = 680.\ \text{torr}$$

(There is no need to convert mass to moles because the ratio of masses equals the ratio of moles.)

5.5 $$n = \frac{PV}{RT} = \frac{1.37\ \text{atm} \times 438\ \text{L}}{0.0821\ \frac{\text{atm·L}}{\text{mol·K}} \times 294\ \text{K}} = 24.9\ \text{mol}\ O_2$$

$$\text{Mass (g) of } O_2 = 24.9\ \text{mol}\ O_2 \times \frac{32.00\ \text{g}\ O_2}{1\ \text{mol}\ O_2} = 7.97\times10^2\ \text{g}\ O_2$$

5.6 The balanced equation is $2CD(g) \longrightarrow C_2(g) + D_2(g)$, so n does not change. Therefore, given constant P, the temperature, T, must double: $T_1 = -73°C + 273.15 = 200$ K; so $T_2 = 400$ K, or 400 K − 273.15 = 127°C.

5.7 $$d(\text{at } 0°\text{C and } 380\ \text{torr}) = \frac{44.01\ \text{g/mol} \times \frac{380\ \text{torr}}{760\ \text{torr/atm}}}{0.0821\ \frac{\text{atm·L}}{\text{mol·K}} \times 273\ \text{K}} = 0.982\ \text{g/L}$$

The density is lower at the smaller P because V is larger. In this case, d is lowered by one-half because P is one-half as much.

5.8

$$\mathcal{M} = \frac{(68.697\ \text{g} - 68.322\ \text{g}) \times 0.0821\ \frac{\text{atm·L}}{\text{mol·K}} \times (273.15 + 95.0)\ \text{K}}{\frac{740.\ \text{torr}}{760\ \text{torr/atm}} \times \frac{149\ \text{mL}}{1000\ \text{mL/L}}}$$

$$= 78.1\ \text{g/mol}$$

5.9 $n_{total} = \left(5.50 \text{ g He} \times \frac{1 \text{ mol He}}{4.003 \text{ g He}}\right) + \left(15.0 \text{ g Ne} \times \frac{1 \text{ mol Ne}}{20.18 \text{ g Ne}}\right) + \left(35.0 \text{ g Kr} \times \frac{1 \text{ mol Kr}}{83.80 \text{ g Kr}}\right)$

$= 2.53 \text{ mol}$

$$P_{He} = \left(\frac{5.50 \text{ g He} \times \frac{1 \text{ mol He}}{4.003 \text{ g He}}}{2.53 \text{ mol}}\right) \times 1 \text{ atm} = 0.543 \text{ atm}$$

$P_{Ne} = 0.294$ atm $P_{Kr} = 0.165$ atm

5.10 $P_{H_2} = 752 \text{ torr} - 13.6 \text{ torr} = 738 \text{ torr}$

$$\text{Mass (g) of } H_2 = \left(\frac{\frac{738 \text{ torr}}{760 \text{ torr/atm}} \times 1.495 \text{ L}}{0.0821 \frac{\text{atm·L}}{\text{mol·K}} \times 289 \text{ K}}\right) \times \frac{2.016 \text{ g } H_2}{1 \text{ mol } H_2}$$

$= 0.123 \text{ g } H_2$

5.11 $H_2SO_4(aq) + 2NaCl(s) \longrightarrow Na_2SO_4(aq) + 2HCl(g)$

$$n_{HCl} = 0.117 \text{ kg NaCl} \times \frac{10^3 \text{ g}}{1 \text{ kg}} \times \frac{1 \text{ mol NaCl}}{58.44 \text{ g NaCl}} \times \frac{2 \text{ mol HCl}}{2 \text{ mol NaCl}}$$

$= 2.00 \text{ mol HCl}$

$$\text{At STP, } V \text{(mL)} = 2.00 \text{ mol} \times \frac{22.4 \text{ L}}{1 \text{ mol}} \times \frac{10^3 \text{ mL}}{1 \text{ L}}$$

$= 4.48 \times 10^4 \text{ mL}$

5.12 $NH_3(g) + HCl(g) \longrightarrow NH_4Cl(s)$

$n_{NH_3} = 0.187$ mol and $n_{HCl} = 0.0522$ mol; thus, HCl is the limiting reactant.

n_{NH_3} after reaction

$$= 0.187 \text{ mol } NH_3 - \left(0.0522 \text{ mol HCl} \times \frac{1 \text{ mol } NH_3}{1 \text{ mol HCl}}\right)$$

$= 0.135 \text{ mol } NH_3$

$$P = \frac{0.135 \text{ mol} \times 0.0821 \frac{\text{atm·L}}{\text{mol·K}} \times 295 \text{ K}}{10.0 \text{ L}} = 0.327 \text{ atm}$$

5.13 $$\frac{\text{Rate of He}}{\text{Rate of } C_2H_6} = \sqrt{\frac{30.07 \text{ g/mol}}{4.003 \text{ g/mol}}} = 2.741$$

Time for C_2H_6 to effuse $= 1.25 \text{ min} \times 2.741 = 3.43 \text{ min}$

PROBLEMS

Problems with **colored** numbers are answered in Appendix E and worked in detail in the Student Solutions Manual. Problem sections match those in the text and provide the numbers of relevant sample problems. Most offer Concept Review Questions, Skill-Building Exercises (grouped in pairs covering the same concept), and Problems in Context. The Comprehensive Problems are based on material from any section or previous chapter.

An Overview of the Physical States of Matter

Concept Review Questions

5.1 How does a sample of gas differ in its behavior from a sample of liquid in each of the following situations?
(a) The sample is transferred from one container to a larger one.
(b) The sample is heated in an expandable container, but no change of state occurs.
(c) The sample is placed in a cylinder with a piston, and an external force is applied.

5.2 Are the particles in a gas farther apart or closer together than the particles in a liquid? Use your answer to explain each of the following general observations:
(a) Gases are more compressible than liquids.
(b) Gases have lower viscosities than liquids.
(c) After thorough stirring, all gas mixtures are solutions.
(d) The density of a substance in the gas state is lower than in the liquid state.

Gas Pressure and Its Measurement
(Sample Problem 5.1)

Concept Review Questions

5.3 How does a barometer work? Is the column of mercury in a barometer shorter when it is on a mountaintop or at sea level? Explain.

5.4 How can a unit of length such as millimeter of mercury (mmHg) be used as a unit of pressure, which has the dimensions of force per unit area?

5.5 In a closed-end manometer, the mercury level in the arm attached to the flask can never be higher than the mercury level in the other arm, whereas in an open-end manometer, it *can* be higher. Explain.

Skill-Building Exercises (grouped in similar pairs)

5.6 On a cool, rainy day, the barometric pressure is 730 mmHg. Calculate the barometric pressure in centimeters of water (cmH_2O) (d of Hg = 13.5 g/mL; d of H_2O = 1.00 g/mL).

5.7 A long glass tube, sealed at one end, has an inner diameter of 10.0 mm. The tube is filled with water and inverted into a pail of water. If the atmospheric pressure is 755 mmHg, how high (in mmH_2O) is the column of water in the tube (d of Hg = 13.5 g/mL; d of H_2O = 1.00 g/mL)?

5.8 Convert the following:
(a) 0.745 atm to mmHg (b) 992 torr to bar
(c) 365 kPa to atm (d) 804 mmHg to kPa

5.9 Convert the following:
(a) 76.8 cmHg to atm (b) 27.5 atm to kPa
(c) 6.50 atm to bar (d) 0.937 kPa to torr

5.10 In Figure P5.10, what is the pressure of the gas in the flask (in atm) if the barometer reads 738.5 torr?

5.11 In Figure P5.11, what is the pressure of the gas in the flask (in kPa) if the barometer reads 765.2 mmHg?

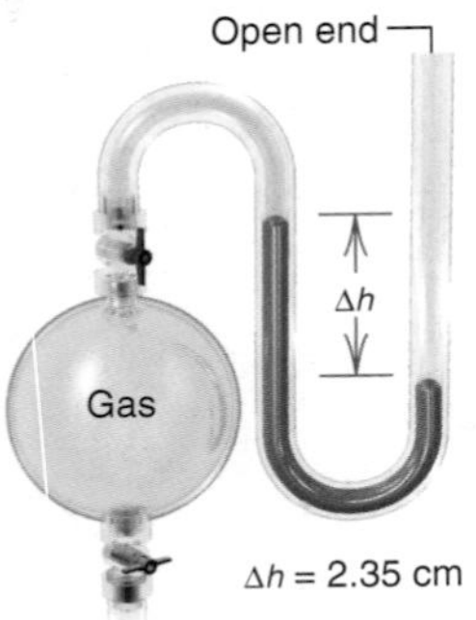

Figure P5.10

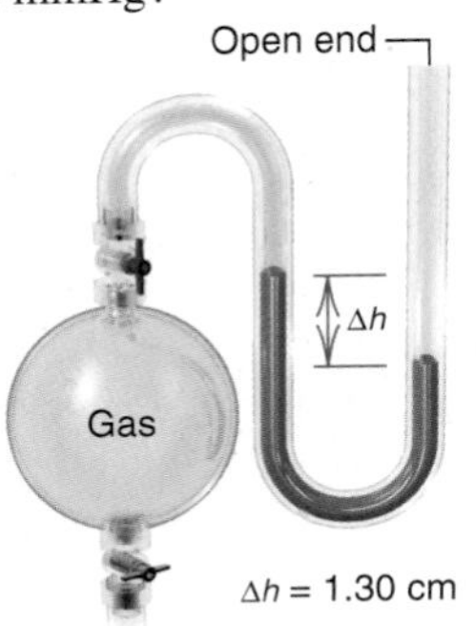

Figure P5.11

5.12 If the sample flask in Figure P5.12 is open to the air, what is the atmospheric pressure (in atm)?

5.13 What is the pressure (in Pa) of the gas in the flask in Figure P5.13?

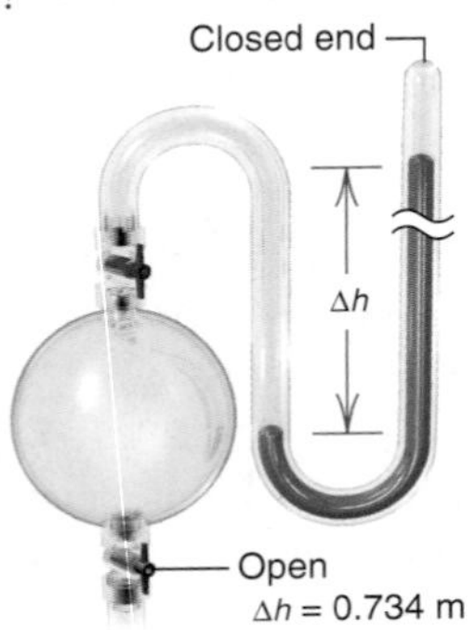

Figure P5.12

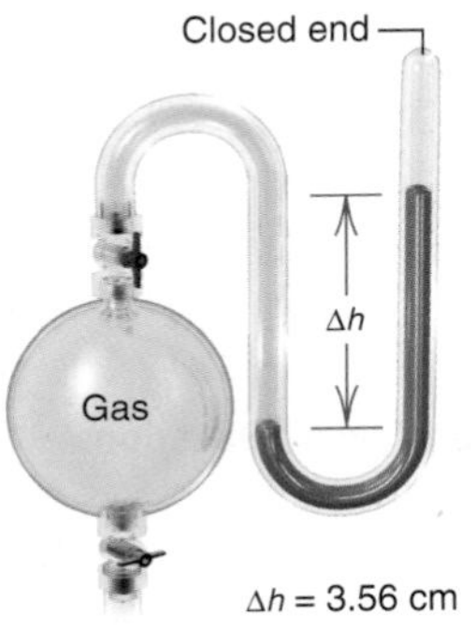

Figure P5.13

Problems in Context

5.14 Convert each of the pressures described below to atm:
(a) At the peak of Mt. Everest, atmospheric pressure is only 2.75×10^2 mmHg.
(b) A cyclist fills her bike tires to 86 psi.
(c) The surface of Venus has an atmospheric pressure of 9.15×10^6 Pa.
(d) At 100 ft below sea level, a scuba diver experiences a pressure of 2.54×10^4 torr.

5.15 The gravitational force exerted by an object is given by $F = mg$, where F is the force in newtons, m is the mass in kilograms, and g is the acceleration due to gravity (9.81 m/s^2).
(a) Use the definition of the pascal to calculate the mass (in kg) of the atmosphere above 1 m^2 of ocean.
(b) Osmium ($Z = 76$) is a transition metal in Group 8B(8) and has the highest density of any element (22.6 g/mL). If an osmium column is 1 m^2 in area, how high must it be for its pressure to equal atmospheric pressure? [Use the answer from part (a) in your calculation.]

The Gas Laws and Their Experimental Foundations

(Sample Problems 5.2 to 5.6)

Concept Review Questions

5.16 A student states Boyle's law as follows: "The volume of a gas is inversely proportional to its pressure." How is this statement incomplete? Give a correct statement of Boyle's law.

5.17 In the following relationships, which quantities are variables and which are fixed: (a) Charles's law; (b) Avogadro's law; (c) Amontons's law?

5.18 Boyle's law relates gas volume to pressure, and Avogadro's law relates gas volume to amount (mol). State a relationship between gas pressure and amount (mol).

5.19 Each of the following processes caused the gas volume to double, as shown. For each process, tell how the remaining gas variable changed or state that it remained fixed:
(a) T doubles at fixed P.
(b) T and n are fixed.
(c) At fixed T, the reaction is $CD_2(g) \longrightarrow C(g) + D_2(g)$.
(d) At fixed P, the reaction is $A_2(g) + B_2(g) \longrightarrow 2AB(g)$.

Skill-Building Exercises (grouped in similar pairs)

5.20 What is the effect of the following on the volume of 1 mol of an ideal gas?
(a) The pressure is tripled (at constant T).
(b) The absolute temperature is increased by a factor of 3.0 (at constant P).
(c) Three more moles of the gas are added (at constant P and T).

5.21 What is the effect of the following on the volume of 1 mol of an ideal gas?
(a) The pressure is reduced by a factor of 4 (at constant T).
(b) The pressure changes from 760 torr to 202 kPa, and the temperature changes from 37°C to 155 K.
(c) The temperature changes from 305 K to 32°C, and the pressure changes from 2 atm to 101 kPa.

5.22 What is the effect of the following on the volume of 1 mol of an ideal gas?
(a) Temperature decreases from 800 K to 400 K (at constant P).
(b) Temperature increases from 250°C to 500°C (at constant P).
(c) Pressure increases from 2 atm to 6 atm (at constant T).

5.23 What is the effect of the following on the volume of 1 mol of an ideal gas?
(a) Half the gas escapes (at constant P and T).
(b) The initial pressure is 722 torr, and the final pressure is 0.950 atm; the initial temperature is 32°F, and the final temperature is 273 K.
(c) Both the pressure and temperature decrease to one-fourth of their initial values.

5.24 A sample of sulfur hexafluoride gas occupies 9.10 L at 198°C. Assuming that the pressure remains constant, what temperature (in °C) is needed to reduce the volume to 2.50 L?

5.25 A 93-L sample of dry air cools from 145°C to −22°C while the pressure is maintained at 2.85 atm. What is the final volume?

5.26 A sample of Freon-12 (CF_2Cl_2) occupies 25.5 L at 298 K and 153.3 kPa. Find its volume at STP.

5.27 A sample of carbon monoxide occupies 3.65 L at 298 K and 745 torr. Find its volume at −14°C and 367 torr.

5.28 A sample of chlorine gas is confined in a 5.0-L container at 328 torr and 37°C. How many moles of gas are in the sample?

5.29 If 1.47×10^{-3} mol of argon occupies a 75.0-mL container at 26°C, what is the pressure (in torr)?

5.30 You have 357 mL of chlorine trifluoride gas at 699 mmHg and 45°C. What is the mass (in g) of the sample?

5.31 A 75.0-g sample of dinitrogen monoxide is confined in a 3.1-L vessel. What is the pressure (in atm) at 115°C?

Problems in Context

5.32 In preparation for a demonstration, your professor brings a 1.5-L bottle of sulfur dioxide into the lecture hall before class to allow the gas to reach room temperature. If the pressure gauge reads 85 psi and the temperature in the hall is 23°C, how many moles of sulfur dioxide are in the bottle? (*Hint:* The gauge reads zero when 14.7 psi of gas remains.)

5.33 A gas-filled weather balloon with a volume of 65.0 L is released at sea-level conditions of 745 torr and 25°C. The balloon can expand to a maximum volume of 835 L. When the balloon rises to an altitude at which the temperature is −5°C and the pressure is 0.066 atm, will it reach its maximum volume?

Rearrangements of the Ideal Gas Law

(Sample Problems 5.7 to 5.12)

Concept Review Questions

5.34 Why is moist air less dense than dry air?

5.35 To collect a beaker of H_2 gas by displacing the air already in the beaker, would you hold the beaker upright or inverted? Why? How would you hold the beaker to collect CO_2?

5.36 Why can we use a gas mixture, such as air, to study the general behavior of an ideal gas under ordinary conditions?

5.37 How does the partial pressure of gas A in a mixture compare to its mole fraction in the mixture? Explain.

5.38 The scene at right represents a portion of a mixture of four gases A (*purple*), B (*black*), C (*green*), and D_2 (*orange*). (a) Which has the highest partial pressure? (b) Which has the lowest partial pressure? (c) If the total pressure is 0.75 atm, what is the partial pressure of D_2?

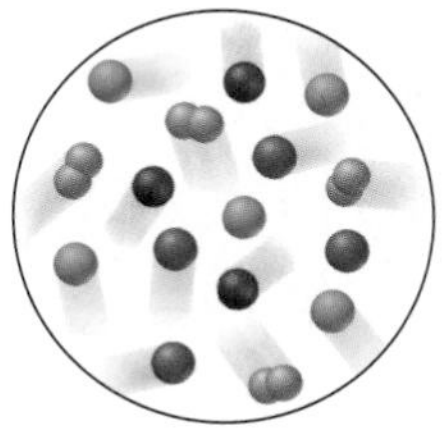

Skill-Building Exercises (grouped in similar pairs)

5.39 What is the density of Xe gas at STP?

5.40 Find the density of Freon-11 ($CFCl_3$) at 120°C and 1.5 atm.

5.41 How many moles of gaseous arsine (AsH_3) occupy 0.0400 L at STP? What is the density of gaseous arsine?

5.42 The density of a noble gas is 2.71 g/L at 3.00 atm and 0°C. Identify the gas.

5.43 Calculate the molar mass of a gas at 388 torr and 45°C if 206 ng occupies 0.206 μL.

5.44 When an evacuated 63.8-mL glass bulb is filled with a gas at 22°C and 747 mmHg, the bulb gains 0.103 g in mass. Is the gas N_2, Ne, or Ar?

5.45 After 0.600 L of Ar at 1.20 atm and 227°C is mixed with 0.200 L of O_2 at 501 torr and 127°C in a 400-mL flask at 27°C, what is the pressure in the flask?

5.46 A 355-mL container holds 0.146 g of Ne and an unknown amount of Ar at 35°C and a total pressure of 626 mmHg. Calculate the number of moles of Ar present.

5.47 How many grams of phosphorus react with 35.5 L of O_2 at STP to form tetraphosphorus decaoxide?

$$P_4(s) + 5O_2(g) \longrightarrow P_4O_{10}(s)$$

5.48 How many grams of potassium chlorate decompose to potassium chloride and 638 mL of O_2 at 128°C and 752 torr?

$$2KClO_3(s) \longrightarrow 2KCl(s) + 3O_2(g)$$

5.49 How many grams of phosphine (PH_3) can form when 37.5 g of phosphorus and 83.0 L of hydrogen gas react at STP?

$$P_4(s) + H_2(g) \longrightarrow PH_3(g) \quad [\text{unbalanced}]$$

5.50 When 35.6 L of ammonia and 40.5 L of oxygen gas at STP burn, nitrogen monoxide and water form. After the products return to STP, how many grams of nitrogen monoxide are present?

$$NH_3(g) + O_2(g) \longrightarrow NO(g) + H_2O(l) \quad [\text{unbalanced}]$$

5.51 Aluminum reacts with excess hydrochloric acid to form aqueous aluminum chloride and 35.8 mL of hydrogen gas over water at 27°C and 751 mmHg. How many grams of aluminum reacted?

5.52 How many liters of hydrogen gas are collected over water at 18°C and 725 mmHg when 0.84 g of lithium reacts with water? Aqueous lithium hydroxide also forms.

Problems in Context

5.53 The air in a hot-air balloon at 744 torr is heated from 17°C to 60.0°C. Assuming that the amount (mol) of air and the pressure remain constant, what is the density of the air at each temperature? (The average molar mass of air is 28.8 g/mol.)

5.54 On a certain winter day in Utah, the average atmospheric pressure is 650. torr. What is the molar density (in mol/L) of the air if the temperature is −25°C?

5.55 A sample of a liquid hydrocarbon known to consist of molecules with five carbon atoms is vaporized in a 0.204-L flask by immersion in a water bath at 101°C. The barometric pressure is 767 torr, and the remaining gas weighs 0.482 g. What is the molecular formula of the hydrocarbon?

5.56 A sample of air contains 78.08% nitrogen, 20.94% oxygen, 0.05% carbon dioxide, and 0.93% argon, by volume. How many molecules of each gas are present in 1.00 L of the sample at 25°C and 1.00 atm?

5.57 An environmental chemist sampling industrial exhaust gases from a coal-burning plant collects a CO_2-SO_2-H_2O mixture in a 21-L steel tank until the pressure reaches 850. torr at 45°C.
(a) How many moles of gas are collected?

(b) If the SO_2 concentration in the mixture is 7.95×10^3 parts per million by volume (ppmv), what is its partial pressure? [*Hint:* ppmv = (volume of component/volume of mixture) $\times 10^6$.]

5.58 "Strike anywhere" matches contain the compound tetraphosphorus trisulfide, which burns to form tetraphosphorus decaoxide and sulfur dioxide gas. How many milliliters of sulfur dioxide, measured at 725 torr and 32°C, can be produced from burning 0.800 g of tetraphosphorus trisulfide?

5.59 Freon-12 (CF_2Cl_2), widely used as a refrigerant and aerosol propellant, is a dangerous air pollutant. In the troposphere, it traps heat 25 times as effectively as CO_2, and in the stratosphere, it participates in the breakdown of ozone. Freon-12 is prepared industrially by reaction of gaseous carbon tetrachloride with hydrogen fluoride. Hydrogen chloride gas also forms. How many grams of carbon tetrachloride are required for the production of 16.0 dm^3 of Freon-12 at 27°C and 1.20 atm?

5.60 Xenon hexafluoride was one of the first noble gas compounds synthesized. The solid reacts rapidly with the silicon dioxide in glass or quartz containers to form liquid $XeOF_4$ and gaseous silicon tetrafluoride. What is the pressure in a 1.00-L container at 25°C after 2.00 g of xenon hexafluoride reacts? (Assume that silicon tetrafluoride is the only gas present and that it occupies the entire volume.)

5.61 In the four cylinder-piston assemblies below, the reactant in the left cylinder is about to undergo a reaction at constant *T* and *P*:

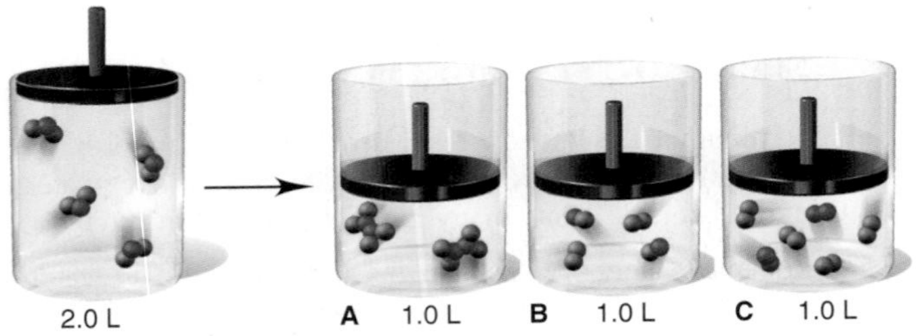

Which of the other three depictions best represents the products of the reaction?

5.62 Roasting galena [lead(II) sulfide] is a step in the industrial isolation of lead. How many liters of sulfur dioxide, measured at STP, are produced by the reaction of 3.75 kg of galena with 228 L of oxygen gas at 220°C and 2.0 atm? Lead(II) oxide also forms.

5.63 In one of his most critical studies into the nature of combustion, Lavoisier heated mercury(II) oxide and isolated elemental mercury and oxygen gas. If 40.0 g of mercury(II) oxide is heated in a 502-mL vessel and 20.0% (by mass) decomposes, what is the pressure (in atm) of the oxygen that forms at 25.0°C? (Assume that the gas occupies the entire volume.)

The Kinetic-Molecular Theory: A Model for Gas Behavior

(Sample Problem 5.13)

Concept Review Questions

5.64 Use the kinetic-molecular theory to explain the change in gas pressure that results from warming a sample of gas.

5.65 How does the kinetic-molecular theory explain why 1 mol of krypton and 1 mol of helium have the same volume at STP?

5.66 Is the rate of effusion of a gas higher than, lower than, or equal to its rate of diffusion? Explain. For two gases with molecules of approximately the same size, is the ratio of their effusion rates higher than, lower than, or equal to the ratio of their diffusion rates? Explain.

5.67 Consider two 1-L samples of gas: one is H_2 and the other is O_2. Both are at 1 atm and 25°C. How do the samples compare in terms of (a) mass, (b) density, (c) mean free path, (d) average molecular kinetic energy, (e) average molecular speed, and (f) time for a given fraction of molecules to effuse?

5.68 Three 5-L flasks, fixed with pressure gauges and small valves, each contain 4 g of gas at 273 K. Flask A contains H_2, flask B contains He, and flask C contains CH_4. Rank the flask contents in terms of (a) pressure, (b) average molecular kinetic energy, (c) diffusion rate after the valve is opened, (d) total kinetic energy of the molecules, (e) density, and (f) collision frequency.

Skill-Building Exercises (grouped in similar pairs)

5.69 What is the ratio of effusion rates for the lightest gas, H_2, and the heaviest known gas, UF_6?

5.70 What is the ratio of effusion rates for O_2 and Kr?

5.71 The graph below shows the distribution of molecular speeds for argon and helium at the same temperature.

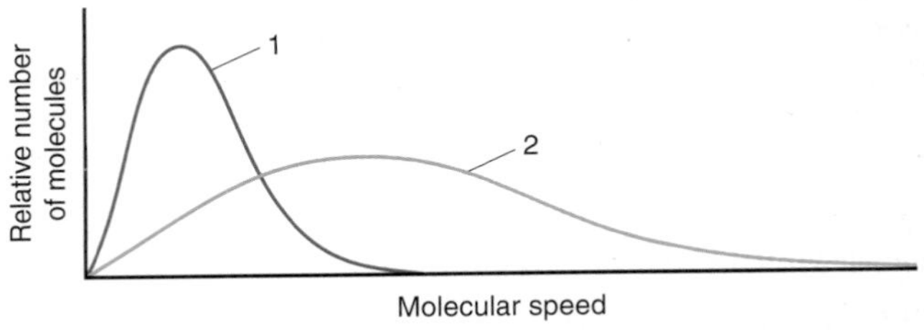

(a) Does curve 1 or 2 better represent the behavior of argon?
(b) Which curve represents the gas that effuses more slowly?
(c) Which curve more closely represents the behavior of fluorine gas? Explain.

5.72 The graph below shows the distribution of molecular speeds for a gas at two different temperatures.

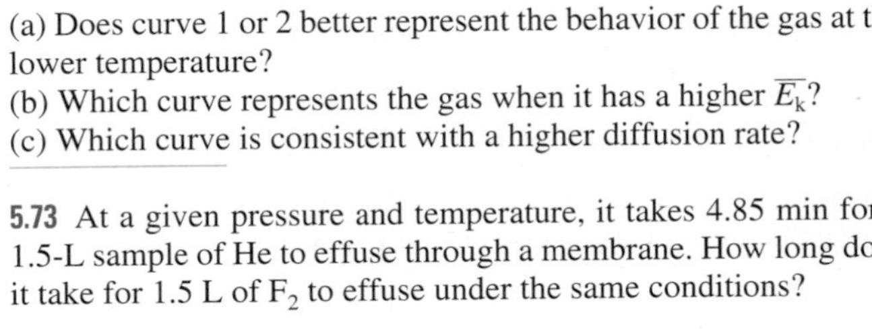

(a) Does curve 1 or 2 better represent the behavior of the gas at the lower temperature?
(b) Which curve represents the gas when it has a higher $\overline{E_k}$?
(c) Which curve is consistent with a higher diffusion rate?

5.73 At a given pressure and temperature, it takes 4.85 min for a 1.5-L sample of He to effuse through a membrane. How long does it take for 1.5 L of F_2 to effuse under the same conditions?

5.74 A sample of an unknown gas effuses in 11.1 min. An equal volume of H_2 in the same apparatus under the same conditions effuses in 2.42 min. What is the molar mass of the unknown gas?

Problems in Context

5.75 White phosphorus melts and then vaporizes at high temperature. The gas effuses at a rate that is 0.404 times that of neon in the same apparatus under the same conditions. How many atoms are in a molecule of gaseous white phosphorus?

5.76 Helium (He) is the lightest noble gas component of air, and xenon (Xe) is the heaviest. [For this problem, use $R = 8.314$ J/(mol·K) and $\mathcal{M}$ in kg/mol.] (a) Find the rms speed of He in winter (0.°C) and in summer (30.°C). (b) Compare the rms speed of He with that of Xe at 30.°C. (c) Find the average kinetic energy per mole of He and of Xe at 30.°C. (d) Find the average kinetic energy per molecule of He at 30.°C.

5.77 A mixture of gaseous disulfur difluoride, dinitrogen tetrafluoride, and sulfur tetrafluoride is placed in an effusion apparatus. (a) Rank the gases in order of increasing effusion rate. (b) Find the ratio of effusion rates of disulfur difluoride and dinitrogen tetrafluoride. (c) If gas X is added, and it effuses at 0.935 times the rate of sulfur tetrafluoride, find the molar mass of X.

Real Gases: Deviations from Ideal Behavior

Skill-Building Exercises (grouped in similar pairs)

5.78 Do interparticle attractions cause negative or positive deviations from the *PV/RT* ratio of an ideal gas? Use Table 5.3 to rank Kr, CO_2, and N_2 in order of increasing magnitude of these deviations.

5.79 Does particle volume cause negative or positive deviations from the *PV/RT* ratio of an ideal gas? Use Table 5.3 to rank Cl_2, H_2, and O_2 in order of increasing magnitude of these deviations.

5.80 Does N_2 behave more ideally at 1 atm or at 500 atm? Explain.

5.81 Does SF_6 (boiling point = 16°C at 1 atm) behave more ideally at 150°C or at 20°C? Explain.

Comprehensive Problems

5.82 An "empty" gasoline can with dimensions 15.0 cm by 40.0 cm by 12.5 cm is attached to a vacuum pump and evacuated. If the atmospheric pressure is 14.7 lb/in^2, what is the total force (in pounds) on the outside of the can?

5.83 Hemoglobin is the protein that transports O_2 through the blood from the lungs to the rest of the body. In doing so, each molecule of hemoglobin combines with four molecules of O_2. If 1.00 g of hemoglobin combines with 1.53 mL of O_2 at 37°C and 743 torr, what is the molar mass of hemoglobin?

5.84 A baker uses sodium hydrogen carbonate (baking soda) as the leavening agent in a banana-nut quickbread. The baking soda decomposes in either of two possible reactions:

(1) $2NaHCO_3(s) \longrightarrow Na_2CO_3(s) + H_2O(l) + CO_2(g)$

(2) $NaHCO_3(s) + H^+(aq) \longrightarrow H_2O(l) + CO_2(g) + Na^+(aq)$

Calculate the volume (in mL) of CO_2 that forms at 200.°C and 0.975 atm per gram of $NaHCO_3$ by each of the reaction processes.

5.85 A weather balloon containing 600. L of He is released near the equator at 1.01 atm and 305 K. It rises to a point where conditions are 0.489 atm and 218 K and eventually lands in the northern hemisphere under conditions of 1.01 atm and 250 K. If one-fourth of the helium leaked out during this journey, what is the volume (in L) of the balloon at landing?

5.86 Chlorine is produced from sodium chloride by the electrochemical chlor-alkali process. During the process, the chlorine is collected in a container that is isolated from the other products to prevent unwanted (and explosive) reactions. If a 15.50-L container holds 0.5950 kg of Cl_2 gas at 225°C, calculate:

(a) P_{IGL} (b) P_{VDW} $\left(\text{use } R = 0.08206 \dfrac{\text{atm·L}}{\text{mol·K}}\right)$

5.87 In a certain experiment, magnesium boride (Mg_3B_2) reacted with acid to form a mixture of four boron hydrides (B_xH_y), three as liquids (labeled I, II, and III) and one as a gas (IV).
(a) When a 0.1000-g sample of each liquid was transferred to an evacuated 750.0-mL container and volatilized at 70.00°C, sample I had a pressure of 0.05951 atm; sample II, 0.07045 atm; and sample III, 0.05767 atm. What is the molar mass of each liquid?
(b) Boron is 85.63% by mass in sample I, 81.10% in II, and 82.98% in III. What is the molecular formula of each sample?
(c) Sample IV was found to be 78.14% boron. Its rate of effusion was compared to that of sulfur dioxide; under identical conditions, 350.0 mL of sample IV effused in 12.00 min and 250.0 mL of sulfur dioxide effused in 13.04 min. What is the molecular formula of sample IV?

5.88 Three equal volumes of gas mixtures, all at the same *T*, are depicted below (with gas A *red*, gas B *green*, and gas C *blue*):

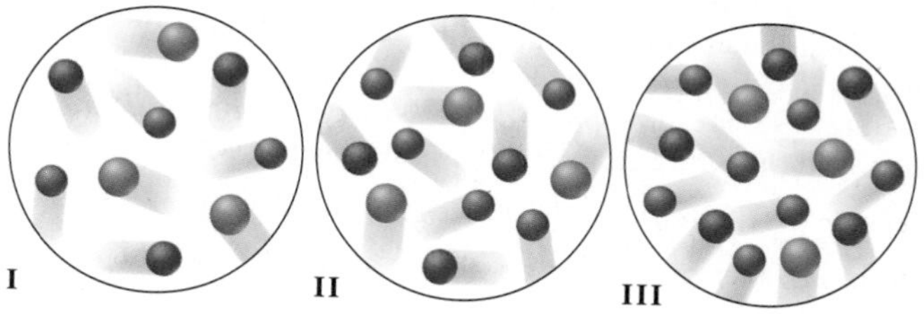

(a) Which sample, if any, has the highest partial pressure of A?
(b) Which sample, if any, has the lowest partial pressure of B?
(c) In which sample, if any, do the gas particles have the highest average kinetic energy?

5.89 Will the volume of a gas increase, decrease, or remain unchanged for each of the following sets of changes?
(a) The pressure is decreased from 2 atm to 1 atm, while the temperature is decreased from 200°C to 100°C.
(b) The pressure is increased from 1 atm to 3 atm, while the temperature is increased from 100°C to 300°C.
(c) The pressure is increased from 3 atm to 6 atm, while the temperature is increased from −73°C to 127°C.
(d) The pressure is increased from 0.2 atm to 0.4 atm, while the temperature is decreased from 300°C to 150°C.

5.90 When air is inhaled, it enters the alveoli of the lungs, and varying amounts of the component gases exchange with dissolved gases in the blood. The resulting alveolar gas mixture is quite different from the atmospheric mixture. The following table presents selected data on the composition and partial pressure of four gases in the atmosphere and in the alveoli:

	Atmosphere (sea level)		Alveoli	
Gas	Mole %	Partial Pressure (torr)	Mole %	Partial Pressure (torr)
N_2	78.6	—	—	569
O_2	20.9	—	—	104
CO_2	00.04	—	—	40
H_2O	00.46	—	—	47

If the total pressure of each gas mixture is 1.00 atm, calculate:
(a) The partial pressure (in torr) of each gas in the atmosphere
(b) The mole % of each gas in the alveoli
(c) The number of O_2 molecules in 0.50 L of alveolar air (volume of an average breath of a person at rest) at 37°C

5.91 Radon (Rn) is the heaviest, and only radioactive, member of Group 8A(18) (noble gases). It is a product of the disintegration of heavier radioactive nuclei found in minute concentrations in many common rocks used for building and construction. In recent years, health concerns about the cancers caused from inhaled residential radon have grown. If 1.0×10^{15} atoms of radium (Ra) produce an average of 1.373×10^{4} atoms of Rn per second, how many liters of Rn, measured at STP, are produced per day by 1.0 g of Ra?

5.92 At 1450. mmHg and 286 K, a skin diver exhales a 208-mL bubble of air that is 77% N_2, 17% O_2, and 6.0% CO_2 by volume. (a) How many milliliters would the volume of the bubble be if it were exhaled at the surface at 1 atm and 298 K?
(b) How many moles of N_2 are in the bubble?

5.93 Nitrogen dioxide is used industrially to produce nitric acid, but it contributes to acid rain and photochemical smog. What volume (in L) of nitrogen dioxide is formed at 735 torr and 28.2°C by reacting 4.95 cm^3 of copper (d = 8.95 g/cm^3) with 230.0 mL of nitric acid (d = 1.42 g/cm^3, 68.0% HNO_3 by mass)?

$$Cu(s) + 4HNO_3(aq) \longrightarrow Cu(NO_3)_2(aq) + 2NO_2(g) + 2H_2O(l)$$

5.94 In the average adult male, the residual volume (RV) of the lungs, the volume of air remaining after a forced exhalation, is 1200 mL. (a) How many moles of air are present in the RV at 1.0 atm and 37°C? (b) How many molecules of gas are present under these conditions?

5.95 In a bromine-producing plant, how many liters of gaseous elemental bromine at 300°C and 0.855 atm are formed by the reaction of 275 g of sodium bromide and 175.6 g of sodium bromate in aqueous acid solution? (Assume no Br_2 dissolves.)

$$5NaBr(aq) + NaBrO_3(aq) + 3H_2SO_4(aq) \longrightarrow 3Br_2(g) + 3Na_2SO_4(aq) + 3H_2O(g)$$

5.96 In a collision of sufficient force, automobile air bags respond by electrically triggering the explosive decomposition of sodium azide (NaN_3) to its elements. A 50.0-g sample of sodium azide was decomposed, and the nitrogen gas generated was collected over water at 26°C. The total pressure was 745.5 mmHg. How many liters of dry N_2 were generated?

5.97 An anesthetic gas contains 64.81% carbon, 13.60% hydrogen, and 21.59% oxygen, by mass. If 2.00 L of the gas at 25°C and 0.420 atm weighs 2.57 g, what is the molecular formula of the anesthetic?

5.98 Aluminum chloride is easily vaporized above 180°C. The gas escapes through a pinhole 0.122 times as fast as helium at the same conditions of temperature and pressure in the same apparatus. What is the molecular formula of aluminum chloride gas?

5.99 (a) What is the total volume (in L) of gaseous *products,* measured at 350°C and 735 torr, when an automobile engine burns 100. g of C_8H_{18} (a typical component of gasoline)?
(b) For part (a), the source of O_2 is air, which is 78% N_2, 21% O_2, and 1.0% Ar by volume. Assuming all the O_2 reacts, but no N_2 or Ar does, what is the total volume (in L) of gaseous *exhaust?*

5.100 An atmospheric chemist studying the pollutant SO_2 places a mixture of SO_2 and O_2 in a 2.00-L container at 800. K and 1.90 atm. When the reaction occurs, gaseous SO_3 forms, and the pressure falls to 1.65 atm. How many moles of SO_3 form?

5.101 The thermal decomposition of ethylene occurs during the compound's transit in pipelines and during the formation of polyethylene. The decomposition reaction is

$$CH_2{=}CH_2(g) \longrightarrow CH_4(g) + C(graphite)$$

If the decomposition begins at 10°C and 50.0 atm with a gas density of 0.215 g/mL and the temperature increases by 950 K,
(a) What is the final pressure of the confined gas (ignore the volume of graphite and use the van der Waals equation)?
(b) How does the PV/RT value of CH_4 compare to that in Figure 5.23? Explain.

5.102 Ammonium nitrate, a common fertilizer, was used by terrorists in the tragic explosion in Oklahoma City in 1995. How many liters of gas at 307°C and 1.00 atm are formed by the explosive decomposition of 15.0 kg of ammonium nitrate to nitrogen, oxygen, and water vapor?

5.103 An environmental engineer analyzes a sample of air contaminated with sulfur dioxide. To a 500.-mL sample at 700. torr and 38°C, she adds 20.00 mL of 0.01017 M aqueous iodine, which reacts as follows:

$$SO_2(g) + I_2(aq) + H_2O(l) \longrightarrow HSO_4^-(aq) + I^-(aq) + H^+(aq) \quad \text{[unbalanced]}$$

Excess I_2 reacts with 11.37 mL of 0.0105 M sodium thiosulfate:

$$I_2(aq) + S_2O_3^{2-}(aq) \longrightarrow I^-(aq) + S_4O_6^{2-}(aq) \quad \text{[unbalanced]}$$

What is the volume % of SO_2 in the air sample?

5.104 Canadian chemists have developed a modern variation of the 1899 Mond process for preparing extremely pure metallic nickel. A sample of impure nickel reacts with carbon monoxide at 50°C to form gaseous nickel carbonyl, $Ni(CO)_4$.
(a) How many grams of nickel can be converted to the carbonyl with 3.55 m^3 of CO at 100.7 kPa?
(b) The carbonyl is then decomposed at 21 atm and 155°C to pure (>99.95%) nickel. How many grams of nickel are obtained per cubic meter of the carbonyl?
(c) The released carbon monoxide is cooled and collected for reuse by passing it through water at 35°C. If the barometric pressure is 769 torr, what volume (in m^3) of CO is formed per cubic meter of carbonyl?

5.105 Analysis of a newly discovered gaseous silicon-fluorine compound shows that it contains 33.01 mass % silicon. At 27°C, 2.60 g of the compound exerts a pressure of 1.50 atm in a 0.250-L vessel. What is the molecular formula of the compound?

5.106 A gaseous organic compound containing only carbon, hydrogen, and nitrogen is burned in oxygen gas, and the volume of each reactant and product is measured under the same conditions of temperature and pressure. Reaction of four volumes of the compound produces four volumes of CO_2, two volumes of N_2, and ten volumes of water vapor. (a) How many volumes of O_2 were required? (b) What is the empirical formula of the compound?

5.107 Containers A, B, and C are attached by closed stopcocks of negligible volume.

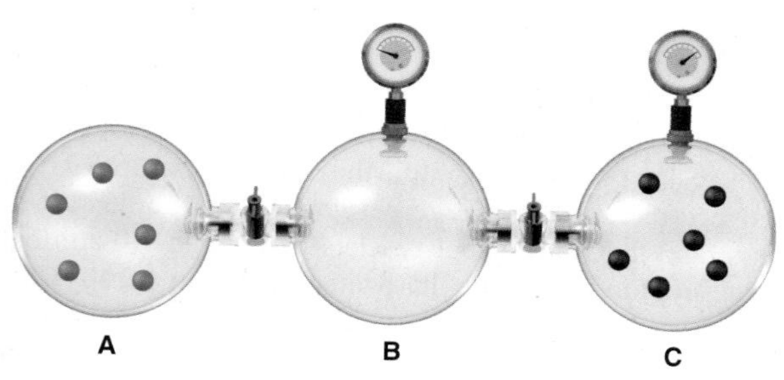

If each particle shown in the picture represents 10^6 particles,
(a) How many blue particles and black particles are in B after the stopcocks are opened and the system reaches equilibrium?
(b) How many blue particles and black particles are in A after the stopcocks are opened and the system reaches equilibrium?
(c) If the pressure in C, P_C, is 750 torr before the stopcocks are opened, what is P_C afterward? (d) What is P_B afterward?

5.108 Combustible vapor-air mixtures are flammable over a limited range of concentrations. The minimum volume % of vapor that gives a combustible mixture is called the *lower flammable limit* (LFL). Generally, the LFL is about half the stoichiometric mixture, the concentration required for complete combustion of the vapor in air. (a) If oxygen is 20.9 vol % of air, estimate the LFL for *n*-hexane, C_6H_{14}. (b) What volume (in mL) of *n*-hexane ($d = 0.660$ g/cm^3) is required to produce a flammable mixture of hexane in 1.000 m^3 of air at STP?

5.109 By what factor would a scuba diver's lungs expand if she ascended rapidly to the surface from a depth of 125 ft without inhaling or exhaling? If an expansion factor greater than 1.5 causes lung rupture, how far could she safely ascend from 125 ft without breathing? Assume constant temperature (d of seawater = 1.04 g/mL; d of Hg = 13.5 g/mL).

5.110 When 15.0 g of fluorite (CaF_2) reacts with excess sulfuric acid, hydrogen fluoride gas is collected at 744 torr and 25.5°C. Solid calcium sulfate is the other product. What gas temperature is required to store the gas in an 8.63-L container at 875 torr?

5.111 Dilute aqueous hydrogen peroxide is used as a bleaching agent and for disinfecting surfaces and small cuts. Its concentration is sometimes given as a certain number of "volumes hydrogen peroxide," which refers to the number of volumes of O_2 gas, measured at STP, that a given volume of hydrogen peroxide solution will release when it decomposes to O_2 and liquid H_2O. How many grams of hydrogen peroxide are in 0.100 L of "20 volumes hydrogen peroxide" solution?

5.112 At a height of 300 km above Earth's surface, an astronaut finds that the atmospheric pressure is about 10^{-8} mmHg and the temperature is 500 K. How many molecules of gas are there per milliliter at this altitude?

5.113 (a) What is the rms speed of O_2 at STP? (b) If the mean free path of O_2 molecules at STP is 6.33×10^{-8} m, what is their collision frequency? [Use $R = 8.314$ J/(mol·K) and $\mathcal{M}$ in kg/mol.]

5.114 Acrylic acid ($CH_2{=}CHCOOH$) is used to prepare polymers, adhesives, and paints. The first step in making acrylic acid involves the vapor-phase oxidation of propylene ($CH_2{=}CHCH_3$) to acrolein ($CH_2{=}CHCHO$). This step is carried out at 330°C and 2.5 atm in a large bundle of tubes around which circulates a heat-transfer agent. The reactants spend an average of 1.8 s in the tubes, which have a void space of 100 ft^3. How many pounds of propylene must be added per hour in a mixture whose mole fractions are 0.07 propylene, 0.35 steam, and 0.58 air?

5.115 Standard conditions are based on relevant environmental conditions. If normal average surface temperature and pressure on Venus are 730. K and 90 atm, respectively, what is the standard molar volume of an ideal gas on Venus?

5.116 A barometer tube is 1.00×10^2 cm long and has a cross-sectional area of 1.20 cm^2. The height of the mercury column is 74.0 cm, and the temperature is 24°C. A small amount of N_2 is introduced into the evacuated space above the mercury, which causes the mercury level to drop to a height of 64.0 cm. How many grams of N_2 were introduced?

5.117 What is the molarity of the cleaning solution formed when 10.0 L of ammonia gas at 33°C and 735 torr dissolves in enough water to give a final volume of 0.750 L?

5.118 The Hawaiian volcano Kilauea emits an average of 1.5×10^3 m^3 of gas each day, when corrected to 298 K and 1.00 atm. The mixture contains gases that contribute to global warming and acid rain, and some are toxic. An atmospheric chemist analyzes a sample and finds the following mole fractions: 0.4896 CO_2, 0.0146 CO, 0.3710 H_2O, 0.1185 SO_2, 0.0003 S_2, 0.0047 H_2, 0.0008 HCl, and 0.0003 H_2S. How many metric tons (t) of each gas are emitted per year (1 t = 1000 kg)?

5.119 To study a key fuel-cell reaction, a chemical engineer has 20.0-L tanks of H_2 and of O_2 and wants to use up both tanks to form 28.0 mol of water at 23.8°C. (a) Use the ideal gas law to find the pressure needed in each tank. (b) Use the van der Waals equation to find the pressure needed in each tank. (c) Compare the results from the two equations.

5.120 For each of the following, which shows the greater deviation from ideal behavior at the same set of conditions? Explain.
(a) Argon or xenon (b) Water vapor or neon
(c) Mercury vapor or radon (d) Water vapor or methane

5.121 How many liters of gaseous hydrogen bromide at 29°C and 0.965 atm will a chemist need if she wishes to prepare 3.50 L of 1.20 *M* hydrobromic acid?

5.122 A mixture consisting of 7.0 g of CO and 10.0 g of SO_2, two atmospheric pollutants, has a pressure of 0.33 atm when placed in a sealed container. What is the partial pressure of CO?

5.123 Sulfur dioxide is used to make sulfuric acid. One method of producing it is by roasting mineral sulfides, for example,

$$FeS_2(s) + O_2(g) \xrightarrow{\Delta} SO_2(g) + Fe_2O_3(s) \quad \text{[unbalanced]}$$

A production error leads to the sulfide being placed in a 950-L vessel with insufficient oxygen. Initially, the partial pressure of O_2 is 0.64 atm, and the total pressure is 1.05 atm, with the balance due to N_2. The reaction is run until 85% of the O_2 is consumed, and the vessel is then cooled to its initial temperature. What is the total pressure and the partial pressure of each gas in the vessel?

5.124 A mixture of CO_2 and Kr weighs 35.0 g and exerts a pressure of 0.708 atm in its container. Since Kr is expensive, you wish to recover it from the mixture. After the CO_2 is completely removed by absorption with NaOH(*s*), the pressure in the container is 0.250 atm. How many grams of CO_2 were originally present? How many grams of Kr can you recover?

5.125 When a car accelerates quickly, the passengers feel a force that presses them back into their seats, but a balloon filled with helium floats forward. Why?

5.126 Gases such as CO are gradually oxidized in the atmosphere, not by O_2 but by the hydroxyl radical, •OH, a species with one fewer electron than a hydroxide ion. At night, the •OH concentration is nearly zero, but it increases to 2.5×10^{12} molecules/m^3 in polluted air during the day. At daytime conditions of 1.00 atm and 22°C, what is the partial pressure and mole percent of •OH in air?

5.127 Aqueous sulfurous acid (H_2SO_3) was made by dissolving 0.200 L of sulfur dioxide gas at 19°C and 745 mmHg in water to yield 500.0 mL of solution. The acid solution required 10.0 mL of sodium hydroxide solution to reach the titration end point. What was the molarity of the sodium hydroxide solution?

5.128 In the 19th century, J. B. A. Dumas devised a method for finding the molar mass of a volatile liquid from the volume, temperature, pressure, and mass of its vapor. He placed a sample of such a liquid in a flask that was closed with a stopper fitted with a narrow tube, immersed the flask in a hot water bath to vaporize the liquid, and then cooled the flask. Find the molar mass of a volatile liquid from the following:

Mass of empty flask = 65.347 g
Mass of flask filled with water at 25°C = 327.4 g
Density of water at 25°C = 0.997 g/mL
Mass of flask plus condensed unknown liquid = 65.739 g
Barometric pressure = 101.2 kPa
Temperature of water bath = 99.8°C

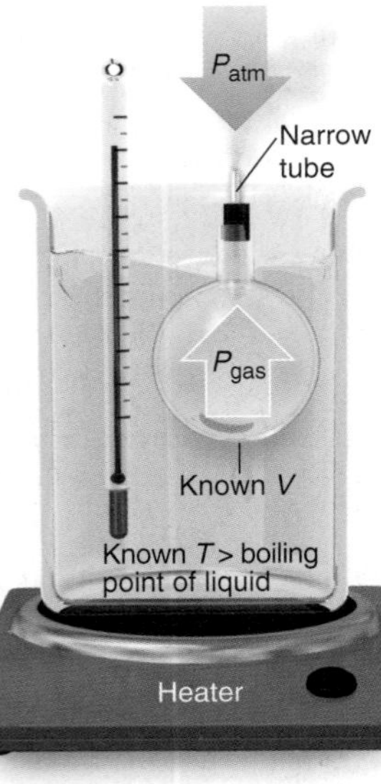

5.129 During World War II, a portable source of hydrogen gas was needed for weather balloons, and solid metal hydrides were the most convenient form. Many metal hydrides react with water to generate the metal hydroxide and hydrogen. Two candidates were lithium hydride and magnesium hydride. What volume (in L) of gas is formed from 1.00 lb of each hydride reacting with excess water at 750. torr and 27°C?

5.130 The lunar surface reaches 370 K at midday. The atmosphere consists of neon, argon, and helium at a total pressure of only 2×10^{-14} atm. Calculate the rms speed of each component in the lunar atmosphere. [Use $R = 8.314$ J/(mol•K) and $\mathcal{M}$ in kg/mol.]

5.131 A person inhales air richer in O_2 and exhales air richer in CO_2 and water vapor. During each hour of sleep, a person exhales a total of about 300 L of this CO_2-enriched and H_2O-enriched air. (a) If the partial pressures of CO_2 and H_2O in exhaled air are each 30.0 torr at 37.0°C, calculate the mass (g) of CO_2 and of H_2O exhaled in 1 h of sleep. (b) How many grams of body mass does the person lose in an 8-h sleep if all the CO_2 and H_2O exhaled come from the metabolism of glucose?

$$C_6H_{12}O_6(s) + 6O_2(g) \longrightarrow 6CO_2(g) + 6H_2O(g)$$

5.132 Popcorn pops because the horny endosperm, a tough, elastic material, resists gas pressure within the heated kernel until it reaches explosive force. A 0.25-mL kernel has a water content of 1.6% by mass, and the water vapor reaches 170°C and 9.0 atm before the kernel ruptures. Assume that water vapor can occupy 75% of the kernel's volume. (a) What is the mass (in g) of the kernel? (b) How many milliliters would this amount of water vapor occupy at 25°C and 1.00 atm?

5.133 Sulfur dioxide emissions from coal-burning power plants are removed by *flue-gas desulfurization.* The flue gas passes through a scrubber, and a slurry of wet calcium carbonate reacts with it to form carbon dioxide and calcium sulfite. The calcium sulfite then reacts with oxygen to form calcium sulfate, which is sold as gypsum. (a) If the sulfur dioxide concentration is 1000 times higher than its mole fraction in clean dry air (2×10^{-10}), how much calcium sulfate (kg) can be made from scrubbing 4 GL of flue gas (1 GL = 1×10^9 L)? A state-of-the-art scrubber removes at least 95% of the sulfur dioxide. (b) If the mole fraction of oxygen in air is 0.209, what volume (L) of air at 1.00 atm and 25°C is needed to react with all the calcium sulfite?

5.134 Many water treatment plants use chlorine gas to kill microorganisms before the water is released for residential use. A plant engineer has to maintain the chlorine pressure in a tank below the 85.0-atm rating and, to be safe, decides to fill the tank to 80.0% of this maximum pressure. (a) How many moles of Cl_2 gas can be kept in an 850.-L tank at 298 K if she uses the ideal gas law in the calculation? (b) What is the tank pressure if she uses the van der Waals equation for this amount of gas? (c) Did the engineer fill the tank to the desired pressure?

5.135 At 10.0°C and 102.5 kPa, the density of dry air is 1.26 g/L. What is the average "molar mass" of dry air at these conditions?

5.136 In A, the picture shows a cylinder with 0.1 mol of a gas that behaves ideally. Choose the cylinder (B, C, or D) that correctly represents the volume of the gas after each of the following changes. If none of the cylinders is correct, specify "none."
(a) P is doubled at fixed n and T.
(b) T is reduced from 400 K to 200 K at fixed n and P.
(c) T is increased from 100°C to 200°C at fixed n and P.
(d) 0.1 mol of gas is added at fixed P and T.
(e) 0.1 mol of gas is added and P is doubled at fixed T.

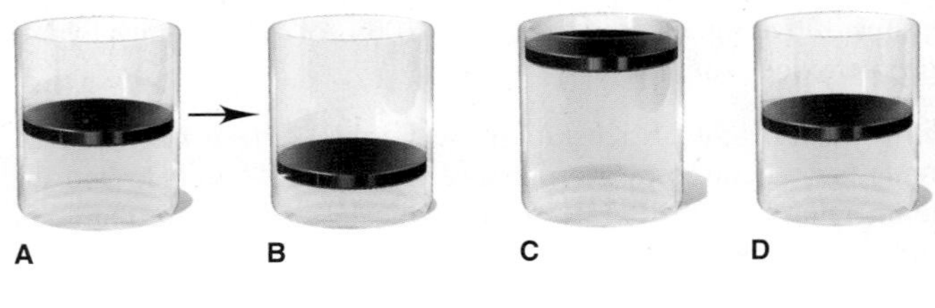

5.137 Ammonia is essential to so many industries that, on a molar basis, it is the most heavily produced substance in the world. Calculate P_{IGL} and P_{VDW} (in atm) of 51.1 g of ammonia in a 3.000-L container at 0°C and 400.°C, the industrial temperature. (See Table 5.4 for the values of the van der Waals constants.)

5.138 A 6.0-L flask contains a mixture of methane (CH_4), argon, and helium at 45°C and 1.75 atm. If the mole fractions of helium and argon are 0.25 and 0.35, respectively, how many molecules of methane are present?

5.139 A large portion of metabolic energy arises from the biological combustion of glucose:

$$C_6H_{12}O_6(s) + 6O_2(g) \longrightarrow 6CO_2(g) + 6H_2O(g)$$

(a) If this reaction is carried out in an expandable container at 37°C and 780. torr, what volume of CO_2 is produced from 20.0 g of glucose and excess O_2? (b) If the reaction is carried out at the same conditions with the stoichiometric amount of O_2, what is the partial pressure of each gas when the reaction is 50% complete (10.0 g of glucose remains)?

5.140 What is the average kinetic energy and rms speed of N_2 molecules at STP? Compare these values with those of H_2 molecules at STP. [Use $R = 8.314$ J/(mol·K) and $\mathcal{M}$ in kg/mol.]

5.141 According to government standards, the *8-h threshold limit value* is 5000 ppmv for CO_2 and 0.1 ppmv for Br_2 (1 ppmv is 1 part by volume in 10^6 parts by volume). Exposure to either gas for 8 h above these limits is unsafe. At STP, which of the following would be unsafe for 8 h of exposure?
(a) Air with a partial pressure of 0.2 torr of Br_2
(b) Air with a partial pressure of 0.2 torr of CO_2
(c) 1000 L of air containing 0.0004 g of Br_2 gas
(d) 1000 L of air containing 2.8×10^{22} molecules of CO_2

5.142 One way to prevent emission of the pollutant NO from industrial plants is by a catalyzed reaction with NH_3:

$$4NH_3(g) + 4NO(g) + O_2(g) \xrightarrow{\text{catalyst}} 4N_2(g) + 6H_2O(g)$$

(a) If the NO has a partial pressure of 4.5×10^{-5} atm in the flue gas, how many liters of NH_3 are needed per liter of flue gas at 1.00 atm? (b) If the reaction takes place at 1.00 atm and 365°C, how many grams of NH_3 are needed per kL of flue gas?

5.143 An equimolar mixture of Ne and Xe is accidentally placed in a container that has a tiny leak. After a short while, a very small proportion of the mixture has escaped. What is the mole fraction of Ne in the effusing gas?

5.144 From the relative rates of effusion of $^{235}UF_6$ and $^{238}UF_6$, find the number of steps needed to produce a sample of the enriched fuel used in many nuclear reactors, which is 3.0 mole % ^{235}U. The natural abundance of ^{235}U is 0.72%.

5.145 A slight deviation from ideal behavior exists even at normal conditions. If it behaved ideally, 1 mol of CO would occupy 22.414 L and exert 1 atm pressure at 273.15 K. Calculate P_{VDW} for 1.000 mol of CO at 273.15 K. $\left(\text{Use } R = 0.08206 \dfrac{\text{atm}\cdot\text{L}}{\text{mol}\cdot\text{K}}.\right)$

5.146 In preparation for a combustion demonstration, a professor fills a balloon with equal molar amounts of H_2 and O_2, but the demonstration has to be postponed until the next day. During the night, both gases leak through pores in the balloon. If 35% of the H_2 leaks, what is the O_2/H_2 ratio in the balloon the next day?

5.147 Phosphorus trichloride is important in the manufacture of insecticides, fuel additives, and flame retardants. Phosphorus has only one naturally occurring isotope, ^{31}P, whereas chlorine has two, ^{35}Cl (75%) and ^{37}Cl (25%). (a) What different molecular masses (in amu) can be found for PCl_3? (b) Which is the most abundant? (c) What is the ratio of the effusion rates of the heaviest and the lightest PCl_3 molecules?

5.148 A truck tire has a volume of 218 L and is filled with air to 35.0 psi at 295 K. After a drive, the air heats up to 318 K. (a) If the tire volume is constant, what is the pressure (in psi)? (b) If the tire volume increases 2.0%, what is the pressure (in psi)? (c) If the tire leaks 1.5 g of air per minute and the temperature is constant, how many minutes will it take for the tire to reach the original pressure of 35.0 psi ($\mathcal{M}$ of air = 28.8 g/mol)?

5.149 Allotropes are different molecular forms of an element, such as dioxygen (O_2) and ozone (O_3). (a) What is the density of each oxygen allotrope at 0°C and 760 torr? (b) Calculate the ratio of densities, d_{O_3}/d_{O_2}, and explain the significance of this number.

5.150 When gaseous F_2 and solid I_2 are heated to high temperatures, the I_2 sublimes and gaseous iodine heptafluoride forms. If 350. torr of F_2 and 2.50 g of solid I_2 are put into a 2.50-L container at 250. K and the container is heated to 550. K, what is the final pressure (in torr)? What is the partial pressure of I_2 gas?

Intermolecular Forces: Liquids, Solids, and Phase Changes

12

Concepts and skills to review before you study this chapter

- properties of gases, liquids, and solids (Section 5.1)
- kinetic-molecular theory of gases (Section 5.5)
- kinetic and potential energy (Section 6.1)
- enthalpy change, heat capacity, and Hess's law (Sections 6.2, 6.3, and 6.5)
- diffraction of light (Section 7.1)
- Coulomb's law (Section 9.2)
- chemical bonding models (Chapter 9)
- molecular polarity (Section 10.3)
- molecular orbital treatment of diatomic molecules (Section 11.3)

All the matter in and around you occurs in one or more of the three physical states—gas, liquid, or solid. Under different conditions, many substances can occur in any of the states. We're all familiar with the states of water: we inhale and exhale gaseous water; drink, excrete, and wash with liquid water; and shovel, slide on, or cool our drinks with solid water. And, given the right conditions, even other solids (gold jewelry, table salt), liquids (gasoline, antifreeze), and gases (air, CO_2 bubbles) can exist in one or both of the other states.

The three states were introduced in Chapter 1 and their properties were compared when we examined gases in Chapter 5. You saw there that the particles in gases are, on average, very far apart. Now, we examine liquids and solids, which are called *condensed* states because their *particles are very close together.*

IN THIS CHAPTER . . . We explore the interplay of forces that give rise to the three states of matter and their changes, with special attention to liquids and solids.

- We use kinetic-molecular theory to see how relative magnitudes of potential and kinetic energy account for the behavior of gases, liquids, and solids and how temperature is related to phase changes.
- We calculate the heat associated with warming or cooling a phase and with a phase change.
- We highlight the effects of temperature and pressure on phases and their changes with phase diagrams.
- We describe the types and relative strengths of the intermolecular forces that occur within pure substances.
- We see how intermolecular forces give rise to the properties of liquids.
- As a special case, we trace the unique and vital physical properties of water to the electron configurations of its atoms.
- We discuss the properties of solids, emphasizing the relationship between type of bonding and predominant intermolecular force, and we examine the methods used to study crystal structure.
- We introduce key features of several kinds of advanced materials—semiconductors, liquid crystals, ceramics, polymers, and nanostructures.

12.1 • AN OVERVIEW OF PHYSICAL STATES AND PHASE CHANGES

Each physical state is called a **phase,** a physically distinct, homogeneous part of system. The water in a closed container constitutes one phase; the water vapor above the liquid is a second phase; add some ice, and there are three.

In this section, you'll see that interactions between the potential energy and the kinetic energy of the particles give rise to the properties of each phase:

- The *potential energy* in the form of **intermolecular forces** (or, more generally, *interparticle forces*) tends to draw the molecules together. According to Coulomb's law, the electrostatic potential energy depends on the charges of the particles and the distances between them (Section 9.2).
- The *kinetic energy* associated with the random motion of the molecules tends to disperse them. It is related to their average speed and is proportional to the absolute temperature (Section 5.5).

These interactions also explain **phase changes,** changes in physical state from one phase to another—liquid to solid, solid to gas, and so forth.

A Kinetic-Molecular View of the Three States Imagine yourself among the particles in any of the three states of water. Look closely and you'll discover two types of electrostatic forces at work:

1. *Intra*molecular (bonding) forces exist *within* each molecule. The *chemical* behavior of the three states is identical because each consists of the same bent, polar H—O—H molecules held together by identical covalent bonding forces.
2. *Inter*molecular (nonbonding) forces exist *between* the molecules. The *physical* behavior of the states is different because the strengths of these forces differ from state to state.

Whether a substance occurs as a gas, liquid, or solid depends on the interplay of the potential and kinetic energy:

- *In a gas,* the potential energy (energy of attraction) is small relative to the kinetic energy (energy of motion); thus, on average, the particles are far apart. This large distance has several macroscopic consequences: a gas fills its container, is highly compressible, and flows easily through another gas (Table 12.1).
- *In a liquid,* attractions are stronger because the particles are touching, but they have enough kinetic energy to move randomly around each other. Thus, a liquid conforms to the shape of its container but has a surface, it resists an applied force and thus compresses very slightly, and it flows, but *much* more slowly than gases.
- *In a solid,* the attractions dominate the motion so much that the particles are fixed in position relative to one another, just jiggling in place. Thus, a solid has its own shape, compresses even less than liquids, and does not flow significantly.

How does ability to flow influence composition in nature?

The environment provides a perfect demonstration of these differences in ability to flow (*see photo*). Atmospheric gases mix so well that the lowest 80 km of air has a uniform composition. Much less mixing in the oceans allows the composition at various depths to support different species. And rocks intermingle so little that adjacent strata remain separated for millions of years.

Table 12.1 A Macroscopic Comparison of Gases, Liquids, and Solids

State	Shape and Volume	Compressibility	Ability to Flow
Gas	Conforms to shape and volume of container	High	High
Liquid	Conforms to shape of container; volume limited by surface	Very low	Moderate
Solid	Maintains its own shape and volume	Almost none	Almost none

Types of Phase Changes and Their Enthalpies When we consider phase changes, understanding the effect of temperature is critical:

- As *temperature increases,* the average kinetic energy does too, so the faster moving particles overcome attractions more easily.
- As *temperature decreases,* particles slow, so attractions can pull them together.

Each phase change has a name and an associated enthalpy change:

1. *Gas to liquid, and vice versa.* As the temperature drops, the molecules in the gas phase come together and form a liquid in the process of **condensation;** the opposite process, changing from a liquid to a gas, is **vaporization.**

2. *Liquid to solid, and vice versa.* As the temperature drops further, the particles move slower and become fixed in position in the process of **freezing;** the opposite change is called **melting,** or **fusion.** In common speech, *freezing* implies low temperature because we think of water. But, molten metals, for example, freeze (solidify) at much higher temperatures and have medical, industrial, and artistic applications, such as gold dental crowns, steel auto bodies, and bronze statues.

3. *Gas to solid, and vice versa.* All three states of water are familiar because they are stable under ordinary conditions. Carbon dioxide, on the other hand, is familiar as a gas and a solid (dry ice), but liquid CO_2 occurs only at pressures of 5.1 atm or greater. At ordinary conditions, solid CO_2 changes directly to a gas, a process called **sublimation.** Freeze-dried foods are prepared by sublimation. The opposite process, changing from a gas directly into a solid, is called **deposition**—ice crystals form on a cold window from the deposition of water vapor (Figure 12.1A).

The accompanying enthalpy changes are either exothermic or endothermic:

- *Exothermic changes.* As the molecules of a gas attract each other into a liquid, and then become fixed in a solid, the system of particles *loses* energy, which is released as heat. Thus, *condensing, freezing, and depositing are exothermic changes.*
- *Endothermic changes.* Heat must be absorbed by the system to overcome the attractive forces that keep the particles fixed in place in a solid or near each other in a liquid. Thus, *melting, vaporizing, and subliming are endothermic changes.*

Sweating has a cooling effect because heat from your body vaporizes the water. To achieve this cooling, cats lick themselves and dogs pant (Figure 12.1B).

For a pure substance, each phase change is accompanied by a standard enthalpy change, given in units of *kilojoules per mole* (measured at 1 atm and the temperature of the change). For vaporization, it is the **heat** (or *enthalpy*) **of vaporization** (ΔH°_{vap}), and for fusion (melting), it is the **heat** (or *enthalpy*) **of fusion** (ΔH°_{fus}). In the case of water, we have

$$H_2O(l) \longrightarrow H_2O(g) \qquad \Delta H = \Delta H^\circ_{vap} = 40.7\ \text{kJ/mol (at } 100^\circ\text{C)}$$
$$H_2O(s) \longrightarrow H_2O(l) \qquad \Delta H = \Delta H^\circ_{fus} = 6.02\ \text{kJ/mol (at } 0^\circ\text{C)}$$

The reverse processes, condensing and freezing, have enthalpy changes of the *same magnitude but opposite sign:*

$$H_2O(g) \longrightarrow H_2O(l) \qquad \Delta H = -\Delta H^\circ_{vap} = -40.7\ \text{kJ/mol}$$
$$H_2O(l) \longrightarrow H_2O(s) \qquad \Delta H = -\Delta H^\circ_{fus} = -6.02\ \text{kJ/mol}$$

Water behaves typically in that it takes much less energy to melt the solid than to vaporize the liquid: $\Delta H^\circ_{fus} < \Delta H^\circ_{vap}$; that is, it takes less energy to reduce the intermolecular forces enough for the molecules to move out of their fixed positions (melt a solid) than to separate them completely (vaporize a liquid) (Figure 12.2).

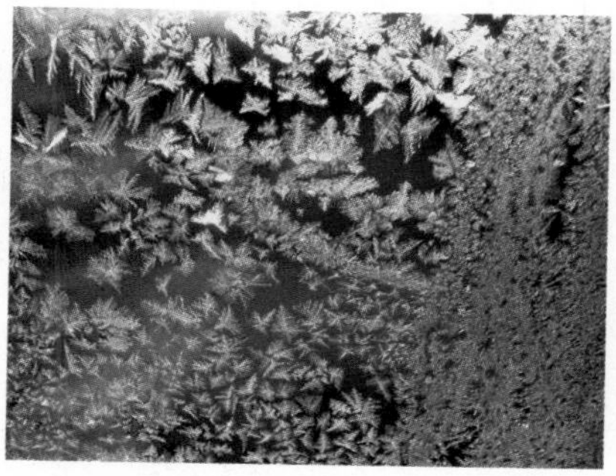
A Deposition

B Vaporization

Figure 12.1 Two familiar phase changes.

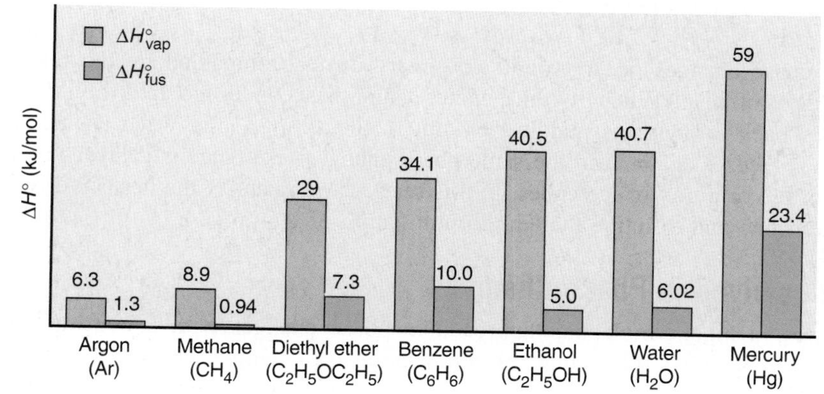

Figure 12.2 Heats of vaporization and fusion for several common substances.

The **heat** (or *enthalpy*) **of sublimation** (ΔH°_{subl}) is the enthalpy change when 1 mol of a substance sublimes, and the negative of this value is the change when 1 mol of the substance deposits. Since sublimation can be considered a combination of melting and vaporizing, Hess's law (Section 6.5) says that the heat of sublimation equals the sum of the heats of fusion and vaporization:

$$\begin{array}{lll} \text{Solid} \longrightarrow \text{liquid} & \Delta H^\circ_{fus} \\ \text{Liquid} \longrightarrow \text{gas} & \Delta H^\circ_{vap} \\ \hline \text{Solid} \longrightarrow \text{gas} & \Delta H^\circ_{subl} \end{array}$$

Figure 12.3 on the next page summarizes the phase changes and their enthalpy changes.

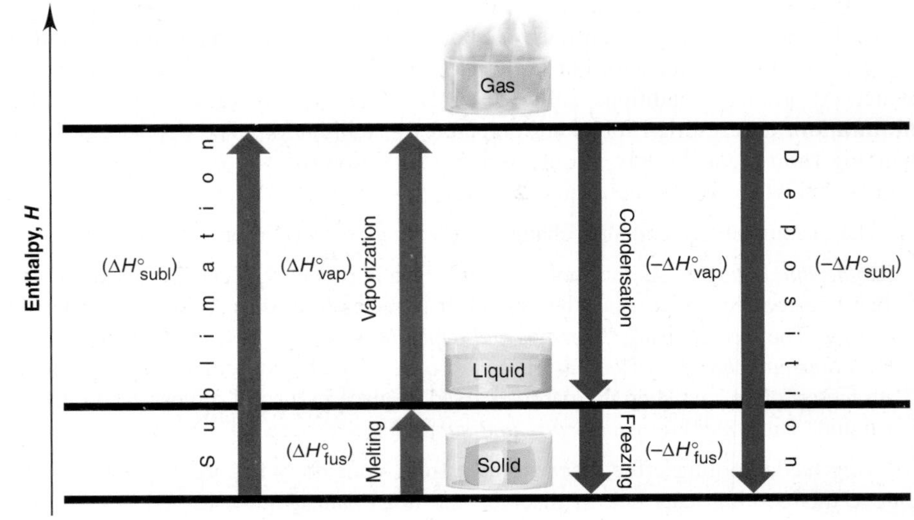

Figure 12.3 Phase changes and their enthalpy changes. Fusion (or melting), vaporization, and sublimation are endothermic changes (positive ΔH°), whereas freezing, condensation, and deposition are exothermic changes (negative ΔH°).

Summary of Section 12.1

- Because of the relative magnitudes of intermolecular forces (potential energy) and average speed (kinetic energy), the particles in a gas are far apart and moving randomly, those in a liquid are in contact and moving relative to each other, and those in a solid are in contact and in fixed positions. These molecular-level differences account for macroscopic differences in shape, compressibility, and ability to flow.
- When a solid becomes a liquid (melting, or fusion), a liquid becomes a gas (vaporization), or a solid becomes a gas (sublimation), energy is absorbed to overcome intermolecular forces and increase the average distance between particles. As particles come closer together in the reverse changes (freezing, condensation, and deposition), energy is released. Each phase change is associated with a given enthalpy change under specified conditions.

12.2 • QUANTITATIVE ASPECTS OF PHASE CHANGES

Many phase changes occur around you every day, accompanied by the release or absorption of heat. When it rains, water vapor has condensed to a liquid, which changes back to a gas as puddles dry up. In the spring, solid water melts, and in winter, it freezes again. And the same phase changes take place whenever you make a pot of tea or a tray of ice cubes. In this section, we quantify the heat involved in a phase change and examine the equilibrium nature of the process.

Heat Involved in Phase Changes

We apply a kinetic-molecular approach to phase changes with a **heating-cooling curve,** which shows the changes in temperature of a sample when heat is absorbed or released at a constant rate. Let's examine what happens when 2.50 mol of gaseous water in a closed container undergoes a change from 130°C to −40°C at a constant pressure of 1 atm. We'll divide this process into five heat-releasing (exothermic) stages (Figure 12.4):

Stage 1. Gaseous water cools. Water molecules zoom chaotically at a range of speeds, smashing into each other and the container walls. At the starting temperature, the most probable speed of the molecules, and thus their average kinetic energy (E_k), is high enough to overcome the potential energy (E_p) of attractions. As the temperature falls, the average E_k decreases and attractions become more important. The change is

$$H_2O(g)\,[130°C] \longrightarrow H_2O(g)\,[100°C]$$

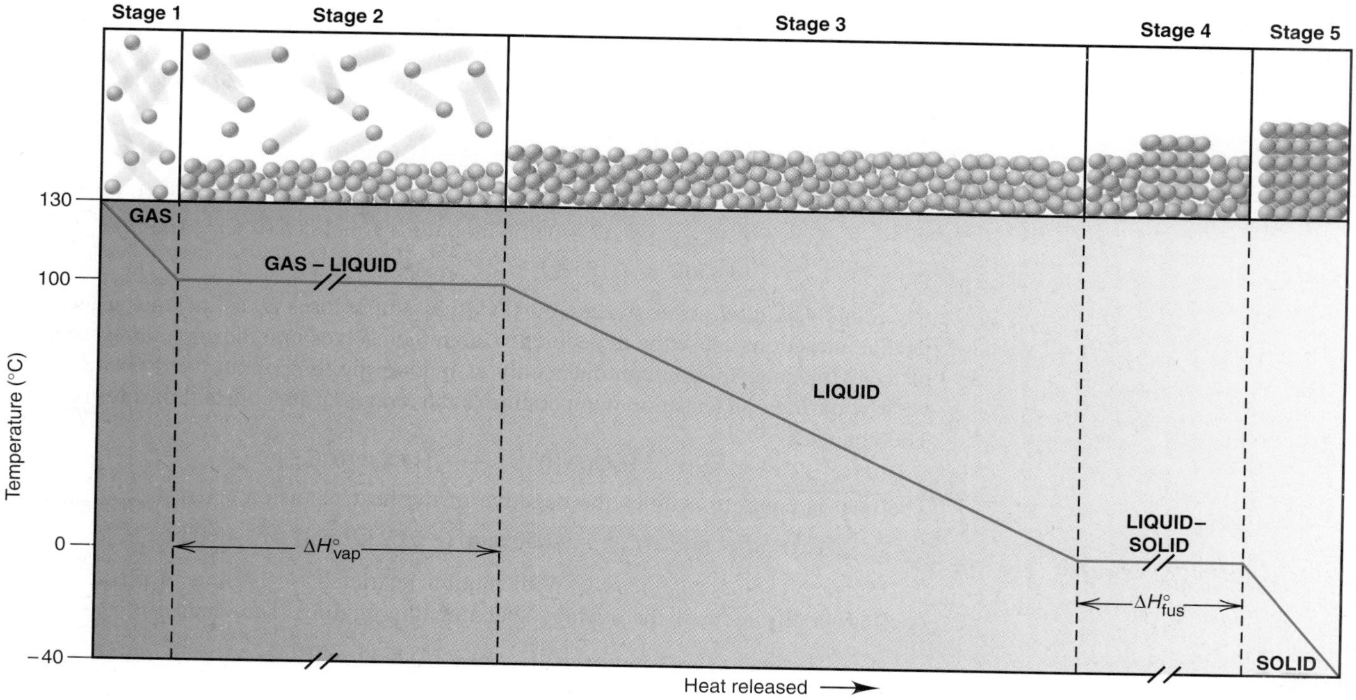

Figure 12.4 A cooling curve for the conversion of gaseous water to ice. A plot of temperature vs. heat released as gaseous water changes to ice is shown, with a molecular-level depiction for each stage. The slopes of the lines in stages 1, 3, and 5 reflect the molar heat capacities of the phases. Although not drawn to scale, the line in stage 2 is longer than the line in stage 4 because ΔH°_{vap} of water is greater than ΔH°_{fus}. A plot of temperature vs. heat absorbed starting at −40°C would have the same steps but in reverse order.

The heat (q) is the product of the amount (number of moles, n) of water, the molar heat capacity of *gaseous* water, $C_{water(g)}$, and the temperature change, ΔT ($T_{final} - T_{initial}$):

$$q = n \times C_{water(g)} \times \Delta T = (2.50\text{ mol})(33.1\text{ J/mol·°C})(100°C - 130°C)$$
$$= -2482\text{ J} = -2.48\text{ kJ}$$

The minus sign indicates that heat is released.*

Stage 2. Gaseous water condenses. At the condensation point, intermolecular attractions cause the slowest of the molecules to aggregate into microdroplets and then a bulk liquid. Note that, during the phase change,

- The temperature of the sample, and thus its average E_k, is constant. At the same temperature, molecules move farther between collisions in a gas than in a liquid, but their *average* speed is the same.
- Releasing heat from the sample decreases the average E_p as the molecules approach each other.

Thus, at 100°C, gaseous and liquid water have the same average E_k, but the liquid has lower average E_p. The change is

$$H_2O(g)\,[100°C] \longrightarrow H_2O(l)\,[100°C]$$

The heat is the amount (n) times the negative of the heat of vaporization ($-\Delta H^\circ_{vap}$):

$$q = n(-\Delta H^\circ_{vap}) = (2.50\text{ mol})(-40.7\text{ kJ/mol}) = -102\text{ kJ}$$

This stage contributes the *greatest portion of the total heat released* because of the large decrease in E_p as the molecules become so much closer in the liquid than they were in the gas.

*For purposes of canceling, the units for molar heat capacity, C, include °C, rather than K, but this doesn't affect the magnitude of C because these two units represent the same temperature increment.

Stage 3. Liquid water cools. The molecules in the liquid state continue to lose heat, which appears as a decrease in temperature, that is, as a decrease in the most probable molecular speed and, thus, the average E_k. The temperature decreases as long as the sample remains liquid. The change is

$$H_2O(l)\ [100°C] \longrightarrow H_2O(l)\ [0°C]$$

The heat depends on amount (n), the molar heat capacity of *liquid* water, and ΔT:

$$q = n \times C_{water(l)} \times \Delta T = (2.50\ mol)(75.4\ J/mol{\cdot}°C)(0°C - 100°C)$$
$$= -18{,}850\ J = -18.8\ kJ$$

Stage 4. Liquid water freezes. At 0°C, the sample loses E_p as increasing intermolecular attractions cause the molecules to align themselves into the crystalline structure of ice. Molecular motion continues only as random jiggling about fixed positions. As we saw during condensation, temperature and average E_k are constant during freezing. The change is

$$H_2O(l)\ [0°C] \longrightarrow H_2O(s)\ [0°C]$$

The heat is equal to n times the negative of the heat of fusion ($-\Delta H^\circ_{fus}$):

$$q = n(-\Delta H^\circ_{fus}) = (2.50\ mol)(-6.02\ kJ/mol) = -15.0\ kJ$$

Stage 5. Solid water cools. With motion restricted to jiggling in place, further cooling merely reduces the average speed of this jiggling. The change is

$$H_2O(s)\ [0°C] \longrightarrow H_2O(s)\ [-40°C]$$

The heat depends on n, the molar heat capacity of *solid* water, and ΔT:

$$q = n \times C_{water(s)} \times \Delta T = (2.50\ mol)(37.6\ J/mol{\cdot}°C)(-40°C - 0°C)$$
$$= -3760\ J = -3.76\ kJ$$

According to Hess's law, the total heat released is the sum of the heats released for the individual stages. The sum of q for stages 1 to 5 is -142 kJ. Two key points stand out for this or any similar process, whether exothermic or endothermic:

- *Within a phase,* heat flow is accompanied by *a change in temperature,* which is associated with a change in average E_k, as *the most probable speed of the molecules changes.* The heat released or absorbed depends on the amount of substance, the molar heat capacity *for that phase,* and the change in temperature.
- *During a phase change,* heat flow occurs at a *constant temperature,* which is associated with a change in average E_p, as *the average distance between molecules changes.* Both phases are present and (as you'll see below) are in equilibrium during the change. The heat released or absorbed depends on the amount of substance and the enthalpy change for that phase change.

Let's work a molecular-scene sample problem to make sure these ideas are clear.

Sample Problem 12.1 Finding the Heat of a Phase Change Depicted by Molecular Scenes

Problem The scenes below represent a phase change of water. Select data from the previous discussion to find the heat (in kJ) released or absorbed when 24.3 g of H_2O undergoes this change.

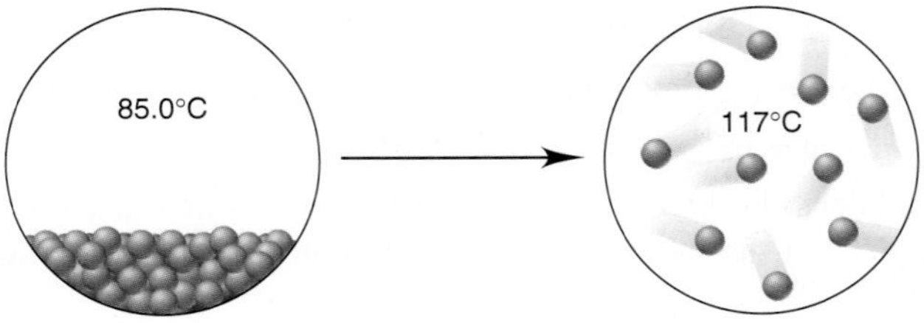

Plan From the molecular scenes, data in the text, and the given mass (24.3 g) of water, we have to find the heat that accompanies this change. The scenes show a disorderly, condensed phase at 85.0°C changing to separate molecules at 117°C. Thus, the phase change they depict is vaporization, an endothermic process. The text data are given per mole, so we first convert the mass (g) of water to amount (mol). There are three stages: (1) heating the liquid from 85.0°C to 100.°C, (2) converting liquid water at 100.°C to gaseous water at 100.°C, and (3) heating the gas from 100.°C to 117°C (*see margin*). We add the values of q for these stages to obtain the total heat.

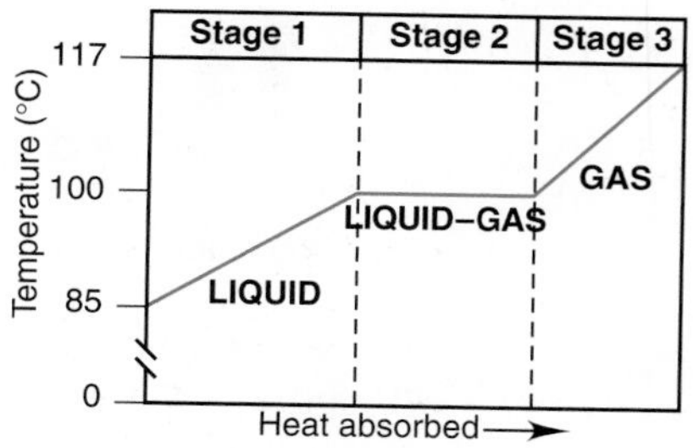

Solution Converting from mass (g) of H_2O to amount (mol):

$$\text{Amount (mol) of } H_2O = 24.3 \text{ g } H_2O \times \frac{1 \text{ mol}}{18.02 \text{ g } H_2O} = 1.35 \text{ mol}$$

Finding the flow accompanying stage 1, $H_2O(l)\ [85.0°C] \longrightarrow H_2O(l)\ [100.°C]$:

$$q = n \times C_{\text{water}(l)} \times \Delta T = (1.35 \text{ mol})(75.4 \text{ J/mol}\cdot°C)(100.°C - 85.0°C)$$
$$= 1527 \text{ J} = 1.53 \text{ kJ}$$

Finding the heat accompanying stage 2, $H_2O(l)\ [100.°C] \longrightarrow H_2O(g)\ [100.°C]$:

$$q = n(\Delta H^\circ_{\text{vap}}) = (1.35 \text{ mol})(40.7 \text{ kJ/mol}) = 54.9 \text{ kJ}$$

Finding the heat accompanying stage 3, $H_2O(g)\ [100.°C] \longrightarrow H_2O(g)\ [117°C]$:

$$q = n \times C_{\text{water}(g)} \times \Delta T = (1.35 \text{ mol})(33.1 \text{ J/mol}\cdot°C)(117°C - 100.°C)$$
$$= 759.6 \text{ J} = 0.760 \text{ kJ}$$

Adding the three heats together to find the total heat of the process:

$$\text{Total heat (kJ)} = 1.53 \text{ kJ} + 54.9 \text{ kJ} + 0.760 \text{ kJ} = 57.2 \text{ kJ}$$

Check The heat should have a positive value because it is absorbed. Be sure to round to check each value of q; for example, in stage 1, 1.33 mol × 75 J/mol·°C × 15°C = 1500 J. Note that the phase change itself (stage 2) requires the most energy and, thus, dominates the final answer. The $\Delta H^\circ_{\text{vap}}$ units include kJ, whereas the molar heat capacity units include J, which is a thousandth as large.

Follow-Up Problem 12.1 The scenes below represent a phase change of water. Select data from the text discussion to find the heat (in kJ) released or absorbed when 2.25 mol of H_2O undergoes this change.

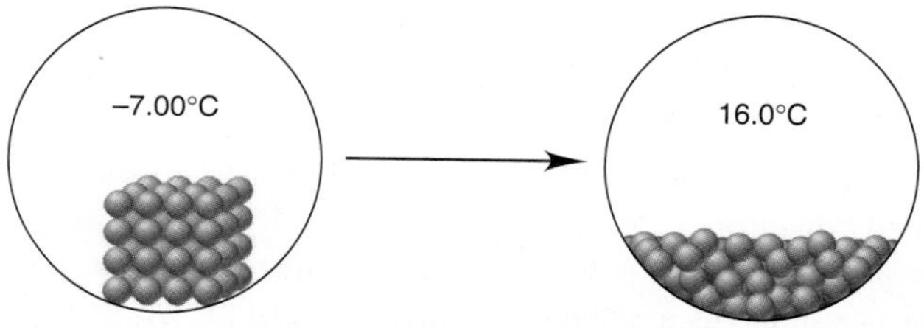

The Equilibrium Nature of Phase Changes

In everyday experience, phase changes take place in *open* containers—the outdoors, a pot on a stove, the freezer compartment of a refrigerator—so they are not reversible. But, in a *closed* container, *phase changes* ***are*** *reversible and reach equilibrium,* just as chemical changes do. In this discussion, we examine the three phase equilibria.

Liquid-Gas Equilibria Vaporization and condensation are familar events. Let's see how these processes differ in open and closed systems of a liquid in a flask:

1. *Open system: nonequilibrium process.* Picture an *open* flask containing a pure liquid at constant temperature. Within their range of speeds, some molecules at the surface have a high enough E_k to overcome attractions and vaporize. Nearby molecules fill the gap, and with heat supplied by the constant-temperature surroundings, the process continues until the entire liquid phase is gone.

2. *Closed system: equilibrium process.* Now picture a *closed* flask at constant temperature and assume a vacuum exists above a liquid (Figure 12.5A, *next page*). Two processes take place: Some molecules at the surface have a high enough E_k to *vaporize*. After a short time, molecules in the vapor collide with the surface, and the slower ones are attracted strongly enough to *condense*.

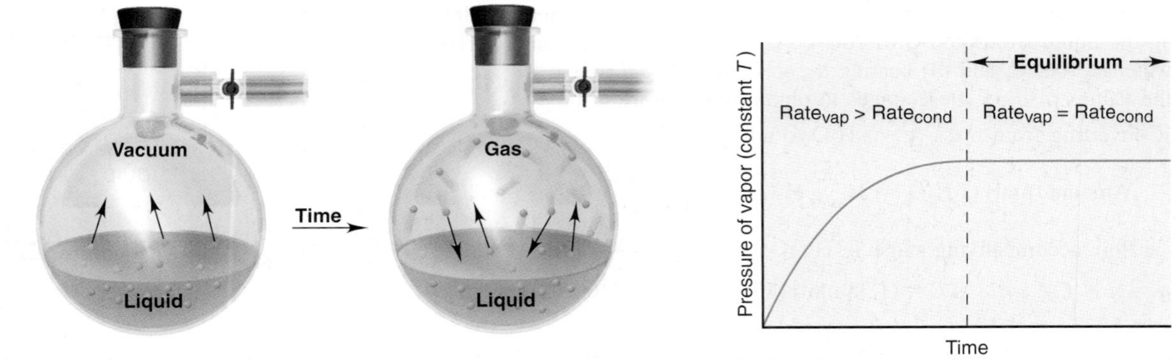

A Molecules in the liquid vaporize. **B** Molecules vaporize and condense at the same rate. **C** Plot of pressure vs. time.

Figure 12.5 Liquid-gas equilibrium. **A,** Molecules leave the surface at a constant rate and the pressure rises. **B,** At equilibrium, the same number of molecules leave and enter the liquid in a given time. **C,** Pressure increases until, at equilibrium, it is constant.

At first, these two processes occur at different rates. The number of molecules in a given surface area is constant, so the number of molecules leaving the surface per unit time—the rate of vaporization—is also constant, and the pressure increases. With time, the number of molecules colliding with and entering the surface—the rate of condensation—increases as the vapor becomes more populated, so the increase in pressure slows. Eventually, the rate of condensation equals the rate of vaporization; from this time onward, *the pressure is constant* (Figure 12.5B).

Macroscopically, the situation at this point seems static, but at the molecular level, molecules are entering and leaving the liquid at equal rates. The system has reached a state of *dynamic equilibrium:*

$$\text{liquid} \rightleftharpoons \text{gas}$$

The pressure exerted by the vapor at equilibrium is called the *equilibrium vapor pressure,* or just the **vapor pressure,** of the liquid at that temperature. Figure 12.5C depicts the entire process graphically. If we started with a larger flask, the number of molecules in the vapor would be greater at equilibrium. But, as long as the temperature is constant and some liquid is present, the vapor pressure will be the same.

3. *Disturbing a system at equilibrium.* Let's see what happens if we alter certain conditions, called "disturbing" the system:

- *Decrease in pressure.* Suppose we pump some vapor out of the flask, immediately lowering the pressure. (In a cylinder fitted with a piston, we lower the pressure by moving the piston outward, thus increasing the volume.) The rate of condensation temporarily falls below the rate of vaporization (the forward process is faster) because fewer molecules enter the liquid than leave it. The pressure rises until, after a short time, the condensation rate increases enough for equilibrium to be reached again.
- *Increase in pressure.* Suppose we pump more vapor in (or move the piston inward, thus decreasing the volume), thereby immediately raising the pressure. The rate of condensation temporarily exceeds the rate of vaporization because more molecules enter the liquid than leave it (the reverse process is faster). Soon, however, the condensation rate decreases until the pressure again reaches the equilibrium value.

This general behavior of a liquid and its vapor is seen in any system at equilibrium: *when a system at equilibrium is disturbed, it counteracts the disturbance until it re-establishes equilibrium.* We'll return to this key idea often in later chapters.

The Effects of Temperature and Intermolecular Forces on Vapor Pressure

While the vapor pressure is not affected by the removal or addition of gas, it is affected by two other factors—a change in temperature and a change in the gas, that is, in the types of intermolecular forces:

1. *Effect of temperature.* Temperature has a major effect on vapor pressure because it changes the fraction of molecules moving fast enough to escape the liquid and, by the same token, the fraction moving slowly enough to be recaptured. In Figure 12.6, we see the familiar skewed bell-shaped curve of the distribution of molecular speeds (see also Figure 5.6, page 188). At the higher temperature, T_2, more molecules have

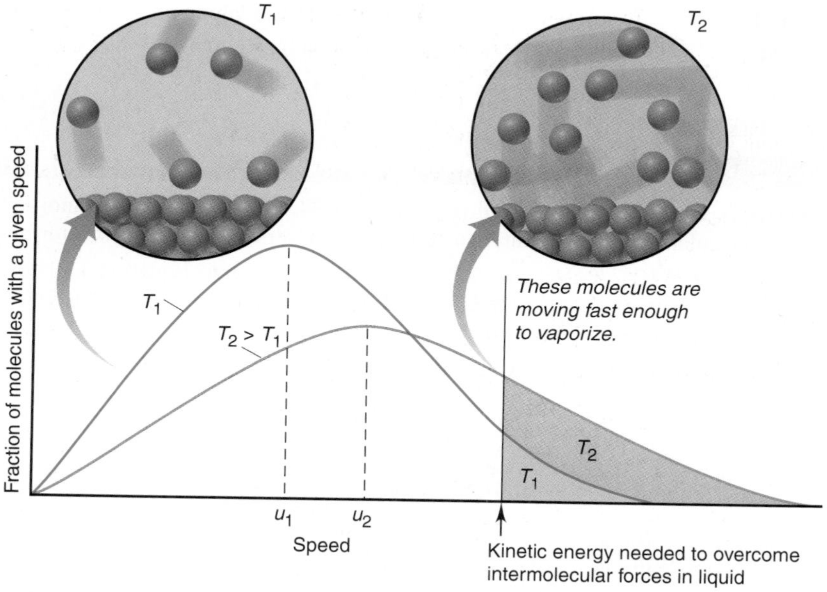

Figure 12.6 The effect of temperature on the distribution of molecular speeds.

enough energy to leave the surface. Thus, in general, *the higher the temperature is, the higher the vapor pressure:*

$$\text{higher } T \Longrightarrow \text{higher } P$$

2. *Effect of intermolecular forces.* At a given T, all substances have the same average E_k. Therefore, molecules with weaker intermolecular forces are held less tightly at the surface and vaporize more easily. In general, *the weaker the intermolecular forces are, the higher the vapor pressure:*

$$\text{weaker forces} \Longrightarrow \text{higher } P$$

Figure 12.7 shows the vapor pressure of three liquids as a function of temperature:

- The effect of temperature is seen in the steeper rise as the temperature increases.
- The effect of intermolecular forces is seen in the values of the vapor pressure, the short, horizontal dashed lines intersecting the vertical (pressure) axis at a given temperature *(vertical dashed line at 20°C)*: the intermolecular forces in diethyl ether (highest vapor pressure) are weaker than those in ethanol, which are weaker than those in water (lowest vapor pressure).

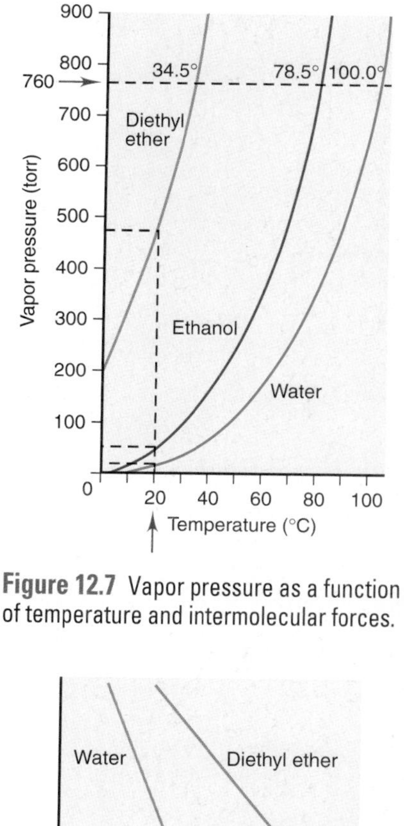

Figure 12.7 Vapor pressure as a function of temperature and intermolecular forces.

Quantifying the Effect of Temperature The nonlinear relationship between P and T is converted to a linear one with the **Clausius-Clapeyron equation:**

$$\ln P = \frac{-\Delta H_{\text{vap}}}{R}\left(\frac{1}{T}\right) + C$$
$$y \quad = \quad m \qquad x \quad + b$$

where $\ln P$ is the natural logarithm of the vapor pressure, ΔH_{vap} is the heat of vaporization, R is the universal gas constant (8.314 J/mol·K), T is the absolute temperature, and C is a constant (not related to heat capacity). The equation is often used to find the heat of vaporization. The equation for a straight line is shown under it in blue, with $y = \ln P$, $x = 1/T$, m (the slope) $= -\Delta H_{\text{vap}}/R$, and b (the y-axis intercept) $= C$. A plot of $\ln P$ vs. $1/T$ gives a straight line, as shown for diethyl ether and water in Figure 12.8.

A two-point version of the Clausius-Clapeyron equation allows us to calculate ΔH_{vap} if vapor pressures at two temperatures are known:

$$\ln \frac{P_2}{P_1} = \frac{-\Delta H_{\text{vap}}}{R}\left(\frac{1}{T_2} - \frac{1}{T_1}\right) \qquad (12.1)$$

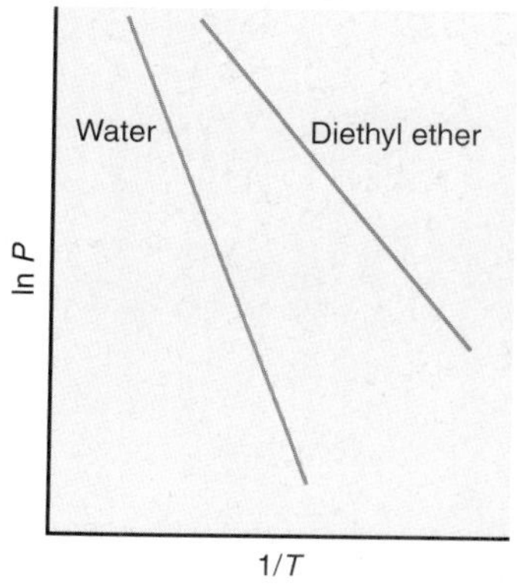

Figure 12.8 Linear plots of the relationship between vapor pressure and temperature. The slope is steeper for water because its ΔH_{vap} is greater.

If ΔH_{vap} and P_1 at T_1 are known, we can also calculate the vapor pressure (P_2) at any other temperature (T_2) or the temperature at any other pressure.

Sample Problem 12.2 Applying the Clausius-Clapeyron Equation

Problem The vapor pressure of ethanol is 115 torr at 34.9°C. If ΔH_{vap} of ethanol is 40.5 kJ/mol, calculate the temperature (in °C) when the vapor pressure is 760 torr.

Plan We are given ΔH_{vap}, P_1, P_2, and T_1 and substitute them into Equation 12.1 to solve for T_2. The value of R here is 8.314 J/mol·K, so we must convert T_1 to K to obtain T_2, and then convert T_2 back to °C.

Solution Substituting the values into Equation 12.1 and solving for T_2:

$$\ln\frac{P_2}{P_1} = \frac{-\Delta H_{vap}}{R}\left(\frac{1}{T_2} - \frac{1}{T_1}\right)$$

$$T_1 = 34.9°\text{C} + 273.15 = 308.0\ \text{K}$$

$$\ln\frac{760\ \text{torr}}{115\ \text{torr}} = \left(-\frac{40.5\times10^3\ \text{J/mol}}{8.314\ \text{J/mol·K}}\right)\left(\frac{1}{T_2} - \frac{1}{308.0\ \text{K}}\right)$$

$$1.888 = (-4.87\times10^3)\left[\frac{1}{T_2} - (3.247\times10^{-3})\right]$$

$$T_2 = 350.\ \text{K}$$

Converting T_2 from K to °C:

$$T_2 = 350.\ \text{K} - 273.15 = 77°\text{C}$$

Check Round off to check the math. The change is in the right direction: higher P should occur at higher T. As we discuss next, a substance has a vapor pressure of 760 torr at its *normal boiling point.* Checking the *CRC Handbook of Chemistry and Physics* shows that the boiling point of ethanol is 78.5°C, very close to our answer.

Follow-Up Problem 12.2 At 34.1°C, the vapor pressure of water is 40.1 torr. What is the vapor pressure at 85.5°C? The ΔH_{vap} of water is 40.7 kJ/mol.

Vapor Pressure and Boiling Point Let's discuss what is happening when a liquid boils and then see the effect of pressure on boiling point.

1. *How a liquid boils.* In an *open* container, the weight of the atmosphere bears down on a liquid surface. As the temperature rises, molecules move more quickly throughout the liquid. At some temperature, the average E_k of the molecules in the liquid is great enough for them to form bubbles of vapor *in the interior,* and the liquid boils. At any lower temperature, the bubbles collapse as soon as they start to form because the external pressure is greater than the vapor pressure inside the bubbles. Thus, the **boiling point** *is the temperature at which the vapor pressure equals the external pressure,* which is usually that of the atmosphere. As in condensation and freezing, once boiling begins, the temperature of the liquid remains constant until all of the liquid is gone.

2. *Effect of pressure on boiling point.* The boiling point of a liquid varies with elevation. At high elevations, a lower atmospheric pressure is exerted on the liquid surface, so molecules in the interior need less kinetic energy to form bubbles. Thus, *the boiling point depends on the applied pressure.*

In mountainous regions, food takes *more* time to cook because the boiling point is lower and the boiling liquid is not as hot; for instance, in Boulder, Colorado (elevation 5430 ft, or 1655 m), water boils at 94°C. On the other hand, in a pressure cooker, food takes *less* time to cook because the boiling point is higher at the higher pressure. The *normal boiling point* is observed at standard atmospheric pressure (760 torr, or 101.3 kPa; *long, horizontal dashed line* in Figure 12.7).

Solid-Liquid Equilibria The particles in a crystal are continually jiggling about their fixed positions. As the temperature rises, the particles jiggle more rapidly, until some have enough kinetic energy to break free of their positions. At this point, melting begins. As more molecules enter the liquid (molten) phase, some collide with the solid and become fixed in position again. Because the phases remain in contact, a dynamic equilibrium is established when the melting rate equals the freezing rate. The temperature at which this occurs is called the **melting point.** The temperature remains fixed at the melting point until all the solid melts.

Because liquids and solids are nearly incompressible, pressure has little effect on the rates of melting and freezing: a plot of pressure vs. temperature for a solid-liquid phase change is typically a *nearly* vertical straight line.

Solid-Gas Equilibria Sublimation is not very familiar because solids have *much* lower vapor pressures than liquids. A substance sublimes rather than melts because the intermolecular attractions are not great enough to keep the molecules near each other when they leave the solid state. Some solids *do* have high enough vapor pressures to sublime at ordinary conditions, including dry ice (carbon dioxide), iodine (Figure 12.9), and moth repellants, all nonpolar molecules with weak intermolecular forces.

The plot of pressure vs. temperature for a solid-gas phase change reflects the large effect of temperature on vapor pressure; thus, it resembles the liquid-gas curve in rising steeply with higher temperatures.

Figure 12.9 Iodine subliming. After the solid sublimes, I_2 vapor deposits on a cold surface (water-filled inner test tube).

Phase Diagrams: Effect of Pressure and Temperature on Physical State

The **phase diagram** of a substance combines the liquid-gas, solid-liquid, and solid-gas curves and gives the conditions of temperature and pressure at which each phase is stable and where phase changes occur.

The Phase Diagram for CO_2 and Most Substances The diagram for CO_2, which is typical of most substances, has four general features (Figure 12.10):

1. *Regions of the diagram.* Each region presents the conditions of pressure and temperature for which the phase is stable. If another phase is placed under those conditions, it will change to the stable phase. In general, the solid is stable at low temperature and high pressure, the gas at high temperature and low pressure, and the liquid at intermediate conditions.

2. *Lines between regions.* The lines are the phase-transition curves discussed earlier. Any point along a line shows the pressure and temperature at which the phases are in equilibrium. The solid-liquid line has a slightly *positive* slope (slants to the *right* with increasing pressure) because, for most substances, the solid is more dense than the liquid: an increase in pressure converts the liquid to the solid. (Water is *the* major exception.)

3. *The triple point.* The three phase-transition curves meet at the **triple point,** at which all three phases are in equilibrium. As strange as it sounds, at the triple point in Figure 12.10, CO_2 is subliming and depositing, melting and freezing, and vaporizing and condensing simultaneously! Substances with several solid and/or liquid forms can have more than one triple point.

The CO_2 phase diagram shows why dry ice (solid CO_2) doesn't melt under ordinary conditions. The triple-point pressure is 5.1 atm, so liquid CO_2 doesn't occur at 1 atm because it is not stable. The horizontal dashed line at 1.0 atm crosses the solid-gas line, so when solid CO_2 is heated, it sublimes at −78°C rather than melts. If our normal atmospheric pressure were 5.2 atm, liquid CO_2 *would* occur.

4. *The critical point.* Heat a liquid in a closed container and its density decreases. At the same time, more of the liquid vaporizes, so the density of the vapor increases. At the **critical point,** the two densities become equal and the phase boundary disappears. The temperature at

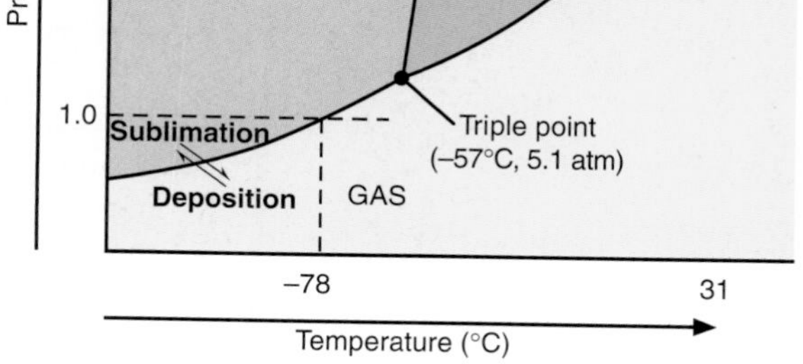

Figure 12.10 Phase diagram for CO_2. (The slope of the solid-liquid line is exaggerated, and the axes are not linear in both this figure and Figure 12.11.)

the critical point is the *critical temperature* (T_c), and the pressure is the *critical pressure* (P_c). The average E_k is so high at this point that the vapor cannot be condensed at any pressure. The two most common gases in air have critical temperatures far below room temperature: O_2 cannot be condensed above $-119°C$, and N_2 above $-147°C$.

Beyond the critical temperature, a *supercritical fluid* (SCF) exists rather than separate liquid and gaseous phases. An SCF expands and contracts like a gas and has unusual solvent properties. Supercritical CO_2 is used to extract caffeine from coffee beans, nicotine from tobacco, and fats from potato chips, and acts as a dry cleaning agent. Lower the pressure, and the SCF disperses as a harmless gas. Supercritical H_2O dissolves nonpolar substances, even though liquid water cannot. Studies are under way to use supercritical H_2O for removing nonpolar organic toxins, such as PCBs, from industrial waste.

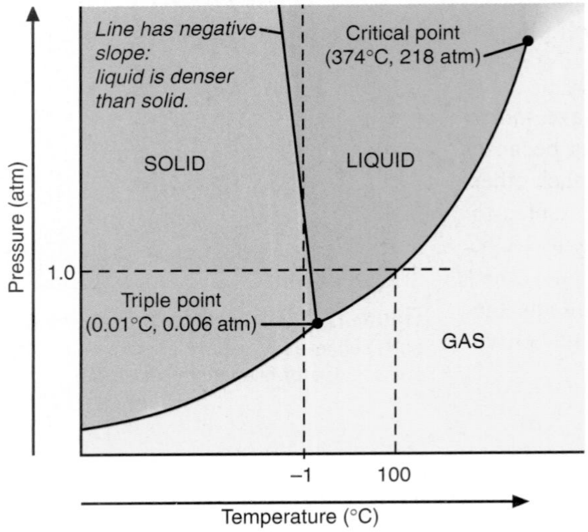

Figure 12.11 Phase diagram for H_2O.

The Solid-Liquid Line for Water The phase diagram for water differs from others in one major respect that reveals a key property. Unlike almost any other substance, the solid form is *less dense* than the liquid; that is, *water expands upon freezing*. Thus, the solid-liquid line has a *negative* slope (slants to the *left* with increasing pressure): an increase in pressure converts the solid to the liquid, and the higher the pressure, the lower the temperature at which water freezes (Figure 12.11). The vertical dashed line at $-1°C$ crosses the solid-liquid line, which means that ice melts with only an increase in pressure.

The triple point of water occurs at low pressure (0.006 atm). Therefore, when solid water is heated at 1.0 atm (*horizontal dashed line*), the solid-liquid line is crossed at 0°C, the normal melting point. Thus, ice melts rather than sublimes. The horizontal dashed line then crosses the liquid-gas curve at 100°C, the normal boiling point.

Summary of Section 12.2

- A heating-cooling curve depicts the change in temperature when a substance absorbs or releases heat at a constant rate. Within a phase, temperature (and average E_k) changes. During a phase change, temperature (and average E_k) is constant, but E_p changes. The total enthalpy change for the system is found using Hess's law.
- In a closed container, the liquid and gas phases of a substance reach equilibrium. The vapor pressure, the pressure of the gas at equilibrium, is related directly to temperature and inversely to the strength of the intermolecular forces.
- The Clausius-Clapeyron equation relates the vapor pressure to the temperature and is often used to find ΔH_{vap}.
- A liquid in an open container boils when its vapor pressure equals the external pressure.
- Solid-liquid equilibrium occurs at the melting point. Some solids sublime because they have very weak intermolecular forces.
- The phase diagram of a substance shows the phase that is stable at any P and T, the conditions at which phase changes occur, and the conditions at the critical point and the triple point. Water differs from most substances in that its solid phase is less dense than its liquid phase, so its solid-liquid line has a negative slope.

12.3 • TYPES OF INTERMOLECULAR FORCES

In Chapter 9, we saw that bonding (*intra*molecular) forces are due to the attraction between cations and anions (ionic bonding), nuclei and electron pairs (covalent bonding), or metal cations and delocalized electrons (metallic bonding). But the nature of the phases and their changes are due primarily to *inter*molecular (nonbonding) forces, which arise from the attraction between molecules with partial charges or between ions and molecules. Coulomb's law explains why the two types of forces differ in magnitude:

- *Bonding forces are relatively strong* because larger charges are closer together.
- *Intermolecular forces are relatively weak* because smaller charges are farther apart.

How Close Can Molecules Approach Each Other?

To see the minimum distance *between* molecules, consider solid Cl_2. When we measure the distances between two Cl nuclei, we obtain two different values (Figure 12.12A):

- *Bond length and covalent radius.* The shorter distance, called the *bond length,* is between *two bonded Cl atoms in the* ***same*** *molecule*. One-half this distance is the *covalent radius.*
- *Van der Waals distance and radius.* The longer distance is between *two nonbonded Cl atoms in* ***adjacent*** *molecules.* It is called the *van der Waals (VDW) distance.* At this distance, intermolecular attractions balance electron-cloud repulsions; thus, the VDW distance is as close as one Cl_2 molecule can approach another. The **van der Waals radius** is one-half the closest distance between nuclei of identical *nonbonded* atoms. The VDW radius of an atom is *always larger than its covalent radius.* Like covalent radii, VDW radii decrease across a period and increase down a group (Figure 12.12B).

As we discuss intermolecular forces (also called *van der Waals forces*), consult Table 12.2, which compares them with bonding forces.

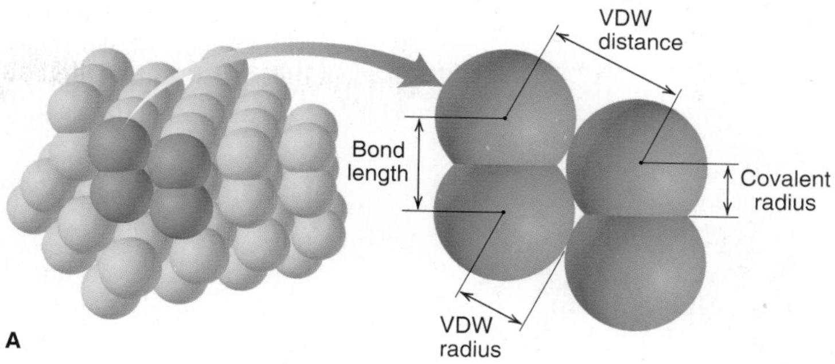

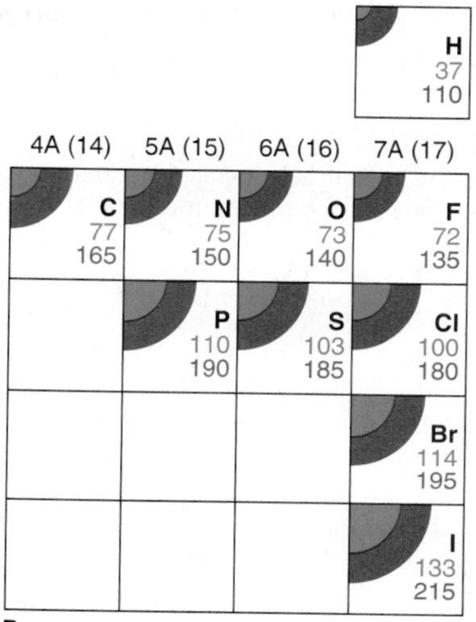

Figure 12.12 Covalent and van der Waals radii and their periodic trends. **A,** The van der Waals (VDW) radius is one-half the distance between adjacent *nonbonded* atoms ($\frac{1}{2}$ × VDW distance). **B,** Like covalent radii (*blue quarter-circles and numbers*), VDW radii (*red quarter-circles and numbers*) increase down a group and decrease across a period.

Table 12.2 Comparison of Bonding and Nonbonding (Intermolecular) Forces

Force	Model	Basis of Attraction	Energy (kJ/mol)	Example
Bonding				
Ionic	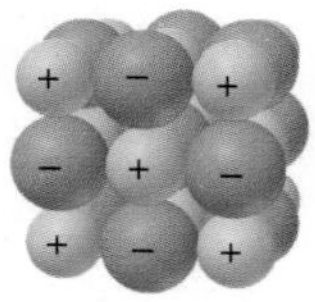	Cation–anion	400–4000	NaCl
Covalent	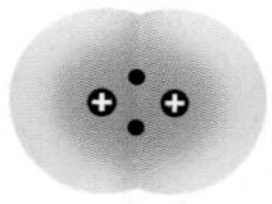	Nuclei–shared e^- pair	150–1100	H—H
Metallic	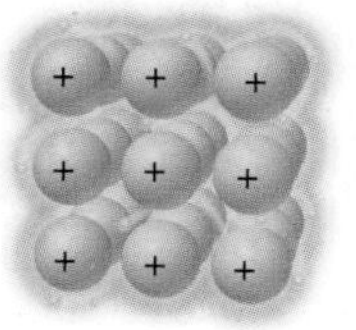	Cations–delocalized electrons	75–1000	Fe
Nonbonding (Intermolecular)				
Ion-dipole		Ion charge–dipole charge	40–600	$Na^+\cdots O$ (bonded to two H)
H bond	$\overset{\delta-}{—A}—\overset{\delta+}{H}\cdots\cdots\overset{\delta-}{:B}—$	Polar bond to H–dipole charge (high EN of N, O, F)	10–40	:Ö—H···:Ö—H (each O bonded to H below)
Dipole-dipole		Dipole charges	5–25	I—Cl···I—Cl
Ion–induced dipole		Ion charge–polarizable e^- cloud	3–15	$Fe^{2+}\cdots O_2$
Dipole–induced dipole	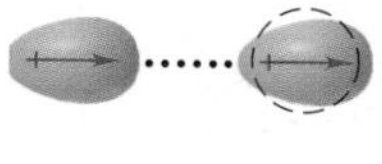	Dipole charge–polarizable e^- cloud	2–10	H—Cl···Cl—Cl
Dispersion (London)	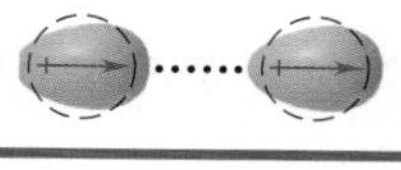	Polarizable e^- clouds	0.05–40	F—F···F—F

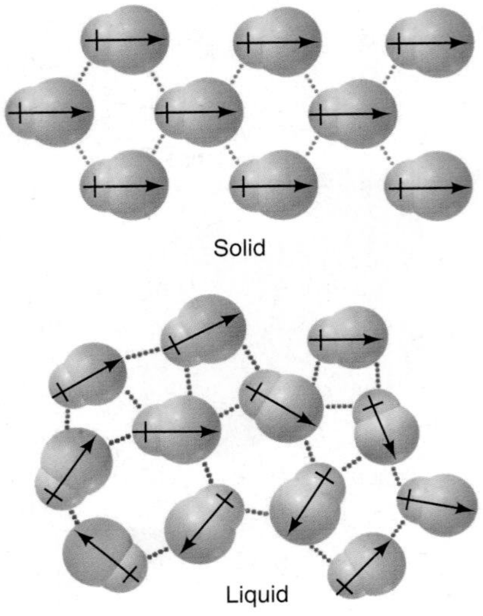

Figure 12.13 Polar molecules and dipole-dipole forces. (Spaces between the molecules are exaggerated.)

Ion-Dipole Forces

When an ion and a nearby polar molecule (dipole) attract each other, an **ion-dipole force** results. The most important example takes place when an ionic compound dissolves in water. The ions become separated because the attractions between the ions and the oppositely charged poles of the H_2O molecules are stronger than the attractions between the ions themselves. Ion-dipole forces in solutions and their associated energy are discussed fully in Chapter 13.

Dipole-Dipole Forces

In Figure 10.13 (p. 383), an external electric field orients gaseous polar molecules. The polar molecules in liquids and solids lie near each other, and their partial charges act as tiny electric fields and give rise to **dipole-dipole forces:** the positive pole of one molecule attracts the negative pole of another (Figure 12.13). The orientation is more orderly in a solid than in a liquid because the average kinetic energy is lower.

These forces depend on the magnitude of the molecular dipole moment. For compounds of similar molar mass, the greater the molecular dipole moment, the greater the dipole-dipole forces, so the more energy it takes to separate the molecules; thus the boiling point is higher. Methyl chloride, for instance, has a smaller dipole moment than acetaldehyde and boils at a lower temperature (Figure 12.14).

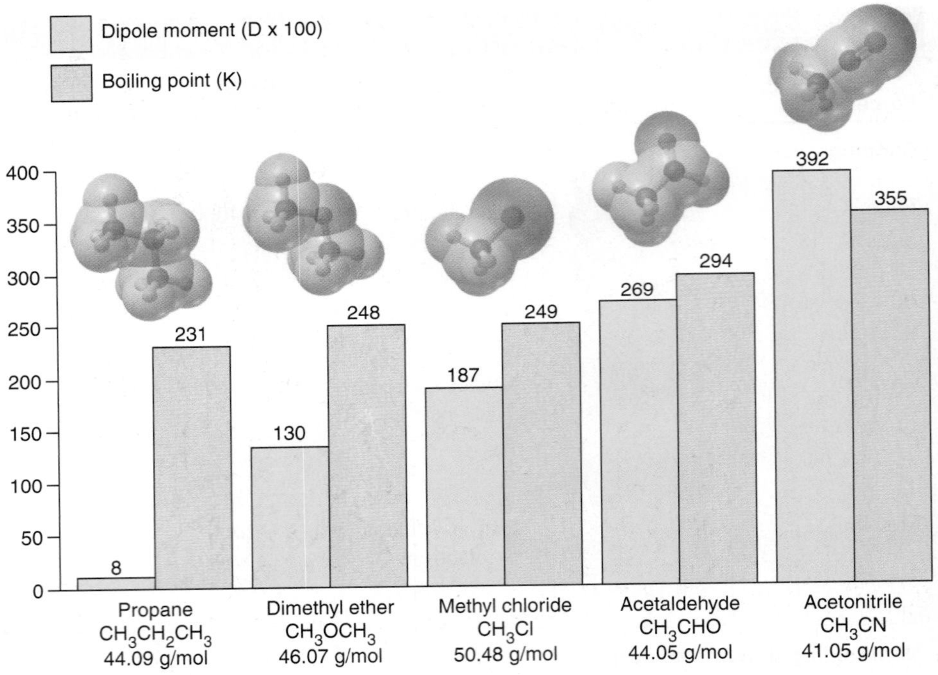

Figure 12.14 Dipole moment and boiling point. (Relative strength of the dipole moments is indicated by color intensities in the electron-density models.)

The Hydrogen Bond

A special type of dipole-dipole force arises between molecules that have *an H atom bonded to a small, highly electronegative atom with lone electron pairs, specifically N, O, or F*. The H—N, H—O, and H—F bonds are very polar. When the partially positive H of one molecule is attracted to the partially negative lone pair on the N, O, or F of another molecule, a **hydrogen bond (H bond)** forms. Thus, the atom sequence of an H bond (dotted line) is —B:····H—A—, where A *and* B are N, O, or F. Three examples are

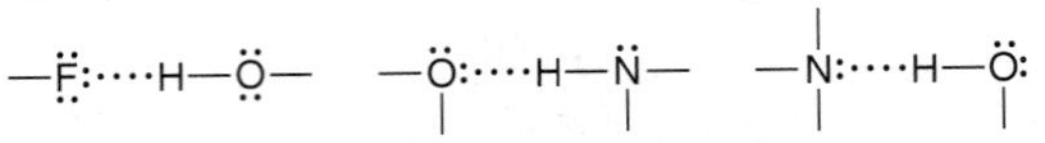

The small sizes of N, O, and F are essential to H bonding for two reasons:

1. The atoms are so electronegative that their covalently bonded H is highly positive.
2. The lone pair on the N, O, or F of the other molecule can come close to the H.

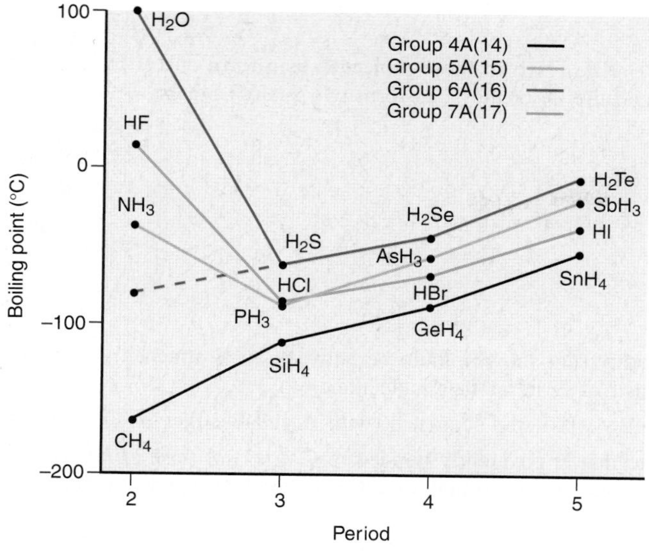

Figure 12.15 Hydrogen bonding and boiling point. NH_3, H_2O, and HF have exceptionallly high boiling points because they form H bonds.

The Significance of Hydrogen Bonding Hydrogen bonding has a profound impact in many systems. We'll examine one effect on physical properties and preview its importance in biological systems, which we address in Chapters 13 and 15.

Figure 12.15 shows the effect of H bonding on the boiling points of the binary hydrides of Groups 4A(14) through 7A(17). For reasons we'll discuss shortly, boiling points rise with molar mass, as the Group 4A(14) hydrides show. However, the first member in each of the other groups—NH_3, H_2O, and HF—deviates enormously from this expected trend. Within samples of these substances, the molecules form strong H bonds, so it takes more energy for the molecules to separate and enter the gas phase. For example, on the basis of molar mass alone, we would expect water to boil about 200°C lower than it actually does (*red dashed line*). (In Section 12.5 we'll discuss the effects that H bonds in water have in nature.)

The significance of hydrogen bonding in biological systems cannot be emphasized too strongly. In Chapter 13, you'll see that it is a key feature in the structure and function of the biological macromolecules—proteins and nucleic acids. It is also responsible for the action of many *enzymes,* the proteins that speed metabolic reactions.

Sample Problem 12.3 Drawing Hydrogen Bonds Between Molecules of a Substance

Problem Which of the following substances exhibits H bonding? For any that do, show the H bonds between two of its molecules.

(a) C_2H_6 **(b)** CH_3OH **(c)** $CH_3\overset{\overset{\displaystyle O}{\|}}{C}—NH_2$

Plan If the molecule does *not* contain N, O, or F, it cannot form H bonds. If it contains any of these atoms covalently bonded to H, we draw two molecules in the —B:····H—A— pattern.

Solution **(a)** For C_2H_6. No N, O, or F, so no H bonds can form.
(b) For CH_3OH. The H covalently bonded to the O in one molecule forms an H bond to the lone pair on the O of an adjacent molecule:

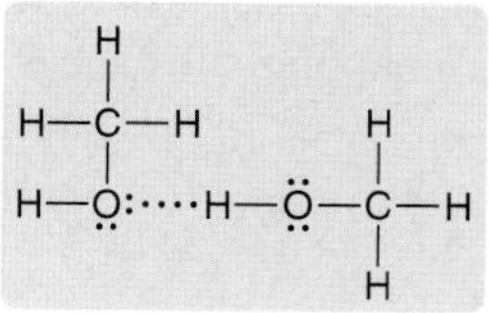

(c) For $CH_3C(=O)—NH_2$. Two of these molecules can form one H bond between an H bonded to N and the O, or they can form two such H bonds:

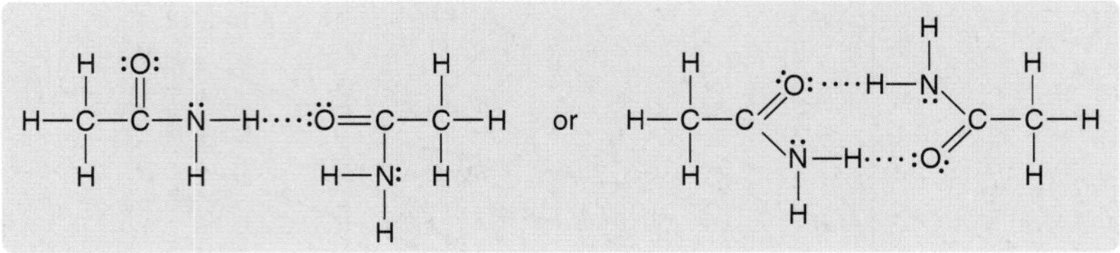

A third possibility (not shown) could be between an H attached to N in one molecule and the lone pair of N in another molecule.

Check The —B:····H—A— sequence (with A and B either N, O, or F) is present.

Comment Note that H covalently bonded to C *does not form H bonds* because carbon is not electronegative enough to make the C—H bond sufficiently polar.

Follow-Up Problem 12.3 Which of these substances exhibits H bonding? Draw the H bond(s) between two molecules of the substance where appropriate.

(a) $CH_3C(=O)—OH$ **(b)** CH_3CH_2OH **(c)** $CH_3C(=O)CH_3$

Polarizability and Induced Dipole Forces

Even though electrons are attracted to nuclei and localized in bonding and lone pairs, we often picture them as "clouds" of negative charge because they are in constant motion. A nearby electric field can *induce* a distortion in the cloud, pulling electron density toward a positive pole of a field or pushing it away from a negative one:

- *For a nonpolar molecule,* the distortion induces a temporary dipole moment.
- *For a polar molecule,* it enhances the dipole moment already present.

In addition to charged plates connected to a battery, the source of the electric field can be the charge of an ion or the partial charges of a polar molecule.

How easily an electron cloud can be distorted is called its **polarizability.** Smaller atoms (or ions) are less polarizable than larger ones because their electrons are closer to the nucleus and therefore held more tightly. Thus, we observe several trends:

- Polarizability *increases down a group* because atomic size increases and larger electron clouds are easier to distort.
- Polarizability *decreases across a period* because increasing Z_{eff} makes the atoms smaller and holds the electrons more tightly.
- Cations are *less* polarizable than their parent atoms because they are smaller; anions are *more* polarizable because they are larger.

Ion–induced dipole and dipole–induced dipole forces are the two types of charge-induced dipole forces; they are most important in solution, so we'll focus on them in Chapter 13. Nevertheless, *polarizability affects all intermolecular forces.*

Dispersion (London) Forces

So far, we've discussed forces that depend on the existing charge of an ion or a polar molecule. But what forces cause nonpolar substances like octane, chlorine, and argon to condense and solidify? As you'll see, polarizability plays the central role in the most universal intermolecular force.

The intermolecular force responsible for the condensed states of nonpolar substances is the **dispersion force** (or **London force,** named for Fritz London, the physicist who explained its quantum-mechanical basis). Dispersion forces *are present between all particles (atoms, ions, and molecules)* because they are caused by the *motion of electrons in atoms.* Let's examine key aspects of this force:

1. *Source.* Picture one atom in a sample of, say, argon gas. Over time, its 18 electrons are distributed uniformly, so the atom is nonpolar. But at any instant, there may be more electrons on one side of the nucleus than the other, which gives the atom an *instantaneous dipole.* When a pair of argon atoms is far apart, they don't influence each other, but when close together, *the instantaneous dipole in one atom induces a dipole in its neighbor,* and they attract each other. This process spreads to other atoms and throughout the sample. At low temperatures, these attractions keep the atoms together (Figure 12.16). Thus, dispersion forces are *instantaneous dipole–induced dipole forces.*

2. *Prevalence.* While they are the *only* force existing between nonpolar particles, *dispersion forces contribute to the energy of attraction in all substances* because they exist between *all* particles. In fact, except for the forces between small, highly polar molecules or between molecules forming H bonds, the *dispersion force is the dominant intermolecular force.* Calculations show, for example, that 85% of the attraction between HCl molecules is due to dispersion forces and only 15% to dipole-dipole forces. Even for water, 75% of the attraction comes from H bonds and 25% from dispersion forces.

3. *Relative strength.* The relative strength of dispersion forces depends on the polarizability of the particles, so they are weak for small particles, like H_2 and He, but stronger for larger particles, like I_2 and Xe. *Polarizability depends on the number of electrons, which correlates closely with molar mass* because heavier particles are either larger atoms or molecules with more atoms and, thus, more electrons. For this reason, as molar mass increases down the Group 4A(14) hydrides (see Figure 12.15), or down the halogens or the noble gases, dispersion forces increase and so do boiling points (Figure 12.17).

4. *Effect of molecular shape.* For a pair of nonpolar substances with the same molar mass, a molecular shape that has more area over which electron clouds can be distorted allows stronger attractions. For example, the two five-carbon alkanes, *n*-pentane and neopentane (2,2-dimethylpropane) are structural isomers—same molecular formula (C_5H_{12}) but different properties. *n*-Pentane is more cylindrical and neopentane more spherical (Figure 12.18). Thus, two *n*-pentane molecules make more contact than do two neopentane molecules, so dispersion forces act at more points, and *n*-pentane has a higher boiling point.

Figure 12.19 on the next page shows how to determine the intermolecular forces in a sample.

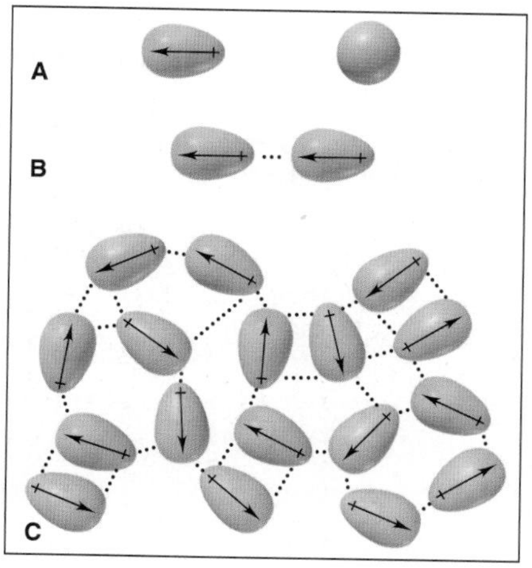

Figure 12.16 Dispersion forces among nonpolar particles. **A,** When atoms are far apart, an instantaneous dipole in one atom (*left*) doesn't influence another. **B,** When atoms are close together, the instantaneous dipole in one atom induces a dipole in the other. **C,** The process occurs through the sample.

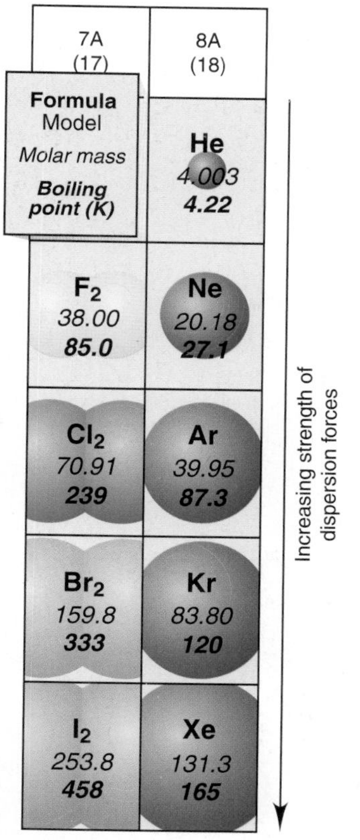

Figure 12.17 Molar mass and trends in boiling point.

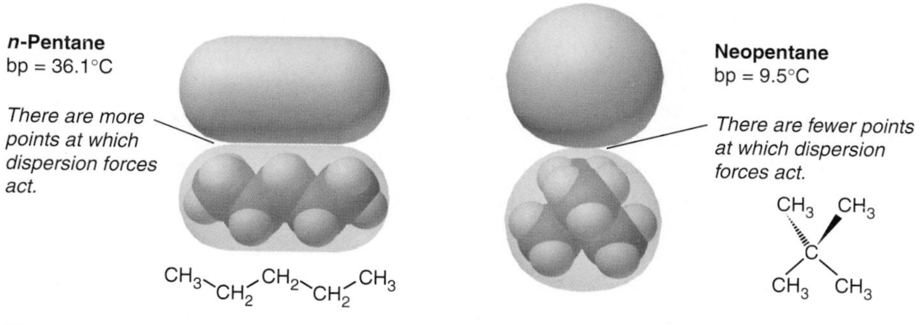

Figure 12.18 Molecular shape, intermolecular contact, and boiling point.

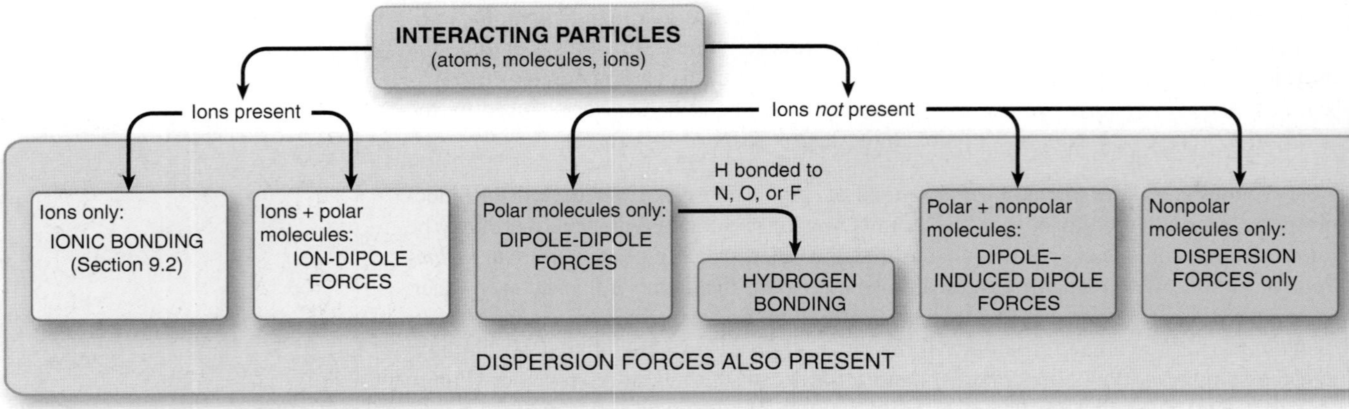

Figure 12.19 Determining the intermolecular forces in a sample.

Sample Problem 12.4 Predicting the Types of Intermolecular Forces

Problem For each substance, identify the key bonding and/or intermolecular force(s), and predict which one of the pair has the higher boiling point:
(a) $MgCl_2$ or PCl_3
(b) CH_3NH_2 or CH_3F
(c) CH_3OH or CH_3CH_2OH
(d) Hexane ($CH_3CH_2CH_2CH_2CH_2CH_3$) or 2,2-dimethylbutane

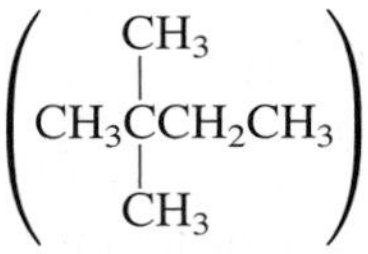

Plan We examine the formulas and structures for key differences between members of the pair: Are ions present? Are molecules polar or nonpolar? Is N, O, or F bonded to H? Do the molecules have different masses or shapes?
To rank boiling points, we consult Figure 12.19 and Table 12.2. Remember that
- Bonding forces are stronger than intermolecular forces.
- Hydrogen bonding is a strong type of dipole-dipole force.
- Dispersion forces are decisive when the difference is molar mass or molecular shape.

Solution (a) $MgCl_2$ consists of Mg^{2+} and Cl^- ions held together by ionic bonding forces; PCl_3 consists of polar molecules, so intermolecular dipole-dipole forces are present. The forces in $MgCl_2$ are stronger, so it should have a higher boiling point.
(b) CH_3NH_2 and CH_3F both consist of polar molecules of about the same molar mass. CH_3NH_2 has N—H bonds, so it can form H bonds (*see margin*). CH_3F contains a C—F bond but no H—F bond, so dipole-dipole forces occur but not H bonds. Therefore, CH_3NH_2 should have the higher boiling point.
(c) CH_3OH and CH_3CH_2OH molecules both contain an O—H bond, so they can form H bonds (*see margin*). CH_3CH_2OH has an additional —CH_2— group and thus a larger molar mass, which correlates with stronger dispersion forces; therefore, it should have a higher boiling point.
(d) Hexane and 2,2-dimethylbutane are nonpolar molecules of the same molar mass but different molecular shapes (*see margin*). Cylindrical hexane molecules make more intermolecular contact than more compact 2,2-dimethylbutane molecules do, so hexane should have stronger dispersion forces and a higher boiling point.

Check The actual boiling points show that our predictions are correct:
(a) $MgCl_2$ (1412°C) and PCl_3 (76°C)
(b) CH_3NH_2 (−6.3°C) and CH_3F (−78.4°C)
(c) CH_3OH (64.7°C) and CH_3CH_2OH (78.5°C)
(d) Hexane (69°C) and 2,2-dimethylbutane (49.7°C)

Comment Dispersion forces are *always* present, but in parts (a) and (b), they are much less significant than the other forces that occur.

(b)
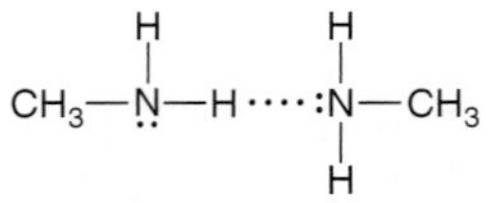

(c)
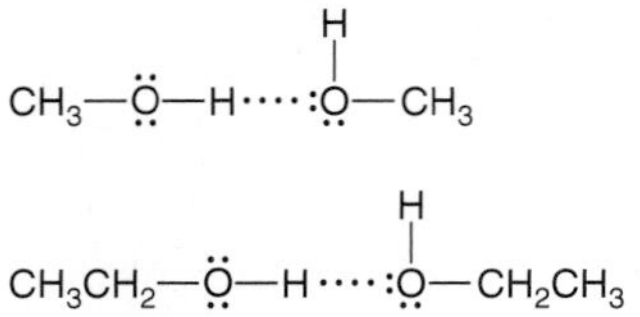

(d)
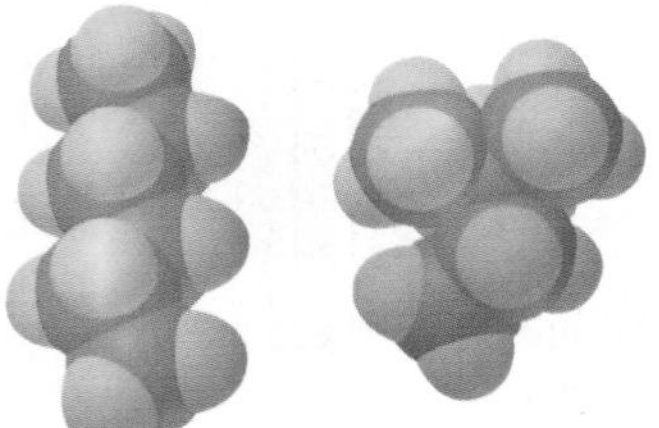
2,2-Dimethylbutane
Hexane

Follow-Up Problem 12.4 In each pair, identify the intermolecular forces present for each substance, and predict which substance has the higher boiling point:
(a) CH_3Br or CH_3F **(b)** $CH_3CH_2CH_2OH$ or $CH_3CH_2OCH_3$ **(c)** C_2H_6 or C_3H_8

Summary of Section 12.3

- The van der Waals radius determines the shortest distance over which intermolecular forces operate; it is always larger than the covalent radius.
- Intermolecular forces are much weaker than bonding (intramolecular) forces.
- Ion-dipole forces occur between ions and polar molecules.
- Dipole-dipole forces occur between oppositely charged poles on polar molecules.
- Hydrogen bonding, a special type of dipole-dipole force, occurs when H bonded to N, O, or F is attracted to the lone pair of N, O, or F in another molecule.
- Electron clouds can be distorted (polarized) in an electric field.
- Ion– and dipole–induced dipole forces arise between a charge and the dipole it induces in another molecule.
- Dispersion (London) forces are instantaneous dipole–induced dipole forces that occur among all particles and increase with number of electrons (molar mass). Molecular shape determines the extent of contact between molecules and can be a factor in the strength of dispersion forces.

12.4 • PROPERTIES OF THE LIQUID STATE

Of the three states, only liquids combine the ability to flow with the effects of strong intermolecular forces. We understand this state least at the molecular level. Because of the *random* arrangement of the particles in a gas, any region of the sample is virtually identical to any other. And, different regions of a crystalline solid are identical because of the *orderly* arrangement of the particles (Section 12.6). Liquids, however, have regions that are orderly one moment and random the next. Despite this complexity, many macroscopic properties, such as surface tension, capillarity, and viscosity are well understood.

Surface Tension

Intermolecular forces have different effects on a molecule at the surface compared with one in the interior (Figure 12.20):

- An interior molecule is attracted by others on all sides.
- A surface molecule is only attracted by others below and to the sides, so it experiences a *net attraction downward.*

Figure 12.20 The molecular basis of surface tension.

Therefore, to increase attractions and become more stable, a surface molecule tends to move into the interior. For this reason, *a liquid surface has the fewest molecules and, thus, the smallest area possible.* In effect, the surface behaves like a "taut skin" covering the interior.

The only way to increase the surface area is for molecules to move up by breaking attractions in the interior, which requires energy. The **surface tension** is the energy required to increase the surface area and has units of J/m^2 (Table 12.3). In general, *the stronger the forces are between particles, the more energy it takes to increase the surface area, so the greater the surface tension.* Water has a high surface tension because its molecules form multiple H bonds. *Surfactants* (*surf*ace-*act*ive age*nts*), such as soaps, petroleum recovery agents, and fat emulsifiers, decrease the surface tension of water by congregating at the surface and disrupting the H bonds.

Table 12.3 Surface Tension and Forces Between Particles

Substance	Formula	Surface Tension (J/m^2) at 20°C	Major Force(s)
Diethyl ether	$CH_3CH_2OCH_2CH_3$	1.7×10^{-2}	Dipole-dipole; dispersion
Ethanol	CH_3CH_2OH	2.3×10^{-2}	H bonding
Butanol	$CH_3CH_2CH_2CH_2OH$	2.5×10^{-2}	H bonding; dispersion
Water	H_2O	7.3×10^{-2}	H bonding
Mercury	Hg	48×10^{-2}	Metallic bonding

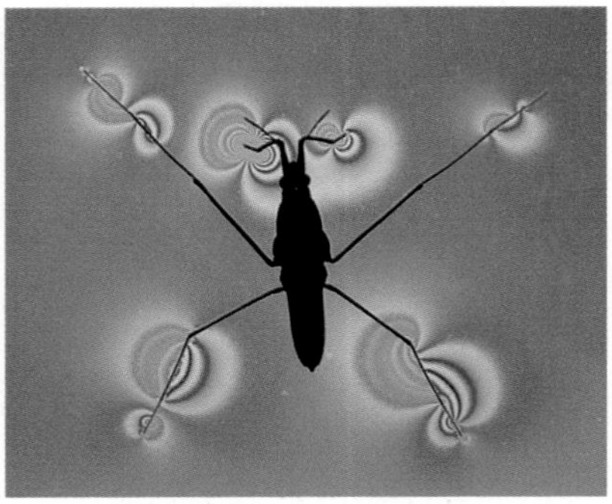

A water strider's widespread legs don't exert enough pressure to exceed the surface tension.

Surface tension is the cause of many familiar phenomena. Bubbles are round because this shape minimizes the surface area around the gas, and surface tension is the reason some insects can walk on water (*see photo*).

Capillarity

The rising of a liquid against the pull of gravity through a narrow space, such as a thin tube, is called *capillary action,* or **capillarity.** Capillarity results from a competition between the intermolecular forces within the liquid (cohesive forces) and those between the liquid and the tube walls (adhesive forces). Let's look at the difference between the capillarities of water and mercury in glass:

1. *Water in glass.* When you place a narrow glass tube in water, why does the liquid rise up the tube and form a concave meniscus? Glass is mostly silicon dioxide (SiO_2), so water molecules form adhesive H bonding forces with the O atoms of the glass. As a result, a thin film of water creeps up the wall. At the same time, cohesive H bonding forces between water molecules, which give rise to surface tension, make the surface taut. These adhesive and cohesive forces combine to raise the water level and produce the concave meniscus (Figure 12.21A). The liquid rises until gravity pulling down is balanced by adhesive forces pulling up.

2. *Mercury in glass.* When you place a glass tube in a dish of mercury, why does the liquid drop below the level in the dish and form a convex meniscus? The cohesive forces among the mercury atoms are metallic bonds, so they are *much* stronger than the mostly dispersion adhesive forces between mercury and glass. As a result, the liquid pulls away from the walls. At the same time, the surface atoms are being pulled toward the interior by mercury's high surface tension, so the level drops. These combined forces produce the concave meniscus seen in a laboratory barometer (Figure 12.21B).

Capillarity plays a key role in many everyday events. The adhesive (dipole–induced dipole) forces between water and a nonpolar surface are much weaker than the cohesive (H-bond) forces within water. As a result, water pulls away from a nonpolar surface and forms beaded droplets, as on a freshly waxed car or on the waxy coating of a leaf after a rainfall. Even more familiar, after a shower, capillary action draws water away from your body through the closely spaced fibers in the cotton towel, which is made of cellulose molecules, so the water molecules also form H bonds with the —OH groups of cellulose.

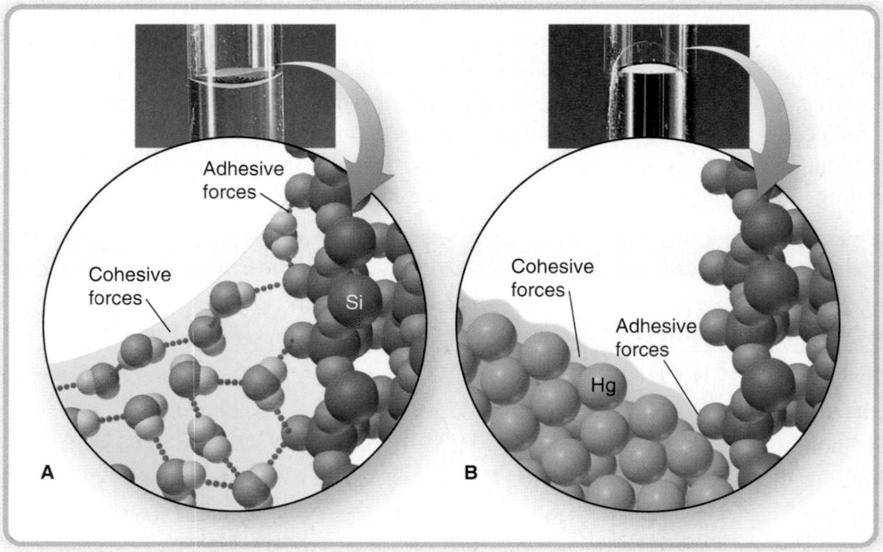

Figure 12.21 Capillary action and the shape of the water or mercury meniscus in glass. **A,** Water displays a concave meniscus. **B,** Mercury displays a convex meniscus.

Viscosity

Viscosity is the resistance of a fluid to flow, and it results from intermolecular attractions that impede the movement of molecules around and past each other. Both gases and liquids flow, but liquid viscosities are *much* higher because there are many more points for intermolecular forces to act due to the much shorter distances. Let's examine two factors—temperature and molecular shape—that influence viscosity:

- *Effect of temperature. Viscosity decreases with heating* (Table 12.4). Faster moving molecules overcome intermolecular forces more easily, so the resistance to flow decreases. Next time you heat cooking oil, watch the oil flow more easily and spread out in the pan as it warms.
- *Effect of molecular shape.* Small, spherical molecules make little contact and pour easily, like buckshot from a bowl. Long molecules make more contact and become entangled and pour slowly, like cooked spaghetti from a bowl. Thus, given the same types of intermolecular forces, liquids consisting of longer molecules have higher viscosities.

To protect engine parts during long drives, motor oils contain *polymeric viscosity improvers.* As the oil warms, these additive molecules change from compact spheres to long strands that become tangled with the long hydrocarbon molecules of the oil. Greater dispersion forces increase the viscosity to compensate for the oil thinning due to heating.

Table 12.4 Viscosity of Water at Several Temperatures

Temperature (°C)	Viscosity ($N \cdot s/m^2$)*
20	1.00×10^{-3}
40	0.65×10^{-3}
60	0.47×10^{-3}
80	0.35×10^{-3}

*The units of viscosity are newton-seconds per square meter.

Summary of Section 12.4

- Surface tension is a measure of the energy required to increase a liquid's surface area. Greater intermolecular forces within a liquid create higher surface tension.
- Capillarity, the rising of a liquid through a narrow space, occurs when the forces between a liquid and a surface (adhesive) are greater than those within the liquid (cohesive).
- Viscosity, the resistance to flow, depends on molecular shape and decreases with temperature. Stronger intermolecular forces create higher viscosity.

12.5 • THE UNIQUENESS OF WATER

Water is absolutely amazing stuff, with some of the most unusual properties of any substance, but it is so familiar we take it for granted. Like any substance, its properties arise inevitably from those of its atoms. Each O and H atom attains a filled outer level by sharing electrons in single bonds. With two bonding pairs and two lone pairs around O and a large electronegativity difference in each O—H bond, the H_2O molecule is bent and highly polar. This arrangement is crucial because it allows each molecule to engage in four H bonds with its neighbors (Figure 12.22). From these basic atomic and molecular facts emerges unique and remarkable macroscopic behavior.

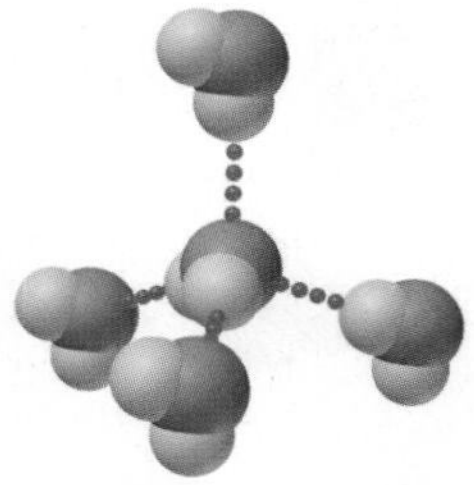

Figure 12.22 H-bonding ability of water. One H_2O molecule can form four H bonds to other molecules, resulting in a tetrahedral arrangement.

Solvent Properties of Water

The *great solvent power* of water results from its polarity and H-bonding ability:

- It dissolves ionic compounds through ion-dipole forces that separate the ions from the solid and keep them in solution (see Figure 4.2, p. 138).
- It dissolves polar nonionic substances, such as ethanol (CH_3CH_2OH) and glucose ($C_6H_{12}O_6$), by H bonding.
- It dissolves nonpolar atmospheric gases to a limited extent through dipole–induced dipole and dispersion forces.

Water is the environmental and biological solvent, forming the complex solutions we know as oceans, lakes, and cytoplasm. Aquatic animals could not survive without dissolved O_2, nor could aquatic plants without dissolved CO_2. Tiny marine animals form coral reefs made of carbonates from dissolved CO_2 and HCO_3^-. Life began in a "primordial soup," an aqueous mixture of simple molecules from which emerged larger molecules capable of self-sustaining reactions. From a chemical point of view, all organisms, from bacteria to humans, are highly organized systems of membranes enclosing and compartmentalizing complex aqueous solutions.

Thermal Properties of Water

When a substance is heated, some of the added energy increases average molecular speed, some increases molecular vibration and rotation, and some is used to overcome intermolecular forces.

1. *Specific heat capacity*. Because water has so many strong H bonds, its *specific heat capacity* is higher than any common liquid. With oceans covering 70% of Earth's surface, daytime energy from the Sun causes relatively small changes in temperature, allowing life to survive. On the waterless, airless Moon, temperatures range from 100°C to −150°C during a complete lunar day. Even in Earth's deserts, day-night temperature differences of 40°C are common.

2. *Heat of vaporization*. Numerous strong H bonds give water a very *high heat of vaporization*. Two examples show why this is crucial. The average adult has 40 kg of body water and generates about 10,000 kJ of heat a day from metabolism. If this heat were used to increase the average E_k of water molecules in the body, the rise in body temperaure of tens of degrees would mean immediate death. Instead, the heat is converted to E_p as it breaks H bonds and evaporates sweat, resulting in a stable body temperature and minimal loss of body fluid. On a planetary scale, the Sun's energy vaporizes ocean water in warm latitudes, and the potential energy is released as heat to warm cooler regions when the vapor condenses to rain. This global-scale cycling of water powers many weather patterns.

Surface Properties of Water

Hydrogen bonding is also responsible for water's *high surface tension* and *high capillarity*. Except for some molten metals and salts, water has the highest surface tension of any liquid. It keeps plant debris resting on a pond surface, providing shelter and nutrients for fish and insects. High capillarity means water rises through the tiny spaces between soil particles, so plant roots can absorb deep groundwater during dry periods.

The Unusual Density of Solid Water

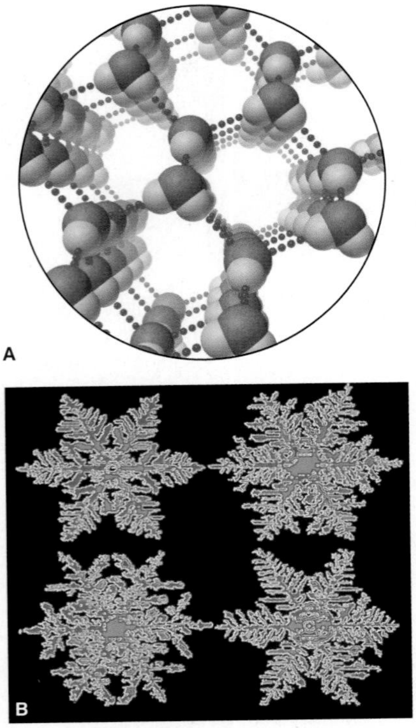

Figure 12.23 The hexagonal structure of ice. **A,** The open, hexagonal molecular structure of ice. **B,** The beauty of six-pointed snowflakes reflects this hexagonal structure.

In the solid state, the tetrahedral pattern of H bonding (see Figure 12.22) leads to the hexagonal, *open structure* of ice (Figure 12.23A), and the symmetrical beauty of snowflakes (Figure 12.23B) reflects this hexagonal organization. The large spaces within ice make *the solid less dense than the liquid* and explain the negative slope of the solid-liquid line in the phase diagram for water (see Figure 12.11, p. 430). As pressure is applied, some H bonds break, so the ordered crystal structure is disrupted, and the ice liquefies. When ice melts at 0°C, the loosened molecules pack much more closely, filling spaces in the collapsing solid structure. As a result, liquid water is most dense (1.000 g/mL) at around 4°C (3.98°C). With more heating, the density decreases through normal thermal expansion. This behavior has major effects in nature:

- *Surface ice of lakes*. When the surface of a lake freezes in winter, the ice floats. If the solid were denser than the liquid, as is true for nearly every other substance, the surface water would freeze and sink until the entire lake was solid. Aquatic life would not survive from year to year.
- *Nutrient turnover*. As lake water becomes colder in early winter, it becomes more dense *before* it freezes. Similarly, in spring, less dense ice thaws to form more dense water *before* the water expands. During both of these seasonal density changes, the top layer of water reaches maximum density first and sinks. The next layer of water rises because it is slightly less dense, reaches 4°C, and likewise sinks. This alternation of sinking and rising distributes nutrients and dissolved oxygen.
- *Soil formation*. When rain fills crevices in rocks and freezes, an outward force is applied that is relieved when the ice melts. In time, this repeated freeze-thaw stress cracks the rock. Over eons, this effect helps produce sand and soil.

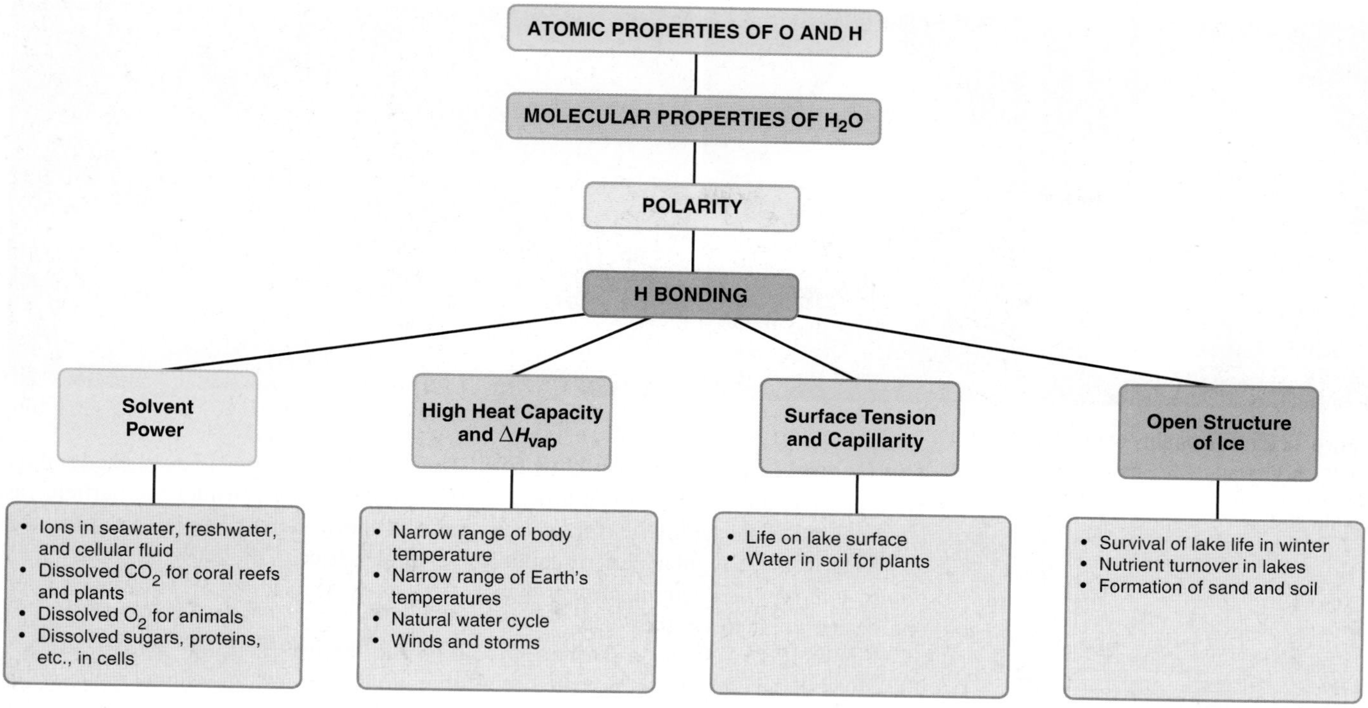

Figure 12.24 The unique macroscopic behavior of water that emerges from its atomic and molecular properties.

The far-reaching consequences of the properties of water illustrate chemistry's central theme: the macroscopic world we know is the cumulative outcome of the atomic world we seek to know (Figure 12.24).

Summary of Section 12.5

- The atomic properties of H and O result in water's bent molecular shape, polarity, and H-bonding ability.
- These properties give water the ability to dissolve many ionic and polar compounds.
- Water's high specific heat capacity and heat of vaporization give Earth and its organisms a narrow temperature range.
- The high surface tension and capillarity are essential to plants and animals.
- Because water expands on freezing, lake life survives in winter, nutrients mix from seasonal density changes, and soil forms through freeze-thaw stress on rocks.

12.6 • THE SOLID STATE: STRUCTURE, PROPERTIES, AND BONDING

Stroll through a museum's mineral collection, and you'll be struck by the variety and beauty of crystalline solids. In this section, we discuss the structural features of these and other solids and the intermolecular forces that create them. We also consider the main bonding model that explains many properties of solids.

Structural Features of Solids

We can divide solids into two broad categories:

- **Crystalline solids** have well defined shapes because their particles—atoms, molecules, or ions—occur in an orderly arrangement (Figure 12.25, *next page*).
- **Amorphous solids** have poorly defined shapes because their particles lack an orderly arrangement throughout the sample.

Figure 12.25 The beauty of crystalline solids. **A,** Wulfanite. **B,** Barite (*left*) on calcite (*right*). **C,** Beryl (emerald). **D,** Quartz (amethyst).

The Crystal Lattice and the Unit Cell The particles in a crystal are packed tightly in an orderly, three-dimensional array. As the simplest case, consider the particles as *identical* spherical atoms, and imagine a point at the center of each. The collection of points forms a regular pattern called the crystal **lattice.** The lattice consists of *all points with identical surroundings;* that is, there is no way to tell if you moved from one lattice point to another.

Figure 12.26A shows a portion of a lattice and the **unit cell,** the *smallest* portion that gives the crystal if it is repeated in all directions. A two-dimensional analogy for a unit cell and the resulting crystal lattice appears in a checkerboard (Figure 12.26B), a section of tiled floor, a strip of wallpaper, or any other pattern that is constructed from a repeating unit.

There are 7 crystal systems and 14 types of unit cells that occur in nature, but we will be concerned primarily with the *cubic system.* The solid states of a majority of metallic elements, some covalent compounds, and many ionic compounds occur as cubic lattices. A key parameter of any lattice is the **coordination number**, the number of *nearest* neighbors of a particle. There are three types of cubic unit cells within the cubic system:

1. In the **simple cubic unit cell** (Figure 12.27A), the centers of eight identical particles define the corners of a cube (shown in the expanded view, *top row*). The particles touch along the cube edges (see the space-filling view, *second row*), but they do not touch diagonally along the cube faces or through its center. An expanded portion of the crystal (*third row*) shows that the coordination number of each particle is 6: four in its own layer, one in the layer above, and one in the layer below.
2. In the **body-centered cubic unit cell** (Figure 12.27B), identical particles lie at each corner *and* in the center of the cube. Those at the corners do not touch each other, but they all touch the one in the center. Each particle is surrounded by eight nearest neighbors, four above and four below, so the coordination number is 8.
3. In the **face-centered cubic unit cell** (Figure 12.27C), identical particles lie at each corner *and* in the center of each face but not in the center of the cube. Particles at the corners touch those in the faces but not each other. The coordination number is 12.

How many particles make up a unit cell? For particles of the same size, *the higher the coordination number is, the greater the number of particles in a given volume.* Since one unit cell touches another, with no gaps, a particle at a corner or face is *shared* by adjacent cells. In the cubic unit cells, the particle at each corner is part of eight adjacent cells (Figure 12.27, *third row*), so one-eighth of each particle belongs to each cell (*bottom row*). There are eight corners in a cube, so

- A simple cubic unit cell contains $8 \times \frac{1}{8}$ particle $= 1$ particle.
- A body-centered cubic unit cell contains $8 \times \frac{1}{8}$ particle $= 1$ particle plus 1 particle in the center, for a total of 2 particles.
- A face-centered cubic unit cell contains $8 \times \frac{1}{8}$ particle $= 1$ particle plus one-half particle in each of the six faces, or $6 \times \frac{1}{2}$ particle $= 3$ particles, for a total of 4 particles.

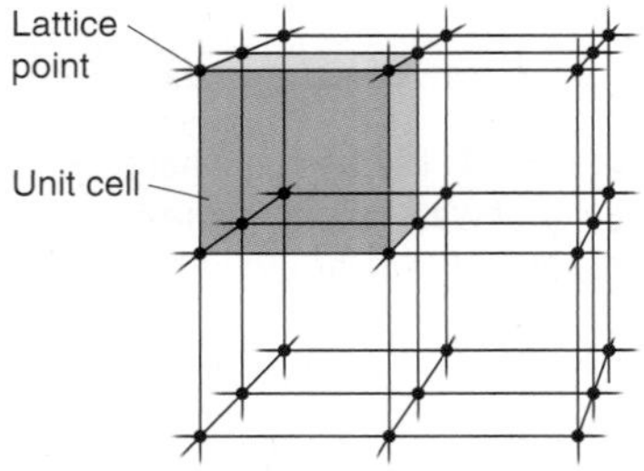

A Portion of 3-D lattice

B 2-D analogy for unit cell and lattice

Figure 12.26 The crystal lattice and the unit cell. **A,** A small portion of a lattice is shown as points connected by lines, with a unit cell (*colored*). **B,** A checkerboard analogy for a lattice.

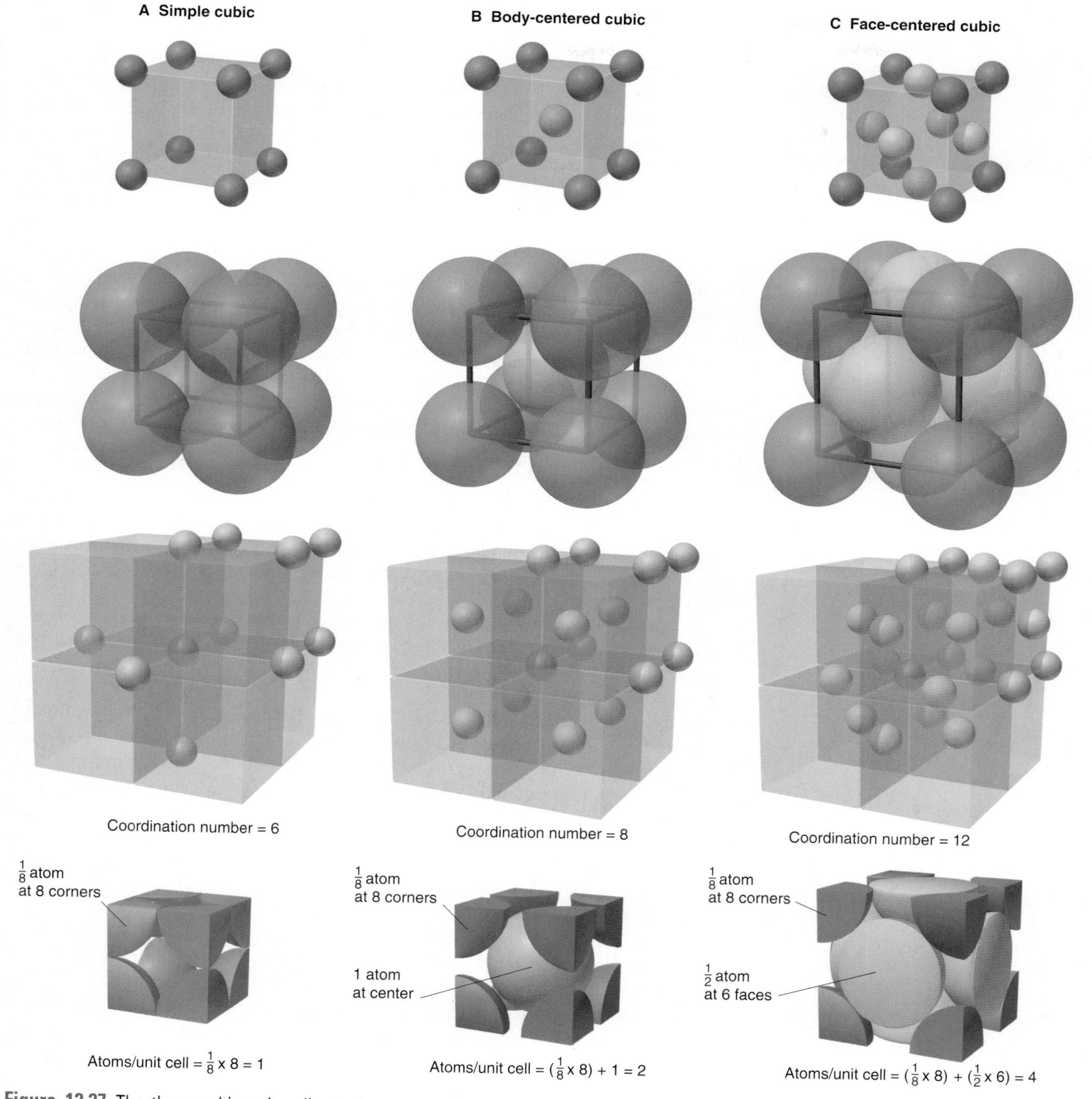

Figure 12.27 The three cubic unit cells. **A,** Simple cubic unit cell. **B,** Body-centered cubic unit cell. **C,** Face-centered cubic unit cell. *Top row:* Cubic arrangements of atoms in expanded view. *Second row:* Space-filling view of these cubic arrangements. All atoms are identical but, for clarity, corner atoms are blue, body-centered atoms pink, and face-centered atoms yellow. *Third row:* A unit cell (*shaded blue*) in an expanded portion of the crystal. The number of nearest neighbors around one particle (*dark blue in center*) is the coordination number. *Bottom row:* The total numbers of atoms in the actual unit cell. The simple cubic has one atom, the body-centered has two, and the face-centered has four.

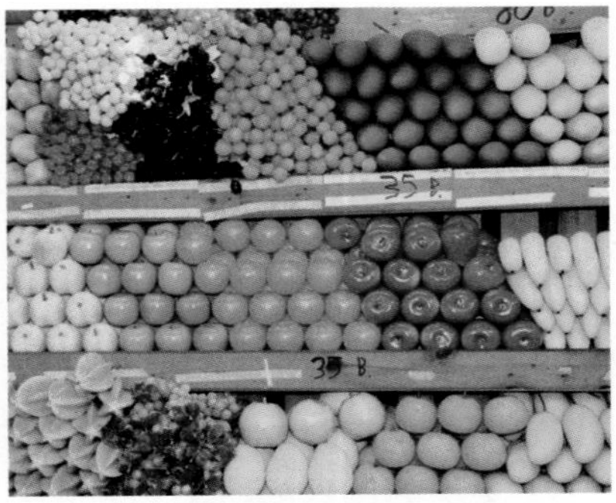
The efficient packing of fruit.

Packing Efficiency and the Creation of Unit Cells Unit cells result from the ways atoms pack together, which are similar to the ways that macroscopic spheres—marbles, golf balls, fruit—are packed (*see photo*). Let's pack *identical* spheres to create the three cubic unit cells and the hexagonal unit cell and determine the **packing efficiency,** the percentage of the total volume occupied by the spheres themselves:

1. *The simple cubic unit cell.* When we arrange the first layer of spheres in vertical and horizontal rows, large diamond-shaped spaces are formed (Figure 12.28A, *cutaway portion*). If we place the next layer of spheres *directly above* the first, we obtain an arrangement based on the *simple* cubic unit cell (Figure 12.28B). The spheres occupy only 52% of the unit-cell volume, so 48% is empty space between them. This is a very inefficient way to pack spheres, so neither fruit nor atoms are typically packed this way.

2. *The body-centered cubic unit cell.* Rather than placing the second layer (colored *green* for clarity) directly above the first, we use space more efficiently by placing it on the diamond-shaped spaces in the first layer (Figure 12.28C). Then we pack the third layer onto the diamond-shaped spaces in the second, which makes the first and third layers line up vertically. This arrangement is based on the *body-centered* cubic unit cell, and its packing efficiency is much higher at 68%. Several metallic elements, including chromium, iron, and all the Group 1A(1) elements, have a crystal structure based on this unit cell.

3. *The hexagonal and face-centered cubic unit cells.* Spheres are packed most efficiently in these cells. First, in the bottom layer (labeled *a*, *orange*), we shift every other row laterally so that the large diamond-shaped spaces become smaller triangular spaces. Then we place the second layer (labeled *b*, *green*) over these spaces (Figure 12.28D).

In layer *b*, notice that some spaces are orange because they lie above *spheres* in layer *a,* whereas other spaces are white because they lie above *spaces* in layer *a*. We can place the third layer in either of two ways, which gives rise to two different unit cells:

- *Hexagonal unit cell.* If we place the third layer of spheres (*orange*) over the orange spaces (look down and left to Figure 12.28E), they lie directly over the spheres in layer *a*. Every other layer is placed identically (an *abab*. . . layering pattern), and we obtain **hexagonal closest packing,** which is based on the *hexagonal* unit cell.
- *Face-centered unit cell.* If we place the third layer of spheres (*blue*) over the white spaces in layer *b* (look down and right to Figure 12.28F), the placement is different from layers *a* and *b* (an *abcabc*. . . pattern) and we obtain **cubic closest packing,** which is based on the *face-centered cubic* unit cell.

The packing efficiency of both hexagonal and cubic closest packing is 74%, and the coordination number of both is 12. Most metallic elements crystallize in one or the other of these arrangements. Magnesium, titanium, and zinc are some that adopt the hexagonal structure; nickel, copper, and lead adopt the cubic structure, as do many ionic compounds and other substances, such as CO_2, CH_4, and most noble gases.

In Sample Problem 12.5, we use density and our knowledge of unit cells to find an atomic radius.

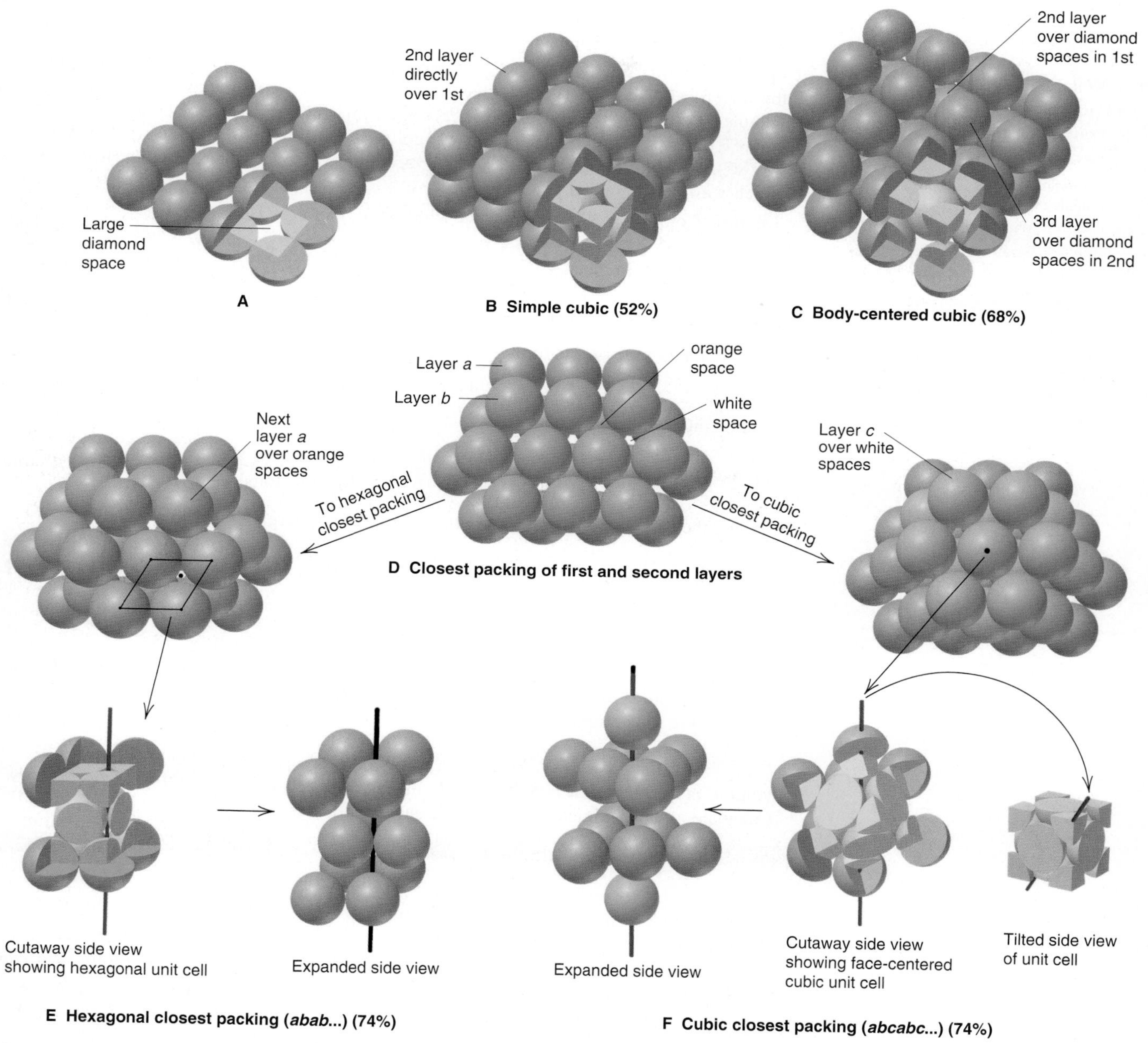

Figure 12.28 Packing spheres to obtain three cubic and hexagonal unit cells. **A,** In the first layer, each sphere lies next to another horizontally and vertically; note the large diamond-shaped spaces (*see cutaway*). **B,** If the spheres in the next layer lie directly over those in the first, the packing is based on the simple cubic unit cell (*pale orange cube, lower right corner*). **C,** If the spheres in the next layer lie in the diamond-shaped spaces of the first layer, the packing is based on the *body-centered cubic* unit cell (*lower right corner*). **D,** The closest possible packing of the first layer (*layer a, orange*) is obtained by shifting every other row in part A to obtain smaller triangular spaces. The spheres of the second layer (*layer b, green*) are placed above these spaces; note the orange and white spaces that result. **E,** When the third layer (*next layer a, orange*) is placed over the orange spaces, we obtain an *abab*. . . pattern and the hexagonal unit cell. **F,** When the third layer (*layer c, blue*) covers the white spaces, we get an *abcabc*. . . pattern and the face-centered cubic unit cell.

Sample Problem 12.5 Determining Atomic Radius

Road Map

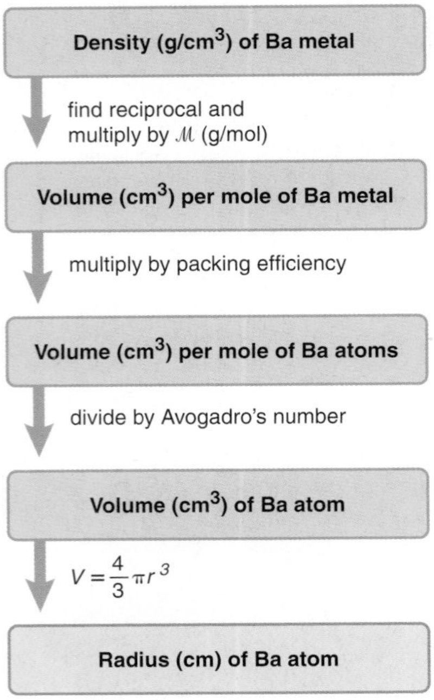

Problem Barium is the largest nonradioactive alkaline earth metal. It has a body-centered cubic unit cell and a density of 3.62 g/cm^3. What is the atomic radius of barium? (Volume of a sphere: $V = \frac{4}{3}\pi r^3$.)

Plan An atom is spherical, so we can find its radius from its volume. If we multiply the reciprocal of density (volume/mass) by the molar mass (mass/mole), we find the volume/mole of Ba metal. The metal crystallizes in the body-centered cubic structure, so 68% of this volume is occupied by 1 mol of the Ba atoms themselves (see Figure 12.28C). Dividing by Avogadro's number gives the volume of one Ba atom, from which we find the radius.

Solution Combining steps to find the volume of 1 mol of Ba metal:

$$\text{Volume/mole of Ba metal} = \frac{1}{\text{density}} \times \mathcal{M} = \frac{1\ \text{cm}^3}{3.62\ \text{g Ba}} \times \frac{137.3\ \text{g Ba}}{1\ \text{mol Ba}} = 37.9\ \text{cm}^3\text{/mol Ba}$$

Finding the volume (cm^3) of 1 mol of Ba *atoms:*

$$\text{Volume/mole of Ba atoms} = \text{cm}^3\text{/mol Ba} \times \text{packing efficiency}$$
$$= 37.9\ \text{cm}^3\text{/mol Ba} \times 0.68 = 26\ \text{cm}^3\text{/mol Ba atoms}$$

Finding the volume of one Ba atom:

$$\text{Volume of Ba atom} = \frac{26\ \text{cm}^3}{1\ \text{mol Ba atoms}} \times \frac{1\ \text{mol Ba atoms}}{6.022\times10^{23}\ \text{Ba atoms}} = 4.3\times10^{-23}\ \text{cm}^3\text{/Ba atom}$$

Finding the atomic radius of Ba from the volume of a sphere:

$$V \text{ of Ba atom} = \tfrac{4}{3}\pi r^3 \qquad \text{so} \qquad r^3 = \frac{3V}{4\pi}$$

Thus,

$$r = \sqrt[3]{\frac{3V}{4\pi}} = \sqrt[3]{\frac{3(4.3\times10^{-23}\ \text{cm}^3)}{4 \times 3.14}} = 2.2\times10^{-8}\ \text{cm}$$

Check The order of magnitude is correct for an atom ($\sim10^{-8}$ cm $\approx 10^{-10}$ m). The actual value for barium is, in fact, 2.22×10^{-8} cm (see Figure 8.9).

Follow-Up Problem 12.5 Iron crystallizes in a body-centered cubic structure. The volume of one Fe atom is 8.38×10^{-24} cm^3, and the density of Fe is 7.874 g/cm^3. Calculate an approximate value for Avogadro's number.

Our understanding of crystal structures comes from our ability to "see" them. Two techniques for doing this are described in Tools of the Laboratory.

The edge length of the unit cell is obtained from x-ray crystallography. We can then apply the Pythagorean theorem and some arithmetic to find atomic (or ionic) radii in the three cubic unit cells (Figure 12.29). Sample Problem 12.6 shows this approach.

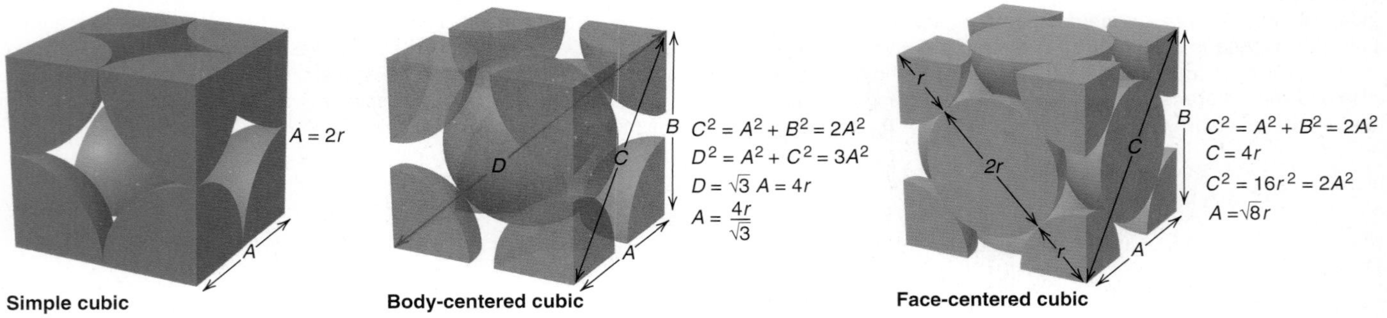

Figure 12.29 Edge length and atomic (ionic) radius in the three cubic unit cells.

TOOLS OF THE LABORATORY | X-Ray Diffraction Analysis and Scanning Tunneling Microscopy

Various tools exist for measuring atomic-scale dimensions, and two of the most powerful are **x-ray diffraction analysis** and **scanning tunneling microscopy.**

X-Ray Diffraction Analysis

In Chapter 7, we saw how diffraction patterns of bright and dark regions appear when light passes through slits spaced as far apart as the wavelength (see Figure 7.5, p. 265). X-ray wavelengths are about the same size as the spaces between layers of spheres in a crystal, so we use the spaces as "slits" to diffract x-rays.

As one example, let's use this approach to measure the distance (d) between two adjacent layers of atoms in a simplified lattice (Figure B12.1). Two waves impinge on the crystal at an angle θ and are diffracted at that angle by the layers. When the first wave strikes the top layer and the second strikes the next layer, they are *in phase* (peaks aligned with peaks and troughs with troughs). If they are still in phase after being diffracted, they form a spot on a photographic plate. This will occur only if the additional distance traveled by the second wave ($DE + EF$ in the figure) is a whole number of wavelengths, $n\lambda$, where n is a positive integer referred to as the *order* of the diffraction. From trigonometry, we find that

$$n\lambda = 2d \sin \theta$$

where θ is the angle of incoming light and d, the unknown, is the distance between layers. This is the *Bragg equation,* named for W. H. Bragg and his son W. L. Bragg, who shared the Nobel Prize in physics in 1915 for their work on crystal structure analysis.

Rotating the crystal changes θ and produces different sets of spots. Eventually, the complete diffraction pattern reveals distances and angles in the lattice (Figure B12.2). X-ray diffraction analysis is used in many studies, but its greatest recent impact is uncovering the structures of DNA and proteins.

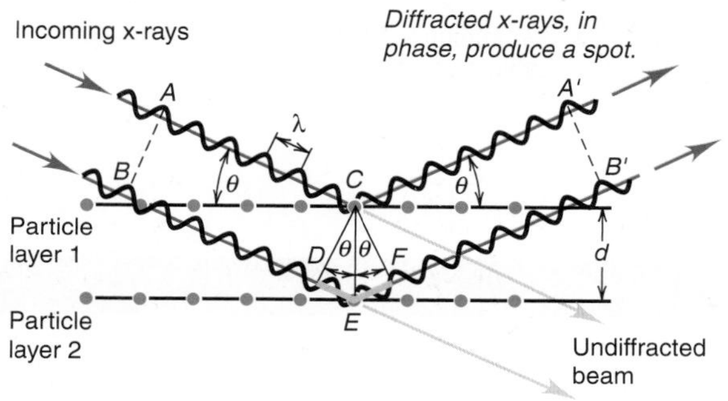

Figure B12.1 Diffraction of x-rays by crystal planes.

Scanning Tunneling Microscopy

This technique, invented by Gerd Binnig and Heinrich Rohrer, who won the Nobel Prize in physics in 1986, is used to observe surfaces. It is based on the idea that an electron has a small, but finite, probability of being so far from its nucleus that it can move ("tunnel") closer to another atom.

In practice, an extremely sharp tungsten-tipped probe, the source of the tunneling electrons, is placed very close (about

(continued)

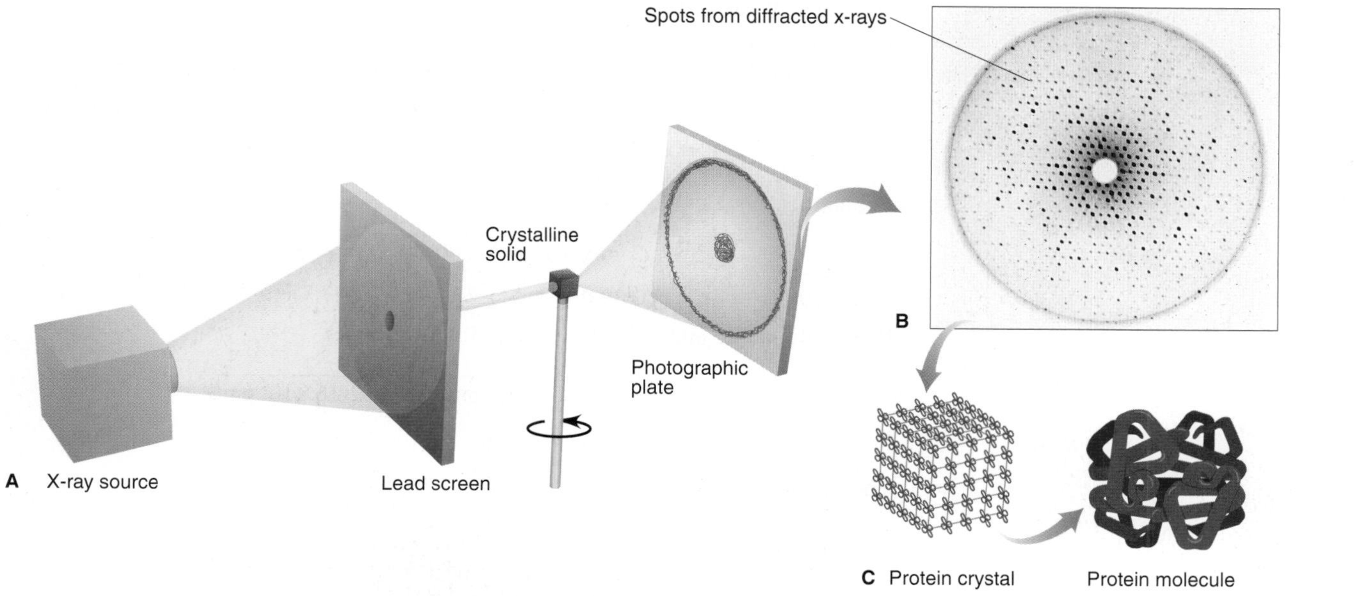

Figure B12.2 Formation of an x-ray diffraction pattern of the protein hemoglobin. **A,** A sample of crystalline protein is rotated to obtain different angles of incoming and diffracted x-rays. **B,** The diffraction pattern is a complex series of spots. **C,** Computerized analysis provides a picture of the molecule.

0.5 nm) to the surface under study. A small applied electric potential increases the probability that the electrons will tunnel across this minute gap. The probe moves tiny distances up and down to maintain the constant current across the gap, thus following the surface at the atomic scale. This movement is monitored electronically, and after many scans, a three-dimensional map of the surface is obtained. The method has revealed images of atoms and molecules coated on surfaces and is being used to study the nature of defects and many other surface features (Figure B12.3).

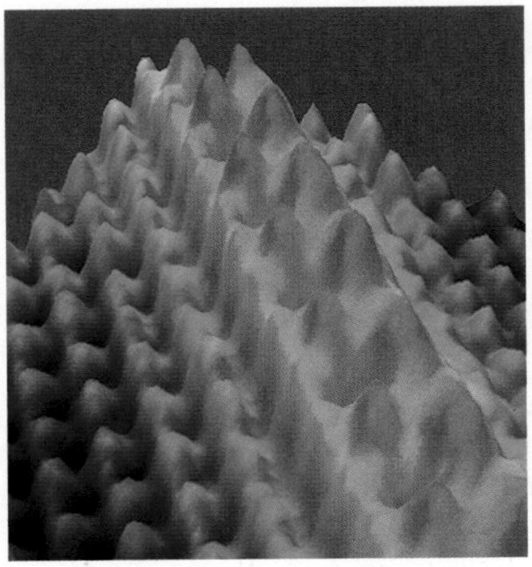

Figure B12.3 A scanning tunneling micrograph of cesium atoms (*red*) on gallium arsenide.

Problems

B12.1 X-rays of wavelength $\lambda = 0.709\times10^{-10}$ m undergo a first-order ($n = 1$) diffraction of 11.6° when aimed at crystalline nickel. What is the spacing between layers of Ni atoms?

B12.2 A first-order ($n = 1$) diffraction of x-rays aimed at a crystal of NaCl occurs at 15.9°.
(a) What is the wavelength (in pm) of the x-rays?
(b) At what angle would a second-order ($n = 2$) diffraction appear?

Sample Problem 12.6 Determining Atomic Radius from the Unit Cell

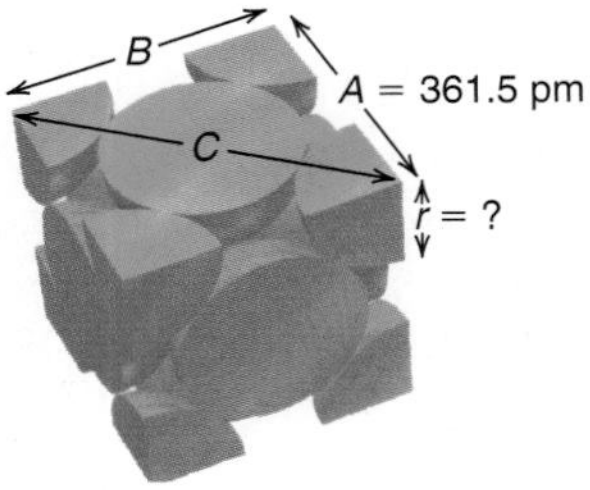

Problem Copper adopts cubic closest packing, and the edge length of the unit cell is 361.5 pm. What is the atomic radius of copper?

Plan Cubic closest packing has a face-centered cubic unit cell, and we know the edge length. With Figure 12.29 and A = 361.5 pm, we solve for r (*see margin*).

Solution Using the Pythagorean theorem to find C, the diagonal of the cell's face:

$$C = \sqrt{A^2 + B^2}$$

The unit cell is a cube, so $A = B$. Therefore,

$$C = \sqrt{2A^2} = \sqrt{2(361.5\text{ pm})^2} = 511.2\text{ pm}$$

Finding r: $C = 4r$. Therefore, $r = 511.2\text{ pm}/4 = 127.8\text{ pm.}$

Check Rounding and quickly checking the math gives

$$C = \sqrt{2(4\times10^2\text{ pm})^2} = \sqrt{2(16\times10^4\text{ pm}^2)}$$

or ~500–600 pm; thus, $r \approx$ 125–150 pm.

The actual value for copper is 128 pm (see Figure 8.15, p. 311).

Follow-Up Problem 12.6 Iron crystallizes in a body-centered cubic structure. If the atomic radius of Fe is 126 pm, find the edge length (in nm) of the unit cell.

Types and Properties of Crystalline Solids

The five most important types of solids are defined by the type(s) of particle(s) in the crystal (Table 12.5). We'll highlight interparticle forces and physical properties.

Atomic Solids Individual atoms held together only by *dispersion forces* form an **atomic solid,** and the noble gases [Group 8A(18)] are the only substances that form such solids. The very weak forces among the atoms mean melting and boiling points and heats of vaporization and fusion are all very low, rising smoothly with increasing molar mass. Argon crystallizes in a cubic closest packed structure (Figure 12.30), as do the other noble gases.

Figure 12.30 Cubic closest packing of frozen argon (face-centered cubic unit cell).

Molecular Solids In the many thousands of **molecular solids,** individual molecules occupy the lattice points. Various combinations of dipole-dipole, dispersion, and H-bonding forces account for a wide range of physical properties. Dispersion forces in nonpolar substances lead to melting points that generally increase with molar mass (Table 12.5). Among polar molecules, dipole-dipole forces and, where possible, H bonding occur. Most molecular solids have much higher melting points than atomic solids (noble gases) but much lower melting points than other types of solids. Methane crystallizes in a face-centered cubic structure with the center of each carbon as the lattice point (Figure 12.31).

Figure 12.31 Cubic closest packing (face-centered unit cell) of frozen CH_4.

Ionic Solids To maximize attractions in a binary **ionic solid,** cations are surrounded by as many anions as possible, and vice versa, with *the smaller of the ions (usually the cation) lying in the spaces (holes) formed by the packing of the larger (usually the anion).* The unit cell is the smallest portion that maintains the composition; that is, *the unit cell has the same cation/anion ratio as the empirical formula.*

Table 12.5 Characteristics of the Major Types of Crystalline Solids

Type	Particle(s)	Interparticle Forces	Physical Properties	Examples [mp, °C]
Atomic	Atoms	Dispersion	Soft, very low mp, poor thermal and electrical conductors	Group 8A(18) (Ne [−249] to Rn [−71])
Molecular	Molecules	Dispersion, dipole-dipole, H bonds	Fairly soft, low to moderate mp, poor thermal and electrical conductors	*Nonpolar** O_2 [−219], C_4H_{10} [−138] Cl_2 [−101], C_6H_{14} [−95], P_4 [44.1] *Polar* SO_2 [−73], $CHCl_3$ [−64], HNO_3 [−42], H_2O [0.0], CH_3COOH [17]
Ionic	Positive and negative ions	Ion-ion attraction	Hard and brittle, high mp, good thermal and electrical conductors when molten	NaCl [801] CaF_2 [1423] MgO [2852]
Metallic	Atoms	Metallic bond	Soft to hard, low to very high mp, excellent thermal and electrical conductors, malleable and ductile	Na [97.8] Zn [420] Fe [1535]
Network covalent	Atoms	Covalent bond	Very hard, very high mp, usually poor thermal and electrical conductors	SiO_2 (quartz) [1610] C (diamond) [~4000]

*Nonpolar molecular solids are arranged in order of increasing molar mass. Note the correlation with increasing melting point (mp).

As a result of cation-anion contact, the interparticle forces (ionic bonds) are *much* stronger than the van der Waals forces in atomic or molecular solids. The properties of ionic solids are a direct consequence of the *fixed ion positions* and *very strong attractive forces,* which create a high lattice energy. Thus, ionic solids typically have high melting points and low electrical conductivities. When a large quantity of heat is supplied and the ions gain enough kinetic energy to break free of their positions, the solid melts and the mobile ions conduct a current. Ionic compounds are hard because only a strong external force can change the relative positions of the huge number of ions attracting one another. If enough force *is* applied to move them, ions of like charge are brought near each other, and their repulsions crack the crystal (see Figure 9.8, p. 336).

Ionic solids often adopt cubic closest packed crystal structures. We'll describe two examples with a 1/1 ratio of ions and then two with a 2/1 (or 1/2) ratio:

1. The *sodium chloride structure* is found in many ionic compounds, including most alkali [Group 1A(1)] halides and hydrides, alkaline earth [Group 2A(2)] oxides and sulfides, and several transition-metal oxides and sulfides. To visualize this structure, imagine Cl^- anions and Na^+ cations in separate face-centered cubic arrays. Now picture the two arrays penetrating each other, the smaller Na^+ ions ending up in the holes between the larger Cl^- ions (Figure 12.32A). Thus, each Na^+ is surrounded by six Cl^-, and vice versa (coordination number = 6). Figure 12.32B is a space-filling depiction of the unit cell: four Cl^- $[(8 \times \frac{1}{8}) + (6 \times \frac{1}{2}) = 4\ Cl^-]$ and four Na^+ $[(12 \times \frac{1}{4}) + 1$ in the center $= 4\ Na^+]$, give a 1/1 ion ratio.

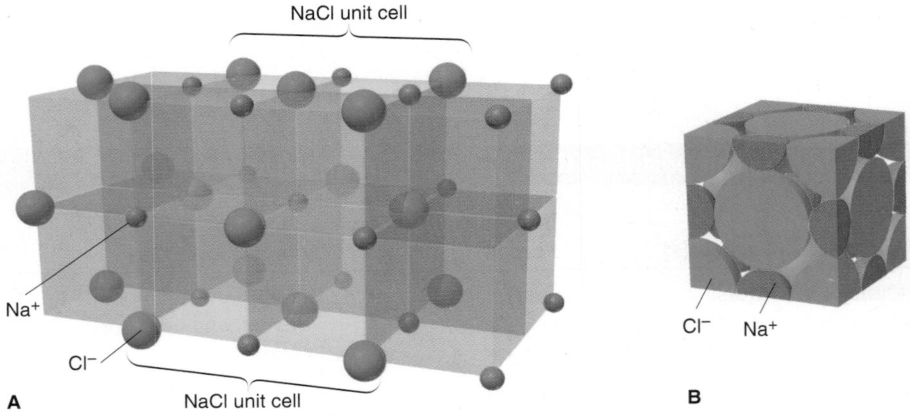

Figure 12.32 The sodium chloride structure. **A,** Expanded view. **B,** Space-filling model of the NaCl unit cell.

2. The *zinc blende (ZnS) structure* can be pictured as two face-centered cubic arrays, one of Zn^{2+} ions (*gray*) and the other of S^{2-} ions (*yellow*), penetrating each other such that each ion is tetrahedrally surrounded by four of the other ions (coordination number = 4) (Figure 12.33). There are four $[(8 \times \frac{1}{8}) + (6 \times \frac{1}{2}) = 4]\ S^{2-}$ ions and four Zn^{2+} ions for a 1/1 ion ratio. Many other compounds, including AgI, CdS, and the copper(I) halides, adopt the zinc blende structure.

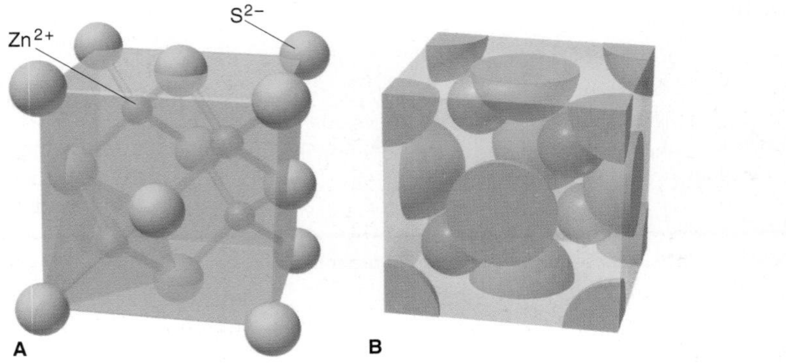

Figure 12.33 The zinc blende structure. **A,** Expanded view (with bonds shown for clarity). **B,** The unit cell is expanded a bit to show interior ions.

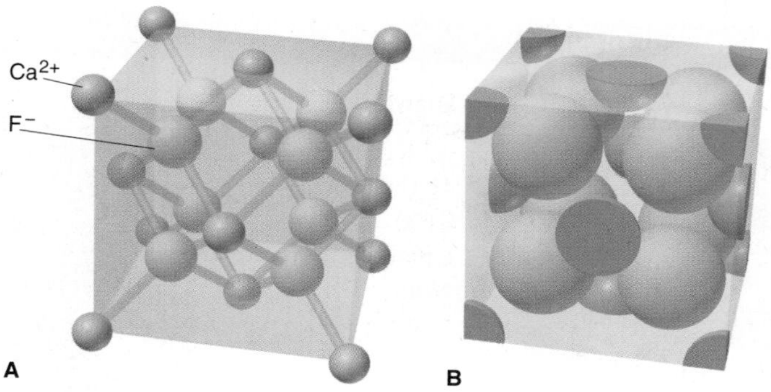

Figure 12.34 The fluorite structure. **A,** Expanded view (with bonds shown for clarity). **B,** The unit cell is expanded a bit to show interior ions.

3. The *fluorite (CaF_2) structure* is common among salts with a 1/2 cation/anion ratio that have relatively large cations and small anions, such as SrF_2 and $BaCl_2$. In CaF_2, the unit cell is a face-centered cubic array of Ca^{2+} ions with F^- ions occupying *all* eight available holes (Figure 12.34). This results in a Ca^{2+}/F^- ratio of 4/8, or 1/2.

4. The *antifluorite structure* is common in compounds with a 2/1 cation/anion ratio and a relatively large anion (such as K_2S). The ion arrangment is the opposite of that in the fluorite structure: the cations occupy all eight holes formed by the cubic closest packing of the anions.

Metallic Solids Most metallic elements crystallize in one of the two closest packed structures (Figure 12.35). In contrast to the weak dispersion forces in atomic solids, powerful metallic bonding forces hold atoms together in **metallic solids.** The properties of metals—high electrical and thermal conductivity, luster, and malleability—result from their delocalized electrons (Section 9.6). Melting points and hardnesses are related to the packing efficiency and number of valence electrons. For example, Group 2A metals are harder and melt higher than Group 1A metals (see Figure 9.27, pp. 352–353), because the 2A metals have twice as many delocalized valence electrons.

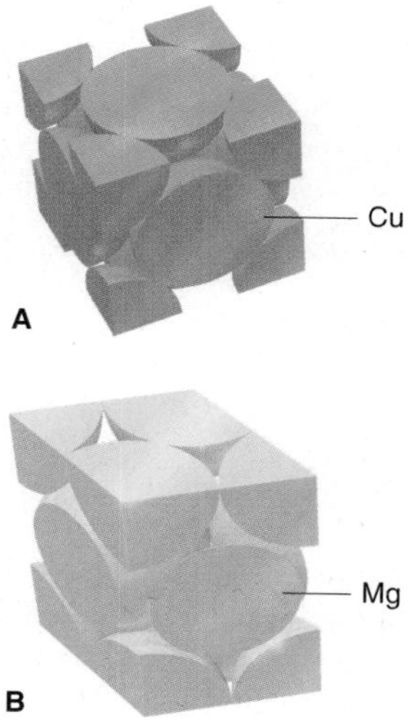

Figure 12.35 Crystal structures of metals. **A,** Copper adopts cubic closest packing. **B,** Magnesium adopts hexagonal closest packing.

Network Covalent Solids Strong covalent bonds link the atoms together in a **network covalent solid;** thus, separate particles are not present. These substances adopt a variety of crystal structures depending on the details of their bonding.

As a consequence of strong bonding, all network covalent solids have extremely high melting and boiling points, but their conductivity and hardness vary. Two examples with the same composition but strikingly different properties are the two common crystalline forms of elemental carbon, graphite and diamond:

- *Graphite* occurs as stacked flat sheets of hexagonal carbon rings with a strong σ-bond framework and delocalized π bonds, reminiscent of benzene; the arrangement looks like chicken wire or honeycomb. Whereas the π-bonding electrons of benzene are delocalized over one ring, those of graphite are delocalized over the entire sheet. Thus, graphite conducts electricity well—it is a common electrode material—but only in the plane of the sheets. The sheets interact via dispersion forces, and impurities, such as O_2, between the sheets allow them to slide past each other, which explains why graphite is soft and used as a lubricant.
- *Diamond* adopts a face-centered cubic unit cell, with each C tetrahedrally bonded to four others in an endless array. Throughout the crystal, strong single bonds make diamond the hardest natural substance known. Like most network covalent solids, diamond does not conduct electricity because the bonding electrons are localized.

These properties are compared in Table 12.6 on the next page.

The most important network covalent solids are the *silicates,* which consist of extended arrays of covalently bonded silicon and oxygen atoms. Quartz (SiO_2) is a common example. We'll discuss silicates, which form the structure of clays, rocks, and many minerals, when we consider the chemistry of silicon in Chapter 14.

Table 12.6 Comparison of the Properties of Diamond and Graphite

Property	Graphite	Diamond
Density (g/cm^3)	2.27	3.51
Hardness	<1 (very soft)	10 (hardest)
Melting point (K)	4100	4100
Color	Shiny black	Colorless transparent
Electrical conductivity	High (along sheet)	None
ΔH°_{rxn} for combustion (kJ/mol)	−393.5	−395.4
ΔH°_f (kJ/mol)	0 (standard state)	1.90

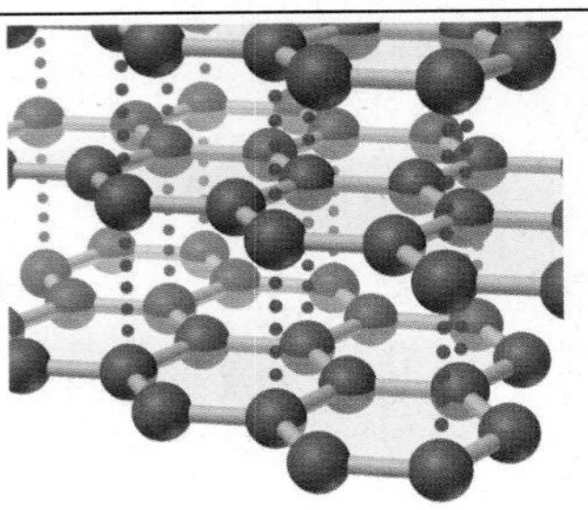

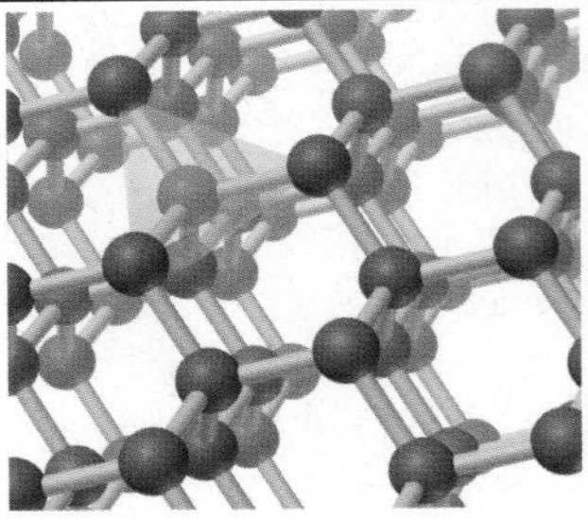

Amorphous Solids

Amorphous solids are noncrystalline. Many have small, somewhat ordered regions interspersed among large disordered regions. Charcoal, rubber, and glass are examples.

The process that forms quartz glass is typical of many amorphous solids. Crystalline quartz (SiO_2), which adopts cubic closest packing, is melted and the viscous liquid is cooled rapidly to prevent it from recrystallizing. The chains of Si and O atoms cannot orient themselves quickly enough, so they solidify in a distorted jumble containing gaps and misaligned rows (Figure 12.36). The absence of regularity confers some properties of a liquid; in fact, glasses are sometimes referred to as *supercooled liquids.*

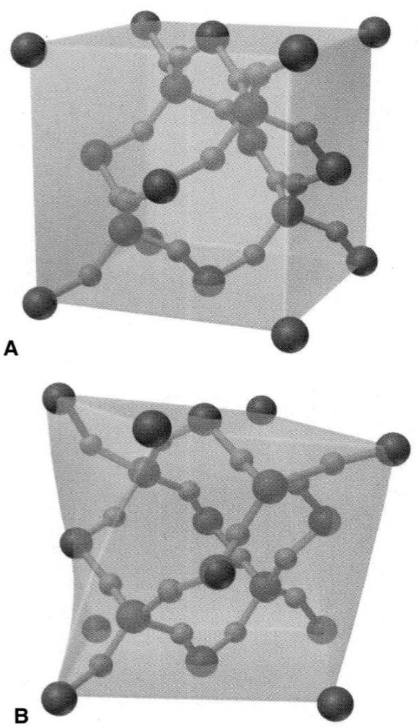

Figure 12.36 Crystalline and amorphous silicon dioxide. **A,** Cristobalite, a crystalline form of silica (SiO_2), shows cubic closest packing. **B,** Quartz glass is amorphous with a generally disordered structure.

Bonding in Solids: Molecular Orbital Band Theory

Chapter 9 introduced a qualitative model of metallic bonding, with metal ions submerged in a "sea" of mobile, delocalized valence electrons. Molecular orbital (MO) theory offers a more quantitative, and therefore more useful, model called **band theory.** We'll focus on bonding in metals and the conductivity of metals, metalloids, and nonmetals.

Formation of Valence and Conduction Bands Recall from Section 11.3 that when two atoms form a diatomic molecule, their atomic orbitals (AOs) combine to form an equal number of molecular orbitals (MOs). Figure 12.37 shows the formation of MOs in lithium. To form Li_2, each Li atom has four valence orbitals (one 2*s* and three

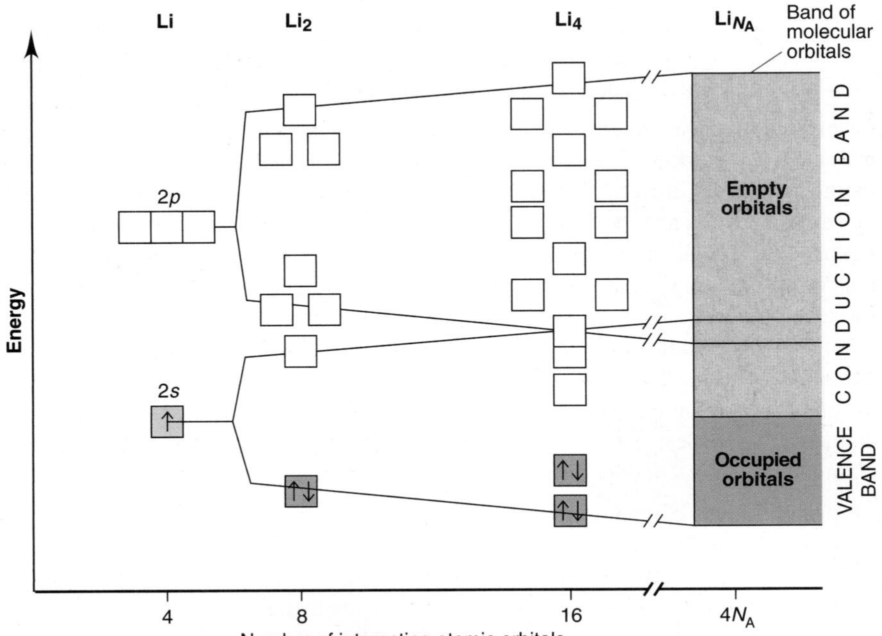

Figure 12.37 The band of molecular orbitals in lithium metal.

2*p*) that combine to form eight MOs, four bonding and four antibonding. The order of MOs shows 2*s*-2*p* mixing (Figure 11.21B, p. 409). Two more Li atoms form Li_4, a slightly larger aggregate, with 16 delocalized MOs. As more Li atoms join the cluster, more MOs are created, and their energy levels lie closer and closer together. Extending this process to 7 g (1 mol) of lithium results in 6×10^{23} Li atoms (Li_{N_A}) combining to form an extremely large number (4 × Avogadro's number) of delocalized MOs. *The energies of the MOs are so close that they form a continuum, or band, of MOs.*

The lower energy MOs are occupied by the $2s^1$ valence electrons and make up the **valence band.** The empty MOs that are higher in energy make up the **conduction band.** In Li metal, the valence band is derived from the 2*s* AOs, and the conduction band is derived from 2*s* and mostly 2*p* AOs. In Li_2, two valence electrons fill the lowest energy bonding MO and leave the antibonding MO empty. In Li metal, 1 mol of valence electrons fills the valence band and leaves the conduction band empty.

How Band Theory Explains Metallic Properties The key to understanding the properties of metals is that *the valence and conduction bands are contiguous,* that is, the highest level of one touches the lowest of the other. This means that, given an infinitesimal quantity of energy, electrons jump from the filled valence band to the unfilled conduction band: the electrons are completely delocalized.

- *Electrical conductivity.* Metals conduct so well because an applied field easily excites the highest energy valence electrons into empty conduction orbitals, allowing them to move through the sample.
- *Luster.* With so many closely spaced levels available, electrons absorb and release photons of many frequencies as they move between the valence and conduction bands.
- *Malleability.* Under an applied force, layers of positive metal ions move past each other, always protected from mutual repulsions by the delocalized electrons.
- *Thermal conductivity.* When a metal wire is heated, the highest energy electrons are excited and their extra energy is transferred as kinetic energy along the wire's length.

Conductivity of Solids and the Size of the Energy Gap Like metal atoms, large numbers of nonmetal and metalloid atoms can form bands of MOs. Band theory explains differences in electrical conductivity and the effect of temperature among these three classes of substances in terms of the presence of an energy gap between their valence and conduction bands (Figure 12.38):

1. *Conductors (metals).* The valence and conduction bands of a **conductor** have *no energy gap* between them, so electrons flow when a tiny electrical potential difference is applied. When the temperature is raised, greater random motion of the atoms hinders electron movement: conductivity *decreases* when a metal is heated.
2. *Semiconductors (metalloids).* In a **semiconductor,** a *small energy gap* exists between the valence and conduction bands. Thermally excited electrons can cross the gap, allowing a small current to flow: in contrast to a conductor, conductivity *increases* when a semiconductor is heated.
3. *Insulators (nonmetals).* In an **insulator,** a *large energy gap* exists between the bands: no current is observed even when the substance is heated.

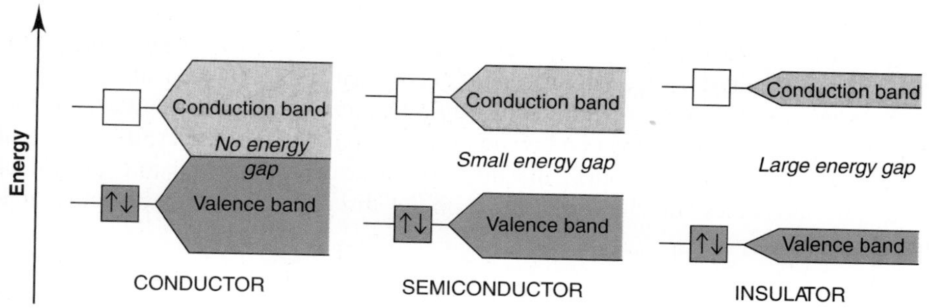

Figure 12.38 Electrical conductivity in a conductor, semiconductor, and insulator.

Another type of electrical conductivity, called **superconductivity,** has been the focus of intensive research for the past few decades. When metals conduct at ordinary temperatures, moving electrons collide with vibrating atoms; the reduction in their flow appears as resistive heating and represents a loss of energy.

For many years, to conduct with no energy loss—to superconduct—required minimizing atom movement by cooling with liquid helium (bp = 4 K; price ≈ $11/L). Then, in 1986, certain ionic oxides that superconduct near the boiling point of liquid nitrogen (bp = 77 K; price = $0.20/L) were prepared. Like metal conductors, oxide superconductors, such as $YBa_2Cu_3O_7$, have no gap between bands. In 1989, oxides with Bi and Tl instead of Y and Ba were synthesized and found to superconduct at 125 K; and in 1993, an oxide with Hg, Ba, and Ca, in addition to Cu and O, superconducted at 133 K. Such materials could transmit electricity with no loss of energy, allowing power plants to be located far from cities. They could be part of ultrasmall microchips for ultrafast computers, electromagnets to levitate superfast trains, and inexpensive medical diagnostic equipment with superb image clarity. However, the oxides are brittle and not easy to machine, and when warmed, the superconductivity may disappear and not return on cooling. Addressing these and related problems will involve chemists, physicists, and engineers for many years.

Summary of Section 12.6

- Particles in crystalline solids lie at points that form a structure of repeating unit cells.
- The three types of unit cells of the cubic system are simple, body-centered, and face-centered. The highest packing efficiency occurs with cubic (face-centered) and hexagonal closest packing.
- Bond angles and distances in a crystal are determined with x-ray diffraction analysis and scanning tunneling microscopy. These data are used to determine atomic radii.
- Atomic [Group 8A(18)] solids adopt cubic closest packing, with atoms held together by weak dispersion forces.
- Molecular solids have molecules at the lattice points and often adopt cubic closest packing. Combinations of intermolecular forces (dispersion, dipole-dipole, and H bonding) result in physical properties that vary greatly.
- Ionic solids crystallize with one ion filling holes in the cubic closest packed array of the other. High melting points, hardness, and low conductivity arise from strong ionic attractions.
- Most metals have a closest packed structure. Their physical properties result from the high packing efficiency and the presence of delocalized electrons.
- Atoms of network covalent solids are covalently bonded throughout the sample, so these substances have very high melting and boiling points.
- Amorphous solids have little regularity in their structure.
- Band theory proposes that atomic orbitals of many atoms combine to form a continuum, or band, of molecular orbitals. Metals are electrical conductors because electrons move freely from the filled (valence) band to the empty (conduction) band. Insulators have a large energy gap between the two portions, and semiconductors have a small gap, which can be bridged by heating.

12.7 • ADVANCED MATERIALS

In the last few decades, the exciting field of materials science has grown from solid-state chemistry, physics, and engineering. Objects that were once considered futuristic fantasies are becoming realities: powerful, ultrafast computers smaller than this book; cars powered by sunlight and made of nonmetallic parts stronger than steel and lighter than aluminum; ultrasmall machines constructed by manipulating individual atoms and molecules. In this section, we briefly discuss some of these remarkable materials.

Electronic Materials

The ideal of a perfectly ordered crystal is attainable only if the crystal is grown very slowly under carefully controlled conditions. When crystals form more rapidly, **crystal defects** inevitably form. Planes of particles are misaligned, particles are out of place or missing entirely, and foreign particles replace those that belong in the lattice. Although defects usually weaken a substance, they can be introduced intentionally to improve materials, giving them increased strength, hardness, or conductivity. Centuries of metal-working exemplify the traditional importance of defects, which is the basis of modern electronic materials.

Introducing Defects in Welding and Alloying In the process of *welding* two metals together, *vacancies* form near the surface when atoms vaporize, and then these vacancies move deeper as atoms from lower rows rise to fill the gaps. Welding causes the two types of metal atoms to intermingle and fill each other's vacancies. Metal *alloying* introduces several kinds of crystal defects, as when some atoms of a second metal occupy lattice sites of the first. Often, the alloy is harder than the pure metal; an example is brass, an alloy of copper with zinc. One reason the welded metals are stronger and the alloy is harder is that the second metal contributes additional valence electrons for metallic bonding.

Doped Semiconductors By controlling the number of valence electrons through the creation of specific types of crystal defects, chemists and engineers can greatly increase the conductivity of a semiconductor. Pure silicon [Si; Group 4A(14)], conducts poorly at room temperature because an energy gap separates its filled valence band from its conduction band (Figure 12.39A). Its conductivity can be greatly enhanced by **doping,** adding small amounts of other elements to increase or decrease the number of valence electrons in the bands:

- *n-Type semiconductor: increasing the number of valence electrons.* When Si is doped with phosphorus [or another Group 5A(15) element], P atoms occupy some of the lattice sites. Since P has one more valence electron than Si, this additional electron must enter an empty orbital in the conduction band, thus bridging the energy gap and increasing conductivity. Such doping creates an *n-type semiconductor,* so called because extra *n*egative charges (electrons) are present (Figure 12.39B).
- *p-Type semiconductor: decreasing the number of valence electrons.* When Si is doped with gallium [or another Group 3A(13) element], Ga atoms occupy some sites (Figure 12.39C). Since Ga has one fewer valence electron than Si, some of the orbitals in the valence band are empty, which creates a positive site. Si electrons can migrate to these empty orbitals, thereby increasing conductivity. Such doping creates a *p-type semiconductor,* so called because the empty orbitals act as *p*ositive holes.

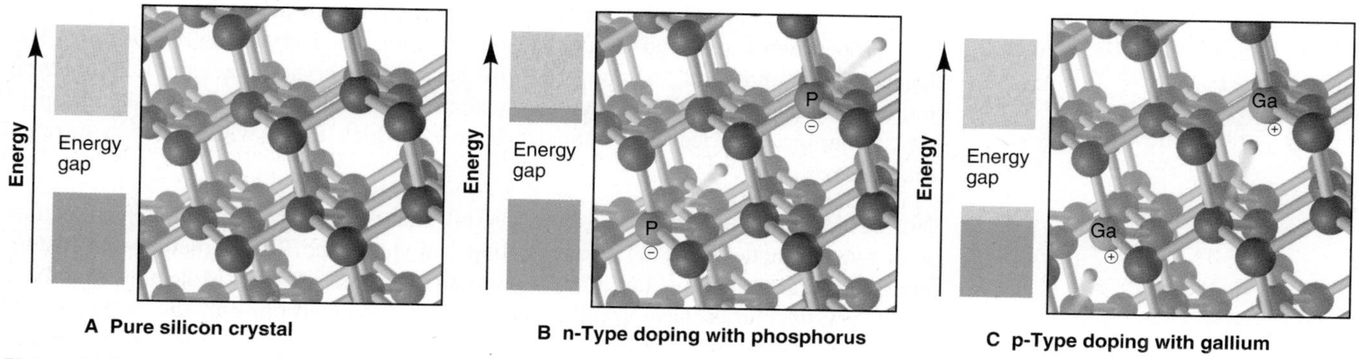

Figure 12.39 Crystal structures and band representations of doped semiconductors. **A,** Pure silicon has an energy gap between its valence and conduction bands, which keeps conductivity low at room temperature. **B,** Doping silicon with phosphorus (*purple*) adds additional valence electrons. **C,** Doping silicon with gallium (*orange*) removes electrons from the valence band and introduces positive holes.

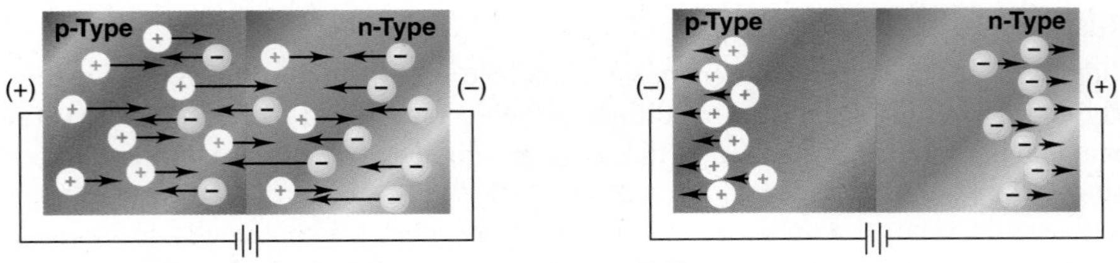

A Flow of electrons and holes creates a current. **B** No current.

Figure 12.40 The p-n junction. Placing a p-type semiconductor adjacent to an n-type creates a p-n junction.

In contact with each other, an n-type and a p-type semiconductor form a *p-n junction.* When the negative terminal of a battery is connected to the n-type portion and the positive terminal to the p-type portion, electrons (*yellow, negative spheres*) flow freely in the n-to-p direction, which has the simultaneous effect of moving holes (*white, positive spheres*) in the p-to-n direction (Figure 12.40A). No current flows if the terminals are reversed (Figure 12.40B). Such unidirectional current flow makes a p-n junction act as a *rectifier,* a device that converts alternating current into direct current. A p-n junction in a modern integrated circuit can be made smaller than a square 10 μm on a side.

A modern computer chip the size of a nickel may incorporate millions of p-n junctions in the form of *transistors*. One of the most common types, an n-p-n transistor, is made by sandwiching a p-type portion between two n-type portions to form adjacent p-n junctions. The current flowing through one junction controls the current flowing through the other and results in an amplified signal.

One of the more common types of *solar cell* is, in essence, a p-n junction with an n-type surface exposed to a light source. Light provides the energy to free electrons from the n-type region and accelerate them through an external circuit into the p-type region, thus producing a current.

Liquid Crystals

Incorporated in the membrane of every cell in your body and in the display of every electronic device are **liquid crystals.** These materials flow like liquids but, like crystalline solids, pack at the molecular level with a high degree of order.

Ordering of the Particles Let's examine how particles are ordered in the three physical states and how this affects their properties. Both gases and liquids are *isotropic*—their physical properties are the same in every direction within the phase. For example, the viscosity of a gas or a liquid is the same regardless of direction. Glasses and other amorphous solids are also isotropic because they have no regular lattice structure.

In contrast, crystalline solids have a high degree of order among their particles. The properties of a crystal *do* depend on direction, so a crystal is *anisotropic.* The facets in a cut diamond, for instance, arise because the crystal cracks in one direction more easily than in another. Liquid crystals are anisotropic in several physical properties, including electrical and optical properties, which differ with direction through the phase.

Molecular Characteristics Liquid crystal phases consist of individual molecules with two characteristics: (1) a long, cylindrical shape and (2) a structure that fosters intermolecular attractions but inhibits perfect crystalline packing. Molecules that form liquid crystal phases have rodlike shapes and certain groups—in the cases shown in Figure 12.41, flat, benzene-like ring systems—that keep the molecules extended. Many of these molecules also have polarity associated with the long molecular axis. A strong electric field can orient these polar molecules like compass needles in a magnetic field.

The viscosity of a liquid crystal phase is lowest in the direction parallel to the long axis. Like moistened microscope slides, it is easier for the molecules to slide along each other (because the total attractive force remains the same), than it is for

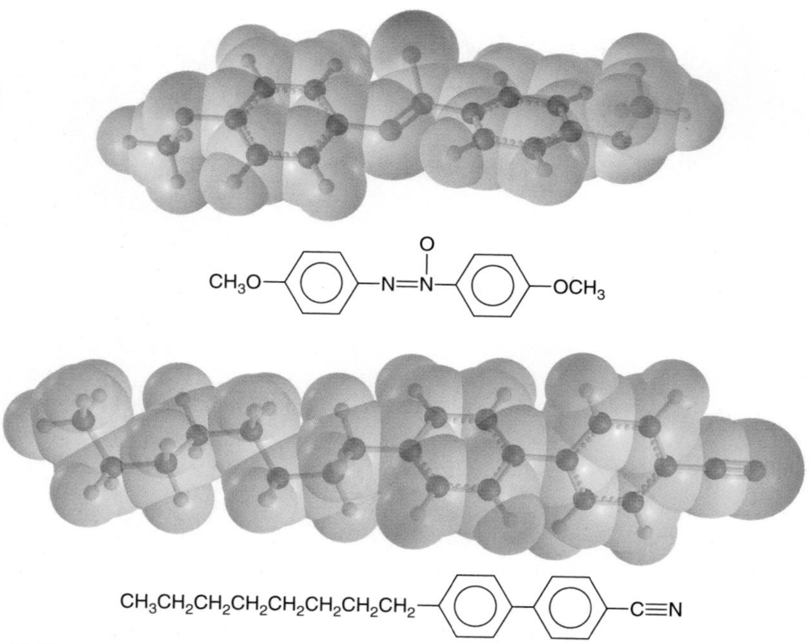

Figure 12.41 Structures of two typical molecules that form liquid crystal phases. Note the long, extended shapes and the regions of high (*red*) and low (*blue*) electron density.

them to pull apart from each other sideways. As a result, the molecules tend to align while the phase flows.

Controlling Conditions to Form Phases Liquid crystal phases can arise in two general ways, and, sometimes, either way can occur in the same substance:

1. *Thermotropic phases* develop as a result of a change in temperature. As a crystalline solid is heated, the molecules leave their lattice sites, but the intermolecular interactions are still strong enough to keep the molecules aligned with each other along their long axes. Like any other phase, the liquid crystal phase has sharp transition temperatures, but they occur over a relatively small temperature range. Further heating provides enough kinetic energy for the molecules to become disordered, as in a normal liquid. The typical range for liquid crystal phases of pure substances is from $<1°C$ to as much as 10°C, but mixing phases of two or more substances can greatly extend this range. For this reason, the liquid crystal phases used within display devices, as well as those within cell membranes, consist of mixtures of molecules.

2. *Lyotropic phases* occur in solution as the result of changes in concentration, but the conditions for forming such a phase vary for different substances. For example, when purified, some biomolecules that exist in cell membranes form lyotropic phases in water at the temperature that occurs within the organism. At the other extreme, Kevlar, a fiber used in bulletproof vests and high-performance sports equipment, forms a lyotropic phase in concentrated H_2SO_4 solution.

In some cases, a substance that forms a given liquid crystal phase under one set of conditions forms other phases under different conditions. Thus, a given thermotropic liquid crystal substance can pass from disordered liquid through a series of distinct liquid crystal phases to an ordered crystal through a decrease in temperature. A lyotropic substance can undergo similar changes through an increase in concentration.

Types of Order in Liquid Crystal Phases Molecules that form liquid crystal phases can exhibit various types of order. Three common types are nematic, cholesteric, and smectic:

1. In a *nematic phase,* the molecules lie in the same direction but their ends are not aligned, much like a school of fish swimming in synchrony (Figure 12.42A, *next page*). The nematic phase is the least ordered type of liquid crystal phases.

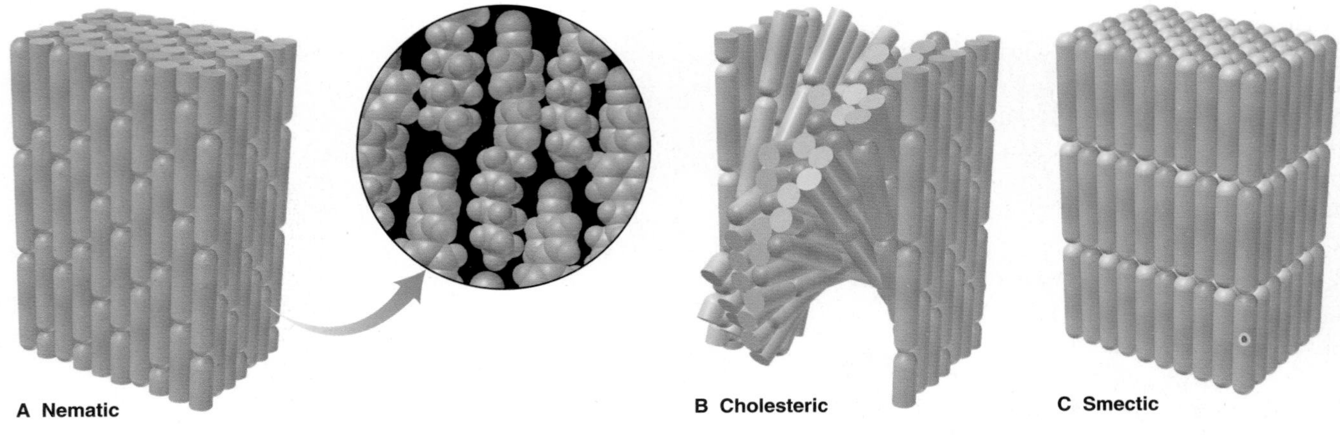

Figure 12.42 The three common types of ordering in liquid crystal phases.

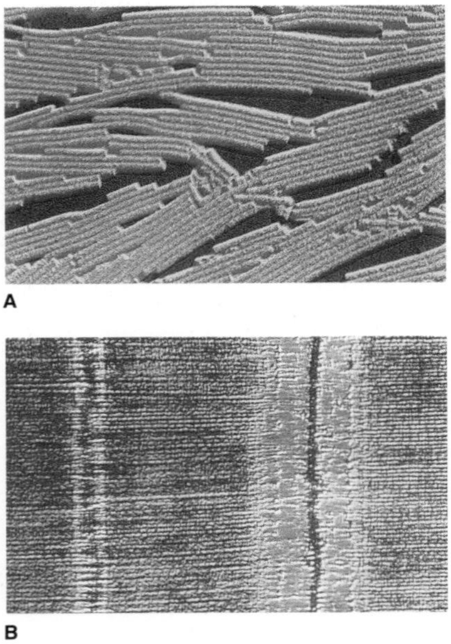

Figure 12.43 Liquid crystal–type phases in biological systems. **A,** Nematic arrays of tobacco mosaic virus particles within the fluid of a tobacco leaf. **B,** The smectic-like arrangement of actin and myosin protein filaments in voluntary muscle cells.

2. In a *cholesteric phase,* which is somewhat more ordered, the molecules lie in layers that each exhibit nematic-type ordering. Rather than lying in parallel fashion, however, each layer is rotated by a fixed angle with respect to the next layer to give a helical (corkscrew) arrangement. A cholesteric phase is often called a *twisted nematic phase* (Figure 12.42B).
3. In a *smectic phase,* which is the most ordered, the molecules lie parallel to each other, *with* their ends aligned, in layers that are stacked directly over each other (Figure 12.42C). The long molecular axis has a well-defined angle (shown in the figure as 90°) with respect to the plane of the layer. The molecules in Figure 12.41 form nematic or smectic phases. Liquid crystal–type phases appear in many biological systems (Figure 12.43).

Applications of Liquid Crystals The ability to control the orientation of the molecules in a liquid crystal allows us to produce materials with high strength or unique optical properties:

1. *High-strength applications* involve the use of extremely long molecules called *polymers.* While in a thermotropic liquid crystal phase and during their flow through the processing equipment, these molecules become highly aligned, like the fibers in wood. Cooling solidifies them into fibers, rods, and sheets that can be shaped into materials with superior mechanical properties. Sporting equipment, supersonic aircraft parts, and the sails used in the America's Cup races are fabricated from these polymeric materials. (We discuss the structure and physical behavior of polymers later in this section and their synthesis in Chapter 15.)

2. *Optical applications* include the liquid crystal displays (LCDs) used in countless devices, such as watches, calculators, cell phones, and computers. All depend on *changes in molecular orientation in an electric field.* Figure 12.44 shows a small portion of a wristwatch LCD. Layers of nematic phases are sandwiched between thin glass plates that incorporate transparent electrodes. The long molecular axis lies parallel to the plane of the plates. The distance between plates (6–8 μm) allows the molecular axis within each succeeding layer to twist just enough for the molecular orientation at the bottom plate to be 90° from that at the top plate. Above and below this "sandwich" are thin polarizing filters that allow light waves oriented in only one direction to pass through. The filters are placed in a "crossed" arrangement, so that light passing through the top filter must twist 90° to pass through the bottom filter. This whole grouping of filters, plates, and liquid crystal phase lies on a mirror.

A current generated by the watch battery controls the orientation of the molecules. With the current on in one region of the display, the molecules become oriented *toward* the field, and thus block the light from passing through to the bottom filter, so that region appears dark. With the current off in another region, light passes through the molecules and bottom filter to the mirror and back again, so that region appears bright.

Cholesteric liquid crystals are used in applications that involve color changes with temperature. The twisted molecular orientation "unwinds" with heating, and the extent of the unwinding determines the color. Liquid crystal thermometers include a mixture of substances to widen their range of temperatures. Newer uses include "mapping" the area of a tumor, detecting faulty connections in electronic circuit boards, and nondestructive testing of materials under stress.

Ceramic Materials

First developed by Stone Age people, **ceramics** are nonmetallic, nonpolymeric solids hardened by high temperature. Clay ceramics consist of silicate microcrystals suspended in a glassy cementing medium. In "firing" a ceramic pot, for example, a kiln heats the object made of an aluminosilicate clay, such as kaolinite, to 1500°C and the clay loses water:

$$Si_2Al_2O_5(OH)_4(s) \longrightarrow Si_2Al_2O_7(s) + 2H_2O(g)$$

During the heating process, the structure rearranges to an extended network of Si-centered and Al-centered tetrahedra of O atoms (Section 14.6).

Bricks, porcelain, glazes, and other clay ceramics are hard and resistant to heat and chemicals. Today's high-tech ceramics have these characteristics in addition to superior electrical and magnetic properties (Table 12.7). As just one example, consider the unusual electrical behavior of certain zinc oxide (ZnO) composites. Ordinarily a semiconductor, ZnO can be doped so that it becomes a conductor. Imbedding particles of the doped oxide into an insulating ceramic produces a variable resistor: at low voltage, the material conducts poorly, but at high voltage, it conducts well. The changeover voltage can be "preset" by controlling the size of the ZnO particles and the thickness of the insulating medium.

Preparing Modern Ceramics Among the important modern ceramics are silicon carbide (SiC) and nitride (Si_3N_4), boron nitride (BN), and the superconducting oxides. They are prepared by standard chemical methods that involve driving off a volatile component during the reaction:

1. *SiC ceramics* are made from compounds used in silicone polymer manufacture (we'll discuss these polymers in Section 14.6):

$$n(CH_3)_2SiCl_2(l) + 2nNa(s) \longrightarrow 2nNaCl(s) + [(CH_3)_2Si]_n(s)$$

This product is heated to 800°C to form the ceramic:

$$[(CH_3)_2Si]_n \longrightarrow nCH_4(g) + nH_2(g) + nSiC(s)$$

Silicon carbide can also be prepared by the direct reaction of silicon and graphite under vacuum:

$$Si(s) + C(graphite) \xrightarrow{\sim 1500°C} SiC(s)$$

Table 12.7 Some Uses of Modern Ceramics and Ceramic Mixtures

Ceramic	Applications
SiC, Si_3N_4, TiB_2, Al_2O_3	Whiskers (fibers) to strengthen Al and other ceramics
Si_3N_4	Car engine parts; turbine rotors for "turbo" cars; electronic sensor units
Si_3N_4, BN, Al_2O_3	Support or layering materials (as insulators) in electronic microchips
SiC, Si_3N_4, TiB_2, ZrO_2, Al_2O_3, BN	Cutting tools, edge sharpeners (as coatings and whole devices), scissors, surgical tools, industrial "diamond"
BN, SiC	Armor-plating reinforcement fibers (as in Kevlar composites)
ZrO_2, Al_2O_3	Surgical implants (hip and knee joints)

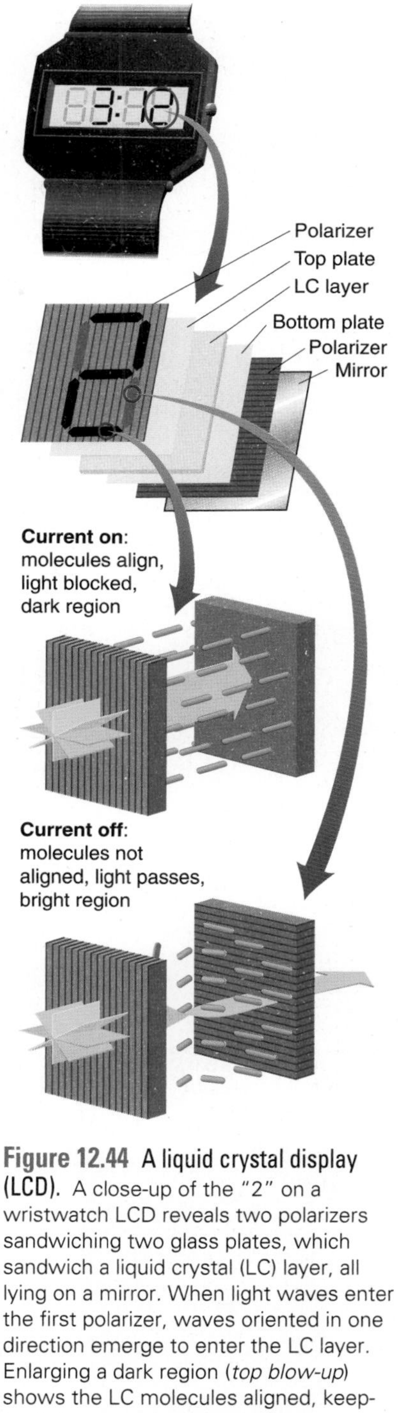

Figure 12.44 A liquid crystal display (LCD). A close-up of the "2" on a wristwatch LCD reveals two polarizers sandwiching two glass plates, which sandwich a liquid crystal (LC) layer, all lying on a mirror. When light waves enter the first polarizer, waves oriented in one direction emerge to enter the LC layer. Enlarging a dark region (*top blow-up*) shows the LC molecules aligned, keeping light waves from passing through; thus, the viewer sees no light. Enlarging a bright region (*bottom blow-up*) shows the LC molecules rotating the plane of the light waves, which can then pass through and reach the viewer.

The nitride is also prepared by reaction of the elements:

$$3Si(s) + 2N_2(g) \xrightarrow{>1300^\circ C} Si_3N_4(s)$$

2. *BN ceramics* are produced through the reaction of boron trichloride or boric acid with ammonia:

$$B(OH)_3(s) + 3NH_3(g) \longrightarrow B(NH_2)_3(s) + 3H_2O(g)$$

Heat drives off some of the bound nitrogen as NH_3 to yield the ceramic:

$$B(NH_2)_3(s) \xrightarrow{\Delta} 2NH_3(g) + BN(s)$$

3. One type of *superconducting oxide* is made by heating a mixture of barium carbonate with copper and yttrium oxides, followed by further heating in the presence of O_2:

$$4BaCO_3(s) + 6CuO(s) + Y_2O_3(s) \xrightarrow{\Delta} 2YBa_2Cu_3O_{6.5}(s) + 4CO_2(g)$$

$$YBa_2Cu_3O_{6.5}(s) + \tfrac{1}{4}O_2(g) \xrightarrow{\Delta} YBa_2Cu_3O_7(s)$$

Ceramic Structures and Uses Structures of several ceramic materials are shown in Figure 12.45.

1. *Silicon carbide* has a diamond-like structure. Network covalent bonding gives this material great strength. It is made into thin fibers, called *whiskers,* to reinforce other ceramics and prevent cracking in a composite structure, much like steel rods reinforcing concrete.

2. *Silicon nitride* is virtually inert chemically, retains its strength and wear resistance for extended periods above 1000°C, is dense and hard, and acts as an electrical insulator. Many automakers are testing it in high-efficiency car and truck engines because of its low weight, tolerance of high operating temperature, and little need for lubrication.

3. *BN ceramics* exist in two structures, analogous to the common crystalline forms of carbon. In the graphite-like form, BN has extraordinary properties as an electrical insulator. At high temperature and very high pressure (1800°C and 8.5×10^4 atm), it converts to a diamond-like structure, which is extremely hard and durable. Both forms are virtually invisible to radar.

4. *Superconducting oxides* often contain copper in an unusual oxidation state. In $YBa_2Cu_3O_7$, for instance, assuming oxidation states of +3 for Y, +2 for Ba, and −2 for O, the three Cu atoms have a total oxidation state of +7. This is allocated as $Cu(II)_2Cu(III)$, with one Cu in the unusual +3 state. X-ray diffraction analysis indicates that a distortion in the structure makes four of the oxide ions unusually close to the Y^{3+} ion, which aligns the Cu ions into chains within the crystal. It is suspected that a specific half-filled 3*d* orbital in Cu oriented toward a neighboring O^{2-} ion may be associated with superconductivity.

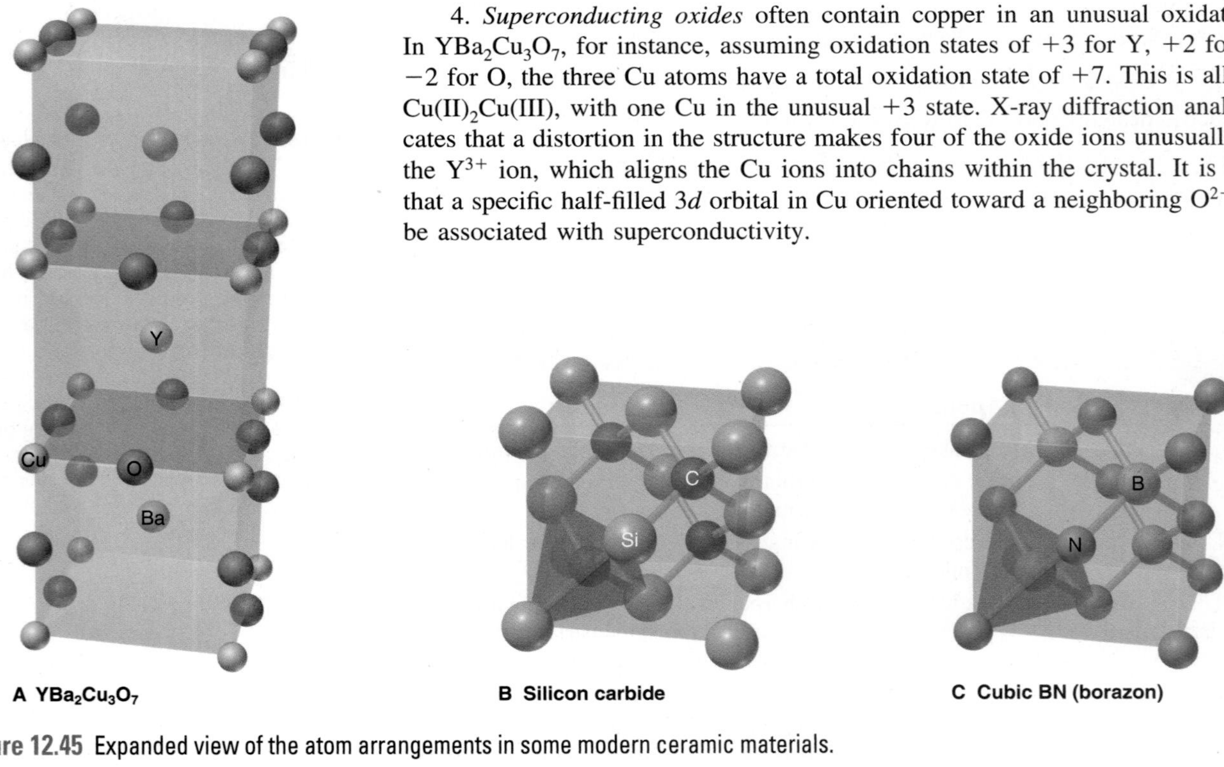

A $YBa_2Cu_3O_7$ **B Silicon carbide** **C Cubic BN (borazon)**

Figure 12.45 Expanded view of the atom arrangements in some modern ceramic materials.

Because of brittleness, it is difficult to fashion these ceramics into wires, but methods for making films and ribbons have been developed. The brittleness arises from the strength of the ionic-covalent bonding and the resulting inability to deform. Under stress, a microfine defect widens until the material cracks. One new method forms defect-free superconducting oxide ceramics using controlled packing and heat-treating of extremely small, uniform oxide particles coated with organic polymers. Another method is aimed at arresting a widening crack. The ceramics are embedded with zirconia (ZrO_2), whose crystal structure expands up to 5% under mechanical stress. When an advancing crack reaches them, the zirconia particles pinch it shut. A third method prepares the material of precisely grown crystals of Al_2O_3 and $GdAlO_3$, which become entangled during the solidification process. The resulting material bends without cracking above 1800 K.

Polymeric Materials

A **polymer** (Greek, "many parts") is an extremely large molecule, or **macromolecule,** consisting of a covalently linked chain of smaller molecules, called **monomers** (Greek, "one part"). The monomer is the *repeat unit* of the polymer, and a polymer may have hundreds to hundreds of thousands of repeat units. Many types of monomers give polymers the complete repertoire of intermolecular forces.

- *Synthetic* polymers are created in the laboratory.
- *Natural* polymers (or *biopolymers*) are created within organisms.

In this section, we examine the physical nature of synthetic polymers and explore the role of intermolecular forces in their properties and uses. In Chapter 15, we'll examine the types of monomers, the preparation of synthetic polymers, and the monomers, structures, and functions of some biopolymers.

Dimensions of a Polymer Chain Polymers differ from smaller molecules in terms of molar mass, chain length, shape, and size. We'll discuss these, using polyethylene, by far the most common synthetic polymer, as an example.

1. *Polymer mass*. The molar mass of a polymer chain ($\mathcal{M}_{\text{polymer}}$, in g/mol, often referred to as the *molecular weight*) depends on the molar mass of the repeat unit ($\mathcal{M}_{\text{repeat}}$) and the **degree of polymerization (*n*),** the number of repeat units in the chain:

$$\mathcal{M}_{\text{polymer}} = \mathcal{M}_{\text{repeat}} \times n$$

For example, the molar mass of the ethylene repeat unit ($-CH_2-CH_2-$) is 28 g/mol. If an individual polyethylene chain in a plastic grocery bag has a degree of polymerization of 7100, the molar mass of that chain is

$$\mathcal{M}_{\text{polymer}} = \mathcal{M}_{\text{repeat}} \times n = (28 \text{ g/mol})(7.1\times10^3) = 2.0\times10^5 \text{ g/mol}$$

Table 12.8 shows some other examples.

Table 12.8 Molar Masses of Some Common Polymers

Name	$\mathcal{M}_{\text{polymer}}$ (g/mol)	*n*	Uses
Acrylates	2×10^5	2×10^3	Rugs, carpets
Polyamide (nylons)	1.5×10^4	1.2×10^2	Tires, fishing line
Polycarbonate	1×10^5	4×10^2	Compact discs
Polyethylene	3×10^5	1×10^4	Grocery bags
Polyethylene (ultrahigh molecular weight)	5×10^6	2×10^5	Hip joints
Poly(ethylene terephthalate)	2×10^4	1×10^2	Soda bottles
Polystyrene	3×10^5	3×10^3	Packing, coffee cups
Poly(vinyl chloride)	1×10^5	1.5×10^3	Plumbing

However, even though the monomer repeat unit in any given chain has the same molar mass, the degree of polymerization often varies considerably from chain to chain. Thus, *a sample of a synthetic polymer has a distribution of chain lengths and molar masses*. Polymer chemists use various definitions of the *average* molar mass, and a common one is the *number-average molar mass*, $\mathcal{M}_n$:

$$\mathcal{M}_n = \frac{\text{total mass of all chains}}{\text{number of moles of chains}}$$

If the number-average molar mass of the polyethylene in grocery bags is, say, 1.6×10^5 g/mol, the chains may vary in molar mass from about 7.0×10^4 to 3.0×10^5 g/mol.

2. *Polymer chain length*. The long axis of a polymer chain is called its *backbone*. The length of an *extended* backbone is simply the number of repeat units (degree of polymerization, n) times the length of each repeat unit (l_0). For instance, the length of an ethylene repeat unit is about 250 pm, so the extended length of our particular grocery-bag polyethylene chain is

$$\text{Length of extended chain} = n \times l_0 = (7.1\times10^3)\,(2.5\times10^2\text{ pm}) = 1.8\times10^6\text{ pm}$$

Comparing this length with the thickness of the chain, which is about 40 pm, shows the threadlike nature of the extended chain (length about 50,000 times width).

3. *Coiled shape and size*. A polymer molecule, however, whether pure or in solution, doesn't exist as an extended chain. In principle, the shape of the molecule arises from free rotation around all the single bonds. Thus, as each repeat unit rotates randomly, the chain continuously changes direction, turning back on itself many times and eventually arriving at the **random coil** shape that most polymers adopt (Figure 12.46). In reality, rotation is not completely free because intermolecular forces between chain portions, between different chains, and/or between chain and solvent have significant effects on the actual shape of a polymer chain.

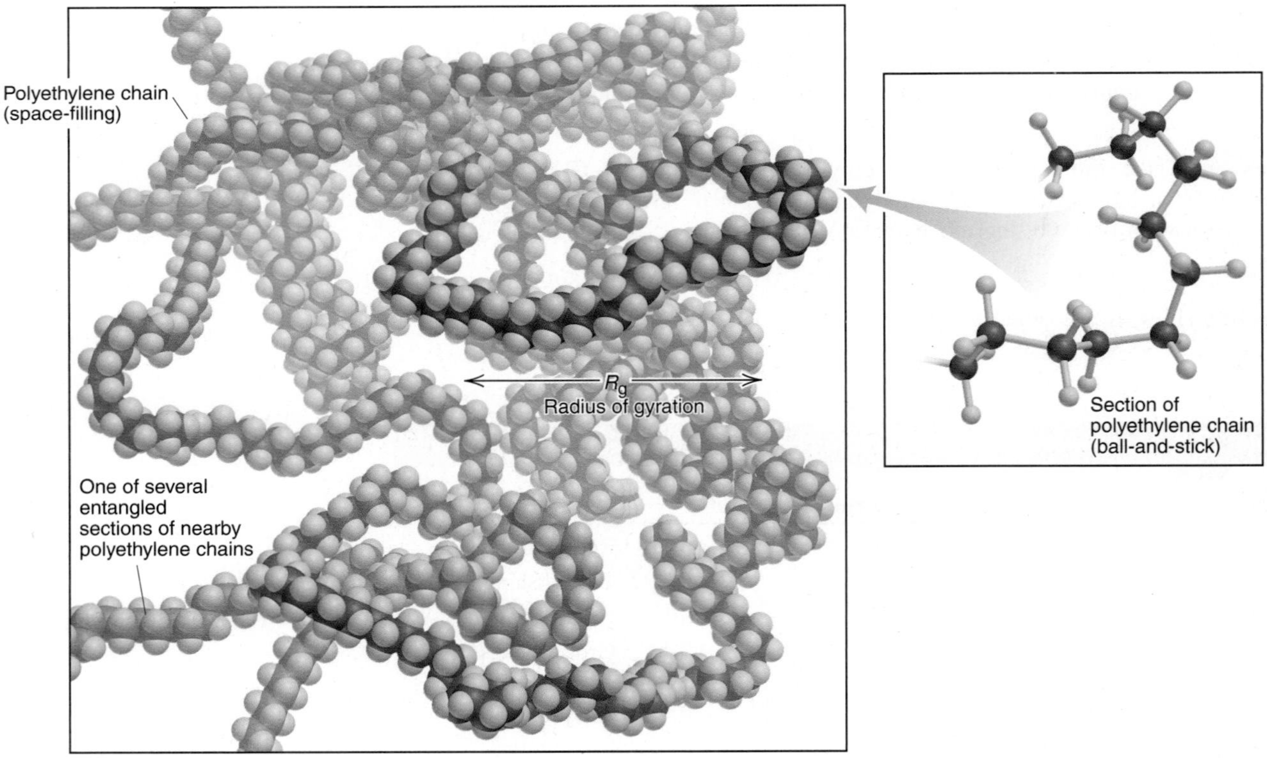

Figure 12.46 The random-coil shape of a polymer chain. Note the random coiling of the chain's carbon atoms (*black*). Sections of several nearby chains (*red, green,* and *yellow*) are entangled with this chain, kept near one another by dispersion forces. In reality, entangling chains fill any gaps shown here.

The size of the coiled chain is expressed by its **radius of gyration, R_g,** the average distance from the center of mass of the molecule to the outer edge of the coil (Figure 12.46). Even though R_g is reported as a single value for a given polymer, it represents an average value for many chains. The mathematical expression for the radius of gyration includes the length of each repeat unit and the degree of polymerization:*

$$R_g = \sqrt{\frac{nl_0^2}{6}}$$

As expected, the radius of gyration increases with the degree of polymerization, and thus with the molar mass as well. Light-scattering measurements correlate with these calculated results, so for many polymers the radius of gyration can be determined experimentally.

For our grocery-bag polyethylene chain, we have

$$R_g = \sqrt{\frac{nl_0^2}{6}} = \sqrt{\frac{(7.1\times10^3)(2.5\times10^2 \text{ pm})^2}{6}} = 8.6\times10^3 \text{ pm}$$

Doubling the radius gives a diameter of 1.7×10^4 pm for the coiled chain, less than one-hundredth the length of the extended chain!

Polymer Crystallinity A sample of a given polymer is not just a disorderly jumble of chains. If the molecular structure allows neighboring chains to pack together and if the chemical groups lead to favorable dipole-dipole, H-bonding, and/or dispersion forces, portions of the chains can align regularly and exhibit crystallinity.

However, the crystallinity of a polymer is very different from the crystal structures we discussed earlier. In those structures, the orderly array extends over many atoms or molecules, and the unit cell includes at least one atom or molecule. In contrast, the orderly regions of a polymer rarely involve even one whole molecule (Figure 12.47). At best, a polymer is *semicrystalline,* because parts of the molecule align with parts of neighboring molecules (or with other parts of the same chain), while most of the chain remains as a random coil.

*The mathematical derivation of R_g is beyond the scope of this text, but it is analogous to the two-dimensional "walk of the drunken sailor." With each step, the sailor stumbles in random directions and, given enough time, ends up very close to the starting position. The radius of gyration quantifies how far the end of the polymer chain (the sailor) has gone from the origin.

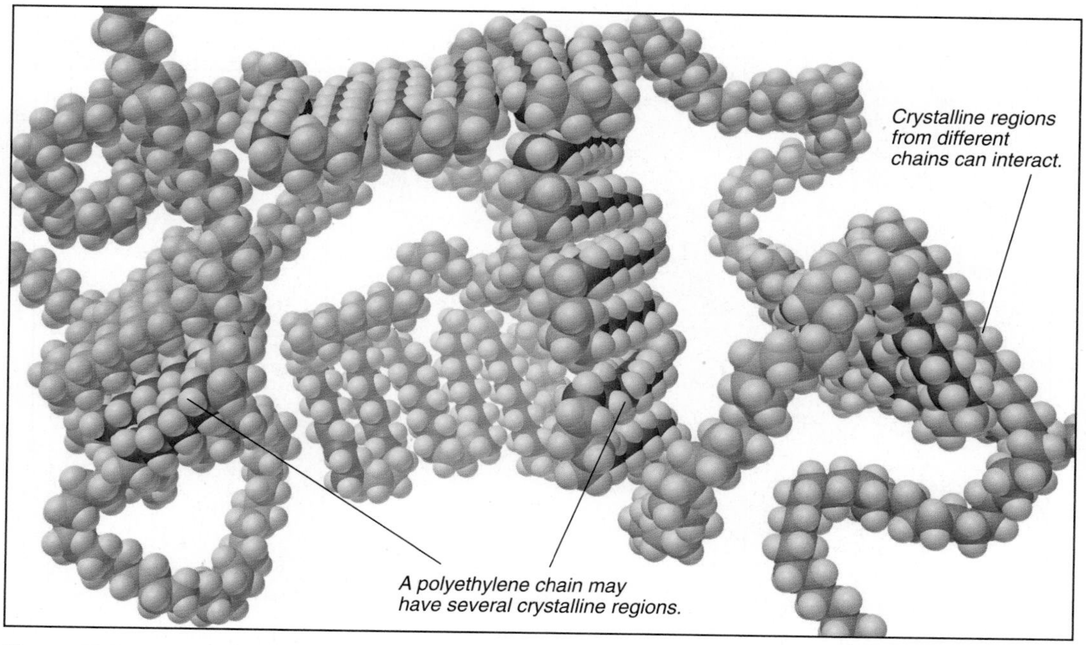

Figure 12.47 The semicrystallinity of a polymer chain. Several crystalline regions (*darker color*) have randomly coiled regions between them. Crystalline regions from nearby chains (*red* and *yellow*) align with those in the main chain.

Viscosity of Pure and Dissolved Polymers Some of the most important uses of polymers arise from their ability to change the viscosity of a solvent in which they are dissolved and to undergo temperature-dependent changes in their own viscosity.

1. *Dissolved polymers.* When an appreciable amount of polymer (about 5–15 mass %) dissolves, the viscosity of the solution is much higher than that of the pure solvent. In fact, polymers are added to increase the viscosity of many common materials, such as motor oil, paint, and salad dressing. As the random coil of a polymer moves through a solution, solvent molecules are attracted to it through intermolecular forces (Figure 12.48). Thus, as the solution flows, the polymer coil drags along solvent molecules that are interacting with other solvent molecules and other coils, and flow is reduced. Increasing the polymer concentration increases the viscosity because coils are more likely to become entangled.

Viscosity is a property of a particular polymer-solvent pair at a given temperature. The size (radius of gyration) of a random coil in solution increases with molar mass, and so does the viscosity. To improve polymer manufacture, chemists have developed equations to predict the viscosity of polymers of different molar masses in a variety of solvents (see Problem 12.142).

2. *Pure polymers.* Intermolecular forces also play a major role in the flow of a pure polymer sample. At temperatures high enough to melt them, many polymers exist as viscous liquids, flowing more like honey than water. The forces between the chains, as well as the entangling of chains, hinder the flow. As the temperature decreases, the intermolecular attractions exert a greater effect, and the eventual result is a rigid solid. If the chains don't crystallize, the resulting material is called a *polymer glass.* The transition from a liquid to a glass occurs over a narrow temperature range (10–20°C) for a given polymer; temperature at the midpoint of the range is

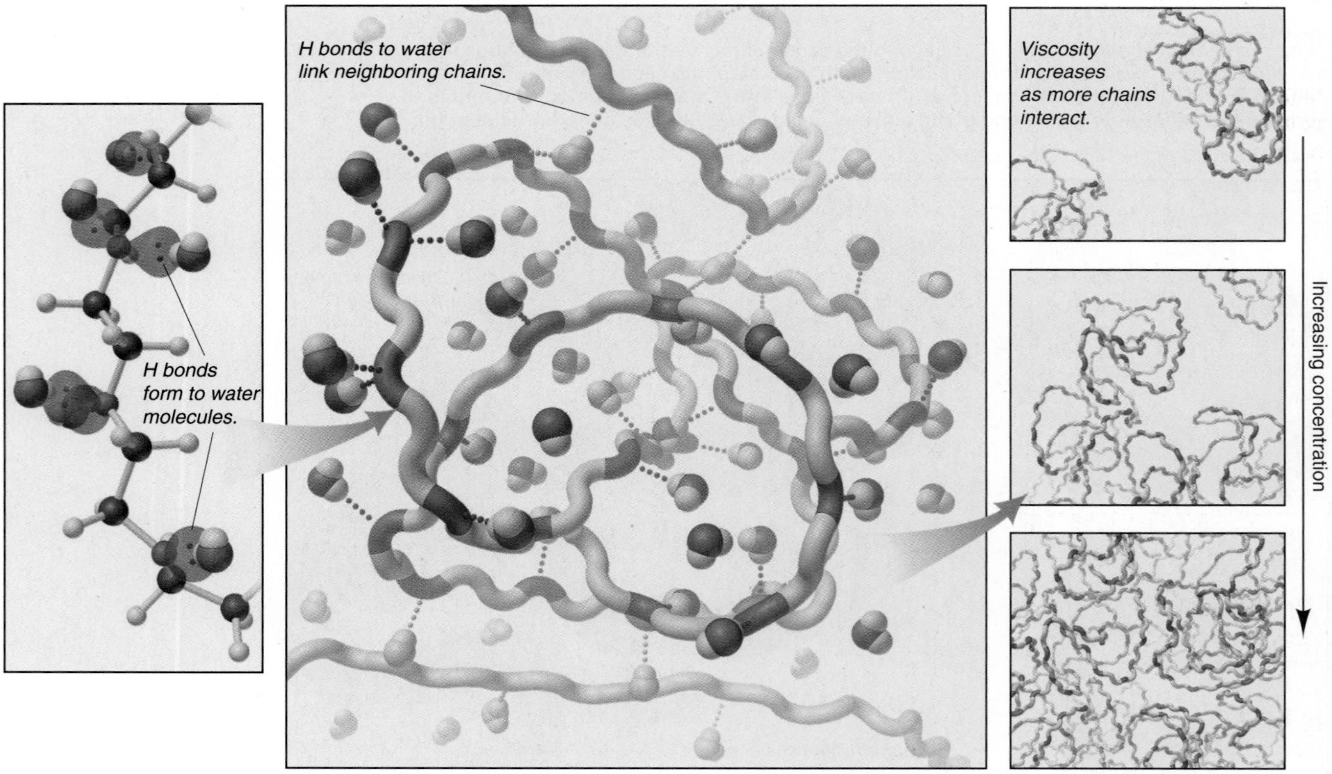

Figure 12.48 The viscosity of a polymer in aqueous solution. A section of a poly(ethylene oxide) chain *(left panel)* forms H bonds between the lone pairs of the chain's O atoms and the H atoms of water molecules. A polymer chain *(blue and red coiled rod, center panel)* forms many H bonds with water molecules that allow the chain to interact with other chains. As the concentration of polymer increases *(three right panels)*, the viscosity of the solution increases.

called the *glass transition temperature*, T_g. Like window glass, many polymer glasses are transparent, such as polystyrene in drinking cups and polycarbonate in eyeglass lenses.

Plasticity of Polymers The flow-related properties of polymers give rise to their familiar **plastic** mechanical behavior. The word "plastic" refers to a material that, when deformed, retains its new shape; in contrast, when an "elastic" object is deformed, it returns to its original shape. Many polymers can be deformed (stretched, bent, twisted) when warm and retain their deformed shape when cooled. In this way, they are made into milk bottles, car parts, and countless other everyday objects.

Molecular Architecture of Polymers A polymer's architecture—its overall spatial layout and molecular structure—is crucial to its properties. In addition to linear chains, more complex architectures arise through branching and crosslinking:

1. **Branches** are smaller chains appended to a polymer backbone. As the number of branches increases, the chains cannot pack as well, so the degree of crystallinity decreases and the polymer is less rigid. A small amount of branching occurs as a side reaction in the preparation of high-density polyethylene (HDPE). It is still largely linear and rigid enough for use in milk containers. In contrast, much more branching is intentionally induced to prepare low-density polyethylene (LDPE). The chains cannot pack well, so crystallinity is low. This polymer is used in flexible, transparent food storage bags.

Dendrimers are prepared from monomers with three or more attachment points, so each monomer forms branches. In essence, then, dendrimers have no backbone and consist only of branches. A dendrimer has a constantly increasing number of branches and an incredibly large number of end groups at its outer edge. Chemists use dendrimers to bind one polymer to another to create films and fibers and to deliver drugs in medical applications.

2. **Crosslinks** can be thought of as branches that link one chain to another. The extent of crosslinking leads to remarkable differences in properties. A small degree of crosslinking often yields a *thermoplastic* polymer, one that still flows at high temperatures. But, as the extent of crosslinking increases, a thermoplastic polymer is transformed into a *thermoset* polymer, one that can no longer flow because it has become a single network. Below their glass transition temperatures, some thermosets are extremely rigid and strong, making them ideal as matrix materials in high-strength composites (*see photo*).

Bicycle helmet containing a thermoset polymer.

Above their glass transition temperatures, many thermosets become **elastomers,** polymers that can be stretched and immediately spring back to their initial shapes when released, like a trampoline or a rubber band. When you stretch a rubber band, individual polymer chains flow for only a short distance before the connectivity of the network returns them to their original positions. Table 12.9 lists some elastomers.

Table 12.9 Some Common Elastomers

Name	T_g (°C)	Uses
Poly(dimethyl siloxane)	−123	Breast implants
Polybutadiene	−106	Rubber bands
Polyisoprene	−65	Surgical gloves
Polychloroprene (neoprene)	−43	Footwear; medical tubing

Impact of Monomer Sequence Differences in monomer sequences influence polymer properties as well. A *homopolymer* consists of one type of monomer (A—A—A—A—A— · · ·), whereas a **copolymer** consists of two or more types. The simplest copolymer is called an *AB block copolymer* because a chain (block) of monomer A and a chain of monomer B are linked at one point:

$$\cdots —A—A—A—A—A—B—B—B—B—B— \cdots$$

If the intermolecular forces between the A and B portions of the chain are weaker than those between different regions within each portion, the A and B portions form their own random coils. This ability makes AB block copolymers ideal *adhesives* for joining two polymer surfaces covalently. An ABA block copolymer has A chains linked at each end of a B chain:

$$\cdots\ \text{—A—A—A—B—}(\text{B})_n\text{—B—A—A—A—}\ \cdots$$

Some of these block copolymers act as *thermoplastic elastomers,* materials shaped at high temperature that become elastomers at room temperature; many are used in the modern footwear industry.

Silicone polymers are described briefly in Chapter 14, and organic reactions that form polymer chains from monomers are examined in Chapter 15.

Nanotechnology: Designing Materials Atom by Atom

Nanotechnology is the science and engineering of nanoscale systems, whose sizes range from 1 to 100 nm. (Recall that 1 nm is 10^{-9} m—about one-billionth the width of your dorm-room desk or one-millionth the width of your pen tip. A nanometer is to a meter as a marble is to Earth!) Nanotechnology joins scientists from physics, materials science, chemistry, biology, environmental science, medicine, and many branches of engineering.

Nanoscale materials behave neither like atoms, which are smaller (1×10^1 nm), nor like crystals, which are at least 1×10^5 nm. The different behavior is due to a surface area that is similar to their interior volume—for example, a 5-nm particle has about half of its atoms on its surface. Cut a piece of ordinary aluminum foil into pieces just large enough to see with a light microscope and they still behave like the original piece. But, if you could cut the original piece into 20–30-nm pieces, they would explode. Indeed, aluminum nanoparticles are used in fireworks and propellants.

As so often happens in science, a technological advance allows a new field to blossom. Nanotechnologists can use the scanning tunneling microscope (see Tools of the Laboratory, pp. 447–448) and the similar scanning probe and atomic force microscopes to examine the chemical and physical properties of nanostructures and build them up, in many cases, atom by atom.

Two features of nanoscale engineering occur routinely in nature:

1. *Self-assembly* is the ability of smaller, simpler parts to organize themselves into a larger, more complex whole. On the molecular scale, self-assembly refers to atoms or small molecules aggregating through intermolecular forces. Oppositely charged regions on two such particles make contact to form a larger particle, which in turn aggregates with another to form a still larger one.
2. *Controlled orientation* is the positioning of two molecules near each other long enough for intermolecular forces to result in a change, often a bond breaking or forming. All enzymes function this way.

Because this new field changes many times faster than a textbook does, we can only provide a glimpse of a few exciting research directions in nanotechnology.

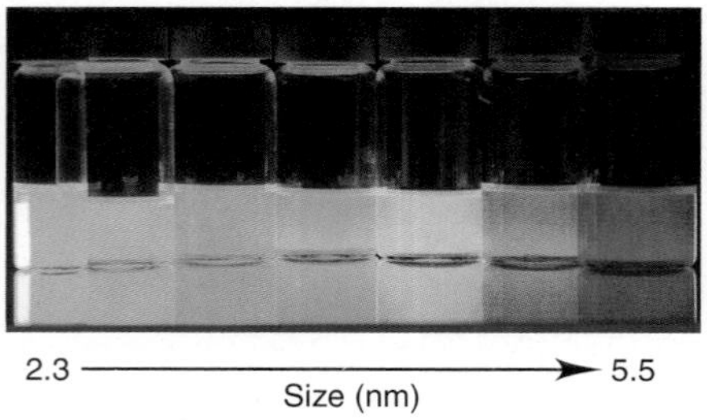

Figure 12.49 The colors of quantum dots. The smaller the dots, the shorter the emitted wavelengths.

Nanoscale Optical Materials *Quantum dots* are nanoparticles of semiconducting materials, such as gallium arsenide (GaAs) or gallium selenide (GaSe), that are smaller than 10 nm. Rather than having a band of energy levels, the dot has discrete energy levels, much like a single atom. As in atoms, the energy levels can be studied with spectroscopy; unlike atoms, quantum dots can be modified chemically. When high-energy (short-wavelength) UV light irradiates a suspension of quantum dots, they become excited and emit radiation of lower energy (longer wavelength). Most importantly, the emitted wavelengths depend on the size of the dots: the larger the particles, the longer the wavelength emitted. Thus, the color of the emitted light can be "tuned" by varying the dimensions of the nanoparticles (Figure 12.49). One use for quantum dots is the imaging of specific cells. The dot is encapsulated in a coating and then bonded to a particular protein used by a target organ. The cells in the target incorporate the protein, along with its attached quantum dot, and the location of the protein is viewed spectroscopically.

Nanostructured Materials *Nanostructuring,* the construction of bulk materials from nanoscale building blocks, increases strength, ductility, plasticity, and many other properties. The resulting *nanocomposites* behave as liquid magnets, ductile cements, conducting elastomers, and many other unique materials.

One example mimics a familiar natural material. Bones are natural nanocomposites of hydroxyapatite (a type of calcium phosphate) and other minerals. Synthetic nanocrystalline hydroxyapatite has been made with weight-bearing properties identical to bone that provides a framework for natural bone tissue to grow into and heal a fracture. Another material, called a *ferrofluid,* consists of magnetic nanoparticles (usually magnetite, Fe_3O_4) dispersed in a viscous fluid. When placed in a magnetic field, the particles align to conform to the shape of the field (Figure 12.50). Ferrofluids find uses in automobile shock absorbers, magnetic plastics, audio speakers, computer hard drives, high-vacuum valves, and many other devices.

Figure 12.50 The magnetic behavior of a ferrofluid. Nanoparticles of magnetite (Fe_3O_4) dispersed in a viscous fluid are suspended between the poles of a magnet.

High-Surface-Area Materials Carbon nanotubes have remarkable mechanical and electrical properties. But, a possible future application involves storing H_2 gas for hydrogen-powered vehicles. Currently, H_2 is stored in metal cylinders at high pressures (>70 atm). Porous solids, such as carbon nanotubes, can store the same amount of gas at much lower pressures because they have surface areas of 4500 m^2/g—about four football fields per gram of material! Thus, a medium-sized container of nanotubes could store a large amount of H_2 fuel under conditions safe enough for a family car.

Other high-surface-area materials being developed are porous membranes for water purification or batteries and multilayer films that incorporate photosynthetic molecules for high-efficiency solar cells. A very exciting development is the molecule-specific biosensor, which can detect as little as 10^{-14} mol of DNA using color changes in gold nanoparticles. Such biosensors could circulate freely in the bloodstream to measure levels of specific disease-related molecules, deliver drugs to individual cells, and even alter individual genes.

Nanomachines In nature, the virus is a marvel of nanoscale engineering, designed for delivering genetic material to infect a host cell. For example, the T4 virus latches onto a bacterial cell with its tail fibers, bores through the bacterial membrane with its end plate, and then injects the payload of DNA, packaged in its head, into the bacterium. These complex functions are performed by a biological "machine" measuring 60×200 nm. Researchers are exploring ways for viruses to deliver medicinal agents to specific cells. In other feats of nanoscale engineering, researchers have created nanovalves, nanopropellers, and even a nanocar, complete with a chassis, axles, and buckyball wheels, that is only 4 nm wide and is "driven" on a gold surface under the direction of an atomic force microscope (Figure 12.51).

Figure 12.51 Driving a nanocar.

Summary of Section 12.7

- Doping increases the conductivity of semiconductors and is essential to modern electronic materials. Doping silicon with Group 5A(15) atoms introduces negative sites (n-type semiconductor) by adding valence electrons to the conduction band, whereas doping with Group 3A(13) atoms adds positive holes (p-type semiconductor) by emptying some orbitals in the valence band. Placing these two types of semiconductors in contact with one another forms a p-n junction. Sandwiching a p-type portion between two n-type portions forms a transistor.

- Liquid crystal phases flow like liquids but have molecules ordered like crystalline solids. Typically, the molecules have rodlike shapes, and their intermolecular forces keep them aligned. Thermotropic phases are prepared by heating the solid; lyotropic phases form when the solvent concentration is varied. The nematic, cholesteric, and smectic phases of liquid crystals differ in their molecular order. Liquid crystal applications depend on controlling the orientation of the molecules.
- Ceramics are very resistant to heat and chemicals. Most are network covalent solids formed at high temperature from simple reactants. They add lightweight strength to other materials.
- Polymers are extremely large molecules that adopt the shape of a random coil, as a result of intermolecular forces. A polymer sample has an average molar mass because it consists of chains with a range of lengths. The high viscosity of a polymer arises from attractions between chains or, in the case of a dissolved polymer, between chains and solvent. By varying the degrees of branching, crosslinking, and ordering (crystallinity), chemists tailor polymers with specific properties.
- Nanoscale materials can be made through construction processes involving self-assembly and controlled orientation of molecules.

CHAPTER REVIEW GUIDE

Learning Objectives

Relevant section (§) and/or sample problem (SP) numbers appear in parentheses.

Understand These Concepts

1. How the interplay between kinetic and potential energy underlies the properties of the three states of matter and their phase changes (§12.1)
2. The processes involved, both within a phase and during a phase change, when heat is added or removed from a pure substance (§12.2)
3. The meaning of vapor pressure and how phase changes are dynamic equilibrium processes (§12.2)
4. How temperature and intermolecular forces influence vapor pressure (§12.2)
5. The relation between vapor pressure and boiling point (§12.2)
6. How a phase diagram shows the phases of a substance at differing conditions of pressure and temperature (§12.2)
7. The distinction between bonding and intermolecular forces on the basis of Coulomb's law and the meaning of the van der Waals radius of an atom (§12.3)
8. The types and relative strengths of intermolecular forces acting in a substance (dipole-dipole, H-bonding, dispersion), the impact of H bonding on physical properties, and the meaning of polarizability (§12.3)
9. The meanings of surface tension, capillarity, and viscosity and how intermolecular forces influence their magnitudes (§12.4)
10. How the important macroscopic properties of water arise from atomic and molecular properties (§12.5)
11. The meaning of *crystal lattice* and the characteristics of the three types of cubic unit cells (§12.6)
12. How packing of spheres gives rise to the hexagonal and cubic unit cells (§12.6)
13. Types of crystalline solids and how their intermolecular forces give rise to their properties (§12.6)
14. How band theory accounts for the properties of metals and the relative conductivities of metals, nonmetals, and metalloids (§12.6)
15. The structures, properties, and functions of modern materials (doped semiconductors, liquid crystals, ceramics, polymers, and nanostructures) (§12.7)

Master These Skills

1. Calculating the overall enthalpy change when heat is gained or lost by a pure substance (§12.2 and SP 12.1)
2. Using the Clausius-Clapeyron equation to examine the relationship between vapor pressure and temperature (SP 12.2)
3. Using a phase diagram to predict the physical state and/or phase change of a substance (§12.2)
4. Determining whether a substance can form H bonds and drawing the H-bonded structures (SP 12.3)
5. Predicting the types and relative strength of the bonding and intermolecular forces acting within a substance from its structure (SP 12.4)
6. Finding the number of particles in a unit cell (§12.6)
7. Calculating atomic radius from the crystal structure of an element (SP 12.5, 12.6)

Key Terms

Page numbers appear in parentheses.

Section 12.1
phase (419)
intermolecular forces (419)
phase change (420)
condensation (420)
vaporization (420)
freezing (420)
melting (fusion) (420)
sublimation (421)
deposition (421)
heat of vaporization (ΔH°_{vap}) (421)
heat of fusion (ΔH°_{fus}) (421)
heat of sublimation (ΔH°_{subl}) (421)

Section 12.2
heating-cooling curve (422)
vapor pressure (426)
Clausius-Clapeyron equation (427)
boiling point (428)
melting point (429)
phase diagram (429)
triple point (429)
critical point (429)

Section 12.3
van der Waals radius (431)
ion-dipole force (432)
dipole-dipole force (432)
hydrogen bond (H bond) (432)
polarizability (434)
dispersion (London) force (435)

Section 12.4
surface tension (437)
capillarity (438)
viscosity (439)

Section 12.6
crystalline solid (441)
amorphous solid (441)
lattice (442)
unit cell (442)
coordination number (442)
simple cubic unit cell (442)
body-centered cubic unit cell (442)
face-centered cubic unit cell (442)
packing efficiency (444)
hexagonal closest packing (444)
cubic closest packing (444)
x-ray diffraction analysis (447)
scanning tunneling microscopy (447)
atomic solid (449)
molecular solid (449)
ionic solid (449)
metallic solid (451)
network covalent solid (451)
band theory (452)
valence band (453)
conduction band (453)
conductor (453)
semiconductor (453)
insulator (453)
superconductivity (454)

Section 12.7
crystal defect (455)
doping (455)
liquid crystal (456)
ceramic (459)
polymer (461)
macromolecule (461)
monomer (461)
degree of polymerization (n) (461)
random coil (462)
radius of gyration (R_g) (463)
plastic (465)
branch (465)
crosslink (465)
elastomer (465)
copolymer (465)
nanotechnology (466)

Key Equations and Relationships

Page number appears in parentheses.

12.1 Using the vapor pressure at one temperature to find the vapor pressure at another temperature (two-point form of the Clausius-Clapeyron equation) (427):

$$\ln \frac{P_2}{P_1} = \frac{-\Delta H_{vap}}{R}\left(\frac{1}{T_2} - \frac{1}{T_1}\right)$$

Brief Solutions to Follow-Up Problems

12.1 The scenes represent solid water at −7.00°C melting to liquid water at 16.0°C, so there are three stages.

Stage 1, $H_2O(s)$ [−7.00°C] ⟶ $H_2O(s)$ [0.00°C]:

$$q = n \times C_{water(s)} \times \Delta T = (2.25\ mol)(37.6\ J/mol{\cdot}°C)(7.00°C) = 592\ J = 0.592\ kJ$$

Stage 2, $H_2O(s)$ [0.00°C] ⟶ $H_2O(l)$ [0.00°C]:

$$q = n(\Delta H^\circ_{fus}) = (2.25\ mol)(6.02\ kJ/mol) = 13.5\ kJ$$

Stage 3, $H_2O(l)$ [0.00°C] ⟶ $H_2O(l)$ [16.0°C]:

$$q = n \times C_{water(l)} \times \Delta T = (2.25\ mol)(75.4\ J/mol{\cdot}°C)(16.0°C) = 2714\ J = 2.71\ kJ$$

Total heat (kJ) = 0.592 kJ + 13.5 kJ + 2.71 kJ = 16.8 kJ

12.2
$$\ln \frac{P_2}{P_1} = \left(\frac{-40.7\times10^3\ J/mol}{8.314\ J/mol{\cdot}K}\right) \times \left(\frac{1}{273.15 + 85.5\ K} - \frac{1}{273.15 + 34.1\ K}\right)$$
$$= (-4.90\times10^3\ K)(-4.6\times10^{-4}\ K^{-1}) = 2.28$$

$\frac{P_2}{P_1} = 9.8$; thus, $P_2 = 40.1\ torr \times 9.8 = 3.9\times10^2\ torr$

12.3 (a)

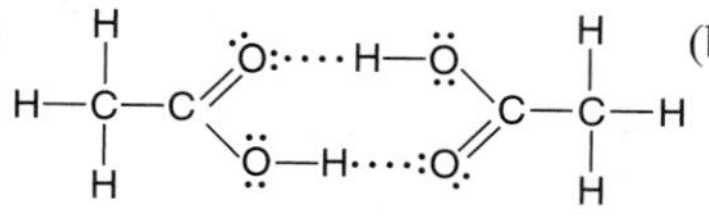

(b)

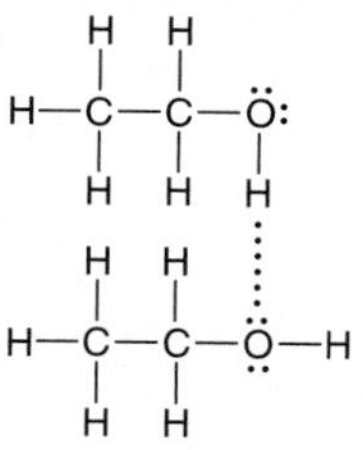

(c) No H bonding

12.4 (a) Dipole-dipole, dispersion; CH_3Br
(b) H bonds, dipole-dipole, dispersion; $CH_3CH_2CH_2OH$
(c) Dispersion; C_3H_8

12.5
$$\text{Avogadro's no.} = \frac{1\ cm^3}{7.874\ g\ Fe} \times \frac{55.85\ g\ Fe}{1\ mol\ Fe} \times 0.68 \times \frac{1\ Fe\ atom}{8.38\times10^{-24}\ cm^3}$$
$$= 5.8\times10^{23}\ Fe\ atoms/mol\ Fe$$

12.6 From Figure 12.29B,

$$A = \frac{4r}{\sqrt{3}} = \frac{4(126\ pm)}{\sqrt{3}} = 291\ pm$$

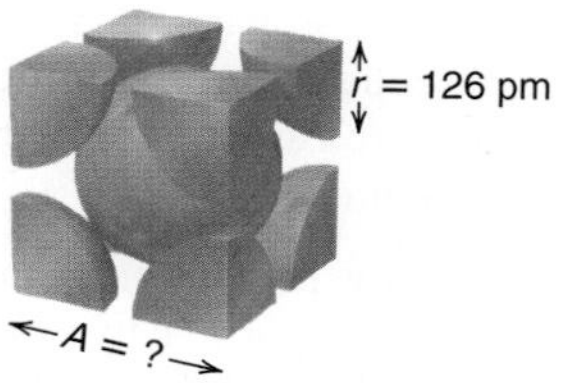

PROBLEMS

Problems with **colored** numbers are in Appendix E and worked in detail in the Student Solutions Manual. Problem sections match those in the text and provide the numbers of relevant sample problems. Most offer Concept Review Questions, Skill-Building Exercises (grouped in pairs covering the same concept), and Problems in Context. The Comprehensive Problems are based on material from any section or previous chapter.

Overview of Physical States and Phase Changes

Concept Review Questions

12.1 How does the energy of attraction between particles compare with their energy of motion in a gas and in a solid? As part of your answer, identify two macroscopic properties that differ between a gas and a solid.

12.2 (a) Why are gases more easily compressed than liquids? (b) Why do liquids have a greater ability to flow than solids?

12.3 What type of forces, intramolecular or intermolecular:
(a) Prevent ice cubes from adopting the shape of their container?
(b) Are overcome when ice melts?
(c) Are overcome when liquid water is vaporized?
(d) Are overcome when gaseous water is converted to hydrogen gas and oxygen gas?

12.4 (a) Why is the heat of fusion (ΔH_{fus}) of a substance smaller than its heat of vaporization (ΔH_{vap})?
(b) Why is the heat of sublimation (ΔH_{subl}) of a substance greater than its ΔH_{vap}?
(c) At a given temperature and pressure, how does the magnitude of the heat of vaporization of a substance compare with that of its heat of condensation?

Skill-Building Exercises (grouped in similar pairs)

12.5 Which forces are intramolecular and which intermolecular?
(a) Those preventing oil from evaporating at room temperature
(b) Those preventing butter from melting in a refrigerator
(c) Those allowing silver to tarnish
(d) Those preventing O_2 in air from forming O atoms

12.6 Which forces are intramolecular and which intermolecular?
(a) Those allowing fog to form on a cool, humid evening
(b) Those allowing water to form when H_2 is sparked
(c) Those allowing liquid benzene to crystallize when cooled
(d) Those responsible for the low boiling point of hexane

12.7 Name the phase change in each of these events: (a) Dew appears on a lawn in the morning. (b) Icicles change into liquid water. (c) Wet clothes dry on a summer day.

12.8 Name the phase change in each of these events: (a) A diamond film forms on a surface from gaseous carbon atoms in a vacuum. (b) Mothballs in a bureau drawer disappear over time. (c) Molten iron from a blast furnace is cast into ingots ("pigs").

Problems in Context

12.9 Liquid propane, a widely used fuel, is produced by compressing gaseous propane. During the process, approximately 15 kJ of energy is released for each mole of gas liquefied. Where does this energy come from?

12.10 Many heat-sensitive and oxygen-sensitive solids, such as camphor, are purified by warming under vacuum. The solid vaporizes directly, and the vapor crystallizes on a cool surface. What phase changes are involved in this method?

Quantitative Aspects of Phase Changes

(Sample Problems 12.1 and 12.2)

Concept Review Questions

12.11 Describe the changes (if any) in potential energy and in kinetic energy among the molecules when gaseous PCl_3 condenses to a liquid at a fixed temperature.

12.12 When benzene is at its melting point, two processes occur simultaneously and balance each other. Describe these processes on the macroscopic and molecular levels.

12.13 Liquid hexane (bp = 69°C) is placed in a closed container at room temperature. At first, the pressure of the vapor phase increases, but after a short time, it stops changing. Why?

12.14 Explain the effect of strong intermolecular forces on each of these parameters: (a) critical temperature; (b) boiling point; (c) vapor pressure; (d) heat of vaporization.

12.15 Match each numbered point in the phase diagram for compound Q with the correct molecular depiction below:

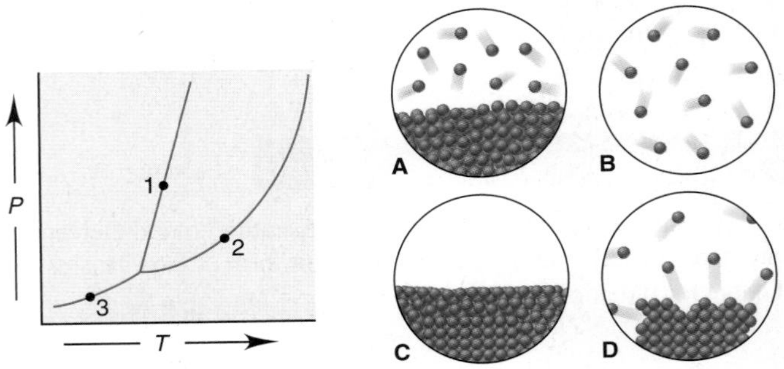

12.16 A liquid is in equilibrium with its vapor in a closed vessel at a fixed temperature. The vessel is connected by a stopcock to an evacuated vessel. When the stopcock is opened, will the final pressure of the vapor be different from the initial value if (a) some liquid remains; (b) all the liquid is first removed? Explain.

12.17 The phase diagram for substance A has a solid-liquid line with a positive slope, and that for substance B has a solid-liquid line with a negative slope. What macroscopic property can distinguish A from B?

12.18 Why does water vapor at 100°C cause a more severe burn than liquid water at 100°C?

Skill-Building Exercises (grouped in similar pairs)

12.19 From the data below, calculate the total heat (in J) needed to convert 22.00 g of ice at −6.00°C to liquid water at 0.500°C:

mp at 1 atm:	0.0°C	ΔH°_{fus}:	6.02 kJ/mol
c_{liquid}:	4.21 J/g·°C	c_{solid}:	2.09 J/g·°C

12.20 From the data below, calculate the total heat (in J) needed to convert 0.333 mol of gaseous ethanol at 300°C and 1 atm to liquid ethanol at 25.0°C and 1 atm:

bp at 1 atm:	78.5°C	ΔH°_{vap}:	40.5 kJ/mol
c_{gas}:	1.43 J/g·°C	c_{liquid}:	2.45 J/g·°C

12.21 A liquid has a ΔH°_{vap} of 35.5 kJ/mol and a boiling point of 122°C at 1.00 atm. What is its vapor pressure at 113°C?

12.22 Diethyl ether has a ΔH°_{vap} of 29.1 kJ/mol and a vapor pressure of 0.703 atm at 25.0°C. What is its vapor pressure at 95.0°C?

12.23 What is the ΔH°_{vap} of a liquid that has a vapor pressure of 621 torr at 85.2°C and a boiling point of 95.6°C at 1 atm?

12.24 Methane (CH_4) has a boiling point of −164°C at 1 atm and a vapor pressure of 42.8 atm at −100°C. What is the heat of vaporization of CH_4?

12.25 Use these data to draw a qualitative phase diagram for ethylene (C_2H_4). Is $C_2H_4(s)$ more or less dense than $C_2H_4(l)$?

bp at 1 atm:	−103.7°C
mp at 1 atm:	−169.16°C
Critical point:	9.9°C and 50.5 atm
Triple point:	−169.17°C and 1.20×10^{-3} atm

12.26 Use these data to draw a qualitative phase diagram for H_2. Does H_2 sublime at 0.05 atm? Explain.

mp at 1 atm:	13.96 K
bp at 1 atm:	20.39 K
Triple point:	13.95 K and 0.07 atm
Critical point:	33.2 K and 13.0 atm
Vapor pressure of solid at 10 K:	0.001 atm

Problems in Context

12.27 Sulfur dioxide is produced in enormous amounts for sulfuric acid production. It melts at −73°C and boils at −10.°C. Its ΔH°_{fus} is 8.619 kJ/mol and its ΔH°_{vap} is 25.73 kJ/mol. The specific heat capacities of the liquid and gas are 0.995 J/g·K and 0.622 J/g·K, respectively. How much heat is required to convert 2.500 kg of solid SO_2 at the melting point to a gas at 60.°C?

12.28 Butane is a common fuel used in cigarette lighters and camping stoves. Normally supplied in metal containers under pressure, the fuel exists as a mixture of liquid and gas, so high temperatures may cause the container to explode. At 25.0°C, the vapor pressure of butane is 2.3 atm. What is the pressure in the container at 135°C (ΔH°_{vap} = 24.3 kJ/mol)?

12.29 Use Figure 12.10, p. 429, to answer the following:
(a) Carbon dioxide is sold in steel cylinders under pressures of approximately 20 atm. Is there liquid CO_2 in the cylinder at room temperature (~20°C)? At 40°C? At −40°C? At −120°C?
(b) Carbon dioxide is also sold as solid chunks, called *dry ice,* in insulated containers. If the chunks are warmed by leaving them in an open container at room temperature, will they melt?
(c) If a container is nearly filled with dry ice and then sealed and warmed to room temperature, will the dry ice melt?
(d) If dry ice is compressed at a temperature below its triple point, will it melt?

Types of Intermolecular Forces
(Sample Problems 12.3 and 12.4)

Concept Review Questions

12.30 Why are covalent bonds typically much stronger than intermolecular forces?

12.31 (a) Name the type of force depicted in each scene below. (b) Rank the forces in order of increasing strength.

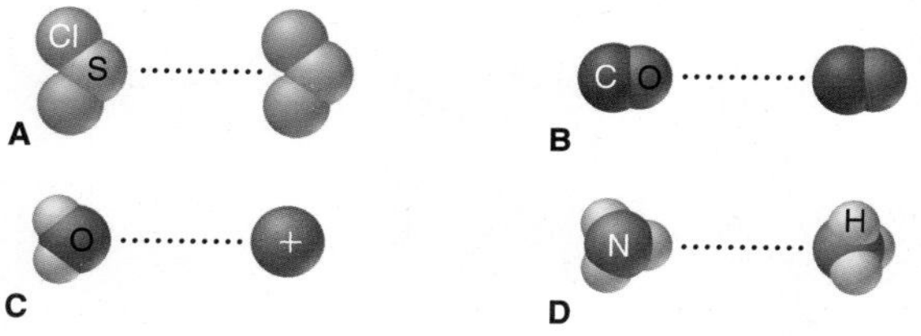

12.32 Oxygen and selenium are members of Group 6A(16). Water forms H bonds, but H_2Se does not. Explain.

12.33 In solid I_2, is the distance between the two I nuclei of one I_2 molecule longer or shorter than the distance between two I nuclei of adjacent I_2 molecules? Explain.

12.34 Polar molecules exhibit dipole-dipole forces. Do they also exhibit dispersion forces? Explain.

12.35 Distinguish between *polarizability* and *polarity*. How does each influence intermolecular forces?

12.36 How can one nonpolar molecule induce a dipole in a nearby nonpolar molecule?

Skill-Building Exercises (grouped in similar pairs)

12.37 What is the strongest interparticle force in each substance?
(a) CH_3OH (b) CCl_4 (c) Cl_2

12.38 What is the strongest interparticle force in each substance?
(a) H_3PO_4 (b) SO_2 (c) $MgCl_2$

12.39 What is the strongest interparticle force in each substance?
(a) CH_3Cl (b) CH_3CH_3 (c) NH_3

12.40 What is the strongest interparticle force in each substance?
(a) Kr (b) BrF (c) H_2SO_4

12.41 Which member of each pair of compounds forms intermolecular H bonds? Draw the H-bonded structures in each case:
(a) CH_3CHCH_3 (with OH on the central C) or CH_3SCH_3 (b) HF or HBr

12.42 Which member of each pair of compounds forms intermolecular H bonds? Draw the H-bonded structures in each case:
(a) $(CH_3)_2NH$ or $(CH_3)_3N$ (b) $HOCH_2CH_2OH$ or FCH_2CH_2F

12.43 Which forces oppose vaporization of each substance?
(a) Hexane (b) Water (c) $SiCl_4$

12.44 Which forces oppose vaporization of each substance?
(a) Br_2 (b) SbH_3 (c) CH_3NH_2

12.45 Which has the greater polarizability? Explain.
(a) Br^- or I^- (b) $CH_2{=}CH_2$ or $CH_3{-}CH_3$ (c) H_2O or H_2Se

12.46 Which has the greater polarizability? Explain.
(a) Ca^{2+} or Ca (b) CH_3CH_3 or $CH_3CH_2CH_3$ (c) CCl_4 or CF_4

12.47 Which member in each pair of liquids has the *higher* vapor pressure at a given temperature? Explain.
(a) C_2H_6 or C_4H_{10} (b) CH_3CH_2OH or CH_3CH_2F
(c) NH_3 or PH_3

12.48 Which member in each pair of liquids has the *lower* vapor pressure at a given temperature? Explain.
(a) $HOCH_2CH_2OH$ or $CH_3CH_2CH_2OH$
(b) CH_3COOH or $(CH_3)_2C{=}O$ (c) HF or HCl

12.49 Which substance has the *lower* boiling point? Explain.
(a) LiCl or HCl (b) NH_3 or PH_3 (c) Xe or I_2

12.50 Which substance has the *higher* boiling point? Explain.
(a) CH_3CH_2OH or $CH_3CH_2CH_3$ (b) NO or N_2
(c) H_2S or H_2Te

12.51 Which substance has the *lower* boiling point? Explain.
(a) $CH_3CH_2CH_2CH_3$ or $CH_2{-}CH_2$ / $CH_2{-}CH_2$ (cyclic, bonded in a ring) (b) NaBr or PBr_3
(c) H_2O or HBr

12.52 Which substance has the *higher* boiling point? Explain.
(a) CH_3OH or CH_3CH_3 (b) FNO or ClNO
(c)
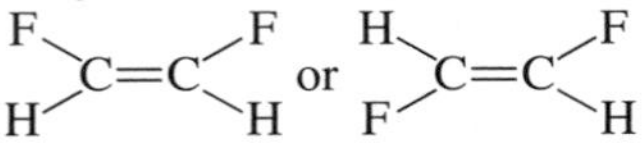

Problems in Context

12.53 For pairs of molecules in the gas phase, average H-bond dissociation energies are 17 kJ/mol for NH_3, 22 kJ/mol for H_2O, and 29 kJ/mol for HF. Explain this increase in H-bond strength.

12.54 Dispersion forces are the only intermolecular forces present in motor oil, yet it has a high boiling point. Explain.

12.55 Why does the antifreeze ingredient ethylene glycol ($HOCH_2CH_2OH$; $\mathcal{M} = 62.07$ g/mol) have a boiling point of 197.6°C, whereas propanol ($CH_3CH_2CH_2OH$; $\mathcal{M} = 60.09$ g/mol), a compound with a similar molar mass, has a boiling point of only 97.4°C?

Properties of the Liquid State

Concept Review Questions

12.56 Before the phenomenon of surface tension was understood, physicists described the surface of water as being covered with a "skin." What causes this skinlike phenomenon?

12.57 Small, equal-sized drops of oil, water, and mercury lie on a waxed floor. How does each liquid behave? Explain.

12.58 Why does an aqueous solution of ethanol (CH_3CH_2OH) have a lower surface tension than water?

12.59 Why are units of energy per area (J/m^2) used for surface tension values?

12.60 Does the *strength* of the intermolecular forces in a liquid change as the liquid is heated? Explain. Why does liquid viscosity decrease with rising temperature?

Skill-Building Exercises (grouped in similar pairs)

12.61 Rank the following in order of *increasing* surface tension at a given temperature, and explain your ranking:
(a) $CH_3CH_2CH_2OH$ (b) $HOCH_2CH(OH)CH_2OH$
(c) $HOCH_2CH_2OH$

12.62 Rank the following in order of *decreasing* surface tension at a given temperature, and explain your ranking:
(a) CH_3OH (b) CH_3CH_3 (c) $H_2C{=}O$

12.63 Rank the compounds in Problem 12.61 in order of *decreasing* viscosity at a given temperature; explain your ranking.

12.64 Rank the compounds in Problem 12.62 in order of *increasing* viscosity at a given temperature; explain your ranking.

Problems in Context

12.65 Soil vapor extraction (SVE) is used to remove volatile organic pollutants, such as chlorinated solvents, from soil at hazardous waste sites. Vent wells are drilled, and a vacuum pump is applied to the subsurface. (a) How does this remove pollutants? (b) Why does heating combined with SVE speed the process?

12.66 Use Figure 12.2, p. 421 to answer the following: (a) Does it take more heat to melt 12.0 g of CH_4 or 12.0 g of Hg? (b) Does it take more heat to vaporize 12.0 g of CH_4 or 12.0 g of Hg? (c) What is the principal intermolecular force in each sample?

12.67 Pentanol ($C_5H_{11}OH$; $\mathcal{M} = 88.15$ g/mol) has nearly the same molar mass as hexane (C_6H_{14}; $\mathcal{M} = 86.17$ g/mol) but is more than 12 times as viscous at 20°C. Explain.

The Uniqueness of Water

Concept Review Questions

12.68 For what types of substances is water a good solvent? For what types is it a poor solvent? Explain.

12.69 A water molecule can engage in as many as four H bonds. Explain.

12.70 Warm-blooded animals have a narrow range of body temperature because their bodies have a high water content. Explain.

12.71 What property of water keeps plant debris on the surface of lakes and ponds? What is the ecological significance of this?

12.72 A drooping plant can be made upright by watering the ground around it. Explain.

12.73 Describe the molecular basis of the property of water responsible for the presence of ice on the surface of a frozen lake.

12.74 Describe in molecular terms what occurs when ice melts.

The Solid State: Structure, Properties, and Bonding

(Sample Problems 12.5 and 12.6)

Concept Review Questions

12.75 What is the difference between an amorphous solid and a crystalline solid on the macroscopic and molecular levels? Give an example of each.

12.76 How are a solid's unit cell and crystal structure related?

12.77 For structures consisting of identical atoms, how many atoms are contained in the simple, body-centered, and face-centered cubic unit cells? Explain how you obtained the values.

12.78 An element has a crystal structure in which the width of the cubic unit cell equals the diameter of an atom. What type of unit cell does it have?

12.79 What specific difference in the positioning of spheres gives a crystal structure based on the face-centered cubic unit cell less empty space than one based on the body-centered cubic unit cell?

12.80 Both solid Kr and solid Cu consist of individual atoms. Why do their physical properties differ so much?

12.81 What is the energy gap in band theory? Compare its size in superconductors, conductors, semiconductors, and insulators.

12.82 Predict the effect (if any) of an increase in temperature on the electrical conductivity of (a) a conductor; (b) a semiconductor; (c) an insulator.

12.83 Besides the type of unit cell, what information is needed to find the density of a solid consisting of identical atoms?

Skill-Building Exercises (grouped in similar pairs)

12.84 What type of crystal lattice does each metal form? (The number of atoms per unit cell is given in parentheses.)
(a) Ni (4) (b) Cr (2) (c) Ca (4)

12.85 What is the number of atoms per unit cell for each metal?
(a) Polonium, Po (b) Manganese, Mn (c) Silver, Ag

12.86 When cadmium oxide reacts to form cadmium selenide, a change in unit cell occurs, as depicted below:

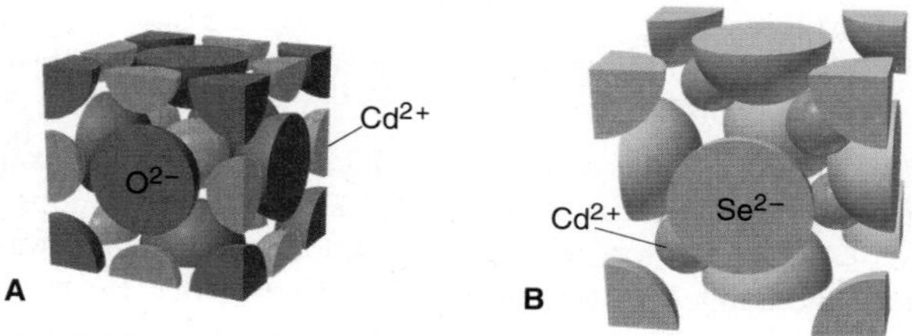

(a) What is the change in unit cell?
(b) Does the coordination number of cadmium change? Explain.

12.87 As molten iron cools to 1674 K, it adopts one type of cubic unit cell; then, as the temperature drops below 1181 K, it changes to another, as depicted below:

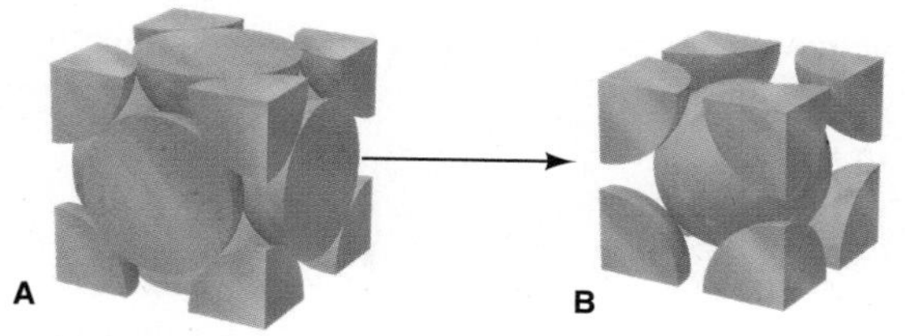

(a) What is the change in unit cell?
(b) Which crystal structure has the greater packing efficiency?

12.88 Of the five major types of crystalline solid, which does each of the following form, and why: (a) Ni; (b) F_2; (c) CH_3OH; (d) Sn; (e) Si; (f) Xe?

12.89 Of the five major types of crystalline solid, which does each of the following form, and why: (a) SiC; (b) Na_2SO_4; (c) SF_6; (d) cholesterol ($C_{27}H_{45}OH$); (e) KCl; (f) BN?

12.90 Zinc oxide adopts the zinc blende crystal structure (Figure P12.90). How many Zn^{2+} ions are in the ZnO unit cell?

12.91 Calcium sulfide adopts the sodium chloride crystal structure (Figure P12.91). How many S^{2-} ions are in the CaS unit cell?

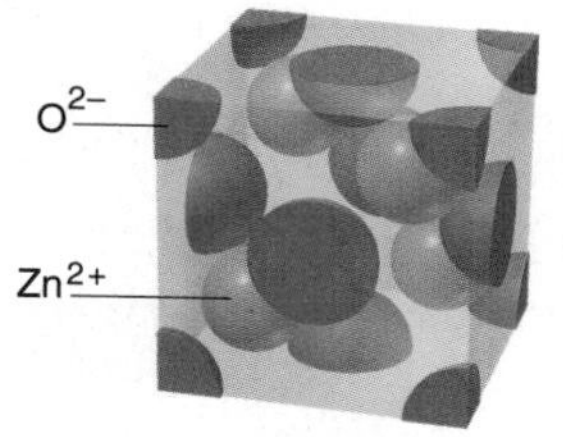

Figure P12.90

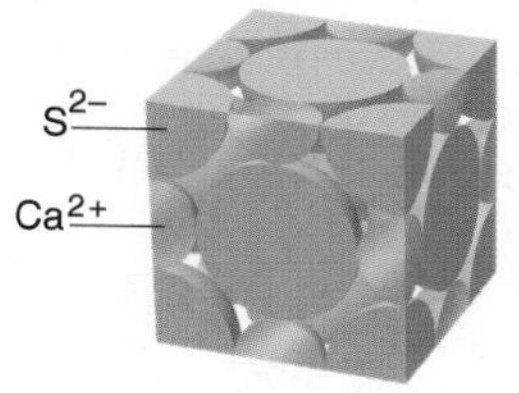

Figure P12.91

12.92 Zinc selenide (ZnSe) crystallizes in the zinc blende structure (see Figure P12.90) and has a density of 5.42 g/cm^3.
(a) How many Zn and Se ions are in each unit cell?
(b) What is the mass of a unit cell?
(c) What is the volume of a unit cell?
(d) What is the edge length of a unit cell?

12.93 An element crystallizes in a face-centered cubic lattice and has a density of 1.45 g/cm^3. The edge of its unit cell is 4.52×10^{-8} cm.
(a) How many atoms are in each unit cell?
(b) What is the volume of a unit cell?
(c) What is the mass of a unit cell?
(d) Calculate an approximate atomic mass for the element.

12.94 Classify each of the following as a conductor, insulator, or semiconductor: (a) phosphorus; (b) mercury; (c) germanium.

12.95 Classify each of the following as a conductor, insulator, or semiconductor: (a) carbon (graphite); (b) sulfur; (c) platinum.

12.96 Predict the effect (if any) of an increase in temperature on the electrical conductivity of (a) antimony; (b) tellurium; (c) bismuth.

12.97 Predict the effect (if any) of a decrease in temperature on the electrical conductivity of (a) silicon; (b) lead; (c) germanium.

Problems in Context

12.98 Polonium, the Period 6 member of Group 6A(16), is a rare radioactive metal that is the only element with a crystal structure based on the simple cubic unit cell. If its density is 9.142 g/cm^3, calculate an approximate atomic radius for polonium.

12.99 The coinage metals—copper, silver, and gold—crystallize in a cubic closest packed structure. Use the density of copper (8.95 g/cm^3) and its molar mass (63.55 g/mol) to calculate an approximate atomic radius for copper.

12.100 One of the most important enzymes in the world—nitrogenase, the plant protein that catalyzes nitrogen fixation—contains active clusters of iron, sulfur, and molybdenum atoms. Crystalline molybdenum (Mo) has a body-centered cubic unit cell (d of Mo = 10.28 g/cm^3). (a) Determine the edge length of the unit cell. (b) Calculate the atomic radius of Mo.

12.101 Tantalum (Ta; d = 16.634 g/cm^3 and $\mathcal{M}$ = 180.9479 g/mol) has a body-centered cubic structure with a unit-cell edge length of 3.3058 Å. Use these data to calculate Avogadro's number.

Advanced Materials

Concept Review Questions

12.102 When tin is added to copper, the resulting alloy (bronze) is much harder than copper. Explain.

12.103 In the process of doping a semiconductor, certain impurities are added to increase its electrical conductivity. Explain this process for an n-type and a p-type semiconductor.

12.104 State two molecular characteristics of substances that typically form liquid crystals. How is each related to function?

12.105 Distinguish between isotropic and anisotropic substances. To which category do liquid crystals belong?

12.106 How are the properties of high-tech ceramics the same as those of traditional clay ceramics, and how are they different? Refer to specific substances in your answer.

12.107 Why is the average molar mass of a polymer sample different from the molar mass of an individual chain?

12.108 How does the random coil shape relate to the radius of gyration of a polymer chain?

12.109 What factor(s) influence the viscosity of a polymer solution? What factor(s) influence the viscosity of a molten polymer? What is a polymer glass?

12.110 Use an example to show how branching and crosslinking can affect the physical behavior of a polymer.

Skill-Building Exercises (grouped in similar pairs)

12.111 Silicon and germanium are both semiconducting elements from Group 4A(14) that can be doped to improve their conductivity. Would each of the following form an n-type or a p-type semiconductor: (a) Ge doped with P; (b) Si doped with In?

12.112 Would each of the following form an n-type or a p-type semiconductor: (a) Ge doped with As; (b) Si doped with B?

12.113 The repeat unit in a polystyrene coffee cup has the formula $C_6H_5CHCH_2$. If the molar mass of the polymer is 3.5×10^5 g/mol, what is the degree of polymerization?

12.114 The monomer of poly(vinyl chloride) has the formula C_2H_3Cl. If there are 1565 repeat units in a single chain of the polymer, what is the molecular mass (in amu) of that chain?

12.115 The polypropylene (repeat unit CH_3CHCH_2) in a plastic toy has a molar mass of 2.8×10^5 g/mol and a repeat unit length of 0.252 pm. Calculate the radius of gyration.

12.116 The polymer that is used to make 2-L soda bottles [poly(ethylene terephthalate)] has a repeat unit with molecular formula $C_{10}H_8O_4$ and length 1.075 nm. Calculate the radius of gyration of a chain with molar mass of 2.30×10^4 g/mol.

Comprehensive Problems

12.117 A 0.75-L bottle is cleaned, dried, and closed in a room where the air is 22°C and 44% relative humidity (that is, the water vapor in the air is 0.44 of the equilibrium vapor pressure at 22°C). The bottle is then brought outside and stored at 0.0°C.
(a) What mass of liquid water condenses inside the bottle?
(b) Would liquid water condense at 10°C? (See Table 5.2, p. 200.)

12.118 In an experiment, 5.00 L of N_2 is saturated with water vapor at 22°C and then compressed to half its volume at constant T. (a) What is the partial pressure of H_2O in the compressed gas mixture? (b) What mass of water vapor condenses to liquid?

12.119 Barium is the largest nonradioactive alkaline earth metal. It has a body-centered cubic unit cell and a density of 3.62 g/cm^3. What is the atomic radius of barium? (Volume of a sphere: $V = \frac{4}{3}\pi r^3$.)

12.120 Two important characteristics used to evaluate the risk of fire or explosion are a compound's *lower flammable limit* (LFL) and *flash point*. The LFL is the minimum percentage by volume in air that is ignitable. Below that, the mixture is too "lean" to burn. The flash point is the temperature at which the air over a confined liquid becomes ignitable. *n*-Hexane boils at 68.7°C at 1 atm. At 20.0°C, its vapor pressure is 121 mmHg. The LFL of *n*-hexane is 1.1%. Calculate the flash point of *n*-hexane.

12.121 Bismuth is used to calibrate instruments employed in high-pressure studies because it has several well-characterized crystalline phases. Its phase diagram (*right*) shows the liquid phase and five solid phases that are stable above 1 katm (1000 atm) and up to 300°C. (a) Which solid phases are stable at 25°C? (b) Which phase is stable at 50 katm and 175°C? (c) As the pressure is reduced from 100 to 1 katm at 200°C, what phase transitions does bismuth undergo? (d) What phases are present at each of the triple points?

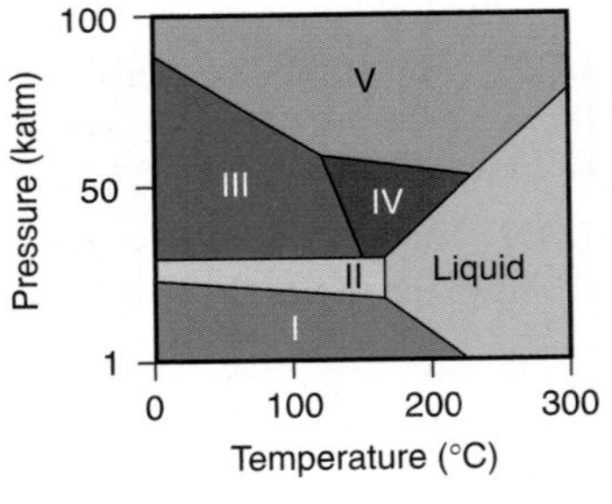

12.122 In making computer chips, a 4.00-kg cylindrical ingot of ultrapure n-type doped silicon that is 5.20 inches in diameter is sliced into wafers 1.12×10^{-4} m thick.
(a) Assuming no waste, how many wafers can be made?
(b) What is the mass of a wafer (d of Si = 2.34 g/cm^3; V of a cylinder = $\pi r^2 h$)?
(c) A key step in making p-n junctions for the chip is chemical removal of the oxide layer on the wafer through treatment with gaseous HF. Write a balanced equation for this reaction.
(d) If 0.750% of the Si atoms are removed during the treatment in part (c), how many moles of HF are required per wafer, assuming 100% reaction yield?

12.123 Methyl salicylate, $C_8H_8O_3$, the odorous constituent of oil of wintergreen, has a vapor pressure of 1.00 torr at 54.3°C and 10.0 torr at 95.3°C. (a) What is its vapor pressure at 25°C? (b) What is the minimum number of liters of air that must pass over a sample of the compound at 25°C to vaporize 1.0 mg of it?

12.124 Mercury (Hg) vapor is toxic and readily absorbed from the lungs. At 20.°C, mercury (ΔH_{vap} = 59.1 kJ/mol) has a vapor pressure of 1.20×10^{-3} torr, which is high enough to be hazardous. To reduce the danger to workers in processing plants, Hg is cooled to lower its vapor pressure. At what temperature would the vapor pressure of Hg be at the safer level of 5.0×10^{-5} torr?

12.125 Polytetrafluoroethylene (Teflon) has a repeat unit with the formula $F_2C{-}CF_2$. A sample of the polymer consists of fractions with the following distribution of chains:

Fraction	Average no. of repeat units	Amount (mol) of polymer
1	273	0.10
2	330	0.40
3	368	1.00
4	483	0.70
5	525	0.30
6	575	0.10

(a) Determine the molar mass of each fraction.
(b) Determine the number-average molar mass of the sample.
(c) Another type of average molar mass of a polymer sample is called the *weight-average molar mass*, $\mathcal{M}_w$:

$$\mathcal{M}_w = \frac{\Sigma\ (\mathcal{M} \text{ of fraction} \times \text{mass of fraction})}{\text{total mass of all fractions}}$$

Calculate the weight-average molar mass of the above sample.

12.126 A greenhouse contains 256 m^3 of air at a temperature of 26°C, and a humidifier in it vaporizes 4.20 L of water. (a) What is the pressure of water vapor in the greenhouse, assuming that none escapes and that the air was originally completely dry (d of H_2O = 1.00 g/mL)? (b) What total volume of liquid water would have to be vaporized to saturate the air (i.e., achieve 100% relative humidity)? (See Table 5.2, p. 200.)

12.127 Like most transition metals, tantalum (Ta) exhibits several oxidation states. Give the formula of each tantalum compound whose unit cell is depicted below:

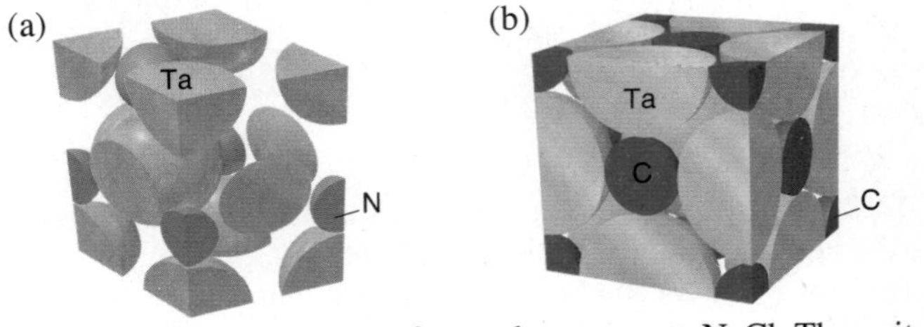

12.128 KF has the same type of crystal structure as NaCl. The unit cell of KF has an edge length of 5.39 Å. Find the density of KF.

12.129 Furfural, which is prepared from corncobs, is an important solvent in synthetic rubber manufacturing, and it is reduced to furfuryl alcohol, which is used to make polymer resins. Furfural can also be oxidized to 2-furoic acid.

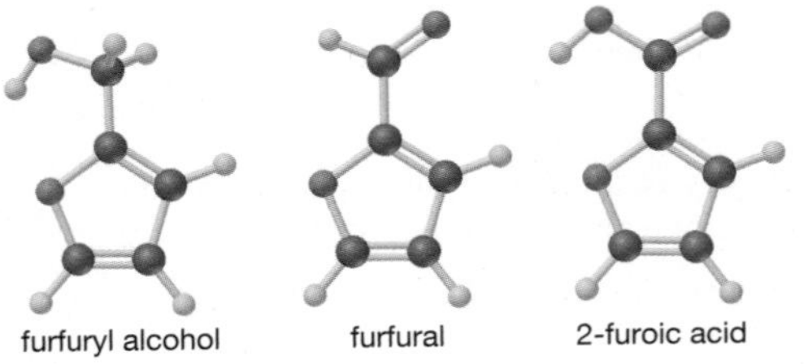

(a) Which of these compounds can form H bonds? Draw structures in each case.
(b) The molecules of some substances can form an "internal" H bond, that is, an H bond *within* a molecule. This takes the form of a polygon with atoms as corners and bonds as sides and an H bond as one of the sides. Which of these molecules is (are) likely to form a stable internal H bond? Draw the structure. (*Hint:* Structures with 5 or 6 atoms as corners are most stable.)

12.130 On a humid day in New Orleans, the temperature is 22.0°C, and the partial pressure of water vapor in the air is 31.0 torr. The 9000-ton air-conditioning system in the Louisiana Superdome maintains an inside air temperature of 22.0°C also, but a partial pressure of water vapor of 10.0 torr. The volume of air in the dome is 2.4×10^6 m^3, and the total pressure is 1.0 atm both inside and outside the dome. (a) What mass of water (in metric tons) must be removed every time the inside air is completely replaced with outside air? (*Hint:* How many moles of gas are in the dome? How many moles of water vapor? How many moles of dry air? How many moles of outside air must be added to the air in the dome to simulate the composition of outside air?) (b) Find the heat released when this mass of water condenses.

12.131 The boiling point of amphetamine, $C_9H_{13}N$, is 201°C at 760 torr and 83°C at 13 torr. What is the concentration (in g/m^3) of amphetamine when it is in contact with 20.°C air?

12.132 Diamond has a face-centered cubic unit cell, with four more C atoms in tetrahedral holes within the cell. Densities of diamonds vary from 3.01 g/cm^3 to 3.52 g/cm^3 because C atoms are missing from some holes. (a) Calculate the unit-cell edge length of the densest diamond. (b) Assuming the cell dimensions are fixed, how many C atoms are in the unit cell of the diamond with the lowest density?

12.133 Is it possible for a salt of formula AB_3 to have a face-centered cubic unit cell of anions with cations in all the eight available holes? Explain.

12.134 The density of solid gallium at its melting point is 5.9 g/cm^3, whereas that of liquid gallium is 6.1 g/cm^3. Is the temperature at the triple point higher or lower than the normal melting point? Is the slope of the solid-liquid line for gallium positive or negative?

12.135 A 4.7-L sealed bottle containing 0.33 g of liquid ethanol, C_2H_6O, is placed in a refrigerator and reaches equilibrium with its vapor at −11°C. (a) What mass of ethanol is present in the vapor? (b) When the container is removed and warmed to room temperature, 20.°C, will all the ethanol vaporize? (c) How much liquid ethanol would be present at 0.0°C? The vapor pressure of ethanol is 10. torr at −2.3°C and 40. torr at 19°C.

12.136 Substance A has the following properties.

mp at 1 atm:	−20.°C	bp at 1 atm:	85°C
ΔH_{fus}:	180. J/g	ΔH_{vap}:	500. J/g
c_{solid}:	1.0 J/g·°C	c_{liquid}:	2.5 J/g·°C
c_{gas}:	0.5 J/g·°C		

At 1 atm, a 25-g sample of A is heated from −40.°C to 100.°C at a constant rate of 450. J/min. (a) How many minutes does it take to heat the sample to its melting point? (b) How many minutes does it take to melt the sample? (c) Perform any other necessary calculations, and draw a curve of temperature vs. time for the entire heating process.

12.137 An aerospace manufacturer is building a prototype experimental aircraft that cannot be detected by radar. Boron nitride is chosen for incorporation into the body parts, and the boric acid/ammonia method is used to prepare the ceramic material. Given 85.5% and 86.8% yields for the two reaction steps, how much boron nitride can be prepared from 1.00 metric ton of boric acid and 12.5 m^3 of ammonia at 275 K and 3.07×10^3 kPa? Assume that ammonia does not behave ideally under these conditions and is recycled completely in the reaction process.

12.138 The ball-and-stick models below represent three compounds with the same molecular formula, $C_4H_8O_2$:

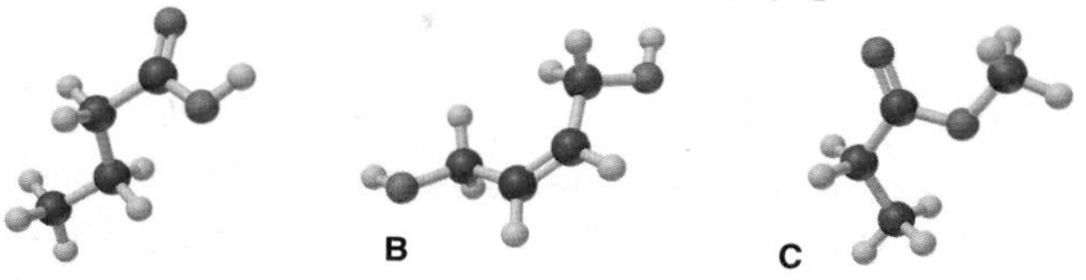

(a) Which compound(s) can form intermolecular H bonds?
(b) Which has the highest viscosity?

12.139 The ΔH°_f of gaseous dimethyl ether (CH_3OCH_3) is −185.4 kJ/mol; the vapor pressure is 1.00 atm at −23.7°C and 0.526 atm at −37.8°C. (a) Calculate ΔH°_{vap} of dimethyl ether. (b) Calculate ΔH°_f of liquid dimethyl ether.

12.140 The crystal structure of sodium is based on the body-centered cubic unit cell. What is the mass of one unit cell of Na?

12.141 The *intrinsic viscosity* of a solute in a solvent, $[\eta]_{solvent}$, is the portion of the total viscosity due to the solute and is related to solute shape. In polymer science, it relates as well to intermolecular interactions between solvent and polymer: higher $[\eta]_{solvent}$ means stronger interaction. The $[\eta]_{solvent}$ values of polymers in solution are given by the Mark-Houwink equation, $[\eta]_{solvent} = K\mathcal{M}^a$, where $\mathcal{M}$ is the molar mass of the polymer, and K and a are constants specific to the polymer and solvent. Use the data below for 25°C to answer the following questions:

Polymer	Solvent	K (mL/g)	a
Polystyrene	Benzene	9.5×10^{-3}	0.74
	Cyclohexane	8.1×10^{-2}	0.50
Polyisobutylene	Benzene	8.3×10^{-2}	0.50
	Cyclohexane	2.6×10^{-1}	0.70

(a) A polystyrene sample has a molar mass of 104,160 g/mol. Calculate the intrinsic viscosity in benzene and in cyclohexane. Which solvent has stronger interactions with the polymer?
(b) A different polystyrene sample has a molar mass of 52,000 g/mol. Calculate its $[\eta]_{benzene}$. Given a polymer standard of known $\mathcal{M}$, how could you use its measured $[\eta]$ in a given solvent to determine the molar mass of any sample of that polymer?
(c) Compare $[\eta]$ of a polyisobutylene sample [repeat unit $(CH_3)_2CCH_2$] with a molar mass of 104,160 g/mol with that of the polystyrene in part (a). What does this suggest about the solvent-polymer interactions of the two samples?

12.142 One way of purifying gaseous H_2 is to pass it under high pressure through the holes of a metal's crystal structure. Palladium, which adopts a cubic closest packed structure, absorbs more H_2 than any other element and is one of the metals used for this purpose. How the metal and H_2 interact is unclear, but it is estimated that the density of absorbed H_2 approaches that of liquid hydrogen (70.8 g/L). What volume (in L) of gaseous H_2 (at STP) can be packed into the spaces of 1 dm^3 of palladium metal?

The Properties of Mixtures: Solutions and Colloids

13

Concepts and skills to review before you study this chapter

- separation of mixtures (Section 2.9)
- calculations involving mass percent (Section 3.1) and molarity (Section 3.5)
- electrolytes; water as solvent (Sections 4.1 and 12.5)
- mole fraction and Dalton's law (Section 5.4)
- intermolecular forces and polarizability (Section 12.3)
- monomers and polymers (Section 12.7)
- vapor pressure of liquids (Section 12.2)

Virtually all the gases, liquids, and solids in the real world are *mixtures*—two or more substances mixed together physically, not combined chemically. Synthetic mixtures, such as glass and soap, usually contain only a dozen or so components, but natural mixtures, such as seawater and soil, often contain over 50. Living mixtures, such as trees and students, are the most complex—even a simple bacterial cell (*photo*) contains well over 5000 different compounds (Table 13.1).

Recall from Chapter 2 that a mixture has two defining characteristics: *its composition is variable,* and *it retains some properties of its components.* We focus here on two common types of mixtures—solutions and colloids—whose main differences relate to particle size and number of phases:

Table 13.1 Approximate Composition of a Bacterium

Substance	Mass % of Cell	Number of Types	Number of Molecules
Water	~70	1	5×10^{10}
Ions	1	20	?
Sugars*	3	200	3×10^{8}
Amino acids*	0.4	100	5×10^{7}
Lipids*	2	50	3×10^{7}
Nucleotides*	0.4	200	1×10^{7}
Other small molecules	0.2	~200	?
Macromolecules (proteins, nucleic acids, polysaccharides)	23	~5000	6×10^{6}

*Includes precursors and metabolites.

- A *solution* is a *homogeneous* mixture; thus, it exists as one phase. In a solution, the particles are individual atoms, ions, or small molecules.
- A *colloid* is a type of *heterogeneous* mixture. A heterogeneous mixture has two or more phases. They may be visibly distinct, like pebbles in concrete, or not, like the much smaller particles in the colloids smoke and milk. In a colloid, the particles are typically macromolecules or aggregations of small molecules that are dispersed so finely they don't settle out.

IN THIS CHAPTER . . . We focus on how intermolecular forces and other energy considerations affect a solute dissolving in a solvent, how we calculate concentrations, and how solutions differ from pure substances. We also briefly consider the behavior and applications of colloids.

- We survey intermolecular forces between solute and solvent and find that substances with similar types of forces form a solution.
- We see how the dual polarity of organic molecules gives rise to these same intermolecular forces, which determine the structures and functions of soaps, antibiotics, biological macromolecules, and cell membranes.
- We use a stepwise cycle to see why a substance dissolves and examine the roles of the heat of solution and the dispersal of matter. To understand the latter factor, we introduce the concept of entropy.
- We examine the equilibrium nature of solubility and see how temperature and pressure affect it.
- We define various solution concentration units and see how to interconvert them mathematically.
- We see why the physical properties of solutions are different from those of pure substances and how we apply those differences.
- We investigate colloids and apply solution and colloid chemistry to the purification of water.

13.1 • TYPES OF SOLUTIONS: INTERMOLECULAR FORCES AND SOLUBILITY

A **solute** dissolves in a **solvent** to form a solution. In general, *the solvent is the most abundant component,* but in some cases, the substances are **miscible**—soluble in each other in any proportion—so the terms "solute" and "solvent" lose their meaning. *The physical state of the solvent usually determines the physical state of the solution.* Solutions can be gaseous, liquid, or solid, but we focus mostly on liquid solutions because they are by far the most important.

The **solubility (*S*)** of a solute is the maximum amount that dissolves in a fixed quantity of a given solvent at a given temperature, where an excess of the solute is present. Different solutes have different solubilities:

- Sodium chloride (NaCl), S = 39.12 g/100. mL water at 100.°C.
- Silver chloride (AgCl), S = 0.0021 g/100. mL water at 100.°C.

Solubility is a *quantitative* term, but *dilute* and *concentrated* are qualitative, referring to the *relative* amounts of dissolved solute; the NaCl solution above is concentrated, and the AgCl solution is dilute.

A given solute may dissolve in one solvent and not another. The explanation lies in the relative strengths of the intermolecular forces within both solute and solvent and between them. The useful rule-of-thumb **"like dissolves like"** says that *substances with similar types of intermolecular forces dissolve in each other.* Thus, by knowing the forces, we can often predict whether a solute will dissolve in a solvent.

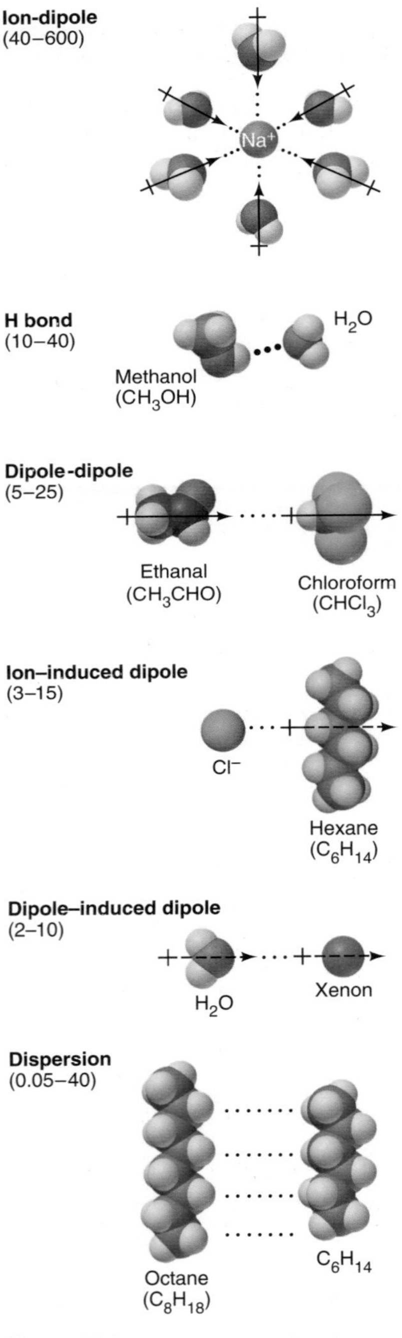

Figure 13.1 **Types of intermolecular forces in solutions.** Forces are listed in order of decreasing strength (values are in kJ/mol), with an example of each.

Intermolecular Forces in Solution

All the intermolecular forces we discussed for pure substances also occur in solutions (Figure 13.1; also see Section 12.3):

1. *Ion-dipole forces* are the principal force involved when an ionic compound dissolves in water. Two events occur simultaneously:
   - *Forces compete.* When a salt is added to water, an ion and the oppositely charged pole of a water molecule attract each other. These attractions compete with and overcome attractions between the ions, and the crystal structure breaks down.
   - *Hydration shells form.* As an ion separates, water molecules cluster around it in **hydration shells.** The number of water molecules in the closest shell depends on the ion's size: four fit tetrahedrally around small ions like Li^+, while the larger Na^+ and F^- have six water molecules surrounding them octahedrally (Figure 13.2). In the innermost shell, normal H bonding is disrupted to form the ion-dipole forces. But these water molecules are H bonded to others in the next shell, and those are H bonded to others still farther away.
2. *Hydrogen bonding* is the principal force in solutions of polar, O- and N-containing organic and biological compounds, such as alcohols, amines, and amino acids.
3. *Dipole-dipole forces,* in the absence of H bonding, allow polar molecules like propanal (CH_3CH_2CHO) to dissolve in polar solvents like dichloromethane (CH_2Cl_2).
4. **Ion–induced dipole forces,** one type of *charge-induced dipole force,* rely on polarizability. They arise when an ion's charge distorts the electron cloud of a nearby nonpolar molecule. This type of force initiates the binding of the Fe^{2+} ion in hemoglobin to an O_2 molecule entering a red blood cell.
5. **Dipole–induced dipole forces,** also based on polarizability, arise when a polar molecule distorts the electron cloud of a nonpolar molecule. They are weaker than ion–induced dipole forces because the charge of each pole is less than an ion's (Coulomb's law). The solubility in water of atmospheric O_2, N_2, and noble gases, while limited, is due in part to these forces. Paint thinners and grease solvents also use them.
6. *Dispersion forces* contribute to the solubility of all solutes in all solvents, but they are the *principal* intermolecular force in solutions of nonpolar substances, such as those in petroleum or gasoline.

The same forces keep biological macromolecules in their active shapes (Section 13.2).

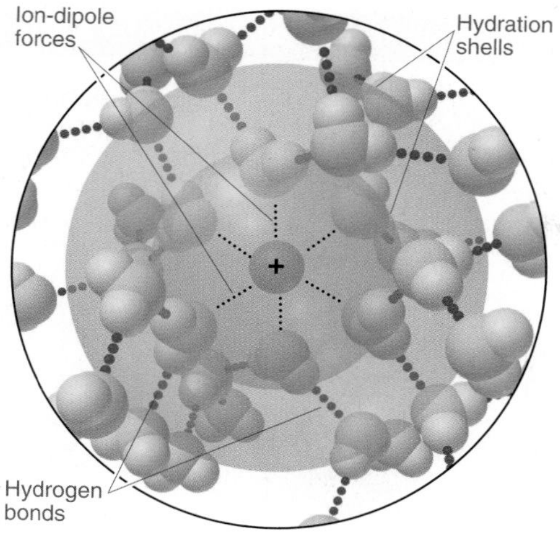

Figure 13.2 Hydration shells around an Na^+ ion. Ion-dipole forces orient water molecules around an ion. In the innermost shell here, six water molecules surround the cation octahedrally.

Liquid Solutions and the Role of Molecular Polarity

From cytoplasm to tree sap, gasoline to cleaning fluid, iced tea to urine, liquid solutions are very familiar. Water is the most prominent solvent, but there are many other liquid solvents, with polarities from very polar to nonpolar.

Applying the Like-Dissolves-Like Rule The like-dissolves-like rule says that when the forces *within* the solute are *similar* to those *within* the solvent, the forces *replace* each other and a solution forms. Thus,

- *Salts are soluble in water* because the strong ion-dipole attractions between ion and water are so similar to the strong attractions between the ions and the strong H bonds between water molecules that they *can* replace each other.
- *Salts are insoluble in hexane* (C_6H_{14}) because the weak ion–induced dipole forces between ion and nonpolar hexane *cannot* replace attractions between the ions.
- *Oil is insoluble in water* because the weak dipole–induced dipole forces between oil and water molecules cannot replace the strong H bonds within water molecules and the extensive dispersion forces within the oil.
- *Oil is soluble in hexane* because dispersion forces in one readily replace dispersion forces in the other.

Dual Polarity and Effects on Solubility To examine these ideas further, let's compare the solubilities of a series of alcohols in water and hexane, solvents with very different intermolecular forces. Alcohols are organic compounds that have a dual polarity, a polar hydroxyl (—OH) group bonded to a nonpolar hydrocarbon group:

- The —OH portion interacts through strong H bonds with water and through weak dipole–induced dipole forces with hexane.
- The hydrocarbon portion interacts through many dispersion forces with hexane and through weak dipole–induced dipole forces with water.

The general formula for an alcohol is $CH_3(CH_2)_nOH$, and we'll look at straight-chain examples with one to six carbons ($n = 0$ to 5):

1. *Solubility in water is high for smaller alcohols.* From the models in Table 13.2 *(next page)*, we see that the —OH group is a relatively large portion of the alcohols with one to three carbons ($n = 0$ to 2). These molecules interact with each other through H bonding, just as water molecules do. When they mix with water, H bonding in solute and in solvent is replaced by H bonding *between* solute and solvent (Figure 13.3, *next page*). As a result, these smaller alcohols are miscible with water.

Table 13.2 Solubility* of a Series of Alcohols in Water and in Hexane

Alcohol	Model	Solubility in Water	Solubility in Hexane
CH_3OH (methanol)		∞	1.2
CH_3CH_2OH (ethanol)	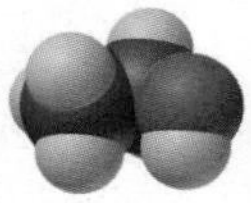	∞	∞
$CH_3(CH_2)_2OH$ (1-propanol)		∞	∞
$CH_3(CH_2)_3OH$ (1-butanol)		1.1	∞
$CH_3(CH_2)_4OH$ (1-pentanol)		0.30	∞
$CH_3(CH_2)_5OH$ (1-hexanol)		0.058	∞

*Expressed in mol alcohol/1000 g solvent at 20°C.

2. *Solubility in water is low for larger alcohols.* Solubility decreases dramatically for alcohols larger than three carbons ($n > 2$); in fact, those with chains longer than six carbons are insoluble in water. For larger alcohols to dissolve, the nonpolar chains have to move among the water molecules, replacing weak attractions with water for strong H bonds between water molecules. While the —OH portion of such an alcohol forms H bonds to water, these cannot make up for all the other H bonds between water molecules that have to break to make room for the hydrocarbon portion.

Table 13.2 shows that the opposite trend occurs with hexane:

1. *Solubility in hexane is low for smaller alcohols.* For alcohols in hexane, in addition to dispersion forces, weak dipole–induced dipole forces exist between the —OH of methanol (CH_3OH) and hexane. These cannot replace the strong H bonding between CH_3OH molecules, so solubility is low.

2. *Solubility in hexane is high for larger alcohols.* In any larger alcohol ($n > 0$), dispersion forces between the hydrocarbon portion and hexane *can* replace dispersion forces between hexane molecules. With only weak forces within the solvent to be replaced, even ethanol, with a two-carbon chain, has enough dispersion forces between it and hexane to be miscible.

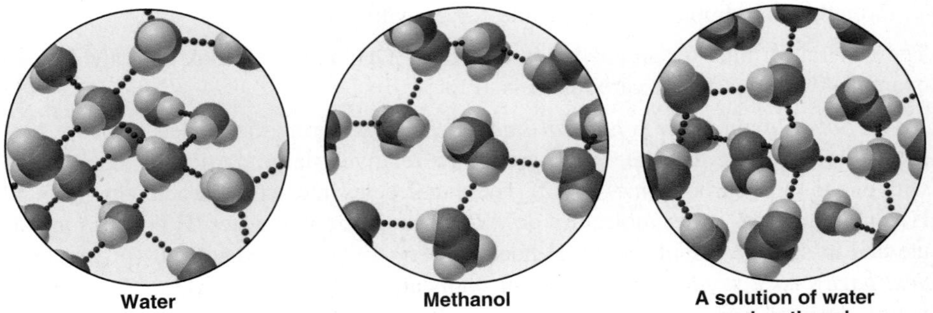

Figure 13.3 Like dissolves like: solubility of methanol in water. H bonds in water and in methanol replace one another when the two substances form a solution.

Many organic molecules have polar and nonpolar portions, which determine their solubility. For example, carboxylic acids and amines behave like alcohols: methanoic acid (HCOOH, formic acid) and methanamine (CH_3NH_2) are miscible with water and slightly soluble in hexane, whereas hexanoic acid [$CH_3(CH_2)_4COOH$] and 1-hexanamine [$CH_3(CH_2)_5NH_2$] are slightly soluble in water and very soluble in hexane.

Sample Problem 13.1 Predicting Relative Solubilities

Problem Predict which solvent will dissolve more of the given solute:
(a) Sodium chloride in methanol (CH_3OH) or in 1-propanol ($CH_3CH_2CH_2OH$)
(b) Ethylene glycol ($HOCH_2CH_2OH$) in hexane ($CH_3CH_2CH_2CH_2CH_2CH_3$) or in water
(c) Diethyl ether ($CH_3CH_2OCH_2CH_3$) in water or in ethanol (CH_3CH_2OH)

Plan We examine the formulas of solute and solvent to determine the forces in and between solute and solvent. A solute is more soluble in a solvent whose intermolecular forces are similar to, and therefore can replace, its own.

Solution (a) Methanol. NaCl is ionic, so it dissolves through ion-dipole forces. Both methanol and 1-propanol have a polar —OH group, but the hydrocarbon portion of each alcohol interacts only weakly with the ions and 1-propanol has a longer hydrocarbon portion than methanol.
(b) Water. Ethylene glycol molecules have two —OH groups, so they interact with each other through H bonding. H bonds formed with H_2O can replace these H bonds between solute molecules better than dipole–induced dipole forces with hexane can.
(c) Ethanol. Diethyl ether molecules interact through dipole-dipole and dispersion forces. They can form H bonds to H_2O or to ethanol. But ethanol can also interact with the ether effectively through dispersion forces because it has a hydrocarbon chain.

Follow-Up Problem 13.1 Which solute is more soluble in the given solvent: **(a)** 1-butanol ($CH_3CH_2CH_2CH_2OH$) or 1,4-butanediol ($HOCH_2CH_2CH_2CH_2OH$) in water; **(b)** chloroform ($CHCl_3$) or carbon tetrachloride (CCl_4) in water?

Gas-Liquid Solutions A substance with very weak intermolecular attractions has a low boiling point and is a gas under ordinary conditions. Likewise, it is not very soluble in water because solute-solvent forces are weak. Thus, for nonpolar or slightly polar gases, boiling point generally correlates with solubility in water (Table 13.3).

The small amount of a nonpolar gas that *does* dissolve may be vital. At 25°C and 1 atm, the solubility of O_2 is only 3.2 mL/100. mL of water, but aquatic animal life requires it. At times, the solubility of a nonpolar gas may *seem* high because it is also *reacting* with solvent. Oxygen seems more soluble in blood than in water because it bonds to hemoglobin in red blood cells. Carbon dioxide, which is essential for aquatic plants and coral-reef growth, seems very soluble in water (~81 mL of CO_2/100. mL of H_2O at 25°C and 1 atm) because it is dissolving *and* reacting:

$$CO_2(g) + H_2O(l) \longrightarrow H^+(aq) + HCO_3^-(aq)$$

Table 13.3 Correlation Between Boiling Point and Solubility in Water

Gas	Solubility (*M*)*	bp (K)
He	4.2×10^{-4}	4.2
Ne	6.6×10^{-4}	27.1
N_2	10.4×10^{-4}	77.4
CO	15.6×10^{-4}	81.6
O_2	21.8×10^{-4}	90.2
NO	32.7×10^{-4}	121.4

*At 273 K and 1 atm.

Gas Solutions and Solid Solutions

Gas solutions and solid solutions also have vital importance and numerous applications.

Gas-Gas Solutions *All gases are miscible with each other.* Air is the classic example of a gaseous solution, consisting of about 18 gases in widely differing proportions. Anesthetic gas proportions are finely adjusted to the needs of the patient and the length of the surgical procedure. The proportions of many industrial gas mixtures, such as CO/H_2 in syngas production or N_2/H_2 in ammonia production, are controlled to optimize product yield under varying conditions of temperature and pressure.

Gas-Solid Solutions *When a gas dissolves in a solid, it occupies the spaces between the closely packed particles.* Hydrogen gas can be purified by passing an impure sample through palladium. Only H_2 molecules are small enough to fit between the

Pd atoms, where they form Pd—H bonds. The H atoms move from one Pd atom to another and emerge from the metal as H_2 molecules (see Figure 14.2, p. 525).

The ability of gases to dissolve in a solid also has disadvantages. The electrical conductivity of copper is greatly reduced by the presence of O_2, which dissolves into the crystal structure and reacts to form copper(I) oxide. High-conductivity copper is prepared by melting and recasting the metal in an O_2-free atmosphere.

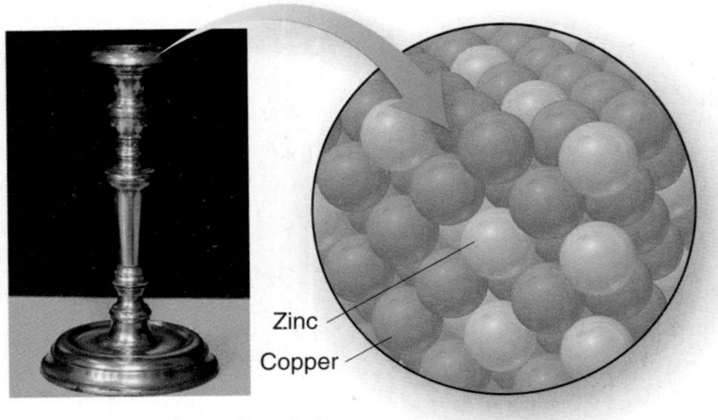

A Brass, a substitutional alloy

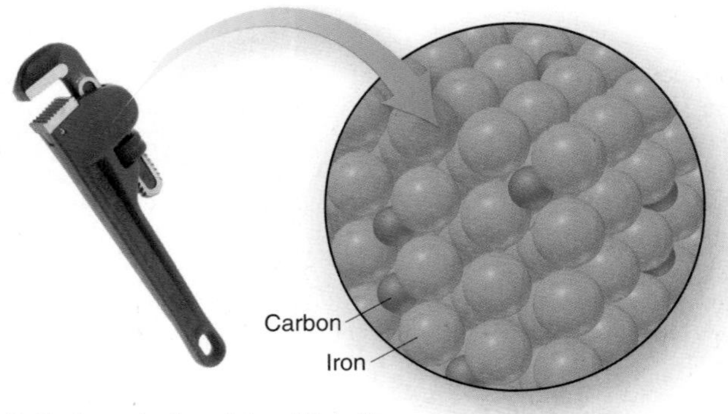

B Carbon steel, an interstitial alloy

Figure 13.4 The arrangement of atoms in two types of alloys.

Solid-Solid Solutions Solids diffuse so little that their mixtures are usually heterogeneous. Some solid-solid solutions can be formed by melting the solids and then mixing them and allowing them to freeze. Many **alloys,** mixtures of elements that have a metallic character, are solid-solid solutions (although several have microscopic heterogeneous regions). In a *substitutional alloy* like brass (Figure 13.4A), atoms of zinc replace atoms of the main element, copper, at some sites in the cubic-closest packing array. In an *interstitial alloy* like carbon steel (Figure 13.4B), atoms of carbon (a nonmetal is typical in this type of alloy) fill some of the spaces (*interstices*) between atoms of the main element, iron, in the body-centered array.

Waxes are also solid-solid solutions. Most are amorphous solids with some small regions of crystalline regularity. A natural *wax* is defined as a solid of biological origin that is insoluble in water and soluble in nonpolar solvents. Beeswax, which bees secrete to build their combs, is a homogeneous mixture of fatty acids, long-chain carboxylic acids, and hydrocarbons in which some of the molecules contain chains more than 40 carbon atoms long. Carnauba wax, from a South American palm, is a mixture of compounds, each consisting of a fatty acid bound to a long-chain alcohol. It is hard but forms a thick gel in nonpolar solvents, so it is perfect for waxing cars.

Summary of Section 13.1

- A solution is a homogeneous mixture of a solute dissolved in a solvent through the action of intermolecular forces.
- Ion-dipole, ion–induced dipole, and dipole–induced dipole forces occur in solutions, in addition to all the intermolecular forces that also occur in pure substances.
- If similar intermolecular forces occur in solute and solvent, they replace each other when the substances mix and a solution is likely to form ("like dissolves like").
- When ionic compounds dissolve in water, the ions become surrounded by hydration shells of H-bonded water molecules.
- Solubility of organic molecules in various solvents depends on the relative sizes of their polar and nonpolar portions.
- The solubility of nonpolar gases in water is low because of weak intermolecular forces. Gases are miscible with one another and dissolve in solids by fitting into spaces in the crystal structure.
- Solid-solid solutions include alloys and waxes, and some are formed by mixing molten components.

13.2 • INTERMOLECULAR FORCES AND BIOLOGICAL MACROMOLECULES

The three-dimensional shapes of proteins, nucleic acids, and cell membranes and the functions of soaps and antibiotics depend on intermolecular forces and are explained by two ideas:

- Polar and ionic groups attract water, but nonpolar groups do not.
- Just as separate molecules attract each other, so do distant groups on the same molecule.

The Structures of Proteins

Proteins are unbranched polymers formed from about 20 different monomers called **amino acids.** They range in size from about 50 amino acids ($\mathcal{M} \approx 5\times10^3$ g/mol) to several thousand ($\mathcal{M} \approx 5\times10^5$ g/mol). Proteins with a few types of amino acids in repeating patterns have extended helical or sheetlike shapes and give structure to hair, skin, and so forth. Proteins with many types of amino acids have complex, globular shapes and function as antibodies, enzymes and so forth. Let's see how intermolecular forces among amino acids influence the shapes of globular proteins.

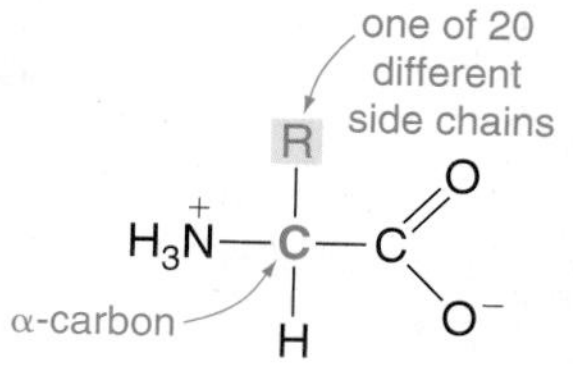

Figure 13.5 The charged form of an amino acid under physiological conditions.

The Polarity of Amino-Acid Side Chains In the cell, a free amino acid has four groups bonded to its α-carbon (Figure 13.5): charged carboxyl (—COO^-) and amine (—NH_3^+) groups, an H atom, and a *side chain,* which ranges from an H atom to a two-ringed C_9H_8N group. Amino acids can be classified by the polarity or charge of their side chains: nonpolar, polar, and ionic. A few examples are

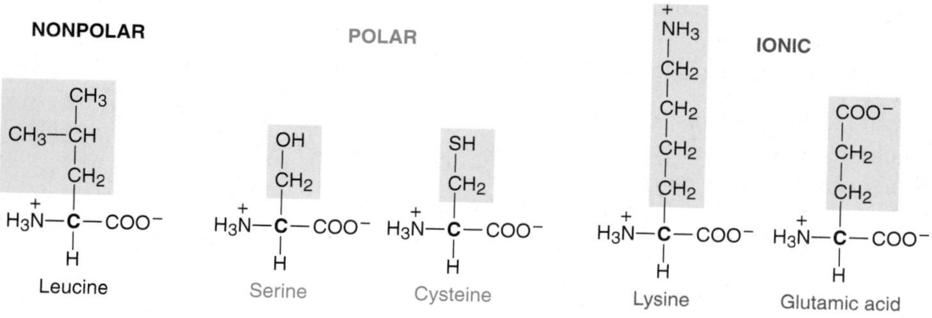

In a protein, the carboxyl group of one amino acid is linked covalently to the amine group of the next by a *peptide* bond. (We discuss amino acid structures and peptide bond formation in Chapter 15.) Thus, as Figure 13.6 shows, the *backbone* of a protein is a polypeptide chain: an *α-carbon connected through a peptide bond (orange screen) to the next α-carbon,* and so forth. The various side chains (*gray screens*) dangle off the α-carbons on alternate sides of the chain.

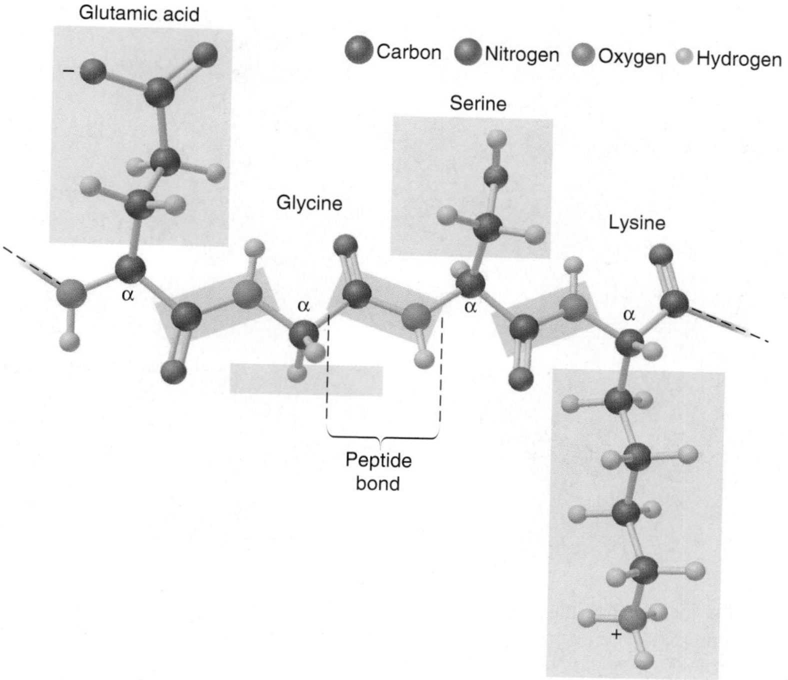

Figure 13.6 A portion of a polypeptide chain. Three peptide bonds (*orange screens*) join four amino acids in this chain portion.

Intermolecular Forces and Protein Shape The same forces that act between separate molecules are responsible for a protein's shape, because *distant groups on the protein chain end up near each other as the chain bends.* Figure 13.7 depicts the forces within the protein and between the protein and the aqueous medium of the cell. In general order of importance, they are

- Covalent peptide bonds create the backbone (polypeptide chain).
- Helical and sheetlike segments arise from *H bonds between the C=O of one peptide bond and the N—H of another.*
- Polar and ionic side chains protrude into the surrounding cell fluid, interacting with water through ion-dipole forces and H bonds.
- Nonpolar side chains interact through dispersion forces within the nonaqueous protein interior.
- The —SH ends of two cysteine side chains form a covalent —S—S— bond, a *disulfide bridge,* between distant parts of the chain that fixes a bend.
- Oppositely charged ends of ionic side chains, $—COO^-$ and $—NH_3^+$ groups, that lie near each other form an electrostatic *salt link* (or *ion pair*) that creates bend in the protein chain.
- Other H bonds between side chains keep distant chain portions near each other.

Thus, *soluble proteins have polar-ionic exteriors and nonpolar interiors.* As we emphasize in Chapter 15, *the amino acid sequence of a protein determines its shape, which determines its function.*

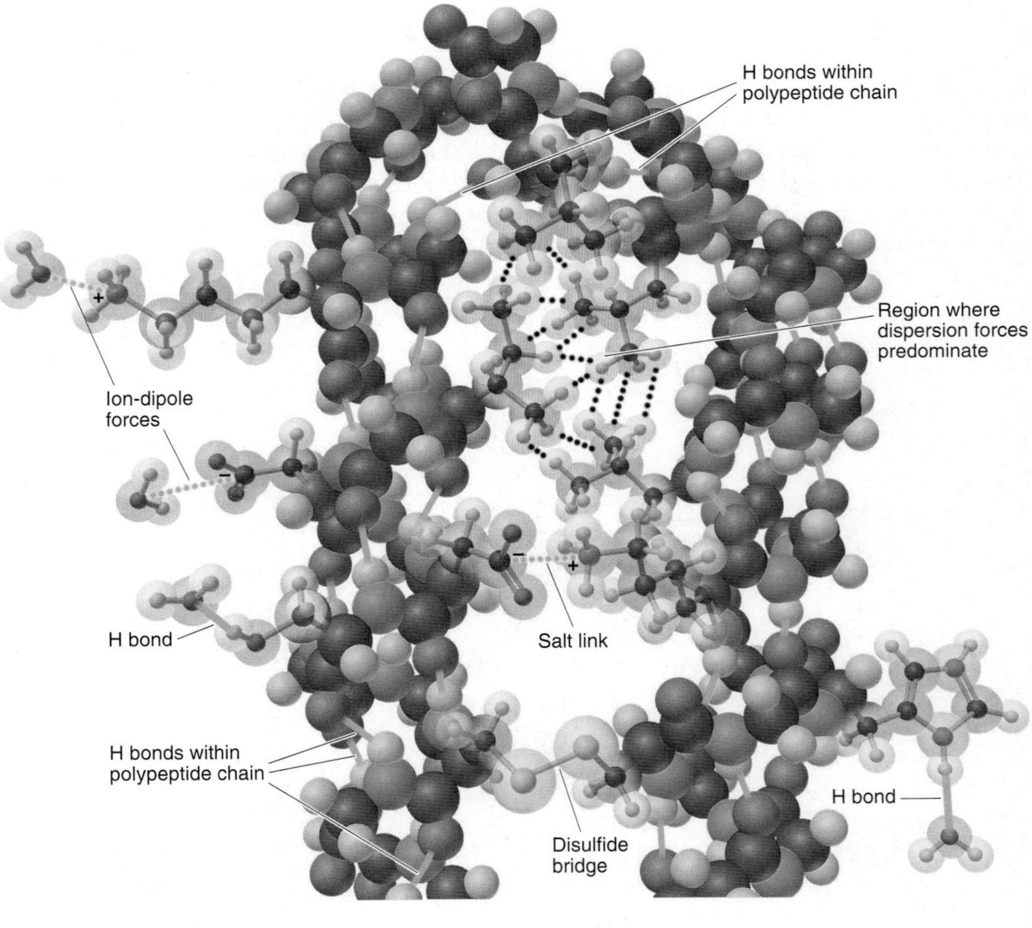

Figure 13.7 The forces that maintain protein structure. Covalent, ionic, and intermolecular forces act between parts of a protein and between the protein and surrounding H_2O molecules to determine the protein's shape. (Water molecules and some amino-acid side chains are shown as ball-and-stick models within space-filling contours.)

Dual Polarity in Soaps, Membranes, and Antibiotics

Dual polarity, which we discussed in regard to the solubility of alcohols, also helps explain how soaps, cell membranes, and antibiotics function.

Action of Soaps A **soap** is the salt formed when a strong base (metal hydroxide) reacts with a *fatty acid,* a carboxylic acid with a long hydrocarbon chain. A typical soap molecule is made up of a nonpolar "tail" 15–19 carbons long and a polar-ionic "head" consisting of a $—COO^-$ group and the cation of the strong base. The cation greatly influences a soap's properties. Lithium soaps are hard and high melting and used in car lubricants. Potassium soaps are low melting and used in liquid form. Softer, more water-soluble sodium soaps, including sodium stearate, $CH_3(CH_2)_{16}COONa$, are components of common bar soaps:

Sodium stearate, $C_{17}H_{35}COONa$

When grease on your hands or clothes is immersed in soapy water, the soap molecule's nonpolar tails interact with the nonpolar grease molecules through dispersion forces, while the polar-ionic heads attract water molecules through ion-dipole forces and H bonds. Tiny aggregates of grease molecules, embedded with soap molecules whose polar-ionic heads stick into the water, are flushed away by added water (Figure 13.8).

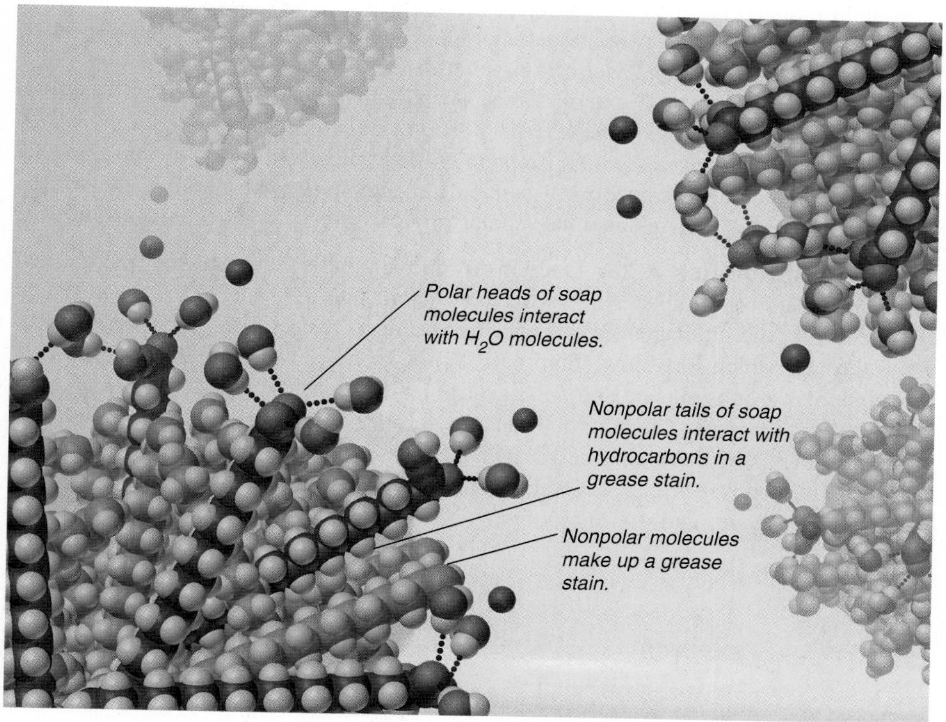

Figure 13.8 The cleaning ability of a soap depends on the dual polarity of its molecules.

Lipid Bilayers and the Structure of the Cell Membrane The most abundant molecules in cell membranes are *phospholipids.* Like soaps, they have a dual polarity—a nonpolar tail consists of two fatty acid chains, and an organophosphate group is the polar-ionic head (Figure 13.9). Remarkably, phospholipids self-assemble in water into a sheetlike double layer called a **lipid bilayer,** with the tails of the two layers touching and the heads in the water. In the laboratory, bilayers form spherical vesicles that trap water inside. These structures are favored energetically because of their intermolecular forces:

- Ion-dipole forces occur between polar heads and water inside and outside.
- Dispersion forces occur between nonpolar tails within the bilayer interior.
- Minimal contact exists between nonpolar tails and water.

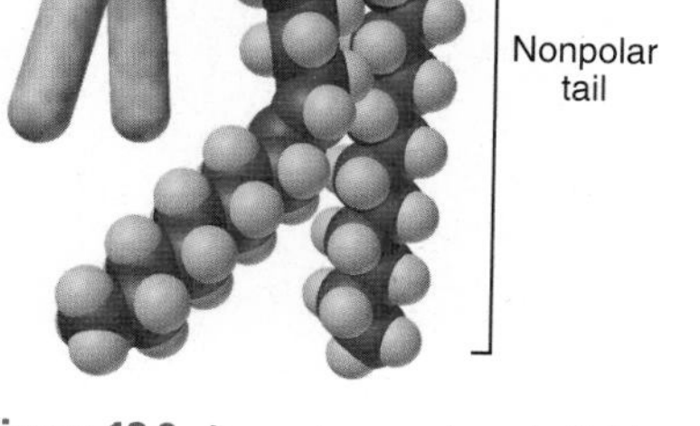

Figure 13.9 **A membrane phospholipid.** Lecithin (phosphatidylcholine), a phospholipid, is shown as a space-filling model and as a simplified purple-and-gray shape.

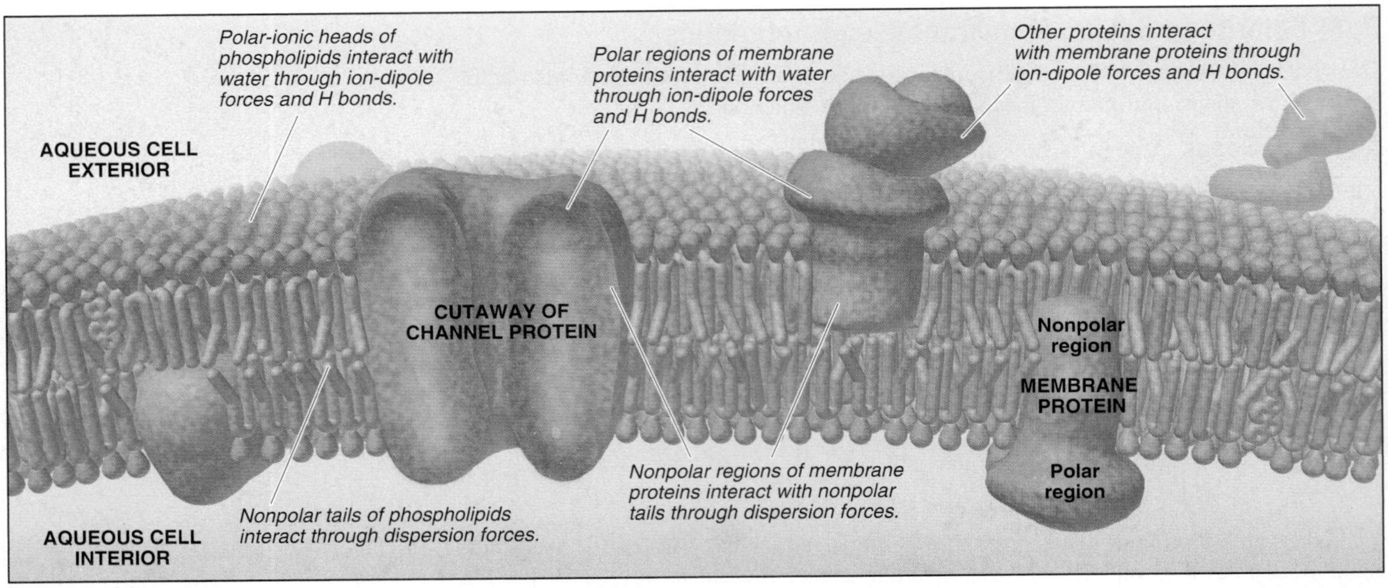

Figure 13.10 Intermolecular forces and cell membrane structure.

A typical animal cell membrane consists of a phospholipid bilayer with proteins partially embedded in it (Figure 13.10). Membrane proteins, which play countless essential roles, differ fundamentally from soluble proteins in terms of their dual polarity:

- Soluble proteins have polar exteriors and nonpolar interiors. They form ion-dipole and H-bonding forces between water and *polar groups on the exterior* and dispersion forces between *nonpolar groups in the interior* (see Figure 13.7).
- Membrane proteins have exteriors that are partially polar and partially nonpolar. They have polar groups on the *exterior portion that juts into the aqueous surroundings* and nonpolar groups on *the exterior portion embedded in the membrane*. The nonpolar groups thus can form dispersion forces with the phospholipid tails of the bilayer. Channel proteins also have polar groups lining the aqueous channel.

Action of Antibiotics A key function of the membrane is to balance internal and external ion concentrations: Na^+ is excluded from the cell, and K^+ is kept inside. Gramicidin A and similar antibiotics act by forming channels in the bacterial membrane through which ions flow (Figure 13.11). Two helical gramicidin A molecules, their nonpolar groups outside and polar groups inside, lie end to end to form a channel through the membrane. The nonpolar outside stabilizes the molecule in the membrane through dispersion forces, and the polar inside passes the ions along using ion-dipole forces, like a "bucket brigade." Over 10^7 ions pass in and out through each of these channels per second, and the microorganism soon dies.

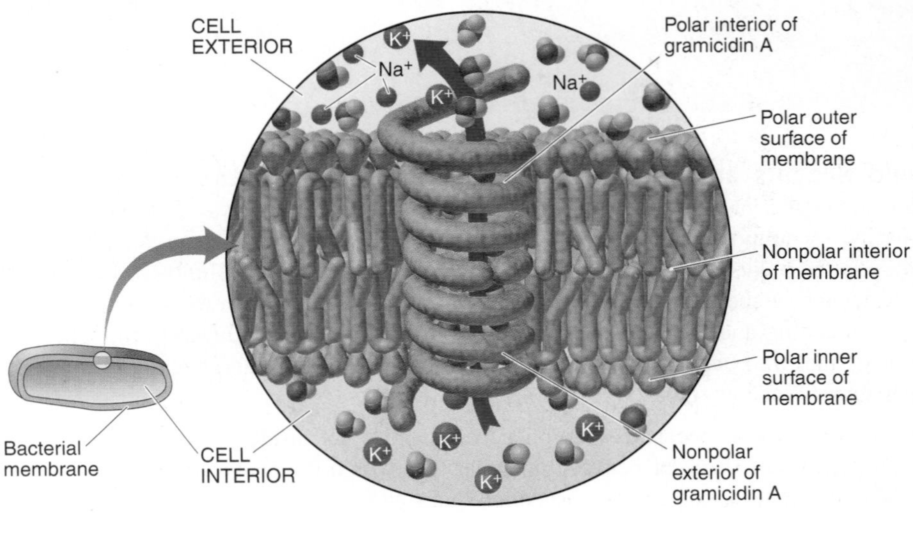

Figure 13.11 The mode of action of the antibiotic gramicidin A. The K^+ ions are shown leaving the cell. At the same time (not shown), Na^+ ions enter the cell.

The Structure of DNA

The chemical information that guides the design and construction, and therefore the function, of all proteins is contained in **nucleic acids,** unbranched polymers made up of monomers called **mononucleotides.** Each mononucleotide consists of an N-containing base, a sugar, and a phosphate group (Figure 13.12). In DNA (***d****eoxyri*-*bo****n****ucleic* ***a****cid*), the sugar is *2-deoxyribose,* in which —H substitutes for —OH on the second C atom of the five-C sugar ribose.

The repeating pattern of the DNA chain is *sugar linked to phosphate linked to sugar linked to phosphate,* and so on. Attached to each sugar is one of four N-containing bases, flat ring structures that dangle off the polynucleotide chain, similar to the way amino-acid side chains dangle off the polypeptide chain.

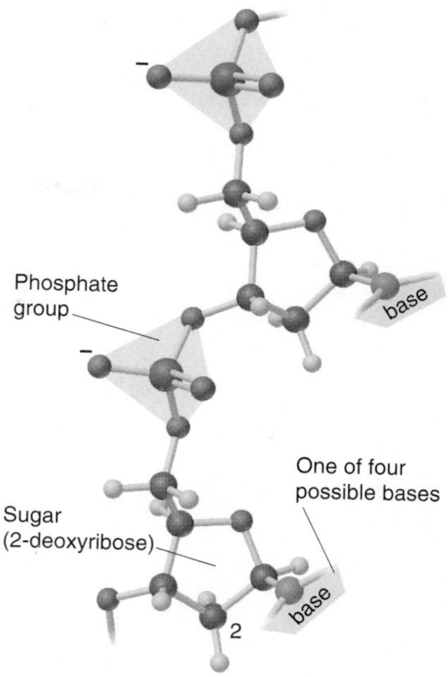

Figure 13.12 A short portion of the polynucleotide chain of DNA.

Intermolecular Forces and the Double Helix DNA exists as two chains wrapped around each other in a **double helix** stabilized by intermolecular forces (Figure 13.13):

- *On the more polar exterior,* negatively charged sugar-phosphate groups interact with the aqueous surroundings via ion-dipole forces and H bonds.
- *In the less polar interior,* flat, N-containing bases stack above each other and interact by dispersion forces.
- *Bases form specific interchain H bonds;* that is, each base in one chain is always H bonded with its complementary base in the other chain. Thus, *the base sequence of one chain is the H-bonded complement of the base sequence of the other.*

A DNA molecule contains millions of H bonds linking bases in these prescribed pairs. The *total* energy of the H bonds keeps the chains together, but each H bond is weak enough (around 5% of a typical covalent single bond) that a few at a time can break as the chains separate during crucial cellular processes. (In Chapter 15, we'll see how H-bonded base pairs are essential for protein synthesis and DNA replication.)

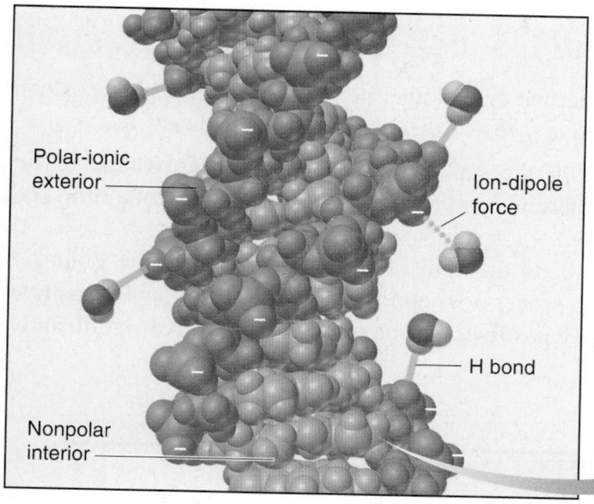

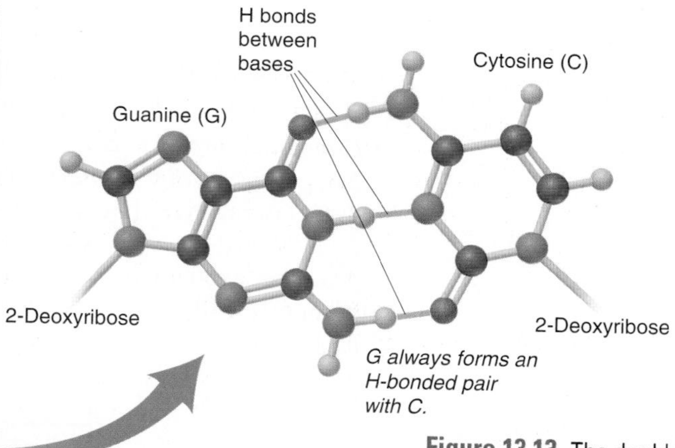

Figure 13.13 The double helix of DNA. A segment of DNA (*left*) has its polar-ionic sugar-phosphate portion (*pink*) facing the water and the nonpolar bases (*gray*) stacking in the interior. The expanded portion (*right*) shows an H-bonded pair of the bases guanine and cytosine.

Summary of Section 13.2

- In soluble proteins, polar and ionic amino-acid side chains on the exterior interact with surrounding water, and nonpolar side chains in the interior interact with each other.
- With polar-ionic heads *and* nonpolar tails, a soap dissolves grease *and* interacts with water.
- Like soaps, phospholipids also have dual polarity. They assemble into a water-impermeable lipid bilayer. In a cell membrane, the embedded portion of membrane proteins has exterior nonpolar side chains that face the nonpolar tails in the lipid bilayer. Some antibiotics form channels with nonpolar exteriors and polar interiors that shuttle ions through the cell membrane.
- DNA forms a double helix with a sugar-phosphate, polar-ionic exterior. In the interior, N-containing bases H bond in specific pairs and stack through dispersion forces.

13.3 • WHY SUBSTANCES DISSOLVE: UNDERSTANDING THE SOLUTION PROCESS

The qualitative *macroscopic* rule "like dissolves like" is based on *molecular* interactions between solute and solvent. To see *why* like dissolves like, we'll break down the solution process conceptually into steps and examine them quantitatively.

Heat of Solution: Solution Cycles

Before a solution forms, solute particles are attracting each other, as are solvent particles. For one to dissolve in the other, three steps must take place, each accompanied by an enthalpy change:

Step 1. Solute particles separate from each other. This step involves overcoming intermolecular attractions, so it is *endothermic:*

$$\text{Solute (aggregated)} + \textit{heat} \longrightarrow \text{solute (separated)} \qquad \Delta H_{\text{solute}} > 0$$

Step 2. Solvent particles separate from each other. This step also involves overcoming attractions, so it is *endothermic,* too:

$$\text{Solvent (aggregated)} + \textit{heat} \longrightarrow \text{solvent (separated)} \qquad \Delta H_{\text{solvent}} > 0$$

Step 3. Solute and solvent particles mix and form a solution. The different particles attract each other and come together, so this step is *exothermic:*

$$\text{Solute (separated)} + \text{solvent (separated)} \longrightarrow \text{solution} + \textit{heat} \qquad \Delta H_{\text{mix}} < 0$$

The overall process is called a *thermochemical solution cycle,* and in yet another application of Hess's law, we combine the three individual enthalpy changes to find the **heat of solution (ΔH_{soln}),** the total enthalpy change that occurs when solute and solvent form a solution:

$$\Delta H_{\text{soln}} = \Delta H_{\text{solute}} + \Delta H_{\text{solvent}} + \Delta H_{\text{mix}} \tag{13.1}$$

Overall solution formation is exothermic or endothermic, and ΔH_{soln} is either positive or negative, depending on the relative sizes of the individual ΔH values:

- *Exothermic process:* $\Delta H_{\text{soln}} < 0$. If the sum of the endothermic terms ($\Delta H_{\text{solute}} + \Delta H_{\text{solvent}}$) is *smaller* than the exothermic term (ΔH_{mix}), the process is exothermic and ΔH_{soln} is negative (Figure 13.14A).
- *Endothermic process:* $\Delta H_{\text{soln}} > 0$. If the sum of the endothermic terms is *larger* than the exothermic term, the process is endothermic and ΔH_{soln} is positive (Figure 13.14B). If ΔH_{soln} is highly positive, the solute may not dissolve significantly in that solvent.

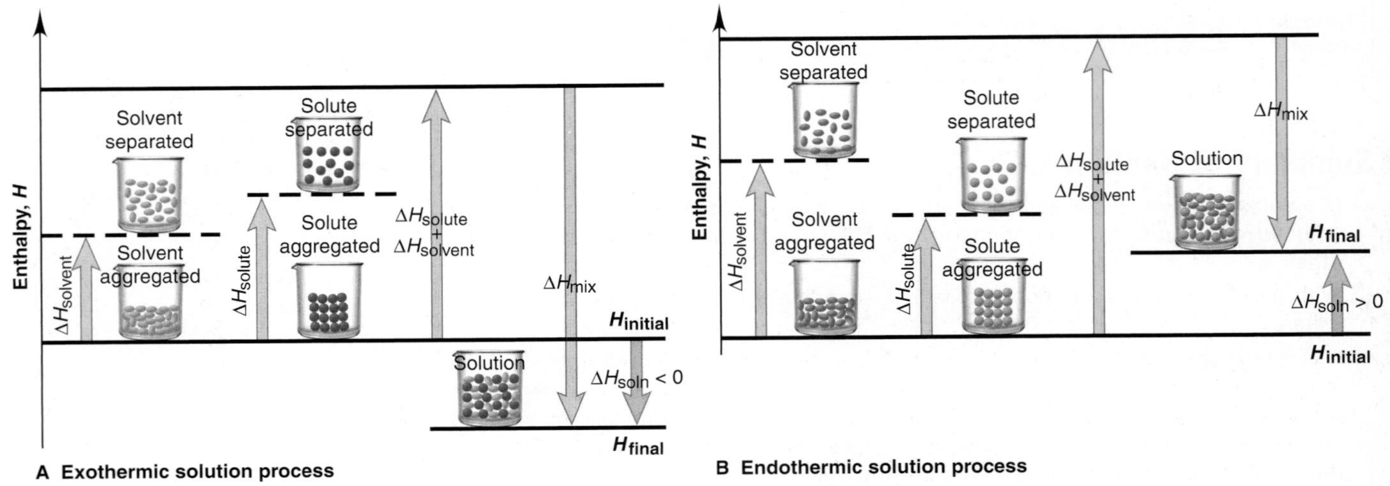

Figure 13.14 Enthalpy components of the heat of solution. **A,** ΔH_{mix} is larger than the sum of ΔH_{solute} and $\Delta H_{\text{solvent}}$, so ΔH_{soln} is negative. **B,** ΔH_{mix} is smaller than the sum of ΔH_{solute} and $\Delta H_{\text{solvent}}$, so ΔH_{soln} is positive.

Heat of Hydration: Ionic Solids in Water

The $\Delta H_{solvent}$ and ΔH_{mix} components of the solution cycle are difficult to measure individually. Combined, they equal the enthalpy change for **solvation,** the process of surrounding a solute particle with solvent particles:

$$\Delta H_{solvation} = \Delta H_{solvent} + \Delta H_{mix}$$

Solvation in water is called **hydration.** Thus, enthalpy changes for separating the water molecules ($\Delta H_{solvent}$) and mixing the separated solute with them (ΔH_{mix}) are combined into the **heat of hydration (ΔH_{hydr}).** In water, Equation 13.1 becomes

$$\Delta H_{soln} = \Delta H_{solute} + \Delta H_{hydr}$$

The heat of hydration is a key factor in dissolving an ionic solid. Breaking H bonds in water is more than compensated for by forming the stronger ion-dipole forces, so hydration of an ion is *always* exothermic. The ΔH_{hydr} of an ion is defined as the enthalpy change for the hydration of 1 mol of separated (gaseous) ions:

$$M^+(g)\ [\text{or } X^-(g)] \xrightarrow{H_2O} M^+(aq)\ [\text{or } X^-(aq)] \qquad \Delta H_{\text{hydr of the ion}}\ (\text{always} < 0)$$

Importance of Charge Density Heats of hydration exhibit trends based on the ion's **charge density,** the ratio of its charge to its volume. In general, the higher the charge density, the more negative ΔH_{hydr} is. Coulomb's law explains why: the higher the charge of an ion and the smaller its radius, the closer it gets to the oppositely charged pole of an H_2O (see Figure 2.12, p. 57), and the stronger the attraction. Thus,

- A 2+ ion attracts H_2O molecules more strongly than a 1+ ion of similar size.
- A small 1+ ion attracts H_2O molecules more strongly than a large 1+ ion.

Periodic trends in ΔH_{hydr} values are based on trends in charge density (Table 13.4):

- *Down a group,* the charge stays the same and the size increases; thus, the charge densities decrease, as do the ΔH_{hydr} values.
- *Across a period,* say, from Group 1A(1) to Group 2A(2), the 2A ion has a smaller radius *and* a higher charge, so its charge density and ΔH_{hydr} are greater.

Components of Aqueous Heats of Solution To separate an ionic solute, MX, into gaseous ions (ΔH_{solute}) requires a lot of energy; recall from Chapter 9 that this is the lattice energy, and it is highly positive:

$$MX(s) \longrightarrow M^+(g) + X^-(g) \qquad \Delta H_{solute}\ (\text{always} > 0) = \Delta H_{lattice}$$

Thus, for ionic compounds in water, the heat of solution is the lattice energy (always positive) plus the combined heats of hydration of the ions (always negative):

$$\Delta H_{soln} = \Delta H_{lattice} + \Delta H_{\text{hydr of the ions}} \qquad (13.2)$$

Once again, the sizes of the individual terms determine the sign of ΔH_{soln}.

Figure 13.15 (*next page*) shows enthalpy diagrams for three ionic solutes dissolving in water:

- *NaCl.* Sodium chloride has a small positive ΔH_{soln} (3.9 kJ/mol) because its lattice energy is only slightly greater than the combined ionic heats of hydration: if you dissolve NaCl in water in a flask, you don't feel any temperature change.
- *NaOH.* Sodium hydroxide has a large negative ΔH_{soln} (−44.5 kJ/mol) because its lattice energy is much *smaller* than the combined ionic heats of hydration: if you dissolve NaOH in water, the flask feels hot.
- *NH_4NO_3.* Ammonium nitrate has a large positive ΔH_{soln} (25.7 kJ/mol) because its lattice energy is much *larger* than the combined ionic heats of hydration: if you dissolve NH_4NO_3 in water, the flask feels cold.

Hot and cold packs consist of a thick outer pouch of water and a thin inner pouch of a salt. A squeeze breaks the inner pouch, and the salt dissolves. Most hot packs use anhydrous $CaCl_2$ (ΔH_{soln} = −82.8 kJ/mol), and cold packs use NH_4NO_3 (ΔH_{soln} = 25.7 kJ/mol). A cold pack can keep the solution at 0°C for about half an hour. In Japan, some soup is sold in double-walled cans with a salt in a packet immersed in water between the walls. Open the can and the packet breaks, the salt dissolves, and the soup quickly warms to about 90°C.

Table 13.4 Trends in Ionic Heats of Hydration

Ion	Ionic Radius (pm)	ΔH_{hydr} (kJ/mol)
Group 1A(1)		
Na^+	102	−410
K^+	138	−336
Rb^+	152	−315
Cs^+	167	−282
Group 2A(2)		
Mg^{2+}	72	−1903
Ca^{2+}	100	−1591
Sr^{2+}	118	−1424
Ba^{2+}	135	−1317
Group 7A(17)		
F^-	133	−431
Cl^-	181	−313
Br^-	196	−284
I^-	220	−247

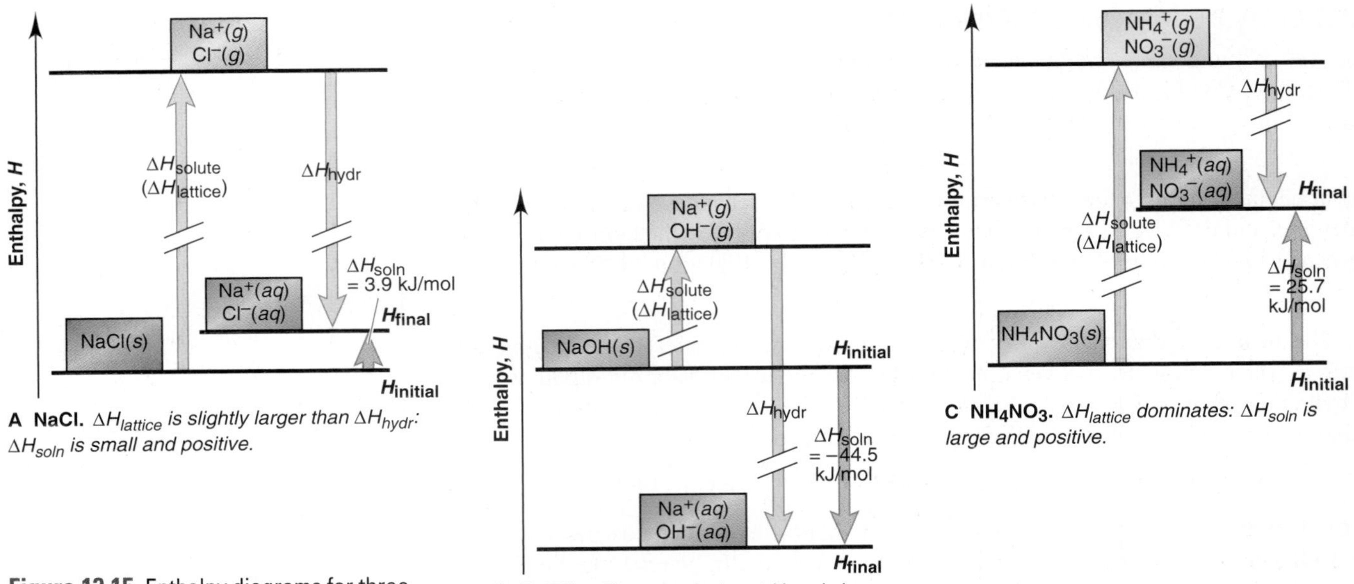

A NaCl. *$\Delta H_{lattice}$ is slightly larger than ΔH_{hydr}: ΔH_{soln} is small and positive.*

B NaOH. *ΔH_{hydr} dominates: ΔH_{soln} is large and negative.*

C NH_4NO_3. *$\Delta H_{lattice}$ dominates: ΔH_{soln} is large and positive.*

Figure 13.15 Enthalpy diagrams for three ionic compounds dissolving in water.

The Solution Process and the Change in Entropy

The heat of solution (ΔH_{soln}) is one of two factors that determine whether a solute dissolves. The other factor is the natural tendency of a system of particles to spread out and the system's kinetic energy to become more dispersed or distributed. A thermodynamic variable called **entropy (S)** is directly related to the number of ways a system can disperse its energy, which is closely related to the freedom of motion of the particles.

Let's see what it means for a system to "distribute its energy." We'll first compare the three physical states and then compare solute and solvent with solution.

Entropy and the Three Physical States The states of matter differ significantly in their entropy.

- In a solid, the particles are fixed in their positions with little freedom of motion. In a liquid, they can move around each other and so have greater freedom of motion. And in a gas, the particles have little restriction and much more freedom of motion.
- The more freedom of motion the particles have, the more ways they can distribute their kinetic energy; thus, a liquid has higher entropy than a solid, and a gas has higher entropy than a liquid:

$$S_{gas} > S_{liquid} > S_{solid}$$

- We can also look at the *change* in entropy (ΔS) of a phase change. Thus, for example, the change in entropy when a liquid vaporizes ($\Delta S_{vap} = S_{gas} - S_{liquid}$) is positive ($\Delta S_{vap} > 0$), the change in entropy when a liquid freezes (fusion) ($\Delta S_{fus} = S_{solid} - S_{liquid}$) is negative ($\Delta S_{fus} < 0$), and so forth.

Entropy and the Formation of Solutions The formation of solutions also involves a change in entropy. *A solution usually has higher entropy than the pure solute and pure solvent* because the number of ways to distribute the energy is related to the number of interactions between different molecules. There are far more interactions possible when solute and solvent are mixed than when they are pure; thus,

$$S_{soln} > (S_{solute} + S_{solvent}) \qquad \text{or} \qquad \Delta S_{soln} > 0$$

You know from everyday experience that solutions form naturally, but pure solutes and solvents don't: you've seen sugar dissolve in water, but you've never seen a sugar solution separate into pure sugar and water. In Chapter 20, we'll see that energy is needed to reverse the natural tendency of systems to distribute their energy—to get "mixed up." Water treatment plants, oil refineries, steel mills, and many other industrial facilities expend a lot of energy to separate mixtures into pure components.

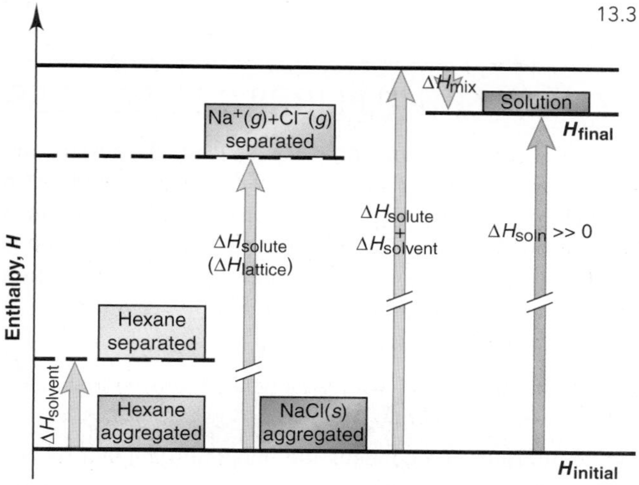

A **NaCl.** ΔH_{mix} *is* ***much*** *smaller than* ΔH_{solute}*;* ΔH_{soln} *is so much larger than the entropy increase due to mixing that NaCl does* ***not*** *dissolve.*

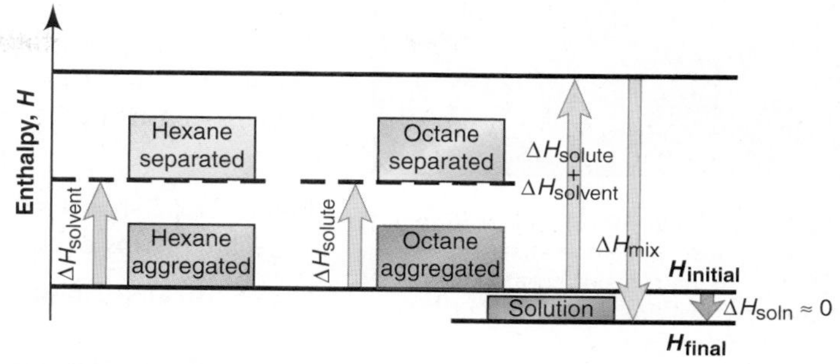

B Octane. ΔH_{soln} *is very small, but the entropy increase due to mixing is large, so octane dissolves.*

Figure 13.16 Enthalpy diagrams for dissolving (A) NaCl and (B) octane in hexane.

Enthalpy vs. Entropy Changes in Solution Formation Solution formation involves the interplay of two factors: systems change toward a state of *lower enthalpy* and *higher entropy,* so the relative sizes of ΔH_{soln} and ΔS_{soln} determine whether a solution forms. Let's consider three solute-solvent pairs to see which factor dominates:

1. *NaCl in hexane*. Given their very different intermolecular forces, we predict that sodium chloride does *not* dissolve in hexane (C_6H_{14}) (Figure 13.16A). Separating the solvent is easy because the dispersion forces are weak ($\Delta H_{solvent} \geq 0$), but separating the solute requires supplying the very large $\Delta H_{lattice}$ ($\Delta H_{solute} >> 0$). Mixing releases little heat because ion–induced dipole forces between Na^+ (or Cl^-) and hexane are weak ($\Delta H_{mix} \leq 0$). Because the sum of the endothermic terms is *much* larger than the exothermic term, $\Delta H_{soln} >> 0$. *A solution does not form because the entropy increase from mixing solute and solvent would be much smaller than the enthalpy increase required to separate the solute:* $\Delta S_{mix} << \Delta H_{solute}$.

2. *Octane in hexane*. We predict that octane (C_8H_{18}) is soluble in hexane because both are held together by dispersion forces of similar strength; in fact, they are miscible. That is, both ΔH_{solute} and $\Delta H_{solvent}$ are around zero. The similar forces mean that ΔH_{mix} is around zero also. And a lot of heat is not released; in fact, ΔH_{soln} is around zero (Figure 13.16B). So why does a solution form so readily? *With no enthalpy change driving the process, octane dissolves in hexane because the entropy increases greatly when the pure substances mix:* $\Delta S_{mix} >> \Delta H_{soln}$.

3. *NH_4NO_3 in water.* A large enough increase in entropy can sometimes cause a solution to form even when the enthalpy increase is large ($\Delta H_{soln} >> 0$). As we saw in Figure 13.15C, when ammonium nitrate (NH_4NO_3) dissolves in water, the process is highly endothermic; that is, $\Delta H_{lattice} >> \Delta H_{\text{hydr of the ions}}$. Nevertheless, *the increase in entropy that occurs when the crystal breaks down and the ions mix with water molecules is greater than the increase in enthalpy:* $\Delta S_{soln} > \Delta H_{soln}$.

In Chapter 20, we'll return in depth to the relation between enthalpy and entropy to understand physical and chemical systems.

Summary of Section 13.3

- In a thermochemical solution cycle, the heat of solution is the sum of the endothermic separations of solute and of solvent and the exothermic mixing of their particles.
- In water, the combination of solvent separation and mixing with solute particles is hydration. For ions, heats of hydration depend on the ion's charge density but are always negative because ion-dipole forces are strong.
- Systems naturally increase their entropy (distribute their energy in more ways). A gas has higher entropy than a liquid, which has higher entropy than a solid, and a solution has higher entropy than the pure solute and solvent.
- Relative sizes of the enthalpy and entropy changes determine solution formation. A substance with a positive ΔH_{soln} dissolves *only* if ΔS_{soln} is larger than ΔH_{soln}.

Figure 13.17 Equilibrium in a saturated solution. At some temperature, the number of solute particles dissolving (*white arrows*) per unit time equals the number recrystallizing (*black arrows*).

13.4 • SOLUBILITY AS AN EQUILIBRIUM PROCESS

When an excess amount of solid is added to a solvent, particles leave the crystal, are surrounded by solvent, and move away. Some dissolved solute particles collide with undissolved solute and recrystallize, but, as long as the rate of dissolving is greater than the rate of recrystallizing, the concentration rises. At a given temperature, when solid is dissolving at the same rate as dissolved particles are recrystallizing, the concentration remains constant and *undissolved solute is in equilibrium with dissolved solute:*

$$\text{Solute (undissolved)} \rightleftharpoons \text{solute (dissolved)}$$

Figure 13.17 shows an ionic solid in equilibrium with dissolved cations and anions.

Three terms express the extent of this solution process:

- A **saturated solution** is at equilibrium and contains the maximum amount of dissolved solute at a given temperature in the presence of undissolved solute. Therefore, if you filter off the solution and add more solute, it doesn't dissolve.
- An **unsaturated solution** contains *less* than the equilibrium concentration of dissolved solute; add more solute, and more dissolves until the solution is saturated.
- A **supersaturated solution** contains *more* than the equilibrium concentration and is unstable relative to the saturated solution; add a "seed" crystal of solute or tap the container, and the excess solute crystallizes immediately, leaving a saturated solution (Figure 13.18). You can often prepare a supersaturated solution if the solute is more soluble at higher temperature. While heating, dissolve more than the amount required for saturation at some lower temperature, and then slowly cool the solution. If the excess solute remains dissolved, the solution is supersaturated.

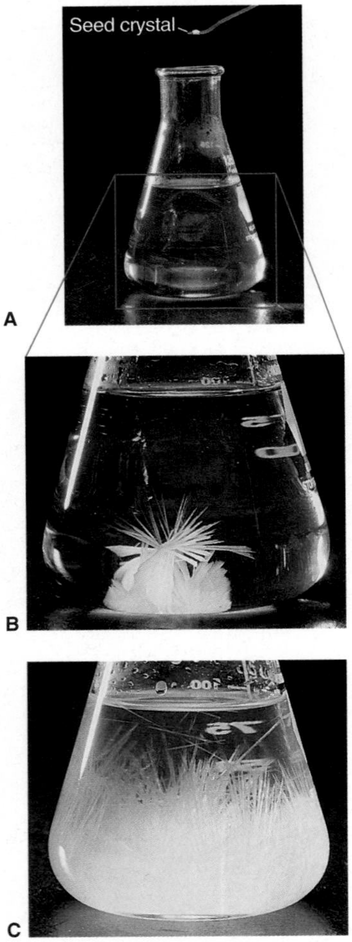

Figure 13.18 Sodium acetate crystallizing from a supersaturated solution. When a seed crystal of sodium acetate is added to a supersaturated solution of it **(A)**, solute begins to crystallize **(B)** and continues until the remaining solution is saturated **(C)**.

Effect of Temperature on Solubility

You know that more sugar dissolves in hot tea than in iced tea; in fact, temperature affects the solubility of most substances. Let's examine the effects of temperature on the solubility of solids and gases.

Temperature and the Solubility of Solids in Water Like sugar, *most solids are more soluble at higher temperatures* (Figure 13.19). Note that cerium sulfate is one of several exceptions, mostly other sulfates. Some salts have higher solubility up to a certain temperature and then lower solubility at still higher temperatures.

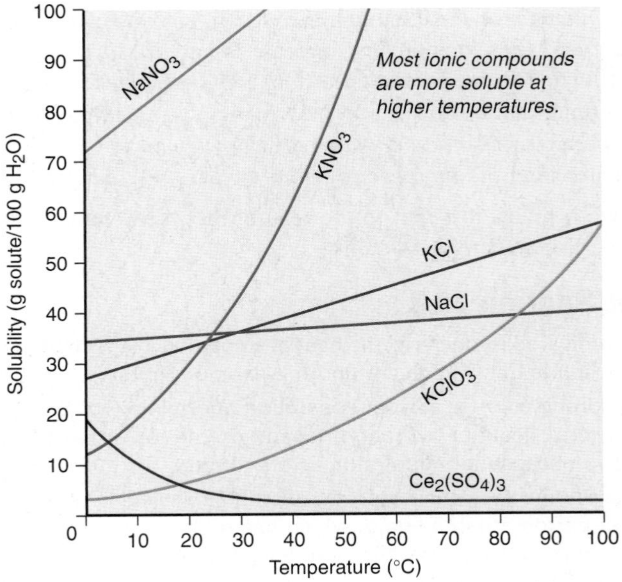

Figure 13.19 Relation between solubility and temperature for several ionic compounds.

Unfortunately, the effect of temperature on solubility is a complex phenomenon, and the sign of ΔH_{soln} does not reflect that complexity. Tabulated ΔH_{soln} values give the enthalpy change for making a solution at the standard state of 1 *M*; but in order to understand the effect of temperature, we need to know the sign of the enthalpy change very close to the point of saturation, which may differ from the sign of the tabulated value. For example, tables give a negative ΔH_{soln} for NaOH and a positive one for NH_4NO_3, yet both compounds are more soluble at higher temperatures. The point is that, although the effect of temperature reflects the equilibrium nature of solubility, no single measure can predict the effect for a given solute.

Temperature and the Solubility of Gases in Water The effect of temperature on *gas* solubility is much more predictable. When a solid dissolves in a liquid, the solute particles must separate, so $\Delta H_{solute} > 0$. In contrast, gas particles are already separated, so $\Delta H_{solute} \approx 0$. Because hydration is exothermic ($\Delta H_{hydr} < 0$), the sum of these two terms is negative. Thus, $\Delta H_{soln} < 0$ for all gases in water:

$$\text{Solute}(g) + \text{water}(l) \rightleftharpoons \text{saturated solution}(aq) + \text{heat}$$

Thus, *gas solubility in water* ***decreases*** *with rising temperature (addition of heat).* Gases have weak intermolecular forces with water. When the temperature rises, the average kinetic energy increases, allowing the gas particles to easily overcome these forces and re-enter the gas phase.

This behavior leads to *thermal pollution.* Many electric power plants use large amounts of water from a nearby river or lake for cooling, and the warmed water is returned to the source. The metabolic rates of fish and other aquatic animals increase in this warmer water, increasing their need for O_2. But the concentration of dissolved O_2 is lower in warm water, so they become "oxygen deprived." Also, the less dense warm water floats and prevents O_2 from reaching the cooler water below. Thus, even creatures at deeper levels become oxygen deprived. Farther from the plant, the water temperature and O_2 solubility return to normal. To mitigate the problem, cooling towers lower the temperature of the water before it exits the plant (Figure 13.20); nuclear power plants use a similar approach (Section 24.7).

Figure 13.20 Preventing thermal pollution with cooling towers.

Effect of Pressure on Solubility

Pressure has little effect on the solubility of liquids and solids because they are almost incompressible. But it has a *major* effect on the solubility of gases. Consider a piston-cylinder assembly with a gas above a saturated aqueous solution of the gas (Figure 13.21A). At equilibrium, at a given pressure, the same number of gas molecules enter and leave the solution per unit time:

$$\text{Gas} + \text{solvent} \rightleftharpoons \text{saturated solution}$$

Push down on the piston, and you disturb the equilibrium: gas volume decreases, so gas pressure (and concentration) increases, and gas particles collide with the liquid surface more often. Thus, more particles enter than leave the solution per unit time (Figure 13.21B). More gas dissolves to reduce this disturbance (a shift to the right in the preceding equation) until the system re-establishes equilibrium (Figure 13.21C).

The relation between gas pressure and solubility has many familiar applications. In a closed can of cola, dissolved CO_2 is in equilibrium with 4 atm of CO_2 in the small

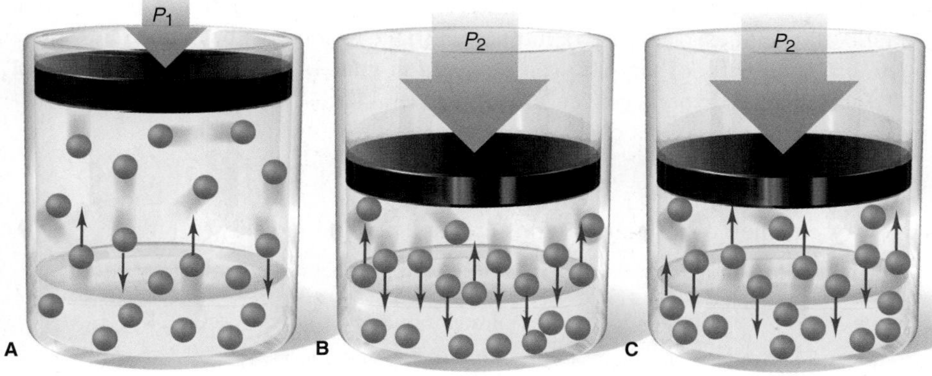

Figure 13.21 The effect of pressure on gas solubility.

What happens to gases dissolved in the blood of a scuba diver?

volume above the solution. Open the can and the dissolved CO_2 bubbles out of solution until the drink goes "flat" because it reaches equilibrium with CO_2 in air ($P_{CO_2} = 3\times10^{-4}$ atm). In a different situation (*see photo*), scuba divers who breathe compressed air have a high concentration of N_2 dissolved in their blood. If they ascend too quickly, they may suffer decompression sickness (the "bends"), in which lower external pressure allows the dissolved N_2 to form bubbles in the blood that block capillaries.

Henry's law expresses the quantitative relationship between gas pressure and solubility: *the solubility of a gas (S_{gas}) is directly proportional to the partial pressure of the gas (P_{gas}) above the solution:*

$$S_{gas} = k_H \times P_{gas} \qquad (13.3)$$

where k_H is the *Henry's law constant* and is specific for a given gas-solvent combination at a given temperature. With S_{gas} in mol/L and P_{gas} in atm, the units of k_H are mol/L·atm.

Sample Problem 13.2 Using Henry's Law to Calculate Gas Solubility

Problem The partial pressure of carbon dioxide gas inside a bottle of cola is 4 atm at 25°C. What is the solubility of CO_2? The Henry's law constant for CO_2 in water is 3.3×10^{-2} mol/L·atm at 25°C.

Plan We know P_{CO_2} (4 atm) and the value of k_H (3.3×10^{-2} mol/L·atm), so we substitute them into Equation 13.3 to find S_{CO_2}.

Solution $S_{CO_2} = k_H \times P_{CO_2} = (3.3\times10^{-2}\ \text{mol/L·atm})(4\ \text{atm}) = 0.1\ \text{mol/L}$

Check The units are correct. We rounded to one significant figure because there is one in the pressure value. A 0.5-L bottle of cola has about 0.2 g of dissolved CO_2.

Follow-Up Problem 13.2 If air contains 78% N_2 by volume, what is the solubility of N_2 in water at 25°C and 1 atm (k_H for N_2 in H_2O at 25°C $= 7\times10^{-4}$ mol/L·atm)?

Summary of Section 13.4

- A solution that contains the maximum amount of dissolved solute in the presence of excess undissolved solute is saturated. A saturated solution is in equilibrium with excess solute, because solute particles are entering and leaving the solution at the same rate.
- Most solids are more soluble at higher temperatures.
- All gases have a negative ΔH_{soln} in water, so heating lowers gas solubility in water.
- Henry's law says that the solubility of a gas is directly proportional to its partial pressure above the solution.

13.5 • CONCENTRATION TERMS

Concentration is the *proportion* of a substance in a mixture, so it is an *intensive* property (like density and temperature), one that does not depend on the quantity of mixture: 1.0 L or 1.0 mL of 0.1 *M* NaCl have the same concentration. Concentration is a ratio of quantities (Table 13.5), most often solute to *solution,* but sometimes solute to *solvent.* Both parts of the ratio can be given in units of mass, volume, or amount (mol), and chemists express concentration by several terms, including molarity, molality, and various expressions of "parts of solute per part by solution."

Molarity and Molality

Two very common concentration terms are molarity and molality:

1. Molarity (*M*) is the *number of moles of solute dissolved in 1 L of solution:*

$$\text{Molarity } (M) = \frac{\text{amount (mol) of solute}}{\text{volume (L) of solution}} \qquad (13.4)$$

Table 13.5 Concentration Definitions

Concentration Term	Ratio
Molarity (M)	$\frac{\text{amount (mol) of solute}}{\text{volume (L) of solution}}$
Molality (m)	$\frac{\text{amount (mol) of solute}}{\text{mass (kg) of solvent}}$
Parts by mass	$\frac{\text{mass of solute}}{\text{mass of solution}}$
Parts by volume	$\frac{\text{volume of solute}}{\text{volume of solution}}$
Mole fraction (X)	$\frac{\text{amount (mol) of solute}}{\text{amount (mol) of solute + amount (mol) of solvent}}$

In Chapter 3, we used molarity to convert liters of solution into amount of dissolved solute. Molarity has two drawbacks that affect its use in precise work:

- *Effect of temperature*. A liquid expands when heated, so a unit volume of hot solution contains less solute than one of cold solution; thus, the molarity is different.
- *Effect of mixing*. Because of solute-solvent interactions that are difficult to predict, *volumes may not be additive:* adding 500. mL of one solution to 500. mL of another may not give 1000. mL of final solution.

2. **Molality (m)** does not contain volume in its ratio; it is *the number of moles of solute dissolved in 1000 g (1 kg) of solvent:*

$$\text{Molality } (m) = \frac{\text{amount (mol) of solute}}{\text{mass (kg) of solvent}} \qquad (13.5)$$

Note that molality includes the quantity of *solvent,* not solution. Molality has two advantages over molarity for precise work:

- *Effect of temperature*. Molal solutions are based on *masses* of components, not *volume*. And since mass does not change with temperature, neither does molality.
- *Effect of mixing*. Unlike volumes, masses *are* additive: adding 500. g of one solution to 500. g of another *does* give 1000. g of final solution.

For these reasons, molality is the preferred term when temperature, and hence density, may change, as in a study of physical properties. Note that, in the case of water, 1 L has a mass of 1 kg, so *molality and molarity are nearly the same for dilute aqueous solutions.*

Sample Problem 13.3 Calculating Molality

Problem What is the molality of a solution prepared by dissolving 32.0 g of $CaCl_2$ in 271 g of water?

Plan To use Equation 13.5, we convert mass of $CaCl_2$ (32.0 g) to amount (mol) with the molar mass (g/mol) and then divide by the mass of water (271 g), being sure to convert from grams to kilograms (see the road map).

Road Map

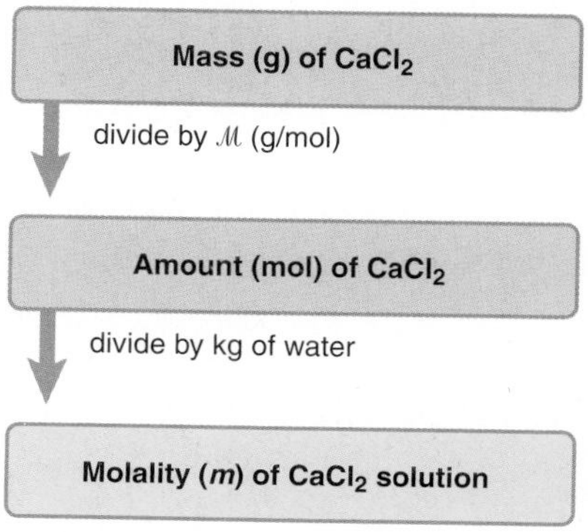

Solution Converting from grams of solute to moles:

$$\text{Amount (mol) of CaCl}_2 = 32.0 \text{ g CaCl}_2 \times \frac{1 \text{ mol CaCl}_2}{110.98 \text{ g CaCl}_2} = 0.288 \text{ mol CaCl}_2$$

Finding molality:

$$\text{Molality} = \frac{\text{mol solute}}{\text{kg solvent}} = \frac{0.288 \text{ mol CaCl}_2}{271 \text{ g} \times \frac{1 \text{ kg}}{10^3 \text{ g}}} = 1.06\ m \text{ CaCl}_2$$

Check The answer seems reasonable: the given amount (mol) of $CaCl_2$ and mass (kg) of H_2O are about the same, so their ratio is about 1.

Follow-Up Problem 13.3 How many grams of glucose ($C_6H_{12}O_6$) must be dissolved in 563 g of ethanol (C_2H_5OH) to prepare a 2.40×10^{-2} *m* solution?

Parts of Solute by Parts of Solution

Several concentration terms relate the number of solute (or solvent) parts to a number of *solution* parts. Both can be expressed in units of mass, volume, or amount (mol).

Parts by Mass The most common of these terms is **mass percent, % (w/w),** which you encountered in Chapter 3. The word *percent* means "per hundred," so mass percent means mass of solute dissolved in 100. parts by mass of solution:

$$\text{Mass percent} = \frac{\text{mass of solute}}{\text{mass of solute} + \text{mass of solvent}} \times 100 = \frac{\text{mass of solute}}{\text{mass of solution}} \times 100 \quad (13.6)$$

Mass percent values appear on jars of solid chemicals to indicate impurities.

Two very similar terms are parts per million (ppm) by mass and parts per billion (ppb) by mass, or grams of solute per million or per billion grams of solution: in Equation 13.6, you multiply by 10^6 or by 10^9, respectively, instead of by 100. Environmental toxicologists use these units to measure pollutants. For example, TCDD (*t*etra*c*hloro*d*ibenzo*d*ioxin) (*see margin*), a byproduct of paper bleaching, is unsafe at soil levels above 1 ppb. From normal contact with air, water, and soil, North Americans have an average of 0.01 ppb TCDD in their tissues.

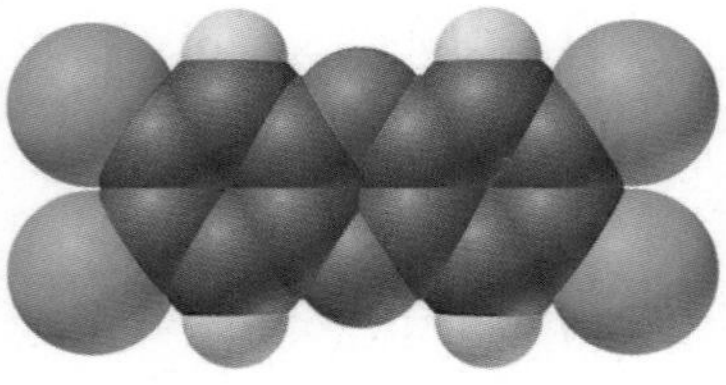

Is this deadly toxin in your body?

Parts by Volume The most common parts-by-volume term is **volume percent, % (v/v),** the volume of solute in 100. volumes of solution:

$$\text{Volume percent} = \frac{\text{volume of solute}}{\text{volume of solution}} \times 100 \quad (13.7)$$

For example, rubbing alcohol is an aqueous solution of isopropanol (a three-carbon alcohol) that contains 70 volumes of alcohol in 100. volumes of solution, or 70% (v/v).

Parts by volume is often used to express tiny concentrations of liquids or gases. Minor atmospheric components occur in parts per million by volume (ppmv). For example, about 0.05 ppmv of the toxic gas carbon monoxide (CO) is in clean air, 1000 times as much (50 ppmv of CO) in air over urban traffic, and 10,000 times as much (500 ppmv of CO) in cigarette smoke. *Pheromones* are compounds secreted by members of a species to signal food, danger, sexual readiness, and so forth. Many organisms, including dogs and monkeys, release pheromones, and researchers suspect that humans do as well. Some insect pheromones, such as the sexual attractant of the gypsy moth, are active at a few hundred molecules per milliliter of air, 100 parts per quadrillion by volume.

A concentration term often used in health-related facilities for aqueous solutions is % (w/v), a ratio of solute *weight* (actually mass) to solution *volume*. Thus, a 1.5% (w/v) NaCl solution contains 1.5 g of NaCl per 100. mL of *solution*.

Mole Fraction The **mole fraction (*X*)** of a solute is the ratio of number of moles of solute to the total number of moles (solute plus solvent), that is, parts by mole:

$$\text{Mole fraction } (X) = \frac{\text{amount (mol) of solute}}{\text{amount (mol) of solute} + \text{amount (mol) of solvent}} \quad (13.8)$$

Put another way, the mole fraction gives the proportion of solute (or solvent) particles in solution. The *mole percent* is the mole fraction expressed as a percentage:

$$\text{Mole percent (mol \%)} = \text{mole fraction} \times 100$$

Sample Problem 13.4 **Expressing Concentrations in Parts by Mass, Parts by Volume, and Mole Fraction**

Problem **(a)** Find the concentration of calcium ion (in ppm) in a 3.50-g pill that contains 40.5 mg of Ca^{2+}.
(b) The label on a 0.750-L bottle of Italian chianti indicates "11.5% alcohol by volume." How many liters of alcohol does the wine contain?
(c) A sample of rubbing alcohol contains 142 g of isopropyl alcohol (C_3H_7OH) and 58.0 g of water. What are the mole fractions of alcohol and water?

Plan **(a)** We know the mass of Ca^{2+} (40.5 mg) and the mass of the pill (3.50 g). We convert the mass of Ca^{2+} from mg to g, find the mass ratio of Ca^{2+} to pill, and multiply by 10^6 to obtain ppm. **(b)** We know the volume % (11.5%, or 11.5 parts by volume of alcohol to 100. parts of chianti) and the total volume (0.750 L), so we use Equation 13.7 to find liters of alcohol. **(c)** We know the mass and formula of each component, so we convert masses to amounts (mol) and apply Equation 13.8 to find the mole fractions.

Solution **(a)** Finding parts per million by mass of Ca^{2+}. Combining the steps, we have

$$\text{ppm } Ca^{2+} = \frac{\text{mass of } Ca^{2+}}{\text{mass of pill}} \times 10^6 = \frac{40.5 \text{ mg } Ca^{2+} \times \dfrac{1 \text{ g}}{10^3 \text{ mg}}}{3.50 \text{ g}} \times 10^6$$

$$= 1.16\times10^4 \text{ ppm } Ca^{2+}$$

(b) Finding volume (L) of alcohol:

$$\text{Volume (L) of alcohol} = 0.750 \text{ L chianti} \times \frac{11.5 \text{ L alcohol}}{100. \text{ L chianti}}$$

$$= 0.0862 \text{ L}$$

(c) Finding mole fractions. Converting from mass (g) to amount (mol):

$$\text{Amount (mol) of } C_3H_7OH = 142 \text{ g } C_3H_7OH \times \frac{1 \text{ mol } C_3H_7OH}{60.09 \text{ g } C_3H_7OH} = 2.36 \text{ mol } C_3H_7OH$$

$$\text{Amount (mol) of } H_2O = 58.0 \text{ g } H_2O \times \frac{1 \text{ mol } H_2O}{18.02 \text{ g } H_2O} = 3.22 \text{ mol } H_2O$$

Calculating mole fractions:

$$X_{C_3H_7OH} = \frac{\text{moles of } C_3H_7OH}{\text{total moles}} = \frac{2.36 \text{ mol}}{2.36 \text{ mol} + 3.22 \text{ mol}} = 0.423$$

$$X_{H_2O} = \frac{\text{moles of } H_2O}{\text{total moles}} = \frac{3.22 \text{ mol}}{2.36 \text{ mol} + 3.22 \text{ mol}} = 0.577$$

Check **(a)** The mass ratio is about 0.04 g/4 g = 10^{-2}, and $10^{-2}\times10^6 = 10^4$ ppm, so it seems correct. **(b)** The volume % is a bit more than 10%, so the volume of alcohol should be a bit more than 75 mL (0.075 L). **(c)** Always check that the *mole fractions add up to 1:* 0.423 + 0.577 = 1.000.

Follow-Up Problem 13.4 An alcohol solution contains 35.0 g of 1-propanol (C_3H_7OH) and 150. g of ethanol (C_2H_5OH). Calculate the mass percent and the mole fraction of each alcohol.

Interconverting Concentration Terms

All the terms we just discussed represent different ways of expressing concentration, so they are interconvertible. Keep these points in mind:

- To convert a term based on amount to one based on mass, you need the molar mass. These conversions are similar to the mass-mole conversions you've done earlier.
- To convert a term based on mass to one based on volume, you need the solution *density.* Given the mass of solution, the density (mass/volume) gives the volume, or vice versa.
- Molality includes quantity of *solvent;* the other terms include quantity of *solution.*

Sample Problem 13.5 Interconverting Concentration Terms

Problem Hydrogen peroxide is a powerful oxidizing agent; it is used in concentrated solution in rocket fuel, but in dilute solution in hair bleach. An aqueous solution of H_2O_2 is 30.0% by mass and has a density of 1.11 g/mL. Calculate the **(a)** molality, **(b)** mole fraction of H_2O_2, and **(c)** molarity.

Plan We know the mass % (30.0) and the density (1.11 g/mL). **(a)** For molality, we need the amount (mol) of solute and the mass (kg) of *solvent.* If we assume 100.0 g of solution, the mass % equals the grams of H_2O_2, which we subtract to obtain the grams of solvent. To find molality, we convert grams of H_2O_2 to moles and divide by mass of solvent (converting g to kg). **(b)** To find the mole fraction, we use the moles of H_2O_2 [from part (a)] and convert the grams of H_2O to moles. Then we divide the moles of H_2O_2 by the total moles. **(c)** To find molarity, we assume 100.0 g of solution and use the solution density to find the volume. Then we divide the moles of H_2O_2 [from part (a)] by *solution* volume (in L).

Solution **(a)** From mass % to molality. Finding mass of solvent (assuming 100.0 g of solution):

$$\text{Mass (g) of } H_2O = 100.0 \text{ g solution} - 30.0 \text{ g } H_2O_2 = 70.0 \text{ g } H_2O$$

Converting from grams of H_2O_2 to moles:

$$\text{Amount (mol) of } H_2O_2 = 30.0 \text{ g } H_2O_2 \times \frac{1 \text{ mol } H_2O_2}{34.02 \text{ g } H_2O_2} = 0.882 \text{ mol } H_2O_2$$

Calculating molality:

$$\text{Molality of } H_2O_2 = \frac{0.882 \text{ mol } H_2O_2}{70.0 \text{ g} \times \dfrac{1 \text{ kg}}{10^3 \text{ g}}} = 12.6\, m\ H_2O_2$$

(b) From mass % to mole fraction:

$$\text{Amount (mol) of } H_2O_2 = 0.882 \text{ mol } H_2O_2 \text{ [from part (a)]}$$

$$\text{Amount (mol) of } H_2O = 70.0 \text{ g } H_2O \times \frac{1 \text{ mol } H_2O}{18.02 \text{ g } H_2O} = 3.88 \text{ mol } H_2O$$

$$X_{H_2O_2} = \frac{0.882 \text{ mol}}{0.882 \text{ mol} + 3.88 \text{ mol}} = 0.185$$

(c) From mass % and density to molarity. Converting from solution mass to volume:

$$\text{Volume (mL) of solution} = 100.0 \text{ g} \times \frac{1 \text{ mL}}{1.11 \text{ g}} = 90.1 \text{ mL}$$

Calculating molarity:

$$\text{Molarity} = \frac{\text{mol } H_2O_2}{\text{L soln}} = \frac{0.882 \text{ mol } H_2O_2}{90.1 \text{ mL} \times \dfrac{1 \text{ L soln}}{10^3 \text{ mL}}} = 9.79\, M\ H_2O_2$$

Check Rounding shows the answers to be reasonable: **(a)** The ratio of ~0.9 mol/0.07 kg is greater than 10. **(b)** ~0.9 mol H_2O_2/(1 mol + 4 mol) ≈ 0.2. **(c)** The ratio of moles to liters (0.9/0.09) is around 10.

Follow-Up Problem 13.5 Concentrated hydrochloric acid is 11.8 *M* HCl and has a density of 1.190 g/mL. Calculate the mass %, molality, and mole fraction of HCl.

Summary of Section 13.5

- The concentration of a solution is independent of the quantity of solution and can be expressed as molarity (mol solute/L solution), molality (mol solute/kg solvent), parts by mass (mass solute/mass solution), parts by volume (volume solute/volume solution), or mole fraction [mol solute/(mol solute + mol solvent)] (Table 13.5).
- Molality is based on mass, so it is independent of temperature; the mole fraction gives the proportion of dissolved particles.
- If, in addition to the quantities of solute and solution, the solution density is known, the various ways of expressing concentration are interconvertible.

13.6 • COLLIGATIVE PROPERTIES OF SOLUTIONS

The presence of solute gives a solution different physical properties than the pure solvent. But, in the case of four important properties, it is the *number* of solute particles, *not* their chemical identity, that makes the difference. These **colligative properties** (*colligative* means "collective") are vapor pressure lowering, boiling point elevation, freezing point depression, and osmotic pressure. Most of the effects are small, but they have many applications, including some vital to organisms.

We predict the magnitude of a colligative property from the solute formula, which shows the number of particles in solution and is closely related to our classification of solutes (Chapter 4) by their ability to conduct an electric current (Figure 13.22):

1. *Electrolytes.* An aqueous solution of an **electrolyte** conducts because the solute separates into ions as it dissolves.
   - *Strong electrolytes*—soluble salts, strong acids, and strong bases—dissociate completely, so their solutions conduct well.
   - *Weak electrolytes*—weak acids and weak bases—dissociate very little, so their solutions conduct poorly.
2. *Nonelectrolytes.* Compounds such as sugar and alcohol do not dissociate into ions at all. They are **nonelectrolytes** because their solutions do not conduct a current.

Thus we can predict that

- *For nonelectrolytes,* 1 mol of compound yields 1 mol of particles in solution. For example, 0.35 *M* glucose contains 0.35 mol of solute particles per liter.
- *For strong electrolytes,* 1 mol of compound yields the amount (mol) of ions in the formula unit: 0.4 *M* Na_2SO_4 has 0.8 mol of Na^+ ions and 0.4 mol of SO_4^{2-} ions, or 1.2 mol of particles, per liter (see Sample Problem 4.1, p. 138).
- *For weak electrolytes,* the calculation is complicated because the solution reaches equilibrium; we examine these systems in Chapters 18 and 19.

In this section, we discuss colligative properties of three types of solute—nonvolatile nonelectrolytes, volatile nonelectrolytes, and strong electrolytes.

Nonvolatile Nonelectrolyte Solutions

We start with solutions of *nonvolatile nonelectrolytes,* because they provide the clearest examples of the colligative properties. These solutes do not dissociate and have negligible vapor pressure at the boiling point of the solvent; sucrose (table sugar) dissolved in water is an example.

Vapor Pressure Lowering *The vapor pressure of a nonvolatile nonelectrolyte solution is always lower than the vapor pressure of the pure solvent.* The difference in vapor pressures is the **vapor pressure lowering (ΔP).**

1. *Why the vapor pressure of a solution is lower.* We can explain this lowering in terms of maintaining equilibrium or increasing entropy (Figure 13.23, *next page*):

- *Maintaining equilibrium.* In pure solvent, the opposing rates of vaporization (molecules leaving the liquid) and of condensation (molecules entering the liquid) are equal at equilibrium. In a solution, some solute molecules are on the surface, so the number of solvent molecules on the surface is lower; therefore, fewer vaporize per unit time. To maintain equilibrium, fewer gas molecules must enter the liquid, which happens if the vapor pressure is lower.
- *Increasing entropy.* A solvent vaporizes because the gaseous state has higher entropy than the liquid. But, with dissolved particles present, the solution already has higher entropy, so the solvent has less tendency to vaporize.

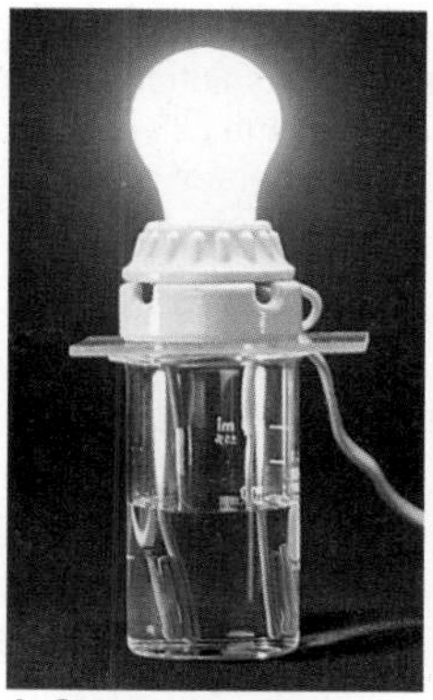

A Strong electrolyte

B Weak electrolyte

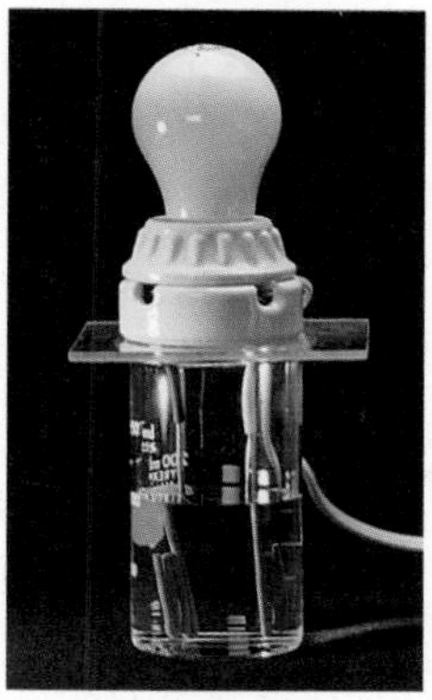

C Nonelectrolyte

Figure 13.22 Conductivity of three types of electrolyte solutions. **A,** For strong electrolytes, the number of particles equals the number of ions in a formula unit. **B,** Weak electrolytes form few ions. **C,** For nonelectrolytes, the number of particles equals the number of molecules.

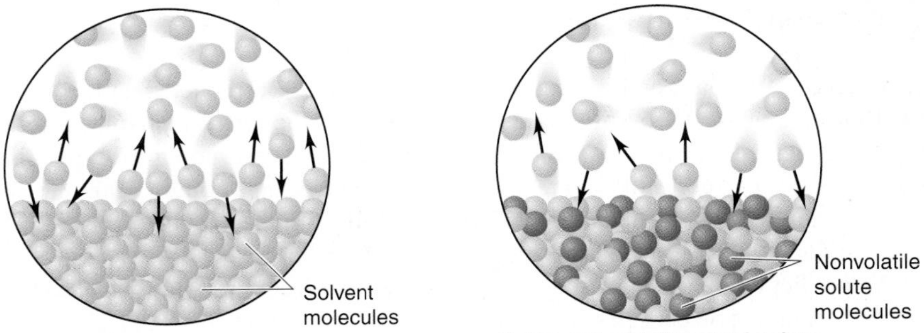

Figure 13.23 Effect of solute on the vapor pressure of solution. **A,** Equilibrium between a liquid and its vapor occurs when equal numbers of molecules vaporize and condense in a given time. **B,** Solute molecules decrease the number of solvent molecules at the surface *and* increase the entropy, so equilibrium occurs at a lower vapor pressure.

2. *Quantifying vapor pressure lowering.* **Raoult's law** says that the vapor pressure of solvent above a solution ($P_{solvent}$) equals the mole fraction of solvent ($X_{solvent}$) times the vapor pressure of the pure solvent ($P^\circ_{solvent}$):

$$P_{solvent} = X_{solvent} \times P^\circ_{solvent} \quad (13.9)$$

Since $X_{solvent}$ is less than 1 in a solution, $P_{solvent}$ is less than $P^\circ_{solvent}$. An **ideal solution** is one that follows Raoult's law at any concentration. However, just as real gases deviate from ideality, so do real solutions. In practice, Raoult's law works reasonably well for *dilute* solutions and becomes exact at infinite dilution.

Let's see how the *amount* of dissolved solute affects ΔP. The solution consists of solvent and solute, so the sum of their mole fractions equals 1:

$$X_{solvent} + X_{solute} = 1; \quad \text{thus,} \quad X_{solvent} = 1 - X_{solute}$$

From Raoult's law, we have

$$P_{solvent} = X_{solvent} \times P^\circ_{solvent} = (1 - X_{solute}) \times P^\circ_{solvent}$$

Multiplying through on the right side gives

$$P_{solvent} = P^\circ_{solvent} - (X_{solute} \times P^\circ_{solvent})$$

Rearranging and introducing ΔP gives

$$P^\circ_{solvent} - P_{solvent} = \Delta P = X_{solute} \times P^\circ_{solvent} \quad (13.10)$$

Thus, ΔP equals the mole fraction of solute times the vapor pressure of the pure solvent—a relationship applied in the next sample problem.

Sample Problem 13.6 Using Raoult's Law to Find ΔP

Road Map

- Volume (mL) of glycerol (or H_2O)
  - ↓ multiply by density (g/mL)
- Mass (g) of glycerol (or H_2O)
  - ↓ divide by $\mathcal{M}$ (g/mol)
- Amount (mol) of glycerol (or H_2O)
  - ↓ divide by total number of moles
- Mole fraction (X) of glycerol
  - ↓ multiply by $P^\circ_{H_2O}$
- Vapor pressure lowering (ΔP)

Problem Find the vapor pressure lowering, ΔP, when 10.0 mL of glycerol ($C_3H_8O_3$) is added to 500. mL of water at 50.°C. At this temperature, the vapor pressure of pure water is 92.5 torr and its density is 0.988 g/mL. The density of glycerol is 1.26 g/mL.

Plan To calculate ΔP, we use Equation 13.10. We are given the vapor pressure of pure water ($P^\circ_{H_2O} = 92.5$ torr), so we just need the mole fraction of glycerol, $X_{glycerol}$. We convert the given volume of glycerol (10.0 mL) to mass using the given density (1.26 g/L), find the molar mass from the formula, and convert mass (g) to amount (mol). The same procedure gives amount of H_2O. From these amounts, we find $X_{glycerol}$ and ΔP.

Solution Calculating the amount (mol) of glycerol and of water:

$$\text{Amount (mol) of glycerol} = 10.0 \text{ mL glycerol} \times \frac{1.26 \text{ g glycerol}}{1 \text{ mL glycerol}} \times \frac{1 \text{ mol glycerol}}{92.09 \text{ g glycerol}}$$
$$= 0.137 \text{ mol glycerol}$$

$$\text{Amount (mol) of } H_2O = 500. \text{ mL } H_2O \times \frac{0.988 \text{ g } H_2O}{1 \text{ mL } H_2O} \times \frac{1 \text{ mol } H_2O}{18.02 \text{ g } H_2O} = 27.4 \text{ mol } H_2O$$

Calculating the mole fraction of glycerol:

$$X_{glycerol} = \frac{0.137 \text{ mol}}{0.137 \text{ mol} + 27.4 \text{ mol}} = 0.00498$$

Finding the vapor pressure lowering:

$$\Delta P = X_{glycerol} \times P^\circ_{H_2O} = 0.00498 \times 92.5 \text{ torr} = 0.461 \text{ torr}$$

Check The amount of each component seems correct: for glycerol, ~10 mL × 1.25 g/mL ÷ 100 g/mol = 0.125 mol; for H_2O, ~500 mL × 1 g/mL ÷ 20 g/mol = 25 mol. The small ΔP is reasonable because the mole fraction of solute is small.

Comment 1. The calculation assumes that glycerol is nonvolatile. At 1 atm, glycerol boils at 290.0°C, so the vapor pressure of glycerol at 50°C is negligible. **2.** To introduce the calculation, we assume the solution is close to ideal and Raoult's law holds.

Follow-Up Problem 13.6 Calculate the vapor pressure lowering of a solution of 2.00 g of aspirin ($\mathcal{M}$ = 180.15 g/mol) in 50.0 g of methanol (CH_3OH) at 21.2°C. Pure methanol has a vapor pressure of 101 torr at this temperature.

Boiling Point Elevation *A solution boils at a higher temperature than the pure solvent.* This colligative property results from the previous vapor pressure lowering:

1. *Why a solution boils at a higher T.* Recall that the boiling point, T_b, of a liquid is the temperature at which its vapor pressure equals the external pressure, P_{ext}. But, the vapor pressure of a solution is always lower than that of the pure solvent. Therefore, it is lower than P_{ext} at T_b of the solvent, so the solution doesn't boil. Thus, the **boiling point elevation (ΔT_b)** results because a higher temperature is needed to raise the solution's vapor pressure to equal P_{ext}.

   We superimpose a phase diagram for the solution on one for the solvent to see ΔT_b (Figure 13.24): the gas-liquid line for the solution lies *below* the line for the solvent at any T and to the right of it at any P, and the line crosses 1 atm (P_{ext}, or P_{atm}) at a higher T.

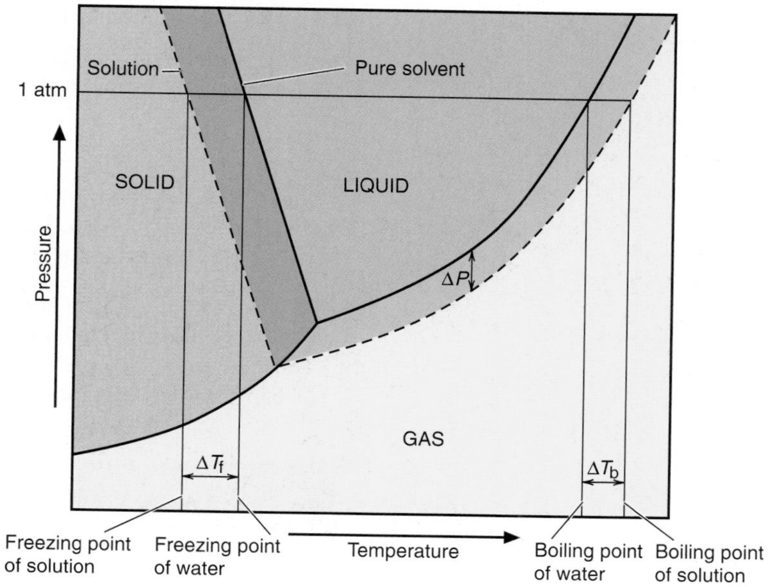

Figure 13.24 Boiling and freezing points of solvent and solution. Phase diagrams of an aqueous solution (*dashed lines*) and of pure water (*solid lines*) show that, by lowering the vapor pressure (ΔP), a solute elevates the boiling point (ΔT_b) and depresses the freezing point (ΔT_f). (The slope of the solid-liquid line is exaggerated.)

2. *Quantifying boiling point elevation.* Like vapor pressure lowering, boiling point elevation is proportional to the concentration of solute:

$$\Delta T_b \propto m \quad \text{or} \quad \Delta T_b = K_b m \qquad (13.11)$$

where m is the solution molality and K_b is the *molal boiling point elevation constant.* Since $\Delta T_b > 0$, we subtract the lower solvent T_b from the higher solution T_b:

$$\Delta T_b = T_{b(solution)} - T_{b(solvent)}$$

Molality is used because it relates to mole fraction and, thus, to particles of solute, and it is not affected by temperature.

The constant K_b has units of degrees Celsius per molal unit (°C/m) and is specific for a given solvent (Table 13.6). The K_b for water is 0.512°C/m, so ΔT_b for aqueous

Table 13.6 Molal Boiling Point Elevation and Freezing Point Depression Constants of Several Solvents

Solvent	Boiling Point (°C)*	K_b (°C/m)	Melting Point (°C)	K_f (°C/m)
Acetic acid	117.9	3.07	16.6	3.90
Benzene	80.1	2.53	5.5	4.90
Carbon disulfide	46.2	2.34	−111.5	3.83
Carbon tetrachloride	76.5	5.03	−23	30.
Chloroform	61.7	3.63	−63.5	4.70
Diethyl ether	34.5	2.02	−116.2	1.79
Ethanol	78.5	1.22	−117.3	1.99
Water	100.0	0.512	0.0	1.86

*At 1 atm.

solutions is quite small. For example, if you dissolve 1.00 mol of glucose (180. g; 1.00 mol of particles) or 0.500 mol of NaCl (29.2 g; also 1.00 mol of particles) in 1.00 kg of water at 1 atm, the solutions will boil at 100.512°C instead of 100.000°C.

Freezing Point Depression *A solution freezes at a lower temperature than the pure solvent,* and this colligative property also results from vapor pressure lowering:

1. *Why a solution freezes at a lower T.* Only solvent vaporizes from solution, so solute molecules are left behind. Similarly, *only solvent freezes,* again leaving solute molecules behind. The freezing point of a solution is the temperature at which its vapor pressure equals that of the pure solvent, that is, when solid solvent and liquid solution are in equilibrium. The **freezing point depression (ΔT_f)** occurs because the vapor pressure of the solution is always lower than that of the solvent, so the solution freezes at a lower temperature; that is, only at a lower temperature will solvent particles leave and enter the solid at the same rate. In Figure 13.24, the solid-liquid line for the solution is to the left of the pure solvent line at 1 atm, or any pressure.

2. *Quantifying freezing point depression.* Like ΔT_b, the freezing point depression is proportional to the molal concentration of solute:

$$\Delta T_f \propto m \quad \text{or} \quad \Delta T_f = K_f m \qquad (13.12)$$

where K_f is the *molal freezing point depression constant,* which also has units of °C/*m* (see Table 13.6). Also, like ΔT_b, $\Delta T_f > 0$, but in this case, we subtract the lower solution T_f from the higher solvent T_f:

$$\Delta T_f = T_{f(solvent)} - T_{f(solution)}$$

Here, too, the effect in aqueous solution is small because K_f for water is just 1.86°C/*m*. Thus, at 1 atm, 1 *m* glucose, 0.5 *m* NaCl, and 0.33 *m* K_2SO_4, all solutions with 1 mol of particles per kilogram of water, freeze at −1.86°C instead of at 0.00°C.

Sample Problem 13.7 Determining Boiling and Freezing Points of a Solution

Problem You add 1.00 kg of ethylene glycol ($C_2H_6O_2$) antifreeze to 4450 g of water in your car's radiator. What are the boiling and freezing points of the solution?

Plan To find the boiling and freezing points, we need ΔT_b and ΔT_f. We first find the molality by converting mass of solute (1.00 kg) to amount (mol) and dividing by mass of solvent (4450 g, converted to kg). Then we calculate ΔT_b and ΔT_f from Equations 13.11 and 13.12 (using constants from Table 13.6). We add ΔT_b to the solvent boiling point and subtract ΔT_f from its freezing point. The road map shows the steps.

Road Map

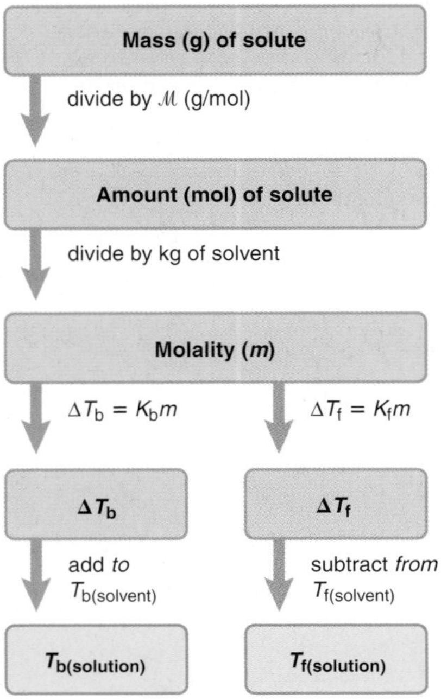

Solution Calculating the molality:

$$\text{Amount (mol) of } C_2H_6O_2 = 1.00 \text{ kg } C_2H_6O_2 \times \frac{10^3 \text{ g}}{1 \text{ kg}} \times \frac{1 \text{ mol } C_2H_6O_2}{62.07 \text{ g } C_2H_6O_2}$$
$$= 16.1 \text{ mol } C_2H_6O_2$$

$$\text{Molality} = \frac{\text{mol solute}}{\text{kg solvent}} = \frac{16.1 \text{ mol } C_2H_6O_2}{4450 \text{ g } H_2O \times \frac{1 \text{ kg}}{10^3 \text{ g}}} = 3.62\ m\ C_2H_6O_2$$

Finding the boiling point elevation and $T_{b(solution)}$, with $K_b = 0.512°C/m$:

$$\Delta T_b = \frac{0.512°C}{m} \times 3.62\ m = 1.85°C$$

$$T_{b(solution)} = T_{b(solvent)} + \Delta T_b = 100.00°C + 1.85°C = 101.85°C$$

Finding the freezing point depression and $T_{f(solution)}$, with $K_f = 1.86°C/m$:

$$\Delta T_f = \frac{1.86°C}{m} \times 3.62\ m = 6.73°C$$

$$T_{f(solution)} = T_{f(solvent)} - \Delta T_f = 0.00°C - 6.73°C = -6.73°C$$

Check The changes in boiling and freezing points should be in the same proportion as the constants used. That is, $\Delta T_b/\Delta T_f$ should equal K_b/K_f: 1.85/6.73 = 0.275 = 0.512/1.86.

Comment These answers are approximate because the concentration far exceeds that of a *dilute* solution, for which Raoult's law is most accurate.

Follow-Up Problem 13.7 What is the lowest molality of ethylene glycol solution that will protect your car's coolant from freezing at 0.00°F? (Assume the solution is ideal.)

Osmotic Pressure This colligative property occurs when solutions of higher and lower concentrations are separated by a **semipermeable membrane,** one that allows solvent, but *not* solute, to pass through. The phenomenon is called **osmosis:** a net flow of solvent into the more concentrated solution causes a pressure difference known as *osmotic pressure*. Many organisms regulate internal concentrations by osmosis.

1. *Why osmotic pressure arises.* Consider a simple apparatus in which a semipermeable membrane lies at the curve of a U tube and separates an aqueous sugar solution from pure water. Water molecules pass in *either* direction, but the larger sugar molecules do not. Because sugar molecules are on the solution side of the membrane, fewer water molecules touch that side, so fewer leave the solution than enter it in a given time (Figure 13.25A). The *net flow of water into the solution* increases its volume and thus decreases its concentration.

As the height of the solution rises and the height of the water falls, a pressure difference forms that resists more water entering and pushes some water back through the membrane. When water is being pushed out of the solution at the same rate it is entering, the system is at equilibrium (Figure 13.25B). The pressure difference at this point is the **osmotic pressure (Π),** which is the same as the pressure that must be applied to *prevent* net movement of water from solvent to solution (or from lower to higher concentration, Figure 13.25C).

2. *Quantifying osmotic pressure.* The osmotic pressure is proportional to the number of solute particles in a given solution *volume,* that is, to the molarity (M):

$$\Pi \propto \frac{n_{\text{solute}}}{V_{\text{soln}}} \quad \text{or} \quad \Pi \propto M$$

The proportionality constant is R times the absolute temperature T. Thus,

$$\Pi = \frac{n_{\text{solute}}}{V_{\text{soln}}} RT = MRT \tag{13.13}$$

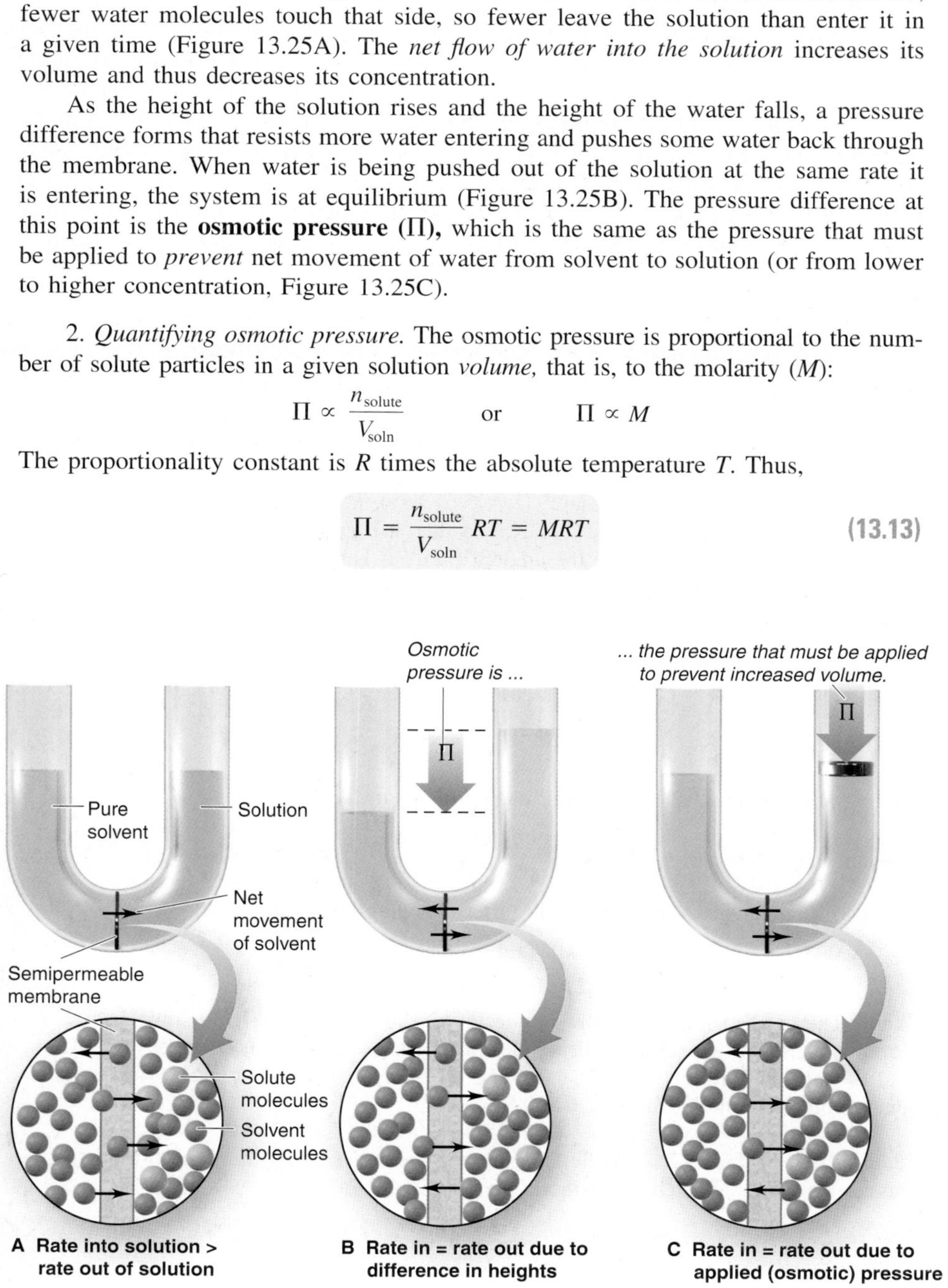

Figure 13.25 The development of osmotic pressure. **A,** In a given time, more solvent enters the solution through the membrane than leaves. **B,** At equilibrium, solvent flow is equalized. **C,** The *osmotic pressure* (Π) *prevents* the volume change.

The similarity of Equation 13.13 to the ideal gas law ($P = nRT/V$) is not surprising, because both relate the pressure of a system to its concentration and temperature.

The Underlying Theme of Colligative Properties A common theme runs through our explanations of the four colligative properties of nonvolatile solutes. Each property arises because solute particles cannot move between two phases:

- They cannot enter the gas phase, which leads to *vapor pressure lowering* and *boiling point elevation.*
- They cannot enter the solid phase, which leads to *freezing point depression.*
- They cannot cross a semipermeable membrane, which leads to *osmotic pressure.*

In each situation, the presence of solute decreases the mole fraction of solvent, which lowers the number of solvent particles leaving the solution per unit time. This lowering requires a new balance in numbers of particles moving between two phases per unit time, and this new balance results in the measured colligative property.

Using Colligative Properties to Find Solute Molar Mass

Each colligative property is proportional to solute concentration. Thus, by measuring the property—lower freezing point, higher boiling point, and so forth—we determine the amount (mol) of solute particles and, given the mass of solute, the molar mass.

In principle, any of the colligative properties can be used but, of the four, osmotic pressure creates the largest changes and, thus, the most precise measurements. Polymer chemists and biochemists estimate molar masses as great as 10^5 g/mol by measuring osmotic pressure. Because only a tiny fraction of a mole of a macromolecular solute dissolves, the change in the other colligative properties would be too small.

Sample Problem 13.8 Determining Molar Mass from Osmotic Pressure

Problem Biochemists have discovered more than 400 mutant varieties of hemoglobin, the blood protein that carries O_2. A physician dissolves 21.5 mg of one variety in water to make 1.50 mL of solution at 5.0°C. She measures an osmotic pressure of 3.61 torr. What is the molar mass of the protein?

Plan We know the osmotic pressure (Π = 3.61 torr), R, and T (5.0°C). We convert Π from torr to atm, and T from °C to K, and then use Equation 13.13 to solve for molarity (M). Then we calculate the amount (mol) of hemoglobin from the known volume (1.50 mL) and use the known mass (21.5 mg) to find $\mathcal{M}$.

Road Map

Π (atm)

↓ $M = \Pi/RT$

M (mol/L)

↓ multiply by volume (L) of solution

Amount (mol) of solute

↓ divide *into* mass (g) of solute

$\mathcal{M}$ (g/mol)

Solution Combining unit conversion steps and solving for molarity:

$$M = \frac{\Pi}{RT} = \frac{\dfrac{3.61\ \text{torr}}{760\ \text{torr}/1\ \text{atm}}}{\left(0.0821\ \dfrac{\text{atm·L}}{\text{mol·K}}\right)(273.15\ \text{K} + 5.0)} = 2.08\times10^{-4}\ M$$

Finding amount (mol) of solute (after changing mL to L):

$$\text{Amount (mol) of solute} = M \times V = \frac{2.08\times10^{-4}\ \text{mol}}{1\ \text{L soln}} \times 0.00150\ L\ \text{soln} = 3.12\times10^{-7}\ \text{mol}$$

Calculating molar mass of hemoglobin (after changing mg to g):

$$\mathcal{M} = \frac{0.0215\ \text{g}}{3.12\times10^{-7}\ \text{mol}} = 6.89\times10^{4}\ \text{g/mol}$$

Check The small osmotic pressure implies a very low molarity. Hemoglobin is a biopolymer, so we expect a small number of moles [($\sim$2×10^{-4} mol/L)(1.5×10^{-3} L) = 3×10^{-7} mol] and a high $\mathcal{M}$ ($\sim$21×10^{-3} g/3×10^{-7} mol = 7×10^{4} g/mol). Mammalian hemoglobin has a molar mass of 64,500 g/mol.

Follow-Up Problem 13.8 At 37°C, 0.30 M sucrose has about the same osmotic pressure as blood. What is the osmotic pressure of blood?

Volatile Nonelectrolyte Solutions

What is the effect on vapor pressure when the solute *is* volatile, that is, when the vapor consists of solute *and* solvent molecules? From Raoult's law (Equation 13.9),

$$P_{\text{solvent}} = X_{\text{solvent}} \times P^{\circ}_{\text{solvent}} \quad \text{and} \quad P_{\text{solute}} = X_{\text{solute}} \times P^{\circ}_{\text{solute}}$$

where X_{solvent} and X_{solute} are the mole fractions in the *liquid* phase. According to Dalton's law (p. 99), the total vapor pressure is the sum of the partial vapor pressures:

$$P_{\text{total}} = P_{\text{solvent}} + P_{\text{solute}} = (X_{\text{solvent}} \times P^{\circ}_{\text{solvent}}) + (X_{\text{solute}} \times P^{\circ}_{\text{solute}})$$

Thus, just as a nonvolatile solute lowers the vapor pressure of the solvent by making the solvent's mole fraction less than 1, *the presence of each volatile component lowers the vapor pressure of the other* by making each mole fraction less than 1.

Let's examine this idea with a solution of benzene (C_6H_6) and toluene (C_7H_8), which are miscible, in which the mole fractions in the liquid are equal: $X_{\text{ben}} = X_{\text{tol}} = 0.500$. At 25°C, the vapor pressures of the pure substances are 95.1 torr for benzene (P°_{ben}) and 28.4 torr for toluene (P°_{tol}). Note that benzene is *more volatile* than toluene. We find the partial pressures from Raoult's law:

$$P_{\text{ben}} = X_{\text{ben}} \times P^{\circ}_{\text{ben}} = 0.500 \times 95.1 \text{ torr} = 47.6 \text{ torr}$$
$$P_{\text{tol}} = X_{\text{tol}} \times P^{\circ}_{\text{tol}} = 0.500 \times 28.4 \text{ torr} = 14.2 \text{ torr}$$

Thus, the presence of benzene in the liquid lowers the vapor pressure of toluene, and vice versa.

Now let's calculate the mole fraction of each substance *in the vapor* by applying Dalton's law. Recall from Section 5.4 that $X_A = P_A/P_{\text{total}}$. Therefore, for benzene and toluene in the vapor,

$$X_{\text{ben}} = \frac{P_{\text{ben}}}{P_{\text{total}}} = \frac{47.6 \text{ torr}}{47.6 \text{ torr} + 14.2 \text{ torr}} = 0.770$$

$$X_{\text{tol}} = \frac{P_{\text{tol}}}{P_{\text{total}}} = \frac{14.2 \text{ torr}}{47.6 \text{ torr} + 14.2 \text{ torr}} = 0.230$$

The key point is that *the vapor has a higher mole fraction of the* ***more*** *volatile component.* Through a single vaporization-condensation step, a 50/50 *liquid* ratio of benzene-to-toluene created a 77/23 *vapor* ratio. Condense this vapor into a separate container, and the new *liquid* would have this 77/23 composition, and the new *vapor* above it would be enriched still further in the more volatile benzene.

In the laboratory method of **fractional distillation,** a solution of two or more volatile components is attached to a *fractionating column* packed with glass beads (or ceramic chunks) and connected to a condenser and collection flask. As the solution is heated and the vapor mixture meets the beads, numerous vaporization-condensation steps enrich the mixture until the vapor leaving the column, and thus the liquid finally collected, consists only of the most volatile component (see Figure 13.28).

Strong Electrolyte Solutions

For colligative properties of strong electrolyte solutions, the solute formula tells us the number of particles. For instance, the boiling point elevation (ΔT_b) of 0.050 m NaCl should be $2 \times \Delta T_b$ of 0.050 m glucose ($C_6H_{12}O_6$), because NaCl dissociates into two particles per formula unit. Thus, we use a multiplying factor called the *van't Hoff factor (i),* named after the Dutch chemist Jacobus van't Hoff (1852–1911):

$$i = \frac{\text{measured value for electrolyte solution}}{\text{expected value for nonelectrolyte solution}}$$

To calculate colligative properties for strong electrolyte solutions, we include i:

For vapor pressure lowering:	$\Delta P = i(X_{\text{solute}} \times P^{\circ}_{\text{solvent}})$
For boiling point elevation:	$\Delta T_b = i(K_b m)$
For freezing point depression:	$\Delta T_f = i(K_f m)$
For osmotic pressure:	$\Pi = i(MRT)$

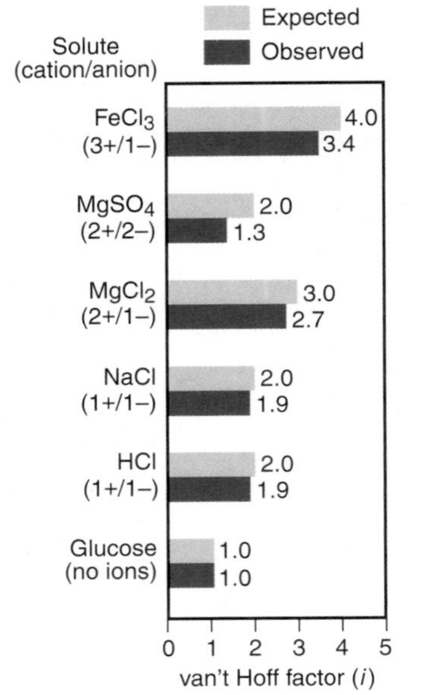

Figure 13.26 Nonideal behavior of strong electrolyte solutions. Van't Hoff factors (i) for 0.050 m solutions show the largest deviation for salts with multiply-charged ions. Glucose (a nonelectrolyte) behaves as expected.

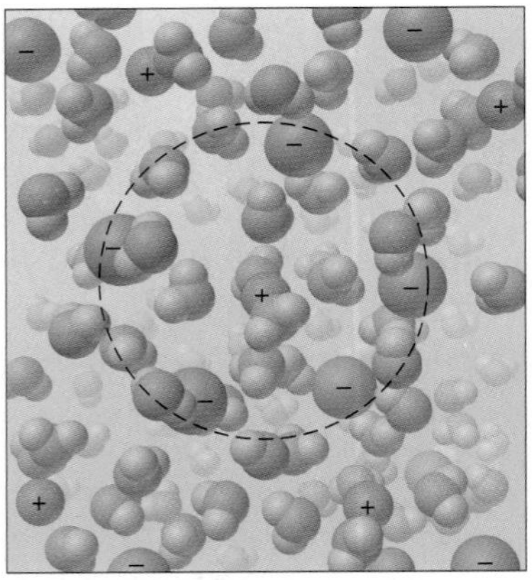

Figure 13.27 An ionic atmosphere model for nonideal behavior of electrolyte solutions.

Nonideal Solutions and Ionic Atmospheres *If* strong electrolyte solutions behaved ideally, the factor i would be the amount (mol) of particles in solution divided by the amount (mol) of dissolved solute; that is, i would be 2 for KBr, 3 for $Mg(NO_3)_2$, and so forth. However, *most strong electrolyte solutions are **not** ideal,* and the measured value of i is typically *lower* than the value expected from the formula. For example, for the boiling point elevation of 0.050 m NaCl, the expected value is 2.0, but, from experiment, we have

$$i = \frac{\Delta T_b \text{ of } 0.050\ m \text{ NaCl}}{\Delta T_b \text{ of } 0.050\ m \text{ glucose}} = \frac{0.049°\text{C}}{0.026°\text{C}} = 1.9$$

It seems as though the ions are not behaving independently, even though other evidence indicates that soluble salts dissociate completely. One clue to understanding the results is that multiply-charged ions cause a larger deviation (Figure 13.26).

To explain this nonideal behavior, we picture positive ions clustered, on average, near negative ions, and vice versa, to form an **ionic atmosphere** of net opposite charge (Figure 13.27). In effect, each type of ion acts "tied up," so its actual concentration seems *lower*. The *effective* concentration is the *stoichiometric* concentration, which is based on the formula multiplied by i. The greater the charge, the stronger the attractions, which explains the larger deviation for salts with multiply-charged ions.

Comparing Real Solutions and Real Gases At ordinary conditions and concentrations, particles are *much* closer together in liquids than in gases. And, as a result, nonideal behavior is much more common, and the deviations much larger. Nevertheless, the two systems have similarities:

- Gases display nearly ideal behavior at low pressures because the distances between particles are large. Similarly, the van't Hoff factor (i) approaches the ideal value as the solution becomes more dilute, that is, as the distance between ions increases.
- Attractions between particles cause deviations from the expected pressure in gases and from the expected size of a colligative property in ionic solutions.
- For both real gases and real solutions, we use empirically determined numbers (van der Waals constants or van't Hoff factors) to transform theories (the ideal gas law or Raoult's law) into more useful relations.

Sample Problem 13.9 Depicting Strong Electrolyte Solutions

Problem A 0.952-g sample of magnesium chloride dissolves in 100. g of water in a flask.

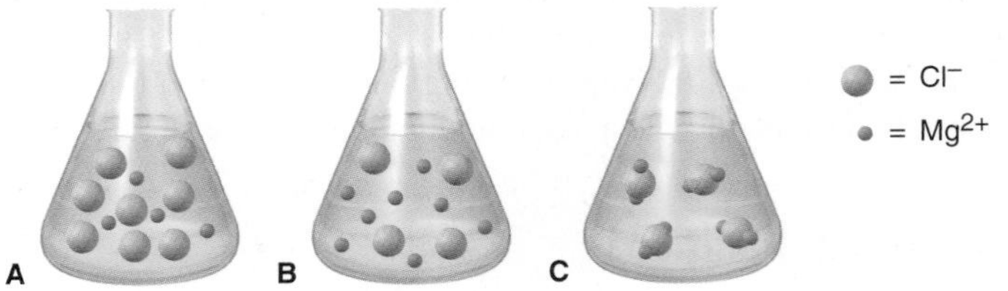

(a) Which scene depicts the solution best?
(b) What is the amount (mol) represented by each green sphere?
(c) Assuming the solution is ideal, what is its freezing point (at 1 atm)?

Plan **(a)** We find the numbers of cations and anions per formula unit from the name and compare it with the three scenes. **(b)** We convert the given mass to amount (mol), use the answer from part (a) to find moles of chloride ions (*green spheres*), and divide by the number of green spheres to get moles/sphere. **(c)** We find the molality (m) from amount (mol) of solute divided by the given mass of water (changed to kg). We multiply K_f for water (Table 13.6) by m to get ΔT_f, and then subtract that from 0.000°C to get the solution freezing point.

Solution **(a)** The formula is $MgCl_2$; only scene A has 1 Mg^{2+} for every 2 Cl^-.

(b) $$\text{Amount (mol) of } MgCl_2 = \frac{0.952 \text{ g } MgCl_2}{95.21 \text{ g/mol } MgCl_2} = 0.0100 \text{ mol } MgCl_2$$

Therefore, $\text{Amount (mol) of Cl}^- = 0.0100 \text{ mol MgCl}_2 \times \dfrac{2\text{ Cl}^-}{1\text{ MgCl}_2} = 0.0200 \text{ mol Cl}^-$

$$\text{Moles/sphere} = \frac{0.0200 \text{ mol Cl}^-}{8 \text{ spheres}} = 2.50\times10^{-3} \text{ mol/sphere}$$

(c) $$\text{Molality } (m) = \frac{\text{mol of solute}}{\text{kg of solvent}} = \frac{0.0100 \text{ mol MgCl}_2}{100.\text{ g} \times \dfrac{1\text{ kg}}{1000\text{ g}}} = 0.100\ m \text{ MgCl}_2$$

Assuming an ideal solution, $i = 3$ for $MgCl_2$ (3 ions per formula unit), so we have

$$\Delta T_f = i(K_f m) = 3(1.86°\text{C}/m \times 0.100\ m) = 0.558°\text{C}$$

and $$T_f = 0.000°\text{C} - 0.558°\text{C} = -0.558°\text{C}$$

Check Let's quickly check the ΔT_f in part (c): We have 0.01 mol dissolved in 0.1 kg, or 0.1 m. Then, rounding K_f, we have about $3(2°\text{C}/m \times 0.1\ m) = 0.6°\text{C}$.

Follow-Up Problem 13.9 The $MgCl_2$ solution in the sample problem has a density of 1.006 g/mL at 20.0°C. **(a)** What is the osmotic pressure of the solution? **(b)** A U tube, with semipermeable membrane, is filled with the solution in the left arm and a glucose solution of equal molarity in the right. After time, which scene depicts the U tube best?

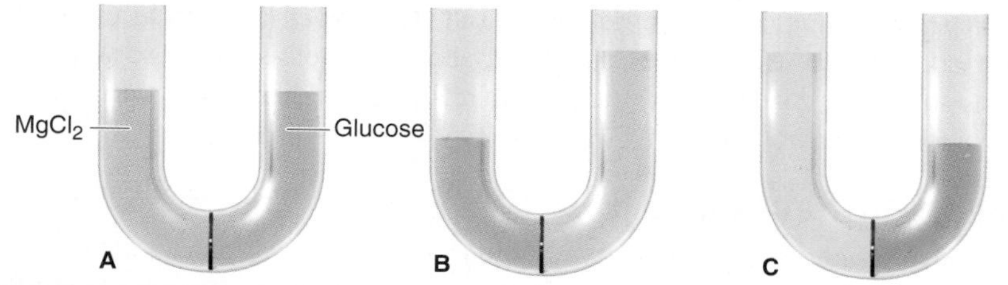

Applications of Colligative Properties

Two colligative properties in particular, freezing point depression and osmotic pressure, have key applications that involve all three types of solutes we've discussed, nonvolatile and volatile nonelectrolytes and strong electrolytes.

Uses of Freezing Point Depression Applications of this property appear in everyday life, nature, and industry:

- *Plane de-icer and car antifreeze.* The main ingredient in plane de-icer and car antifreeze, ethylene glycol ($C_2H_6O_2$), lowers the freezing point of water in winter and raises its boiling point in summer. Due to extensive H bonding, ethylene glycol is miscible with water and nonvolatile at 100°C.

- *Biological antifreeze.* Structurally similar to ethylene glycol and also miscible with water, glycerol ($C_3H_8O_3$) is produced by some fish and insects, including the common housefly, to lower the freezing point of their blood and thus allow them to survive winters.

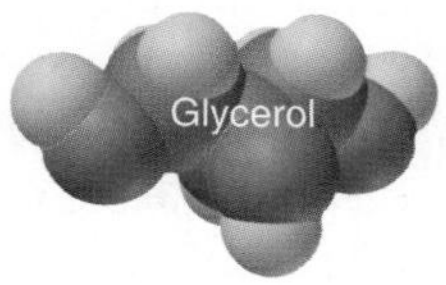

- *De-icing sidewalks and roads.* NaCl, or a mixture of it with $CaCl_2$, is used to melt ice on roads. A small amount dissolves in the ice by lowering its freezing point and melting it. More salt dissolves, more ice melts, and so forth. An advantage of $CaCl_2$ is that it has a highly negative ΔH_{soln}, so heat is released when it dissolves, which melts more ice.
- *Refining petroleum and silicon.* Countless vaporization-condensation steps within a 30-m fractionating tower separate the hundreds of volatile compounds in crude oil into a few "fractions" based on boiling point range (Figure 13.28). Impure silicon is refined by continuous melting and refreezing into a sample pure enough for use in computer chips (Chapter 22).

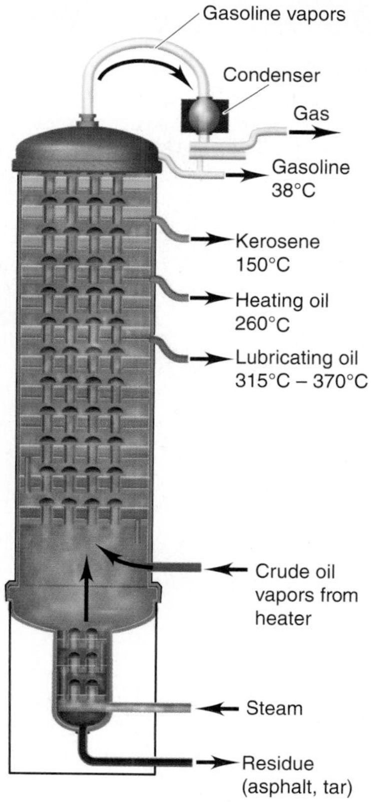

Figure 13.28 Fractional distillation in petroleum refining.

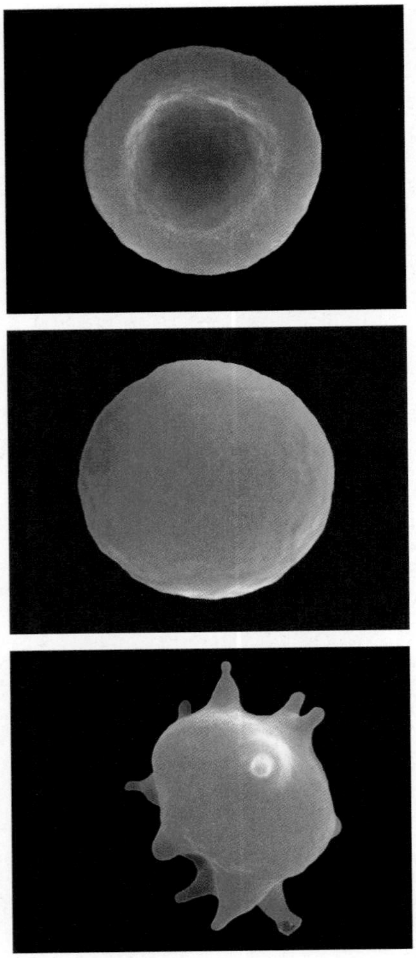

Figure 13.29 Osmotic pressure and cell shape. Isotonic (*top*), hypotonic (*middle*), and hypertonic (*bottom*) solutions influence the shape of a red blood cell.

Uses of Osmotic Pressure Of the four colligative properties, this one has the most applications vital to organisms.

- *Tonicity and cell shape.* The term *tonicity* refers to the tone, or firmness, of a cell. Placing the cell in an *isotonic* solution, one that has the same concentration of particles as the cell fluid, maintains the cell's normal shape because water enters and leaves the cell at the same rate (Figure 13.29, *top*). A *hypotonic* solution has a lower concentration of particles, so water enters the cell faster than it leaves, causing the cell to burst (*middle*). In contrast, a *hypertonic* solution has a higher concentration, so the cell shrinks because water leaves faster than it enters (*bottom*). To maintain cell shape, contact-lens rinse is isotonic saline (0.15 *M* NaCl), as are solutions used to deliver nutrients or drugs intravenously.
- *Absorption of water by trees.* Tree sap is a more concentrated solution than surrounding groundwater, so water passes through root membranes into the tree, creating an osmotic pressure that can exceed 20 atm in the tallest trees.
- *Regulation of water volume in the body.* Of the four major biological cations—Na^+, K^+, Mg^{2+}, and Ca^{2+}—sodium ion has the primary role of regulating water volume. It accounts for over 90 mol % of cations *outside* a cell: high Na^+ draws water out of the cell and low Na^+ leaves more inside. And the primary role of the kidneys is to regulate Na^+ concentration.
- *Food preservation.* Before refrigeration, salt was valued as a preservative. Packed onto food, salt causes microbes on the surface to shrivel as they lose water. In fact, it was so highly prized for this purpose that Roman soldiers were paid in salt, from which comes the word *salary*.

Summary of Section 13.6

- Colligative properties arise from the number, not type, of dissolved solute particles.
- Compared to pure solvent, a solution has lower vapor pressure (Raoult's law), elevated boiling point, and depressed freezing point, and it gives rise to osmotic pressure.
- Colligative properties are used to determine solute molar mass; osmotic pressure gives the most precise measurements.
- When solute *and* solvent are volatile, each lowers the vapor pressure of the other, with the vapor pressure of the more volatile component greater. When the vapor is condensed, the new solution is richer in that component than the original solution.
- Calculating colligative properties of electrolyte solutions requires a factor (i) that adjusts for the number of ions per formula unit. These solutions exhibit nonideal behavior because charge attractions effectively reduce the concentration of ions.

13.7 • THE STRUCTURE AND PROPERTIES OF COLLOIDS

Particle size plays a defining role in three types of mixtures:

- *Suspensions.* Stir a handful of fine sand into a glass of water, and the particles are suspended at first but gradually settle to the bottom. Sand in water is a **suspension,** a *heterogeneous* mixture containing particles large enough (>1000 nm) to be visibly distinct from the surrounding fluid.
- *Solutions.* In contrast, stirring sugar into water forms a solution, a *homogeneous* mixture in which the particles are invisible, individual sugar molecules (around 1 nm) distributed evenly throughout the surrounding fluid.
- *Colloids.* Between these extremes is a large group of mixtures called *colloidal dispersions,* or **colloids,** in which a dispersed (solute-like) substance is distributed throughout a dispersing (solvent-like) substance. The particles are larger than simple molecules but too small to settle out.

In this section, we examine the classification and key features of colloids.

1. *Particle size and surface area.* Colloidal particles range in diameter from 1 to 1000 nm (10^{-9} to 10^{-6} m). It may be a single macromolecule (natural or synthetic) or an aggregate of many atoms, ions, or molecules. As a result of the small particle size, a

colloid has a *very large total surface area*. A cube with 1-cm sides has a total surface area of 6 cm^2. If it's divided equally into 10^{12} cubes, the cubes are the size of large colloidal particles and have a total surface area of 60,000 cm^2, or 6 m^2. The enormous surface area of a colloid attracts other particles through various intermolecular forces.

2. *Classification of colloids*. Colloids are commonly classified by the physical state of the dispersed and dispersing substances (Table 13.7). Many familiar commercial products and natural objects are colloids. Whipped cream and shaving cream are *foams,* a gas dispersed in a liquid. Styrofoam is a *solid foam,* a gas dispersed in a solid. Most biological fluids are aqueous *sols,* solids dispersed in water: proteins and nucleic acids are the colloidal-size particles dispersed in an aqueous fluid of ions and small molecules within a cell. Soaps and detergents work by forming an *emulsion,* a liquid dispersed in another liquid. Other emulsions are mayonnaise and hand cream. Bile salts convert fats to an emulsion in the watery fluid of the small intestine.

Table 13.7 Types of Colloids

Colloid Type	Dispersed Substance	Dispersing Medium	Example(s)
Aerosol	Liquid	Gas	Fog
Aerosol	Solid	Gas	Smoke
Foam	Gas	Liquid	Whipped cream
Solid foam	Gas	Solid	Marshmallow
Emulsion	Liquid	Liquid	Milk
Solid emulsion	Liquid	Solid	Butter
Sol	Solid	Liquid	Paint, cell fluid
Solid sol	Solid	Solid	Opal

3. *Tyndall effect and Brownian motion*. Light passing through a colloid is scattered randomly because the dispersed particles have sizes similar to wavelengths of visible light (400 to 750 nm). The scattered light beam appears broader than one passing through a solution, an example of the **Tyndall effect** (Figure 13.30). Dust scatters sunlight shining through it, as does mist pierced by headlights.

Under low magnification, colloidal particles exhibit *Brownian motion,* an erratic change of speed and direction. Brownian motion results from collisions with molecules of the dispersing medium, and Einstein's explanation of it in 1905 led many to accept the molecular nature of matter.

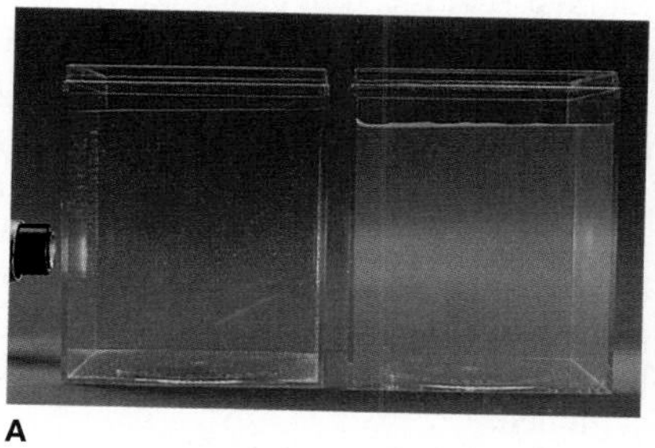

A

B

Figure 13.30 Light scattering and the Tyndall effect. **A,** The narrow, barely visible light beam that passes through a solution (*left*), is scattered and broadened by passing through a colloid (*right*). **B,** Sunlight is scattered by dust in air.

4. *Stabilizing and destabilizing colloids*. Why don't colloidal particles aggregate and settle out? Colloidal particles dispersed in water have charged surfaces that stabilize the colloid through ion-dipole forces. Molecules with dual polarities, like lipids and soaps, form spherical *micelles,* with the charged heads on the exterior and hydrocarbon tails in the interior (Section 13.2). Aqueous proteins mimic this arrangement, with charged amino acid groups facing the water and nonpolar groups buried within the molecule. Oily particles can be dispersed in water by adding ions, which are adsorbed onto their surfaces. Repulsions between the ions on the oil and partial charges on water molecules prevent the particles from aggregating.

Despite these forces, various methods that coagulate the particles destabilize the colloid. Heating makes the particles collide more often and with enough force to coalesce and settle out. Addition of an electrolyte solution containing oppositely charged ions neutralizes the surface charges, so the particles coagulate and settle. In smokestack gases from a coal-burning power plant, ions become adsorbed onto uncharged colloidal particles, which are then attracted to the charged plates of a device called a *Cotrell precipitator* installed in the stack. At the mouths of rivers, where salt concentrations increase near an ocean or sea, colloidal clay particles coalesce into muddy deltas, like those of the Mississippi and the Nile (Figure 13.31). Thus, the city of New Orleans and the ancient Egyptian empire were made possible by such large-scale colloid chemistry.

Figure 13.31 The Nile delta (reddish-brown area).

The upcoming Chemical Connections essay applies solution and colloid chemistry to the purification of water for residential and industrial use.

CHEMICAL CONNECTIONS TO ENVIRONMENTAL ENGINEERING | Solutions and Colloids in Water Purification

Most water destined for human use comes from lakes, rivers, reservoirs, or groundwater. Present in this essential resource may be soluble toxic organic compounds and high concentrations of NO_3^- and Fe^{3+}, colloidal clay and microbes, and suspended debris. Let's see how water is treated to remove these dissolved, dispersed, and suspended particles.

Water Treatment Plants

Treating water involves several steps (Figure B13.1):

Step 1. Screening and settling. As water enters the facility, screens remove debris, and settling removes particles such as sand.

Step 2. Coagulating. This step and the next two remove colloids. These particles have negative surfaces that repel each other. Added aluminum sulfate [cake alum; $Al_2(SO_4)_3$] or iron(III) chloride ($FeCl_3$), which supply Al^{3+} or Fe^{3+} that neutralize the charges, coagulates the particles through intermolecular forces.

Step 3. Flocculating and sedimenting. Mixing water and flocculating agents in large basins causes a fluffy *floc* to form. Added cationic polymers form long-chain bridges between floc particles, which grow bigger and heavier and flow into other basins, where they form a sediment and are removed. Some plants use *dissolved air flotation* (DAF) instead: bubbles forced through the water attach to the floc, and the floating mass is skimmed.

Step 4. Filtering. Various filters remove remaining particles. In *slow sand filters,* the water passes through sand and/or gravel of increasing particle size. In *rapid sand filters,* the sand is backwashed with water, and the colloidal mass is removed. Membrane filters (*not shown*) with pore sizes of 0.1–10 μm are thin tubes bundled together inside a vessel. The water is forced into these tubes, and the colloid-free filtrate is collected from a large central tube. Filtration is very effective at removing microorganisms resistant to disinfecting.

Step 5. Disinfecting. Water sources often contain harmful microorganisms that are killed by one of three agents:

- Chlorine, as aqueous bleach (ClO^-) or Cl_2, is most common, but carcinogenic chlorinated organic compounds can form.
- UV light emitted by high-intensity fluorescent tubes disinfects by disrupting microorganisms' DNA.
- Ozone (O_3) gas is a powerful oxidizing agent.

Sodium fluoride (NaF) to prevent tooth decay and phosphate salts to prevent leaching of lead from pipes may then be added.

Step 6 (not shown). Adsorbing onto granular activated carbon (GAC). Petroleum and other organic contaminants are removed by adsorption. GAC is a highly porous agent formed by "activating" wood, coal, or coconut shells with steam: 1 kg of GAC has a surface area of 275 acres!

Water Softening via Ion Exchange

Water with large amounts of 2+ ions, such as Ca^{2+} and Mg^{2+}, is called **hard water.** Combined with fatty-acid anions in soap, these cations form solid deposits on clothes, washing machines, and sinks:

$$Ca^{2+}(aq) + \underset{\text{soap}}{2C_{17}H_{35}COONa(aq)} \longrightarrow \underset{\text{insoluble deposit}}{(C_{17}H_{35}COO)_2Ca(s)} + 2Na^+(aq)$$

When a large amount of HCO_3^- is present, the cations form *scale,* a carbonate deposit in boilers and hot-water pipes that interferes with the transfer of heat:

$$Ca^{2+}(aq) + 2HCO_3^-(aq) \longrightarrow CaCO_3(s) + CO_2(g) + H_2O(l)$$

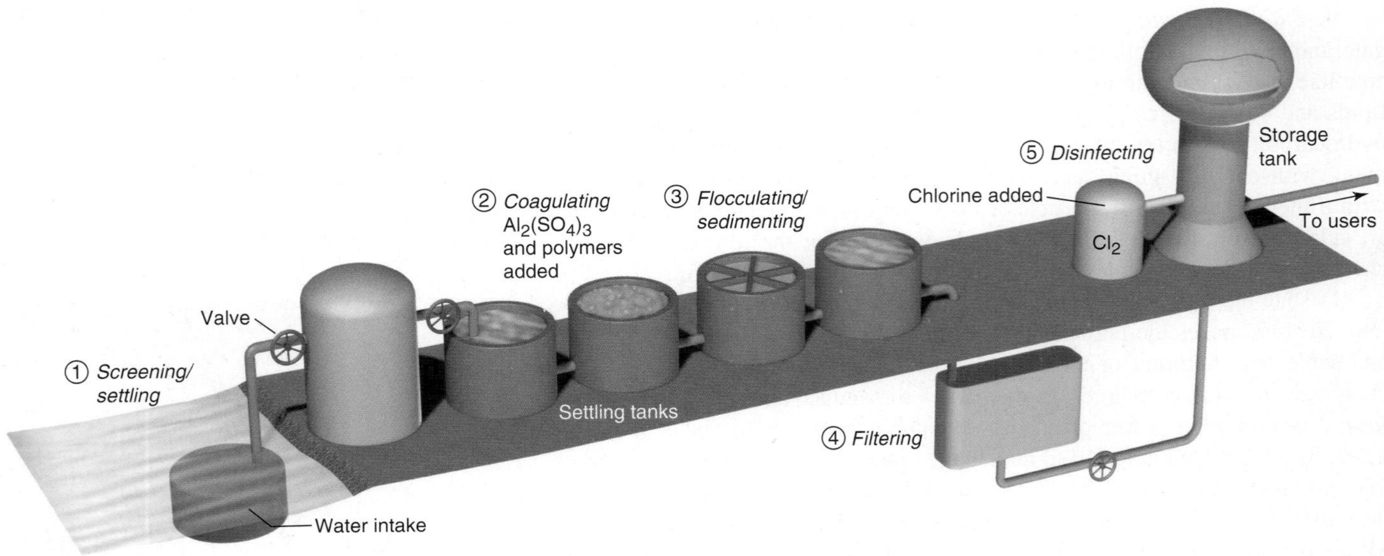

Figure B13.1 The typical steps in municipal water treatment.

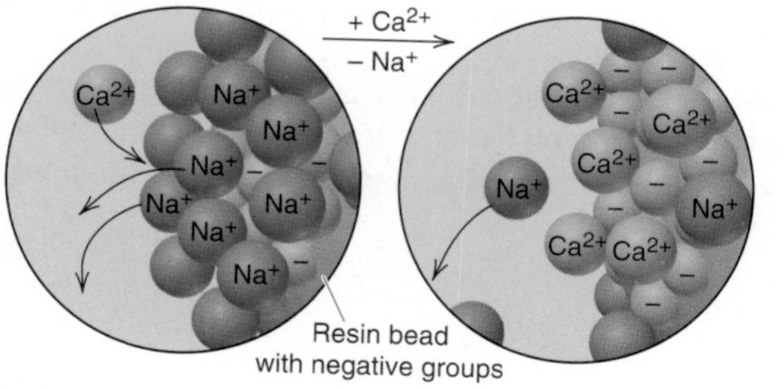

Figure B13.2 Ion exchange to remove hard-water cations.

Removing hard-water cations, called **water softening,** is done by exchanging Na^+ ions for Ca^{2+} and Mg^{2+} ions. A domestic **ion exchange** system contains an insoluble polymer *resin* with bonded anionic groups, such as $—SO_3^-$ or $—COO^-$, and Na^+ ions for charge balance (Figure B13.2). The hard-water cations displace the Na^+ ions and bind to the anionic groups. When the resin sites are occupied, the resin is regenerated with concentrated Na^+ solution that exchanges Na^+ ions for bound Ca^{2+} and Mg^{2+}.

Membrane Processes and Reverse Osmosis

Membranes with 0.0001–0.01 μm pores can remove unwanted ions from water. Recall that solutions of different concentrations separated by a semipermeable membrane create osmotic pressure. In **reverse osmosis,** a pressure *greater* than the osmotic pressure is *applied* to the more concentrated solution to force water back through the membrane and filter out ions. In homes, toxic *heavy-metal ions,* such as Pb^{2+}, Cd^{2+}, and Hg^{2+}, are removed this way. On a large scale, reverse osmosis is used for **desalination,** which can convert seawater (40,000 ppm of ions) to drinking water (400 ppm) (Figure B13.3).

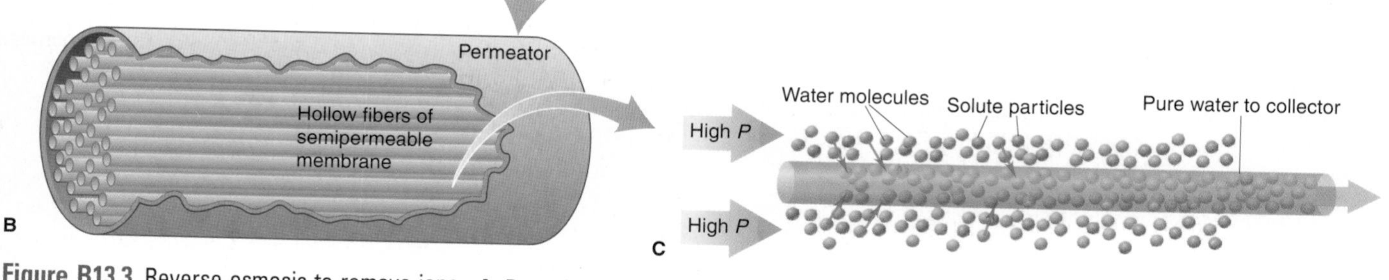

Figure B13.3 Reverse osmosis to remove ions. **A,** Part of a reverse-osmosis permeator. **B,** Each permeator contains a bundle of hollow fibers of semipermeable membrane. **C,** Pumping seawater at high pressure removes ions and purer water enters the fibers and is collected.

Wastewater Treatment

Wastewater, used domestic or industrial water, is treated in several ways before being returned to a natural source:

- In *primary* treatment, the water enters a settling basin to remove particles.
- In *biological* treatment, bacteria metabolize organic compounds and are then removed by settling.
- In *advanced* treatment, a process is tailored to remove a specific pollutant. For example, ammonia, which causes excessive growth of plants and algae, is removed in two steps:
  1. *Nitrification.* Certain bacteria oxidize ammonia (electron donor) with O_2 (electron acceptor) to form nitrate ion:
  $$NH_4^+ + 2O_2 \longrightarrow NO_3^- + 2H^+ + H_2O$$
  2. *Denitrification.* Other bacteria oxidize an added compound like methanol (CH_3OH) using the NO_3^-:
  $$5CH_3OH + 6NO_3^- \longrightarrow 3N_2 + 5CO_2 + 7H_2O + 6OH^-$$
  Thus, the process converts NH_3 in wastewater to N_2, which is released to the atmosphere.

Problems

B13.1 Briefly answer each of the following:
(a) Why is cake alum [$Al_2(SO_4)_3$] added during water purification?
(b) Why is water that contains large amounts of Ca^{2+} and Mg^{2+} difficult to use for cleaning?
(c) What is the meaning of "reverse" in reverse osmosis?
(d) Why might a water treatment plant use ozone as a disinfectant instead of chlorine?
(e) How does passing a saturated NaCl solution through a "spent" ion-exchange resin regenerate the resin?

B13.2 Wastewater discharged into a stream by a sugar refinery contains 3.55 g of sucrose ($C_{12}H_{22}O_{11}$) per liter. A government-sponsored study is testing the feasibility of removing the sugar by reverse osmosis. What pressure must be applied to the apparatus at 20.°C to produce pure water?

Summary of Section 13.7

- Particles in a colloid are smaller than those in a suspension and larger than those in a solution.
- Colloids are classified by the physical states of the dispersed and dispersing substances and involve many combinations of gas, liquid, and/or solid.
- Colloids have extremely large surface areas, scatter incoming light (Tyndall effect), and exhibit random (Brownian) motion.
- Colloidal particles in water are stabilized by charged surfaces that keep them dispersed, but they can be coagulated by heating or by the addition of ions.
- Solution behavior and colloid chemistry are applied to water treatment and purification.

CHAPTER REVIEW GUIDE

Learning Objectives

Relevant section (§) and/or sample problem (SP) numbers appear in parentheses.

Understand These Concepts

1. The quantitative meaning of solubility (§13.1)
2. The major types of intermolecular forces in solution and their relative strengths (§13.1)
3. How the like-dissolves-like rule depends on intermolecular forces (§13.1)
4. Why gases have relatively low solubilities in water (§13.1)
5. General characteristics of solutions formed by various combinations of gases, liquids, and solids (§13.1)
6. How intermolecular forces stabilize the structures of proteins, the cell membrane, and DNA (§13.2)
7. The enthalpy components of a solution cycle and their effect on ΔH_{soln} (§13.3)
8. The dependence of ΔH_{hydr} on ionic charge density and the factors that determine whether ionic solution processes are exothermic or endothermic (§13.3)
9. The meaning of entropy and how the balance between the change in enthalpy and the change in entropy governs the solution process (§13.3)
10. The distinctions among saturated, unsaturated, and supersaturated solutions, and the equilibrium nature of a saturated solution (§13.4)
11. The relation between temperature and the solubility of solids (§13.4)
12. Why the solubility of gases in water decreases with a rise in temperature (§13.4)
13. The effect of gas pressure on solubility and its quantitative expression as Henry's law (§13.4)
14. The meaning of molarity, molality, mole fraction, and parts by mass or by volume of a solution, and how to convert among them (§13.5)
15. The distinction between electrolytes and nonelectrolytes in solution (§13.6)
16. The four colligative properties and their dependence on number of dissolved particles (§13.6)
17. Ideal solutions and the importance of Raoult's law (§13.6)
18. How the phase diagram of a solution differs from that of the pure solvent (§13.6)
19. Why the vapor over a solution of volatile nonelectrolyte is richer in the more volatile component (§13.6)
20. Why electrolyte solutions are not ideal and the meanings of the van't Hoff factor and ionic atmosphere (§13.6)
21. How particle size distinguishes suspensions, colloids, and solutions (§13.7)
22. How colloidal behavior is demonstrated by the Tyndall effect and Brownian motion (§13.7)

Master These Skills

1. Predicting relative solubilities from intermolecular forces (SP 13.1)
2. Using Henry's law to calculate the solubility of a gas (SP 13.2)
3. Expressing concentration in terms of molality, parts by mass, parts by volume, and mole fraction (SPs 13.3, 13.4)
4. Interconverting among the various terms for expressing concentration (SP 13.5)
5. Using Raoult's law to calculate the vapor pressure lowering of a solution (SP 13.6)
6. Determining boiling point elevation and freezing point depression of a solution (SP 13.7)
7. Using a colligative property to calculate the molar mass of a solute (SP 13.8)
8. Calculating the composition of vapor over a solution of volatile nonelectrolyte (§13.6)
9. Calculating the van't Hoff factor i from the magnitude of a colligative property (§13.6)
10. Using a solution depiction to determine colligative properties (SP 13.9)

Key Terms

Page numbers appear in parentheses.

Section 13.1
solute (478)
solvent (478)
miscible (478)
solubility (S) (478)
like-dissolves-like rule (478)
hydration shell (478)
ion–induced dipole force (478)
dipole–induced dipole force (478)
alloy (482)

Section 13.2
protein (483)
amino acid (483)
soap (485)
lipid bilayer (485)
nucleic acid (487)
mononucleotide (487)
double helix (487)

Section 13.3
heat of solution (ΔH_{soln}) (488)
solvation (489)
hydration (489)
heat of hydration (ΔH_{hydr}) (489)
charge density (489)
entropy (S) (490)

Section 13.4
saturated solution (492)
unsaturated solution (492)
supersaturated solution (492)
Henry's law (494)

Section 13.5
molality (m) (495)
mass percent [% (w/w)] (496)
volume percent [% (v/v)] (496)
mole fraction (X) (496)

Section 13.6
colligative property (499)
electrolyte (499)
nonelectrolyte (499)
vapor pressure lowering (ΔP) (499)
Raoult's law (500)
ideal solution (500)
boiling point elevation (ΔT_b) (501)
freezing point depression (ΔT_f) (502)
semipermeable membrane (503)
osmosis (503)
osmotic pressure (Π) (503)
fractional distillation (505)
ionic atmosphere (506)

Section 13.7
suspension (508)
colloid (508)
Tyndall effect (509)
hard water (510)
water softening (511)
ion exchange (511)
reverse osmosis (511)
desalination (511)
wastewater (511)

Key Equations and Relationships

Page numbers appear in parentheses.

13.1 Dividing the general heat of solution into component enthalpies (488):

$$\Delta H_{soln} = \Delta H_{solute} + \Delta H_{solvent} + \Delta H_{mix}$$

13.2 Dividing the heat of solution of an ionic compound in water into component enthalpies (489):

$$\Delta H_{soln} = \Delta H_{lattice} + \Delta H_{\text{hydr of the ions}}$$

13.3 Relating gas solubility to its partial pressure (Henry's law) (494):

$$S_{gas} = k_H \times P_{gas}$$

13.4 Defining concentration in terms of molarity (494):

$$\text{Molarity } (M) = \frac{\text{amount (mol) of solute}}{\text{volume (L) of solution}}$$

13.5 Defining concentration in terms of molality (495):

$$\text{Molality } (m) = \frac{\text{amount (mol) of solute}}{\text{mass (kg) of solvent}}$$

13.6 Defining concentration in terms of mass percent (496):

$$\text{Mass percent } [\% \text{ (w/w)}] = \frac{\text{mass of solute}}{\text{mass of solution}} \times 100$$

13.7 Defining concentration in terms of volume percent (496):

$$\text{Volume percent } [\% \text{ (v/v)}] = \frac{\text{volume of solute}}{\text{volume of solution}} \times 100$$

13.8 Defining concentration in terms of mole fraction (496):
Mole fraction (X)

$$= \frac{\text{amount (mol) of solute}}{\text{amount (mol) of solute} + \text{amount (mol) of solvent}}$$

13.9 Expressing the relationship between the vapor pressure of solvent above a solution and its mole fraction in the solution (Raoult's law) (500):

$$P_{solvent} = X_{solvent} \times P^{\circ}_{solvent}$$

13.10 Calculating the vapor pressure lowering due to solute (500):

$$\Delta P = X_{solute} \times P^{\circ}_{solvent}$$

13.11 Calculating the boiling point elevation of a solution (501):

$$\Delta T_b = K_b m$$

13.12 Calculating the freezing point depression of a solution (502):

$$\Delta T_f = K_f m$$

13.13 Calculating the osmotic pressure of a solution (503):

$$\Pi = \frac{n_{solute}}{V_{soln}} RT = MRT$$

Brief Solutions to Follow-Up Problems

13.1 (a) 1,4-Butanediol is more soluble in water because it can form more H bonds.
(b) Chloroform is more soluble in water because of dipole-dipole forces.

13.2 $S_{N_2} = (7\times10^{-4}\ \text{mol/L·atm})(0.78\ \text{atm})$
$= 5\times10^{-4}\ \text{mol/L}$

13.3 Mass (g) of glucose

$$= 563\ \text{g ethanol} \times \frac{1\ \text{kg}}{10^3\ \text{g}} \times \frac{2.40\times10^{-2}\ \text{mol glucose}}{1\ \text{kg ethanol}} \times \frac{180.16\ \text{g glucose}}{1\ \text{mol glucose}}$$
$$= 2.43\ \text{g glucose}$$

13.4 $$\text{Mass \% } C_3H_7OH = \frac{35.0\ \text{g}}{35.0\ \text{g} + 150.\ \text{g}} \times 100 = 18.9\ \text{mass \%}$$

$$\text{Mass \% } C_2H_5OH = 100.0 - 18.9 = 81.1\ \text{mass \%}$$

$$X_{C_3H_7OH} = \frac{35.0\ \text{g } C_3H_7OH \times \frac{1\ \text{mol } C_3H_7OH}{60.09\ \text{g } C_3H_7OH}}{\left(35.0\ \text{g } C_3H_7OH \times \frac{1\ \text{mol } C_3H_7OH}{60.09\ \text{g } C_3H_7OH}\right) + \left(150.\ \text{g } C_2H_5OH \times \frac{1\ \text{mol } C_2H_5OH}{46.07\ \text{g } C_2H_5OH}\right)} = 0.152$$

$$X_{C_2H_5OH} = 1.000 - 0.152 = 0.848$$

13.5 $$\text{Mass \% HCl} = \frac{\text{mass of HCl}}{\text{mass of soln}} \times 100$$
$$= \frac{\frac{11.8\ \text{mol HCl}}{1\ \text{L soln}} \times \frac{36.46\ \text{g HCl}}{1\ \text{mol HCl}}}{\frac{1.190\ \text{g}}{1\ \text{mL soln}} \times \frac{10^3\ \text{mL}}{1\ \text{L}}} \times 100$$
$$= 36.2\ \text{mass \% HCl}$$

$$\text{Mass (kg) of soln} = 1\ \text{L soln} \times \frac{1.190\times10^{-3}\ \text{kg soln}}{1\times10^{-3}\ \text{L soln}} = 1.190\ \text{kg soln}$$

$$\text{Mass (kg) of HCl} = 11.8\ \text{mol HCl} \times \frac{36.46\ \text{g HCl}}{1\ \text{mol HCl}} \times \frac{1\ \text{kg}}{10^3\ \text{g}} = 0.430\ \text{kg HCl}$$

$$\text{Molality of HCl} = \frac{\text{mol HCl}}{\text{kg water}} = \frac{\text{mol HCl}}{\text{kg soln} - \text{kg HCl}}$$
$$= \frac{11.8\ \text{mol HCl}}{0.760\ \text{kg } H_2O} = 15.5\ m\ \text{HCl}$$

$$X_{HCl} = \frac{\text{mol HCl}}{\text{mol HCl} + \text{mol } H_2O}$$
$$= \frac{11.8\ \text{mol}}{11.8\ \text{mol} + \left(760\ \text{g } H_2O \times \frac{1\ \text{mol}}{18.02\ \text{g } H_2O}\right)} = 0.219$$

13.6 $$\Delta P = X_{\text{aspirin}} \times P^\circ_{\text{methanol}}$$
$$= \frac{\frac{2.00\ \text{g}}{180.15\ \text{g/mol}}}{\frac{2.00\ \text{g}}{180.15\ \text{g/mol}} + \frac{50.0\ \text{g}}{32.04\ \text{g/mol}}} \times 101\ \text{torr}$$
$$= 0.713\ \text{torr}$$

13.7 $$\text{Molality of } C_2H_6O_2 = \frac{(32°\text{F} - 0.00°\text{F})\left(\frac{5°\text{C}}{9°\text{F}}\right)}{1.86°\text{C}/m} = 9.56\ m$$

13.8 $$\Pi = MRT = (0.30\ \text{mol/L})\left(0.0821\ \frac{\text{atm·L}}{\text{mol·K}}\right)(37°\text{C} + 273.15)$$
$$= 7.6\ \text{atm}$$

13.9 (a) Mass of 0.100 m solution
$= 1\ \text{kg water} + 0.100\ \text{mol } MgCl_2$
$= 1000\ \text{g} + 9.52\ \text{g} = 1009.52\ \text{g}$

$$\text{Volume of solution} = 1009.52\ \text{g} \times \frac{1\ \text{mL}}{1.006\ \text{g}} = 1003\ \text{mL}$$

$$\text{Molarity} = \frac{9.52\ \text{g } MgCl_2}{1003\ \text{mL soln}} \times \frac{1\ \text{mol}}{95.21\ \text{g } MgCl_2} \times \frac{10^3\ \text{mL}}{1\ \text{L}}$$
$$= 9.97\times10^{-2}\ M$$

Osmotic pressure (Π)
$$= i(MRT)$$
$$= 3(9.97\times10^{-2}\ \text{mol/L})\left(0.0821\ \frac{\text{atm·L}}{\text{mol·K}}\right)(293\ \text{K})$$
$$= 7.19\ \text{atm}$$

(b) Scene C

PROBLEMS

Problems with **colored** numbers are answered in Appendix E and worked in detail in the Student Solutions Manual. Problem sections match those in the text and provide the numbers of relevant sample problems. Most offer Concept Review Questions, Skill-Building Exercises (grouped in pairs covering the same concept), and Problems in Context. The Comprehensive Problems are based on material from any section or previous chapter.

Types of Solutions: Intermolecular Forces and Solubility

(Sample Problem 13.1)

Concept Review Questions

13.1 Describe how properties of seawater illustrate the two characteristics that define mixtures.

13.2 What types of intermolecular forces give rise to hydration shells in an aqueous solution of sodium chloride?

13.3 Acetic acid is miscible with water. Would you expect carboxylic acids with general formula $CH_3(CH_2)_nCOOH$ to become more or less water soluble as n increases? Explain.

13.4 Which would you expect to be more effective as a soap, sodium acetate or sodium stearate? Explain.

13.5 Hexane and methanol are miscible as gases but only slightly soluble in each other as liquids. Explain.

13.6 Hydrogen chloride (HCl) gas is much more soluble than propane gas (C_3H_8) in water, even though HCl has a lower boiling point. Explain.

Skill-Building Exercises (grouped in similar pairs)

13.7 Which gives the more concentrated solution, (a) KNO_3 in H_2O or (b) KNO_3 in carbon tetrachloride (CCl_4)? Explain.

13.8 Which gives the more concentrated solution, stearic acid $[CH_3(CH_2)_{16}COOH]$ in (a) H_2O or (b) CCl_4? Explain.

13.9 What is the strongest type of intermolecular force between solute and solvent in each solution?

(a) $CsCl(s)$ in $H_2O(l)$ (b) $CH_3\overset{O}{\overset{\|}{C}}CH_3(l)$ in $H_2O(l)$
(c) $CH_3OH(l)$ in $CCl_4(l)$

13.10 What is the strongest type of intermolecular force between solute and solvent in each solution?

(a) $Cu(s)$ in $Ag(s)$ (b) $CH_3Cl(g)$ in $CH_3OCH_3(g)$
(c) $CH_3CH_3(g)$ in $CH_3CH_2CH_2NH_2(l)$

13.11 What is the strongest type of intermolecular force between solute and solvent in each solution?

(a) $CH_3OCH_3(g)$ in $H_2O(l)$ (b) $Ne(g)$ in $H_2O(l)$
(c) $N_2(g)$ in $C_4H_{10}(g)$

13.12 What is the strongest type of intermolecular force between solute and solvent in each solution?

(a) $C_6H_{14}(l)$ in $C_8H_{18}(l)$ (b) $H_2C{=}O(g)$ in $CH_3OH(l)$
(c) $Br_2(l)$ in $CCl_4(l)$

13.13 Which member of each pair is more soluble in diethyl ether? Why?

(a) $NaCl(s)$ or $HCl(g)$ (b) $H_2O(l)$ or $CH_3\overset{O}{\overset{\|}{C}}H(l)$
(c) $MgBr_2(s)$ or $CH_3CH_2MgBr(s)$

13.14 Which member of each pair is more soluble in water? Why?

(a) $CH_3CH_2OCH_2CH_3(l)$ or $CH_3CH_2OCH_3(g)$
(b) $CH_2Cl_2(l)$ or $CCl_4(l)$
(c)

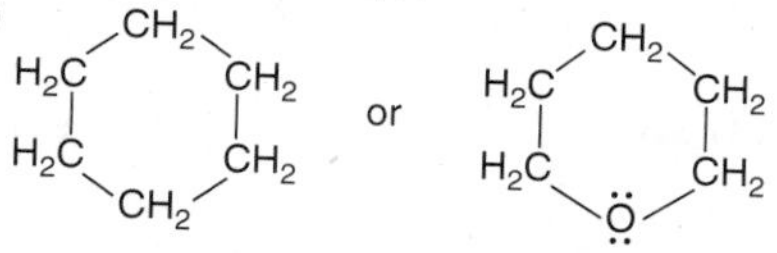

cyclohexane tetrahydropyran

Problems in Context

13.15 The dictionary defines *homogeneous* as "uniform in composition throughout." River water is a mixture of dissolved compounds, such as calcium bicarbonate, and suspended soil particles. Is river water homogeneous? Explain.

13.16 Gluconic acid is a derivative of glucose used in cleaners and in the dairy and brewing industries. Caproic acid is a carboxylic acid used in the flavoring industry. Although both are six-carbon acids (*see structures below*), gluconic acid is soluble in water and nearly insoluble in hexane, whereas caproic acid has the opposite solubility behavior. Explain.

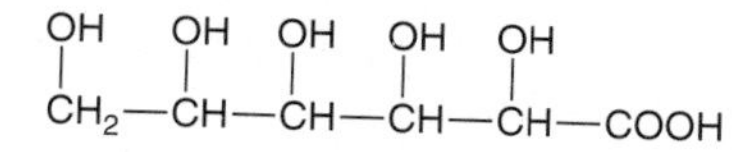

gluconic acid

$CH_3—CH_2—CH_2—CH_2—CH_2—COOH$

caproic acid

Intermolecular Forces and Biological Macromolecules

Concept Review Questions

13.17 Name three intermolecular forces that stabilize the shape of a soluble, globular protein, and explain how they act.

13.18 Name three intermolecular forces that stabilize the structure of DNA, and explain how they act.

13.19 How can relatively weak H bonds hold the double helix together yet allow DNA to function?

13.20 Is the sodium salt of propanoic acid as effective a soap as sodium stearate? Explain.

13.21 What intermolecular forces stabilize a lipid bilayer?

13.22 In what way do proteins embedded in a membrane differ structurally from soluble proteins?

13.23 Histones are proteins that control gene function by attaching through salt links to exterior regions of DNA. Name an amino acid whose side chain is often found on the exterior of histones.

Why Substances Dissolve: Understanding the Solution Process

Concept Review Questions

13.24 What is the relationship between solvation and hydration?

13.25 For a general solvent, which enthalpy terms in the thermochemical solution cycle are combined to obtain $\Delta H_{solvation}$?

13.26 (a) What is the charge density of an ion, and what two properties of an ion affect it?
(b) Arrange the following in order of increasing charge density:

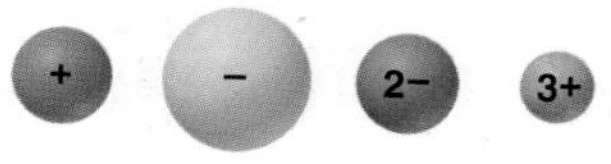

(c) How do the two properties in part (a) affect the ionic heat of hydration, ΔH_{hydr}?

13.27 For ΔH_{soln} to be very small, what quantities must be nearly equal in magnitude? Will their signs be the same or opposite?

13.28 Water is added to a flask containing solid NH_4Cl. As the salt dissolves, the solution becomes colder.
(a) Is the dissolving of NH_4Cl exothermic or endothermic?
(b) Is the magnitude of $\Delta H_{lattice}$ of NH_4Cl larger or smaller than the combined ΔH_{hydr} of the ions? Explain.
(c) Given the answer to (a), why does NH_4Cl dissolve in water?

13.29 An ionic compound has a highly negative ΔH_{soln} in water. Would you expect it to be very soluble or nearly insoluble in water? Explain in terms of enthalpy and entropy changes.

Skill-Building Exercises (grouped in similar pairs)

13.30 Sketch an enthalpy diagram for the process of dissolving $KCl(s)$ in H_2O (endothermic).

13.31 Sketch an enthalpy diagram for the process of dissolving $NaI(s)$ in H_2O (exothermic).

13.32 Which ion in each pair has greater charge density? Explain.
(a) Na^+ or Cs^+ (b) Sr^{2+} or Rb^+ (c) Na^+ or Cl^-
(d) O^{2-} or F^- (e) OH^- or SH^- (f) Mg^{2+} or Ba^{2+}
(g) Mg^{2+} or Na^+ (h) NO_3^- or CO_3^{2-}

13.33 Which ion has the lower ratio of charge to volume? Explain.
(a) Br^- or I^- (b) Sc^{3+} or Ca^{2+} (c) Br^- or K^+
(d) S^{2-} or Cl^- (e) Sc^{3+} or Al^{3+} (f) SO_4^{2-} or ClO_4^-
(g) Fe^{3+} or Fe^{2+} (h) Ca^{2+} or K^+

13.34 Which has the *larger* ΔH_{hydr} in each pair of Problem 13.32?

13.35 Which has the *smaller* ΔH_{hydr} in each pair of Problem 13.33?

13.36 (a) Use the following data to calculate the combined heat of hydration for the ions in potassium bromate ($KBrO_3$):
$$\Delta H_{lattice} = 745 \text{ kJ/mol} \qquad \Delta H_{soln} = 41.1 \text{ kJ/mol}$$
(b) Which ion contributes more to the answer to part (a)? Why?

13.37 (a) Use the following data to calculate the combined heat of hydration for the ions in sodium acetate ($NaC_2H_3O_2$):
$$\Delta H_{lattice} = 763 \text{ kJ/mol} \qquad \Delta H_{soln} = 17.3 \text{ kJ/mol}$$
(b) Which ion contributes more to the answer to part (a)? Why?

13.38 State whether the entropy of the system increases or decreases in each of the following processes:
(a) Gasoline burns in a car engine.
(b) Gold is extracted and purified from its ore.
(c) Ethanol (CH_3CH_2OH) dissolves in 1-propanol ($CH_3CH_2CH_2OH$).

13.39 State whether the entropy of the system increases or decreases in each of the following processes:
(a) Pure gases are mixed to prepare an anesthetic.
(b) Electronic-grade silicon is prepared from sand.
(c) Dry ice (solid CO_2) sublimes.

Problems in Context

13.40 Besides its use in making black-and-white film, silver nitrate ($AgNO_3$) is used similarly in forensic science. The NaCl left behind in the sweat of a fingerprint is treated with $AgNO_3$ solution to form AgCl. This precipitate is developed to show the black-and-white fingerprint pattern. Given $\Delta H_{lattice}$ of $AgNO_3$ = 822 kJ/mol and $\Delta H_{hydr} = -799$ kJ/mol, calculate its ΔH_{soln}.

Solubility as an Equilibrium Process

(Sample Problem 13.2)

Concept Review Questions

13.41 You are given a bottle of solid X and three aqueous solutions of X—one saturated, one unsaturated, and one supersaturated. How would you determine which solution is which?

13.42 Potassium permanganate ($KMnO_4$) has a solubility of 6.4 g/100 g of H_2O at 20°C and a curve of solubility vs. temperature that slopes upward to the right. How would you prepare a supersaturated solution of $KMnO_4$?

13.43 Why does the solubility of any gas in water decrease with rising temperature?

Skill-Building Exercises (grouped in similar pairs)

13.44 For a saturated aqueous solution of each of the following at 20°C and 1 atm, will the solubility increase, decrease, or stay the same when the indicated change occurs?
(a) $O_2(g)$, increase P (b) $N_2(g)$, increase V

13.45 For a saturated aqueous solution of each of the following at 20°C and 1 atm, will the solubility increase, decrease, or stay the same when the indicated change occurs?
(a) $He(g)$, decrease T (b) $RbI(s)$, increase P

13.46 The Henry's law constant (k_H) for O_2 in water at 20°C is 1.28×10^{-3} mol/L·atm. (a) How many grams of O_2 will dissolve in 2.50 L of H_2O that is in contact with pure O_2 at 1.00 atm? (b) How many grams of O_2 will dissolve in 2.50 L of H_2O that is in contact with air, where the partial pressure of O_2 is 0.209 atm?

13.47 Argon makes up 0.93% by volume of air. Calculate its solubility (mol/L) in water at 20°C and 1.0 atm. The Henry's law constant for Ar under these conditions is 1.5×10^{-3} mol/L·atm.

Problems in Context

13.48 Caffeine is about 10 times as soluble in hot water as in cold water. A chemist puts a hot-water extract of caffeine into an ice bath, and some caffeine crystallizes. Is the remaining solution saturated, unsaturated, or supersaturated?

13.49 The partial pressure of CO_2 gas above the liquid in a bottle of champagne at 20°C is 5.5 atm. What is the solubility of CO_2 in champagne? Assume Henry's law constant is the same for champagne as for water: at 20°C, $k_H = 3.7\times10^{-2}$ mol/L·atm.

13.50 Respiratory problems are treated with devices that deliver air with a higher partial pressure of O_2 than normal air. Why?

Concentration Terms

(Sample Problems 13.3 to 13.5)

Concept Review Questions

13.51 Explain the difference between molarity and molality. Under what circumstances would molality be a more accurate measure of the concentration of a prepared solution than molarity? Why?

13.52 Which way of expressing concentration includes (a) volume of solution; (b) mass of solution; (c) mass of solvent?

13.53 A solute has a solubility in water of 21 g/kg solvent. Is this value the same as 21 g/kg solution? Explain.

13.54 You want to convert among molarity, molality, and mole fraction of a solution. You know the masses of solute and solvent and the volume of solution. Is this enough information to carry out all the conversions? Explain.

13.55 When a solution is heated, which ways of expressing concentration change in value? Which remain unchanged? Explain.

Skill-Building Exercises (grouped in similar pairs)

13.56 Calculate the molarity of each aqueous solution:
(a) 32.3 g of table sugar ($C_{12}H_{22}O_{11}$) in 100. mL of solution
(b) 5.80 g of $LiNO_3$ in 505 mL of solution

13.57 Calculate the molarity of each aqueous solution:
(a) 0.82 g of ethanol (C_2H_5OH) in 10.5 mL of solution
(b) 1.27 g of gaseous NH_3 in 33.5 mL of solution

13.58 Calculate the molarity of each aqueous solution:
(a) 78.0 mL of 0.240 *M* NaOH diluted to 0.250 L with water
(b) 38.5 mL of 1.2 *M* HNO_3 diluted to 0.130 L with water

13.59 Calculate the molarity of each aqueous solution:
(a) 25.5 mL of 6.25 *M* HCl diluted to 0.500 L with water
(b) 8.25 mL of 2.00×10^{-2} *M* KI diluted to 12.0 mL with water

13.60 How would you prepare the following aqueous solutions?
(a) 365 mL of 8.55×10^{-2} *M* KH_2PO_4 from solid KH_2PO_4
(b) 465 mL of 0.335 *M* NaOH from 1.25 *M* NaOH

13.61 How would you prepare the following aqueous solutions?
(a) 2.5 L of 0.65 *M* NaCl from solid NaCl
(b) 15.5 L of 0.3 *M* urea [$(NH_2)_2C{=}O$] from 2.1 *M* urea

13.62 How would you prepare the following aqueous solutions?
(a) 1.40 L of 0.288 *M* KBr from solid KBr
(b) 255 mL of 0.0856 *M* $LiNO_3$ from 0.264 *M* $LiNO_3$

13.63 How would you prepare the following aqueous solutions?
(a) 57.5 mL of 1.53×10^{-3} *M* $Cr(NO_3)_3$ from solid $Cr(NO_3)_3$
(b) 5.8×10^3 m^3 of 1.45 *M* NH_4NO_3 from 2.50 *M* NH_4NO_3

13.64 Calculate the molality of the following:
(a) A solution containing 85.4 g of glycine (NH_2CH_2COOH) dissolved in 1.270 kg of H_2O
(b) A solution containing 8.59 g of glycerol ($C_3H_8O_3$) in 77.0 g of ethanol (C_2H_5OH)

13.65 Calculate the molality of the following:
(a) A solution containing 174 g of HCl in 757 g of H_2O
(b) A solution containing 16.5 g of naphthalene ($C_{10}H_8$) in 53.3 g of benzene (C_6H_6)

13.66 What is the molality of a solution consisting of 44.0 mL of benzene (C_6H_6; d = 0.877 g/mL) in 167 mL of hexane (C_6H_{14}; d = 0.660 g/mL)?

13.67 What is the molality of a solution consisting of 2.66 mL of carbon tetrachloride (CCl_4; d = 1.59 g/mL) in 76.5 mL of methylene chloride (CH_2Cl_2; d = 1.33 g/mL)?

13.68 How would you prepare the following aqueous solutions?
(a) 3.10×10^2 g of 0.125 *m* ethylene glycol ($C_2H_6O_2$) from ethylene glycol and water
(b) 1.20 kg of 2.20 mass % HNO_3 from 52.0 mass % HNO_3

13.69 How would you prepare the following aqueous solutions?
(a) 1.50 kg of 0.0355 *m* ethanol (C_2H_5OH) from ethanol and water
(b) 445 g of 13.0 mass % HCl from 34.1 mass % HCl

13.70 A solution contains 0.35 mol of isopropanol (C_3H_7OH) dissolved in 0.85 mol of water. (a) What is the mole fraction of isopropanol? (b) The mass percent? (c) The molality?

13.71 A solution contains 0.100 mol of NaCl dissolved in 8.60 mol of water. (a) What is the mole fraction of NaCl? (b) The mass percent? (c) The molality?

13.72 What mass of cesium bromide must be added to 0.500 L of water (d = 1.00 g/mL) to produce a 0.400 *m* solution? What are the mole fraction and the mass percent of CsBr?

13.73 What are the mole fraction and the mass percent of a solution made by dissolving 0.30 g of KI in 0.400 L of water (d = 1.00 g/mL)?

13.74 Calculate the molality, molarity, and mole fraction of NH_3 in an 8.00 mass % aqueous solution (d = 0.9651 g/mL).

13.75 Calculate the molality, molarity, and mole fraction of $FeCl_3$ in a 28.8 mass % aqueous solution (d = 1.280 g/mL).

Problems in Context

13.76 Wastewater from a cement factory contains 0.25 g of Ca^{2+} ion and 0.056 g of Mg^{2+} ion per 100.0 L of solution. The solution density is 1.001 g/mL. Calculate the Ca^{2+} and Mg^{2+} concentrations in ppm (by mass).

13.77 An automobile antifreeze mixture is made by mixing equal volumes of ethylene glycol (d = 1.114 g/mL; $\mathcal{M}$ = 62.07 g/mol) and water (d = 1.00 g/mL) at 20°C. The density of the mixture is 1.070 g/mL. Express the concentration of ethylene glycol as:
(a) Volume percent (b) Mass percent (c) Molarity
(d) Molality (e) Mole fraction

Colligative Properties of Solutions

(Sample Problems 13.6 to 13.9)

Concept Review Questions

13.78 The chemical formula of a solute does *not* affect the extent of the solution's colligative properties. What characteristic of a solute *does* affect these properties? Name a physical property of a solution that *is* affected by the chemical formula of the solute.

13.79 What is a nonvolatile nonelectrolyte? Why is this type of solute the simplest case for examining colligative properties?

13.80 In what sense is a strong electrolyte "strong"? What property of the substance makes it a strong electrolyte?

13.81 Express Raoult's law in words. Is Raoult's law valid for a solution of a volatile solute? Explain.

13.82 What are the most important differences between the phase diagram of a pure solvent and the phase diagram of a solution of that solvent?

13.83 Is the composition of the vapor at the top of a fractionating column different from the composition at the bottom? Explain.

13.84 Is the boiling point of 0.01 *m* KF(*aq*) higher or lower than that of 0.01 *m* glucose(*aq*)? Explain.

13.85 Which aqueous solution has a boiling point closer to its predicted value, 0.050 *m* NaF or 0.50 *m* KCl? Explain.

13.86 Which aqueous solution has a freezing point closer to its predicted value, 0.01 *m* NaBr or 0.01 *m* $MgCl_2$? Explain.

13.87 The freezing point depression constants of the solvents cyclohexane and naphthalene are 20.1°C/*m* and 6.94°C/*m*, respectively. Which solvent would give a more accurate result if you are using freezing point depression to determine the molar mass of a substance that is soluble in either one? Why?

Skill-Building Exercises (grouped in similar pairs)

13.88 Classify the following substances as strong electrolytes, weak electrolytes, or nonelectrolytes:
(a) Hydrogen chloride (HCl) (b) Potassium nitrate (KNO_3)
(c) Glucose ($C_6H_{12}O_6$) (d) Ammonia (NH_3)

13.89 Classify the following substances as strong electrolytes, weak electrolytes, or nonelectrolytes:
(a) Sodium permanganate ($NaMnO_4$)
(b) Acetic acid (CH_3COOH)
(c) Methanol (CH_3OH)
(d) Calcium acetate [$Ca(C_2H_3O_2)_2$]

13.90 How many moles of solute particles are present in 1 L of each of the following aqueous solutions?
(a) 0.3 *M* KBr (b) 0.065 *M* HNO_3
(c) 10^{-4} *M* $KHSO_4$ (d) 0.06 *M* ethanol (C_2H_5OH)

13.91 How many moles of solute particles are present in 1 mL of each of the following aqueous solutions?
(a) 0.02 *M* $CuSO_4$ (b) 0.004 *M* $Ba(OH)_2$
(c) 0.08 *M* pyridine (C_5H_5N) (d) 0.05 *M* $(NH_4)_2CO_3$

13.92 Which solution has the lower freezing point?
(a) 11.0 g of CH_3OH in 100. g of H_2O *or*
22.0 g of CH_3CH_2OH in 200. g of H_2O
(b) 20.0 g of H_2O in 1.00 kg of CH_3OH *or*
20.0 g of CH_3CH_2OH in 1.00 kg of CH_3OH

13.93 Which solution has the higher boiling point?
(a) 38.0 g of $C_3H_8O_3$ in 250. g of ethanol *or*
38.0 g of $C_2H_6O_2$ in 250. g of ethanol
(b) 15 g of $C_2H_6O_2$ in 0.50 kg of H_2O *or*
15 g of NaCl in 0.50 kg of H_2O

13.94 Rank the following aqueous solutions in order of increasing (a) osmotic pressure; (b) boiling point; (c) freezing point; (d) vapor pressure at 50°C:
(I) 0.100 *m* $NaNO_3$
(II) 0.100 *m* glucose
(III) 0.100 *m* $CaCl_2$

13.95 Rank the following aqueous solutions in order of decreasing (a) osmotic pressure; (b) boiling point; (c) freezing point; (d) vapor pressure at 298 K:
(I) 0.04 *m* urea [$(NH_2)_2C{=}O$]
(II) 0.01 *m* $AgNO_3$
(III) 0.03 *m* $CuSO_4$

13.96 Calculate the vapor pressure of a solution of 34.0 g of glycerol ($C_3H_8O_3$) in 500.0 g of water at 25°C. The vapor pressure of water at 25°C is 23.76 torr. (Assume ideal behavior.)

13.97 Calculate the vapor pressure of a solution of 0.39 mol of cholesterol in 5.4 mol of toluene at 32°C. Pure toluene has a vapor pressure of 41 torr at 32°C. (Assume ideal behavior.)

13.98 What is the freezing point of 0.251 *m* urea in water?

13.99 What is the boiling point of 0.200 *m* lactose in water?

13.100 The boiling point of ethanol (C_2H_5OH) is 78.5°C. What is the boiling point of a solution of 6.4 g of vanillin ($\mathcal{M}$ = 152.14 g/mol) in 50.0 g of ethanol (K_b of ethanol = 1.22°C/*m*)?

13.101 The freezing point of benzene is 5.5°C. What is the freezing point of a solution of 5.00 g of naphthalene ($C_{10}H_8$) in 444 g of benzene (K_f of benzene = 4.90°C/*m*)?

13.102 What is the minimum mass of ethylene glycol ($C_2H_6O_2$) that must be dissolved in 14.5 kg of water to prevent the solution from freezing at −12.0°F? (Assume ideal behavior.)

13.103 What is the minimum mass of glycerol ($C_3H_8O_3$) that must be dissolved in 11.0 mg of water to prevent the solution from freezing at −15°C? (Assume ideal behavior.)

13.104 Calculate the molality and van't Hoff factor (*i*) for the following aqueous solutions:
(a) 1.00 mass % NaCl, freezing point = −0.593°C
(b) 0.500 mass % CH_3COOH, freezing point = −0.159°C

13.105 Calculate the molality and van't Hoff factor (*i*) for the following aqueous solutions:
(a) 0.500 mass % KCl, freezing point = −0.234°C
(b) 1.00 mass % H_2SO_4, freezing point = −0.423°C

Problems in Context

13.106 In a study designed to prepare new gasoline-resistant coatings, a polymer chemist dissolves 6.053 g of poly(vinyl alcohol) in enough water to make 100.0 mL of solution. At 25°C, the osmotic pressure of this solution is 0.272 atm. What is the molar mass of the polymer sample?

13.107 The U.S. Food and Drug Administration lists dichloromethane (CH_2Cl_2) and carbon tetrachloride (CCl_4) among the many cancer-causing chlorinated organic compounds. What are the partial pressures of these substances in the vapor above a solution of 1.60 mol of CH_2Cl_2 and 1.10 mol of CCl_4 at 23.5°C? The vapor pressures of pure CH_2Cl_2 and CCl_4 at 23.5°C are 352 torr and 118 torr, respectively. (Assume ideal behavior.)

The Structure and Properties of Colloids

Concept Review Questions

13.108 Is the fluid inside a bacterial cell considered a solution, a colloid, or both? Explain.

13.109 What type of colloid is each of the following?
(a) Milk (b) Fog (c) Shaving cream

13.110 What is Brownian motion, and what causes it?

13.111 In a movie theater, you can see the beam of projected light. What phenomenon does this exemplify? Why does it occur?

13.112 Why don't soap micelles coagulate and form large globules? Is soap more effective in freshwater or in seawater? Why?

Comprehensive Problems

13.113 The three aqueous ionic solutions below have total volumes of 25. mL for A, 50. mL for B, and 100. mL for C. If each sphere represents 0.010 mol of ions, calculate: (a) the total molarity of ions for each solution; (b) the highest molarity of solute; (c) the lowest molality of solute (assuming the solution densities are equal); (d) the highest osmotic pressure (assuming ideal behavior).

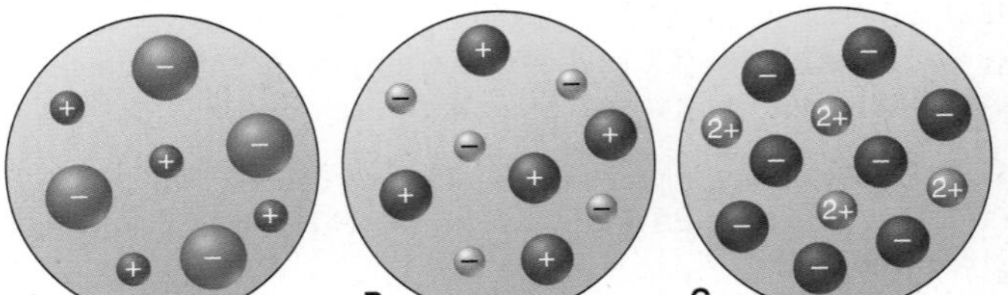

13.114 An aqueous solution is 10.% glucose by mass (*d* = 1.039 g/mL at 20°C). Calculate its freezing point, boiling point at 1 atm, and osmotic pressure.

13.115 Because zinc has nearly the same atomic radius as copper (*d* = 8.95 g/cm³), zinc atoms substitute for some copper atoms in the many types of brass. Calculate the density of the brass with (a) 10.0 atom % Zn and (b) 38.0 atom % Zn.

13.116 Gold occurs in seawater at an average concentration of 1.1×10^{-2} ppb. How many liters of seawater must be processed to recover 1 troy ounce of gold, assuming 81.5% efficiency (*d* of seawater = 1.025 g/mL; 1 troy ounce = 31.1 g)?

13.117 Use atomic properties to explain why xenon is 11 times as soluble as helium in water at 0°C on a mole basis.

13.118 Which of the following best represents a molecular-scale view of an ionic compound in aqueous solution? Explain.

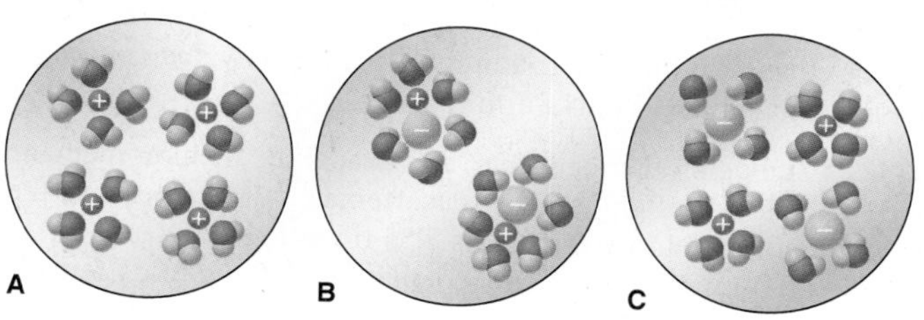

13.119 Four 0.50 *m* aqueous solutions are depicted below. Assume the solutions behave ideally: (a) Which has the highest boiling point? (b) Which has the lowest freezing point? (c) Can you determine which one has the highest osmotic pressure? Explain.

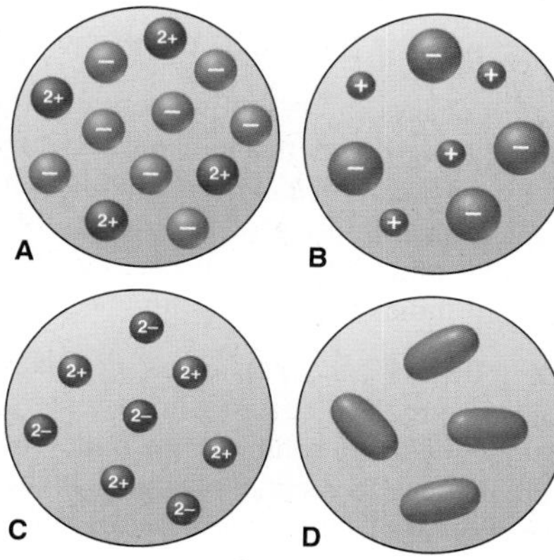

13.120 Thermal pollution from industrial wastewater causes the temperature of river or lake water to increase, which can affect fish survival as the concentration of dissolved O_2 decreases. Use the following data to find the molarity of O_2 at each temperature (assume the solution density is the same as water):

Temperature (°C)	Solubility of O_2 (mg/kg H_2O)	Density of H_2O (g/mL)
0.0	14.5	0.99987
20.0	9.07	0.99823
40.0	6.44	0.99224

13.121 Pyridine (*right*) is an essential portion of many biologically active compounds, such as nicotine and vitamin B_6. Like ammonia, it has a nitrogen with a lone pair, which makes it act as a weak base. Because it is miscible in a wide range of solvents, from water to benzene, pyridine is one of the most important bases and solvents in organic syntheses. Account for its solubility behavior in terms of intermolecular forces.

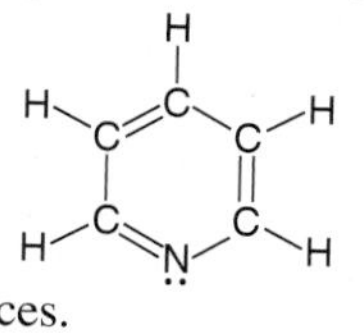

13.122 A chemist is studying small organic compounds for their potential use as an antifreeze. When 0.243 g of a compound is dissolved in 25.0 mL of water, the freezing point of the solution is −0.201°C. (a) Calculate the molar mass of the compound (*d* of water = 1.00 g/mL). (b) Analysis shows that the compound is 53.31 mass % C and 11.18 mass % H, the remainder being O. Calculate the empirical and molecular formulas of the compound. (c) Draw a Lewis structure for a compound with this formula that forms H bonds and another for one that does not.

13.123 Air in a smoky bar contains 4.0×10^{-6} mol/L of CO. What mass of CO is inhaled by a bartender who respires at a rate of 11 L/min during an 8.0-h shift?

13.124 Is 50% by mass of methanol dissolved in ethanol different from 50% by mass of ethanol dissolved in methanol? Explain.

13.125 Three gaseous mixtures of N_2 (blue), Cl_2 (green), and Ne (purple) are depicted below. (a) Which has the smallest mole fraction of N_2? (b) Which have the same mole fraction of Ne? (c) Rank all three in order of increasing mole fraction of Cl_2.

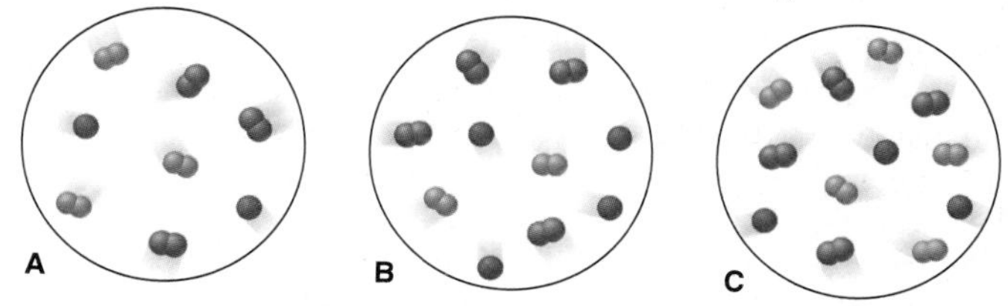

13.126 A water treatment plant needs to attain a fluoride concentration of 4.50×10^{-5} *M*. (a) What mass of NaF must be added to a 5000.-L blending tank of water? (b) What mass per day of fluoride is ingested by a person who drinks 2.0 L of this water?

13.127 Four U tubes each have distilled water in the right arm, a solution in the left arm, and a semipermeable membrane between arms. (a) If the solute is KCl, which solution is most concentrated? (b) If each solute is different but all the solutions have the same molarity, which contains the smallest number of dissolved ions?

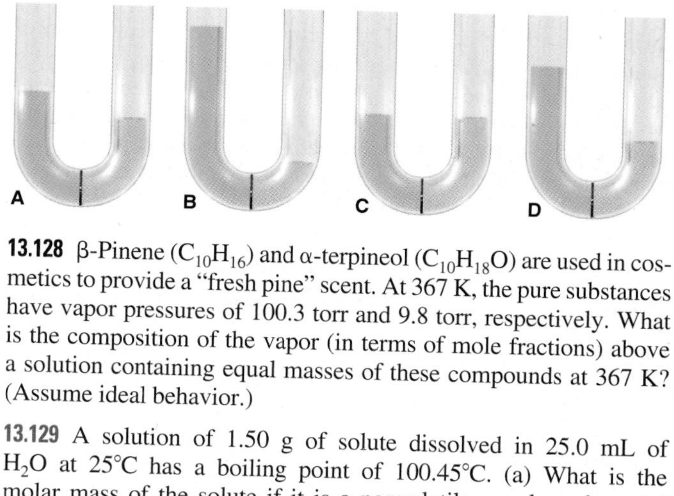

13.128 β-Pinene ($C_{10}H_{16}$) and α-terpineol ($C_{10}H_{18}O$) are used in cosmetics to provide a "fresh pine" scent. At 367 K, the pure substances have vapor pressures of 100.3 torr and 9.8 torr, respectively. What is the composition of the vapor (in terms of mole fractions) above a solution containing equal masses of these compounds at 367 K? (Assume ideal behavior.)

13.129 A solution of 1.50 g of solute dissolved in 25.0 mL of H_2O at 25°C has a boiling point of 100.45°C. (a) What is the molar mass of the solute if it is a nonvolatile nonelectrolyte and the solution behaves ideally (*d* of H_2O at 25°C = 0.997 g/mL)? (b) Conductivity measurements show the solute to be ionic of general formula AB_2 or A_2B. What is the molar mass if the solution behaves ideally? (c) Analysis indicates an empirical formula of CaN_2O_6. Explain the difference between the actual formula mass and that calculated from the boiling point elevation. (d) Find the van't Hoff factor (*i*) for this solution.

13.130 A pharmaceutical preparation made with ethanol (C_2H_5OH) is contaminated with methanol (CH_3OH). A sample of vapor above the liquid mixture contains a 97/1 mass ratio of C_2H_5OH to CH_3OH. What is the mass ratio of these alcohols in the liquid? At the temperature of the liquid, the vapor pressures of C_2H_5OH and CH_3OH are 60.5 torr and 126.0 torr, respectively.

13.131 Water treatment plants commonly use chlorination to destroy bacteria. A byproduct is chloroform ($CHCl_3$), a suspected carcinogen, produced when HOCl, formed by reaction of Cl_2 and water, reacts with dissolved organic matter. The United States, Canada, and the World Health Organization have set a limit of 100. ppb of

$CHCl_3$ in drinking water. Convert this concentration into molarity, molality, mole fraction, and mass percent.

13.132 A saturated Na_2CO_3 solution is prepared, and a small excess of solid is present (white pile in beaker). A seed crystal of $Na_2{}^{14}CO_3$ (^{14}C is a radioactive isotope of ^{12}C) is added (small red piece), and the radioactivity is measured over time. (a) Would you expect radioactivity in the solution? Explain. (b) Would you expect radioactivity in all the solid or just in the seed crystal? Explain.

13.133 A biochemical engineer isolates a bacterial gene fragment and dissolves a 10.0-mg sample in enough water to make 30.0 mL of solution. The osmotic pressure of the solution is 0.340 torr at 25°C. (a) What is the molar mass of the gene fragment? (b) If the solution density is 0.997 g/mL, how large is the freezing point depression for this solution (K_f of water = 1.86°C/*m*)?

13.134 A river is contaminated with 0.65 mg/L of dichloroethylene ($C_2H_2Cl_2$). What is the concentration (in ng/L) of dichloroethylene at 21°C in the air breathed by a person swimming in the river (k_H for $C_2H_2Cl_2$ in water is 0.033 mol/L·atm)?

13.135 At an air-water interface, fatty acids such as oleic acid lie in a one-molecule-thick layer (*monolayer*), with the heads in the water and the tails perpendicular in the air. When 2.50 mg of oleic acid is placed on a water surface, it forms a circular monolayer 38.6 cm in diameter. Find the surface area (in cm^2) occupied by one molecule ($\mathcal{M}$ of oleic acid = 283 g/mol).

13.136 A simple device used for estimating the concentration of total dissolved solids in an aqueous solution works by measuring the electrical conductivity of the solution. The method assumes that equal concentrations of different solids give approximately the same conductivity, and that the conductivity is proportional to concentration. The table below gives some actual electrical conductivities (in arbitrary units) for solutions of selected solids at the indicated concentrations (in ppm by mass):

	Conductivity		
Sample	**0 ppm**	**5.00×10^3 ppm**	**10.00×10^3 ppm**
$CaCl_2$	0.0	8.0	16.0
K_2CO_3	0.0	7.0	14.0
Na_2SO_4	0.0	6.0	11.0
Seawater (dil)	0.0	8.0	15.0
Sucrose ($C_{12}H_{22}O_{11}$)	0.0	0.0	0.0
Urea [$(NH_2)_2C{=}O$]	0.0	0.0	0.0

(a) How reliable are these measurements for estimating concentrations of dissolved solids? (b) For what types of substances might this method have a large error? Why? (c) Based on this method, an aqueous $CaCl_2$ solution has a conductivity of 14.0 units. Calculate its mole fraction and molality.

13.137 Two beakers are placed in a closed container (*left*). One beaker contains water, the other a concentrated aqueous sugar solution. With time, the solution volume increases and the water volume decreases (*right*). Explain on the molecular level.

13.138 The release of volatile organic compounds into the atmosphere is regulated to limit ozone formation. In a laboratory simulation, 5% of the ethanol in a liquid detergent is released. Thus, a "down-the-drain" factor of 0.05 is used to estimate ethanol emissions from the detergent. The k_H values for ethanol and 2-butoxyethanol ($C_4H_9OCH_2CH_2OH$) are 5×10^{-6} atm·m³/mol and 1.6×10^{-6} atm·m³/mol, respectively. (a) Estimate a "down-the-drain" factor for 2-butoxyethanol in the detergent. (b) What is the k_H for ethanol in units of L·atm/mol? (c) Is this value consistent with a value given as 0.64 Pa·m³/mol?

13.139 Although other solvents are available, dichloromethane (CH_2Cl_2) is still often used to "decaffeinate" drinks because the solubility of caffeine in CH_2Cl_2 is 8.35 times that in water.
(a) A 100.0-mL sample of cola containing 10.0 mg of caffeine is extracted with 60.0 mL of CH_2Cl_2. What mass of caffeine remains in the aqueous phase?
(b) A second identical cola sample is extracted with two successive 30.0-mL portions of CH_2Cl_2. What mass of caffeine remains in the aqueous phase after each extraction?
(c) Which approach extracts more caffeine?

13.140 How do you prepare 250. g of 0.150 *m* aqueous $NaHCO_3$?

13.141 Tartaric acid occurs in crystalline residues found in wine vats. It is used in baking powders and as an additive in foods. It contains 32.3% by mass carbon and 3.97% by mass hydrogen; the balance is oxygen. When 0.981 g of tartaric acid is dissolved in 11.23 g of water, the solution freezes at −1.26°C. Find the empirical and molecular formulas of tartaric acid.

13.142 Methanol (CH_3OH) and ethanol (C_2H_5OH) are miscible because the major intermolecular force for each is hydrogen bonding. In some methanol-ethanol solutions, the mole fraction of methanol is higher, but the mass percent of ethanol is higher. What is the range of mole fraction of methanol for these solutions?

13.143 A solution of 5.0 g of benzoic acid (C_6H_5COOH) in 100.0 g of carbon tetrachloride has a boiling point of 77.5°C.
(a) Calculate the molar mass of benzoic acid in the solution.
(b) Suggest a reason for the difference between the molar mass based on the formula and that found in part (a).

13.144 Derive a general equation that expresses the relationship between the molarity and the molality of a solution. Why are the numerical values of these two terms approximately equal for very dilute aqueous solutions?

13.145 A florist prepares a solution of nitrogen-phosphorus fertilizer by dissolving 5.66 g of NH_4NO_3 and 4.42 g of $(NH_4)_3PO_4$ in enough water to make 20.0 L of solution. What are the molarities of NH_4^+ and of PO_4^{3-} in the solution?

13.146 Suppose coal-fired power plants used water in scrubbers to remove SO_2 from smokestack gases (see Chemical Connections, p. 249). (a) If the partial pressure of SO_2 in the stack gases is 2.0×10^{-3} atm, what is the solubility of SO_2 in the scrubber liquid (k_H for SO_2 in water is 1.23 mol/L·atm at 200.°C)? (b) From your answer to part (a), why are basic solutions, such as limewater slurries [$Ca(OH)_2$], used in scrubbers?

13.147 Urea is a white crystalline solid used as a fertilizer, in the pharmaceutical industry, and in the manufacture of certain polymer resins. Analysis of urea reveals that, by mass, it is 20.1% carbon, 6.7% hydrogen, 46.5% nitrogen and the balance oxygen.
(a) Find the empirical formula of urea.
(b) A 5.0 g/L solution of urea in water has an osmotic pressure of 2.04 atm, measured at 25°C. What is the molar mass and molecular formula of urea?

13.148 The total concentration of dissolved particles in blood is 0.30 *M*. An intravenous (IV) solution must be isotonic with blood, which means it must have the same concentration.
(a) To relieve dehydration, a patient is given 100. mL/h of IV glucose ($C_6H_{12}O_6$) for 2.5 h. What mass (g) of glucose did she receive? (b) If isotonic saline (NaCl) is used, what is the molarity of the solution? (c) If the patient is given 150. mL/h of IV saline for 1.5 h, how many grams of NaCl did she receive?

13.149 Deviations from Raoult's law lead to the formation of *azeotropes,* constant boiling mixtures that cannot be separated by distillation, making industrial separations difficult. For components A and B, there is a positive deviation if the A-B attraction is less than A-A and B-B attractions (A and B reject each other), and a negative deviation if the A-B attraction is greater than A-A and B-B attractions. If the A-B attraction is nearly equal to the A-A and B-B attractions, the solution obeys Raoult's law. Explain whether the behavior of each pair will be nearly ideal, have a positive deviation, or a negative deviation:
(a) Benzene (C_6H_6) and methanol
(b) Water and ethyl acetate
(c) Hexane and heptane
(d) Methanol and water
(e) Water and hydrochloric acid

13.150 Acrylic acid ($CH_2{=}CHCOOH$) is a monomer used to make superabsorbent polymers and various compounds for paint and adhesive production. At 1 atm, it boils at 141.5°C but is prone to polymerization. Its vapor pressure at 25°C is 4.1 mbar. What pressure (in mmHg) is needed to distill the pure acid at 65°C?

13.151 To effectively stop polymerization, certain inhibitors require the presence of a small amount of O_2. At equilibrium with 1 atm of air, the concentration of O_2 dissolved in the monomer acrylic acid ($CH_2{=}CHCOOH$) is 1.64×10^{-3} *M*. (a) What is the k_H (mol/L·atm) for O_2 in acrylic acid? (b) If 0.005 atm of O_2 is sufficient to stop polymerization, what is the molarity of O_2? (c) What is the mole fraction? (d) What is the concentration in ppm? (Pure acrylic acid is 14.6 *M*; P_{O_2} in air is 0.2095 atm.)

13.152 Volatile organic solvents have been implicated in adverse health effects in industrial workers. Greener methods are phasing these solvents out. Rank the solvents in Table 13.6 (p. 501) in terms of increasing volatility.

13.153 At ordinary temperatures, water is a poor solvent for organic substances. But at high pressure and above 200°C, water develops many properties of organic solvents. Find the minimum pressure needed to maintain water as a liquid at 200.°C (ΔH_{vap} = 40.7 kJ/mol at 100°C and 1.00 atm; assume it remains constant with temperature).

13.154 In ice-cream making, the ingredients are kept below 0.0°C in an ice-salt bath. (a) Assuming that NaCl dissolves completely and forms an ideal solution, what mass of it is needed to lower the melting point of 5.5 kg of ice to −5.0°C? (b) Given the same assumptions as in part (a), what mass of $CaCl_2$ is needed?

13.155 Perfluorocarbons (PFCs), hydrocarbons with all H atoms replaced by F atoms, have very weak cohesive forces. One unusual application has a live mouse submerged in O_2-saturated PFCs.
(a) At 298 K, perfluorohexane (C_6F_{14}, $\mathcal{M}$ = 338 g/mol, d = 1.674 g/mL) in equilibrium with 101,325 Pa of O_2 has a mole fraction of O_2 of 4.28×10^{-3}. What is the k_H in mol/L·atm?
(b) According to one source, the k_H for O_2 in water at 25°C is 756.7 L·atm/mol. What is the solubility of O_2 in water at 25°C in ppm? (c) Rank the k_H values in descending order for O_2 in water, ethanol, C_6F_{14}, and C_6H_{14}. Explain your ranking.

13.156 The solubility of N_2 in blood is a serious problem for divers breathing compressed air (78% N_2 by volume) at depths greater than 50 ft.
(a) What is the molarity of N_2 in blood at 1.00 atm?
(b) What is the molarity of N_2 in blood at a depth of 50. ft?
(c) Find the volume (in mL) of N_2, measured at 25°C and 1.00 atm, released per liter of blood when a diver at a depth of 50. ft rises to the surface (k_H for N_2 in water at 25°C is 7.0×10^{-4} mol/L·atm and at 37°C is 6.2×10^{-4} mol/L·atm; assume d of water is 1.00 g/mL).

13.157 Figure 12.11 (p. 430) shows the phase changes of pure water. Consider how the diagram would change if air were present at 1 atm and dissolved in the water. (a) Would the three phases of water still attain equilibrium at some temperature? Explain. (b) In principle, would that temperature be higher, lower, or the same as the triple point for pure water? Explain. (c) Would ice sublime at a few degrees below the freezing point under this pressure? Explain. (d) Would the liquid have the same vapor pressure as that shown in Figure 12.9B at 100°C? At 120°C?

13.158 KNO_3, $KClO_3$, KCl, and NaCl are recrystallized as follows:
Step 1. A saturated aqueous solution of the compound is prepared at 50°C.
Step 2. The mixture is filtered to remove undissolved compound.
Step 3. The filtrate is cooled to 0°C.
Step 4. The crystals that form are filtered, dried, and weighed.
(a) Which compound has the highest percent recovery and which the lowest (see Figure 13.19, p. 492)?
(b) Starting with 100. g of each compound, how many grams of each can be recovered?

13.159 Eighty proof whiskey is 40% ethanol (C_2H_5OH) by volume. A man has 7.0 L of blood and drinks 28 mL of the whiskey, of which 22% of the ethanol goes into his blood.
(a) What concentration (in g/mL) of ethanol is in his blood (d of ethanol = 0.789 g/mL)?
(b) What volume (in mL) of whiskey would raise his blood alcohol level to 8.0×10^{-4} g/mL, the level at which a person is considered intoxicated?

13.160 Soft drinks are canned under 4 atm of CO_2 and release CO_2 when opened.
(a) How many moles of CO_2 are dissolved in a 355-mL can of soda before it is opened?
(b) After it has gone flat?
(c) What volume (in L) would the released CO_2 occupy at 1.00 atm and 25°C (k_H for CO_2 at 25°C is 3.3×10^{-2} mol/L·atm; P_{CO_2} in air is 3×10^{-4} atm)?

13.161 Gaseous O_2 in equilibrium with O_2 dissolved in water at 283 K is depicted at right. (a) Which scene below represents the system at 298 K? (b) Which scene represents the system when the pressure of O_2 is increased by half?

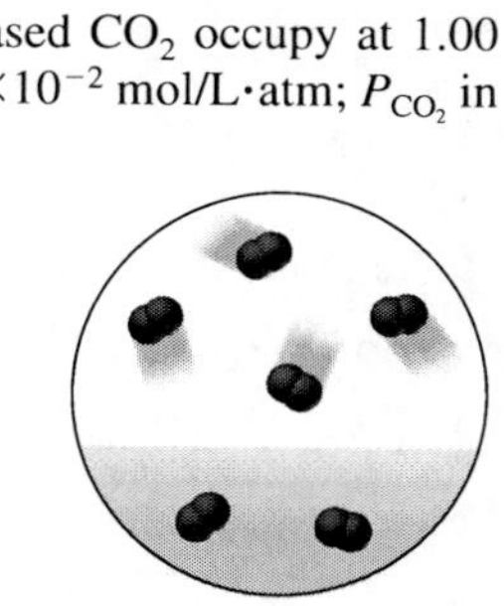

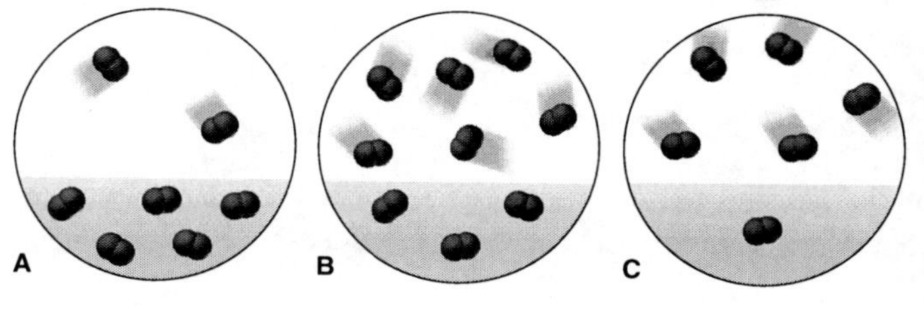

Kinetics: Rates and Mechanisms of Chemical Reactions

16

Concepts and skills to review before you study this chapter

- influence of temperature on molecular speed and collision frequency (Section 5.5)

You are in a small, thermoregulatory minority. About 85% of animal species—all reptiles and most amphibians, insects, and fish—rely predominantly on heat from the environment to maintain the speeds of the reactions that keep them alive. Only mammals (like us) and birds generate enough heat within their bodies for these reactions to proceed at a life-sustaining pace. Temperature, as you'll see, has a critical effect on the speed, or rate, of a reaction.

Until now, we haven't focused quantitatively on factors affecting reactions, other than the amounts of reactants and products and their molecular nature. Yet, while a balanced equation is essential for calculating yields, it tells us nothing about three dynamic aspects of chemical change:

- How fast is the reaction proceeding?
- How far will the reaction proceed toward completion?
- Will the reaction proceed by releasing energy or by requiring it?

This chapter addresses the first of these questions and focuses on the field of *kinetics*. We'll address the other two questions in upcoming chapters. Answering all three is crucial to understanding modern technology, the environment, and the reactions in living things.

IN THIS CHAPTER . . . We examine the rate of a reaction, the factors that affect it, the theories that explain those effects, and the stepwise changes reactants undergo as they transform into products.

- We introduce some general ideas about reaction rates and overview three key factors that affect them—concentration, physical state, and temperature.
- We express rate through a rate law and determine its components.
- We see how concentrations change as a reaction proceeds and discuss the meaning of half-life.
- To understand the effects of concentration and temperature on rate, we examine two related theories of chemical kinetics.
- We discuss reaction mechanisms, noting the steps a reaction goes through and picturing the chemical species that exists as reactant bonds are breaking and product bonds are forming.
- We see how catalysts increase reaction rates, highlighting two vital examples—the reactions in a living cell and the depletion of stratospheric ozone.

16.1 • FOCUSING ON REACTION RATE

By definition, in a chemical reaction, reactants change into products. **Chemical kinetics,** the study of how fast that change occurs, focuses on the **reaction rate,** the change in the concentrations of reactants (or products) as a function of time. Different reactions have different rates: *in a faster reaction (higher rate), the reactant concentration decreases quickly, whereas in a slower reaction (lower rate), it decreases slowly* (Figure 16.1, *next page*). Under any given set of conditions, a rate is determined by the nature of the reactants. At room temperature, for example, hydrogen reacts explosively with fluorine but extremely slowly with nitrogen:

$$H_2(g) + F_2(g) \longrightarrow 2HF(g) \qquad \text{[very fast]}$$
$$3H_2(g) + N_2(g) \longrightarrow 2NH_3(g) \qquad \text{[very slow]}$$

Furthermore, any given reaction has a different rate under different conditions.

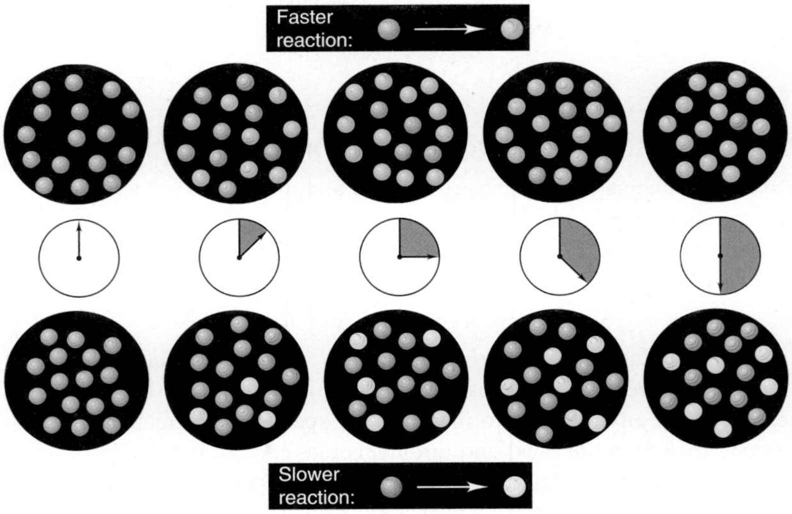

Figure 16.1 A faster reaction (*top*) and a slower reaction (*bottom*). As time elapses, reactant *decreases* and product *increases*.

Chemical processes occur over a wide range of rates (Figure 16.2). Some—like a neutralization, a precipitation, or an explosion—may take a second or less. Processes that include many reactions—like the ripening of fruit—take days to months. Human aging continues for decades, and the formation of coal from dead plants takes hundreds of millions of years. Knowing the reaction rate can be essential: how quickly a medicine acts can make the difference between life and death, and how long a polymer takes to form can make the difference between profit and loss.

We can control four factors that affect rate: the concentrations of reactants, their physical state, the temperature of the reaction, and the use of a catalyst. We consider the first three here and the fourth in Section 16.7.

1. *Concentration: molecules must collide to react.* A major factor influencing reaction rate is reactant concentration. Consider the reaction between ozone and nitrogen monoxide (nitric oxide):

$$NO(g) + O_3(g) \longrightarrow NO_2(g) + O_2(g)$$

This reaction occurs in the stratosphere, where the oxide is released in the exhaust gases of supersonic aircraft, but it can be simulated in the lab. In a reaction vessel, the molecules zoom every which way, crashing into each other and the vessel walls, but a reaction can occur only when NO and O_3 molecules collide. The more molecules present, the more frequently they collide, and the more often they react. Thus, *reaction rate is proportional to the number of collisions, which depends on the concentration of reactants:*

$$\text{Rate} \propto \text{collision frequency} \propto \text{concentration}$$

2. *Physical state: molecules must mix to collide.* Collision frequency also depends on physical state, which determines how easily the reactants mix. When the reactants are in the same phase, as in an aqueous solution, random thermal motion brings them into contact, but gentle stirring mixes them further. When the reactants are in different phases, contact occurs only at the interface between the phases, so vigorous stirring or

Figure 16.2 The wide range of reaction rates.

Figure 16.3 The effect of surface area on reaction rate.

even grinding may be needed. Thus, *the more finely divided a solid or liquid reactant, the greater its surface area, the more contact it makes with the other reactant, and the faster the reaction occurs.* In Figure 16.3, a hot steel nail (*left*) placed in oxygen gas glows feebly, but the same mass of steel wool (*right*) bursts into flame. For the same reason, you start a campfire with twigs, not logs.

3. *Temperature: molecules must collide with enough energy.* Temperature usually has a major effect on the rate of a reaction. Two kitchen appliances employ this effect: a refrigerator slows down chemical processes that spoil food, whereas an oven speeds up other chemical processes that cook it. Temperature affects reaction rate by increasing the *frequency* and, more importantly, the *energy* of collisions:

- *Frequency of collisions.* Recall that molecules in a sample of gas have a range of speeds, with the most probable speed a function of the temperature (see Figure 5.14, p. 205). Thus, *at a higher temperature, collisions occur more frequently, and so more molecules react:*

$$\text{Rate} \propto \text{collision } \textbf{frequency} \propto \text{temperature}$$

- *Energy of collisions.* Even more important is that *temperature affects the kinetic energy* of the molecules. In the jumble of NO and O_3 molecules in the reaction vessel, most collisions have only enough energy for the molecules to bounce off each other. However, some collisions occur with sufficient energy for the molecules to react (Figure 16.4). *At a higher temperature, more sufficiently energetic collisions occur, and so more molecules react:*

$$\text{Rate} \propto \text{collision } \textbf{energy} \propto \text{temperature}$$

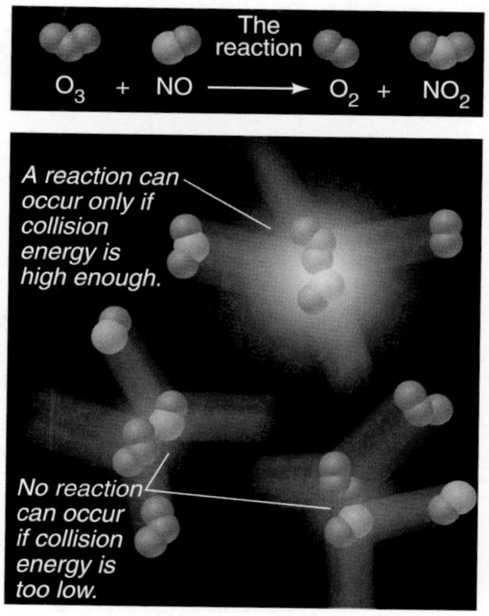

Figure 16.4 Sufficient collision energy is required for a reaction to occur.

Summary of Section 16.1

- Chemical kinetics focuses on reaction rate and the factors that affect it.
- Under a given set of conditions, each reaction has its own rate.
- Concentration affects rate by influencing the frequency of collisions between reactant molecules.
- Physical state affects rate by determining how well reactants can mix.
- Temperature affects rate by influencing the frequency and, more importantly, the energy of the collisions between reactant molecules.

16.2 • EXPRESSING THE REACTION RATE

In general terms, a *rate* is a change in some variable per unit of time. The most familiar examples relate to speed (*see photo*), the change in position of an object divided by the change in time. For instance, if we measure a runner's initial position, x_1, at time t_1, and final position, x_2, at time t_2, the average speed is

$$\text{Rate of motion (speed)} = \frac{\text{change in position}}{\text{change in time}} = \frac{x_2 - x_1}{t_2 - t_1} = \frac{\Delta x}{\Delta t}$$

Runners change positions with time.

For the rate of a *reaction,* we measure the changes in concentrations of reactants or products per unit time: *reactant concentrations decrease while product concentrations increase.* For the general reaction A $\longrightarrow$ B, we measure the initial reactant concentration (A_1) at t_1, allow the reaction to proceed, and then quickly measure the final reactant concentration (A_2) at t_2. The change in concentration divided by the change in time gives the rate:

$$\text{Rate} = -\frac{\text{change in concentration of A}}{\text{change in time}} = -\frac{\text{conc } A_2 - \text{conc } A_1}{t_2 - t_1} = -\frac{\Delta(\text{conc A})}{\Delta t}$$

The negative sign is important because, by convention, reaction rate is a *positive* number. But, since conc A_2 must be *lower* than conc A_1, the *change in concentration (final − initial) of reactant A is negative.* Therefore, we use the negative sign to convert the negative change in reactant concentration to a positive value for the rate. Suppose the concentration of A changes from 1.2 mol/L (conc A_1) to 0.75 mol/L (conc A_2) over a 125-s period. The rate is

$$\text{Rate} = -\frac{0.75 \text{ mol/L} - 1.2 \text{ mol/L}}{125 \text{ s} - 0 \text{ s}} = 3.6\times10^{-3} \text{ mol/L·s}$$

Square brackets, [ ], indicate a concentration in moles per liter. For example, [A] is the concentration of A in mol/L, and the rate expressed in terms of A is

$$\text{Rate} = -\frac{\Delta[\text{A}]}{\Delta t} \qquad (16.1)$$

The units for the rate are moles per liter per second (mol L^{-1} s^{-1}, or mol/L·s), or any time unit convenient for the reaction (minutes, years, and so on).

If instead we measure the *product* concentrations to determine the rate, we find that conc B_2 is always *higher* than conc B_1. Thus, the *change* in product concentration, Δ[B], is *positive,* and the reaction rate for A $\longrightarrow$ B expressed in terms of B is

$$\text{Rate} = +\frac{\Delta[\text{B}]}{\Delta t}$$

The plus sign is usually understood and not shown.

Average, Instantaneous, and Initial Reaction Rates

In most cases, *the rate varies as a reaction proceeds.* Consider the reversible gas-phase reaction between ethylene and ozone, one of many reactions that may be involved in the formation of smog:

$$C_2H_4(g) + O_3(g) \rightleftharpoons C_2H_4O(g) + O_2(g)$$

The equation shows that for every molecule of C_2H_4 that reacts, a molecule of O_3 reacts; thus, $[O_3]$ and $[C_2H_4]$ decrease at the same rate:

$$\text{Rate} = -\frac{\Delta[C_2H_4]}{\Delta t} = -\frac{\Delta[O_3]}{\Delta t}$$

When we start with a known $[O_3]$ in a closed vessel at 30°C (303 K) and measure $[O_3]$ at 10.0-s intervals during the first minute after adding C_2H_4, we obtain the data in Table 16.1 and the plot of $[O_3]$ vs. t in Figure 16.5 *(red curve).* Two key points are

- The data points in Figure 16.5 result in a curved line, which means that the rate is changing (a straight line would mean that the rate is constant).
- The rate *decreases* during the course of the reaction because we are plotting *reactant* concentration versus time: as O_3 molecules react, fewer are present to collide with C_2H_4 molecules, and the rate, the change in $[O_3]$ over time, therefore decreases.

Three types of reaction rates are shown in the figure:

1. *Average rate.* Over a given period of time, the **average rate** is the slope of the line joining two points along the curve. The rate over the entire 60.0 s is the total change in concentration divided by the total change in time (Figure 16.5, *line* ***a***):

$$\text{Rate} = -\frac{\Delta[O_3]}{\Delta t} = -\frac{(1.10\times10^{-5} \text{ mol/L}) - (3.20\times10^{-5} \text{ mol/L})}{60.0 \text{ s} - 0.0 \text{ s}} = 3.50\times10^{-7} \text{ mol/L·s}$$

Table 16.1 Concentration of O_3 at Various Times in Its Reaction with C_2H_4 at 303 K

Time (s)	Concentration of O_3 (mol/L)
0.0	3.20×10^{-5}
10.0	2.42×10^{-5}
20.0	1.95×10^{-5}
30.0	1.63×10^{-5}
40.0	1.40×10^{-5}
50.0	1.23×10^{-5}
60.0	1.10×10^{-5}

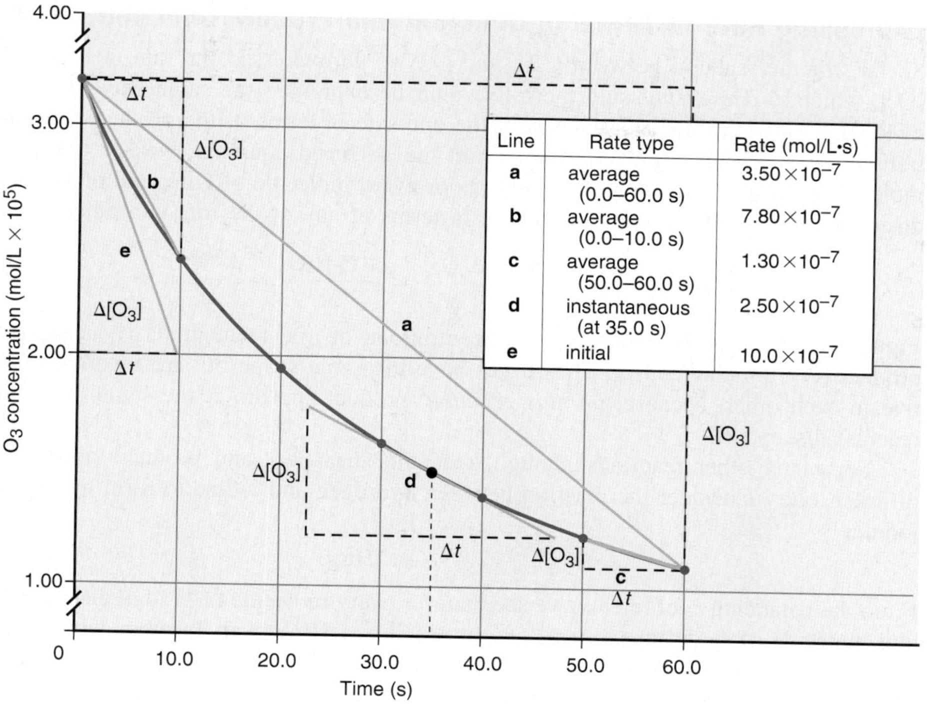

Line	Rate type	Rate (mol/L•s)
a	average (0.0–60.0 s)	3.50×10^{-7}
b	average (0.0–10.0 s)	7.80×10^{-7}
c	average (50.0–60.0 s)	1.30×10^{-7}
d	instantaneous (at 35.0 s)	2.50×10^{-7}
e	initial	10.0×10^{-7}

Figure 16.5 Three types of reaction rates for the reaction of O_3 and C_2H_4.

This quantity, which is the slope of line **a** (that is, $\Delta[O_3]/\Delta t$), is the average rate over the entire period: during the first 60.0 s of the reaction, $[O_3]$ decreases an *average* of 3.50×10^{-7} mol/L each second.

But, when you drive a car or ride a bike for a few miles, your speed over shorter distances may be lower or higher than your average speed. In the same sense, the decrease in $[O_3]$ over the whole time period does not show the rate over any shorter time period. This *change* in reaction rate is evident when we calculate the average rate over two shorter periods. For the first 10.0 s, between 0.0 s and 10.0 s, the average rate (Figure 16.5, *line* ***b***) is

$$\text{Rate} = -\frac{\Delta[O_3]}{\Delta t} = -\frac{(2.42\times10^{-5}\ \text{mol/L}) - (3.20\times10^{-5}\ \text{mol/L})}{10.0\ \text{s} - 0.0\ \text{s}} = 7.80\times10^{-7}\ \text{mol/L·s}$$

And, for the last 10.0 s, between 50.0 s and 60.0 s, the average rate (Figure 16.5, *line* ***c***) is

$$\text{Rate} = -\frac{\Delta[O_3]}{\Delta t} = -\frac{(1.10\times10^{-5}\ \text{mol/L}) - (1.23\times10^{-5}\ \text{mol/L})}{60.0\ \text{s} - 50.0\ \text{s}} = 1.30\times10^{-7}\ \text{mol/L·s}$$

The earlier rate is six times faster than the later rate.

2. *Instantaneous rate.* The shorter the time period we choose, the closer we come to the **instantaneous rate,** the rate at a particular instant during the reaction. *The slope of a line tangent to the curve at any point gives the instantaneous rate at that time.* For example, the rate at 35.0 s is 2.50×10^{-7} mol/L·s, the slope of the line tangent to the curve through the point at $t = 35.0$ s (Figure 16.5, *line* ***d***). In general, we use the term *reaction rate* to mean *instantaneous* reaction rate.

3. *Initial rate.* The instantaneous rate at the moment the reactants are mixed (that is, at $t = 0$) is the **initial rate.** We use this rate to avoid a complication: as a reaction proceeds in the *forward* direction (reactants $\longrightarrow$ products), product increases, causing the *reverse* reaction (reactants $\longleftarrow$ products), to occur more quickly. To find the overall (net) rate, we would have to calculate the difference between the forward and reverse rates. But, for the initial rate, $t = 0$, so product concentrations are negligible, and so is the reverse rate. We find the initial rate from the slope of the line tangent to the curve at $t = 0$ s (Figure 16.5, *line* ***e***). We typically use initial rates to find other kinetic parameters.

Expressing Rate in Terms of Reactant and Product Concentrations

So far, for the reaction between C_2H_4 and O_3, we've expressed the rate in terms of $[O_3]$, which is *decreasing,* and the rate would be expressed the same way in terms of $[C_2H_4]$. However, the rate is exactly the opposite in terms of the product concentrations because they are *increasing*. From the balanced equation, we see that one molecule each of C_2H_4O and of O_2 appear for every molecule of C_2H_4 and of O_3 that disappear. Thus, we can express the rate in terms of any of the four substances:

$$\text{Rate} = -\frac{\Delta[C_2H_4]}{\Delta t} = -\frac{\Delta[O_3]}{\Delta t} = \frac{\Delta[C_2H_4O]}{\Delta t} = \frac{\Delta[O_2]}{\Delta t}$$

Figure 16.6A plots the changes in concentrations of one reactant (C_2H_4) and one product (O_2) simultaneously. The curves have the same shape but are inverted relative to each other, because, *for this reaction,* product appears at the same rate that reactant disappears.

For many other reactions, though, reactants disappear and products appear at different rates. Consider the reaction between hydrogen and iodine to form hydrogen iodide:

$$H_2(g) + I_2(g) \longrightarrow 2HI(g)$$

From the balancing coefficients, we see that, for every molecule of H_2 that disappears, one molecule of I_2 disappears and *two* molecules of HI appear. In other words, the rate of $[H_2]$ decrease is the same as the rate of $[I_2]$ decrease, but both are only half the rate of [HI] increase. Thus, in Figure 16.6B, the [HI] curve rises twice as fast as the $[H_2]$ curve drops. If we refer the changes in $[I_2]$ and [HI] to the change in $[H_2]$, we have

$$\text{Rate} = -\frac{\Delta[H_2]}{\Delta t} = -\frac{\Delta[I_2]}{\Delta t} = \frac{1}{2}\frac{\Delta[HI]}{\Delta t}$$

If, instead, we refer the changes in $[H_2]$ and $[I_2]$ to the change in [HI], we obtain

$$\text{Rate} = \frac{\Delta[HI]}{\Delta t} = -2\frac{\Delta[H_2]}{\Delta t} = -2\frac{\Delta[I_2]}{\Delta t}$$

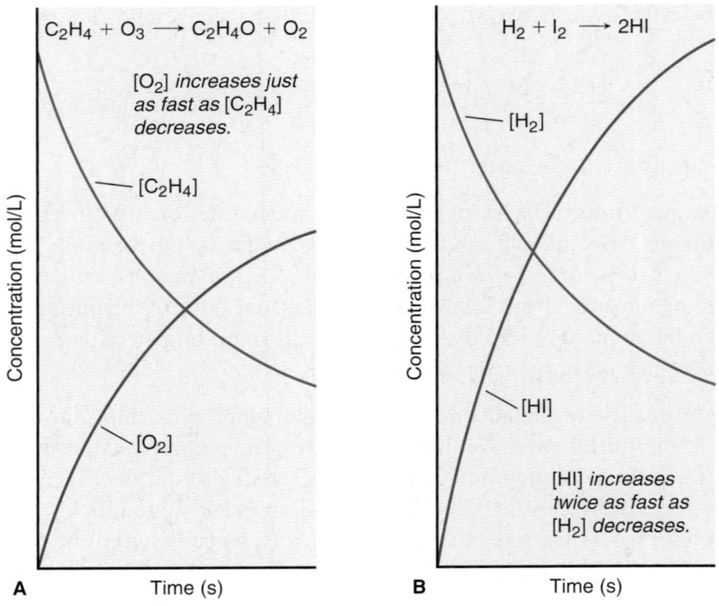

Figure 16.6 Plots of [reactant] and [product] vs. time. **A,** C_2H_4 and O_2. **B,** H_2 and HI.

Note that this expression gives a rate that is double the previous one. Thus, *the expression for the rate of a reaction and its numerical value depend on which substance serves as the reference.*

We can summarize these results for any reaction,

$$aA + bB \longrightarrow cC + dD$$

where a, b, c, and d are coefficients of the balanced equation, as follows:

$$\text{Rate} = -\frac{1}{a}\frac{\Delta[A]}{\Delta t} = -\frac{1}{b}\frac{\Delta[B]}{\Delta t} = \frac{1}{c}\frac{\Delta[C]}{\Delta t} = \frac{1}{d}\frac{\Delta[D]}{\Delta t} \quad (16.2)$$

Sample Problem 16.1 Expressing Rate in Terms of Changes in Concentration with Time

Problem Hydrogen gas has a nonpolluting combustion product (water vapor). It is used as a fuel aboard the space shuttle and in earthbound cars with prototype engines:

$$2H_2(g) + O_2(g) \longrightarrow 2H_2O(g)$$

(a) Express the rate in terms of changes in $[H_2]$, $[O_2]$, and $[H_2O]$ with time.
(b) When $[O_2]$ is decreasing at 0.23 mol/L·s, at what rate is $[H_2O]$ increasing?

Plan (a) Of the three substances in the equation, let's choose O_2 as the reference because its coefficient is 1. For every molecule of O_2 that disappears, two molecules of H_2 disappear. Thus, the rate of $[O_2]$ decrease is one-half the rate of $[H_2]$ decrease. By similar reasoning, the rate of $[O_2]$ decrease is one-half the rate of $[H_2O]$ increase. **(b)** Because $[O_2]$ is decreasing, the change in its concentration must be negative. We substitute the given rate as a negative value (−0.23 mol/L·s) into the expression and solve for $\Delta[H_2O]/\Delta t$.

Solution (a) Expressing the rate in terms of each component:

$$\text{Rate} = -\frac{\Delta[O_2]}{\Delta t} = -\frac{1}{2}\frac{\Delta[H_2]}{\Delta t} = \frac{1}{2}\frac{\Delta[H_2O]}{\Delta t}$$

(b) Calculating the rate of change of $[H_2O]$:

$$\frac{1}{2}\frac{\Delta[H_2O]}{\Delta t} = -\frac{\Delta[O_2]}{\Delta t} = -(-0.23 \text{ mol/L·s})$$

$$\frac{\Delta[H_2O]}{\Delta t} = 2(0.23 \text{ mol/L·s}) = 0.46 \text{ mol/L·s}$$

Check (a) A good check is to use the rate expression to obtain the balanced equation: $[H_2]$ changes twice as fast as $[O_2]$, so two H_2 molecules react for each O_2. $[H_2O]$ changes twice as fast as $[O_2]$, so two H_2O molecules form from each O_2. Thus, we get $2H_2 + O_2 \longrightarrow 2H_2O$. The values of $[H_2]$ and $[O_2]$ decrease, so they have minus signs; $[H_2O]$ increases, so it has a plus sign. Another check is to use Equation 16.2, with A = H_2, $a = 2$; B = O_2, $b = 1$; and C = H_2O, $c = 2$:

$$\text{Rate} = -\frac{1}{a}\frac{\Delta[A]}{\Delta t} = -\frac{1}{b}\frac{\Delta[B]}{\Delta t} = \frac{1}{c}\frac{\Delta[C]}{\Delta t}$$

or

$$\text{Rate} = -\frac{1}{2}\frac{\Delta[H_2]}{\Delta t} = -\frac{\Delta[O_2]}{\Delta t} = \frac{1}{2}\frac{\Delta[H_2O]}{\Delta t}$$

(b) Given the rate expression, it makes sense that the numerical value of the rate of $[H_2O]$ increase is twice that of $[O_2]$ decrease.

Comment Thinking through this type of problem at the molecular level is the best approach, but use Equation 16.2 to confirm your answer.

Follow-Up Problem 16.1 **(a)** Balance the following equation and express the rate in terms of the change in concentration with time for each substance:

$$NO(g) + O_2(g) \longrightarrow N_2O_3(g)$$

(b) How fast is $[O_2]$ decreasing when [NO] is decreasing at a rate of 1.60×10^{-4} mol/L·s?

Summary of Section 16.2

- The average reaction rate is the change in reactant (or product) concentration over a change in time, Δt. The rate slows as the reaction proceeds because reactants are used up.
- The instantaneous rate at time t is the slope of the tangent to a curve that plots concentration vs. time.
- The initial rate, the instantaneous rate at $t = 0$, occurs when reactants have just been mixed and before any product accumulates.
- The expression for a reaction rate and its numerical value depend on which reaction component is being referenced.

16.3 • THE RATE LAW AND ITS COMPONENTS

The centerpiece of any kinetic study of a reaction is the **rate law** (or **rate equation**), which expresses the rate as a function of concentrations and temperature. The rate law is based on experiment, so any hypothesis about how the reaction occurs on the molecular level must conform to it.

In this discussion, we generally consider reactions for which the products do not appear in the rate law, so the rate depends only on *reactant* concentrations and temperature. For a general reaction occurring at a fixed temperature,

$$a\text{A} + b\text{B} + \cdots \longrightarrow c\text{C} + d\text{D} + \cdots$$

the rate law is

$$\text{Rate} = k[\text{A}]^m[\text{B}]^n \cdots \quad (16.3)$$

The term k is a proportionality constant, called the **rate constant,** that is specific for a given reaction at a given temperature and does *not* change as the reaction proceeds. (As we'll see in Section 16.5, k *does* change with temperature.) The exponents m and n, called the **reaction orders,** define how the rate is affected by reactant concentration; we'll see how to determine them shortly. Two key points to remember are

- *The balancing coefficients a and b in the reaction equation are **not** necessarily related in any way to the reaction orders m and n.*
- *The components of the rate law—rate, reaction orders, and rate constant—**must** be found by experiment.*

In the remainder of this section, we'll find the components of the rate law by measuring concentrations to determine the *initial rate,* using initial rates to determine the *reaction orders,* and using these values to calculate the *rate constant.* With the rate law for a reaction, we can predict the rate for any initial concentrations.

Some Laboratory Methods for Determining the Initial Rate

We determine an initial rate from a plot of concentration vs. time, so we need a quick, accurate method for measuring concentration. Let's briefly discuss three common approaches.

1. *Spectrometric methods* measure the concentration of a component that absorbs (or emits) characteristic wavelengths of light. For example, in the reaction of NO and O_3, only NO_2 has a color:

$$\text{NO}(g, \text{colorless}) + \text{O}_3(g, \text{colorless}) \longrightarrow \text{O}_2(g, \text{colorless}) + \text{NO}_2(g, \text{brown})$$

Known amounts of reactants are injected into a tube of known volume within a spectrometer (see Tools of the Laboratory, p. 273), which is set to measure the wavelength and intensity of the brown color. The rate of NO_2 formation is proportional to the increase in that intensity over time.

2. *Conductometric methods* rely on the change in electrical conductivity of the reaction solution when nonionic reactants form ionic products, or vice versa. Con-

sider the reaction between an organic halide, such as 2-bromo-2-methylpropane, and water:

$$(CH_3)_3C{-}Br(l) + H_2O(l) \longrightarrow (CH_3)_3C{-}OH(l) + H^+(aq) + Br^-(aq)$$

The HBr that forms is a strong acid, so it dissociates completely in the water. As time passes, more ions form, so the conductivity of the reaction mixture increases.

3. *Manometric methods* employ a manometer attached to a reaction vessel of fixed volume and temperature. The manometer measures the pressure over time of a reaction that involves a change in the number of moles of gas. Consider the reaction between zinc and acetic acid:

$$Zn(s) + 2CH_3COOH(aq) \longrightarrow Zn^{2+}(aq) + 2CH_3COO^-(aq) + H_2(g)$$

The rate is directly proportional to the increase in H_2 gas pressure.

Determining Reaction Orders

With the initial rate in hand, we can determine reaction orders. Let's first discuss what reaction orders are and then see how to determine them by controlling reactant concentrations.

Meaning and Terminology A reaction has an *individual* order "with respect to" or "in" each reactant, and an *overall* order, the sum of the individual orders.

Consider first the simplest case, a reaction with only one reactant, A:

$$A \longrightarrow \text{products}$$

- *First order.* If the rate doubles when [A] doubles, the rate depends on [A] raised to the first power, $[A]^1$ (the ^{1} is generally omitted). Thus, the reaction is *first order* in (or with respect to) A and *first order* overall:

$$\text{Rate} = k[A]^1 = k[A]$$

- *Second order.* If the rate quadruples when [A] doubles, the rate depends on [A] squared, $[A]^2$. In this case, the reaction is *second order* in A and *second order* overall:

$$\text{Rate} = k[A]^2$$

- *Zero order.* If the rate does not change when [A] doubles, the rate does *not* depend on [A], but we express this fact mathematically by saying that the rate depends on [A] raised to the zero power, $[A]^0$. The reaction is *zero order* in A and *zero order* overall:

$$\text{Rate} = k[A]^0 = k(1) = k$$

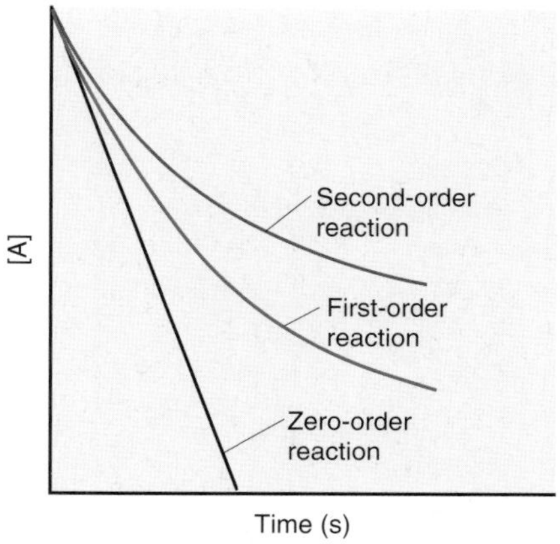

Figure 16.7 Plots of reactant concentration, [A], vs. time for first-, second-, and zero-order reactions.

Figure 16.7 shows plots of [A] vs. time for first-, second-, and zero-order reactions. (In all cases, the value of k was assumed to be the same.) Notice that

- The decrease in [A] doesn't change as time goes on for a zero-order reaction.
- The decrease slows down as time goes on for a first-order reaction.
- The decrease slows even more for a second-order reaction.

These results are reflected in Figure 16.8, which shows plots of rate vs. [A] for the same reaction orders. Notice that

- The plot is a horizontal line for the zero-order reaction because the rate doesn't change no matter what the value of [A].
- The plot is an upward-sloping *line* for the first-order reaction because the rate is directly proportional to [A].
- The plot is an upward-sloping *curve* for the second-order reaction because the rate increases exponentially with [A].

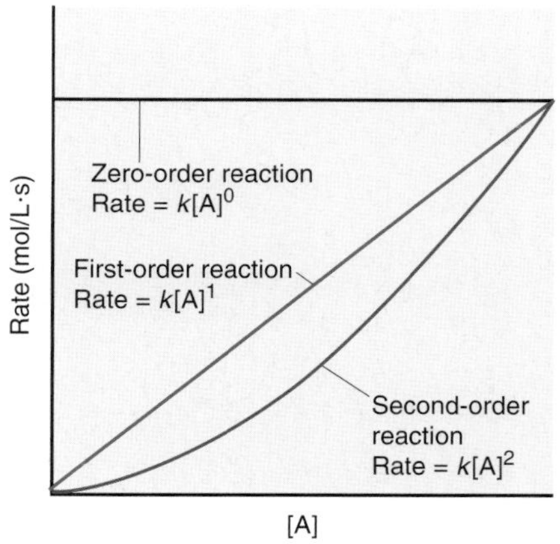

Figure 16.8 Plots of rate vs. reactant concentration, [A], for first-, second-, and zero-order reactions.

Let's look at some examples of observed rate laws and note the reaction orders. For the reaction between NO and hydrogen gas,

$$2NO(g) + 2H_2(g) \longrightarrow N_2(g) + 2H_2O(g)$$

the rate law is

$$\text{Rate} = k[NO]^2[H_2]$$

This reaction is second order in NO. And, even though H_2 has a coefficient of 2 in the balanced equation, the reaction is first order in H_2. It is third order overall (2 + 1 = 3).

For the reaction between nitrogen monoxide and ozone,

$$NO(g) + O_3(g) \longrightarrow NO_2(g) + O_2(g)$$

the rate law is

$$\text{Rate} = k[NO][O_3]$$

This reaction is first order with respect to NO and first order with respect to O_3, so it is second order overall (1 + 1 = 2).

Finally, for the hydrolysis of 2-bromo-2-methylpropane,

$$(CH_3)_3C\text{—}Br(l) + H_2O(l) \longrightarrow (CH_3)_3C\text{—}OH(l) + H^+(aq) + Br^-(aq)$$

the rate law is

$$\text{Rate} = k[(CH_3)_3CBr]$$

This reaction is first order in 2-bromo-2-methylpropane and zero order with respect to H_2O, despite its coefficient of 1 in the balanced equation. If we want to note that water is a reactant, we can write

$$\text{Rate} = k[(CH_3)_3CBr][H_2O]^0$$

Overall, this is a first-order reaction (1 + 0 = 1).

These examples reiterate an important point noted earlier: *reaction orders* ***cannot*** *be deduced from the balanced equation but* ***must*** *be determined from experimental data.*

Although usually positive integers or zero, reaction orders can also be fractional or negative. For the reaction

$$CHCl_3(g) + Cl_2(g) \longrightarrow CCl_4(g) + HCl(g)$$

a fractional order appears in the rate law:

$$\text{Rate} = k[CHCl_3][Cl_2]^{1/2}$$

This reaction order means that if, for example, $[Cl_2]$ increases by a factor of 4, the rate increases by a factor of 2, the square root of the change in $[Cl_2]$. The overall order of this reaction is $\frac{3}{2}$.

A negative reaction order means the rate *decreases* when the concentration of that component increases. Negative orders are often seen when the rate law includes products. For example, for the atmospheric reaction

$$2O_3(g) \rightleftharpoons 3O_2(g)$$

the rate law is

$$\text{Rate} = k[O_3]^2[O_2]^{-1} = k\frac{[O_3]^2}{[O_2]}$$

If $[O_2]$ doubles, the reaction proceeds half as fast. This reaction is second order in O_3 and negative first order in O_2, so it is first order overall [2 + (−1) = 1].

Sample Problem 16.2 Determining Reaction Orders from Rate Laws

Problem For each of the following reactions, use the given rate law to determine the reaction order with respect to each reactant and the overall order:
(a) $2NO(g) + O_2(g) \longrightarrow 2NO_2(g)$; rate = $k[NO]^2[O_2]$
(b) $CH_3CHO(g) \longrightarrow CH_4(g) + CO(g)$; rate = $k[CH_3CHO]^{3/2}$
(c) $H_2O_2(aq) + 3I^-(aq) + 2H^+(aq) \longrightarrow I_3^-(aq) + 2H_2O(l)$; rate = $k[H_2O_2][I^-]$

Plan We inspect the exponents in the rate law, *not* the coefficients of the balanced equation, to find the individual orders, and then take their sum to find the overall reaction order.

Solution **(a)** The exponent of [NO] is 2, so the reaction is second order with respect to NO, first order with respect to O_2, and third order overall.

(b) The reaction is $\frac{3}{2}$ order in CH_3CHO and $\frac{3}{2}$ order overall.

(c) The reaction is first order in H_2O_2, first order in I^-, and second order overall.

The reactant H^+ does not appear in the rate law, so the reaction is zero order in H^+.

Check Be sure that each reactant has an order and that the sum of the individual orders gives the overall order.

Follow-Up Problem 16.2 Experiment shows that the reaction

$$5Br^-(aq) + BrO_3^-(aq) + 6H^+(aq) \longrightarrow 3Br_2(l) + 3H_2O(l)$$

obeys this rate law: rate $= k[Br^-][BrO_3^-][H^+]^2$. What is the reaction order in each reactant and the overall reaction order?

Determining Reaction Orders by Changing Reactant Concentrations Now let's see how reaction orders are found *before* the rate law is known. Before looking at a real reaction, we'll go through the process for substances A and B in this reaction:

$$A + 2B \longrightarrow C + D$$

The rate law, expressed in general terms, is

$$\text{Rate} = k[A]^m[B]^n$$

To find the values of m and n, *we run a series of experiments in which one reactant concentration changes while the other is kept constant, and we measure the effect on the initial rate in each case.* Table 16.2 shows the results.

Table 16.2 Initial Rates for the Reaction Between A and B

Experiment	Initial Rate (mol/L·s)	Initial [A] (mol/L)	Initial [B] (mol/L)
1	1.75×10^{-3}	2.50×10^{-2}	3.00×10^{-2}
2	3.50×10^{-3}	5.00×10^{-2}	3.00×10^{-2}
3	3.50×10^{-3}	2.50×10^{-2}	6.00×10^{-2}
4	7.00×10^{-3}	5.00×10^{-2}	6.00×10^{-2}

1. *Finding m, the order with respect to A.* By comparing experiments 1 and 2, in which [A] doubles and [B] is constant, we can obtain m. First, we take the ratio of the general rate laws for thse two experiments:

$$\frac{\text{Rate 2}}{\text{Rate 1}} = \frac{k[A]_2^m[B]_2^n}{k[A]_1^m[B]_1^n}$$

where $[A]_2$ is the concentration of A in experiment 2, $[B]_1$ is the concentration of B in experiment 1, and so forth. Because k is a constant and [B] does not change between these two experiments, those quantities cancel:

$$\frac{\text{Rate 2}}{\text{Rate 1}} = \frac{\cancel{k}[A]_2^m\cancel{[B]_2^n}}{\cancel{k}[A]_1^m\cancel{[B]_1^n}} = \frac{[A]_2^m}{[A]_1^m} = \left(\frac{[A]_2}{[A]_1}\right)^m$$

Substituting the values from Table 16.2, we have

$$\frac{3.50\times10^{-3}\ \text{mol/L·s}}{1.75\times10^{-3}\ \text{mol/L·s}} = \left(\frac{5.00\times10^{-2}\ \text{mol/L}}{2.50\times10^{-2}\ \text{mol/L}}\right)^m$$

Dividing, we obtain

$$2.00 = (2.00)^m, \qquad \text{so } m = 1$$

Thus, the reaction is first order in A, because when [A] doubles, the rate doubles.

2. *Finding n, the order with respect to B.* To find n, we compare experiments 3 and 1 in which [A] is held constant and [B] doubles:

$$\frac{\text{Rate 3}}{\text{Rate 1}} = \frac{k[A]_3^m\ [B]_3^n}{k[A]_1^m\ [B]_1^n}$$

As before, k is a constant, and in this pair of experiments, [A] does not change, so those quantities cancel, and we have

$$\frac{\text{Rate 3}}{\text{Rate 1}} = \frac{\cancel{k}\cancel{[A]_3^m}[B]_3^n}{\cancel{k}\cancel{[A]_1^m}[B]_1^n} = \frac{[B]_3^n}{[B]_1^n} = \left(\frac{[B]_3}{[B]_1}\right)^n$$

The actual values give

$$\frac{3.50\times10^{-3}\ \text{mol/L·s}}{1.75\times10^{-3}\ \text{mol/L·s}} = \left(\frac{6.00\times10^{-2}\ \text{mol/L}}{3.00\times10^{-2}\ \text{mol/L}}\right)^n$$

Dividing, we obtain

$$2.00 = (2.00)^n, \qquad \text{so } n = 1$$

Thus, the reaction is also first order in B because when [B] doubles, the rate doubles. We can check this conclusion from experiment 4: when *both* [A] and [B] double, the rate should quadruple, and it does. Thus, the rate law, with m and n equal to 1, is

$$\text{Rate} = k[\text{A}][\text{B}]$$

Note, especially, that while the order with respect to B is 1, the coefficient of B in the balanced equation is 2. Thus, as we said earlier, *reaction orders must be determined from experiment.*

Next, let's go through this process for a real reaction, the one between oxygen and nitrogen monoxide, a key step in the formation of acid rain and in the industrial production of nitric acid:

$$O_2(g) + 2NO(g) \longrightarrow 2NO_2(g)$$

The general rate law is

$$\text{Rate} = k[O_2]^m[\text{NO}]^n$$

Table 16.3 shows experiments that change one reactant concentration while keeping the other constant. If we compare experiments 1 and 2, we see the effect of doubling $[O_2]$ on the rate. First, we take the ratio of their rate laws:

$$\frac{\text{Rate 2}}{\text{Rate 1}} = \frac{k[O_2]_2^m[\text{NO}]_2^n}{k[O_2]_1^m[\text{NO}]_1^n}$$

As before, the constant quantities—k and [NO]—cancel:

$$\frac{\text{Rate 2}}{\text{Rate 1}} = \frac{\cancel{k}[O_2]_2^m\cancel{[\text{NO}]_2^n}}{\cancel{k}[O_2]_1^m\cancel{[\text{NO}]_1^n}} = \frac{[O_2]_2^m}{[O_2]_1^m} = \left(\frac{[O_2]_2}{[O_2]_1}\right)^m$$

Table 16.3 Initial Rates for the Reaction Between O_2 and NO

Experiment	Initial Rate (mol/L·s)	Initial Reactant Concentrations (mol/L) $[O_2]$	[NO]
1	3.21×10^{-3}	1.10×10^{-2}	1.30×10^{-2}
2	6.40×10^{-3}	2.20×10^{-2}	1.30×10^{-2}
3	12.8×10^{-3}	1.10×10^{-2}	2.60×10^{-2}
4	9.60×10^{-3}	3.30×10^{-2}	1.30×10^{-2}
5	28.8×10^{-3}	1.10×10^{-2}	3.90×10^{-2}

Substituting the values from Table 16.3, we obtain

$$\frac{6.40\times10^{-3}\ \text{mol/L·s}}{3.21\times10^{-3}\ \text{mol/L·s}} = \left(\frac{2.20\times10^{-2}\ \text{mol/L}}{1.10\times10^{-2}\ \text{mol/L}}\right)^m$$

Dividing, we obtain

$$1.99 = (2.00)^m$$

Rounding to one significant figure gives

$$2 = 2^m, \qquad \text{so } m = 1$$

Sometimes, the exponent is not as easy to find by inspection as it is here. In those cases, we solve for m with an equation of the form $a = b^m$:

$$m = \frac{\log a}{\log b} = \frac{\log 1.99}{\log 2.00} = 0.993$$

which rounds to 1. Thus, the reaction is first order in O_2: when $[O_2]$ doubles, the rate doubles.

To find the order with respect to NO, we compare experiments 3 and 1, in which $[O_2]$ is held constant and [NO] is doubled:

$$\frac{\text{Rate 3}}{\text{Rate 1}} = \frac{k[O_2]_3^m[NO]_3^n}{k[O_2]_1^m[NO]_1^n}$$

Canceling the constant k and unchanging $[O_2]$, we have

$$\frac{\text{Rate 3}}{\text{Rate 1}} = \left(\frac{[NO]_3}{[NO]_1}\right)^n$$

The actual values give

$$\frac{12.8\times10^{-3}\text{ mol/L·s}}{3.21\times10^{-3}\text{ mol/L·s}} = \left(\frac{2.60\times10^{-2}\text{ mol/L}}{1.30\times10^{-2}\text{ mol/L}}\right)^n$$

Dividing, we obtain

$$3.99 = (2.00)^n$$

Solving for n:

$$n = \frac{\log 3.99}{\log 2.00} = 2.00 \quad (\text{or } 2)$$

The reaction is second order in NO: when [NO] doubles, the rate quadruples. Thus, the actual rate law is

$$\text{Rate} = k[O_2][NO]^2$$

In this case, the reaction orders happen to be the same as the equation coefficients; nevertheless, they must *always* be determined by experiment.

The next two sample problems offer practice with this approach; the first is based on data and the second on molecular scenes.

Sample Problem 16.3 Determining Reaction Orders from Rate Data

Problem Many gaseous reactions occur in car engines and exhaust systems. One of these is

$$NO_2(g) + CO(g) \longrightarrow NO(g) + CO_2(g) \qquad \text{rate} = k[NO_2]^m[CO]^n$$

Use the following data to determine the individual and overall reaction orders:

Experiment	Initial Rate (mol/L·s)	Initial $[NO_2]$ (mol/L)	Initial [CO] (mol/L)
1	0.0050	0.10	0.10
2	0.080	0.40	0.10
3	0.0050	0.10	0.20

Plan We need to solve the general rate law for m and for n and then add those orders to get the overall order. To solve for each exponent, we proceed as in the text, taking the ratio of the rate laws for two experiments in which only the reactant in question changes.

Solution Calculating m in $[NO_2]^m$: We take the ratio of the rate laws for experiments 1 and 2, in which $[NO_2]$ varies but [CO] is constant:

$$\frac{\text{Rate 2}}{\text{Rate 1}} = \frac{k[NO_2]_2^m[CO]_2^n}{k[NO_2]_1^m[CO]_1^n} = \left(\frac{[NO_2]_2}{[NO_2]_1}\right)^m \quad \text{or} \quad \frac{0.080\text{ mol/L·s}}{0.0050\text{ mol/L·s}} = \left(\frac{0.40\text{ mol/L}}{0.10\text{ mol/L}}\right)^m$$

This gives $16 = (4.0)^m$, so we have $m = \log 16/\log 4.0 = 2.0$. The reaction is second order in NO_2.

Calculating n in $[CO]^n$: We take the ratio of the rate laws for experiments 1 and 3, in which [CO] varies but $[NO_2]$ is constant:

$$\frac{\text{Rate 3}}{\text{Rate 1}} = \frac{k[NO_2]_3^2[CO]_3^n}{k[NO_2]_1^2[CO]_1^n} = \left(\frac{[CO]_3}{[CO]_1}\right)^n \quad \text{or} \quad \frac{0.0050\text{ mol/L·s}}{0.0050\text{ mol/L·s}} = \left(\frac{0.20\text{ mol/L}}{0.10\text{ mol/L}}\right)^n$$

We have $1.0 = (2.0)^n$, so $n = 0$. The rate does not change when [CO] varies, so the reaction is zero order in CO.

Therefore, the rate law is

$$\text{Rate} = k[NO_2]^2[CO]^0 = k[NO_2]^2(1) = k[NO_2]^2$$

The reaction is second order overall.

Check A good check is to reason through the orders. If $m = 1$, quadrupling $[NO_2]$ would quadruple the rate; but the rate *more* than quadruples, so $m > 1$. If $m = 2$, quadrupling $[NO_2]$ would increase the rate by a factor of 16 (4^2). The ratio of rates is $0.080/0.005 = 16$, so $m = 2$. In contrast, increasing [CO] has no effect on the rate, which can happen only if $[CO]^n = 1$, so $n = 0$.

Follow-Up Problem 16.3 Find the rate law and the individual and overall reaction orders for the reaction $H_2 + I_2 \longrightarrow 2HI$ using the following data at 450°C:

Experiment	Initial Rate (mol/L·s)	Initial $[H_2]$ (mol/L)	Initial $[I_2]$ (mol/L)
1	1.9×10^{-23}	0.0113	0.0011
2	1.1×10^{-22}	0.0220	0.0033
3	9.3×10^{-23}	0.0550	0.0011
4	1.9×10^{-22}	0.0220	0.0056

Sample Problem 16.4 Determining Reaction Orders from Molecular Scenes

Problem At a particular temperature and volume, two gases, A (*red*) and B (*blue*), react. The following molecular scenes represent starting mixtures for four experiments:

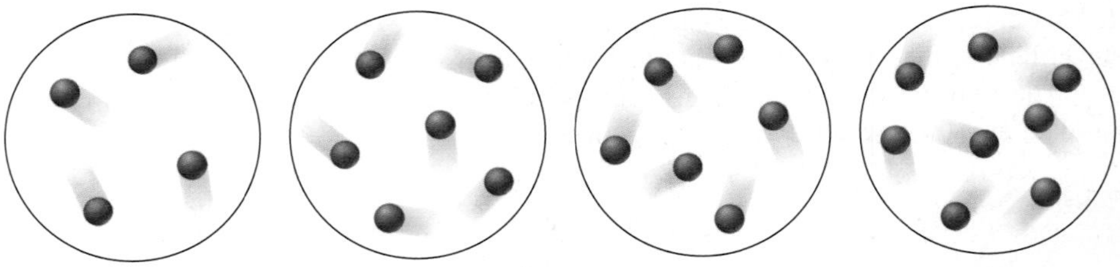

Expt no.:	1	2	3	4
Initial rate (mol/L·s):	0.50×10^{-4}	1.0×10^{-4}	2.0×10^{-4}	?

(a) What is the reaction order with respect to A? With respect to B? The overall order?
(b) Write the rate law for the reaction.
(c) Predict the initial rate of Expt 4.

Plan (a) As before, we find the individual reaction orders by seeing how a change in each reactant changes the rate. In this case, however, instead of using concentration data, we count numbers of particles. The sum of the individual orders is the overall order. **(b)** To write the rate law, we use the orders from part (a) as exponents in the general rate law. **(c)** Using the results from Expts 1 through 3 and the rate law from part (b), we find the unknown initial rate of Expt 4.

Solution (a) Finding the individual and overall orders. For reactant A (*red*): Expts 1 and 2 show that when the number of particles of A doubles (from 2 to 4), with the number of particles of B constant (at 2), the rate doubles (from 0.5×10^{-4} mol/L·s to 1.0×10^{-4} mol/L·s). Thus, the order with respect to A is 1. For reactant B (*blue*): Expts 1 and 3 show that when the number of particles of B doubles (from 2 to 4), with the number of particles of A constant (at 2), the rate quadruples (from 0.5×10^{-4} mol/L·s to 2.0×10^{-4} mol/L·s). Thus, the order with respect to B is 2. The overall order is $1 + 2 = 3$.
(b) Writing the rate law: The general rate law is rate $= k[A]^m[B]^n$, so we have

$$\text{Rate} = k[A][B]^2$$

(c) Finding the initial rate of Expt 4: There are several possibilities, but let's compare Expts 3 and 4, in which the number of particles of A doubles (from 2 to 4) and the number of particles of B doesn't change. Since the rate law shows that the reaction is first order in A, the initial rate in Expt 4 should be double the initial rate in Expt 3, or 4.0×10^{-4} mol/L·s.

Check A good check is to compare other pairs of experiments. **(a)** Comparing Expts 2 and 3 shows that the number of B doubles, which causes the rate to quadruple, and the number of A decreases by half, which causes the rate to halve; so the overall rate change should double (from 1.0×10^{-4} mol/L·s to 2.0×10^{-4} mol/L·s), which it does. **(c)** Comparing Expts 2 and 4, in which the number of A is constant and the number of B doubles, the rate should quadruple, which means the initial rate of Expt 4 would be 4.0×10^{-4} mol/L·s, as we found.

Follow-Up Problem 16.4 The scenes below show three experiments at a given temperature and volume involving reactants X (*black*) and Y (*green*):

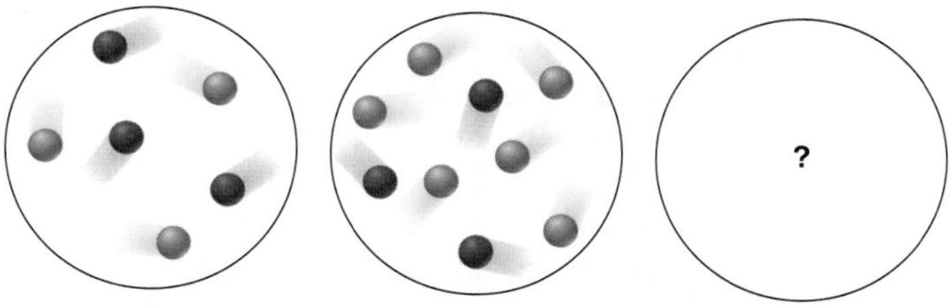

If the rate law for the reaction is rate = $k[X]^2$: **(a)** What is the initial rate of Expt 2? **(b)** Draw a scene for Expt 3 that involves a single change of the scene for Expt 1.

Determining the Rate Constant

Let's find the rate constant for the reaction of O_2 and NO. With the rate, reactant concentrations, and reaction orders known, the sole remaining unknown in the rate law is the rate constant, k. We can use data from any of the experiments in Table 16.3 to solve for k. From experiment 1, for instance, we have

$$\text{Rate} = k[O_2]_1[NO]_1^2$$

$$k = \frac{\text{rate 1}}{[O_2]_1[NO]_1^2} = \frac{3.21\times10^{-3}\ \text{mol/L·s}}{(1.10\times10^{-2}\ \text{mol/L})(1.30\times10^{-2}\ \text{mol/L})^2}$$

$$= \frac{3.21\times10^{-3}\ \text{mol/L·s}}{1.86\times10^{-6}\ \text{mol}^3/\text{L}^3} = 1.73\times10^3\ \text{L}^2/\text{mol}^2\text{·s}$$

Always check that the values of k for a series of experiments are constant within experimental error. To three significant figures, the average value of k for the five experiments in Table 16.3 is 1.72×10^3 L²/mol²·s.

With concentrations in mol/L and the reaction rate in units of mol/L·time, the units for k depend on the order of the reaction and, of course, the time unit. For this reaction, the units for k, L²/mol²·s, are required to give a rate with units of mol/L·s:

$$\frac{\text{mol}}{\text{L·s}} = \frac{\text{L}^2}{\text{mol}^2\text{·s}} \times \frac{\text{mol}}{\text{L}} \times \left(\frac{\text{mol}}{\text{L}}\right)^2$$

The rate constant will *always* have these units for an overall third-order reaction with the time unit in seconds. Table 16.4 shows the units of k for common integer overall orders, but you can always determine the units mathematically.

Figure 16.9 summarizes the steps for studying the kinetics of a reaction.

Table 16.4 Units of the Rate Constant k for Several Overall Reaction Orders

Overall Reaction Order	Units of k (t in seconds)
0	mol/L·s (or mol L^{-1} s^{-1})
1	1/s (or s^{-1})
2	L/mol·s (or L mol^{-1} s^{-1})
3	L²/mol²·s (or L^2 mol^{-2} s^{-1})

General formula:

$$\text{Units of } k = \frac{\left(\frac{\text{L}}{\text{mol}}\right)^{\text{order}-1}}{\text{unit of } t}$$

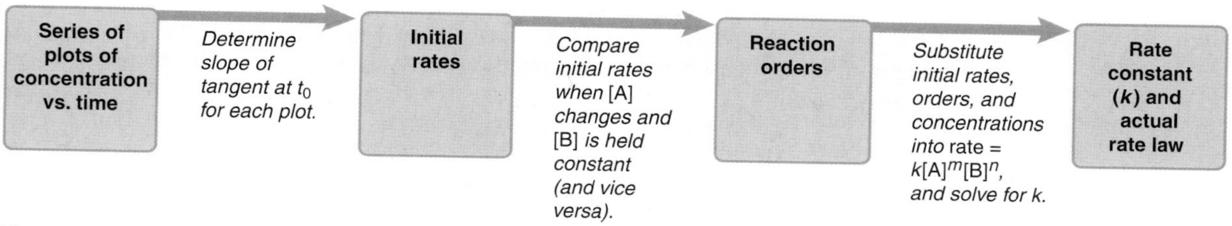

Figure 16.9 Information sequence to determine the kinetic parameters of a reaction.

Summary of Section 16.3

- An experimentally determined rate law shows how the rate of a reaction depends on concentration. Considering only initial rates (that is, no products), the expression for a general rate law is rate $= k[A]^m[B]^n \cdot\cdot\cdot$. This reaction is mth order with respect to A and nth order with respect to B; the overall reaction order is $m + n$.
- With an accurate method for obtaining initial rates, reaction orders are determined experimentally by varying the concentration of one reactant at a time to see its effect on the rate.
- By substituting the known rate, concentrations, and reaction orders into the rate law, we solve for the rate constant, k.

16.4 • INTEGRATED RATE LAWS: CONCENTRATION CHANGES OVER TIME

The rate laws we've developed so far tell us the rate or concentration at a given instant, allowing us to answer questions such as "How fast is the reaction proceeding at the moment y moles per liter of A are mixed with z moles per liter of B?" and "What is [B], when [A] is x moles per liter?" By employing different forms of the rate laws, called **integrated rate laws,** we can include time as a variable and answer questions such as "How long will it take to use up x moles per liter of A?" and "What is [A] after y minutes of reaction?"

Integrated Rate Laws for First-, Second-, and Zero-Order Reactions

As we've seen, for a *general first-order reaction,* the rate is the negative of the change in [A] divided by the change in time:

$$\text{Rate} = -\frac{\Delta[A]}{\Delta t}$$

It can also be expressed in terms of the rate law:

$$\text{Rate} = k[A]$$

Setting these two expressions equal to each other gives

$$-\frac{\Delta[A]}{\Delta t} = k[A] \qquad \text{or} \qquad -\frac{\Delta[A]}{[A]} = k\Delta t$$

Through the methods of calculus, we integrate over time to obtain the integrated rate law for a first-order reaction:

$$\ln\frac{[A]_0}{[A]_t} = kt \qquad \text{(first-order reaction; rate} = k[A]) \qquad \textbf{(16.4)}$$

where ln is the natural logarithm, $[A]_0$ is the concentration of A at $t = 0$, and $[A]_t$ is the concentration of A at any time t.

For a *general second-order reaction* involving two reactants, A and B, the expression including time is complex. In the simpler case, the rate law contains only reactant A. Setting the two rate expressions equal to each other gives

$$\text{Rate} = -\frac{\Delta[A]}{\Delta t} = k[A]^2 \qquad \text{or} \qquad -\frac{\Delta[A]}{[A]^2} = k\Delta t$$

Integrating over time gives the integrated rate law for a second-order reaction involving one reactant:

$$\frac{1}{[A]_t} - \frac{1}{[A]_0} = kt \qquad \text{(second-order reaction; rate} = k[A]^2) \qquad \textbf{(16.5)}$$

For a *general zero-order reaction*, setting the two rate expressions equal to each other gives

$$\text{Rate} = -\frac{\Delta[A]}{\Delta t} = k[A]^0 = k \qquad \text{or} \qquad -\Delta[A] = k\Delta t$$

Integrating over time gives the integrated rate law for a zero-order reaction:

$$[A]_t - [A]_0 = -kt \qquad \text{(zero-order reaction; rate} = k[A]^0 = k) \qquad (16.6)$$

Sample Problem 16.5 shows one way integrated rate laws are applied.

Sample Problem 16.5 Determining the Reactant Concentration after a Given Time

Problem At 1000°C, cyclobutane (C_4H_8) decomposes in a first-order reaction, with the very high rate constant of 87 s^{-1}, to two molecules of ethylene (C_2H_4).
(a) The initial C_4H_8 concentration is 2.00 *M*. What is the concentration after 0.010 s?
(b) What fraction of C_4H_8 has decomposed in this time?

Plan (a) We must find the concentration of cyclobutane at time *t*, $[C_4H_8]_t$. The problem tells us this is a first-order reaction, so we use the integrated first-order rate law:

$$\ln \frac{[C_4H_8]_0}{[C_4H_8]_t} = kt$$

We know *k* (87 s^{-1}), *t* (0.010 s), and $[C_4H_8]_0$ (2.00 *M*), so we can solve for $[C_4H_8]_t$.
(b) The fraction decomposed is the concentration that has decomposed divided by the initial concentration:

$$\text{Fraction decomposed} = \frac{[C_4H_8]_0 - [C_4H_8]_t}{[C_4H_8]_0}$$

Solution (a) Substituting the data into the integrated rate law:

$$\ln \frac{2.00 \text{ mol/L}}{[C_4H_8]_t} = (87 \text{ s}^{-1})(0.010 \text{ s}) = 0.87$$

Taking the antilog of both sides:

$$\frac{2.00 \text{ mol/L}}{[C_4H_8]_t} = e^{0.87} = 2.4$$

Solving for $[C_4H_8]_t$:

$$[C_4H_8]_t = \frac{2.00 \text{ mol/L}}{2.4} = 0.83 \text{ mol/L}$$

(b) Finding the fraction that has decomposed after 0.010 s:

$$\frac{[C_4H_8]_0 - [C_4H_8]_t}{[C_4H_8]_0} = \frac{2.00 \text{ mol/L} - 0.83 \text{ mol/L}}{2.00 \text{ mol/L}} = 0.58$$

Check The concentration remaining after 0.010 s (0.83 mol/L) is less than the starting concentration (2.00 mol/L), which makes sense. Raising *e* to an exponent slightly less than 1 should give a number (2.4) slightly less than the value of *e* (2.718). Moreover, the final result makes sense: a high rate constant indicates a fast reaction, so it's not surprising that so much decomposes in such a short time.

Follow-Up Problem 16.5 At 25°C, hydrogen iodide breaks down very slowly to hydrogen and iodine: rate = $k[HI]^2$. The rate constant at 25°C is 2.4×10^{-21} L/mol·s. If 0.0100 mol of HI(*g*) is placed in a 1.0-L container, how long will it take for the concentration of HI to reach 0.00900 mol/L (10.0% reacted)?

Determining Reaction Orders from an Integrated Rate Law

In Sample Problem 16.3, we found the reaction orders using rate data. If rate data are not available, we rearrange the integrated rate law into an equation for a straight line, $y = mx + b$, where m is the slope and b is the y-axis intercept. We then use a graphical method to find the order:

- For a *first-order reaction,* we have

$$\ln \frac{[\text{A}]_0}{[\text{A}]_t} = kt$$

From Appendix A, we know that $\ln \frac{a}{b} = \ln a - \ln b$, so we have

$$\ln [\text{A}]_0 - \ln [\text{A}]_t = kt$$

Rearranging gives

$$\underset{y}{\ln [\text{A}]_t} \underset{=}{=} \underset{mx}{-kt} \underset{+}{+} \underset{b}{\ln [\text{A}]_0}$$

Therefore, a plot of $\ln [\text{A}]_t$ vs. t gives a straight line with slope $= -k$ and y intercept $= \ln [\text{A}]_0$ (Figure 16.10A).

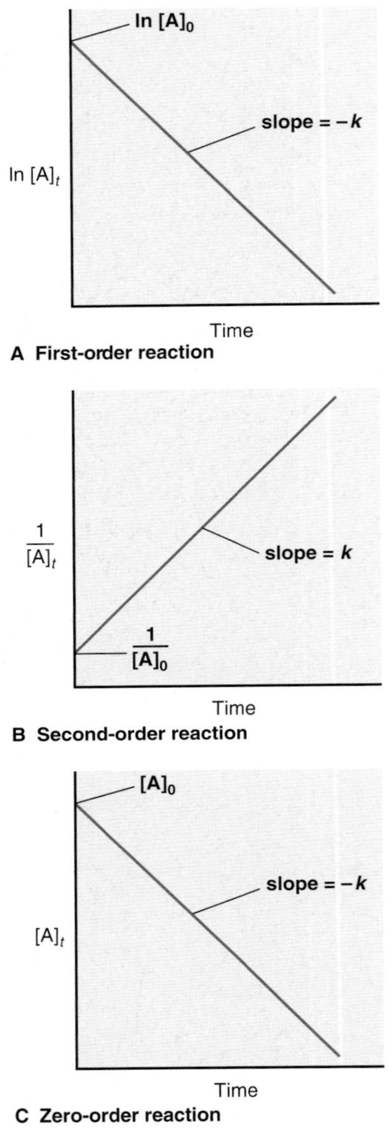

Figure 16.10 Graphical method for finding the reaction order from the integrated rate law.

- For a *second-order reaction* with one reactant, we have

$$\frac{1}{[\text{A}]_t} - \frac{1}{[\text{A}]_0} = kt$$

Rearranging gives

$$\underset{y}{\frac{1}{[\text{A}]_t}} = \underset{mx}{kt} + \underset{b}{\frac{1}{[\text{A}]_0}}$$

In this case, a plot of $1/[\text{A}]_t$ vs. t gives a straight line with slope $= k$ and y intercept $= 1/[\text{A}]_0$ (Figure 16.10B).

- For a *zero-order reaction,* we have

$$[\text{A}]_t - [\text{A}]_0 = -kt$$

Rearranging gives

$$\underset{y}{[\text{A}]_t} = \underset{mx}{-kt} + \underset{b}{[\text{A}]_0}$$

A plot of $[\text{A}]_t$ vs. t gives a straight line with slope $= -k$ and y intercept $= [\text{A}]_0$ (Figure 16.10C).

Some trial-and-error graphical plotting is required to find the reaction order from the concentration and time data:

- If you obtain a straight line when you plot ln [reactant] vs. t, the reaction is *first order* with respect to that reactant.
- If you obtain a straight line when you plot 1/[reactant] vs. t, the reaction is *second order* with respect to that reactant.
- If you obtain a straight line when you plot [reactant] vs. t, the reaction is *zero order* with respect to that reactant.

Figure 16.11 shows how to use this approach to determine the order for the decomposition of N_2O_5. When we plot the data from each column in the table versus time, we find that the plot of $\ln [N_2O_5]$ vs. t *is* linear (part B), while the plots of $[N_2O_5]$ vs. t (part A) and of $1/[N_2O_5]$ vs. t (part C) are *not;* therefore, the decomposition is first order in N_2O_5.

Reaction Half-Life

The **half-life ($t_{1/2}$)** of a reaction is the time it takes for the reactant concentration to reach *half its initial value.* A half-life has time units appropriate for the reaction and

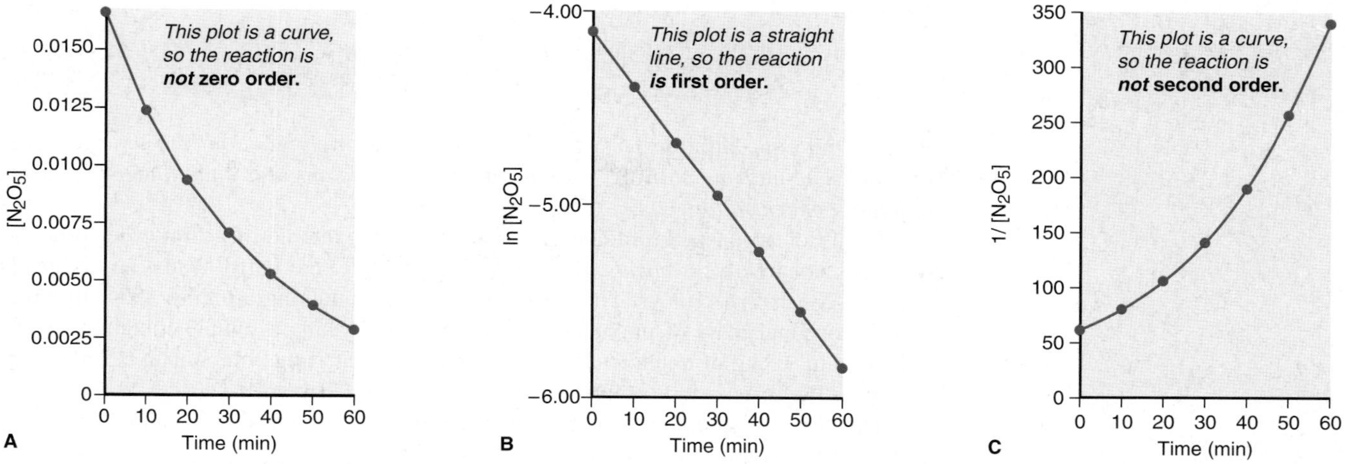

Figure 16.11 Graphical determination of the reaction order for the decomposition of N_2O_5. The time and concentration data in the table are used to obtain the three plots, A, B, and C.

Time (min)	$[N_2O_5]$	ln $[N_2O_5]$	$1/[N_2O_5]$
0	0.0165	−4.104	60.6
10	0.0124	−4.390	80.6
20	0.0093	−4.68	1.1×10^2
30	0.0071	−4.95	1.4×10^2
40	0.0053	−5.24	1.9×10^2
50	0.0039	−5.55	2.6×10^2
60	0.0029	−5.84	3.4×10^2

is characteristic of the reaction at a given temperature. For example, at 45°C, the half-life for the decomposition of N_2O_5, which we know is first order, is 24.0 min. Therefore, if we start with, say, 0.0600 mol/L of N_2O_5 at 45°C, 0.0300 mol/L will have reacted after 24 min (one half-life), and 0.0300 mol/L will remain; after 48 min (two half-lives), 0.0150 mol/L will remain; after 72 min (three half-lives), 0.0075 mol/L will remain, and so forth (Figure 16.12). The mathematical expression for the half-life depends on the overall order of the reaction.

First-Order Reactions We can derive an expression for the half-life of a first-order reaction from the integrated rate law, which is

$$\ln \frac{[A]_0}{[A]_t} = kt$$

By definition, after one half-life, $t = t_{1/2}$, and $[A]_t = \frac{1}{2}[A]_0$. Substituting and canceling $[A]_0$ gives

$$\ln \frac{\cancel{[A]_0}}{\frac{1}{2}\cancel{[A]_0}} = kt_{1/2} \qquad \text{or} \qquad \ln 2 = kt_{1/2}$$

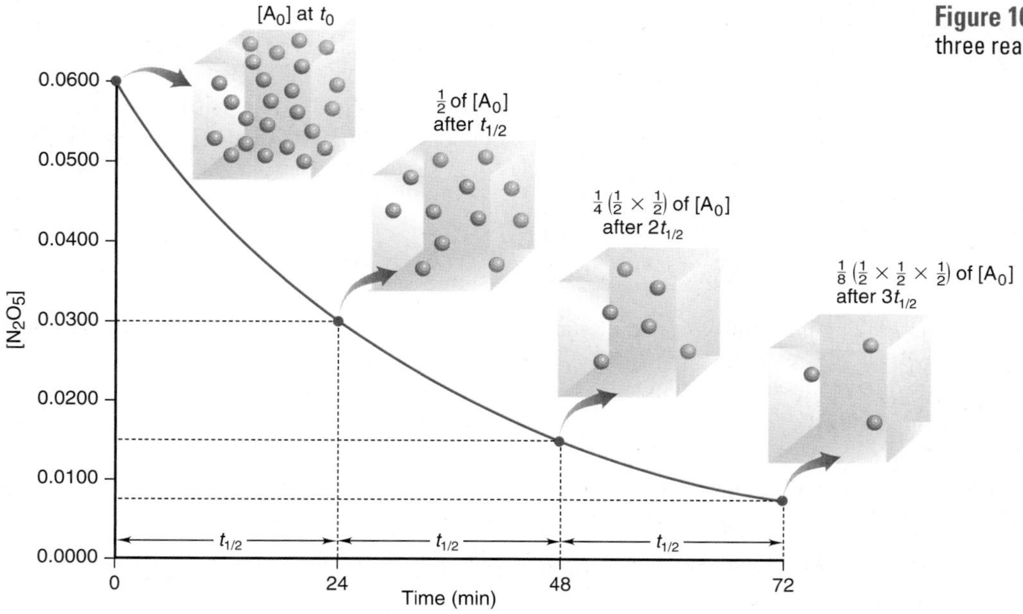

Figure 16.12 A plot of $[N_2O_5]$ vs. time for three reaction half-lives.

Then, solving for $t_{1/2}$, we have

$$t_{1/2} = \frac{\ln 2}{k} = \frac{0.693}{k} \qquad \text{(first-order process; rate} = k[\text{A}]) \qquad (16.7)$$

Because no concentration term appears, *for a first-order reaction, the time it takes to reach one-half the starting concentration is a constant and, thus, independent of reactant concentration.*

Decay of an unstable, radioactive nucleus is an example of a first-order process that does not involve a *chemical* change. For example, the half-life for the decay of uranium-235 is 7.1×10^8 yr. Thus, a sample of ore containing uranium-235 will have half the original mass of uranium-235 after 7.1×10^8 years: a sample containing 1 kg will contain 0.5 kg of uranium-235, a sample containing 1 mg will contain 0.5 mg, and so forth. (We discuss radioactive decay thoroughly in Chapter 24.)

The next two sample problems show some ways to use half-life in calculations: the first is based on molecular scenes.

Sample Problem 16.6 Using Molecular Scenes to Find Quantities at Various Times

Problem Substance A (*green*) decomposes to two other substances, B (*blue*) and C (*yellow*), in a first-order gaseous reaction. The molecular scenes below show a portion of the reaction mixture at two different times:

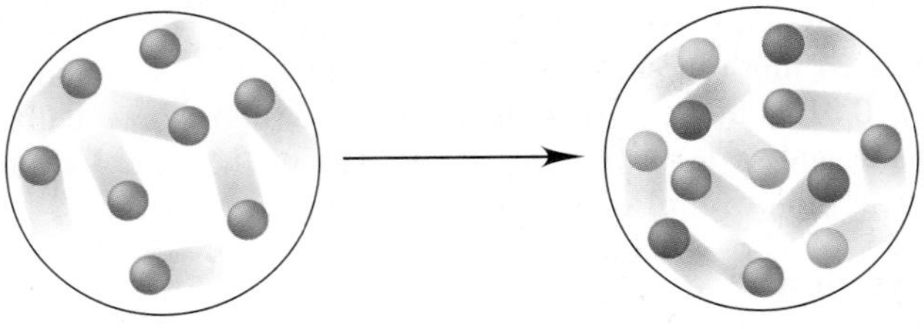

(a) Draw a similar molecular scene of the reaction mixture at $t = 60.0$ s.
(b) Find the rate constant of the reaction.
(c) If the total pressure (P_{total}) of the mixture is 5.00 atm at 90.0 s, what is the partial pressure of substance B (P_B)?

Plan We are shown molecular scenes of a reaction at two times with various numbers of reactant and product particles and have to predict quantities at two later times. **(a)** We count the number of A particles and see that A has decreased by half after 30.0 s; thus, the half-life is 30.0 s. The time $t = 60.0$ s represents two half-lives, so the number of A will decrease by half again, and each A forms one B and one C. **(b)** We substitute the value of the half-life in Equation 16.7 to find k. **(c)** First, we find the numbers of particles at $t = 90.0$ s, which represents three half-lives. To find P_B, we multiply the mole fraction of B, X_B, by P_{total} (5.00 atm) (Chapter 5). To find X_B, we know that the number of particles is equivalent to the number of moles, so we divide the number of B particles by the total number of particles.

Solution **(a)** The number of A particles decreased from 8 to 4 in one half-life (30.0 s), so after two half-lives (60.0 s), the number would be 2 (1/2 of 4) A particles. Each A decomposes to 1 B and 1 C, so 6 (8 – 2) particles of A form 6 particles of B and 6 of C (*see margin*).

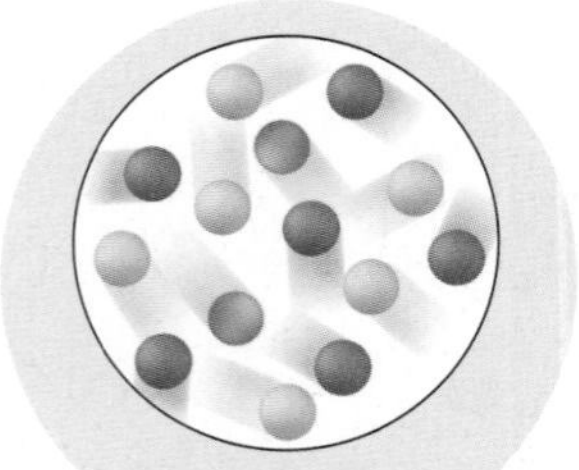

(b) Finding the rate constant, k:

$$t_{1/2} = \frac{0.693}{k} \qquad \text{so} \qquad k = \frac{0.693}{t_{1/2}} = \frac{0.693}{30.0\ \text{s}} = 2.31\times10^{-2}\ \text{s}^{-1}$$

(c) Finding the number of particles after 90.0s: After a third half-life, there would be 1 A, 7 B, and 7 C particles.
Finding the mole fraction of B, X_B:

$$X_B = \frac{7}{1 + 7 + 7} = \frac{7}{15} = 0.467$$

Finding the partial pressure of B, P_B:

$$P_B = X_B \times P_{\text{total}} = 0.467 \times 5.00\ \text{atm} = 2.33\ \text{atm}$$

Check For (b), rounding gives 0.7/30, which is a bit over 0.02, so the answer seems correct. For (c), X_B is almost 0.5, so P_B is a bit less than half of 5 atm, or <2.5 atm.

Follow-Up Problem 16.6 Substance X (*black*) changes to substance Y (*red*) in a first-order gaseous reaction. The scenes below represent the reaction mixture in cubic containers at two different times:

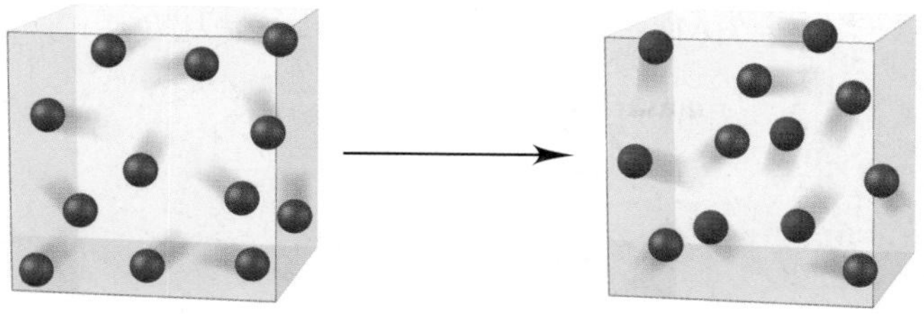

$t = 0.0$ min $\qquad$ $t = 2.5$ min

(a) Draw a scene that represents the mixture at 5.0 min. **(b)** If each sphere represents 0.20 mol of particles and the volume of the cubic container is 0.50 L, what is the molarity of X at 10.0 min?

Sample Problem 16.7 Determining the Half-Life of a First-Order Reaction

Problem Cyclopropane is the smallest cyclic hydrocarbon. Because its 60° bond angles reduce orbital overlap, its bonds are weak. As a result, it is thermally unstable and rearranges to propene at 1000°C via the following first-order reaction:

$$\text{(cyclo-}CH_2\text{—}H_2C\text{—}CH_2)(g) \xrightarrow{\Delta} CH_3\text{—}CH\text{=}CH_2(g)$$

The rate constant is 9.2 s^{-1}. **(a)** What is the half-life of the reaction? **(b)** How long does it take for the concentration of cyclopropane to reach one-quarter of the initial value?

Plan (a) The cyclopropane rearrangement is first order, so to find $t_{1/2}$ we use Equation 16.7 and substitute for k (9.2 s^{-1}). **(b)** Each half-life decreases the concentration to one-half of its initial value, so two half-lives decrease it to one-quarter.

Solution (a) Solving for $t_{1/2}$:

$$t_{1/2} = \frac{\ln 2}{k} = \frac{0.693}{9.2\ s^{-1}} = 0.075\ s$$

It takes 0.075 s for half the cyclopropane to form propene at this temperature.
(b) Finding the time to reach one-quarter of the initial concentration:

$$\text{Time} = 2(t_{1/2}) = 2(0.075\ s) = 0.15\ s$$

Check For part (a), rounding gives $0.7/9\ s^{-1} = 0.08$ s, so the answer seems correct.

Follow-Up Problem 16.7 Iodine-123 is used to study thyroid gland function. This radioactive isotope breaks down in a first-order process with a half-life of 13.1 h. What is the rate constant for the process?

Second-Order Reactions In contrast to the half-life of a first-order reaction, the half-life of a second-order reaction *does* depend on reactant concentration:

$$t_{1/2} = \frac{1}{k[A]_0} \qquad \text{(second-order process; rate } = k[A]^2\text{)}$$

Note that here *the half-life is* ***inversely*** *proportional to the initial reactant concentration.* This relationship means that a second-order reaction with a high initial reactant concentration has a *shorter* half-life, and one with a low initial reactant concentration has a *longer* half-life.

Zero-Order Reactions In contrast to the half-life of a second-order reaction, *the half-life of a zero-order reaction is* ***directly*** *proportional to the initial reactant concentration:*

$$t_{1/2} = \frac{[A]_0}{2k} \qquad \text{(zero-order process; rate } = k\text{)}$$

Thus, if a zero-order reaction begins with a high reactant concentration, it has a longer half-life than if it begins with a low reactant concentration.

Table 16.5 An Overview of Zero-Order, First-Order, and Simple Second-Order Reactions

	Zero Order	First Order	Second Order
Rate law	rate = k	rate = $k[A]$	rate = $k[A]^2$
Units for k	mol/L·s	1/s	L/mol·s
Half-life	$\frac{[A]_0}{2k}$	$\frac{\ln 2}{k}$	$\frac{1}{k[A]_0}$
Integrated rate law in straight-line form	$[A]_t = -kt + [A]_0$	$\ln [A]_t = -kt + \ln [A]_0$	$1/[A]_t = kt + 1/[A]_0$
Plot for straight line	$[A]_t$ vs. t	$\ln [A]_t$ vs. t	$1/[A]_t$ vs. t
Slope, y intercept	$-k$, $[A]_0$	$-k$, $\ln [A]_0$	k, $1/[A]_0$

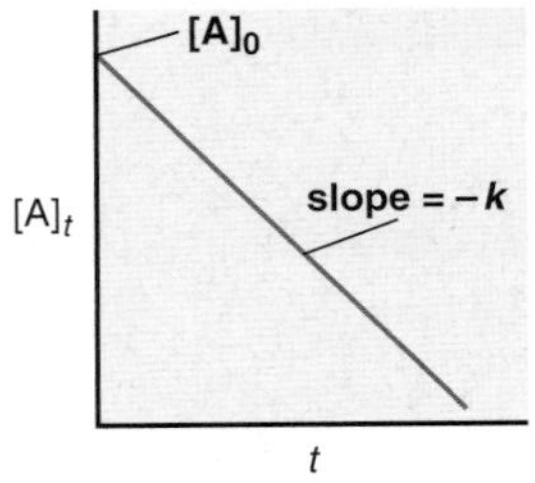

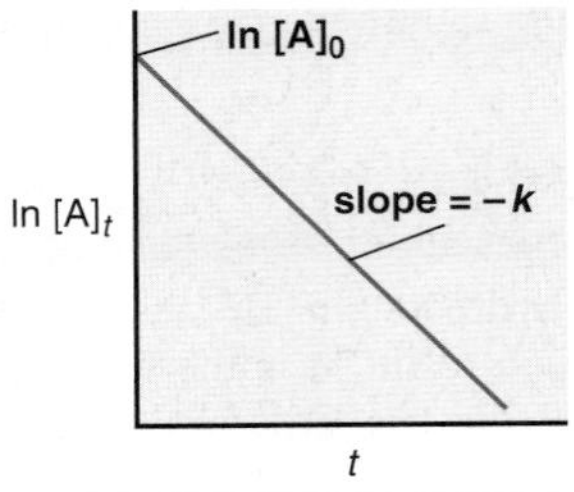

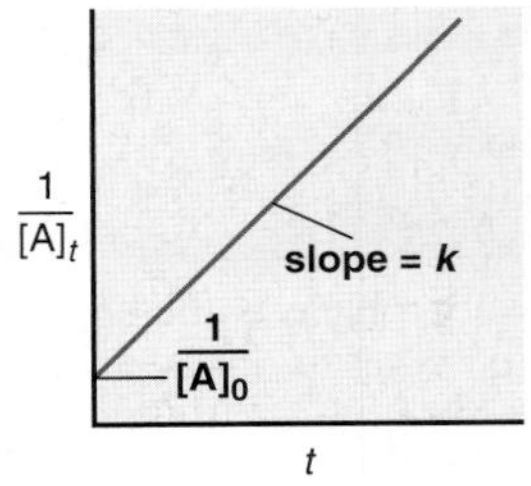

Table 16.5 summarizes the features of zero-, first-, and second-order reactions.

Summary of Section 16.4

- Integrated rate laws are used to find either the time needed to reach a certain concentration of reactant or the concentration present after a given time.
- Rearrangements of the integrated rate laws that give equations in the form of a straight line allow us to determine reaction orders and rate constants graphically.
- The half-life is the time needed for the reactant concentration to reach half its initial value; for first-order reactions, the half-life is constant, that is, independent of concentration.

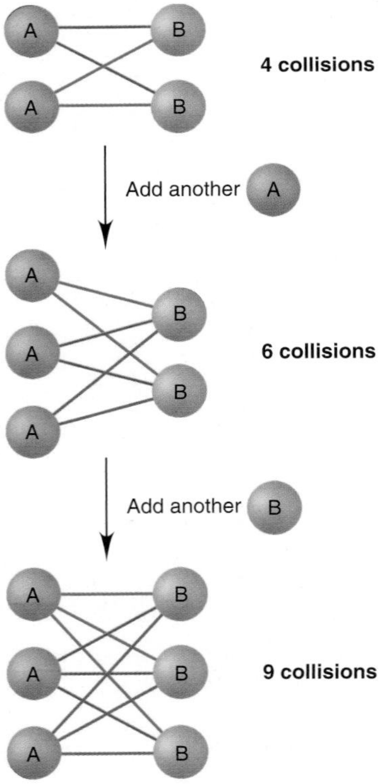

Figure 16.13 The number of possible collisions is the product, not the sum, of reactant concentrations.

16.5 • THEORIES OF CHEMICAL KINETICS

As was pointed out at the beginning of the chapter, concentration and temperature have major effects on reaction rate. Chemists employ two models—*collision theory* and *transition state theory*—to explain these effects.

Collision Theory: Basis of the Rate Law

The basic tenet of **collision theory** is that particles—atoms, molecules, or ions—must collide to react. But number of collisions can't be the only factor determining rate, or all reactions would be over in an instant. For example, at 1 atm and 20°C, the N_2 and O_2 molecules in 1 mL of air experience about 10^{27} collisions per second. If all that was needed for a reaction to occur was an N_2 molecule colliding with an O_2 molecule, our atmosphere would consist of almost all NO; in fact, only traces are present. Thus, this theory also relies on the concepts of collision energy and molecular structure to explain the effects of concentration and temperature on rate.

Why Concentrations Are Multiplied in the Rate Law Particles must collide to react, so the collision frequency, the number of collisions per unit time, provides an *upper limit* on how fast a reaction can take place. In its basic form, collision theory deals with one-step reactions, those in which two particles collide and form products: $A + B \longrightarrow$ products. Suppose we have only two particles of A and two of B confined in a vessel. Figure 16.13 shows that four A-B collisions are possible. The laws of probability tell us that the number of collisions depends on the *product* of

Expt	[Ester]	[H_2O]	T (K)	Rate (mol/L•s)	k (L/mol•s)
1	0.100	0.200	288	1.04×10^{-3}	0.0521
2	0.100	0.200	298	2.02×10^{-3}	0.101
3	0.100	0.200	308	3.68×10^{-3}	0.184
4	0.100	0.200	318	6.64×10^{-3}	0.332

A

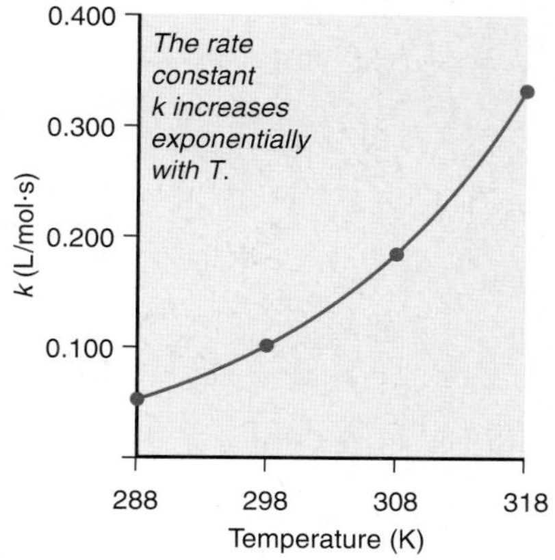

B

Figure 16.14 Increase of the rate constant with temperature for the hydrolysis of an ester.

the numbers of reactant particles, not their sum. Thus, when we add another particle of A, six A-B collisions (3×2) are possible, not just five ($3 + 2$). Similarly, when we add another particle of B, nine A-B collisions (3×3) are possible, not just six ($3 + 3$). Thus, collision theory explains why we *multiply* the concentrations in the rate law to obtain the observed rate.

The Effect of Temperature on the Rate Constant and the Rate Temperature typically has a dramatic effect on reaction rate: for many reactions near room temperature, an increase of 10 K (10°C) doubles or triples the rate. Figure 16.14A shows kinetic data for an organic reaction—hydrolysis, or reaction with water, of the ester ethyl acetate. To understand the effect of temperature, we measure concentrations and times for the reaction run at different temperatures. Solving each rate expression for k and plotting the results (Figure 16.14B), we find that *k increases exponentially as T increases.*

These results are consistent with findings obtained in 1889 by the Swedish chemist Svante Arrhenius. In its modern form, the **Arrhenius equation** is

$$k = Ae^{-E_a/RT} \qquad (16.8)$$

where k is the rate constant, e is the base of natural logarithms, T is the absolute temperature, and R is the universal gas constant. (We'll focus on the term E_a in the next subsection and the term A a bit later.) Note the relationship between k and T, especially that T is in the denominator of a negative exponent. Thus, *as T increases, the value of the negative exponent becomes smaller, which means k becomes larger, so the rate increases:*

$$\text{Higher } T \Longrightarrow \text{larger } k \Longrightarrow \text{increased rate}$$

The Central Importance of Activation Energy The effect of temperature on k is closely related to the **activation energy (E_a)** of a reaction, an energy *threshold* that the colliding molecules must exceed in order to react. As an analogy, in order to succeed at the high jump, an athlete must exert at least enough energy to get over the bar. Similarly, if reactant molecules collide with a certain minimum energy, they reach an *activated state,* from which they can change to products (Figure 16.15).

As you can see from Figure 16.15, a reversible reaction has two activation energies. The activation energy for the forward reaction, $E_{a(fwd)}$, is the energy difference between the activated state and the reactants; the activation energy for the reverse

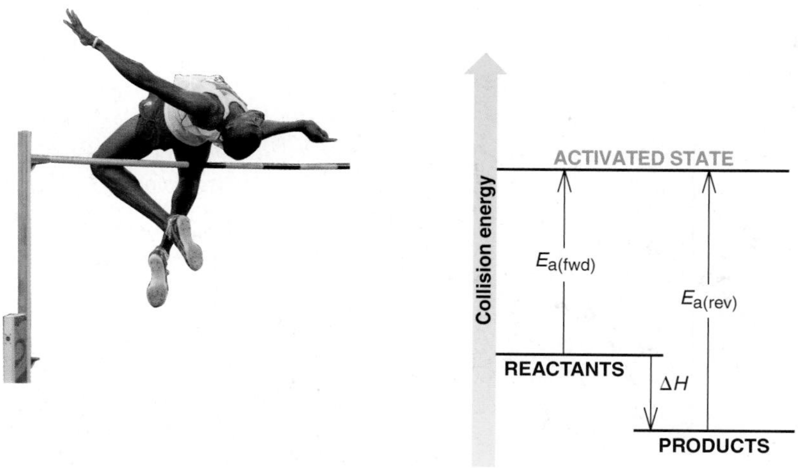

Figure 16.15 **Energy-level diagram for a reaction.** Like a high jumper with enough energy to go over the bar, molecules must collide with enough energy, E_a, to reach an activated state. (This reaction is reversible and is exothermic in the forward direction.)

reaction, $E_{a(rev)}$, is the energy difference between the activated state and the products. The reaction represented in the diagram is exothermic ($\Delta H_{rxn} < 0$) in the forward direction. Thus, the products are at a lower energy than the reactants, and $E_{a(fwd)}$ is less than $E_{a(rev)}$. This difference equals the heat of reaction, ΔH_{rxn}:

$$\Delta H_{rxn} = E_{a(fwd)} - E_{a(rev)} \tag{16.9}$$

The Effect of Temperature on Collision Energy A rise in temperature has two effects on moving particles: it causes a higher collision *frequency* and a higher collision *energy*. Let's see how each affects rate.

- *Collision frequency*. If particles move faster, they collide more often. Calculations show that a 10 K rise in temperature from, say, 288 K to 298 K, increases the average molecular speed by 2%, which would lead to, at most, a 4% increase in rate. Thus, higher collision frequency cannot possibly account for the doubling or tripling of rates observed with a 10 K rise. Indeed, the effect of temperature on collision *frequency* is only a minor factor.
- *Collision energy*. On the other hand, the effect of temperature on collision *energy* is a major factor. At a given temperature, the fraction f of collisions with energy equal to or greater than E_a is

$$f = e^{-E_a/RT}$$

where e is the base of natural logarithms, T is the absolute temperature, and R is the universal gas constant. The right side of this expression appears in the Arrhenius equation (Equation 16.8), which shows that a rise in T causes a larger k. We now see why—because *a rise in temperature enlarges the fraction of collisions with enough energy to exceed* E_a (Figure 16.16).

Table 16.6 The Effect of E_a and T on the Fraction (f) of Collisions with Sufficient Energy to Allow Reaction

E_a (kJ/mol)	f (at T = 298 K)
50	1.70×10^{-9}
75	7.03×10^{-14}
100	2.90×10^{-18}
T	**f (at E_a = 50 kJ/mol)**
25°C (298 K)	1.70×10^{-9}
35°C (308 K)	3.29×10^{-9}
45°C (318 K)	6.12×10^{-9}

Table 16.6 shows that the magnitudes of *both* E_a *and* T *affect the size of this fraction* for the hydrolysis of the ester we discussed above. In the top portion, temperature is held constant, and the fraction of sufficiently energetic collisions shrinks several orders of magnitude with each 25-kJ/mol increase in E_a. (To extend the high jump analogy, as the height of the bar is raised, a smaller fraction of the athletes have enough energy to jump over it.) In the bottom portion, E_a is held constant, and the fraction nearly doubles for each 10 K (10°C) rise in temperature.

Therefore, *the smaller the activation energy (or the higher the temperature), the larger the fraction of sufficiently energetic collisions, the larger the value of k, and the higher the reaction rate:*

Smaller E_a (or higher T) $\Longrightarrow$ larger f $\Longrightarrow$ larger k $\Longrightarrow$ higher rate

Calculating the Activation Energy We can calculate E_a from the Arrhenius equation by taking the natural logarithm of both sides of the equation, which recasts it into the form of an equation for a straight line:

$$k = Ae^{-E_a/RT}$$

$$\ln k = \ln A - \frac{E_a}{R}\left(\frac{1}{T}\right)$$

$$y = b + mx$$

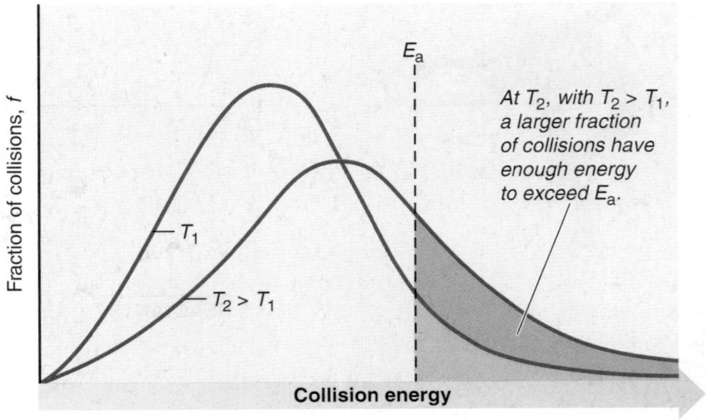

Figure 16.16 The effect of temperature on the distribution of collision energies.

A plot of ln k vs. $1/T$ gives a straight line whose slope is $-E_a/R$ and whose y intercept is ln A (Figure 16.17). We know the constant R, so we can determine E_a graphically from a series of k values at different temperatures.

We can find E_a in another way if we know the rate constants at two temperatures, T_2 and T_1:

$$\ln k_2 = \ln A - \frac{E_a}{R}\left(\frac{1}{T_2}\right) \qquad \ln k_1 = \ln A - \frac{E_a}{R}\left(\frac{1}{T_1}\right)$$

When we subtract ln k_1 from ln k_2, the term ln A drops out and the other terms can be rearranged to give

$$\ln\frac{k_2}{k_1} = -\frac{E_a}{R}\left(\frac{1}{T_2} - \frac{1}{T_1}\right) \qquad (16.10)$$

Then, we can solve for E_a, as in the next sample problem.

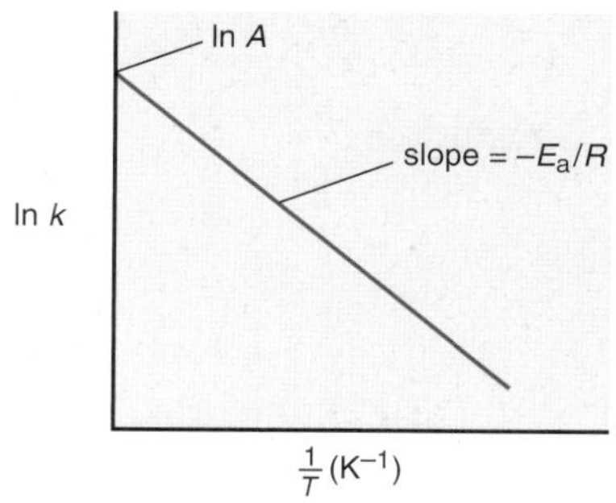

Figure 16.17 Graphical determination of the activation energy.

Sample Problem 16.8 Determining the Energy of Activation

Problem The decomposition of hydrogen iodide, $2HI(g) \longrightarrow H_2(g) + I_2(g)$, has rate constants of 9.51×10^{-9} L/mol·s at 500. K and 1.10×10^{-5} L/mol·s at 600. K. Find E_a.

Plan We are given the rate constants, k_1 and k_2, at two temperatures, T_1 and T_2, so we substitute into Equation 16.10 and solve for E_a.

Solution Rearranging Equation 16.10 to solve for E_a:

$$\ln\frac{k_2}{k_1} = -\frac{E_a}{R}\left(\frac{1}{T_2} - \frac{1}{T_1}\right)$$

$$E_a = -R\left(\ln\frac{k_2}{k_1}\right)\left(\frac{1}{T_2} - \frac{1}{T_1}\right)^{-1}$$

$$= -(8.314 \text{ J/mol·K})\left(\ln\frac{1.10\times10^{-5}\text{ L/mol·s}}{9.51\times10^{-9}\text{ L/mol·s}}\right)\left(\frac{1}{600.\text{ K}} - \frac{1}{500.\text{ K}}\right)^{-1}$$

$$= 1.76\times10^5 \text{ J/mol} = 1.76\times10^2 \text{ kJ/mol}$$

Comment Be sure to retain the same number of significant figures in $1/T$ as you have in T, or a significant error could be introduced. Round to the correct number of significant figures only at the final answer. On most pocket calculators, the expression $(1/T_2 - 1/T_1)$ is entered as follows: $(T_2)(1/x) - (T_1)(1/x) =$

Follow-Up Problem 16.8 The reaction $2NOCl(g) \longrightarrow 2NO(g) + Cl_2(g)$ has an E_a of 1.00×10^2 kJ/mol and a rate constant of 0.286 L/mol·s at 500. K. What is the rate constant at 490. K?

The Effect of Molecular Structure on Rate At ordinary temperatures, the enormous number of collisions per second between reactant particles is reduced by six or more orders of magnitude by counting only those with enough energy to react. And, even this tiny fraction of all collisions is typically much larger than the number of **effective collisions,** those that actually lead to product because *the atoms that become bonded in the product make contact.* Thus, to be effective, a collision must have enough energy *and* the appropriate *molecular orientation.*

In the Arrhenius equation, molecular orientation is contained in the term A:

$$k = Ae^{-E_a/RT}$$

This term is the **frequency factor,** the product of the collision frequency Z and an *orientation probability factor, p,* which is specific for each reaction:

$$A = pZ$$

The factor p is related to the structural complexity of the reactants. You can think of p as the ratio of effectively oriented collisions to all possible collisions. Figure 16.18 shows a few of the collision orientations for the following reaction:

$$NO(g) + NO_3(g) \longrightarrow 2NO_2(g)$$

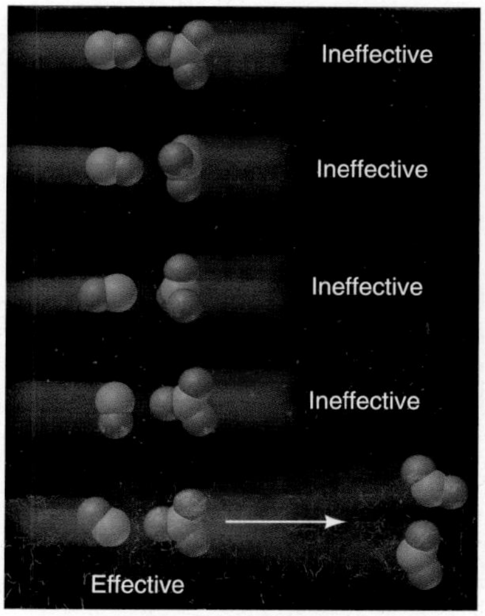

Figure 16.18 The importance of molecular orientation to an effective collision. In the one effective orientation (*bottom*), contact occurs between the atoms that become bonded in the product.

Of the five orientations shown, only one has the effective orientation, with the N of NO making contact with an O of NO_3. Actually, the p value for this reaction is 0.006: only 6 collisions in every 1000 (1 in 167) have the correct orientation.

The more complex the molecular structure, the smaller the p value is. Individual atoms are spherical, so reactions between them have p values near 1: as long as reacting atoms collide with enough energy, the product forms. At the other extreme are biochemical reactions, in which two small molecules (or portions of larger molecules) react only when they collide with enough energy on a specific tiny region of a giant protein. The p value for these reactions is often much less than 10^{-6}, fewer than one in a million. The fact that countless such biochemical reactions are occurring in you right now attests to the astounding number of collisions per second!

Transition State Theory: What the Activation Energy Is Used For

Collision theory explains the importance of effective collisions, and **transition state theory** focuses on the high-energy species that exists at the moment of an effective collision when reactants are becoming product.

Visualizing the Transition State As two molecules approach each other, repulsions between their electron clouds continually increase, so they slow down as some of their kinetic energy is converted to potential energy. If they collide, but the energy of the collision is *less* than the activation energy, the molecules bounce off each other.

However, in a tiny fraction of collisions in which the molecules are moving fast enough, *their kinetic energies push them together with enough force to overcome the repulsions and surpass the activation energy.* And, in an even tinier fraction of these sufficiently energetic collisions, the molecules are oriented effectively. In those cases, nuclei in one molecule attract electrons in the other, atomic orbitals overlap, electron densities shift, and some bonds lengthen and weaken while others shorten and strengthen. At some point during this smooth transformation, *a species with partial bonds exists* that is neither reactant nor product. This very unstable species, called the **transition state** (or **activated complex**) exists only at the instant of highest potential energy. Thus, *the activation energy of a reaction is used to reach the transition state.*

Transition states cannot be isolated, but the work of Ahmed H. Zewail, who received the 1999 Nobel Prize in chemistry, greatly expanded our knowledge of them. Using lasers pulsing at the time scale of bond vibrations (10^{-15} s), he observed transition states forming and decomposing. A few, such as the one that forms as methyl bromide reacts with hydroxide ion, have been well studied:

$$BrCH_3 + OH^- \longrightarrow Br^- + CH_3OH$$

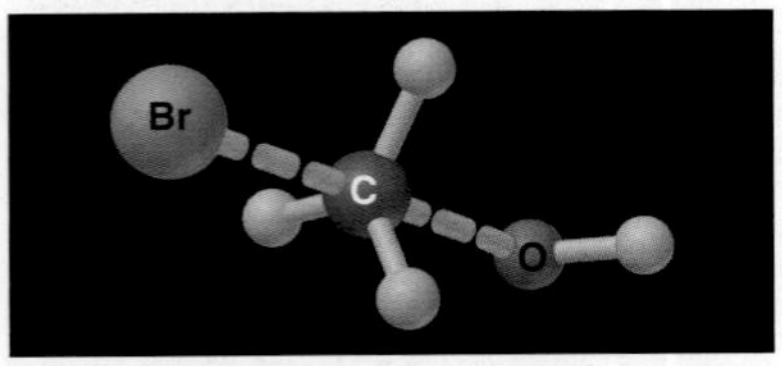

Figure 16.19 The transition state of the reaction between $BrCH_3$ and OH^-. Note the partial (*dashed*) C—O and Br—C bonds and the trigonal bipyramidal shape.

The electronegative bromine makes the carbon in $BrCH_3$ partially positive, and the carbon attracts the negatively charged oxygen in OH^-. As a C—O bond begins to form, the Br—C bond begins to weaken. In the transition state (Figure 16.19), C is surrounded by five atoms (trigonal bipyramidal; Section 10.2), which never occurs in its stable compounds. This high-energy species has three normal C—H bonds and two partial bonds, one from C to O and the other from Br to C.

Reaching the transition state does not guarantee that a reaction will proceed to products because *a transition state can change in either direction.* In this case, if the C—O bond continues to strengthen, products form; but, if the Br—C bond becomes stronger again, the transition state reverts to reactants.

Depicting the Change with a Reaction Energy Diagram A useful way to depict these events is with a **reaction energy diagram,** which plots how potential energy changes as the reaction proceeds from reactants to products (the *reaction progress*). The diagram shows the relative energy levels of reactants, products, and transition state, as well as the forward and reverse activation energies and the enthalpy of reaction.

The bottom of Figure 16.20 shows the diagram for the reaction of $BrCH_3$ and OH^-. This reaction is exothermic, so reactants are higher in energy than products, which means $E_{a(fwd)}$ is less than $E_{a(rev)}$. Above the diagram are molecular-scale views at various points during the reaction and corresponding structural formulas. At the top of

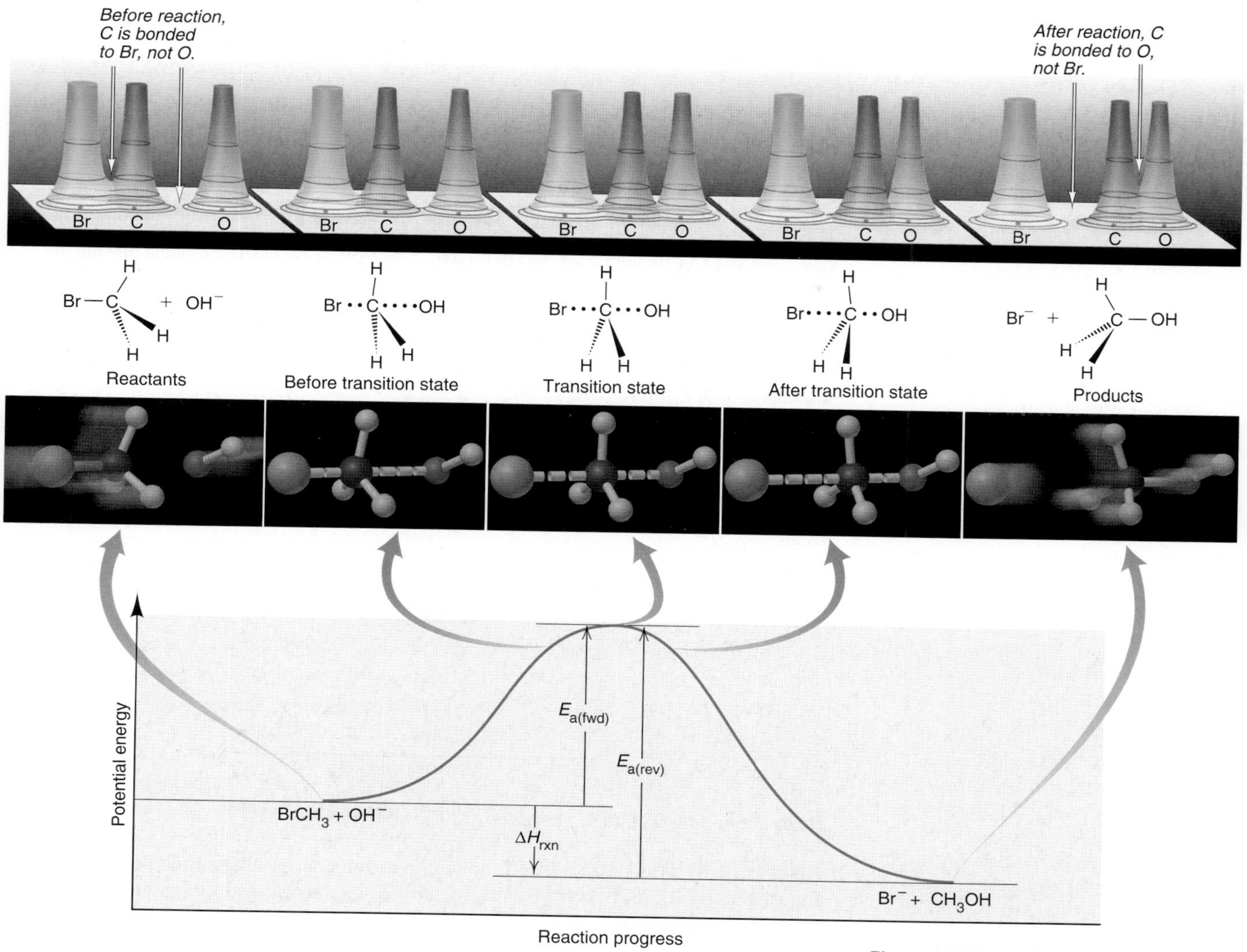

Figure 16.20 Depicting the reaction between $BrCH_3$ and OH^-. In order (*bottom to top*) are the reaction energy diagram with blow-up arrows at five points during the reaction, molecular-scale views, structural formulas, and electron density relief maps. Note the gradual, simultaneous C—O bond forming and Br—C bond breaking.

the figure are electron density relief maps of the Br, C, and O atoms: note the gradual change in electron density from C overlapping Br (*left*) to C overlapping O (*right*).

Transition state theory proposes that *every reaction (or every step in an overall reaction) goes through its own transition state.* Figure 16.21 presents reaction energy diagrams for two gas-phase reactions. In each case, the structure of the transition state is predicted from the orientations of the reactant atoms that must become bonded in the product.

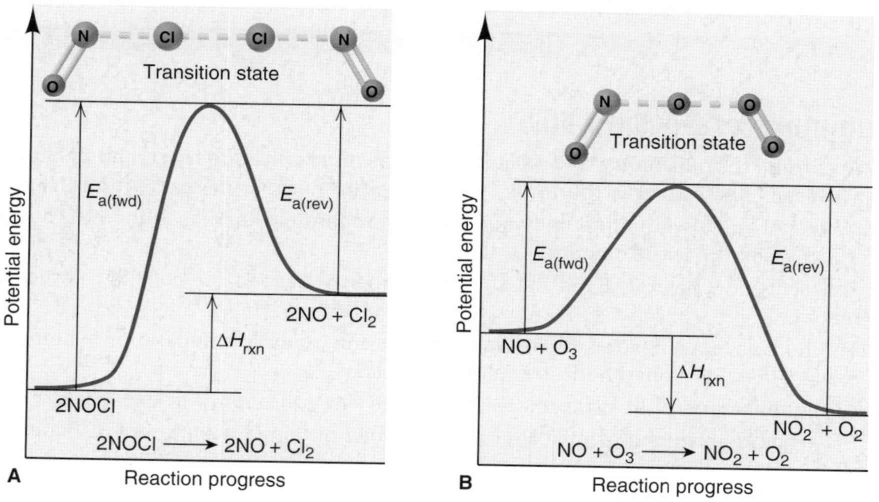

Figure 16.21 Reaction energy diagrams and possible transition states for two reactions.

Sample Problem 16.9 Drawing Reaction Energy Diagrams and Transition States

Problem A key reaction in the upper atmosphere is

$$O_3(g) + O(g) \longrightarrow 2O_2(g)$$

The $E_{a(fwd)}$ is 19 kJ, and the ΔH_{rxn} for the reaction as written is -392 kJ. Draw a reaction energy diagram, predict a structure for the transition state, and calculate $E_{a(rev)}$.

Plan The reaction is highly exothermic ($\Delta H_{rxn} = -392$ kJ), so the products are much lower in energy than the reactants. The small $E_{a(fwd)}$ (19 kJ) means the energy of the reactants lies slightly below that of the transition state. We use Equation 16.9 to calculate $E_{a(rev)}$. To predict the transition state, we sketch the species and note that one of the bonds in O_3 weakens, and this partially bonded O begins forming a bond to the separate O atom.

Solution Solving for $E_{a(rev)}$:

$$\Delta H_{rxn} = E_{a(fwd)} - E_{a(rev)}$$

So, $$E_{a(rev)} = E_{a(fwd)} - \Delta H_{rxn} = 19 \text{ kJ} - (-392 \text{ kJ}) = 411 \text{ kJ}$$

The reaction energy diagram (not drawn to scale), with transition state, is

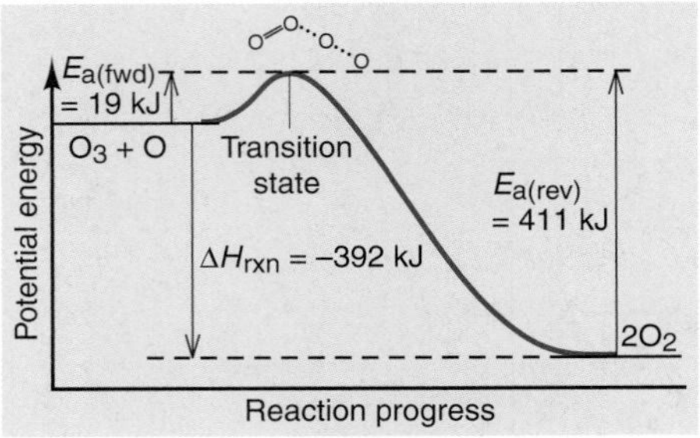

Check Rounding to find $E_{a(rev)}$ gives $\sim 20 + 390 = 410$.

Follow-Up Problem 16.9 The following reaction energy diagram depicts another key atmospheric reaction. Label the axes, identify $E_{a(fwd)}$, $E_{a(rev)}$, and ΔH_{rxn}, draw and label the transition state, and calculate $E_{a(rev)}$ for the reaction.

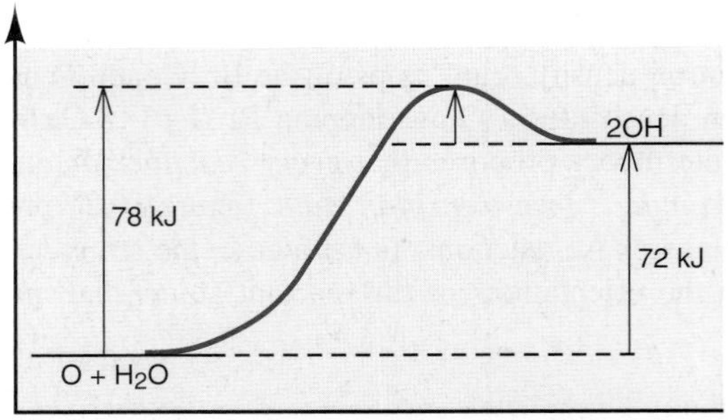

Summary of Section 16.5

- According to collision theory, reactant particles must collide to react, and the number of possible collisions is found by multiplying the number of reactant particles.
- As the Arrhenius equation shows, a rise in temperature increases the rate because it increases the rate constant.
- The activation energy, E_a, is the minimum energy needed for colliding particles to react.
- The relative E_a values for the forward and reverse reactions depend on whether the overall reaction is exothermic or endothermic.
- At higher temperatures, more collisions have enough energy to exceed E_a.
- E_a can be determined graphically from k values obtained at different T values.

- Molecules must collide with an effective orientation for them to react, so structural complexity decreases rate.
- Transition state theory focuses on the change of kinetic energy to potential energy as reactant particles collide and form an unstable transition state.
- Given a sufficiently energetic collision and an effective molecular orientation, the reactant species form the transition state, which either continues toward product(s) or reverts to reactant(s).
- A reaction energy diagram depicts the changing potential energy throughout a reaction's progress from reactants through transition states to products.

16.6 • REACTION MECHANISMS: THE STEPS FROM REACTANT TO PRODUCT

You can't understand how a car works by examining the body, wheels, and dashboard, or even the engine as a whole. You need to look inside the engine to see how its parts fit together and function. Similarly, by examining the overall balanced equation, we can't know how a reaction works. We must look "inside the reaction" to see how reactants change into products.

Most reactions occur through a **reaction mechanism,** a sequence of single reaction steps that sum to the overall equation. For example, a possible mechanism for the overall reaction

$$2A + B \longrightarrow E + F$$

might involve these three simpler steps:

(1) $A + B \longrightarrow C$
(2) $C + A \longrightarrow D$
(3) $D \longrightarrow E + F$

Adding the steps and canceling common substances gives the overall equation:

$$A + B + \cancel{C} + A + \cancel{D} \longrightarrow \cancel{C} + \cancel{D} + E + F \quad \text{or} \quad 2A + B \longrightarrow E + F$$

A mechanism is a hypothesis about how a reaction occurs; chemists *propose* a mechanism and then *test* to see that it fits with the observed rate law.

Elementary Reactions and Molecularity

The individual steps that make up a reaction mechanism are called **elementary reactions** (or **elementary steps**). Each describes a *single molecular event*—one particle decomposing, two particles combining, and so forth.

An elementary step is characterized by its **molecularity,** the number of *reactant* particles in the step. Consider the mechanism for the breakdown of ozone in the stratosphere. The overall equation is

$$2O_3(g) \longrightarrow 3O_2(g)$$

A two-step mechanism has been proposed:

(1) $O_3(g) \longrightarrow O_2(g) + O(g)$
(2) $O_3(g) + O(g) \longrightarrow 2O_2(g)$

The first step is a **unimolecular reaction,** one that involves the decomposition or rearrangement of a single particle (O_3). The second step is a **bimolecular reaction,** one in which two particles (O_3 and O) react. Some *termolecular* elementary steps occur, but they are extremely rare because the probability of three particles colliding simultaneously with enough energy and an effective orientation is very small. Higher molecularities are not known. Therefore, in general, *we propose unimolecular and/or bimolecular reactions as reasonable steps in a mechanism.*

Because an elementary reaction occurs in one step, its rate law, unlike that for an overall reaction, *can* be deduced from the reaction stoichiometry: *reaction order equals molecularity*. Therefore, *only* for an elementary step, *we use the equation coefficients as the reaction orders in the rate law* (Table 16.7, *next page*).

Table 16.7 Rate Laws for General Elementary Steps

Elementary Step	Molecularity	Rate Law
$A \longrightarrow$ product	Unimolecular	Rate $= k[A]$
$2A \longrightarrow$ product	Bimolecular	Rate $= k[A]^2$
$A + B \longrightarrow$ product	Bimolecular	Rate $= k[A][B]$
$2A + B \longrightarrow$ product	Termolecular	Rate $= k[A]^2[B]$

Sample Problem 16.10 Determining Molecularity and Rate Laws for Elementary Steps

Problem The following elementary steps are proposed for a reaction mechanism:

(1) $NO_2Cl(g) \longrightarrow NO_2(g) + Cl(g)$

(2) $NO_2Cl(g) + Cl(g) \longrightarrow NO_2(g) + Cl_2(g)$

(a) Write the overall balanced equation.

(b) Determine the molecularity of each step.

(c) Write the rate law for each step.

Plan We find the overall equation from the sum of the elementary steps. The molecularity of each step equals the total number of *reactant* particles. We write the rate law for each step using the molecularities as reaction orders.

Solution (a) Writing the overall balanced equation:

$$NO_2Cl(g) \longrightarrow NO_2(g) + Cl(g)$$
$$NO_2Cl(g) + Cl(g) \longrightarrow NO_2(g) + Cl_2(g)$$
$$NO_2Cl(g) + NO_2Cl(g) + \cancel{Cl(g)} \longrightarrow NO_2(g) + \cancel{Cl(g)} + NO_2(g) + Cl_2(g)$$
$$2NO_2Cl(g) \longrightarrow 2NO_2(g) + Cl_2(g)$$

(b) Determining the molecularity of each step: The first step has one reactant, NO_2Cl, so it is unimolecular. The second step has two reactants, NO_2Cl and Cl, so it is bimolecular.

(c) Writing rate laws for the elementary steps:

(1) $\text{Rate}_1 = k_1[NO_2Cl]$

(2) $\text{Rate}_2 = k_2[NO_2Cl][Cl]$

Check In part (a), be sure the equation is balanced; in part (c), be sure the substances in brackets are the *reactants* of each elementary step.

Follow-Up Problem 16.10 These elementary steps are proposed for a mechanism:

(1) $2NO(g) \longrightarrow N_2O_2(g)$

(2) $2H_2(g) \longrightarrow 4H(g)$

(3) $N_2O_2(g) + H(g) \longrightarrow N_2O(g) + HO(g)$

(4) $HO(g) + H(g) \longrightarrow H_2O(g)$

(5) $H(g) + N_2O(g) \longrightarrow HO(g) + N_2(g)$

(a) Write the balanced equation for the overall reaction. **(b)** Determine the molecularity of each step. **(c)** Write the rate law for each step.

The Rate-Determining Step of a Reaction Mechanism

All the elementary steps in a mechanism have their own rates. However, one step is usually *much* slower than the others. This step, called the **rate-determining step** (or **rate-limiting step**), limits how fast the overall reaction proceeds. Therefore, *the rate law of the rate-determining step becomes the rate law for the overall reaction.* ●

Consider the reaction between nitrogen dioxide and carbon monoxide:

$$NO_2(g) + CO(g) \longrightarrow NO(g) + CO_2(g)$$

If this reaction were an elementary step—that is, if the mechanism consisted of only one step—we could immediately write the overall rate law as

$$\text{Rate} = k[NO_2][CO]$$

● **A Rate-Determining Step for Traffic Flow** Imagine driving home on a wide street that goes over a toll bridge. Traffic flows smoothly until the road narrows at the approach to the toll booth. Past the bridge, traffic returns to normal, and you proceed a couple of miles further to your destination. Getting through the bottleneck to pay the toll takes longer than the rest of the trip combined and, therefore, determines the time for the whole trip.

But, as you saw in Sample Problem 16.3, experimental data show the rate law is

$$\text{Rate} = k[NO_2]^2$$

Thus, the overall reaction cannot be elementary.

A proposed two-step mechanism is

$$(1)\ NO_2(g) + NO_2(g) \longrightarrow NO_3(g) + NO(g) \quad [\text{slow; rate determining}]$$
$$(2)\ NO_3(g) + CO(g) \longrightarrow NO_2(g) + CO_2(g) \quad [\text{fast}]$$

In this mechanism, NO_3 functions as a **reaction intermediate,** a substance formed and used up during the reaction. Even though it does not appear in the overall balanced equation, a reaction intermediate is essential for the reaction to occur. Intermediates are less stable than the reactants and products, but unlike *much* less stable transition states, they have normal bonds and can sometimes be isolated.

Rate laws for the two elementary steps listed above are

$$(1)\ \text{Rate}_1 = k_1[NO_2][NO_2] = k_1[NO_2]^2$$
$$(2)\ \text{Rate}_2 = k_2[NO_3][CO]$$

Three key points to notice about this mechanism are

- If $k_1 = k$, the rate law for the rate-determining step (step 1) becomes identical to the observed rate law.
- Because the first step is slow, $[NO_3]$ is low. As soon as any NO_3 forms, it is consumed by the fast second step, so the reaction takes as long as the first step does.
- CO does not appear in the rate law (reaction order = 0) because it takes part in the mechanism *after* the rate-determining step.

Correlating the Mechanism with the Rate Law

Coming up with a reasonable reaction mechanism is a classic demonstration of the scientific method. Using observations and data from rate experiments, we hypothesize the individual steps and then test our hypothesis with further evidence. If the evidence supports our mechanism, we can accept it; if not, we must propose a different one. We can never *prove* that a mechanism represents the *actual* chemical change, only that it is consistent with the data.

A valid mechanism must meet three criteria:

1. *The elementary steps must add up to the overall balanced equation.*
2. *The elementary steps must be reasonable.* They should generally involve one reactant particle (unimolecular) or two (bimolecular).
3. *The mechanism must correlate with the rate law,* not the other way around.

Mechanisms with a Slow Initial Step The reaction between NO_2 and CO that we considered earlier has a mechanism with a slow initial step; that is, the first step is rate-determining. The reaction between nitrogen dioxide and fluorine is another example:

$$2NO_2(g) + F_2(g) \longrightarrow 2NO_2F(g)$$

The experimental rate law is first order in NO_2 and in F_2,

$$\text{Rate} = k[NO_2][F_2]$$

and the accepted mechanism is

$$(1)\ NO_2(g) + F_2(g) \longrightarrow NO_2F(g) + F(g) \quad [\text{slow; rate determining}]$$
$$(2)\ NO_2(g) + F(g) \longrightarrow NO_2F(g) \quad [\text{fast}]$$

Note that the free fluorine atom is a reaction intermediate.

Let's see how this mechanism meets the three criteria.

1. The elementary reactions sum to the balanced equation:

$$NO_2(g) + NO_2(g) + F_2(g) + \cancel{F(g)} \longrightarrow NO_2F(g) + NO_2F(g) + \cancel{F(g)}$$

or $$2NO_2(g) + F_2(g) \longrightarrow 2NO_2F(g)$$

2. Both steps are bimolecular and, thus, reasonable.
3. To determine whether the mechanism is consistent with the observed rate law, we first write the rate laws for the elementary steps:

   (1) $\text{Rate}_1 = k_1[NO_2][F_2]$
   (2) $\text{Rate}_2 = k_2[NO_2][F]$

   Step 1 is the rate-determining step, and with $k_1 = k$, it is the same as the overall rate law, so the third criterion is met. Note that the second molecule of NO_2 is involved *after* the rate-determining step, so it does not appear in the overall rate law. Thus, as in the mechanism for the reaction of NO_2 and CO, *the overall rate law includes all the reactants involved in the rate-determining step.*

Mechanisms with a Fast Initial Step If the rate-limiting step in a mechanism is *not* the initial step, the product of the fast initial step builds up and starts reverting to reactant. With time, this *fast, reversible step reaches equilibrium,* as product changes to reactant as fast as it forms. As you'll see, this situation allows us to fit the mechanism to the overall rate law.

Consider once again the oxidation of nitrogen monoxide:

$$2NO(g) + O_2(g) \longrightarrow 2NO_2(g)$$

The observed rate law is

$$\text{Rate} = k[NO]^2[O_2]$$

and a proposed mechanism is

(1) $NO(g) + O_2(g) \rightleftharpoons NO_3(g)$ [fast, reversible]
(2) $NO_3(g) + NO(g) \longrightarrow 2NO_2(g)$ [slow; rate determining]

Let's go through the three criteria to see if this mechanism is valid. With cancellation of the reaction intermediate, NO_3, the sum of the steps gives the overall equation, so the first criterion is met:

$$NO(g) + O_2(g) + \cancel{NO_3(g)} + NO(g) \longrightarrow \cancel{NO_3(g)} + 2NO_2(g)$$

or

$$2NO(g) + O_2(g) \longrightarrow 2NO_2(g)$$

Both steps are bimolecular, so the second criterion is met.

To see whether the third criterion—that the mechanism is consistent with the observed rate law—is met, we first write rate laws for the elementary steps:

(1) $\text{Rate}_{1(\text{fwd})} = k_1[NO][O_2]$
$\text{Rate}_{1(\text{rev})} = k_{-1}[NO_3]$

where k_{-1} is the rate constant and NO_3 is the reactant for the reverse reaction.

(2) $\text{Rate}_2 = k_2[NO_3][NO]$

Next, we show that the rate law for the rate-determining step (step 2) gives the overall rate law. As written, it does not, because it contains the intermediate NO_3, and *an overall rate law includes only reactants (and products).* We eliminate $[NO_3]$ from the rate law for step 2 by expressing it in terms of reactants, as follows. Step 1 reaches equilibrium when the forward and reverse rates are equal:

$$\text{Rate}_{1(\text{fwd})} = \text{Rate}_{1(\text{rev})} \quad \text{or} \quad k_1[NO][O_2] = k_{-1}[NO_3]$$

To express $[NO_3]$ in terms of reactants, we isolate it algebraically:

$$[NO_3] = \frac{k_1}{k_{-1}}[NO][O_2]$$

Then, substituting for $[NO_3]$ in the rate law for the slow step, step 2, we obtain

$$\text{Rate}_2 = k_2[NO_3][NO] = k_2\underbrace{\left(\frac{k_1}{k_{-1}}[NO][O_2]\right)}_{[NO_3]}[NO] = \frac{k_2k_1}{k_{-1}}[NO]^2[O_2]$$

With $k = \dfrac{k_2k_1}{k_{-1}}$, this rate law is identical to the overall rate law.

To summarize, we assess the validity of a mechanism with a fast initial step by

1. Writing rate laws for the fast step (both directions) and for the slow step.
2. Expressing [intermediate] in terms of [reactant] by setting the forward rate law of the reversible step equal to the reverse rate law, and solving for [intermediate].
3. Substituting the expression for [intermediate] into the rate law for the slow step to obtain the overall rate law.

Several end-of-chapter problems, including Problems 16.72 and 16.73, provide additional examples of this approach.

An important point to note is that, *for any mechanism, only reactants involved up to and including the slow (rate-determining) step appear in the overall rate law.*

Depicting a Multistep Mechanism with a Reaction Energy Diagram Figure 16.22 shows reaction energy diagrams for two reactions, each of which has a two-step mechanism. The reaction of NO_2 and F_2 (part A) starts with a slow step, and the reaction of NO and O_2 (part B) starts with a fast step. Both overall reactions are exothermic, so the product is lower in energy than the reactants. Note these key points:

- *Each step in the mechanism has its own peak with the transition state at the top.*
- The intermediates (F in part A and NO_3 in part B) are reactive, unstable species, so they are higher in energy than the reactants or product.
- The slow (rate-determining) step (step 1 in A and step 2 in B) has a *larger* E_a than the other step.

Figure 16.22 Reaction energy diagrams for the two-step reaction of (**A**) NO_2 and F_2 and of (**B**) NO and O_2.

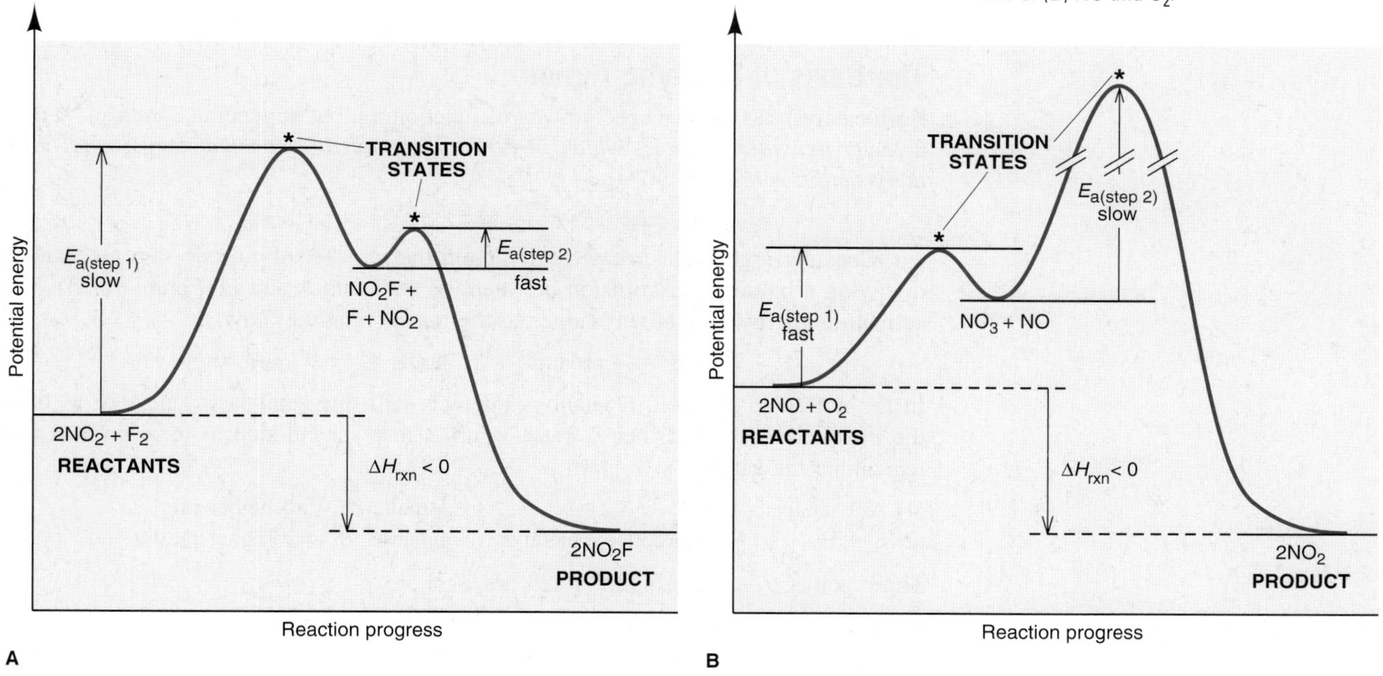

Summary of Section 16.6

- The mechanisms of most common reactions consist of two or more elementary steps, each of which shows a single molecular event.
- The molecularity of an elementary step equals the number of reactant particles and is the same as the total reaction order of the step. Only unimolecular and bimolecular steps are reasonable.
- The rate-determining (slowest) step in a mechanism determines how fast the overall reaction occurs, and its rate law is equivalent to the overall rate law.
- Reaction intermediates are species that form in one step and react in a later one.

- For a mechanism to be valid, (1) the elementary steps must add up to the overall balanced equation, (2) the steps must be reasonable, and (3) the mechanism must correlate with the rate law.
- If a mechanism begins with a slow step, only those reactants involved in the slow step appear in the overall rate law.
- If a mechanism begins with a fast step, the product of the fast step accumulates as an intermediate, and the step reaches equilibrium. To show that the mechanism is valid, we express [intermediate] in terms of [reactant].
- Only reactants involved in steps up to and including the slow (rate-determining) step appear in the overall rate law.
- Each step in a mechanism has its own transition state, which appears at the top of a peak in the reaction-energy diagram. A slower step has a higher peak (larger E_a).

16.7 • CATALYSIS: SPEEDING UP A REACTION

Increasing the rate of a reaction has countless applications, in both engineering and biology. Higher temperature can speed up a reaction, but energy for industrial processes is costly and many organic and biological substances are heat sensitive. More commonly, by far, a reaction is accelerated by a **catalyst,** a substance that increases the rate *without* being consumed. Thus, only a small, nonstoichiometric amount of the catalyst is required to speed the reaction. Despite this, catalysts are employed in so many processes that several million tons are produced annually in the United States alone. Nature is the master designer and user of catalysts: every organism relies on protein catalysts, known as *enzymes,* to speed up life-sustaining reactions, and even the simplest bacterium employs thousands of them.

The Basis of Catalytic Action

Each catalyst has its own specific way of functioning, but in general, *a catalyst causes a lower activation energy, which in turn makes the rate constant larger and, thus, the reaction rate higher:*

$$\text{Catalyst} \Longrightarrow \text{lower } E_a \Longrightarrow \text{larger } k \Longrightarrow \text{higher rate}$$

Consider a general *uncatalyzed* reaction that proceeds by a one-step mechanism involving a bimolecular collision between the reactants A and B (Figure 16.23). The activation energy is relatively large, so the rate is relatively low:

$$\text{A} + \text{B} \longrightarrow \text{product} \qquad [\text{larger } E_a \Longrightarrow \text{lower rate}]$$

In the *catalyzed* reaction, reactant A interacts with the catalyst in one step to form the intermediate C, and then C reacts with B in a second step to form product and regenerate the catalyst:

$$(1)\ \text{A} + \text{catalyst} \longrightarrow \text{C} \qquad [\text{smaller } E_a \Longrightarrow \text{higher rate}]$$
$$(2)\ \text{C} + \text{B} \longrightarrow \text{product} + \text{catalyst} \qquad [\text{smaller } E_a \Longrightarrow \text{higher rate}]$$

Three points to note in Figure 16.23 are

- A catalyst speeds up the forward *and* reverse reactions. Thus, a reaction has the *same yield* with or without a catalyst, but the product forms *faster.*
- A catalyst causes a *lower total activation energy* by providing a *different mechanism* for the reaction. The total of the activation energies for both steps of the catalyzed pathway $[E_{a1(fwd)} + E_{a2(fwd)}]$ is less than the forward activation energy of the uncatalyzed pathway.
- The catalyst is *not* consumed, but rather used and then regenerated.

Homogeneous Catalysis

Chemists classify catalysts based on whether or not they act in the same phase as the reactants and products. A **homogeneous catalyst** exists in solution with the reaction mixture, so it must be a gas, liquid, or soluble solid.

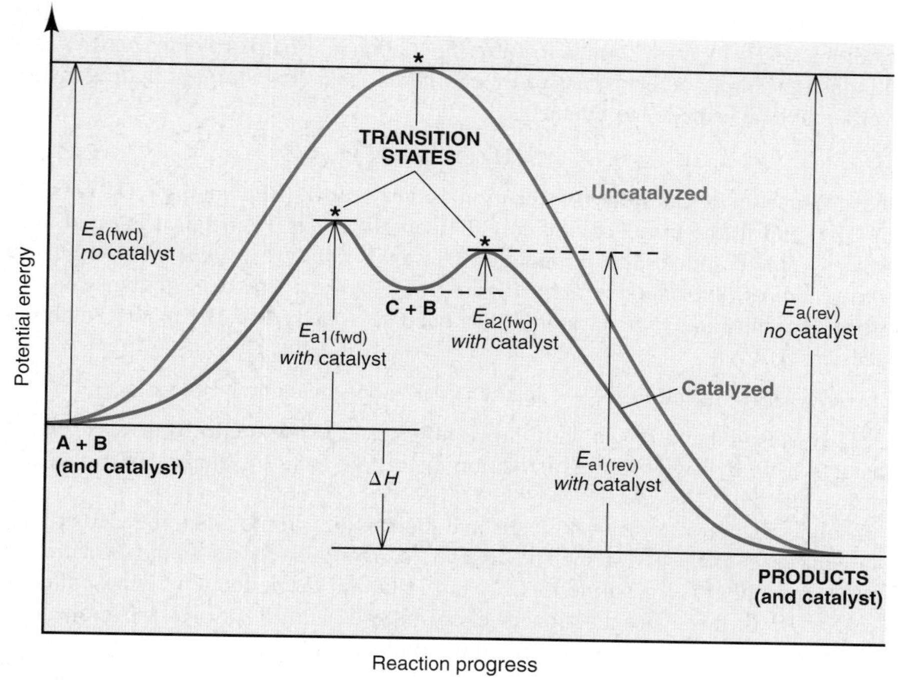

Figure 16.23 **Reaction energy diagram for a catalyzed (*green*) and an uncatalyzed (*red*) process.** A catalyst speeds a reaction by providing a different, lower energy pathway (*green*). (Only the first step of the catalyzed reverse reaction is labeled.)

A thoroughly studied example of homogeneous catalysis in the gas phase was formerly used in sulfuric acid manufacture. The key step, the oxidation of sulfur dioxide to sulfur trioxide, occurs so slowly that it is not economical:

$$SO_2(g) + \tfrac{1}{2}O_2(g) \longrightarrow SO_3(g)$$

In the presence of nitrogen monoxide, however, the reaction speeds up dramatically:

$$NO(g) + \tfrac{1}{2}O_2(g) \longrightarrow NO_2(g)$$
$$NO_2(g) + SO_2(g) \longrightarrow NO(g) + SO_3(g)$$

Note that NO and NO_2 cancel to give the overall reaction. Also, note that NO_2 acts as an intermediate (formed and then consumed) and NO as a catalyst (used and then regenerated).

Another well-studied example of homogeneous catalysis involves the decomposition of hydrogen peroxide in aqueous solution:

$$2H_2O_2(aq) \longrightarrow 2H_2O(l) + O_2(g)$$

Commercial H_2O_2 decomposes in light and in the presence of the small amounts of ions dissolved from glass, but it is quite stable in dark plastic containers. Many other substances speed its decomposition, including bromide ion, Br^- (Figure 16.24). The catalyzed process is thought to occur in two steps:

$$2Br^-(aq) + H_2O_2(aq) + 2H^+(aq) \longrightarrow Br_2(aq) + 2H_2O(l)$$
$$Br_2(aq) + H_2O_2(aq) \longrightarrow 2Br^-(aq) + 2H^+(aq) + O_2(g)$$

In this case, Br_2, Br^-, and H^+ cancel to give the overall balanced equation, Br^- (in the presence of H^+) is the catalyst, and Br_2 is the intermediate.

A

B

Figure 16.24 **The catalyzed decomposition of H_2O_2.** **A,** A small amount of NaBr is added to a solution of H_2O_2. **B,** Oxygen gas forms quickly as $Br^-(aq)$ catalyzes the H_2O_2 decomposition; the intermediate Br_2 turns the solution orange.

Heterogeneous Catalysis

A **heterogeneous catalyst** speeds up a reaction in a different phase. Most often solids interacting with gaseous or liquid reactants, these catalysts have enormous surface areas, sometimes as much as 500 m^2/g. Very early in the reaction, the rate depends on reactant concentration, but almost immediately, the reaction becomes zero order: the rate-determining step occurs on the catalyst's surface, so once the reactant covers it, adding more reactant cannot increase the rate further.

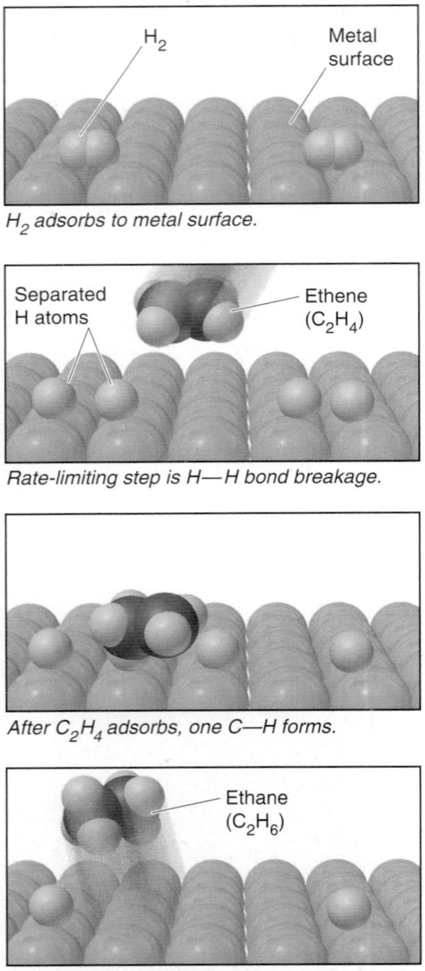

H_2 adsorbs to metal surface.

Rate-limiting step is H—H bond breakage.

After C_2H_4 adsorbs, one C—H forms.

Another C—H bond forms; C_2H_6 leaves surface.

Figure 16.25 The metal-catalyzed hydrogenation of ethene.

A very important organic example of heterogeneous catalysis is **hydrogenation,** the addition of H_2 to C═C bonds to form C—C bonds. The petroleum, plastics, and food industries employ this process on an enormous scale. The simplest hydrogenation converts ethylene (ethene) to ethane:

$$H_2C{=}CH_2(g) + H_2(g) \longrightarrow H_3C{-}CH_3(g)$$

In the absence of a catalyst, the reaction is very slow. But, at high H_2 pressure (high $[H_2]$) and in the presence of finely divided Ni, Pd, or Pt metal, it is rapid even at ordinary temperatures. The Group 8B(10) metals catalyze by *chemically adsorbing the reactants onto their surface* (Figure 16.25). In the rate-determining step, the adsorbed H_2 splits into two H atoms that become weakly bonded to the catalyst's surface (catM):

$$H{-}H(g) + 2\text{catM}(s) \longrightarrow 2\text{catM}{-}H \text{ (H atoms bound to metal surface)}$$

Then, C_2H_4 adsorbs and reacts with the H atoms, one at a time, to form C_2H_6. Thus, the catalyst acts by lowering the activation energy of the slow step as part of a different mechanism.

A solid mixture of transition metals and their oxides forms a heterogeneous catalyst in your car's exhaust system. The catalytic converter speeds both the oxidation of toxic CO and unburned gasoline to CO_2 and H_2O *and* the reduction of the pollutant NO to N_2. As in the hydrogenation mechanism, the catalyst adsorbs the molecules, which weakens and splits their bonds, thus allowing the atoms to form new bonds more quickly. The process is extremely efficient: for example, an NO molecule is split into catalyst-bound N and O atoms in less than 2×10^{-12} s.

Kinetics and Function of Biological Catalysts

Whereas most industrial chemical reactions occur under extreme conditions with high concentrations, thousands of complex reactions occur in every living cell in dilute solution at ordinary temperatures and pressures. Moreover, the rate of each reaction responds to the rates of other reactions, chemical signals from other cells, and environmental stress. In this marvelous chemical harmony, each rate is controlled by an **enzyme,** a protein catalyst whose function has been perfected through evolution.

Enzymes are globular proteins with complex shapes (Section 15.6) and molar masses ranging from about 15,000 to 1,000,000 g/mol. A small part of an enzyme's surface—like a hollow carved into a mountainside—is the **active site,** a region whose shape results from the amino acid side chains involved in catalyzing the reaction. Often far apart in the sequence of the polypeptide chain, these groups lie near each other because of the chain's three-dimensional folding. When the reactant molecules, called **substrates,** collide effectively with the active site, they become attached through *intermolecular forces,* and the chemical change begins.

Characteristics of Enzyme Action The catalytic behavior of enzymes has several common features:

1. *Catalytic activity.* An enzyme behaves like both types of catalyst. Enzymes are typically *much* larger than the substrate, and many enzymes are embedded within cell membranes. Thus, like a heterogeneous catalyst, an enzyme provides a surface on which one reactant is temporarily immobilized to wait until the other reactant lands nearby. But, like many homogeneous catalysts, the active site groups interact with the substrate(s) in multistep sequences in the presence of solvent and other species.

2. *Catalytic efficiency.* Enzymes are incredibly *efficient* in terms of the number of reactions catalyzed per unit time. For example, for the hydrolysis of urea,

$$(NH_2)_2C{=}O(aq) + 2H_2O(l) + H^+(aq) \longrightarrow 2NH_4^+(aq) + HCO_3^-(aq)$$

the rate constant is 3×10^{-10} s^{-1} for the uncatalyzed reaction in water at room temperature. Under the same conditions in the presence of the enzyme *urease* (pronounced "*yur*-ee-ase"), the rate constant is 3×10^{4} s^{-1}, a 10^{14}-fold increase. Enzymes typically increase rates by 10^8 to 10^{20} times, values that industrial chemists who use catalysts can only dream of!

3. *Catalytic specificity*. As a result of the particular groups at the active site, enzymes are also highly *specific:* each enzyme generally catalyzes only one reaction. Urease catalyzes *only* the hydrolysis of urea, and no other enzyme does this.

Models of Enzyme Action Two models of enzyme action have been proposed. According to the earlier **lock-and-key model** (Figure 16.26A), when the "key" (substrate) fits the "lock" (active site), the chemical change begins. However, x-ray crystallographic and spectroscopic methods show that, in most cases, *the enzyme changes shape when the substrate lands at the active site.* Thus, according to the more current **induced-fit model** (Figure 16.26B), the substrate induces the active site to adopt a perfect fit. Rather than a rigid key in a lock, we picture a flexible hand in a glove; the "glove" (active site) does not attain its functional shape until the "hand" (substrate) moves into it.

Kinetics of Enzyme Action Kinetic studies of enzyme catalysis show that substrate (S) and enzyme (E) form an intermediate **enzyme-substrate complex (ES),** whose concentration determines the rate of formation of product (P). In other words, the rate of an enzyme-catalyzed reaction is proportional to the concentration of ES, that is, of reactant bound to catalyst. The steps common to virtually all enzyme-catalyzed reactions are

(1) $E + S \rightleftharpoons ES$ [fast, reversible]
(2) $ES \longrightarrow E + P$ [slow; rate-determining]

Thus, rate = k[ES]. As in the heterogeneous catalysis of hydrogenation (Figure 16.25), [S] is much greater than [E], and once all the enzyme molecules are bound to substrate, [ES] is as high as possible. Then, increasing [S] has no effect on rate, and the process is zero order.

Mechanisms of Enzyme Action Enzymes employ a variety of reaction mechanisms. In some cases, the active-site groups bring specific atoms of the substrate close together. In others, the groups bound to the substrate move apart, stretching the bond to be broken. Many *hydrolases* have acidic groups that provide H^+ ions to speed bond cleavage. Two examples are lysozyme, an enzyme found in tears, which hydrolyzes a polysaccharide in bacterial cell walls to protect the eyes from infection, and chymotrypsin, an enzyme found in the small intestine, which hydrolyzes proteins during digestion.

No matter what their mode of action, *all enzymes catalyze by stabilizing the reaction's transition state.* For instance, in the lysozyme-catalyzed reaction, the transition state is a portion of the polysaccharide whose bonds have been twisted and stretched by the active site groups until it fits the active site well. Stabilizing the transition state lowers the activation energy and thus increases the rate.

Like enzyme-catalyzed reactions, the process of stratospheric ozone depletion includes both homegeneous and heterogeneous catalysis—as you'll see in the following Chemical Connections essay.

Figure 16.26 Two models of enzyme action.

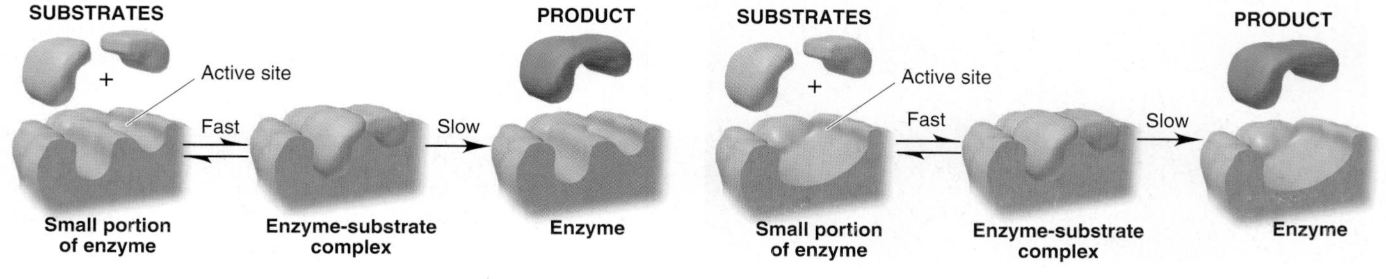

A Lock-and-key model: *fixed shape of active site matches shape of substrate(s).*

B Induced-fit model: *active site changes shape to bind substrate(s) more effectively.*

CHEMICAL CONNECTIONS TO ATMOSPHERIC SCIENCE | Depletion of Earth's Ozone Layer

The stratospheric ozone layer absorbs UV radiation with wavelengths between 280 and 320 nm that is emitted by the Sun. If it reaches Earth's suface, this radiation has enough energy to damage genes by breaking bonds in DNA. Thus, depletion of stratospheric ozone increases human health risks, particularly the risks of skin cancer and cataracts (clouding of the eye's lens). The radiation may also damage plant life, especially forms at the bottom of the food chain. Both homogeneous and heterogeneous catalysts play roles in the depletion of ozone.

Before 1976, stratospheric ozone concentration varied seasonally but remained nearly constant from year to year as a result of a series of atmospheric reactions:

$$O_2 \xrightarrow{UV} 2O \qquad \text{[dissociation of } O_2 \text{ by UV]}$$
$$O + O_2 \longrightarrow O_3 \qquad \text{[ozone formation]}$$
$$O_3 + O \longrightarrow 2O_2 \qquad \text{[ozone breakdown]}$$

Then, in 1985, British scientists reported that a severe reduction of ozone, an *ozone hole,* appeared in the stratosphere over the Antarctic when the Sun ended the long winter darkness. Subsequent research by Paul J. Crutzen, Mario J. Molina, and F. Sherwood Rowland, for which they received the Nobel Prize in chemistry, revealed that industrial chlorofluorocarbons (CFCs) were lowering $[O_3]$ in the stratosphere by catalyzing the breakdown reaction.

Widely used as aerosol propellants, foaming agents, and air-conditioning coolants, large quantities of CFCs were released for years. Unreactive in the troposphere, CFC molecules gradually reach the stratosphere, where UV radiation splits them:

$$CF_2Cl_2 \xrightarrow{UV} CF_2Cl\cdot + Cl\cdot$$

(The dots are lone electrons resulting from C—Cl bond cleavage.)

Like many species with a lone electron (free radicals), atomic Cl is very reactive. It reacts with stratospheric O_3 to produce the intermediate chlorine monoxide ($ClO\cdot$), which then reacts with a free O atom to regenerate a Cl atom:

$$O_3 + Cl\cdot \longrightarrow ClO\cdot + O_2$$
$$ClO\cdot + O \longrightarrow Cl\cdot + O_2$$

The sum of these steps is the ozone breakdown reaction:

$$O_3 + \cancel{Cl\cdot} + \cancel{ClO\cdot} + O \longrightarrow \cancel{ClO\cdot} + O_2 + \cancel{Cl\cdot} + O_2$$

or

$$O_3 + O \longrightarrow 2O_2$$

Studies finding high $[ClO\cdot]$ over Antarctica supported this mechanism. Figure B16.1 shows the ozone hole expanding over the years in which CFCs accumulated.

Figure B16.2 shows the reaction energy diagram for the process. Note that *Cl acts as a homogeneous catalyst:* it exists in the same phase as the reactants, lowers the total activation energy via a different mechanism, and is regenerated. Each Cl atom has a stratospheric half-life of about 2 years, during which it speeds the breakdown of about 100,000 ozone molecules.

Later studies showed that the ozone hole enlarges by heterogeneous catalysis. Stratospheric clouds provide a surface for reactions that convert inactive chlorine compounds, such as HCl and chlorine nitrate ($ClONO_2$), to substances, such as Cl_2, that are cleaved by UV radiation to Cl atoms. Fine particles in the stratosphere act in the same way: dust from the 1991 eruption of Mt. Pinatubo reduced stratospheric ozone for 2 years. The Montreal Protocol of 1987 and later amendments curtailed CFC production and proposed substituting hydrocarbon propellants, such as isobutane, $(CH_3)_3CH$. Nevertheless, because of the long lifetimes of CFCs, complete recovery of the ozone layer may take another century! The good news is that tropospheric halogen levels have begun to fall.

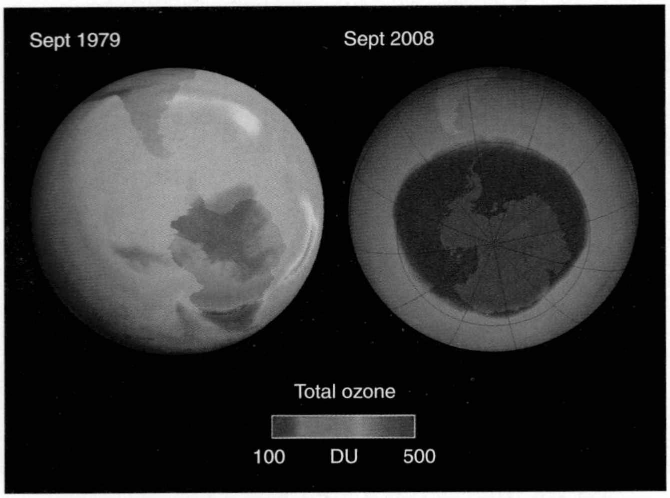

Figure B16.1 Satellite images of the increasing size of the Antarctic ozone hole (*purple*).

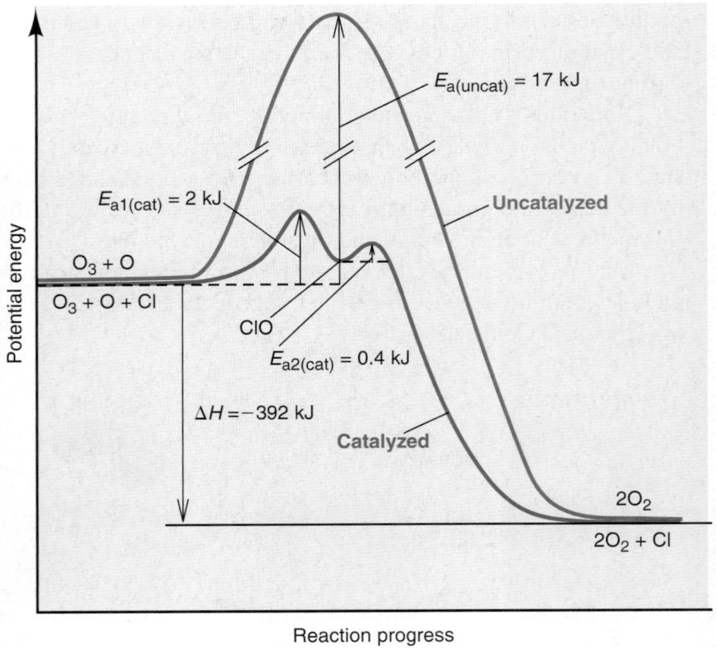

Figure B16.2 Reaction energy diagram for breakdown of O_3 by Cl atoms. (Not drawn to scale.)

Problems

B16.1 The catalytic destruction of ozone occurs via a two-step mechanism, where X can be one of several species:

(1) $X + O_3 \longrightarrow XO + O_2$ [slow]
(2) $XO + O \longrightarrow X + O_2$ [fast]

(a) Write the overall reaction and the rate law for each step.
(b) X acts as ______, and XO acts as ______.

B16.2 Aircraft in the stratosphere release NO, which catalyzes ozone breakdown by the mechanism shown in Problem B16.1.
(a) Write the mechanism.
(b) When $[O_3]$ is 5×10^{12} molecules/cm^3 and [NO] is 1.0×10^9 molecules/cm^3, what is the rate of O_3 depletion (k for the rate-determining step is 6×10^{-15} cm^3/molecule·s)?

B16.3 In the mechanism for O_3 breakdown in Problem B16.1:
(a) Which would you expect to have a higher value for the p factor, step 1 with NO or step 1 with Cl? Explain.
(b) Draw a possible transition state for the step with Cl.

Summary of Section 16.7

- A catalyst increases the rate of a reaction without being consumed. It accomplishes this by providing another mechanism with a lower activation energy.
- Homogeneous catalysts function in the same phase as the reactants. Heterogeneous catalysts act in a different phase from the reactants.
- The hydrogenation of carbon-carbon double bonds takes place on a solid metal catalyst, which speeds up the rate-determining step, the breakage of the H_2 bond.
- Enzymes are protein catalysts of high efficiency and specificity that act by stabilizing the transition state and, thus, lowering the activation energy.
- Chlorine atoms from CFC molecules speed the breakdown of stratospheric O_3 by a process that has aspects of both homogeneous and heterogeneous catalysis.

CHAPTER REVIEW GUIDE

Learning Objectives

Relevant section (§) and/or sample problem (SP) numbers appear in parentheses.

Understand These Concepts

1. How reaction rate depends on concentration, physical state, and temperature (§16.1)
2. The meaning of reaction rate in terms of changing concentrations over time (§16.2)
3. How the rate can be expressed in terms of reactant or product concentrations (§16.2)
4. The distinction between average and instantaneous rate and why the instantaneous rate changes during the reaction (§16.2)
5. The interpretation of reaction rate in terms of reactant and product concentrations (§16.2)
6. The experimental basis of the rate law and the information needed to determine it—initial rate data, reaction orders, and rate constant (§16.3)
7. The importance of reaction order in determining the rate (§16.3)
8. How reaction order is determined from initial rates at different concentrations (§16.3)
9. How integrated rate laws show the dependence of concentration on time (§16.4)
10. What reaction half-life means and why it is constant for a first-order reaction (§16.4)
11. Why concentrations are multiplied in the rate law (§16.5)
12. Activation energy and the effect of temperature on the rate constant (Arrhenius equation) (§16.5)
13. How temperature affects rate by influencing collision energy and, thus, the fraction of collisions with energy exceeding the activation energy (§16.5)
14. Why molecular orientation and complexity influence the number of effective collisions and the rate (§16.5)
15. The transition state as the momentary species between reactants and products whose formation requires the activation energy (§16.5)
16. How an elementary step represents a single molecular event and its molecularity equals the number of colliding particles (§16.6)

17. How a reaction mechanism consists of several elementary steps, with the slowest step determining the overall rate (§16.6)
18. The criteria for a valid reaction mechanism (§16.6)
19. How a catalyst speeds a reaction by lowering the activation energy (§16.7)
20. The distinction between homogeneous and heterogeneous catalysis (§16.7)

Master These Skills

1. Calculating instantaneous rate from the slope of a tangent to a concentration vs. time plot (§16.2)
2. Expressing reaction rate in terms of changes in concentration over time (SP16.1)
3. Determining reaction orders from a known rate law (SP16.2)
4. Determining reaction orders from changes in initial rate with concentration (SPs 16.3, 16.4)
5. Calculating the rate constant and its units (§16.3)
6. Using an integrated rate law to find concentration at a given time or the time to reach a given concentration (SP 16.5)
7. Determining reaction order graphically with a rearranged integrated rate law (§16.4)
8. Determining the half-life of a reaction (SPs 16.6, 16.7)
9. Using a form of the Arrhenius equation to calculate the activation energy (SP 16.8)
10. Using reaction energy diagrams to depict the energy changes during a reaction (SP 16.9)
11. Predicting a transition state for a simple reaction (SP 16.9)
12. Determining the molecularity and rate law for an elementary step (SP 16.10)
13. Constructing a mechanism with either a slow or a fast initial step (§16.6)

Key Terms

Page numbers appear in parentheses.

Section 16.1
chemical kinetics (627)
reaction rate (627)

Section 16.2
average rate (630)
instantaneous rate (631)
initial rate (631)

Section 16.3
rate law (rate equation) (634)
rate constant (634)
reaction orders (634)

Section 16.4
integrated rate law (642)
half-life ($t_{1/2}$) (644)

Section 16.5
collision theory (648)
Arrhenius equation (649)
activation energy (E_a) (649)
effective collision (651)
frequency factor (651)
transition state theory (652)
transition state (activated complex) (652)
reaction energy diagram (652)

Section 16.6
reaction mechanism (655)
elementary reaction (elementary step) (655)
molecularity (655)
unimolecular reaction (655)
bimolecular reaction (655)
rate-determining (rate-limiting) step (656)
reaction intermediate (657)

Section 16.7
catalyst (660)
homogeneous catalyst (660)
heterogeneous catalyst (661)
hydrogenation (662)
enzyme (662)
active site (662)
substrate (662)
lock-and-key model (663)
induced-fit model (663)
enzyme-substrate complex (ES) (663)

Key Equations and Relationships

Page numbers appear in parentheses.

16.1 Expressing reaction rate in terms of reactant A (630):

$$\text{Rate} = -\frac{\Delta[\text{A}]}{\Delta t}$$

16.2 Expressing the rate of a general reaction (633):

$$\text{Rate} = -\frac{1}{a}\frac{\Delta[\text{A}]}{\Delta t} = -\frac{1}{b}\frac{\Delta[\text{B}]}{\Delta t} = \frac{1}{c}\frac{\Delta[\text{C}]}{\Delta t} = \frac{1}{d}\frac{\Delta[\text{D}]}{\Delta t}$$

16.3 Writing a general rate law (in which products do not appear) (634):

$$\text{Rate} = k[\text{A}]^m[\text{B}]^n \cdots$$

16.4 Calculating the time to reach a given [A] in a first-order reaction (rate = k[A]) (642):

$$\ln\frac{[\text{A}]_0}{[\text{A}]_t} = kt$$

16.5 Calculating the time to reach a given [A] in a simple second-order reaction (rate = $k[\text{A}]^2$) (642):

$$\frac{1}{[\text{A}]_t} - \frac{1}{[\text{A}]_0} = kt$$

16.6 Calculating the time to reach a given [A] in a zero-order reaction (rate = k) (643):

$$[\text{A}]_t - [\text{A}]_0 = -kt$$

16.7 Finding the half-life of a first-order process (646):

$$t_{1/2} = \frac{\ln 2}{k} = \frac{0.693}{k}$$

16.8 Relating the rate constant to the temperature (Arrhenius equation) (649):

$$k = Ae^{-E_a/RT}$$

16.9 Relating the heat of reaction to the forward and reverse activation energies (650):

$$\Delta H_{\text{rxn}} = E_{\text{a(fwd)}} - E_{\text{a(rev)}}$$

16.10 Calculating the activation energy (rearranged form of Arrhenius equation) (651):

$$\ln\frac{k_2}{k_1} = -\frac{E_a}{R}\left(\frac{1}{T_2} - \frac{1}{T_1}\right)$$

Brief Solutions to Follow-Up Problems

16.1 (a) $4NO(g) + O_2(g) \longrightarrow 2N_2O_3(g)$;

$$\text{rate} = -\frac{\Delta[O_2]}{\Delta t} = -\frac{1}{4}\frac{\Delta[NO]}{\Delta t} = \frac{1}{2}\frac{\Delta[N_2O_3]}{\Delta t}$$

(b) $$-\frac{\Delta[O_2]}{\Delta t} = -\frac{1}{4}\frac{\Delta[NO]}{\Delta t} = -\frac{1}{4}(-1.60\times10\ \text{mol/L·s})$$

$$= 4.00\times10^{-5}\ \text{mol/L·s}$$

16.2 First order in Br^-, first order in BrO_3^-, second order in H^+, fourth order overall

16.3 Rate $= k[H_2]^m[I_2]^n$. From experiments 1 and 3, $m = 1$. From experiments 2 and 4, $n = 1$. Therefore, rate $= k[H_2][I_2]$; second order overall.

16.4 (a) The rate law shows the reaction is zero order in Y, so the rate is not affected by doubling Y: rate of Expt 2 = 0.25×10^{-5} mol/L·s
(b) The rate of Expt 3 is four times that of Expt 1, so [X] doubles.

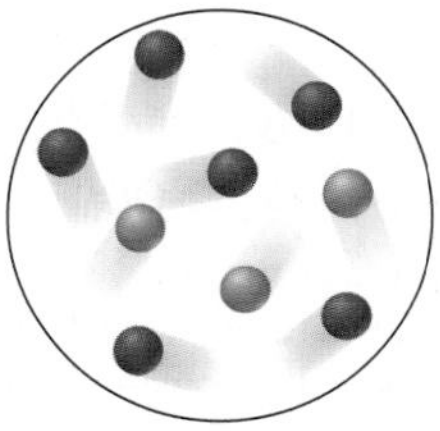

16.5 $1/[HI]_t - 1/[HI]_0 = kt$
111 L/mol − 100. L/mol $= (2.4\times10^{-21}\ \text{L/mol·s})(t)$
$t = 4.6\times10^{21}$ s (or 1.5×10^{14} yr)

16.6 (a)

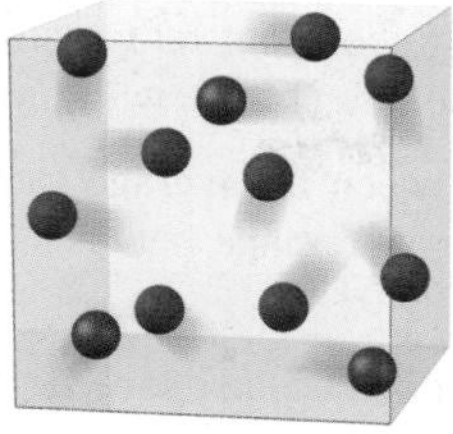

(b) At 10.0 min (4 half-lives), there are 0.75 particles of X.

$$\text{Amount (mol)} = 0.75\ \text{particles} \times \frac{0.20\ \text{mol X}}{1\ \text{particle}} = 0.15\ \text{mol X}$$

$$M = \frac{0.15\ \text{mol X}}{0.50\ \text{L}} = 0.30\ M$$

16.7 $t_{1/2} = (\ln 2)/k$; $k = 0.693/13.1\ \text{h} = 5.29\times10^{-2}\ \text{h}^{-1}$

16.8 $$\ln\frac{0.286\ \text{L/mol·s}}{k_1} = -\frac{1.00\times10^5\ \text{J/mol}}{8.314\ \text{J/mol·K}} \times \left(\frac{1}{500.\ \text{K}} - \frac{1}{490.\ \text{K}}\right) = 0.491$$

$$k_1 = 0.175\ \text{L/mol·s}$$

16.9

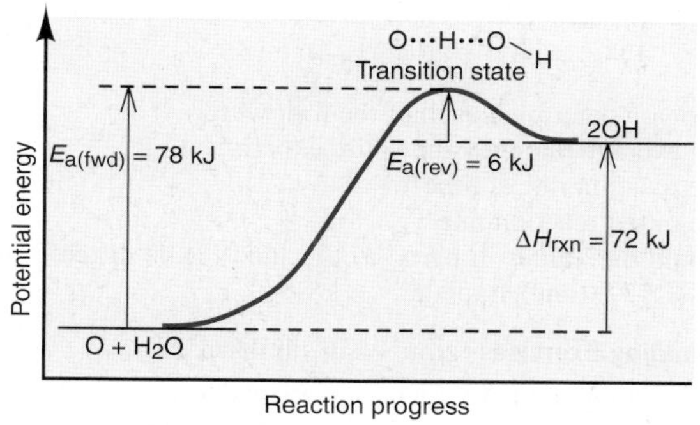

16.10 (a) Balanced equation (after doubling step 4):
$2NO(g) + 2H_2(g) \longrightarrow N_2(g) + 2H_2O(g)$
(b) Step 2 is unimolecular. All others are bimolecular.
(c) $\text{Rate}_1 = k_1[NO]^2$; $\text{rate}_2 = k_2[H_2]$; $\text{rate}_3 = k_3[N_2O_2][H]$; $\text{rate}_4 = k_4[HO][H]$; $\text{rate}_5 = k_5[H][N_2O]$.

PROBLEMS

Problems with **colored** numbers are answered in Appendix E and worked in detail in the Student Solutions Manual. Problem sections match those in the text and provide the numbers of relevant sample problems. Most offer Concept Review Questions, Skill-Building Exercises (grouped in pairs covering the same concept), and Problems in Context. The Comprehensive Problems are based on material from any section or previous chapter.

Focusing on Reaction Rate

Concept Review Questions

16.1 What variable of a chemical reaction is measured over time to obtain the reaction rate?

16.2 How does an increase in pressure affect the rate of a gas-phase reaction? Explain.

16.3 A reaction is carried out with water as the solvent. How does the addition of more water to the reaction vessel affect the rate of the reaction? Explain.

16.4 A gas reacts with a solid that is present in large chunks. Then the reaction is run again with the solid pulverized. How does the increase in the surface area of the solid affect the rate of its reaction with the gas? Explain.

16.5 How does an increase in temperature affect the rate of a reaction? Explain the two factors involved.

16.6 In a kinetics experiment, a chemist places crystals of iodine in a closed reaction vessel, introduces a given quantity of H_2 gas, and obtains data to calculate the rate of HI formation. In a second experiment, she uses the same amounts of iodine and hydrogen, but first warms the flask to 130°C, a temperature above the sublimation point of iodine. In which of these experiments does the reaction proceed at a higher rate? Explain.

Expressing the Reaction Rate

(Sample Problem 16.1)

Concept Review Questions

16.7 Define *reaction rate*. Assuming constant temperature and a closed reaction vessel, why does the rate change with time?

16.8 (a) What is the difference between an average rate and an instantaneous rate? (b) What is the difference between an initial rate and an instantaneous rate?

16.9 Give two reasons to measure initial rates in a kinetics study.

16.10 For the reaction $A(g) \longrightarrow B(g)$, sketch two curves on the same set of axes that show
(a) The formation of product as a function of time
(b) The consumption of reactant as a function of time

16.11 For the reaction $C(g) \longrightarrow D(g)$, [C] vs. time is plotted:

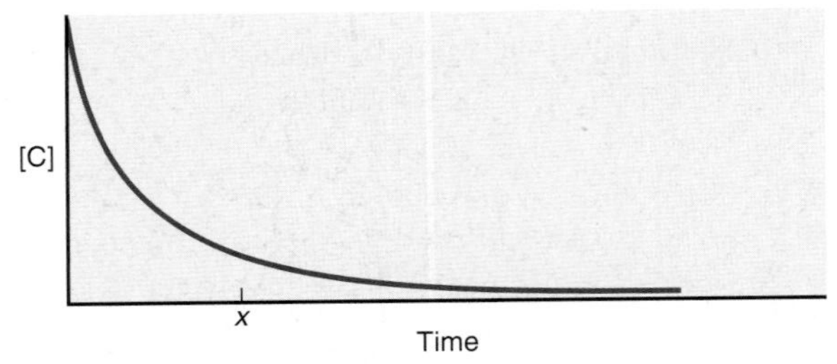

How do you determine each of the following?
(a) The average rate over the entire experiment
(b) The reaction rate at time *x*
(c) The initial reaction rate
(d) Would the values in parts (a), (b), and (c) be different if you plotted [D] vs. time? Explain.

Skill-Building Exercises (grouped in similar pairs)

16.12 The compound AX_2 decomposes according to the equation $2AX_2(g) \longrightarrow 2AX(g) + X_2(g)$. In one experiment, $[AX_2]$ was measured at various times and these data were obtained:

Time (s)	$[AX_2]$ (mol/L)
0.0	0.0500
2.0	0.0448
6.0	0.0300
8.0	0.0249
10.0	0.0209
20.0	0.0088

(a) Find the average rate over the entire experiment.
(b) Is the initial rate higher or lower than the rate in part (a)? Use graphical methods to estimate the initial rate.

16.13 (a) Use the data from Problem 16.12 to calculate the average rate from 8.0 to 20.0 s.
(b) Is the rate at exactly 5.0 s higher or lower than the rate in part (a)? Use graphical methods to estimate the rate at 5.0 s.

16.14 Express the rate of reaction in terms of the change in concentration of each of the reactants and products:

$$2A(g) \longrightarrow B(g) + C(g)$$

When [C] is increasing at 2 mol/L·s, how fast is [A] decreasing?

16.15 Express the rate of reaction in terms of the change in concentration of each of the reactants and products:

$$D(g) \longrightarrow \tfrac{3}{2}E(g) + \tfrac{5}{2}F(g)$$

When [E] is increasing at 0.25 mol/L·s, how fast is [F] increasing?

16.16 Express the rate of reaction in terms of the change in concentration of each of the reactants and products:

$$A(g) + 2B(g) \longrightarrow C(g)$$

When [B] is decreasing at 0.5 mol/L·s, how fast is [A] decreasing?

16.17 Express the rate of reaction in terms of the change in concentration of each of the reactants and products:

$$2D(g) + 3E(g) + F(g) \longrightarrow 2G(g) + H(g)$$

When [D] is decreasing at 0.1 mol/L·s, how fast is [H] increasing?

16.18 Reaction rate is expressed in terms of changes in concentration of reactants and products. Write a balanced equation for

$$\text{Rate} = -\frac{1}{2}\frac{\Delta[N_2O_5]}{\Delta t} = \frac{1}{4}\frac{\Delta[NO_2]}{\Delta t} = \frac{\Delta[O_2]}{\Delta t}$$

16.19 Reaction rate is expressed in terms of changes in concentration of reactants and products. Write a balanced equation for

$$\text{Rate} = -\frac{\Delta[CH_4]}{\Delta t} = -\frac{1}{2}\frac{\Delta[O_2]}{\Delta t} = \frac{1}{2}\frac{\Delta[H_2O]}{\Delta t} = \frac{\Delta[CO_2]}{\Delta t}$$

Problems in Context

16.20 The decomposition of NOBr is studied manometrically because the number of moles of gas changes; it cannot be studied colorimetrically because both NOBr and Br_2 are reddish brown:

$$2NOBr(g) \longrightarrow 2NO(g) + Br_2(g)$$

Use the data below to answer the following:
(a) Determine the average rate over the entire experiment.
(b) Determine the average rate between 2.00 and 4.00 s.
(c) Use graphical methods to estimate the initial reaction rate.
(d) Use graphical methods to estimate the rate at 7.00 s.
(e) At what time does the instantaneous rate equal the average rate over the entire experiment?

Time (s)	[NOBr] (mol/L)
0.00	0.0100
2.00	0.0071
4.00	0.0055
6.00	0.0045
8.00	0.0038
10.00	0.0033

16.21 The formation of ammonia is one of the most important processes in the chemical industry:

$$N_2(g) + 3H_2(g) \longrightarrow 2NH_3(g)$$

Express the rate in terms of changes in $[N_2]$, $[H_2]$, and $[NH_3]$.

16.22 Although the depletion of stratospheric ozone threatens life on Earth today, its accumulation was one of the crucial processes that allowed life to develop in prehistoric times:

$$3O_2(g) \longrightarrow 2O_3(g)$$

(a) Express the reaction rate in terms of $[O_2]$ and $[O_3]$.
(b) At a given instant, the reaction rate in terms of $[O_2]$ is 2.17×10^{-5} mol/L·s. What is it in terms of $[O_3]$?

The Rate Law and Its Components

(Sample Problems 16.2 to 16.4)

Concept Review Questions

16.23 The rate law for the general reaction

$$aA + bB + \cdots \longrightarrow cC + dD + \cdots$$

is rate $= k[A]^m[B]^n \cdots$. (a) Explain the meaning of *k*. (b) Explain the meanings of *m* and *n*. Does $m = a$ and $n = b$? Explain. (c) If the reaction is first order in A and second order in B, and time is measured in minutes (min), what are the units for k?

16.24 You are studying the reaction

$$A_2(g) + B_2(g) \longrightarrow 2AB(g)$$

to determine its rate law. Assuming that you have a valid experimental procedure for obtaining $[A_2]$ and $[B_2]$ at various times, explain how you determine (a) the initial rate, (b) the reaction orders, and (c) the rate constant.

16.25 By what factor does the rate change in each of the following cases (assuming constant temperature)?
(a) A reaction is first order in reactant A, and [A] is doubled.
(b) A reaction is second order in reactant B, and [B] is halved.
(c) A reaction is second order in reactant C, and [C] is tripled.

Skill-Building Exercises (grouped in similar pairs)

16.26 Give the individual reaction orders for all substances and the overall reaction order from the following rate law:

$$\text{Rate} = k[BrO_3^-][Br^-][H^+]^2$$

16.27 Give the individual reaction orders for all substances and the overall reaction order from the following rate law:

$$\text{Rate} = k\frac{[O_3]^2}{[O_2]}$$

16.28 By what factor does the rate in Problem 16.26 change if each of the following changes occurs: (a) $[BrO_3^-]$ is doubled; (b) $[Br^-]$ is halved; (c) $[H^+]$ is quadrupled?

16.29 By what factor does the rate in Problem 16.27 change if each of the following changes occurs: (a) $[O_3]$ is doubled; (b) $[O_2]$ is doubled; (c) $[O_2]$ is halved?

16.30 Give the individual reaction orders for all substances and the overall reaction order from this rate law:

$$\text{Rate} = k[NO_2]^2[Cl_2]$$

16.31 Give the individual reaction orders for all substances and the overall reaction order from this rate law:

$$\text{Rate} = k\frac{[HNO_2]^4}{[NO]^2}$$

16.32 By what factor does the rate in Problem 16.30 change if each of the following changes occurs: (a) $[NO_2]$ is tripled; (b) $[NO_2]$ and $[Cl_2]$ are doubled; (c) $[Cl_2]$ is halved?

16.33 By what factor does the rate in Problem 16.31 change if each of the following changes occurs: (a) $[HNO_2]$ is doubled; (b) [NO] is doubled; (c) $[HNO_2]$ is halved?

16.34 For the reaction

$$4A(g) + 3B(g) \longrightarrow 2C(g)$$

the following data were obtained at constant temperature:

Experiment	Initial Rate (mol/L·min)	Initial [A] (mol/L)	Initial [B] (mol/L)
1	5.00	0.100	0.100
2	45.0	0.300	0.100
3	10.0	0.100	0.200
4	90.0	0.300	0.200

(a) What is the order with respect to each reactant? (b) Write the rate law. (c) Calculate k (using the data from Expt 1).

16.35 For the reaction

$$A(g) + B(g) + C(g) \longrightarrow D(g)$$

the following data were obtained at constant temperature:

Expt	Initial Rate (mol/L·s)	Initial [A] (mol/L)	Initial [B] (mol/L)	Initial [C] (mol/L)
1	6.25×10^{-3}	0.0500	0.0500	0.0100
2	1.25×10^{-2}	0.1000	0.0500	0.0100
3	5.00×10^{-2}	0.1000	0.1000	0.0100
4	6.25×10^{-3}	0.0500	0.0500	0.0200

(a) What is the order with respect to each reactant? (b) Write the rate law. (c) Calculate k (using the data from Expt 1).

16.36 Without consulting Table 16.4, give the units of the rate constants for reactions with the following overall orders: (a) first order; (b) second order; (c) third order; (d) $\frac{5}{2}$ order.

16.37 Give the overall reaction order that corresponds to a rate constant with each of the following units: (a) mol/L·s; (b) yr^{-1}; (c) $(mol/L)^{1/2}\cdot s^{-1}$; (d) $(mol/L)^{-5/2}\cdot min^{-1}$.

Problems in Context

16.38 Phosgene is a toxic gas prepared by the reaction of carbon monoxide with chlorine:

$$CO(g) + Cl_2(g) \longrightarrow COCl_2(g)$$

These data were obtained in a kinetics study of its formation:

Experiment	Initial Rate (mol/L·s)	Initial [CO] (mol/L)	Initial $[Cl_2]$ (mol/L)
1	1.29×10^{-29}	1.00	0.100
2	1.33×10^{-30}	0.100	0.100
3	1.30×10^{-29}	0.100	1.00
4	1.32×10^{-31}	0.100	0.0100

(a) Write the rate law for the formation of phosgene.
(b) Calculate the average value of the rate constant.

Integrated Rate Laws: Concentration Changes over Time

(Sample Problems 16.5 to 16.7)

Concept Review Questions

16.39 How are integrated rate laws used to determine reaction order? What is the order in reactant if a plot of
(a) The natural logarithm of [reactant] vs. time is linear?
(b) The inverse of [reactant] vs. time is linear?
(c) [Reactant] vs. time is linear?

16.40 Define the *half-life* of a reaction. Explain on the molecular level why the half-life of a first-order reaction is constant.

Skill-Building Exercises (grouped in similar pairs)

16.41 For the simple decomposition reaction

$$AB(g) \longrightarrow A(g) + B(g)$$

rate $= k[AB]^2$ and $k = 0.2$ L/mol·s. How long will it take for [AB] to reach one-third of its initial concentration of 1.50 M?

16.42 For the reaction in Problem 16.41, what is [AB] after 10.0 s?

16.43 In a first-order decomposition reaction, 50.0% of a compound decomposes in 10.5 min. (a) What is the rate constant of the reaction? (b) How long does it take for 75.0% of the compound to decompose?

16.44 A decomposition reaction has a rate constant of 0.0012 yr^{-1}. (a) What is the half-life of the reaction? (b) How long does it take for [reactant] to reach 12.5% of its original value?

Problems in Context

16.45 In a study of ammonia production, an industrial chemist discovers that the compound decomposes to its elements N_2 and H_2 in a first-order process. She collects the following data:

Time (s)	0	1.000	2.000
$[NH_3]$ (mol/L)	4.000	3.986	3.974

(a) Use graphical methods to determine the rate constant.
(b) What is the half-life for ammonia decomposition?

Theories of Chemical Kinetics

(Sample Problems 16.8 and 16.9)

Concept Review Questions

16.46 What is the central idea of collision theory? How does this model explain the effect of concentration on reaction rate?

16.47 Is collision frequency the only factor affecting rate? Explain.

16.48 Arrhenius proposed that each reaction has an energy threshold that must be reached for the particles to react. The kinetic theory of gases proposes that the average kinetic energy of the particles is proportional to the absolute temperature. How do these concepts relate to the effect of temperature on rate?

16.49 Use the exponential term in the Arrhenius equation to explain how temperature affects reaction rate.

16.50 How is the activation energy determined from the Arrhenius equation?

16.51 (a) Graph the relationship between k (vertical axis) and T (horizontal axis). (b) Graph the relationship between ln k (vertical axis) and $1/T$ (horizontal axis). How is the activation energy determined from this graph?

16.52 (a) For a reaction with a given E_a, how does an increase in T affect the rate? (b) For a reaction at a given T, how does a decrease in E_a affect the rate?

16.53 In the reaction $AB + CD \rightleftharpoons EF$, 4×10^{-5} mol of AB molecules collide with 4×10^{-5} mol of CD molecules. Will 4×10^{-5} mol of EF form? Explain.

16.54 Assuming the activation energies are equal, which of the following reactions will proceed at a higher rate at 50°C? Explain.

$$NH_3(g) + HCl(g) \longrightarrow NH_4Cl(s)$$
$$N(CH_3)_3(g) + HCl(g) \longrightarrow (CH_3)_3NHCl(s)$$

Skill-Building Exercises (grouped in similar pairs)

16.55 For the reaction $A(g) + B(g) \longrightarrow AB(g)$, how many unique collisions between A and B are possible if there are four particles of A and three particles of B present in the vessel?

16.56 For the reaction $A(g) + B(g) \longrightarrow AB(g)$, how many unique collisions between A and B are possible if 1.01 mol of $A(g)$ and 2.12 mol of $B(g)$ are present in the vessel?

16.57 At 25°C, what is the fraction of collisions with energy equal to or greater than an activation energy of 100. kJ/mol?

16.58 If the temperature in Problem 16.57 is increased to 50.°C, by what factor does the fraction of collisions with energy equal to or greater than the activation energy change?

16.59 The rate constant of a reaction is 4.7×10^{-3} s^{-1} at 25°C, and the activation energy is 33.6 kJ/mol. What is k at 75°C?

16.60 The rate constant of a reaction is 4.50×10^{-5} L/mol·s at 195°C and 3.20×10^{-3} L/mol·s at 258°C. What is the activation energy of the reaction?

16.61 For the reaction $ABC + D \rightleftharpoons AB + CD$, $\Delta H^\circ_{rxn} = -55$ kJ/mol and $E_{a(fwd)} = 215$ kJ/mol. Assuming a one-step reaction, (a) draw a reaction energy diagram; (b) calculate $E_{a(rev)}$; and (c) sketch a possible transition state if ABC is V-shaped.

16.62 For the reaction $A_2 + B_2 \longrightarrow 2AB$, $E_{a(fwd)} = 125$ kJ/mol and $E_{a(rev)} = 85$ kJ/mol. Assuming the reaction occurs in one step, (a) draw a reaction energy diagram; (b) calculate ΔH°_{rxn}; and (c) sketch a possible transition state.

Problems in Context

16.63 Understanding the high-temperature formation and breakdown of the nitrogen oxides is essential for controlling the pollutants generated from power plants and cars. The first-order breakdown of dinitrogen monoxide to its elements has rate constants of 0.76/s at 727°C and 0.87/s at 757°C. What is the activation energy of this reaction?

16.64 Aqua regia, a mixture of HCl and HNO_3, has been used since alchemical times to dissolve many metals, including gold. Its orange color is due to the presence of nitrosyl chloride. Consider this one-step reaction for the formation of this compound:

$$NO(g) + Cl_2(g) \longrightarrow NOCl(g) + Cl(g) \qquad \Delta H^\circ = 83\text{ kJ}$$

(a) Draw a reaction energy diagram, given $E_{a(fwd)}$ is 86 kJ/mol.
(b) Calculate $E_{a(rev)}$.
(c) Sketch a possible transition state for the reaction. (*Note:* The atom sequence of nitrosyl chloride is Cl—N—O.)

Reaction Mechanisms: The Steps from Reactant to Product

(Sample Problem 16.10)

Concept Review Questions

16.65 Is the rate of an overall reaction lower, higher, or equal to the average rate of the individual steps? Explain.

16.66 Explain why the coefficients of an elementary step equal the reaction orders of its rate law but those of an overall reaction do not.

16.67 Is it possible for more than one mechanism to be consistent with the rate law of a given reaction? Explain.

16.68 What is the difference between a reaction intermediate and a transition state?

16.69 Why is a bimolecular step more reasonable physically than a termolecular step?

16.70 If a slow step precedes a fast step in a two-step mechanism, do the substances in the fast step appear in the rate law? Explain.

16.71 If a fast step precedes a slow step in a two-step mechanism, how is the fast step affected? How is this effect used to determine the validity of the mechanism?

Skill-Building Exercises (grouped in similar pairs)

16.72 The proposed mechanism for a reaction is

(1) $A(g) + B(g) \rightleftharpoons X(g)$ [fast]
(2) $X(g) + C(g) \longrightarrow Y(g)$ [slow]
(3) $Y(g) \longrightarrow D(g)$ [fast]

(a) What is the overall equation?
(b) Identify the intermediate(s), if any.
(c) What are the molecularity and the rate law for each step?
(d) Is the mechanism consistent with the actual rate law: rate = $k[A][B][C]$?
(e) Is the following one-step mechanism equally valid: $A(g) + B(g) + C(g) \longrightarrow D(g)$?

16.73 Consider the following mechanism:
(1) $ClO^-(aq) + H_2O(l) \rightleftharpoons HClO(aq) + OH^-(aq)$ [fast]
(2) $I^-(aq) + HClO(aq) \longrightarrow HIO(aq) + Cl^-(aq)$ [slow]
(3) $OH^-(aq) + HIO(aq) \longrightarrow H_2O(l) + IO^-(aq)$ [fast]
(a) What is the overall equation?
(b) Identify the intermediate(s), if any.
(c) What are the molecularity and the rate law for each step?
(d) Is the mechanism consistent with the actual rate law: rate = $k[ClO^-][I^-]$?

Problems in Context

16.74 In a study of nitrosyl halides, a chemist proposes the following mechanism for the synthesis of nitrosyl bromide:

$$NO(g) + Br_2(g) \rightleftharpoons NOBr_2(g) \quad \text{[fast]}$$
$$NOBr_2(g) + NO(g) \longrightarrow 2NOBr(g) \quad \text{[slow]}$$

If the rate law is rate = $k[NO]^2[Br_2]$, is the proposed mechanism valid? If so, show that it satisfies the three criteria for validity.

16.75 The rate law for $2NO(g) + O_2(g) \longrightarrow 2NO_2(g)$ is rate = $k[NO]^2[O_2]$. In addition to the mechanism in the text (p. 658), the following ones have been proposed:

I $2NO(g) + O_2(g) \longrightarrow 2NO_2(g)$

II $2NO(g) \rightleftharpoons N_2O_2(g)$ [fast]
$N_2O_2(g) + O_2(g) \longrightarrow 2NO_2(g)$ [slow]

III $2NO(g) \rightleftharpoons N_2(g) + O_2(g)$ [fast]
$N_2(g) + 2O_2(g) \longrightarrow 2NO_2(g)$ [slow]

(a) Which of these mechanisms is consistent with the rate law?
(b) Which of these mechanisms is most reasonable? Why?

Catalysis: Speeding Up a Reaction

Concept Review Questions

16.76 Consider the reaction $N_2O(g) \xrightarrow{Au} N_2(g) + \frac{1}{2}O_2(g)$.
(a) Does the gold catalyst (Au, above the arrow) act as a homogeneous or a heterogeneous catalyst?
(b) On the same set of axes, sketch the reaction energy diagrams for the catalyzed and the uncatalyzed reaction.

16.77 Does a catalyst increase reaction rate by the same means as a rise in temperature does? Explain.

16.78 In a classroom demonstration, hydrogen gas and oxygen gas are mixed in a balloon. The mixture is stable under normal conditions, but if a spark is applied to it or some powdered metal is added, the mixture explodes. (a) Is the spark acting as a catalyst? Explain. (b) Is the metal acting as a catalyst? Explain.

16.79 A principle of green chemistry is that the energy needs of industrial processes should have minimal environmental impact. How can the use of catalysts lead to "greener" technologies?

16.80 Enzymes are remarkably efficient catalysts that can increase reaction rates by as many as 20 orders of magnitude.
(a) How does an enzyme affect the transition state of a reaction, and how does this effect increase the reaction rate?
(b) What characteristics of enzymes give them this effectiveness as catalysts?

Comprehensive Problems

16.81 Experiments show that each of the following redox reactions is second order overall:
Reaction 1: $NO_2(g) + CO(g) \longrightarrow NO(g) + CO_2(g)$
Reaction 2: $NO(g) + O_3(g) \longrightarrow NO_2(g) + O_2(g)$
(a) When $[NO_2]$ in reaction 1 is doubled, the rate quadruples. Write the rate law for this reaction.
(b) When [NO] in reaction 2 is doubled, the rate doubles. Write the rate law for this reaction.
(c) In each reaction, the initial concentrations of the reactants are equal. For each reaction, what is the ratio of the initial rate to the rate when the reaction is 50% complete?
(d) In reaction 1, the initial $[NO_2]$ is twice the initial [CO]. What is the ratio of the initial rate to the rate at 50% completion?
(e) In reaction 2, the initial [NO] is twice the initial $[O_3]$. What is the ratio of the initial rate to the rate at 50% completion?

16.82 Consider the following reaction energy diagram:

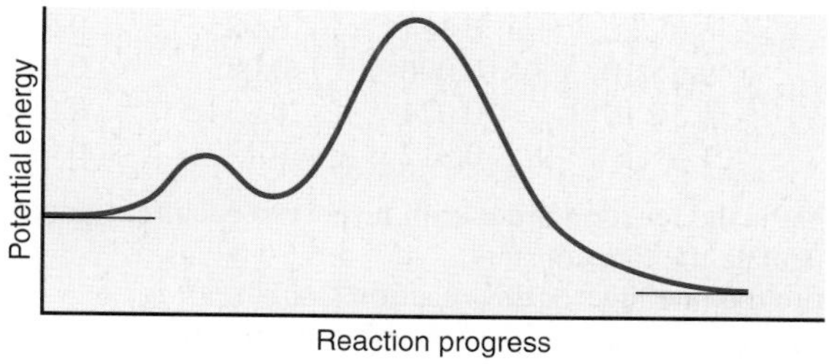

(a) How many elementary steps are in the reaction mechanism?
(b) Which step is rate limiting?
(c) Is the overall reaction exothermic or endothermic?

16.83 Reactions between certain organic (alkyl) halides and water produce alcohols. Consider the overall reaction for *t*-butyl bromide (2-bromo-2-methylpropane):

$$(CH_3)_3CBr(aq) + H_2O(l) \longrightarrow (CH_3)_3COH(aq) + H^+(aq) + Br^-(aq)$$

The experimental rate law is rate = $k[(CH_3)_3CBr]$. The accepted mechanism for the reaction is
(1) $(CH_3)_3C{-}Br(aq) \longrightarrow (CH_3)_3C^+(aq) + Br^-(aq)$ [slow]
(2) $(CH_3)_3C^+(aq) + H_2O(l) \longrightarrow (CH_3)_3C{-}OH_2^{\ +}(aq)$ [fast]
(3) $(CH_3)_3C{-}OH_2^{\ +}(aq) \longrightarrow H^+(aq) + (CH_3)_3C{-}OH(aq)$ [fast]
(a) Why doesn't H_2O appear in the rate law?
(b) Write rate laws for the elementary steps.
(c) What reaction intermediates appear in the mechanism?
(d) Show that the mechanism is consistent with the experimental rate law.

16.84 Archeologists can determine the age of an artifact made of wood or bone by measuring the amount of the radioactive isotope ^{14}C present in the object. The amount of isotope decreases in a first-order process. If 15.5% of the original amount of ^{14}C is present in a wooden tool at the time of analysis, what is the age of the tool? The half-life of ^{14}C is 5730 yr.

16.85 A slightly bruised apple will rot extensively in about 4 days at room temperature (20°C). If it is kept in the refrigerator at 0°C, the same extent of rotting takes about 16 days. What is the activation energy for the rotting reaction?

16.86 Benzoyl peroxide, the substance most widely used against acne, has a half-life of 9.8×10^3 days when refrigerated. How long will it take to lose 5% of its potency (95% remaining)?

16.87 The rate law for the reaction

$$NO_2(g) + CO(g) \longrightarrow NO(g) + CO_2(g)$$

is rate $= k[NO_2]^2$; one possible mechanism is shown on p. 657.
(a) Draw a reaction energy diagram for that mechanism, given that $\Delta H^\circ_{overall} = -226$ kJ/mol.
(b) Consider the following alternative mechanism:

(1) $2NO_2(g) \longrightarrow N_2(g) + 2O_2(g)$ [slow]
(2) $2CO(g) + O_2(g) \longrightarrow 2CO_2(g)$ [fast]
(3) $N_2(g) + O_2(g) \longrightarrow 2NO(g)$ [fast]

Is the alternative mechanism consistent with the rate law? Is one mechanism more reasonable physically? Explain.

16.88 Consider the following general reaction and data:

$$2A + 2B + C \longrightarrow D + 3E$$

Expt	Initial Rate (mol/L·s)	Initial [A] (mol/L)	Initial [B] (mol/L)	Initial [C] (mol/L)
1	6.0×10^{-6}	0.024	0.085	0.032
2	9.6×10^{-5}	0.096	0.085	0.032
3	1.5×10^{-5}	0.024	0.034	0.080
4	1.5×10^{-6}	0.012	0.170	0.032

(a) What is the reaction order with respect to each reactant?
(b) Calculate the rate constant.
(c) Write the rate law for this reaction.
(d) Express the rate in terms of changes in concentration with time for each of the components.

16.89 In acidic solution, the breakdown of sucrose into glucose and fructose has this rate law: rate $= k[H^+][\text{sucrose}]$. The initial rate of sucrose breakdown is measured in a solution that is 0.01 M H^+, 1.0 M sucrose, 0.1 M fructose, and 0.1 M glucose. How does the rate change if
(a) [Sucrose] is changed to 2.5 M?
(b) [Sucrose], [fructose], and [glucose] are all changed to 0.5 M?
(c) $[H^+]$ is changed to 0.0001 M?
(d) [Sucrose] and $[H^+]$ are both changed to 0.1 M?

16.90 The citric acid cycle is the central reaction sequence in human metabolism. One of the key steps is catalyzed by the enzyme isocitrate dehydrogenase and the oxidizing agent NAD^+. In yeast, the reaction is eleventh order:

$$\text{Rate} = k[\text{enzyme}][\text{isocitrate}]^4[\text{AMP}]^2[\text{NAD}^+]^m[\text{Mg}^{2+}]^2$$

What is the order with respect to NAD^+?

16.91 The following molecular scenes represent starting mixtures I and II for the reaction of A (*black*) with B (*orange*):

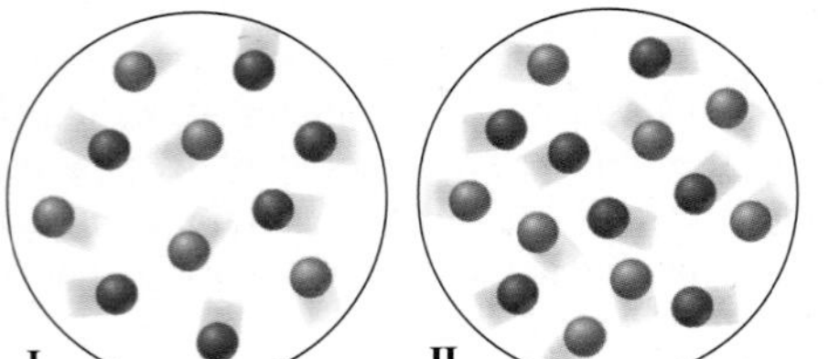

I II

Each sphere represents 0.010 mol, and the volume is 0.50 L. If the reaction is first order in A and first order in B and the initial rate for I is 8.3×10^{-4} mol/L·min, what is the initial rate for II?

16.92 Experiment shows that the rate of formation of carbon tetrachloride from chloroform,

$$CHCl_3(g) + Cl_2(g) \longrightarrow CCl_4(g) + HCl(g)$$

is first order in $CHCl_3$, $\frac{1}{2}$ order in Cl_2, and $\frac{3}{2}$ order overall. Show that the following mechanism is consistent with the rate law:

(1) $Cl_2(g) \rightleftharpoons 2Cl(g)$ [fast]
(2) $Cl(g) + CHCl_3(g) \longrightarrow HCl(g) + CCl_3(g)$ [slow]
(3) $CCl_3(g) + Cl(g) \longrightarrow CCl_4(g)$ [fast]

16.93 A biochemist studying breakdown of the insecticide DDT finds that it decomposes by a first-order reaction with a half-life of 12 yr. How long does it take DDT in a soil sample to decompose from 275 ppbm to 10. ppbm (parts per billion by mass)?

16.94 Insulin is a polypeptide hormone that is released into the blood from the pancreas and stimulates fat and muscle to take up glucose; the insulin is used up in a first-order process. In a certain patient, it has a half-life of 3.5 min. To maintain an adequate blood concentration of insulin, it must be replenished in a time interval equal to $1/k$. How long is the time interval for this patient?

16.95 For the reaction $A(g) + B(g) \longrightarrow AB(g)$, the rate is 0.20 mol/L·s, when $[A]_0 = [B]_0 = 1.0$ mol/L. If the reaction is first order in B and second order in A, what is the rate when $[A]_0 = 2.0$ mol/L and $[B]_0 = 3.0$ mol/L?

16.96 The acid-catalyzed hydrolysis of sucrose occurs by the following overall reaction, whose kinetic data are given below:

$$\underset{\text{sucrose}}{C_{12}H_{22}O_{11}(s)} + H_2O(l) \longrightarrow \underset{\text{glucose}}{C_6H_{12}O_6(aq)} + \underset{\text{fructose}}{C_6H_{12}O_6(aq)}$$

[Sucrose] (mol/L)	Time (h)
0.501	0.00
0.451	0.50
0.404	1.00
0.363	1.50
0.267	3.00

(a) Determine the rate constant and the half-life of the reaction.
(b) How long does it take to hydrolyze 75% of the sucrose?
(c) Other studies have shown that this reaction is actually second order overall but appears to follow first-order kinetics. (Such a reaction is called a *pseudo–first-order reaction.*) Suggest a reason for this apparent first-order behavior.

16.97 At body temperature (37°C), the rate constant of an enzyme-catalyzed decomposition is 2.3×10^{14} times that of the uncatalyzed reaction. If the frequency factor, A, is the same for both processes, by how much does the enzyme lower the E_a?

16.98 Is each of these statements true? If not, explain why.
(a) At a given T, all molecules have the same kinetic energy.
(b) Halving the P of a gaseous reaction doubles the rate.
(c) A higher activation energy gives a lower reaction rate.
(d) A temperature rise of 10°C doubles the rate of any reaction.
(e) If reactant molecules collide with greater energy than the activation energy, they change into product molecules.
(f) The activation energy of a reaction depends on temperature.
(g) The rate of a reaction increases as the reaction proceeds.
(h) Activation energy depends on collision frequency.
(i) A catalyst increases the rate by increasing collision frequency.
(j) Exothermic reactions are faster than endothermic reactions.
(k) Temperature has no effect on the frequency factor (A).
(l) The activation energy of a reaction is lowered by a catalyst.

(m) For most reactions, ΔH_{rxn} is lowered by a catalyst.
(n) The orientation probability factor (p) is near 1 for reactions between single atoms.
(o) The initial rate of a reaction is its maximum rate.
(p) A bimolecular reaction is generally twice as fast as a unimolecular reaction.
(q) The molecularity of an elementary reaction is proportional to the molecular complexity of the reactant(s).

16.99 For the decomposition of gaseous dinitrogen pentaoxide, $2N_2O_5(g) \longrightarrow 4NO_2(g) + O_2(g)$, the rate constant is $k = 2.8\times10^{-3}\ s^{-1}$ at 60°C. The initial concentration of N_2O_5 is 1.58 mol/L. (a) What is $[N_2O_5]$ after 5.00 min? (b) What fraction of the N_2O_5 has decomposed after 5.00 min?

16.100 Even when a mechanism is consistent with the rate law, later work may show it to be incorrect. For example, the reaction between hydrogen and iodine has this rate law: rate $= k[H_2][I_2]$. The long-accepted mechanism had a single bimolecular step; that is, the overall reaction was thought to be elementary:

$$H_2(g) + I_2(g) \longrightarrow 2HI(g)$$

In the 1960s, however, spectroscopic evidence showed the presence of free I atoms during the reaction. Kineticists have since proposed a three-step mechanism:

(1) $I_2(g) \rightleftharpoons 2I(g)$ [fast]
(2) $H_2(g) + I(g) \rightleftharpoons H_2I(g)$ [fast]
(3) $H_2I(g) + I(g) \longrightarrow 2HI(g)$ [slow]

Show that this mechanism is consistent with the rate law.

16.101 Suggest an experimental method for measuring the change in concentration with time for each of the following reactions:
(a) $CH_3CH_2Br(l) + H_2O(l) \longrightarrow CH_3CH_2OH(l) + HBr(aq)$
(b) $2NO(g) + Cl_2(g) \longrightarrow 2NOCl(g)$

16.102 An atmospheric chemist fills a container with gaseous N_2O_5 to a pressure of 125 kPa, and the gas decomposes to NO_2 and O_2. What is the partial pressure of NO_2, P_{NO_2} (in kPa), when the total pressure is 178 kPa?

16.103 Many drugs decompose in blood by a first-order process. (a) Two tablets of aspirin supply 0.60 g of the active compound. After 30 min, this compound reaches a maximum concentration of 2 mg/100 mL of blood. If the half-life for its breakdown is 90 min, what is its concentration (in mg/100 mL) 2.5 h after it reaches its maximum concentration?
(b) For the decomposition of an antibiotic in a person with a normal temperature (98.6°F), $k = 3.1\times10^{-5}\ s^{-1}$; for a person with a fever (temperature of 101.9°F), $k = 3.9\times10^{-5}\ s^{-1}$. If the person with the fever must take another pill when $\frac{2}{3}$ of the first pill has decomposed, how many hours should she wait to take a second pill? A third pill? (Assume the pill is effective immediately.)
(c) Calculate E_a for decomposition of the antibiotic in part (b).

16.104 While developing a catalytic process to make ethylene glycol from synthesis gas ($CO + H_2$), a chemical engineer finds the rate is fourth order with respect to gas pressure. The uncertainty in the pressure reading is 5%. When the catalyst is modified, the rate increases by 10%. If you were the company patent attorney, would you file for a patent on this catalyst modification? Explain.

16.105 Iodide ion reacts with chloromethane to displace chloride ion in a common organic substitution reaction:

$$I^- + CH_3Cl \longrightarrow CH_3I + Cl^-$$

(a) Draw a wedge-bond structure of chloroform and indicate the most effective direction of I^- attack.
(b) The analogous reaction with 2-chlorobutane [Figure P16.105(b)] results in a major change in specific rotation as measured by polarimetry. Explain, showing a wedge-bond structure of the product.
(c) Under different conditions, 2-chlorobutane loses Cl^- in a rate-determining step to form a planar intermediate [Figure P16.105(c)]. This cationic species reacts with HI and then loses H^+ to form a product that exhibits no optical activity. Explain, showing a wedge-bond structure.

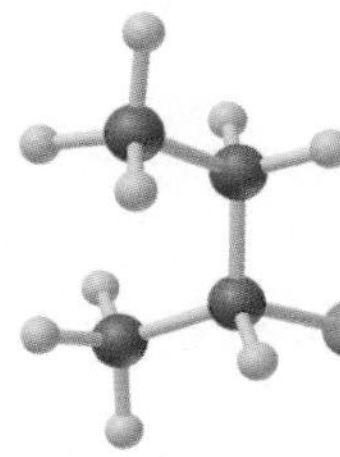
Figure P16.105(b)

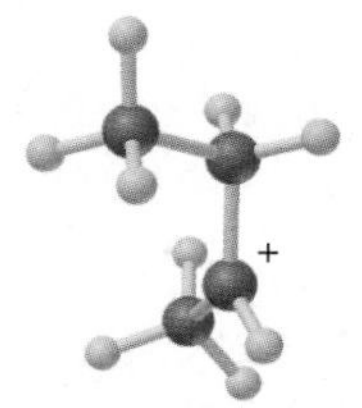
Figure P16.105(c)

16.106 Assume water boils at 100.0°C in Houston (near sea level), and at 90.0°C in Cripple Creek, Colorado (near 9500 ft). If it takes 4.8 min to cook an egg in Cripple Creek and 4.5 min in Houston, what is E_a for this process?

16.107 Sulfonation of benzene has the following mechanism:
(1) $2H_2SO_4 \longrightarrow H_3O^+ + HSO_4^- + SO_3$ [fast]
(2) $SO_3 + C_6H_6 \longrightarrow H(C_6H_5^+)SO_3^-$ [slow]
(3) $H(C_6H_5^+)SO_3^- + HSO_4^- \longrightarrow C_6H_5SO_3^- + H_2SO_4$ [fast]
(4) $C_6H_5SO_3^- + H_3O^+ \longrightarrow C_6H_5SO_3H + H_2O$ [fast]
(a) Write an overall equation for the reaction. (b) Write the overall rate law in terms of the initial rate of the reaction.

16.108 In the lower troposphere, ozone is one of the components of photochemical smog. It is generated in air when nitrogen dioxide, formed by the oxidation of nitrogen monoxide from car exhaust, reacts by the following mechanism:
(1) $NO_2(g) \xrightarrow[h\nu]{k_1} NO(g) + O(g)$
(2) $O(g) + O_2(g) \xrightarrow{k_2} O_3(g)$
Assuming the rate of formation of atomic oxygen in step 1 equals the rate of its consumption in step 2, use the data below to calculate (a) the concentration of atomic oxygen [O]; (b) the rate of ozone formation.

$k_1 = 6.0\times10^{-3}\ s^{-1}$ $\quad [NO_2] = 4.0\times10^{-9}\ M$
$k_2 = 1.0\times10^{6}\ L/mol{\cdot}s$ $\quad [O_2] = 1.0\times10^{-2}\ M$

16.109 Chlorine is commonly used to disinfect drinking water, and inactivation of pathogens by chlorine follows first-order kinetics. The following data show *E. coli* inactivation:

Contact Time (min)	Percent (%) Inactivation
0.00	0.0
0.50	68.3
1.00	90.0
1.50	96.8
2.00	99.0
2.50	99.7
3.00	99.9

(a) Determine the first-order inactivation constant, k. [*Hint:* % inactivation $= 100 \times (1 - [A]_t/[A]_0)$.]
(b) How much contact time is required for 95% inactivation?

16.110 The reaction and law for the gas-phase decomposition of dinitrogen pentaoxide are

$$2N_2O_5(g) \longrightarrow 4NO_2(g) + O_2(g) \qquad \text{rate} = k[N_2O_5]$$

Which of the following can be considered valid mechanisms for the reaction?

I One-step collision

II $2N_2O_5(g) \longrightarrow 2NO_3(g) + 2NO_2(g)$ [slow]
$2NO_3(g) \longrightarrow 2NO_2(g) + 2O(g)$ [fast]
$2O(g) \longrightarrow O_2(g)$ [fast]

III $N_2O_5(g) \rightleftharpoons NO_3(g) + NO_2(g)$ [fast]
$NO_2(g) + N_2O_5(g) \longrightarrow 3NO_2(g) + O(g)$ [slow]
$NO_3(g) + O(g) \longrightarrow NO_2(g) + O_2(g)$ [fast]

IV $2N_2O_5(g) \rightleftharpoons 2NO_2(g) + N_2O_3(g) + 3O(g)$ [fast]
$N_2O_3(g) + O(g) \longrightarrow 2NO_2(g)$ [slow]
$2O(g) \longrightarrow O_2(g)$ [fast]

V $2N_2O_5(g) \longrightarrow N_4O_{10}(g)$ [slow]
$N_4O_{10}(g) \longrightarrow 4NO_2(g) + O_2(g)$ [fast]

16.111 Nitrification is a biological process for removing NH_3 from wastewater as NH_4^+:

$$NH_4^+ + 2O_2 \longrightarrow NO_3^- + 2H^+ + H_2O$$

The first-order rate constant is given as

$$k_1 = 0.47e^{0.095\,(T=15°C)}$$

where k_1 is in day^{-1} and T is in °C.
(a) If the initial concentration of NH_3 is 3.0 mol/m^3, how long will it take to reduce the concentration to 0.35 mol/m^3 in the spring ($T = 20°C$)?
(b) In the winter ($T = 10°C$)?
(c) Using your answer to part (a), what is the rate of O_2 consumption?

16.112 Carbon disulfide, a poisonous, flammable liquid, is an excellent solvent for phosphorus, sulfur, and some other nonmetals. A kinetic study of its gaseous decomposition reveals these data:

Experiment	Initial Rate (mol/L·s)	Initial [CS_2] (mol/L)
1	2.7×10^{-7}	0.100
2	2.2×10^{-7}	0.080
3	1.5×10^{-7}	0.055
4	1.2×10^{-7}	0.044

(a) Write the rate law for the decomposition of CS_2.
(b) Calculate the average value of the rate constant.

16.113 Like any catalyst, palladium, platinum, and nickel catalyze both directions of a reaction: addition of hydrogen to (hydrogenation) and its elimination from (dehydrogenation) carbon double bonds.
(a) Which variable determines whether an alkene will be hydrogenated or dehydrogenated?
(b) Which reaction requires a higher temperature?
(c) How can all-*trans* fats arise during hydrogenation of fats that contain some *cis*- double bonds?

16.114 In a *clock reaction,* a dramatic color change occurs at a time determined by concentration and temperature. Consider the iodine clock reaction, whose overall equation is

$$2I^-(aq) + S_2O_8^{2-}(aq) \longrightarrow I_2(aq) + 2SO_4^{2-}(aq)$$

As I_2 forms, it is immediately consumed by its reaction with a fixed amount of added $S_2O_3^{2-}$:

$$I_2(aq) + 2S_2O_3^{2-}(aq) \longrightarrow 2I^-(aq) + S_4O_6^{2-}(aq)$$

Once the $S_2O_3^{2-}$ is consumed, the excess I_2 forms a blue-black product with starch present in solution:

$$I_2 + \text{starch} \longrightarrow \text{starch}\cdot I_2 \text{ (blue-black)}$$

The rate of the reaction is also influenced by the total concentration of ions, so KCl and $(NH_4)_2SO_4$ are added to maintain a constant value. Use the data below, obtained at 23°C, to determine:
(a) The average rate for each trial
(b) The order with respect to each reactant
(c) The rate constant
(d) The rate law for the overall reaction

	Expt 1	Expt 2	Expt 3
0.200 M KI (mL)	10.0	20.0	20.0
0.100 M $Na_2S_2O_8$ (mL)	20.0	20.0	10.0
0.0050 M $Na_2S_2O_3$ (mL)	10.0	10.0	10.0
0.200 M KCl (mL)	10.0	0.0	0.0
0.100 M $(NH_4)_2SO_4$ (mL)	0.0	0.0	10.0
Time to color (s)	29.0	14.5	14.5

16.115 Heat transfer to and from a reaction flask is often a critical factor in controlling reaction rate. The heat transferred (q) depends on a heat transfer coefficient (h) for the flask material, the temperature difference (ΔT) across the flask wall, and the commonly "wetted" area (A) of the flask and bath, $q = hA\Delta T$. When an exothermic reaction is run at a given T, there is a bath temperature at which the reaction can no longer be controlled, and the reaction "runs away" suddenly. A similar problem is often seen when a reaction is "scaled up" from, say, a half-filled small flask to a half-filled large flask. Explain these behaviors.

16.116 The molecular scenes below represent the first-order reaction in which cyclopropane (*red*) is converted to propene (*green*):

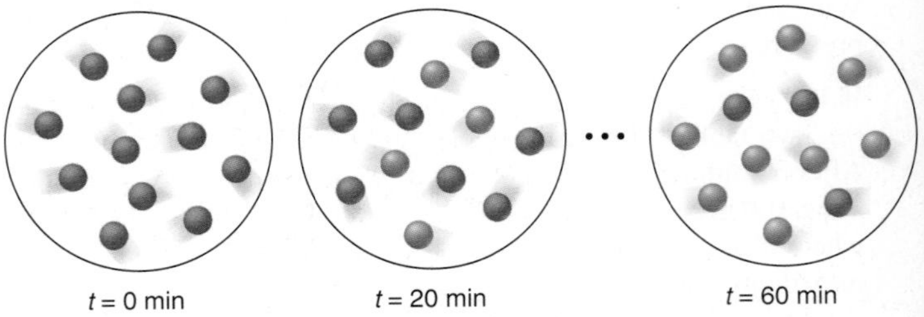

Determine (a) the half-life and (b) the rate constant.

16.117 The growth of *Pseudomonas* bacteria is modeled as a first-order process with $k = 0.035$ min^{-1} at 37°C. The initial *Pseudomonas* population density is 1.0×10^3 cells/L. (a) What is the population density after 2 h? (b) What is the time required for the population to go from 1.0×10^3 to 2.0×10^3 cells/L?

16.118 Consider the following organic reaction, in which one halogen replaces another in an alkyl halide:

$$CH_3CH_2Br + KI \longrightarrow CH_3CH_2I + KBr$$

In acetone, this particular reaction goes to completion because KI is soluble in acetone but KBr is not. In the mechanism, I^- approaches the carbon *opposite* to the Br (see Figure 16.20, with I^- instead of OH^-). After Br^- has been replaced by I^- and precipitates as KBr, other I^- ions react with the ethyl iodide by the same mechanism.

(a) If we designate the carbon bonded to the halogen as C-1, what is the shape around C-1 and the hybridization of C-1 in ethyl iodide?
(b) In the transition state, one of the two lobes of the unhybridized $2p$ orbital of C-1 overlaps a p orbital of I, while the other lobe overlaps a p orbital of Br. What is the shape around C-1 and the hybridization of C-1 in the transition state?
(c) The deuterated reactant, CH_3CHDBr (where D is deuterium, ^2H), has two optical isomers because C-1 is chiral. If the reaction is run with one of the isomers, the ethyl iodide is *not* optically active. Explain.

16.119 Another radioisotope of iodine, ^{131}I, is also used to study thyroid function (see Follow-Up Problem 16.7). A patient is given a sample that is 1.7×10^{-4} M ^{131}I. If the half-life is 8.04 days, what fraction of the radioactivity remains after 30. days?

16.120 The effect of substrate concentration on the first-order growth rate of a microbial population follows the Monod equation:

$$\mu = \frac{\mu_{max} S}{K_s + S}$$

where μ is the first-order growth rate (s^{-1}), μ_{max} is the maximum growth rate (s^{-1}), S is the substrate concentration (kg/m^3), and K_s is the value of S that gives one-half the maximum growth rate (kg/m^3). For $\mu_{max} = 1.5\times10^{-4}$ s^{-1} and $K_s = 0.03$ kg/m^3:
(a) Plot μ vs. S for S between 0.0 and 1.0 kg/m^3.
(b) The initial population density is 5.0×10^3 cells/m^3. What is the density after 1.0 h, if the initial S is 0.30 kg/m^3?
(c) What is it if the initial S is 0.70 kg/m^3?

16.121 The scenes depict four initial reaction mixtures for the reaction of A (*blue*) and B (*yellow*), with and without a solid present (*gray cubes*). The initial rate, $-\Delta[A]/\Delta t$ (in mol/L·s), is shown, with each sphere representing 0.010 mol and the container volume at 0.50 L.

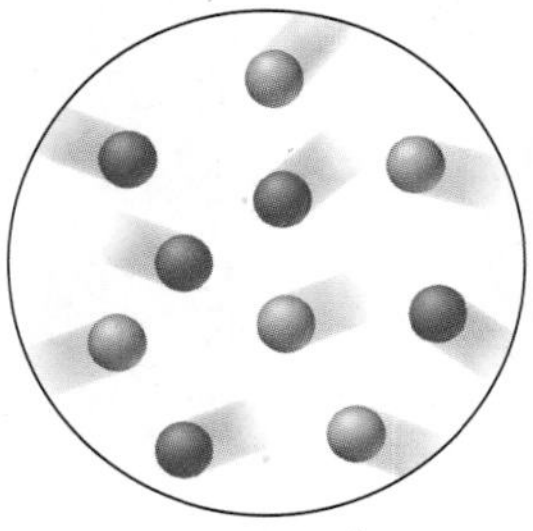

I 3.5×10^{-4}

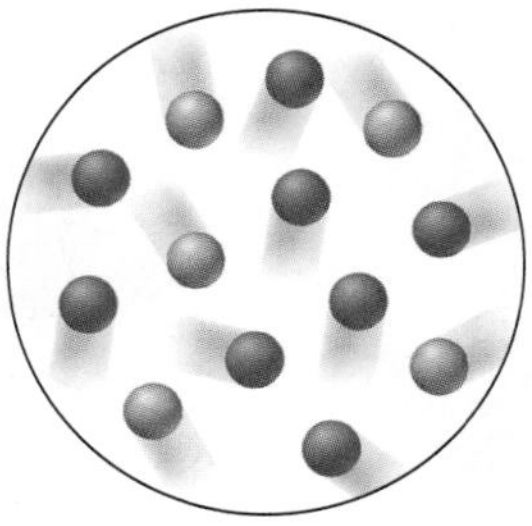

II 5.6×10^{-4}

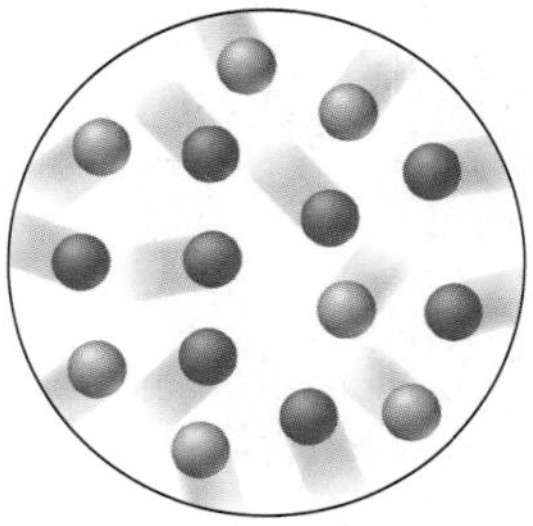

III 5.6×10^{-4}

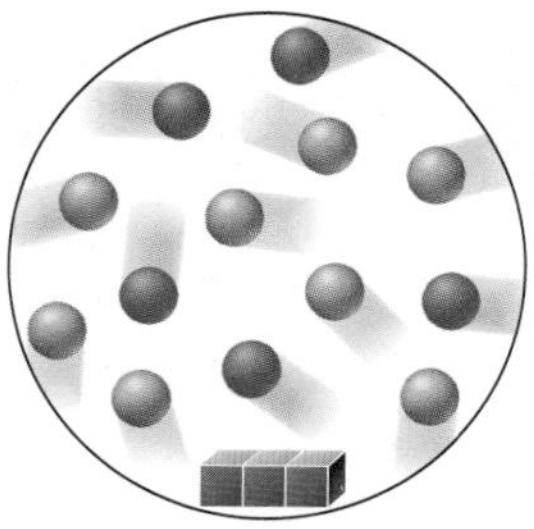

IV 4.9×10^{-4}

(a) What is the rate law in the absence of a catalyst?
(b) What is the overall reaction order?
(c) Find the rate constant.
(d) Do the gray cubes have a catalytic effect? Explain.

16.122 The mathematics of the first-order rate law can be applied to any situation in which a quantity decreases by a constant fraction per unit of time (or unit of any other variable).
(a) As light moves through a solution, its intensity decreases per unit distance traveled in the solution. Show that

$$\ln\left(\frac{\text{intensity of light leaving the solution}}{\text{intensity of light entering the solution}}\right)$$
$$= -\text{fraction of light removed per unit of length} \times \text{distance traveled in solution}$$

(b) The value of your savings declines under conditions of constant inflation. Show that

$$\ln\left(\frac{\text{value remaining}}{\text{initial value}}\right)$$
$$= -\text{fraction lost per unit of time} \times \text{savings time interval}$$

16.123 Figure 16.25 (p. 662) shows key steps in the metal-catalyzed (M) hydrogenation of ethylene:

$$C_2H_4(g) + H_2(g) \xrightarrow{M} C_2H_6(g)$$

Use the following symbols to write a mechanism that gives the overall equation:

$H_2(ads)$	adsorbed hydrogen molecules
M—H	hydrogen atoms bonded to metal atoms
$C_2H_4(ads)$	adsorbed ethylene molecules
$C_2H_5(ads)$	adsorbed ethyl radicals

16.124 Human liver enzymes catalyze the degradation of ingested toxins. By what factor is the rate of a detoxification changed if an enzyme lowers the E_a by 5 kJ/mol at 37°C?

16.125 Acetone is one of the most important solvents in organic chemistry, used to dissolve everything from fats and waxes to airplane glue and nail polish. At high temperatures, it decomposes in a first-order process to methane and ketene ($CH_2{=}C{=}O$). At 600°C, the rate constant is 8.7×10^{-3} s^{-1}.
(a) What is the half-life of the reaction?
(b) How long does it take for 40.% of a sample of acetone to decompose?
(c) How long does it take for 90.% of a sample of acetone to decompose?

16.126 A (*green*), B (*blue*), and C (*red*) are structural isomers. The molecular filmstrip depicts them undergoing a chemical change as time proceeds.

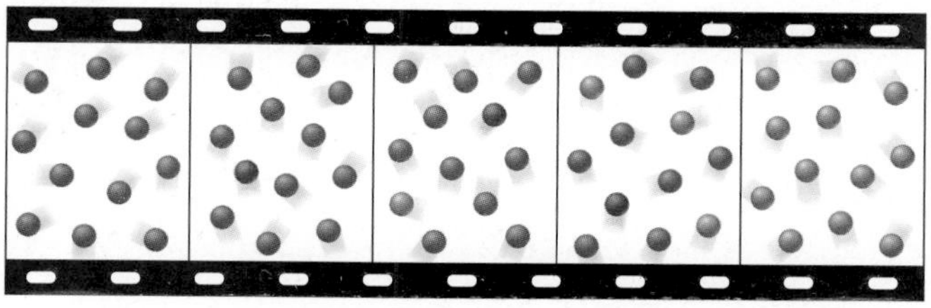

1 $t = 0$ 2 3 4 5 $t = \infty$

(a) Write a mechanism for the reaction.
(b) What role does C play?

Equilibrium: The Extent of Chemical Reactions

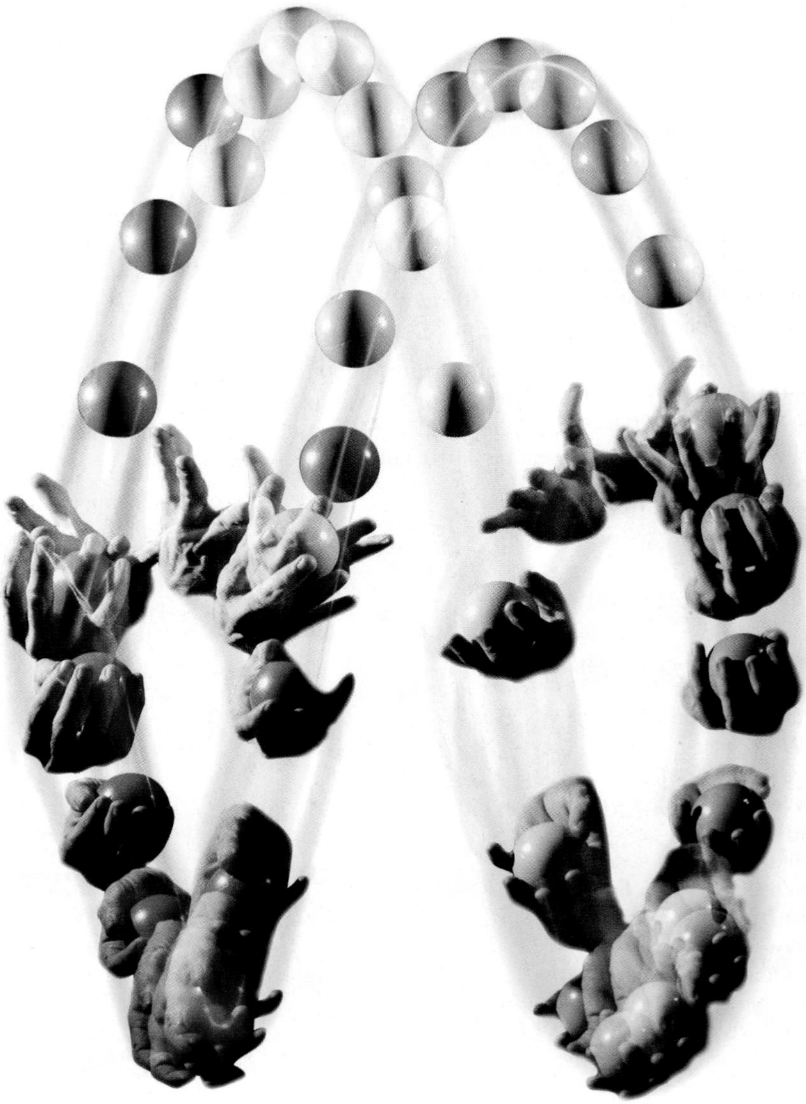

17

Concepts and skills to review before you study this chapter

- reversibility of reactions (Section 4.7)
- equilibrium vapor pressure (Section 12.2)
- equilibrium nature of a saturated solution (Section 13.4)
- dependence of rate on concentration (Sections 16.2 and 16.5)
- rate laws for elementary reactions (Section 16.6)
- function of a catalyst (Section 16.7)

Just as reactions vary greatly in their speed, they also vary greatly in their extent. Indeed, kinetics and equilibrium apply to different aspects of a reaction:

- Kinetics applies to the *speed* (or rate) of a reaction, the concentration of reactant that disappears (or of product that appears) per unit time.
- Equilibrium applies to the *extent* of a reaction, the concentrations of reactant and product present after an unlimited time, that is, when no further change occurs.

As you'll see, at equilibrium, no further *net* change occurs because the forward and reverse reactions reach a *balance*. Like balls being juggled *(photo opposite)* or traffic going back and forth across a bridge or people going up and down an escalator, the change in one direction is balanced by the change in the other. A fast reaction may go almost completely, just partially, or only slightly toward products before this balance is reached. Consider acid dissociation in water. In 1 *M* HCl, virtually all the hydrogen chloride molecules are dissociated into ions, whereas fewer than 1% of the acetic acid molecules are dissociated in 1 *M* CH_3COOH. Yet both reactions take less than a second. Similarly, some slow reactions yield a large amount of product, whereas others yield very little. After a few years, a steel water-storage tank will rust, and it will do so completely given enough time. But, no matter how long you wait, the water inside the tank will not decompose to hydrogen and oxygen.

Knowing the extent of a given reaction is crucial. How much product—medicine, polymer, fuel—can you obtain from a particular reaction mixture? How can you adjust conditions to obtain more? If a reaction is slow but has a good yield, will a catalyst speed it up enough to make it useful?

IN THIS CHAPTER . . . We consider the principles of equilibrium in systems of gases and pure liquids and solids.

- We examine the equilibrium state at the macroscopic and molecular levels and see that equilibrium occurs when the forward and reverse reaction rates are equal.
- We contrast the reaction quotient, *Q*, which changes as the reaction proceeds, with the equilibrium constant, *K*, which applies to the reaction at equilibrium.
- We express the equilibrium condition in terms of concentrations or pressures and see how the two expressions are related.
- We develop a systematic approach to solving a variety of equilibrium problems.
- We compare values of *Q* and *K* to determine the direction in which a system must proceed to reach equilibrium.
- We introduce Le Châtelier's principle, which explains how a change in conditions—concentration, pressure, temperature, or catalyst—affects the equilibrium state, and we apply this principle to a major industrial process.
- We explore how equilibrium concepts operate in metabolic pathways.

17.1 • THE EQUILIBRIUM STATE AND THE EQUILIBRIUM CONSTANT

Experimental results from countless reactions have shown that, *given sufficient time, the concentrations of reactants and products no longer change.* This apparent cessation of chemical change occurs because *all reactions are reversible and reach a state of equilibrium.* Let's examine a chemical system at the macroscopic and molecular

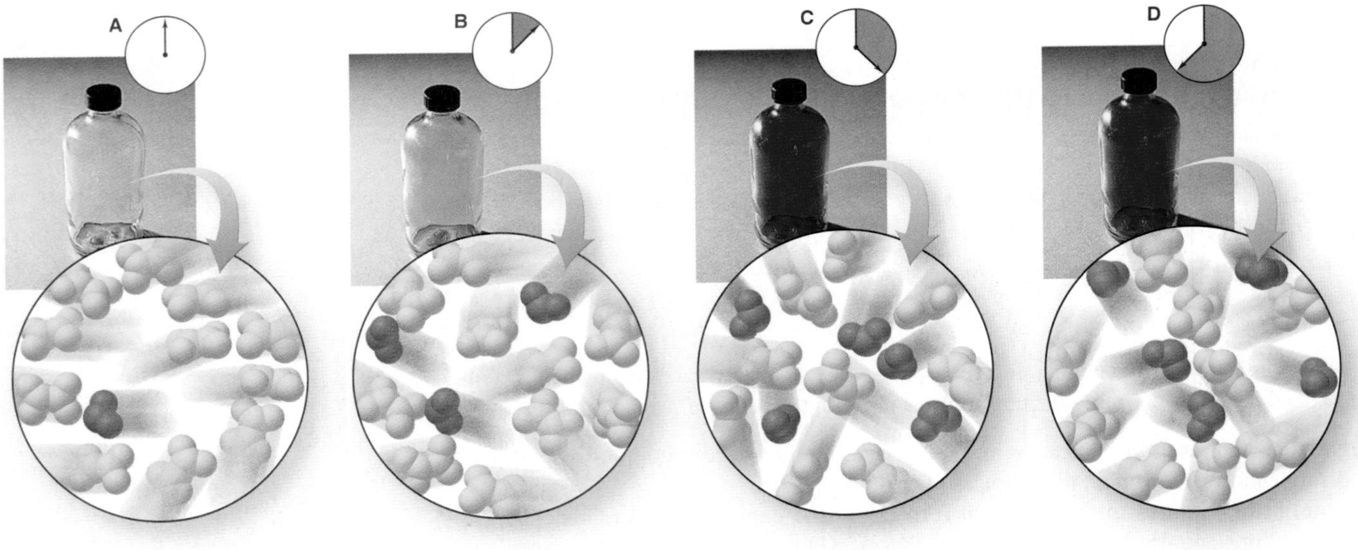

Figure 17.1 Reaching equilibrium on the macroscopic and molecular levels. **A,** The reaction mixture consists mostly of colorless N_2O_4. **B,** As N_2O_4 decomposes to NO_2, the mixture becomes pale brown. **C,** At equilibrium, the color and the concentrations of NO_2 and N_2O_4 no longer change. **D,** The reaction continues in both directions at equal rates, so the concentrations (and color) remain constant.

levels to see how equilibrium arises and then consider some quantitative aspects of the process:

1. *A macroscopic view of equilibrium.* The system we'll consider is the reversible gaseous reaction between colorless dinitrogen tetraoxide and brown nitrogen dioxide:

$$N_2O_4(g;\ \text{colorless}) \rightleftharpoons 2NO_2(g;\ \text{brown})$$

As soon as we introduce some liquid N_2O_4 (bp = 21°C) into a sealed container kept at 200°C, it vaporizes, and the gas begins to turn pale brown. As time passes, the brown darkens, until, after more time, the color stops changing. The first three photos in Figure 17.1 show the color change, and the last photo shows no further change.

2. *A molecular view of equilibrium.* On the molecular level, as shown in the blow-up circles of Figure 17.1, a dynamic scene unfolds. The N_2O_4 molecules fly wildly throughout the container, a few splitting into two NO_2 molecules. As time passes, more N_2O_4 molecules decompose and the concentration of NO_2 rises. As the number of N_2O_4 molecules decreases, N_2O_4 decomposition slows down. At the same time, as the number of NO_2 molecules increases, more collide, and formation of N_2O_4 speeds up. Eventually, the system reaches equilibrium: N_2O_4 molecules are decomposing into NO_2 molecules just as fast as NO_2 molecules are forming N_2O_4.

Thus, at equilibrium, *reactant and product concentrations are constant because a change in one direction is balanced by a change in the other as the forward and reverse rates become equal:*

$$\text{At equilibrium: rate}_{\text{fwd}} = \text{rate}_{\text{rev}} \qquad (17.1)$$

3. *A quantitiative view of equilibrium: a constant ratio of constants.* Let's see how reactant and product concentrations affect this process. At a particular temperature, when the system reaches equilibrium, we have

$$\text{rate}_{\text{fwd}} = \text{rate}_{\text{rev}}$$

In this reaction system, both forward and reverse reactions are elementary steps (Section 16.6), so we can write their rate laws directly from the balanced equation:

$$k_{\text{fwd}}[N_2O_4]_{\text{eq}} = k_{\text{rev}}[NO_2]^2_{\text{eq}}$$

where k_{fwd} and k_{rev} are the forward and reverse rate constants, respectively, and the subscript "eq" refers to concentrations at equilibrium. By rearranging, we set the ratio of the rate constants equal to the ratio of the concentration terms:

$$\frac{k_{\text{fwd}}}{k_{\text{rev}}} = \frac{[NO_2]^2_{\text{eq}}}{[N_2O_4]_{\text{eq}}}$$

The ratio of constants creates a new constant called the **equilibrium constant (K)**:

$$K = \frac{k_{fwd}}{k_{rev}} = \frac{[NO_2]^2_{eq}}{[N_2O_4]_{eq}} \quad (17.2)$$

Thus, *K is a number equal to a particular ratio of equilibrium concentrations of product(s) and reactant(s) at a particular temperature.*

4. *K as a measure of reaction extent.* The *magnitude* of K is an indication of *how far a reaction proceeds toward product at a given temperature*. Different reactions, even at the same temperature, have a wide range of concentrations at equilibrium—from almost all reactant to almost all product—and so, they have a wide range of equilibrium constants. Here are three examples of different magnitudes of K:

- *Small K* (Figure 17.2A). If a reaction yields little product before reaching equilibrium, it has a small K; if K is very small, we may say there is "no reaction." For example, there is "no reaction" between nitrogen and oxygen at 1000 K:*

$$N_2(g) + O_2(g) \rightleftharpoons 2NO(g) \qquad K = 1\times10^{-30}$$

- *Large K* (Figure 17.2B). Conversely, if a reaction reaches equilibrium with little reactant remaining, it has a large K; if K is very large, we say the reaction "goes to completion." The oxidation of carbon monoxide "goes to completion" at 1000 K:

$$2CO(g) + O_2(g) \rightleftharpoons 2CO_2(g) \qquad K = 2.2\times10^{22}$$

- *Intermediate K* (Figure 17.2C). When significant amounts of both reactant and product are present at equilibrium, K has an intermediate value, as when bromine monochloride breaks down to its elements at 1000 K:

$$2BrCl(g) \rightleftharpoons Br_2(g) + Cl_2(g) \qquad K = 5$$

Summary of Section 17.1

- Kinetics and equilibrium are distinct aspects of a reaction system, and the rate and extent of a reaction are not necessarily related.
- When the forward and reverse reactions occur at the same rate, concentrations no longer change and the system has reached equilibrium.
- The equilibrium constant (K) is a number based on a particular ratio of product and reactant concentrations: K is small if a high concentration of reactant(s) is present at equilibrium, and it is large if a high concentration of product(s) is present at equilibrium.

*To distinguish the equilibrium constant from the temperature unit, the kelvin, the equilibrium constant is represented by a capital italic K, whereas the kelvin is a capital roman K. Also, since the kelvin is a unit, it always follows a number.

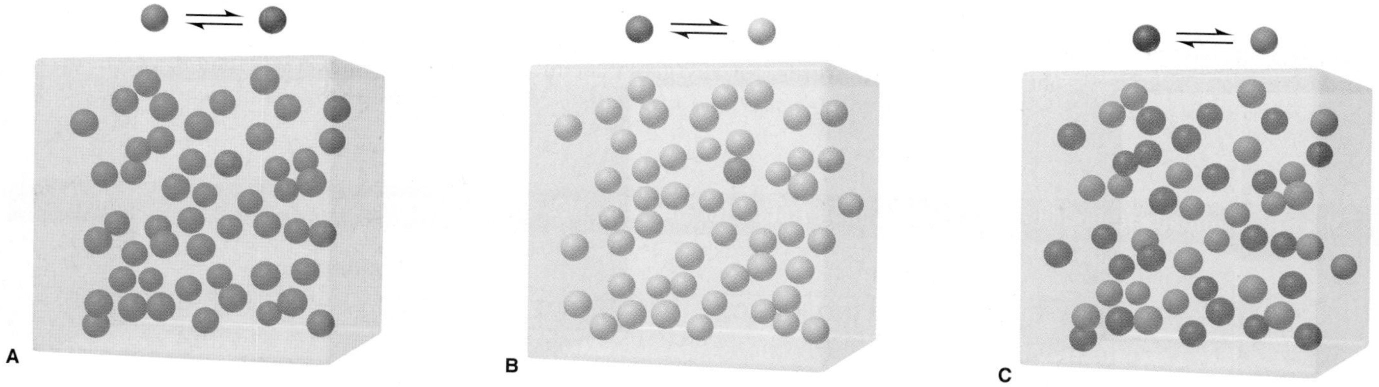

Figure 17.2 The range of equilibrium constants. **A,** For this reaction, $K = 1/49 = 0.020$. **B,** For this reaction, $K = 49/1 = 49$. **C,** For this reaction, $K = 25/25 = 1.0$.

17.2 • THE REACTION QUOTIENT AND THE EQUILIBRIUM CONSTANT

We have introduced the equilibrium constant in terms of a ratio of rate constants, but the original research on chemical equilibrium was developed many years before the principles of kinetics. In 1864, two Norwegian chemists, Cato Guldberg and Peter Waage, observed that *at a given temperature, a chemical system reaches a state in which a particular ratio of reactant and product concentrations has a constant value.* This is a statement of the **law of chemical equilibrium,** or the **law of mass action.**

Changing Value of the Reaction Quotient

The particular ratio of concentration terms that we write for a given reaction is called the **reaction quotient** (***Q,*** also known as the *mass-action expression*). For the reversible breakdown of N_2O_4 to NO_2, the reaction quotient is

$$N_2O_4(g) \rightleftharpoons 2NO_2(g) \qquad Q = \frac{[NO_2]^2}{[N_2O_4]}$$

As the reaction proceeds toward equilibrium, the concentrations of reactants and products change continually, and so does their ratio, the value of Q: at a given temperature, at the beginning of the reaction, the concentrations have initial values, and Q has an initial value; a moment later, the concentrations have slightly different values, and so does Q; after another moment, the concentrations and the value of Q change further. These changes continue, *until the system reaches equilibrium.* At that point, reactant and product concentrations have their equilibrium values and no longer change. Thus, the value of Q no longer changes and equals K at that temperature:

$$\text{At equilibrium: } Q = K \qquad (17.3)$$

In formulating the law of mass action, Guldberg and Waage found that, *for a particular system and temperature, the same equilibrium state is attained regardless of starting concentrations.* For example, for the N_2O_4-NO_2 system at 200°C, the data from four experiments appear in Table 17.1. Two essential points stand out:

- The ratio of *initial* concentrations *(fourth column)* varies widely but always gives the same ratio of *equilibrium* concentrations *(rightmost column).*
- The *individual* equilibrium concentrations are different in each case, but the *ratio* of these equilibrium concentrations is constant.

Thus, monitoring Q tells whether the system has reached equilibrium or, if it hasn't, how far away it is and in which direction it is changing.

The curves in Figure 17.3 show experiment 1 in Table 17.1. Note that $[N_2O_4]$ and $[NO_2]$ change smoothly during the course of the reaction (as indicated by the changing brown color at the top), and so does the value of Q. Once the system reaches equilibrium (constant brown color), the concentrations no longer change and Q equals K. In other words, for any given chemical system, *K is a special value of Q that occurs when the reactant and product concentrations have their equilibrium values.*

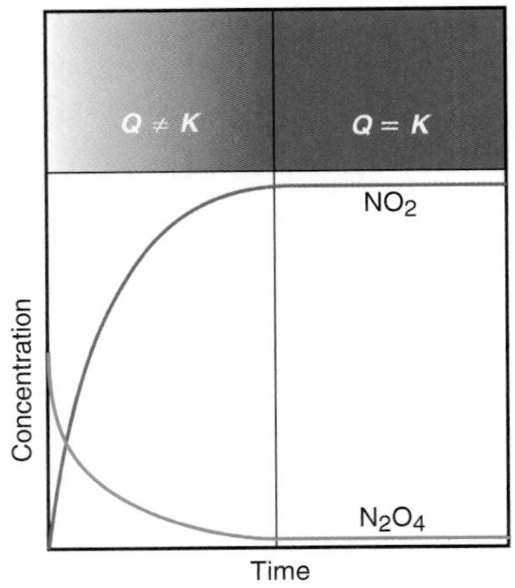

Figure 17.3 The change in Q during the N_2O_4-NO_2 reaction. Based on data from Experiment 1 in Table 17.1.

Table 17.1 Initial and Equilibrium Concentration Ratios for the N_2O_4-NO_2 System at 200°C (473 K)

	Initial			Equilibrium		
Expt	$[N_2O_4]$	$[NO_2]$	Q, $[NO_2]^2/[N_2O_4]$	$[N_2O_4]_{eq}$	$[NO_2]_{eq}$	K, $[NO_2]^2_{eq}/[N_2O_4]_{eq}$
1	0.1000	0.0000	0.0000	0.00357	0.193	10.4
2	0.0000	0.1000	∞	0.000924	0.0982	10.4
3	0.0500	0.0500	0.0500	0.00204	0.146	10.4
4	0.0750	0.0250	0.00833	0.00275	0.170	10.5

Writing the Reaction Quotient in Its Various Forms

The reaction quotient *must* be written directly from the balanced equation. In contrast, as discussed in Chapter 16, the rate law for an overall reaction *cannot* be written from the balanced equation, but must be determined from rate data.

Constructing the Reaction Quotient The most common form of the reaction quotient shows reactant and product terms as molar concentrations, which are designated by square brackets, [ ]. Thus, from now on, we designate the *reaction quotient based on concentrations* as Q_c. (We also designate the *equilibrium constant based on concentrations* as K_c.) For the general equation

$$aA + bB \rightleftharpoons cC + dD$$

where a, b, c, and d are the stoichiometric coefficients, the reaction quotient is

$$Q_c = \frac{[C]^c[D]^d}{[A]^a[B]^b} \quad (17.4)$$

Thus, *Q is a ratio of product concentration terms multiplied together and divided by reactant concentration terms multiplied together, with each term raised to the power of its balancing coefficient.*

Two steps are needed to construct a reaction quotient for any chemical system:

1. *Start with the balanced equation.* For example, for the formation of ammonia from its elements, the balanced equation (with colored coefficients for reference) is
$$N_2(g) + 3H_2(g) \rightleftharpoons 2NH_3(g)$$
2. *Arrange the terms and exponents.* Place the product terms in the numerator and the reactant terms in the denominator, multiplied by each other, and raise each term to the power of its balancing coefficient (colored as in the balanced equation):
$$Q_c = \frac{[NH_3]^2}{[N_2][H_2]^3}$$

Sample Problem 17.1 Writing the Reaction Quotient from the Balanced Equation

Problem Write the reaction quotient, Q_c, for each of the following reactions:
(a) The decomposition of dinitrogen pentaoxide, $N_2O_5(g) \rightleftharpoons NO_2(g) + O_2(g)$
(b) The combustion of propane, $C_3H_8(g) + O_2(g) \rightleftharpoons CO_2(g) + H_2O(g)$

Plan We balance the equations and then construct the reaction quotient (Equation 17.4).

Solution (a) $2N_2O_5(g) \rightleftharpoons 4NO_2(g) + O_2(g)$

$$Q_c = \frac{[NO_2]^4[O_2]}{[N_2O_5]^2}$$

(b) $C_3H_8(g) + 5O_2(g) \rightleftharpoons 3CO_2(g) + 4H_2O(g)$

$$Q_c = \frac{[CO_2]^3[H_2O]^4}{[C_3H_8][O_2]^5}$$

Check Be sure that the exponents in Q_c are the same as the balancing coefficients. A good check is to reverse the process and see if you obtain the balanced equation: change the numerator to products, the denominator to reactants, and the exponents to coefficients.

Follow-Up Problem 17.1 Write the reaction quotient, Q_c, for each of the following reactions:
(a) The first step in nitric acid production, $NH_3(g) + O_2(g) \rightleftharpoons NO(g) + H_2O(g)$
(b) The disproportionation of nitric oxide, $NO(g) \rightleftharpoons N_2O(g) + NO_2(g)$

Why *Q* and *K* Are Unitless In this text (and most others), *the values of Q and K are unitless numbers.* The reason is that each term in Q represents the *ratio* of the quantity of the substance (molar concentration or pressure) to its thermodynamic standard-state quantity. Recall from Section 6.6 that the standard states are 1 M for a substance in solution, 1 atm for a gas, and the pure substance for a liquid or solid. Thus, a concentration of 1.20 M becomes

$$\frac{1.20\ M\ \text{(measured quantity)}}{1\ M\ \text{(standard-state quantity)}} = 1.20$$

Similarly, a pressure of 0.53 atm becomes $\frac{0.53\ \text{atm}}{1\ \text{atm}} = 0.53$. Since the quantity terms are unitless, their ratio, which gives the value of Q (or K), is also unitless.

Form of *Q* for an Overall Reaction We follow the same procedure for writing a reaction quotient whether an equation represents an individual reaction step or an overall multistep reaction. *If an overall reaction is the* ***sum*** *of two or more reactions, the overall reaction quotient (or equilibrium constant) is the* ***product*** *of the reaction quotients (or equilibrium constants) for the steps:*

$$Q_{\text{overall}} = Q_1 \times Q_2 \times Q_3 \times \cdots$$

and

$$K_{\text{overall}} = K_1 \times K_2 \times K_3 \times \cdots \quad (17.5)$$

Sample Problem 17.2 demonstrates this point.

Sample Problem 17.2 Writing the Reaction Quotient and Finding *K* for an Overall Reaction

Problem Nitrogen dioxide is a toxic pollutant that contributes to photochemical smog. One way it forms is through the following sequence:

(1) $N_2(g) + O_2(g) \rightleftharpoons 2NO(g)$ $\qquad K_{c1} = 4.3\times10^{-25}$

(2) $2NO(g) + O_2(g) \rightleftharpoons 2NO_2(g)$ $\qquad K_{c2} = 6.4\times10^{9}$

(a) Show that the overall Q_c for this reaction sequence is the same as the product of the Q_c's for the individual reactions.

(b) Given that both reactions occur at the same temperature, find K_c for the overall reaction.

Plan **(a)** We first write the overall reaction by adding the individual reactions and then write the overall Q_c. Next, we write the Q_c for each step. We *add* the steps and *multiply* their Q_c's, canceling common terms, to obtain the overall Q_c. **(b)** We know the individual K_c's (4.3×10^{-25} and 6.4×10^{9}), so we multiply them to find $K_{c(\text{overall})}$.

Solution **(a)** Writing the overall reaction and its reaction quotient:

$$\begin{array}{ll} (1) & N_2(g) + O_2(g) \rightleftharpoons \cancel{2NO(g)} \\ (2) & \cancel{2NO(g)} + O_2(g) \rightleftharpoons 2NO_2(g) \\ \hline \text{Overall:} & N_2(g) + 2O_2(g) \rightleftharpoons 2NO_2(g) \end{array}$$

$$Q_{c(\text{overall})} = \frac{[NO_2]^2}{[N_2][O_2]^2}$$

Writing the reaction quotients for the individual steps:

For step 1, $$Q_{c1} = \frac{[NO]^2}{[N_2][O_2]}$$

For step 2, $$Q_{c2} = \frac{[NO_2]^2}{[NO]^2[O_2]}$$

Multiplying the individual reaction quotients and canceling:

$$Q_{c1} \times Q_{c2} = \frac{\cancel{[NO]^2}}{[N_2][O_2]} \times \frac{[NO_2]^2}{\cancel{[NO]^2}[O_2]} = \frac{[NO_2]^2}{[N_2][O_2]^2} = Q_{c(\text{overall})}$$

(b) Calculating the overall K_c:

$$K_{c(overall)} = K_{c1} \times K_{c2} = (4.3\times10^{-25})(6.4\times10^{9}) = 2.8\times10^{-15}$$

Check Round off and check the calculation in part (b):

$$K_c \approx (4\times10^{-25})(6\times10^{9}) = 24\times10^{-16} = 2.4\times10^{-15}$$

Follow-Up Problem 17.2 The following sequence of steps has been proposed for the overall reaction between H_2 and Br_2 to form HBr:

(1) $Br_2(g) \rightleftharpoons 2Br(g)$

(2) $Br(g) + H_2(g) \rightleftharpoons HBr(g) + H(g)$

(3) $H(g) + Br(g) \rightleftharpoons HBr(g)$

Write the overall balanced equation and show that the overall Q_c is the product of the Q_c's for the individual steps.

Form of *Q* for a Forward and a Reverse Reaction The form of the reaction quotient depends on the *direction* in which the balanced equation is written. Consider, for example, the oxidation of sulfur dioxide to sulfur trioxide. This reaction is a key step in acid rain formation and sulfuric acid production. The balanced equation is

$$2SO_2(g) + O_2(g) \rightleftharpoons 2SO_3(g)$$

The reaction quotient for this equation *as written* is

$$Q_{c(fwd)} = \frac{[SO_3]^2}{[SO_2]^2[O_2]}$$

If we had written the reverse reaction, the decomposition of sulfur trioxide,

$$2SO_3(g) \rightleftharpoons 2SO_2(g) + O_2(g)$$

the reaction quotient would be the *reciprocal* of $Q_{c(fwd)}$:

$$Q_{c(rev)} = \frac{[SO_2]^2[O_2]}{[SO_3]^2} = \frac{1}{Q_{c(fwd)}}$$

Thus, *a reaction quotient (or equilibrium constant) for a forward reaction is the* ***reciprocal*** *of the reaction quotient (or equilibrium constant) for the reverse reaction:*

$$Q_{c(fwd)} = \frac{1}{Q_{c(rev)}} \quad \text{and} \quad K_{c(fwd)} = \frac{1}{K_{c(rev)}} \qquad (17.6)$$

The K_c values for the forward and reverse reactions shown above at 1000 K are

$$K_{c(fwd)} = 261 \quad \text{and} \quad K_{c(rev)} = \frac{1}{K_{c(fwd)}} = \frac{1}{261} = 3.83\times10^{-3}$$

These values make sense: if the forward reaction goes far to the right (high K_c), the reverse reaction does not (low K_c).

Form of *Q* for a Reaction with Coefficients Multiplied by a Common Factor Multiplying all the coefficients of the equation by some factor also changes the form of *Q*. For example, multiplying all the coefficients in the equation for the formation of SO_3 by $\frac{1}{2}$ gives

$$SO_2(g) + \tfrac{1}{2}O_2(g) \rightleftharpoons SO_3(g)$$

For this equation, the reaction quotient is

$$Q'_{c(fwd)} = \frac{[SO_3]}{[SO_2][O_2]^{1/2}}$$

Notice that Q_c for the halved equation equals Q_c for the original equation raised to the $\frac{1}{2}$ power:

$$Q'_{c(fwd)} = Q^{1/2}_{c(fwd)} = \left(\frac{[SO_3]^2}{[SO_2]^2[O_2]}\right)^{1/2} = \frac{[SO_3]}{[SO_2][O_2]^{1/2}}$$

Once again, the same property holds for the equilibrium constants. Relating the halved reaction to the original, we have

$$K'_{c(fwd)} = K^{1/2}_{c(fwd)} = (261)^{1/2} = 16.2$$

It may seem that we have changed the extent of the reaction, as indicated by a different K, just by changing the coefficients of the equation, but that can't be true. *A particular K has meaning only in relation to a particular equation.* If $K_{c(fwd)}$ and $K'_{c(fwd)}$ relate to different equations, we cannot compare them directly.

In general, *if all the coefficients of the balanced equation are multiplied by some factor, that factor becomes the exponent for relating the reaction quotients and the equilibrium constants.* For a multiplying factor n, which we can write as

$$n(aA + bB \rightleftharpoons cC + dD)$$

the reaction quotient and equilibrium constant are

$$Q' = Q^n = \left(\frac{[C]^c[D]^d}{[A]^a[B]^b}\right)^n \quad \text{and} \quad K' = K^n \qquad (17.7)$$

Sample Problem 17.3 Finding the Equilibrium Constant for an Equation Multiplied by a Common Factor

Problem For the ammonia-formation reaction, the reference (ref) equation is

$$N_2(g) + 3H_2(g) \rightleftharpoons 2NH_3(g)$$

K_c is 2.4×10^{-3} at 1000 K. What are the values of K_c for the following balanced equations?

(a) $\frac{1}{3}N_2(g) + H_2(g) \rightleftharpoons \frac{2}{3}NH_3(g)$ **(b)** $NH_3(g) \rightleftharpoons \frac{1}{2}N_2(g) + \frac{3}{2}H_2(g)$

Plan We compare each equation with the reference equation to see how the direction and coefficients have changed.

Solution The reaction quotient for the reference equation is $Q_{c(ref)} = \dfrac{[NH_3]^2}{[N_2][H_2]^3}$.

(a) This equation is the reference equation multiplied by $\frac{1}{3}$, so K_c equals $K_{c(ref)}$ (2.4×10^{-3}) raised to the $\frac{1}{3}$ power.

$$Q_c = Q^{1/3}_{c(ref)} = \left(\frac{[NH_3]^2}{[N_2][H_2]^3}\right)^{1/3} = \frac{[NH_3]^{2/3}}{[N_2]^{1/3}[H_2]}$$

Thus,

$$K_c = K^{1/3}_{c(ref)} = (2.4\times10^{-3})^{1/3} = 0.13$$

(b) This equation is one-half the *reverse* of the reference equation, so K_c is the reciprocal of $K_{c(ref)}$ raised to the $\frac{1}{2}$ power.

$$Q_c = \left(\frac{1}{Q_{c(ref)}}\right)^{1/2} = \left(\frac{1}{\dfrac{[NH_3]^2}{[N_2][H_2]^3}}\right)^{1/2} = \frac{[N_2]^{1/2}[H_2]^{3/2}}{[NH_3]}$$

Thus,

$$K_c = \left(\frac{1}{K_{c(ref)}}\right)^{1/2} = \left(\frac{1}{2.4\times10^{-3}}\right)^{1/2} = 20.$$

Check A good check is to work the math backwards. **(a)** $(0.13)^3 = 2.2\times10^{-3}$, within rounding of 2.4×10^{-3}. The reaction goes in the same direction, so there should be mostly reactants, as $K_c < 1$ indicates. **(b)** $1/(20.)^2 = 2.5\times10^{-3}$, again within rounding. At equilibrium, the reverse reaction should yield mostly products, as $K_c > 1$ indicates.

Follow-Up Problem 17.3 At 1200 K, the reaction of hydrogen and chlorine to form hydrogen chloride is

$$H_2(g) + Cl_2(g) \rightleftharpoons 2HCl(g) \qquad K_c = 7.6\times10^8$$

Calculate K_c for the following reactions:

(a) $\frac{1}{2}H_2(g) + \frac{1}{2}Cl_2(g) \rightleftharpoons HCl(g)$ **(b)** $\frac{4}{3}HCl(g) \rightleftharpoons \frac{2}{3}H_2(g) + \frac{2}{3}Cl_2(g)$

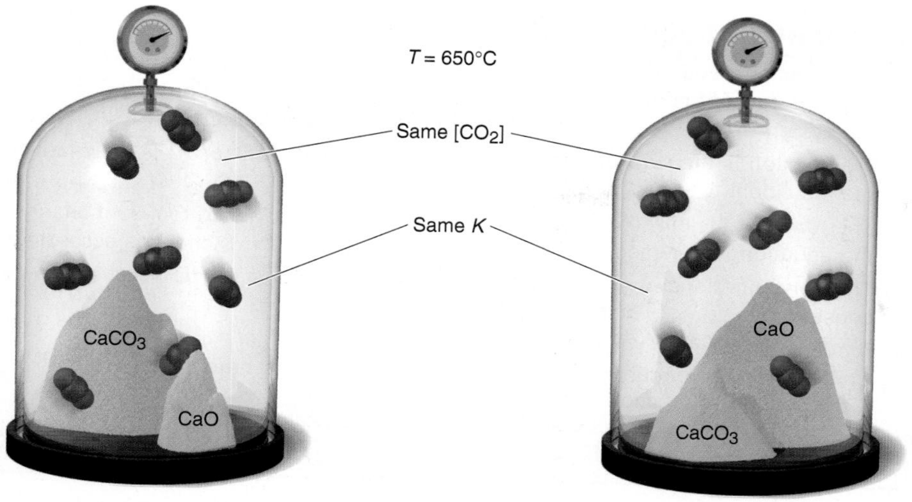

Figure 17.4 The reaction quotient for a heterogeneous system depends only on concentrations that change.

Form of *Q* for a Reaction Involving Pure Liquids or Solids Until now, we've looked at reactions involving only gases. These are *homogeneous* equilibria, systems in which all the components are in the same phase. When the components are in different phases, the system reaches *heterogeneous* equilibrium.

Consider the decomposition of limestone to lime and carbon dioxide:

$$CaCO_3(s) \rightleftharpoons CaO(s) + CO_2(g)$$

Based on the rules for writing the reaction quotient, we have

$$Q_c = \frac{[CaO][CO_2]}{[CaCO_3]}$$

However, like its density, at a given temperature, a pure solid always has the same "concentration" that is, the same number of moles per liter of solid. Therefore, the concentration of a pure solid is constant, as is the concentration of a pure liquid.

Because we are concerned with concentrations that *change* as they approach equilibrium, *we eliminate the terms for pure liquids and solids from the reaction quotient*. To do this, we multiply both sides of the above equation by $[CaCO_3]$ and divide both sides by [CaO] and get a new reaction quotient, Q'_c:

$$Q'_c = Q_c\frac{[CaCO_3]}{[CaO]} = [CO_2]$$

Thus, only the CO_2 concentration changes. As long as some CaO and $CaCO_3$ are present, the reaction quotient equals the CO_2 concentration (Figure 17.4).

Table 17.2 summarizes the ways of writing *Q* and calculating *K*.

Table 17.2 Ways of Expressing *Q* and Calculating *K*

Form of Chemical Equations	Form of *Q*	Value of *K*
Reference reaction: $A \rightleftharpoons B$	$Q_{(ref)} = \frac{[B]}{[A]}$	$K_{(ref)} = \frac{[B]_{eq}}{[A]_{eq}}$
Reference reaction: $B \rightleftharpoons A$	$Q = \frac{1}{Q_{(ref)}} = \frac{[A]}{[B]}$	$K = \frac{1}{K_{(ref)}}$
Reaction as sum of two steps: (1) $A \rightleftharpoons C$	$Q_1 = \frac{[C]}{[A]}; Q_2 = \frac{[B]}{[C]}$	
(2) $C \rightleftharpoons B$	$Q_{overall} = Q_1 \times Q_2 = Q_{(ref)}$ $= \frac{\cancel{[C]}}{[A]} \times \frac{[B]}{\cancel{[C]}} = \frac{[B]}{[A]}$	$K_{overall} = K_1 \times K_2$ $= K_{(ref)}$
Coefficients multiplied by *n*	$Q = Q^n_{(ref)}$	$K = K^n_{(ref)}$
Reaction with pure solid or liquid component, such as A(*s*)	$Q = Q_{(ref)}[A] = [B]$	$K = K_{(ref)}[A] = [B]$

Summary of Section 17.2

- The reaction quotient based on concentration, Q_c, is a particular ratio of product to reactant concentrations. The value of Q_c changes as the reaction proceeds. When the system reaches equilibrium at a particular temperature, $Q_c = K_c$.
- If a reaction is the sum of two or more steps, the overall Q (or K) is the product of the individual Q's (or K's).
- The *form* of Q is based on the balanced equation exactly as written, so it changes if the equation is reversed or multiplied by some factor, and K changes accordingly.
- The concentrations of pure liquids or solids do not appear in Q because they are constant.
- Three criteria define a system at equilibrium:
  1. Reactant and product concentrations are constant over time.
  2. The opposing reaction rates are equal: $\text{rate}_{fwd} = \text{rate}_{rev}$.
  3. The reaction quotient equals the equilibrium constant: $Q = K$.

17.3 • EXPRESSING EQUILIBRIA WITH PRESSURE TERMS: RELATION BETWEEN K_c AND K_p

It is easier to measure gas pressure than concentration, so when a reaction involves gases, we often express the reaction quotient in terms of partial pressures instead of concentrations. As long as the gases behave nearly ideally during the experiment, the ideal gas law (Section 5.3) allows us to relate pressure (P) to concentration (n/V):

$$PV = nRT, \quad \text{so} \quad P = \frac{n}{V}RT \quad \text{or} \quad \frac{P}{RT} = \frac{n}{V}$$

Thus, at constant T, *pressure is directly proportional to molar concentration.* For example, in the reaction between gaseous NO and O_2,

$$2NO(g) + O_2(g) \rightleftharpoons 2NO_2(g)$$

the *reaction quotient based on pressures,* Q_p, is

$$Q_p = \frac{P^2_{NO_2}}{P^2_{NO} \times P_{O_2}}$$

The equilibrium constant obtained when all components are present at their equilibrium partial pressures is designated K_p, the *equilibrium constant based on pressures*. In many cases, K_p has a value different from K_c. But if you know one, the *change in amount (mol) of gas*, Δn_{gas}, from the balanced equation allows you to calculate the other. Let's see how this conversion works for the oxidation of NO:

$$2NO(g) + O_2(g) \rightleftharpoons 2NO_2(g)$$

As the balanced equation shows,

$$3 \text{ mol } (2 \text{ mol} + 1 \text{ mol}) \text{ gaseous reactants} \rightleftharpoons 2 \text{ mol gaseous products}$$

With Δ meaning final *minus* initial (products *minus* reactants), we have

$$\Delta n_{gas} = \text{moles of gaseous product} - \text{moles of gaseous reactant} = 2 - 3 = -1$$

Keep this value of Δn_{gas} in mind because it appears in the conversion that follows.

The reaction quotient based on concentrations is

$$Q_c = \frac{[NO_2]^2}{[NO]^2[O_2]}$$

Rearranging the ideal gas law to $n/V = P/RT$, we write the terms in square brackets as n/V and convert them to partial pressures, P; then we collect the RT terms and cancel:

$$Q_c = \frac{\dfrac{n^2_{NO_2}}{V^2}}{\dfrac{n^2_{NO}}{V^2} \times \dfrac{n_{O_2}}{V}} = \frac{\dfrac{P^2_{NO_2}}{(RT)^2}}{\dfrac{P^2_{NO}}{(RT)^2} \times \dfrac{P_{O_2}}{RT}} = \frac{P^2_{NO_2}}{P^2_{NO} \times P_{O_2}} \times \frac{\dfrac{1}{\cancel{(RT)^2}}}{\dfrac{1}{\cancel{(RT)^2}} \times \dfrac{1}{RT}}$$

$$= \frac{P^2_{NO_2}}{P^2_{NO} \times P_{O_2}} \times RT$$

Note that the far right side of the previous expression is Q_p multiplied by RT. Thus,

$$Q_c = Q_p(RT)$$

Also, at equilibrium, $K_c = K_p(RT)$; thus,

$$K_p = \frac{K_c}{RT} \quad \text{or} \quad K_c(RT)^{-1}$$

Note especially that *the exponent of the RT term equals the change in the amount (mol) of gas (Δn_{gas}) from the balanced equation,* -1. Thus, in general, we have

$$K_p = K_c(RT)^{\Delta n_{gas}} \qquad (17.8)$$

Based on Equation 17.8, *if the amount (mol) of gas does not change in the reaction,* $\Delta n_{gas} = 0$, so the RT term drops out (i.e., equals 1), and $K_p = K_c$. (In calculations, be sure the units for R are consistent with units for pressure.)

Sample Problem 17.4 Converting Between K_c and K_p

Problem A chemical engineer injects limestone ($CaCO_3$) into the hot flue gas of a coal-burning power plant to form lime (CaO), which scrubs SO_2 from the gas and forms gypsum ($CaSO_4 \cdot 2H_2O$). Find K_c for the following reaction:

$$CaCO_3(s) \rightleftharpoons CaO(s) + CO_2(g) \qquad K_p = 2.1\times10^{-4} \text{ (at 1000. K)}$$

Plan We know K_p (2.1×10^{-4}), so to convert between K_p and K_c, we must first determine Δn_{gas} from the balanced equation. Then we rearrange Equation 17.8. (If we assume that pressure is measured in atmospheres, $R = 0.0821$ atm·L/mol·K.)

Solution Determining Δn_{gas}: There is 1 mol of gaseous product and no gaseous reactant, so $\Delta n_{gas} = 1 - 0 = 1$.

Rearranging Equation 17.8 and calculating K_c:

$$K_p = K_c(RT)^1$$

so

$$K_c = K_p(RT)^{-1} = (2.1\times10^{-4})(0.0821 \times 1000.)^{-1}$$
$$= 2.6\times10^{-6}$$

Check Rounding gives

$$(2\times10^{-4})(0.1\times10^3)^{-1} = (2\times10^{-4})(10^{-2})$$
$$= 2\times10^{-6}.$$

Follow-Up Problem 17.4 Calculate K_p for the following reaction:

$$PCl_3(g) + Cl_2(g) \rightleftharpoons PCl_5(g) \qquad K_c = 1.67 \text{ (at 500. K)}$$

Summary of Section 17.3

- For a gaseous reaction, the reaction quotient and the equilibrium constant can be expressed in terms of partial pressures (Q_p and K_p).
- If you know K_p, you can find K_c, and vice versa: $K_p = K_c(RT)^{\Delta n_{gas}}$.

17.4 • COMPARING Q AND K TO DETERMINE REACTION DIRECTION

Suppose you have a mixture of reactants and products and you know K at the temperature of the reaction. By comparing the value of Q with K, you can tell whether the reaction has reached equilibrium or, if not, in which direction it is progressing. With product terms in the numerator of Q and reactant terms in the denominator, *more product makes Q larger, and more reactant makes Q smaller.*

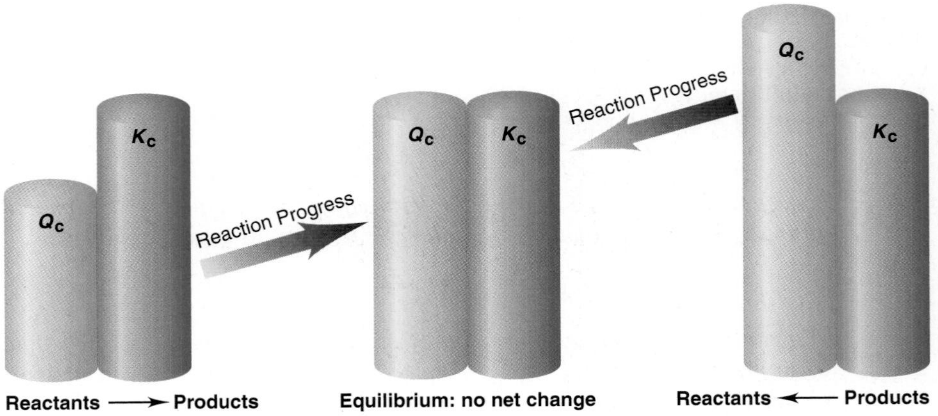

Figure 17.5 Reaction direction and the relative sizes of Q and K. When Q_c is smaller or larger than K_c, the reaction continues until $Q_c = K_c$. Note that K_c remains the same throughout.

There are three possibilities for the relative sizes of Q and K (Figure 17.5):

- $Q < K$. If Q is smaller than K, the denominator (reactants) is large relative to the numerator (products). For Q to equal K, the reactants must decrease and the products increase. The reaction will progress to the right, toward products:

$$\text{If } Q < K, \text{ reactants} \longrightarrow \text{products}$$

- $Q > K$. If Q is larger than K, the numerator (products) will decrease and the denominator (reactants) will increase. The reaction will progress to the left, toward reactants:

$$\text{If } Q > K, \text{ reactants} \longleftarrow \text{products}$$

- $Q = K$. This situation occurs when the reactant and product terms equal their equilibrium values. No further net change takes place:

$$\text{If } Q = K, \text{ reactants} \rightleftharpoons \text{products}$$

Sample Problem 17.5 relies on molecular scenes to determine reaction direction, and Sample Problem 17.6 relies on concentration data.

Sample Problem 17.5 Using Molecular Scenes to Determine Reaction Direction

Problem For the reaction $A(g) \rightleftharpoons B(g)$, the equilibrium mixture at 175°C is $[A] = 2.8\times10^{-4}\ M$ and $[B] = 1.2\times10^{-4}\ M$. The molecular scenes below represent mixtures at various times during runs 1–4 of this reaction (A is *red*; B is *blue*). Does the reaction progress to the right or left or not at all for each mixture to reach equilibrium?

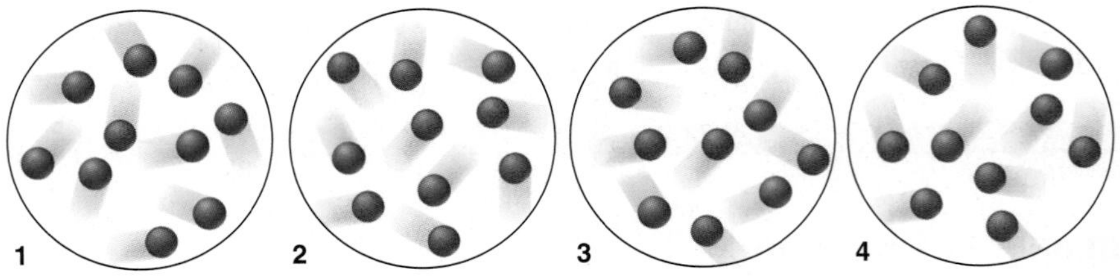

Plan We must compare Q_c with K_c to determine the reaction direction, so we first use the given equilibrium concentrations to find K_c. Then we count spheres and calculate Q_c for each mixture. If $Q_c < K_c$, the reaction progresses to the right (reactants to products); if $Q_c > K_c$, it progresses to the left (products to reactants); and if $Q_c = K_c$, there is no further net change.

Solution Writing the reaction quotient and using the data to find K_c:

$$Q_c = \frac{[B]}{[A]} = \frac{1.2\times10^{-4}}{2.8\times10^{-4}} = 0.43 = K_c$$

Counting red (A) and blue (B) spheres to calculate Q_c for each mixture:

1. $Q_c = 8/2 = 4.0$ 2. $Q_c = 3/7 = 0.43$ 3. $Q_c = 4/6 = 0.67$ 4. $Q_c = 2/8 = 0.25$

Comparing Q_c with K_c to determine reaction direction:

1. $Q_c > K_c$: left 2. $Q_c = K_c$: no net change 3. $Q_c > K_c$: left 4. $Q_c < K_c$: right

Check Making an error in the calculation for K_c would lead to incorrect conclusions throughout, so check that step: the exponents are the same, and 1.2/2.8 is a bit less than 0.5, as is the calculated K_c. You can check the final answers by inspection; for example, for the number of B (8) in mixture 1 to equal the number at equilibrium (3), more B must change to A, so the reaction must proceed to the left.

Follow-Up Problem 17.5 At 338 K, the reaction $X(g) \rightleftharpoons Y(g)$ has a K_c of 1.4. The scenes below represent different mixtures at 338 K, with X orange and Y green. In which direction does the reaction proceed (if at all) for each mixture to reach equilibrium?

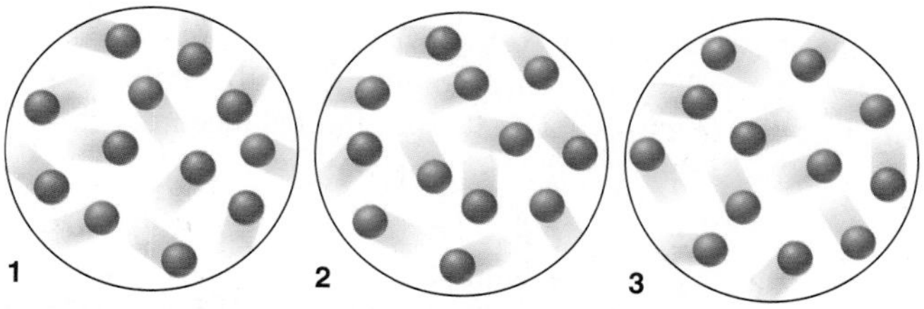

Sample Problem 17.6 Using Concentrations to Determine Reaction Direction

Problem For the reaction $N_2O_4(g) \rightleftharpoons 2NO_2(g)$, $K_c = 0.21$ at 100°C. At a point during the reaction, $[N_2O_4] = 0.12\ M$ and $[NO_2] = 0.55\ M$. Is the reaction at equilibrium? If not, in which direction is it progressing?

Plan We write Q_c, find its value by substituting the given concentrations, and compare its value with the given K_c.

Solution Writing the reaction quotient and solving for Q_c:

$$Q_c = \frac{[NO_2]^2}{[N_2O_4]} = \frac{0.55^2}{0.12} = 2.5$$

With $Q_c > K_c$, the reaction is not at equilibrium and will proceed to the left until $Q_c = K_c$.

Check With $[NO_2] > [N_2O_4]$, we expect to obtain a value for Q_c that is greater than 0.21. If $Q_c > K_c$, the numerator will decrease and the denominator will increase until $Q_c = K_c$; that is, this reaction will proceed toward reactants.

Follow-Up Problem 17.6 Chloromethane forms by the reaction

$$CH_4(g) + Cl_2(g) \rightleftharpoons CH_3Cl(g) + HCl(g)$$

At 1500 K, $K_p = 1.6\times10^4$. In the reaction mixture, $P_{CH_4} = 0.13$ atm, $P_{Cl_2} = 0.035$ atm, $P_{CH_3Cl} = 0.24$ atm, and $P_{HCl} = 0.47$ atm. Is CH_3Cl or CH_4 forming?

Summary of Section 17.4

- We compare the values of Q and K to determine the direction in which a reaction will proceed toward equilibrium.
  - If $Q_c < K_c$, more product forms.
  - If $Q_c > K_c$, more reactant forms.
  - If $Q_c = K_c$, there is no net change.

17.5 • HOW TO SOLVE EQUILIBRIUM PROBLEMS

Many kinds of equilibrium problems arise in the real world—and on chemistry exams—but we can group most of them into two types:

1. We know the equilibrium quantities and solve for K.
2. We know K and the initial quantities and solve for the equilibrium quantities.

Using Quantities to Find the Equilibrium Constant

There are two common variations on this type of problem: one involves substituting quantities to solve for K, and the other requires first finding some of the quantities.

Substituting Equilibrium Quantities into Q to Find K In this type of problem, we use given equilibrium quantities to calculate K. Suppose, for example, that equal amounts of gaseous hydrogen and iodine are injected into a 1.50-L flask at a fixed temperature. In time, the following equilibrium is attained:

$$H_2(g) + I_2(g) \rightleftharpoons 2HI(g)$$

At equilibrium, the flask contains 1.80 mol of H_2, 1.80 mol of I_2, and 0.520 mol of HI. We calculate K_c by finding the concentrations from the amounts and flask volume and substituting into the reaction quotient from the balanced equation:

$$Q_c = \frac{[HI]^2}{[H_2][I_2]}$$

We divide each amount (mol) by the volume (L) to find each concentration (mol/L):

$$[H_2] = \frac{1.80\ \text{mol}}{1.50\ \text{L}} = 1.20\ M$$

Similarly, $[I_2] = 1.20\ M$, and $[HI] = 0.347\ M$.
Substituting these values into the expression for Q_c gives K_c:

$$K_c = \frac{(0.347)^2}{(1.20)(1.20)} = 8.36\times10^{-2}$$

Using a Reaction Table to Find Equilibrium Quantities and K When some quantities are not given, we determine them from the reaction stoichiometry and then find K. In the following example, note the use of the *reaction table.*

In a study of carbon oxidation, an evacuated vessel containing a small amount of powdered graphite is heated to 1080 K. Gaseous CO_2 is added to a pressure of 0.458 atm, and CO forms. At equilibrium, the total pressure is 0.757 atm. Calculate K_p.

As always, we start by writing the balanced equation and the reaction quotient:

$$CO_2(g) + C(\text{graphite}) \rightleftharpoons 2CO(g)$$

The data are given in atmospheres and we must find K_p, so we write the expression for Q_p; note that it does *not* include a term for the solid, C(graphite):

$$Q_p = \frac{P_{CO}^2}{P_{CO_2}}$$

We are given the initial P_{CO_2} and the P_{total} at equilibrium. To find K_p, we must find the equilibrium pressures of CO_2 and CO and then substitute them into Q_p.

Let's think through what happened in the vessel. An unknown portion of the CO_2 reacted with graphite to form an unknown amount of CO. We already know the *relative* amounts of CO_2 and CO from the balanced equation: for each mole of CO_2 that reacts, 2 mol of CO forms, which means that when x atm of CO_2 reacts, $2x$ atm of CO forms:

$$x\ \text{atm}\ CO_2 \longrightarrow 2x\ \text{atm CO}$$

The pressure of CO_2 at equilibrium, $P_{CO_2(eq)}$, is the initial pressure, $P_{CO_2(init)}$, *minus* x, the CO_2 that reacts (the change in P_{CO_2} due to the reaction):

$$P_{CO_2(init)} - x = P_{CO_2(eq)} = 0.458 - x$$

Similarly, the pressure of CO at equilibrium, $P_{CO(eq)}$, is the initial pressure, $P_{CO(init)}$, *plus* $2x$, the CO that forms (the change in P_{CO} due to the reaction). $P_{CO(init)}$ is zero, so

$$P_{CO(init)} + 2x = 0 + 2x = 2x = P_{CO(eq)}$$

We'll summarize this information in a reaction table, similar to those in Chapter 3, but the "Final" quantities are those at equilibrium. The table shows the balanced equation and

- the *initial* quantities (concentrations or pressures) of reactants and products
- the *changes* in these quantities during the reaction
- the *equilibrium* quantities

Pressure (atm)	$CO_2(g)$	+	C(graphite)	$\rightleftharpoons$	$2CO(g)$
Initial	0.458		—		0
Change	$-x$		—		$+2x$
Equilibrium	$0.458 - x$		—		$2x$

We treat each column like a list of numbers to add together: *the initial quantity plus the change in that quantity gives the equilibrium quantity*. Note that we *only* include substances whose concentrations change; thus, the column for C(graphite) is blank.

To solve for K_p, we substitute equilibrium values into Q_p, so we first have to find x. To do this, we use the other piece of data given, $P_{total(eq)}$. According to Dalton's law of partial pressures and using the equilibrium quantities from the reaction table,

$$P_{total(eq)} = 0.757 \text{ atm} = P_{CO_2(eq)} + P_{CO(eq)} = (0.458 \text{ atm} - x) + 2x$$

Thus, $\quad 0.757 \text{ atm} = 0.458 \text{ atm} + x \quad$ and $\quad x = 0.299 \text{ atm}$

With x known, we determine the equilibrium partial pressures:

$$P_{CO_2(eq)} = 0.458 \text{ atm} - x = 0.458 \text{ atm} - 0.299 \text{ atm} = 0.159 \text{ atm}$$
$$P_{CO(eq)} = 2x = 2(0.299 \text{ atm}) = 0.598 \text{ atm}$$

Then we substitute them into Q_p to find K_p:

$$Q_p = \frac{P^2_{CO(eq)}}{P_{CO_2(eq)}} = \frac{0.598^2}{0.159} = 2.25 = K_p$$

(From now on, the subscripts "init" and "eq" appear only when it is not clear whether a quantity is an initial or equilibrium value.)

Sample Problem 17.7 Calculating K_c from Concentration Data

Problem In order to study hydrogen halide decomposition, a researcher fills an evacuated 2.00-L flask with 0.200 mol of HI gas and allows the reaction to proceed at 453°C:

$$2HI(g) \rightleftharpoons H_2(g) + I_2(g)$$

At equilibrium, [HI] = 0.078 *M*. Calculate K_c.

Plan To calculate K_c, we need the equilibrium concentrations. We can find the initial [HI] from the amount (0.200 mol) and the flask volume (2.00 L), and we are given [HI] at equilibrium (0.078 *M*). From the balanced equation, when $2x$ mol of HI reacts, x mol of H_2 and x mol of I_2 form. We set up a reaction table, use the known [HI] at equilibrium to solve for x (the change in $[H_2]$ or $[I_2]$), and substitute the concentrations into Q_c.

Solution Calculating initial [HI]:

$$[HI] = \frac{0.200 \text{ mol}}{2.00 \text{ L}} = 0.100 \, M$$

Setting up the reaction table, with $x = [H_2]$ or $[I_2]$ that forms and $2x$ = [HI] that reacts:

Concentration (*M*)	$2HI(g)$	$\rightleftharpoons$	$H_2(g)$	+	$I_2(g)$
Initial	0.100		0		0
Change	$-2x$		$+x$		$+x$
Equilibrium	$0.100 - 2x$		x		x

Solving for x, using the known [HI] at equilibrium:

$$[HI] = 0.100 \, M - 2x = 0.078 \, M \quad \text{so} \quad x = 0.011 \, M$$

Therefore, the equilibrium concentrations are

$$[H_2] = [I_2] = 0.011 \, M \quad \text{and we are given} \quad [HI] = 0.078 \, M$$

Substituting into the reaction quotient:

$$Q_c = \frac{[H_2][I_2]}{[HI]^2}$$

Thus,

$$K_c = \frac{(0.011)(0.011)}{0.078^2} = 0.020$$

Check Rounding gives $\sim 0.01^2/0.08^2 = 0.02$. Because the initial [HI] of 0.100 *M* fell slightly at equilibrium to 0.078 *M*, relatively little product formed; so we expect $K_c < 1$.

Follow-Up Problem 17.7 The atmospheric oxidation of nitrogen monoxide, $2NO(g) + O_2(g) \rightleftharpoons 2NO_2(g)$, was studied at 184°C with initial pressures of 1.000 atm of NO and 1.000 atm of O_2. At equilibrium, $P_{O_2} = 0.506$ atm. Calculate K_p.

Using the Equilibrium Constant to Find Quantities

The type of problem that involves finding equilibrium quantities also has several variations. Sample Problem 17.8 is one variation, in which we know *K* and some of the equilibrium concentrations and must find another equilibrium concentration.

Sample Problem 17.8 Determining Equilibrium Concentrations from K_c

Problem In a study of the conversion of methane to other fuels, a chemical engineer mixes gaseous CH_4 and H_2O in a 0.32-L flask at 1200 K. At equilibrium, the flask contains 0.26 mol of CO, 0.091 mol of H_2, and 0.041 mol of CH_4. What is $[H_2O]$ at equilibrium? $K_c = 0.26$ for this process at 1200 K.

Plan First, we write the balanced equation and the reaction quotient. We calculate the equilibrium concentrations from the given numbers of moles and the flask volume (0.32 L). Substituting these into Q_c and setting it equal to the given K_c (0.26), we solve for the unknown equilibrium concentration, $[H_2O]$.

Solution Writing the balanced equation and reaction quotient:

$$CH_4(g) + H_2O(g) \rightleftharpoons CO(g) + 3H_2(g) \qquad Q_c = \frac{[CO][H_2]^3}{[CH_4][H_2O]}$$

Determining the equilibrium concentrations:

$$[CH_4] = \frac{0.041 \text{ mol}}{0.32 \text{ L}} = 0.13\ M$$

Similarly, $[CO] = 0.81\ M$ and $[H_2] = 0.28\ M$.
Calculating $[H_2O]$ at equilibrium: Since $Q_c = K_c$, rearranging gives

$$[H_2O] = \frac{[CO][H_2]^3}{[CH_4]K_c} = \frac{(0.81)(0.28)^3}{(0.13)(0.26)} = 0.53\ M$$

Check Always check by substituting the concentrations into Q_c to confirm that the result is equal to K_c:

$$Q_c = \frac{[CO][H_2]^3}{[CH_4][H_2O]} = \frac{(0.81)(0.28)^3}{(0.13)(0.53)} = 0.26 = K_c$$

Follow-Up Problem 17.8 Nitrogen monoxide decomposes by the following equation: $2NO(g) \rightleftharpoons N_2(g) + O_2(g)$; $K_c = 2.3\times10^{30}$ at 298 K. In the atmosphere, $P_{O_2} = 0.209$ atm and $P_{N_2} = 0.781$ atm. What is the equilibrium partial pressure of NO in the air we breathe? (*Hint*: You need K_p to find the partial pressure.)

In a somewhat more involved variation, we know *K* and *initial* quantities and must find *equilibrium* quantities, for which we use a reaction table. Sample Problem 17.9 focuses on this approach.

Sample Problem 17.9 Determining Equilibrium Concentrations from Initial Concentrations and K_c

Problem Fuel engineers use the extent of the change from CO and H_2O to CO_2 and H_2 to regulate the proportions of synthetic fuel mixtures. If 0.250 mol of CO and 0.250 mol of H_2O gases are placed in a 125-mL flask at 900 K, what is the composition of the equilibrium mixture? At this temperature, K_c is 1.56.

Plan We have to find the "composition" of the equilibrium mixture, in other words, the equilibrium concentrations. As always, we write the balanced equation and use it to write the reaction quotient. We find the initial [CO] and [H_2O] from the amounts (0.250 mol of each) and volume (0.125 L), use the balanced equation to define x and set up a reaction table, substitute into Q_c, and solve for x, from which we calculate the concentrations.

Solution Writing the balanced equation and reaction quotient:

$$CO(g) + H_2O(g) \rightleftharpoons CO_2(g) + H_2(g) \qquad Q_c = \frac{[CO_2][H_2]}{[CO][H_2O]}$$

Calculating initial reactant concentrations:

$$[CO] = [H_2O] = \frac{0.250 \text{ mol}}{0.125 \text{ L}} = 2.00\ M$$

Setting up the reaction table, with x = [CO] and [H_2O] that react:

Concentration (M)	$CO(g)$	+	$H_2O(g)$	$\rightleftharpoons$	$CO_2(g)$	+	$H_2(g)$
Initial	2.00		2.00		0		0
Change	$-x$		$-x$		$+x$		$+x$
Equilibrium	$2.00 - x$		$2.00 - x$		x		x

Substituting into the reaction quotient and solving for x:

$$Q_c = \frac{[CO_2][H_2]}{[CO][H_2O]} = \frac{(x)(x)}{(2.00 - x)(2.00 - x)} = \frac{x^2}{(2.00 - x)^2}$$

At equilibrium, we have

$$Q_c = K_c = 1.56 = \frac{x^2}{(2.00 - x)^2}$$

We can apply the following math shortcut in this case *but not in general:* Because the right side of the equation is a perfect square, we take the square root of both sides:

$$\sqrt{1.56} = \frac{x}{2.00 - x} = \pm 1.25$$

A positive number (1.56) has a positive *and* a negative root, but in this case, only the positive root has any chemical meaning, so we ignore the negative root:*

$$1.25 = \frac{x}{2.00 - x} \quad \text{or} \quad 2.50 - 1.25x = x$$

So

$$2.50 = 2.25x \quad \text{therefore} \quad x = 1.11\ M$$

Calculating equilibrium concentrations:

$$[CO] = [H_2O] = 2.00\ M - x = 2.00\ M - 1.11\ M = 0.89\ M$$
$$[CO_2] = [H_2] = x = 1.11\ M$$

Check Given the intermediate size of K_c (1.56), it makes sense that the changes in concentration are moderate. It's a good idea to check that the sign of x in the reaction table is correct—only reactants were initially present, so x has a negative sign for reactants and a positive sign for products. Also check that the equilibrium concentrations give the known K_c: $\frac{(1.11)(1.11)}{(0.89)(0.89)} = 1.56$.

Follow-Up Problem 17.9 The decomposition of HI at low temperature was studied by injecting 2.50 mol of HI into a 10.32-L vessel at 25°C. What is [H_2] at equilibrium for the reaction $2HI(g) \rightleftharpoons H_2(g) + I_2(g)$; $K_c = 1.26 \times 10^{-3}$?

---

*The negative root gives $-1.25 = \frac{x}{2.00 - x}$, or $-2.50 + 1.25x = x$.

So $\quad -2.50 = 0.25x$ and $x = 10.\ M$

This value has no chemical meaning because we started with 2.00 M as the concentration of each reactant, so it is impossible for x to be 10. M. Moreover, the square root of an equilibrium constant is another equilibrium constant, which cannot have a negative value.

Using the Quadratic Formula to Find the Unknown The shortcut we used to simplify the math in Sample Problem 17.9 is a special case that occurred because we started with equal concentrations of the reactants, but typically, we start with different concentrations of reactants. Suppose, for example, we start with 2.00 *M* CO and 1.00 *M* H_2O. Now, the reaction table becomes

Concentration (*M*)	$CO(g)$	+	$H_2O(g)$	$\rightleftharpoons$	$CO_2(g)$	+	$H_2(g)$
Initial	2.00		1.00		0		0
Change	$-x$		$-x$		$+x$		$+x$
Equilibrium	$2.00 - x$		$1.00 - x$		x		x

Substituting these values into Q_c, we obtain

$$Q_c = \frac{[CO_2][H_2]}{[CO][H_2O]} = \frac{(x)(x)}{(2.00 - x)(1.00 - x)} = \frac{x^2}{x^2 - 3.00x + 2.00}$$

At equilibrium, we have

$$1.56 = \frac{x^2}{x^2 - 3.00x + 2.00}$$

To solve for x in this case, we rearrange the previous expression into the form of a *quadratic equation:*

$$a\,x^2 + \quad b\,x + \quad c = 0$$

$$0.56x^2 - 4.68x + 3.12 = 0$$

where $a = 0.56$, $b = -4.68$, and $c = 3.12$. Then we find x with the quadratic formula (Appendix A):

$$x = \frac{-b \pm \sqrt{b^2 - 4ac}}{2a}$$

The $\pm$ sign means that we obtain two possible values for x:

$$x = \frac{4.68 \pm \sqrt{(-4.68)^2 - 4(0.56)(3.12)}}{2(0.56)}$$

$$x = 7.6\text{ M} \qquad \text{and} \qquad x = 0.73\text{ M}$$

But only one of the values makes sense chemically. In this case, the positive root gives the larger value and negative concentrations at equilibrium (for example, 2.00 *M* − 7.6 *M* = −5.6 *M*), which have no meaning. Therefore, $x = 0.73$ *M*, and we have

$$[CO] = 2.00\,M - x = 2.00\,M - 0.73\,M = 1.27\,M$$
$$[H_2O] = 1.00\,M - x = 0.27\,M$$
$$[CO_2] = [H_2] = x = 0.73\,M$$

Checking to see if these values give the known K_c, we have

$$K_c = \frac{(0.73)(0.73)}{(1.27)(0.27)} = 1.6 \text{ (within rounding of 1.56)}$$

A Simplifying Assumption for Finding the Unknown In many cases, we can use chemical "common sense" to make an assumption that simplifies the math by avoiding the need to use the quadratic formula to find x. In general, *if a reaction has a relatively small K and a relatively large initial reactant concentration, the concentration change (x) can often be neglected.* This assumption does not mean that $x = 0$, because then there would be no reaction. It means that if a reaction starts with a high $[\text{reactant}]_{\text{init}}$ and proceeds very little to reach equilibrium (small K), the reactant concentration at equilibrium, $[\text{reactant}]_{\text{eq}}$, will be nearly the same as $[\text{reactant}]_{\text{init}}$.

Here's an everyday analogy for this assumption. On a bathroom scale, you weigh 158 lb. Take off your wristwatch, and you still weigh 158 lb. Within the accuracy of the scale, the weight of the watch is so small compared with your body weight that it can be neglected:

Initial body weight − weight of watch = final body weight ≈ initial body weight

Thus, let's say the initial concentration of A is 0.500 M and, because of a small K_c, the concentration of A that reacts is 0.002 M. We can then assume that

$$0.500\ M - 0.002\ M = 0.498\ M \approx 0.500\ M$$

that is,

$$[\mathrm{A}]_{\mathrm{init}} - [\mathrm{A}]_{\mathrm{reacting}} = [\mathrm{A}]_{\mathrm{eq}} \approx [\mathrm{A}]_{\mathrm{init}} \quad (17.9)$$

To justify the assumption that x is negligible, we make sure the error introduced is not significant. One common criterion for "significant" is the 5% rule: *if the assumption results in a change that is less than 5% of the initial concentration, the error is not significant, and the assumption is justified.* Let's see how making this assumption simplifies the math and if it is justified in the cases of two different $[\text{reactant}]_{\text{init}}$ values.

Sample Problem 17.10 Making a Simplifying Assumption to Calculate Equilibrium Concentrations

Problem Phosgene is a potent chemical warfare agent that is now outlawed by international agreement. It decomposes by the reaction

$$COCl_2(g) \rightleftharpoons CO(g) + Cl_2(g) \qquad K_c = 8.3\times10^{-4} \text{ (at 360°C)}$$

Calculate [CO], $[Cl_2]$, and $[COCl_2]$ when each of the following amounts of phosgene decomposes and reaches equilibrium in a 10.0-L flask:
(a) 5.00 mol of $COCl_2$ **(b)** 0.100 mol of $COCl_2$

Plan We know from the balanced equation that when x mol of $COCl_2$ decomposes, x mol of CO and x mol of Cl_2 form. We use the volume (10.0 L) to convert amount (5.00 mol or 0.100 mol) to molar concentration, define x and set up the reaction table, and substitute the values into Q_c. Before using the quadratic formula, we assume that x is negligibly small. After solving for x, we check the assumption and find the equilibrium concentrations. If the assumption is not justified, we use the quadratic formula to find x.

Solution **(a)** For 5.00 mol of $COCl_2$. Writing the reaction quotient:

$$Q_c = \frac{[CO][Cl_2]}{[COCl_2]}$$

Calculating the initial reactant concentration, $[COCl_2]_{\text{init}}$:

$$[COCl_2]_{\text{init}} = \frac{5.00\text{ mol}}{10.0\text{ L}} = 0.500\ M$$

Setting up the reaction table, with x equal to $[COCl_2]_{\text{reacting}}$:

Concentration (M)	**$COCl_2(g)$**	$\rightleftharpoons$	**$CO(g)$**	**+**	**$Cl_2(g)$**
Initial	0.500		0		0
Change	$-x$		$+x$		$+x$
Equilibrium	$0.500 - x$		x		x

If we use the equilibrium values in Q_c with the given K_c, we obtain

$$Q_c = \frac{[CO][Cl_2]}{[COCl_2]} = \frac{x^2}{0.500 - x} = K_c = 8.3\times10^{-4}$$

Because K_c is small, the reaction does not proceed very far to the right, so let's assume that x ($[COCl_2]_{\text{reacting}}$) can be neglected. In other words, we assume that the equilibrium concentration is nearly the same as the initial concentration, 0.500 M:

$$[COCl_2]_{\text{init}} - [COCl_2]_{\text{reacting}} \approx [COCl_2]_{\text{eq}}$$

$$0.500\ M - x \approx 0.500\ M$$

Using this assumption, we substitute and solve for x:

$$K_c = 8.3\times10^{-4} \approx \frac{x^2}{0.500}$$

$$x^2 \approx (8.3\times10^{-4})(0.500) \qquad \text{so} \qquad x \approx 2.0\times10^{-2}$$

Checking the assumption by seeing if the error is <5%:

$$\frac{[\text{Change}]}{[\text{Initial}]} \times 100 = \frac{2.0\times10^{-2}}{0.500} \times 100 = 4\% \text{ (<5\%, so the assumption is justified)}$$

Solving for the equilibrium concentrations:

$$[\text{CO}] = [\text{Cl}_2] = x = 2.0\times10^{-2}\,M$$
$$[\text{COCl}_2] = 0.500\,M - x = 0.480\,M$$

(b) For 0.100 mol of $COCl_2$. The calculation in this case is the same as the calculation in part (a), except that $[\text{COCl}_2]_{\text{init}} = 0.100 \text{ mol}/10.0 \text{ L} = 0.0100\,M$. Thus, at equilibrium,

$$Q_c = \frac{[\text{CO}][\text{Cl}_2]}{[\text{COCl}_2]} = \frac{x^2}{0.0100 - x} = K_c = 8.3\times10^{-4}$$

Making the assumption that $0.0100\,M - x \approx 0.0100\,M$ and solving for x:

$$K_c = 8.3\times10^{-4} \approx \frac{x^2}{0.0100} \qquad x \approx 2.9\times10^{-3}$$

Checking the assumption:

$$\frac{2.9\times10^{-3}}{0.0100} \times 100 = 29\% \qquad \text{(>5\%, so the assumption is } \textit{not} \text{ justified)}$$

We must solve the quadratic equation:

$$x^2 + (8.3\times10^{-4})x - (8.3\times10^{-6}) = 0$$

The only meaningful value of x is 2.5×10^{-3}.
Solving for the equilibrium concentrations:

$$[\text{CO}] = [\text{Cl}_2] = 2.5\times10^{-3}\,M$$
$$[\text{COCl}_2] = 1.00\times10^{-2}\,M - x = 7.5\times10^{-3}\,M$$

Check Once again, use the calculated values to be sure you obtain the given K_c.

Comment The main point is that the simplifying assumption was justified at the high $[\text{COCl}_2]_{\text{init}}$ but *not* at the low $[\text{COCl}_2]_{\text{init}}$.

Follow-Up Problem 17.10 In a study of the effect of temperature on halogen decomposition, 0.50 mol of I_2 was heated in a 2.5-L vessel, and the following reaction occurred: $I_2(g) \rightleftharpoons 2I(g)$.
(a) Calculate $[I_2]$ and [I] at equilibrium at 600 K; $K_c = 2.94\times10^{-10}$.
(b) Calculate $[I_2]$ and [I] at equilibrium at 2000 K; $K_c = 0.209$.

Predicting When the Assumption Will Be Justified To summarize, we assume that x ($[\text{A}]_{\text{reacting}}$) can be neglected if K_c is relatively small and/or $[\text{A}]_{\text{init}}$ is relatively large. The same holds for K_p and $P_{\text{A(init)}}$. But *how* small or large must these variables be? Here's a benchmark for deciding when to make the assumption:

- If $\frac{[\text{A}]_{\text{init}}}{K_c} > 400$, the assumption is justified: neglecting x introduces an error < 5%.
- If $\frac{[\text{A}]_{\text{init}}}{K_c} < 400$, the assumption is *not* justified; neglecting x introduces an error > 5%, so we solve a quadratic equation to find x.

For example, using the values from Sample Problem 17.10, we have

Part (a): For $[\text{A}]_{\text{init}} = 0.500\,M$, $\frac{0.500}{8.3\times10^{-4}} = 6.0\times10^2$, which is greater than 400.

Part (b): For $[\text{A}]_{\text{init}} = 0.0100\,M$, $\frac{0.0100}{8.3\times10^{-4}} = 12$, which is less than 400.

We will make a similar assumption in many problems in Chapters 18 and 19.

Problems Involving Mixtures of Reactants and Products

In the problems so far, the reaction *had* to go toward products because it started with only reactants. And therefore, in the reaction tables, we knew that the unknown change in reactant concentration had a negative sign ($-x$) and the change in product concentration had a positive sign ($+x$). If, however, we start with a *mixture* of reactants and products, the reaction direction is not obvious. In those cases, we apply the idea from Section 17.4 and first *compare the values of Q and K to find the direction the reaction is proceeding to reach equilibrium.* (To focus on this idea, Sample Problem 17.11 uses concentrations that avoid the need for the quadratic formula.)

Sample Problem 17.11 Predicting Reaction Direction and Calculating Equilibrium Concentrations

Problem The research and development unit of a chemical company is studying the reaction of CH_4 and H_2S, two components of natural gas:

$$CH_4(g) + 2H_2S(g) \rightleftharpoons CS_2(g) + 4H_2(g)$$

In one experiment, 1.00 mol of CH_4, 1.00 mol of CS_2, 2.00 mol of H_2S, and 2.00 mol of H_2 are mixed in a 250.-mL vessel at 960°C. At this temperature, $K_c = 0.036$.
(a) In which direction will the reaction proceed to reach equilibrium?
(b) If $[CH_4] = 5.56\ M$ at equilibrium, what are the equilibrium concentrations of the other substances?

Plan (a) To find the direction, we convert the given initial amounts and volume (0.250 L) to concentrations, calculate Q_c, and compare it with K_c. **(b)** Based on this information, we determine the sign of each concentration change for the reaction table and then use the known $[CH_4]$ at equilibrium (5.56 M) to determine x and the other equilibrium concentrations.

Solution (a) Calculating the initial concentrations:

$$[CH_4] = \frac{1.00\ \text{mol}}{0.250\ \text{L}} = 4.00\ M$$

Similarly, $[H_2S] = 8.00\ M$, $[CS_2] = 4.00\ M$, and $[H_2] = 8.00\ M$.
Calculating the value of Q_c:

$$Q_c = \frac{[CS_2][H_2]^4}{[CH_4][H_2S]^2} = \frac{(4.00)(8.00)^4}{(4.00)(8.00)^2} = 64.0$$

Comparing Q_c and K_c: $Q_c > K_c$ ($64.0 > 0.036$), so the reaction proceeds to the left. Therefore, concentrations of reactants increase and those of products decrease.
(b) Setting up a reaction table, with $x = [CS_2]$ that reacts, which equals $[CH_4]$ that forms:

Concentration (M)	$CH_4(g)$	+	$2H_2S(g)$	$\rightleftharpoons$	$CS_2(g)$	+	$4H_2(g)$
Intial	4.00		8.00		4.00		8.00
Change	$+x$		$+2x$		$-x$		$-4x$
Equilibrium	$4.00 + x$		$8.00 + 2x$		$4.00 - x$		$8.00 - 4x$

Solving for x: At equilibrium,

$$[CH_4] = 5.56\ M = 4.00\ M + x \quad \text{so} \quad x = 1.56\ M$$

Thus,

$$[H_2S] = 8.00\ M + 2x = 8.00\ M + 2(1.56\ M) = 11.12\ M$$
$$[CS_2] = 4.00\ M - x = 2.44\ M$$
$$[H_2] = 8.00\ M - 4x = 1.76\ M$$

Check The comparison of Q_c and K_c showed the reaction proceeding to the left. The given data from part (b) confirm this because $[CH_4]$ increases from 4.00 M to 5.56 M during the reaction. Check that the concentrations give the known K_c:

$$\frac{(2.44)(1.76)^4}{(5.56)(11.12)^2} = 0.0341, \text{ which is close to } 0.036$$

Follow-Up Problem 17.11 An inorganic chemist studying the reactions of phosphorus halides mixes 0.1050 mol of PCl_5 with 0.0450 mol of Cl_2 and 0.0450 mol of PCl_3 in a 0.5000-L flask at 250°C: $PCl_5(g) \rightleftharpoons PCl_3(g) + Cl_2(g)$; $K_c = 4.2\times10^{-2}$.
(a) In which direction will the reaction proceed?
(b) If $[PCl_5] = 0.2065\ M$ at equilibrium, what are the equilibrium concentrations of the other components?

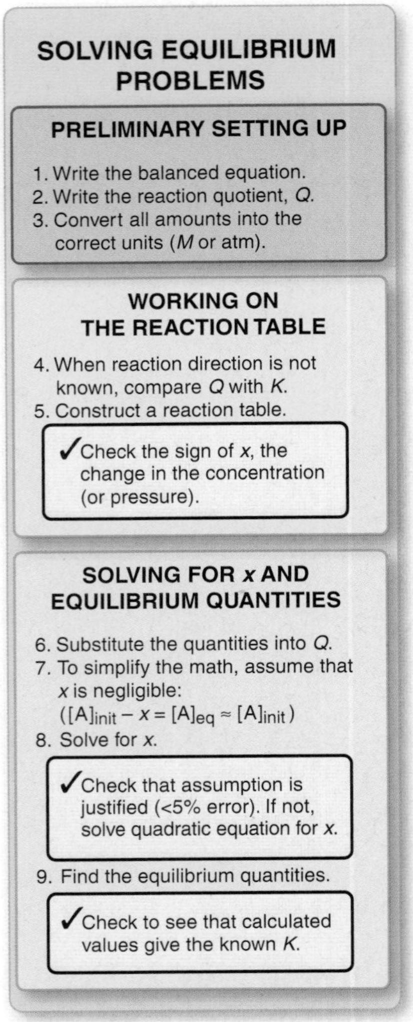

Figure 17.6 Steps in solving equilibrium problems.

Figure 17.6 groups the steps for solving equilibrium problems in which you know K and some initial quantities and must find the equilibrium quantities.

Summary of Section 17.5

- In equilibrium problems, we typically use quantities (concentrations or pressures) of reactants and products to find K, or we use K to find quantities.
- Reaction tables summarize the initial quantities, their changes during the reaction, and the equilibrium quantities. To simplify calculations, we assume that if K is small and the initial quantity of reactant is large, the unknown change in reactant (x) can be neglected. If this assumption is not justified (that is, if the error is greater than 5%), we use the quadratic formula to find x.
- For reactions that start with a mixture of reactants and products, we first determine reaction direction by comparing Q and K to decide on the sign of x.

17.6 • REACTION CONDITIONS AND EQUILIBRIUM: LE CHÂTELIER'S PRINCIPLE

Change conditions so that a system is no longer at equilibrium and it has the remarkable ability to adjust itself and reattain equilibrium. This phenomenon is described by **Le Châtelier's principle:** when a chemical system at equilibrium is disturbed, it reattains equilibrium by undergoing a net reaction that reduces the effect of the disturbance.

Two phrases in this statement need further explanation:

1. How is a system "disturbed"? At equilibrium, Q equals K. The system is disturbed when a change in conditions forces it temporarily out of equilibrium ($Q \neq K$). Three common disturbances are a change in concentration, a change in pressure (caused by a change in volume), or a change in temperature. We'll discuss each below.

2. What does a "net reaction" mean? This phrase refers to a shift in the *equilibrium position* to the right or left. The *equilibrium position* is defined by the specific equilibrium concentrations (or pressures). A shift to the right is a net reaction from reactant to product until equilibrium is reattained; a shift to the left is a net reaction from product to reactant. Thus, *concentrations (or pressures) change in a way that reduces the effect of the change in conditions, and the system attains a new equilibrium position.*

For the remainder of this section, we'll examine a system at equilibrium to see how it responds to changes in concentration, pressure (volume), or temperature; then, we'll see what happens when we add a catalyst. As our example, we use the gaseous reaction between phosphorus trichloride and chlorine to produce phosphorus pentachloride:

$$PCl_3(g) + Cl_2(g) \rightleftharpoons PCl_5(g)$$

Le Châtelier's principle holds for many systems at equilibrium in both the natural and social sciences—the effects of disease or drought on populations of predators and prey on the African plain (*see margin*), a change in the cost of petroleum based on a balance of supply and demand, even the formation of certain elements in the core of a star.

Does Le Châtelier's principle apply to other systems?

The Effect of a Change in Concentration

When a system at equilibrium is disturbed by a change in concentration of one of the components, it reacts in the direction that reduces the change:

- If the concentration of A increases, the system reacts to consume some of it.
- If the concentration of B decreases, the system reacts to produce some of it.

Only components that appear in Q can have an effect, so changes in the amounts of pure liquids and solids cannot.

A Qualitative View of a Concentration Change At 523 K, the PCl_3-Cl_2-PCl_5 system reaches equilibrium when

$$PCl_3(g) + Cl_2(g) \rightleftharpoons PCl_5(g) \qquad Q_c = \frac{[PCl_5]}{[PCl_3][Cl_2]} = 24.0 = K_c$$

Starting with Q_c equal to K_c, let's think through some changes in concentration:

1. *Adding a reactant.* What happens if we disturb the system by adding some Cl_2 gas? To reduce the disturbance, the system will consume some of the added Cl_2 by shifting toward product. With regard to the reaction quotient, when the $[Cl_2]$ term increases, the value of Q_c decreases; thus, $Q_c \neq K_c$. As some of the added Cl_2 reacts with some of the PCl_3 to form more PCl_5, the denominator becomes smaller again and the numerator larger, until eventually $Q_c = K_c$ again. Notice the changes in the new equilibrium concentrations: $[Cl_2]$ and $[PCl_5]$ are higher than in the original equilibrium position, and $[PCl_3]$ is lower. Nevertheless, the ratio of values gives the same K_c. Thus, *the equilibrium position shifts to the right when a component on the left is added:*

$$PCl_3 + Cl_2(\text{added}) \longrightarrow PCl_5$$

2. *Removing a reactant.* What happens if we disturb the system by removing some PCl_3? To reduce this disturbance, the system will replace the PCl_3 by consuming some PCl_5 and proceeding toward reactants. With regard to Q_c, when the $[PCl_3]$ term decreases, Q_c increases, so $Q_c \neq K_c$. As some PCl_5 decomposes to PCl_3 and Cl_2, the numerator decreases and the denominator increases until $Q_c = K_c$ again. Once again, the new and old equilibrium concentrations are different, but the value of K_c is not. Thus, *the equilibrium position shifts to the left when a component on the left is removed:*

$$PCl_3(\text{removed}) + Cl_2 \longleftarrow PCl_5$$

3. *Adding or removing a product.* The same points we just made for a reactant hold for a product. If we add PCl_5, the equilibrium position shifts to the left; if we remove some PCl_5, the equilibrium position shifts to the right.

In other words, no matter how the disturbance in concentration comes about, *the system reacts to consume some of the added substance or produce some of the removed substance* to make $Q_c = K_c$ again (Figure 17.7):

- The equilibrium position shifts to the *right* if a reactant is added or a product is removed: [reactant] increases or [product] decreases.
- The equilibrium position shifts to the *left* if a reactant is removed or a product is added: [reactant] decreases or [product] increases.

A Quantitative View of a Concentration Change As you saw, the system "reduces the effect of the disturbance." But the effect is not completely eliminated, as we can see from a quantitative comparison of original and new equilibrium positions.

Consider what happens when we add Cl_2 to a system whose original equilibrium position was established with $[PCl_3] = 0.200\ M$, $[Cl_2] = 0.125\ M$, and $[PCl_5] = 0.600\ M$. That is,

$$Q_c = \frac{[PCl_5]}{[PCl_3][Cl_2]} = \frac{0.600}{(0.200)(0.125)} = 24.0 = K_c$$

Now we add enough Cl_2 to increase its concentration by 0.075 M to a new $[Cl_2]_{init}$ of 0.200 M. The reaction proceeds, and the system comes to a new equilibrium position. From Le Châtelier's principle, we predict that adding more reactant will shift the equilibrium position to the right. Experimental measurement shows that the new $[PCl_5]_{eq}$ is 0.637 M.

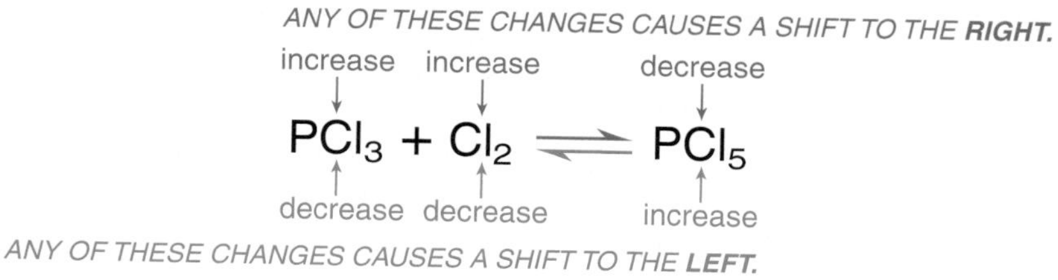

Figure 17.7 The effect of a change in concentration on a system at equilibrium.

Table 17.3 The Effect of Added Cl_2 on the PCl_3-Cl_2-PCl_5 System

Concentration (*M*)	$PCl_3(g)$	+	$Cl_2(g)$	$\rightleftharpoons$	$PCl_5(g)$
Original equilibrium	0.200		0.125		0.600
Disturbance			+0.075		
New initial	0.200		0.200		0.600
Change	$-x$		$-x$		$+x$
New equilibrium	$0.200 - x$		$0.200 - x$		$0.600 + x$ (0.637)*

*Experimentally determined value.

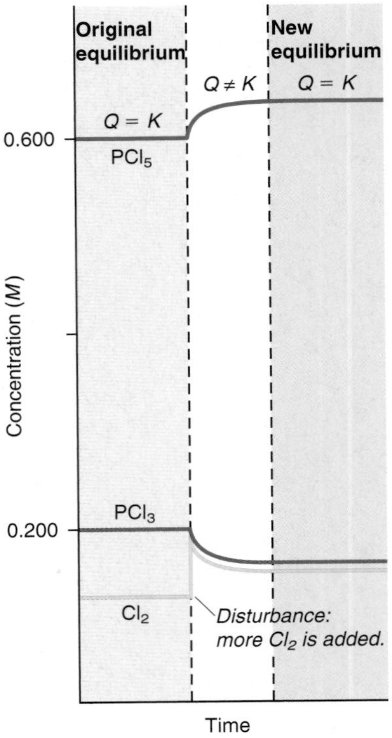

Figure 17.8 The effect of added Cl_2 on the PCl_3-Cl_2-PCl_5 system. The original equilibrium concentrations are shown at left *(gray region)*. When Cl_2 *(yellow curve)* is added, its concentration increases instantly *(vertical part of yellow curve)* and then falls gradually as it reacts with PCl_3 to form more PCl_5. Soon, equilibrium is re-established at new concentrations *(blue region)* but with the same *K*.

Table 17.3 shows a reaction table of the entire process: the original equilibrium position, the disturbance, the (new) initial concentrations, the direction of x (the change needed to reattain equilibrium), and the new equilibrium position. Figure 17.8 depicts the process.

Let's determine the new equilibrium concentrations. From Table 17.3,

$$[PCl_5] = 0.600\ M + x = 0.637\ M \quad \text{so} \quad x = 0.037\ M$$

Thus, $$[PCl_3] = [Cl_2] = 0.200\ M - x = 0.200\ M - 0.037\ M = 0.163\ M$$

Therefore, at equilibrium,

$$K_{c(\text{original})} = \frac{0.600}{(0.200)(0.125)} = 24.0$$

$$K_{c(\text{new})} = \frac{0.637}{(0.163)(0.163)} = 24.0$$

There are several key points to notice about the new equilibrium concentrations:

- As we predicted, $[PCl_5]$ (0.637 *M*) is higher than the original concentration (0.600 *M*).
- $[Cl_2]$ (0.163 *M*) is higher than the *original* equilibrium concentration (0.125 *M*), but lower than the new initial concentration (0.200 *M*); thus, the disturbance is *reduced but not eliminated.*
- $[PCl_3]$ (0.163 *M*), the other reactant, is lower than the original equilibrium concentration (0.200 *M*) because some reacted with the added Cl_2.
- Most importantly, although the position of equilibrium shifted to the right, *at a given temperature, K_c does **not** change with a change in concentration.*

Sample Problem 17.12 Predicting the Effect of a Change in Concentration on the Equilibrium Position

Problem To improve air quality and obtain a useful product, chemists often remove sulfur from coal and natural gas by treating the contaminant hydrogen sulfide with O_2:

$$2H_2S(g) + O_2(g) \rightleftharpoons 2S(s) + 2H_2O(g)$$

What happens to

(a) $[H_2O]$ if O_2 is added? **(b)** $[H_2S]$ if O_2 is added?
(c) $[O_2]$ if H_2S is removed? **(d)** $[H_2S]$ if sulfur is added?

Plan We write the reaction quotient to see how Q_c is affected by each disturbance, relative to K_c. This effect tells us the direction in which the reaction proceeds for the system to reattain equilibrium and how each concentration changes.

Solution Writing the reaction quotient: $Q_c = \dfrac{[H_2O]^2}{[H_2S]^2[O_2]}$

(a) When O_2 is added, the denominator of Q_c increases, so $Q_c < K_c$. The reaction proceeds to the right until $Q_c = K_c$ again, so $[H_2O]$ increases.

(b) As in part (a), when O_2 is added, $Q_c < K_c$. Some H_2S reacts with the added O_2 as the reaction proceeds to the right, so $[H_2S]$ decreases.

(c) When H_2S is removed, the denominator of Q_c decreases, so $Q_c > K_c$. As the reaction proceeds to the left to re-form H_2S, more O_2 forms as well, so $[O_2]$ increases.

(d) The concentration of solid S is unchanged as long as some is present, so it does not appear in the reaction quotient. Adding more S has no effect, so $[H_2S]$ is unchanged (but see Comment 2 below).

Check Apply Le Châtelier's principle to see that the reaction proceeds in the direction that lowers the increased concentration or raises the decreased concentration.

Comment 1. As you know, sulfur exists most commonly as S_8. How would this change in formula affect the answers? The balanced equation and Q_c would be

$$8H_2S(g) + 4O_2(g) \rightleftharpoons S_8(s) + 8H_2O(g) \qquad Q_c = \frac{[H_2O]^8}{[H_2S]^8[O_2]^4}$$

The value of K_c is different for this equation, but the changes described in the problem have the same effects. Thus, shifts in equilibrium position predicted by Le Châtelier's principle are not affected by a change in the balancing coefficients.

2. In (d), you saw that adding a solid has no effect on the concentrations of other components: because *the* ***concentration*** *of the solid cannot change,* it does not appear in Q. But *the* ***amount*** *of solid can change.* Adding H_2S shifts the reaction to the right, so more S forms.

Follow-Up Problem 17.12 In a study of glass etching, a chemist examines the reaction between sand (SiO_2) and hydrogen fluoride at 150°C:

$$SiO_2(s) + 4HF(g) \rightleftharpoons SiF_4(g) + 2H_2O(g)$$

Predict the effect on $[SiF_4]$ when **(a)** $H_2O(g)$ is removed; **(b)** some liquid water is added; **(c)** HF is removed; **(d)** some sand is removed.

The Effect of a Change in Pressure (Volume)

Changes in pressure can have a large effect on equilibrium systems containing gaseous components. (A change in pressure has a negligible effect on liquids and solids because they are nearly incompressible.) Pressure changes can occur in three ways:

- *Changing the concentration of a gaseous component.* We just considered the effect of changing the concentration of a component, and that reasoning applies here.
- *Adding an inert gas (one that does not take part in the reaction).* As long as the volume of the system is constant, adding an inert gas has no effect on the equilibrium position because *all concentrations, and thus partial pressures, remain the same.* Moreover, the inert gas does not appear in Q, so it cannot have an effect.
- *Changing the volume of the reaction vessel.* This change can cause a large shift in equilibrium position, but only for reactions in which the number of moles of gas, n_{gas}, changes.

Let's consider the two possible situations for the third way: changing the volume of the reaction vessel.

1. *Reactions in which n_{gas} changes.* Suppose the PCl_3-Cl_2-PCl_5 system is in a cylinder-piston assembly. We press down on the piston to halve the volume, so the gas pressure doubles. To reduce this disturbance, the system responds by *reducing the number of gas molecules.* And the only way to do that is through a net reaction toward the side with *fewer moles of gas,* in this case, toward product:

$$PCl_3(g) + Cl_2(g) \longrightarrow PCl_5(g)$$
$$\text{2 mol gas} \longrightarrow \text{1 mol gas}$$

Recall that $Q_c = \dfrac{[PCl_5]}{[PCl_3][Cl_2]}$. When the volume is halved, the concentrations double, but the denominator of Q_c is the product of two concentrations, so it quadruples while the numerator only doubles. Thus, Q_c becomes less than K_c. As a result, the system forms more PCl_5 and a new equilibrium position is reached.

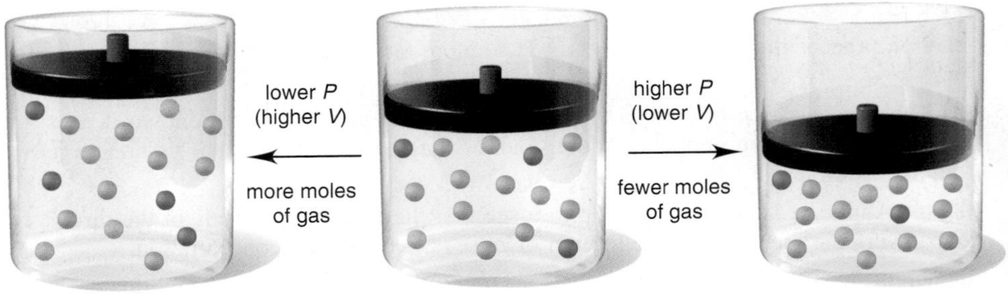

Figure 17.9 The effect of a change in pressure (volume) on a system at equilibrium. The system of gases (*center*) is at equilibrium. For the reaction

an increase in pressure (*right*) decreases the volume, so the equilibrium shifts to form *fewer* molecules. A decrease in pressure (*left*) increases the volume, so the equilibrium shifts to form *more* molecules.

Thus, for a system that consists of gases at equilibrium, in which the amount (mol) of gas, n_{gas}, changes during the reaction (Figure 17.9):

- If the volume becomes smaller (pressure is higher), the reaction shifts so that the total number of gas molecules decreases.
- If the volume becomes larger (pressure is lower), the reaction shifts so that the total number of gas molecules increases.

2. *Reactions in which* n_{gas} *does* ***not*** *change.* For the formation of hydrogen iodide from its elements, we have the same amount (mol) of gas on both sides:

$$H_2(g) + I_2(g) \rightleftharpoons 2HI(g)$$
$$\text{2 mol gas} \longrightarrow \text{2 mol gas}$$

Therefore, Q_c has the same number of terms in the numerator and denominator:

$$Q_c = \frac{[HI]^2}{[H_2][I_2]} = \frac{[HI][HI]}{[H_2][I_2]}$$

Because a change in volume has the same effect on the numerator and denominator, *there is* ***no*** *effect on the equilibrium position.*

In terms of the equilibrium constant, *a change in volume is, in effect, a change in concentration:* a decrease in volume raises the concentration, and vice versa. Therefore, like other changes in concentration, *a change in pressure due to a change in volume does* ***not*** *alter* K_c.

Sample Problem 17.13 Predicting the Effect of a Change in Volume (Pressure) on the Equilibrium Position

Problem How would you change the volume of each of the following reactions to *increase* the yield of the products?

(a) $CaCO_3(s) \rightleftharpoons CaO(s) + CO_2(g)$
(b) $S(s) + 3F_2(g) \rightleftharpoons SF_6(g)$
(c) $Cl_2(g) + I_2(g) \rightleftharpoons 2ICl(g)$

Plan Whenever gases are present, a change in volume causes a change in concentration. For reactions in which the number of moles of gas changes, if the volume decreases (pressure increases), the equilibrium position shifts to lower the pressure by reducing the number of moles of gas. A volume increase (pressure decrease) has the opposite effect.

Solution **(a)** The only gas is the product CO_2. To make the system produce more molecules of gas, that is, more CO_2, we increase the volume (decrease the pressure).
(b) With 3 mol of gas on the left and only 1 mol on the right, we decrease the volume (increase the pressure) to form fewer molecules of gas and, thus, more SF_6.
(c) The number of moles of gas is the same on both sides of the equation, so a change in volume (pressure) will have no effect on the yield of ICl.

Check Let's predict the relative values of Q_c and K_c.
(a) $Q_c = [CO_2]$, so increasing the volume will make $Q_c < K_c$, and the system will yield more CO_2.
(b) $Q_c = [SF_6]/[F_2]^3$. Lowering the volume increases $[F_2]$ and $[SF_6]$ proportionately, but Q_c decreases because of the exponent 3 in the denominator. To make $Q_c = K_c$ again, $[SF_6]$ must increase.
(c) $Q_c = [ICl]^2/[Cl_2][I_2]$. A change in volume (pressure) affects the numerator (2 mol) and denominator (2 mol) equally, so it will have no effect.

Follow-Up Problem 17.13 Would you increase or decrease the pressure (via a volume change) of each of the following reaction mixtures to *decrease* the yield of products?
(a) $2SO_2(g) + O_2(g) \rightleftharpoons 2SO_3(g)$
(b) $4NH_3(g) + 5O_2(g) \rightleftharpoons 4NO(g) + 6H_2O(g)$
(c) $CaC_2O_4(s) \rightleftharpoons CaCO_3(s) + CO(g)$

The Effect of a Change in Temperature

Of the three types of disturbances that may occur—a change in concentration, pressure, or temperature—*only temperature changes alter K.* To see why, let's focus on the sign of ΔH°_{rxn}:

$$PCl_3(g) + Cl_2(g) \rightleftharpoons PCl_5(g) \qquad \Delta H^\circ_{rxn} = -111 \text{ kJ}$$

The forward reaction is exothermic (releases heat; $\Delta H^\circ_{rxn} < 0$), so the reverse reaction is endothermic (absorbs heat; $\Delta H^\circ_{rxn} > 0$):

$$PCl_3(g) + Cl_2(g) \longrightarrow PCl_5(g) + \textbf{heat} \text{ (exothermic)}$$
$$PCl_3(g) + Cl_2(g) \longleftarrow PCl_5(g) + \textbf{heat} \text{ (endothermic)}$$

If we consider *heat as a component of the equilibrium system,* a rise in temperature occurs when heat is "added" to the system and a drop in temperature occurs when heat is "removed" from the system. As with a change in any other component, the system shifts to reduce the effect of the change. Therefore, *a temperature increase (adding heat) favors the endothermic (heat-absorbing) direction, and a temperature decrease (removing heat) favors the exothermic (heat-releasing) direction.*

If we start with the system at equilibrium, Q_c equals K_c. Increase the temperature, and the system absorbs the added heat by decomposing some PCl_5 to PCl_3 and Cl_2. The denominator of Q_c becomes larger and the numerator smaller, so the system reaches a new equilibrium position at a smaller ratio of concentration terms, that is, a lower K_c. Similarly, if the temperature drops, the system releases more heat by forming more PCl_5 from some PCl_3 and Cl_2. The numerator of Q_c becomes larger, the denominator smaller, and the new equilibrium position has a higher K_c. Thus,

- *A temperature rise will increase K_c for a system with a positive ΔH°_{rxn}.*
- *A temperature rise will decrease K_c for a system with a negative ΔH°_{rxn}.*

Let's review these ideas with a sample problem.

Sample Problem 17.14 **Predicting the Effect of a Change in Temperature on the Equilibrium Position**

Problem How does an *increase* in temperature affect the equilibrium concentration of the underlined substance and K for each of the following reactions?
(a) $CaO(s) + H_2O(l) \rightleftharpoons \underline{Ca(OH)_2(aq)} \qquad \Delta H^\circ = -82 \text{ kJ}$
(b) $CaCO_3(s) \rightleftharpoons CaO(s) + \underline{CO_2(g)} \qquad \Delta H^\circ = 178 \text{ kJ}$
(c) $\underline{SO_2(g)} \rightleftharpoons S(s) + O_2(g) \qquad \Delta H^\circ = 297 \text{ kJ}$

Plan We write each equation to show heat as a reactant or product. The temperature increases when we add heat, so the system shifts to absorb the heat; that is, the endothermic reaction occurs. Thus, K will increase if the forward reaction is endothermic and decrease if it is exothermic.

Solution **(a)** $CaO(s) + H_2O(l) \rightleftharpoons Ca(OH)_2(aq)$ + ***heat***
Adding heat shifts the system to the left: $[Ca(OH)_2]$ and K will decrease.
(b) $CaCO_3(s)$ + ***heat*** $\rightleftharpoons CaO(s) + CO_2(g)$
Adding heat shifts the system to the right: $[CO_2]$ and K will increase.
(c) $SO_2(g)$ + ***heat*** $\rightleftharpoons S(s) + O_2(g)$
Adding heat shifts the system to the right: $[SO_2]$ will decrease and K will increase.

Check Check your answers by reasoning through a *decrease* in temperature: heat is removed and the exothermic direction is favored. All the answers should be opposite.

Comment Note that in (a) these ideas hold for solutions as well.

Follow-Up Problem 17.14 How does a *decrease* in temperature affect the partial pressure of the underlined substance and the value of K for each of the following reactions?
(a) $C(graphite) + \underline{2H_2(g)} \rightleftharpoons CH_4(g)$ $\Delta H° = -75$ kJ
(b) $\underline{N_2(g)} + O_2(g) \rightleftharpoons 2NO(g)$ $\Delta H° = 181$ kJ
(c) $P_4(s) + 10Cl_2(g) \rightleftharpoons \underline{4PCl_5(g)}$ $\Delta H° = -1528$ kJ

The van't Hoff Equation: The Effect of *T* on *K* The *van't Hoff equation* shows quantitatively how the equilibrium constant is affected by changes in temperature:

$$\ln \frac{K_2}{K_1} = -\frac{\Delta H^\circ_{rxn}}{R}\left(\frac{1}{T_2} - \frac{1}{T_1}\right) \qquad (17.10)$$

where K_1 is the equilibrium constant at T_1, K_2 is the equilibrium constant at T_2, and R is the universal gas constant (8.314 J/mol·K). If we know ΔH°_{rxn} and K at one temperature, the van't Hoff equation allows us to find K at any other temperature (or to find ΔH°_{rxn}, given the two K's at two T's).

Equation 17.10 confirms the qualitative prediction from Le Châtelier's principle: for a temperature rise, we have

$$T_2 > T_1 \quad \text{and} \quad 1/T_2 < 1/T_1$$

so

$$1/T_2 - 1/T_1 < 0$$

Therefore,

- For an endothermic reaction ($\Delta H^\circ_{rxn} > 0$), the $-(\Delta H^\circ_{rxn}/R)$ term is <0. With $1/T_2 - 1/T_1 < 0$, the right side of the equation is >0. Thus, $\ln (K_2/K_1) > 0$, so $K_2 > K_1$.
- For an exothermic reaction ($\Delta H^\circ_{rxn} < 0$), the $-(\Delta H^\circ_{rxn}/R)$ term is >0. With $1/T_2 - 1/T_1 < 0$, the right side of the equation is <0. Thus, $\ln (K_2/K_1) < 0$, so $K_2 < K_1$.

Here's a typical problem that requires the van't Hoff equation. Many coal gasification processes begin with the formation of syngas from carbon and steam:

$$C(s) + H_2O(g) \rightleftharpoons CO(g) + H_2(g) \qquad \Delta H^\circ_{rxn} = 131 \text{ kJ/mol}$$

An engineer knows that K_p is only 9.36×10^{-17} at 25°C and therefore wants to find a temperature that allows a much higher yield. Calculate K_p at 700.°C.

$$\ln \frac{K_2}{K_1} = -\frac{\Delta H^\circ_{rxn}}{R}\left(\frac{1}{T_2} - \frac{1}{T_1}\right)$$

The temperatures must be in kelvins, and the units of $\Delta H°$ and R must be made consistent:

$$\ln\left(\frac{K_{p2}}{9.36\times10^{-17}}\right) = -\frac{131\times10^3 \text{ J/mol}}{8.314 \text{ J/mol·K}}\left(\frac{1}{973 \text{ K}} - \frac{1}{298 \text{ K}}\right)$$

$$\frac{K_{p2}}{9.36\times10^{-17}} = 8.51\times10^{15}$$

$$K_{p2} = 0.797 \qquad \text{(a much higher yield)}$$

(For further practice with the van't Hoff equation, see Problems 17.73 and 17.74.)

The Lack of Effect of a Catalyst

Let's briefly consider what effect, if any, adding a catalyst would have on the system. Recall from Chapter 16 that a catalyst speeds up a reaction by lowering the activation energy, thereby increasing the forward *and* reverse rates to the same extent. Thus, *a catalyst shortens the time it takes to reach equilibrium but has* **no** *effect on the equilibrium position.* That is, if we add a catalyst to a mixture of PCl_3 and Cl_2 at 523 K, the system attains the *same* equilibrium concentrations of PCl_3, Cl_2, and PCl_5 *more quickly* than it does without the catalyst. Figure 17.10 shows an engine in an imaginary world where catalysts speed a reaction in only one direction. As you'll see in a moment, however, catalysts play key roles in optimizing reaction systems.

Table 17.4 summarizes the effects of changing conditions. Many changes alter the equilibrium *position*, but only temperature changes alter the equilibrium *constant.* Sample Problem 17.15 shows how to visualize equilibrium at the molecular level.

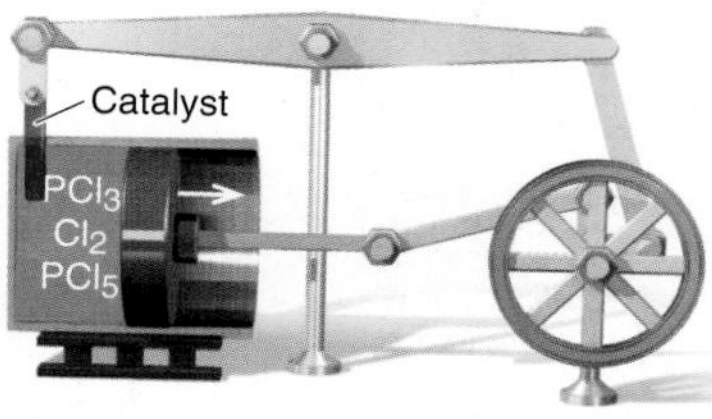

Figure 17.10 Catalyzed perpetual motion? This imaginary engine has a piston attached to a flywheel, whose rocker arm holds a catalyst that speeds PCl_5 breakdown but not formation. With the catalyst in the cylinder, PCl_5 breaks down faster than it forms, so the total gas pressure increases and the piston moves out. With the catalyst out of the cylinder, the old equilibrium returns, gas pressure lowers, and the piston moves in. If a catalyst *could* change the rate in only one direction, this machine would supply power with no input of external energy!

Table 17.4 Effects of Various Disturbances on a System at Equilibrium

Disturbance	Effect on Equilibrium Position	Effect on Value of *K*
Concentration		
Increase [reactant]	Toward formation of product	None
Decrease [reactant]	Toward formation of reactant	None
Increase [product]	Toward formation of reactant	None
Decrease [product]	Toward formation of product	None
Pressure		
Increase *P* (decrease *V*)	Toward formation of fewer moles of gas	None
Decrease *P* (increase *V*)	Toward formation of more moles of gas	None
Increase *P* (add inert gas, no change in *V*)	None; concentrations unchanged	None
Temperature		
Increase *T*	Toward absorption of heat	Increases if $\Delta H^\circ_{rxn} > 0$ Decreases if $\Delta H^\circ_{rxn} < 0$
Decrease *T*	Toward release of heat	Increases if $\Delta H^\circ_{rxn} < 0$ Decreases if $\Delta H^\circ_{rxn} > 0$
Catalyst added	None; forward and reverse rates increase equally; equilibrium attained sooner	None

Sample Problem 17.15 Determining Equilibrium Parameters from Molecular Scenes

Problem For the reaction,

$$X(g) + Y_2(g) \rightleftharpoons XY(g) + Y(g) \qquad \Delta H > 0$$

the following molecular scenes depict different reaction mixtures (X is *green,* Y is *purple*):

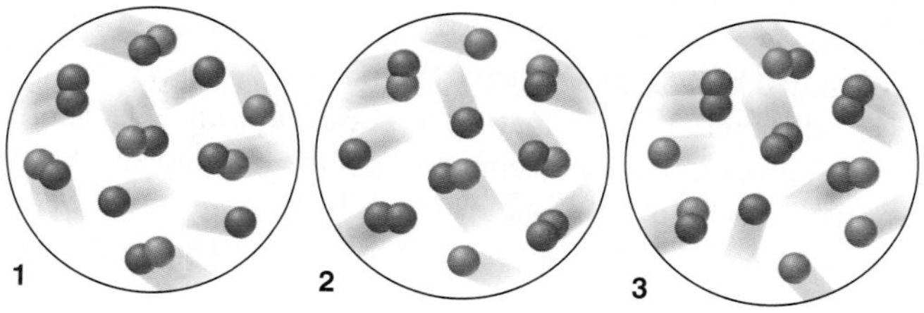

1 2 3

(a) If $K = 2$ at the temperature of the reaction, which scene represents the mixture at equilibrium?
(b) Will the reaction mixtures in the other two scenes proceed toward reactants or toward products to reach equilibrium?
(c) For the mixture at equilibrium, how will a rise in temperature affect $[Y_2]$?

Plan **(a)** We are given the balanced equation and K and must choose the scene that represents the mixture at equilibrium. We write Q, and for each scene, count particles and find the value of Q. Whichever scene gives a Q equal to K (2) represents the mixture at equilibrium. **(b)** For each of the other two reaction mixtures, we compare the value of Q with 2. If $Q > K$, the numerator (product side) is too high, so the reaction proceeds toward reactants; if $Q < K$, the reaction proceeds toward products.
(c) We are given that $\Delta H > 0$, so we must see whether a rise in T increases or decreases $[Y_2]$, one of the reactants.

Solution **(a)** For the reaction, we have $Q = \frac{[XY][Y]}{[X][Y_2]}$. Thus,

$$\text{scene 1: } Q = \frac{5 \times 3}{1 \times 1} = 15 \qquad \text{scene 2: } Q = \frac{4 \times 2}{2 \times 2} = 2 \qquad \text{scene 3: } Q = \frac{3 \times 1}{3 \times 3} = \frac{1}{3}$$

For scene 2, $Q = K$, so scene 2 represents the mixture at equilibrium.

(b) For scene 1, Q (15) $> K$ (2), so the reaction proceeds toward reactants.

For scene 3, Q ($\frac{1}{3}$) $< K$ (2), so the reaction proceeds toward products.

(c) The reaction is endothermic, so heat acts as a reactant:

$$X(g) + Y_2(g) + \textit{heat} \rightleftharpoons XY(g) + Y(g)$$

Therefore, adding heat to the left shifts the reaction to the right, so $[Y_2]$ decreases.

Check **(a)** Remember that quantities in the numerator (or denominator) of Q are multiplied, not added. For example, the denominator for scene 1 is $1 \times 1 = 1$, not $1 + 1 = 2$.
(c) A good check is to imagine that $\Delta H < 0$ and see if you get the opposite result:

$$X(g) + Y_2(g) \rightleftharpoons XY(g) + Y(g) + \textit{heat}$$

If $\Delta H < 0$, adding heat would shift the reaction to the left and increase $[Y_2]$.

Follow-Up Problem 17.15 For the reaction $C_2(g) + D_2(g) \rightleftharpoons 2CD(g)$; $\Delta H < 0$, these molecular scenes depict different reaction mixtures (C is *red,* D is *blue*):

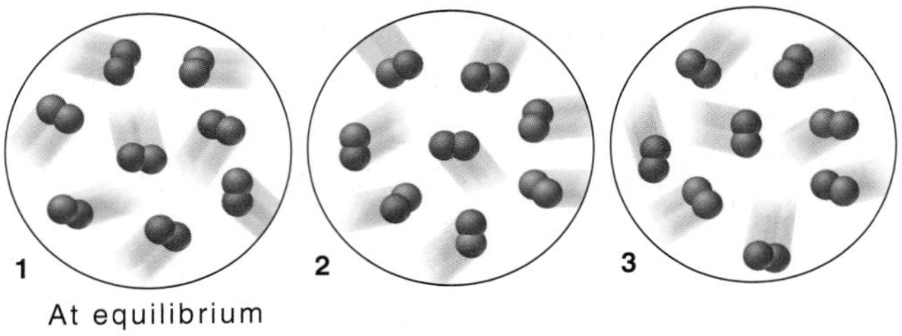

(a) Calculate the value of K_p. **(b)** In which direction will the reaction proceed for the mixtures *not* at equilibrium? **(c)** For the mixture at equilibrium, what effect will a rise in T have on the total amount (mol) of gas (increase, decrease, no effect)? Explain.

Applying Le Châtelier's Principle to the Synthesis of Ammonia

Le Châtelier's principle has countless applications in natural systems and in the chemical industry. As a case study, we'll look at the synthesis of ammonia, which, on a mole basis, is produced industrially in greater amount than any other compound. Then, a Chemical Connections essay applies the principle to metabolism.

Even though four of every five molecules in the atmosphere are N_2, the supply of *usable* nitrogen is limited because the strong triple bond in N_2 lowers its reactivity. Thus, the N atom is very difficult to "fix," that is, to combine with other atoms into useful compounds. Natural nitrogen fixation occurs through the fine-tuned activity of enzymes found in bacteria that live on plant roots, or through the brute force of lightning. But, nearly 13% of nitrogen fixation is done industrially via the **Haber process:**

$$N_2(g) + 3H_2(g) \rightleftharpoons 2NH_3(g) \qquad \Delta H^\circ_{rxn} = -91.8 \text{ kJ}$$

Developed by the German chemist Fritz Haber in 1913 and first used in a plant making 12,000 tons of ammonia a year, the process now yields over 110 million tons a year. Over 80% of this is used as fertilizer, with most of the remainder used to make explosives and nylons and other polymers, and smaller amounts going into production of refrigerants, rubber stabilizers, household cleaners, and pharmaceuticals.

Optimizing Reaction Conditions: Yield vs. Rate The Haber process applies equilibrium *and* kinetics principles to achieve a compromise that makes the process economical. From the balanced equation, we see three ways to maximize NH_3 yield:

1. *Decrease [NH_3].* Removing NH_3 as it forms will make the system shift toward producing more to reattain equilibrium.
2. *Decrease volume (increase pressure).* Because 4 mol of gas reacts to form 2 mol of gas, decreasing the volume will shift the system toward making fewer moles of gas.
3. *Decrease temperature.* Because the formation of NH_3 is exothermic, decreasing the temperature (removing heat) will shift the equilibrium position toward product, thereby increasing K_c (Table 17.5).

Therefore, the conditions for maximizing the yield of product are continual removal of NH_3, high pressure, and low temperature. Figure 17.11 shows the percent yield of NH_3 at various combinations of pressure and temperature. Note the almost complete conversion (98.3%) to product at 1000 atm and 473 K (200.°C).

Although the *yield* is favored at this relatively low temperature, the *rate* of formation is so slow that the process is uneconomical. In practice, a compromise optimizes yield *and* rate. High pressure and continuous removal are used to increase yield, but the temperature is raised to a moderate level and *a catalyst is used to increase the rate.* Achieving the same rate without a catalyst would require much higher temperatures and, thus, result in a much lower yield.

Table 17.5 Effect of Temperature on K_c for Ammonia Synthesis

T(K)	K_c
200.	7.17×10^{15}
300.	2.69×10^{8}
400.	3.94×10^{4}
500.	1.72×10^{2}
600.	4.53×10^{0}
700.	2.96×10^{-1}
800.	3.96×10^{-2}

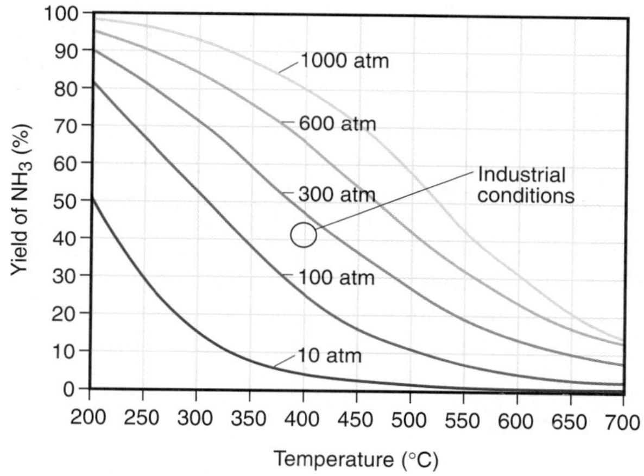

Figure 17.11 Percent yield of ammonia vs. temperature at five different pressures. At very high *P* and low *T (top left)*, the yield is high, but the rate is low. Industrial conditions *(circle)* are between 200 and 300 atm at about 400°C.

The Industrial Process Stages in the industrial production of NH_3 are shown in Figure 17.12. To extend equipment life and minimize cost, modern plants operate at about 200 to 300 atm and around 673 K (400.°C). The stoichiometric ratio of reactant gases (N_2/H_2 = 1/3 by volume) is injected into the heated, pressurized reaction chamber. Some of the needed heat is supplied by ΔH°_{rxn}. The gases flow over catalyst beds that consist of 5-mm to 10-mm chunks of iron crystals embedded in a fused mixture of MgO, Al_2O_3, and SiO_2. The emerging equilibrium mixture contains about 35% NH_3 and is cooled by refrigeration until the NH_3 (b.p. −33.4°C) condenses; it is then removed and stored. Because N_2 and H_2 have much lower boiling points, they are recycled as gases by pumping them back into the reaction chamber.

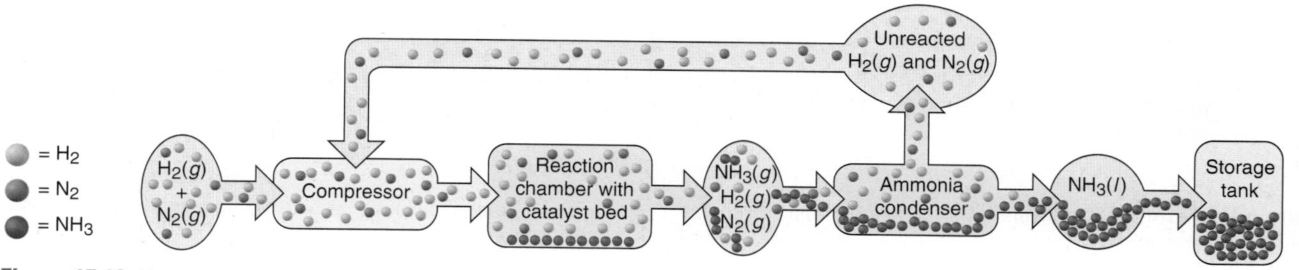

Figure 17.12 Key stages in the Haber process for synthesizing ammonia.

CHEMICAL CONNECTIONS TO CELLULAR METABOLISM | Design and Control of a Metabolic Pathway

From the simplest bacterium to the most specialized neuron, every cell performs thousands of reactions that allow it to grow and reproduce, feed and excrete, move and communicate. Taken together, these myriad feats of breakdown, synthesis, and energy flow constitute the cell's *metabolism* and are organized into reaction sequences called **metabolic pathways.**

Continual Shift Toward Product In principle, each step in a metabolic pathway is a reversible reaction catalyzed by a specific enzyme (Section 16.7). However, equilibrium is never reached in a pathway, because the product of each reaction becomes the reactant of the next. Consider the five-step pathway by which the amino acid threonine is converted into the amino acid isoleucine (Figure B17.1). Threonine, supplied from a different region of the cell, forms ketobutyrate through the catalytic action of enzyme 1. The equilibrium position of reaction 1 shifts to the right because the product, ketobutyrate, is the reactant in reaction 2. Similarly, reaction 2 shifts to the right as its product, acetohydroxybutyrate, is used up in reaction 3. In this way, each subsequent reaction shifts the previous reaction to the right. The final product, isoleucine, is removed to make proteins elsewhere in the cell. Thus, the entire pathway operates in one direction.

Creation of a Steady State This continuous shift in equilibrium position has two consequences for metabolic pathways:

1. *Each step proceeds with nearly 100% yield:* Virtually every molecule of threonine that enters this region of the cell eventually changes to ketobutyrate, every molecule of ketobutyrate to the next product, and so on.
2. *Reactant and product concentrations remain nearly constant,* because they reach a *steady state.*
   - In an equilibrium system, equal rates in *opposing* directions create constant concentrations of reactants and products.
   - In a steady-state system, the rates of reactions in *one* direction—into, through, and out of the system—create constant concentrations of intermediates.

Ketobutyrate, for example, is formed in reaction 1 as fast as it is consumed in reaction 2, so its concentration is constant. (A steady-state amount of water results if you fill a sink and then adjust the flow of faucet and drain so that water enters as fast as it leaves.)

Regulation by Feedback Inhibition Recall from Chapter 16 that substrate concentrations are *much* higher than enzyme concentrations. If the active sites on all the enzyme molecules were always occupied, all cellular reactions would occur at their maximum rates. This might be ideal for an industrial process, but an organism needs to control amounts carefully. To regulate product formation, certain key steps are catalyzed by *regulatory enzymes,* which contain an *inhibitor site* in addition to an active site: when the inhibitor site is occupied, the shape of the active site is deformed and the reaction is not catalyzed (Figure B17.2).

In the simplest case of metabolic regulation (Figure B17.1), *the final product of a pathway is the inhibitor, and the regulatory enzyme catalyzes the first step.* Suppose, for instance, that a cell is temporarily making less protein, so isoleucine is not being removed as quickly. As its concentration rises, isoleucine lands on the inhibitor site of threonine dehydratase, the first enzyme in the pathway, thereby inhibiting its own production. This process is called *end-product feedback inhibition.* More complex pathways have more elaborate regulatory schemes.

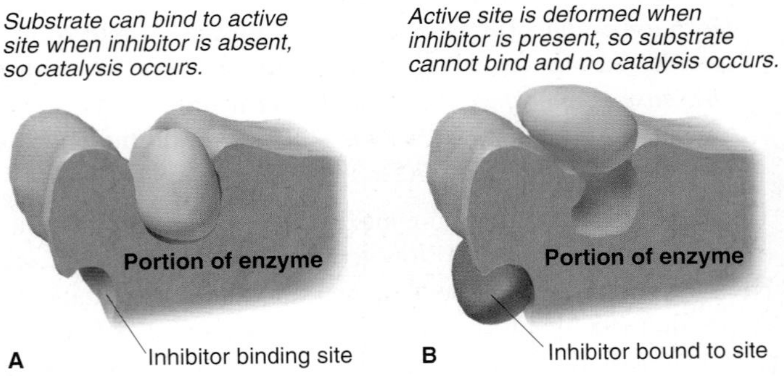

Figure B17.2 Effect of inhibitor binding on shape of active site. **A,** If the inhibitor site is not occupied, the enzyme catalyzes the reaction. **B,** If the inhibitor site is occupied, the enzyme does not function.

Problem

B17.1 Many metabolites are products in branched pathways. In the one below, letters are compounds, and numbers are enzymes:

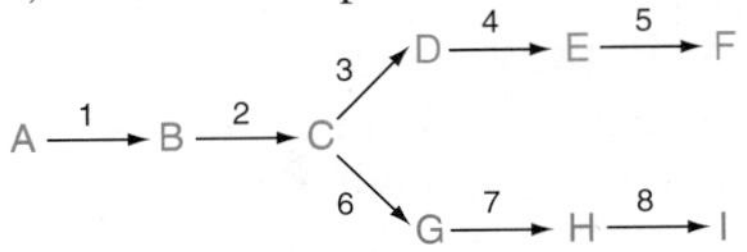

One method of control of these pathways occurs through inhibition of the first enzyme specific for a branch. (a) Which enzyme is inhibited by F? (b) Which enzyme is inhibited by I? (c) What is the disadvantage if F inhibited enzyme 1? (d) What would be the disadvantage if F inhibited enzyme 6?

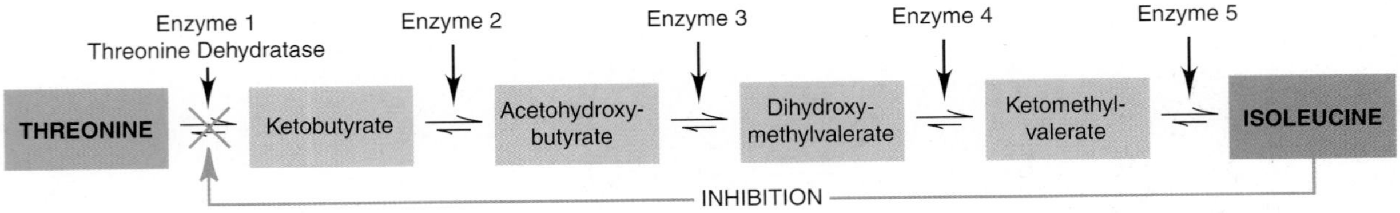

Figure B17.1 The biosynthesis of isoleucine from threonine. Isoleucine is synthesized from threonine in a sequence of five enzyme-catalyzed reactions. Once enough isoleucine is present, its concentration builds up and inhibits threonine dehydratase, the first enzyme in the pathway.

Summary of Section 17.6

- If a system at equilibrium is disturbed, it undergoes a net reaction that reduces the disturbance and returns the system to equilibrium.
- Changes in concentration cause a net reaction to consume the added component or to produce the removed component.
- For a reaction that involves a change in amount (mol) of gas, an increase in pressure (decrease in volume) causes a net reaction toward fewer moles of gas, and a decrease in pressure causes the opposite change.
- Although the equilibrium position changes as a result of a concentration or volume change, *K* does not.
- A temperature change affects *K*: higher *T* increases *K* for an endothermic reaction (positive ΔH°_{rxn}) and decreases *K* for an exothermic reaction (negative ΔH°_{rxn}).
- A catalyst causes the system to reach equilibrium more quickly by speeding forward and reverse reactions equally, but it does not affect the equilibrium position.
- Ammonia is produced in a process favored by high pressure, low temperature, and continual removal of product. To make the process economical, intermediate temperature and pressure and a catalyst are used.
- A metabolic pathway is a cellular reaction sequence with each step shifted completely toward product. Its overall yield is controlled by a feedback system that inhibits the activity of certain key enzymes.

CHAPTER REVIEW GUIDE

Learning Objectives

Relevant section (§) and/or sample problem (SP) numbers appear in parentheses.

Understand These Concepts

1. The distinction between the speed (rate) and the extent of a reaction (Introduction)
2. Why a system attains dynamic equilibrium when forward and reverse reaction rates are equal (§17.1)
3. The equilibrium constant as a number that is equal to a particular ratio of rate constants and of concentration terms (§17.1)
4. How the magnitude of *K* is related to the extent of the reaction (§17.1)
5. Why the same equilibrium state is reached no matter what the starting concentrations of the reacting system (§17.2)
6. How the reaction quotient (*Q*) changes continuously until the system reaches equilibrium, at which point $Q = K$ (§17.2)
7. Why the form of *Q* is based exactly on the balanced equation *as written* (§17.2)
8. How the *sum* of reaction steps gives the overall reaction, and the *product* of *Q*'s (or *K*'s) gives the overall *Q* (or *K*) (§17.2)
9. Why pure solids and liquids do not appear in *Q* (§17.2)
10. How the interconversion of K_c and K_p is based on the ideal gas law and Δn_{gas} (§17.3)
11. How the reaction direction depends on the relative values of *Q* and *K* (§17.4)
12. How a reaction table is used to find an unknown quantity (concentration or pressure) (§17.5)
13. How assuming that the change in [reactant] is relatively small simplifies finding equilibrium quantities (§17.5)
14. How Le Châtelier's principle explains the effects of a change in concentration, pressure (volume), or temperature on a system at equilibrium and on *K* (§17.6)
15. Why a change in temperature *does* affect *K* (§17.6)
16. Why the addition of a catalyst does *not* affect *K* (§17.6)
17. How adjusting reaction conditions and using a catalyst optimizes the synthesis of ammonia (§17.6).

Master These Skills

1. Writing a reaction quotient (*Q*) from a balanced equation (SP 17.1)
2. Writing *Q* and calculating *K* for a reaction consisting of more than one step (SP 17.2)
3. Writing *Q* and finding *K* for an equation multiplied by a common factor (SP 17.3)
4. Writing *Q* for heterogeneous equilibria (§17.2)
5. Converting between K_c and K_p (SP 17.4)
6. Comparing *Q* and *K* to determine reaction direction (SPs 17.5, 17.6)
7. Substituting quantities (concentrations or pressures) into *Q* to find *K* (§17.5)
8. Using a reaction table to determine quantities and find *K* (SP 17.7)
9. Finding one equilibrium quantity from other equilibrium quantities and *K* (SP 17.8)
10. Finding an equilibrium quantity from initial quantities and *K* (SP 17.9)
11. Solving a quadratic equation for an unknown equilibrium quantity (§17.5)
12. Assuming that the change in [reactant] is relatively small to find equilibrium quantities and checking the assumption (SP 17.10)
13. Comparing the values of *Q* and *K* to find reaction direction and *x*, the unknown change in a quantity (SP 17.11)

Learning Objectives *continued*

14. Using the relative values of Q and K to predict the effect of a change in concentration on the equilibrium position and on K (SP 17.12)
15. Using Le Châtelier's principle and Δn_{gas} to predict the effect of a change in pressure (volume) on the equilibrium position (SP 17.13)
16. Using Le Châtelier's principle and $\Delta H°$ to predict the effect of a change in temperature on the equilibrium position and on K (SP 17.14)
17. Using the van't Hoff equation to calculate K at one temperature given K at another temperature (§17.6)
18. Using molecular scenes to find equilibrium parameters (SP 17.15)

Key Terms

Page numbers appear in parentheses.

Section 17.1
equilibrium constant (K) (679)

Section 17.2
law of chemical equilibrium (law of mass action) (680)
reaction quotient (Q) (680)

Section 17.6
Le Châtelier's principle (698)
Haber process (706)
metabolic pathway (708)

Key Equations and Relationships

Page numbers appear in parentheses.

17.1 Defining equilibrium in terms of reaction rates (678):

$$\text{At equilibrium: rate}_{fwd} = \text{rate}_{rev}$$

17.2 Defining the equilibrium constant for the reaction A $\rightleftharpoons$ 2B (679):

$$K = \frac{k_{fwd}}{k_{rev}} = \frac{[B]^2_{eq}}{[A]_{eq}}$$

17.3 Defining the equilibrium constant in terms of the reaction quotient (680):

$$\text{At equilibrium: } Q = K$$

17.4 Expressing Q_c for the reaction aA + bB $\rightleftharpoons$ cC + dD (681):

$$Q_c = \frac{[C]^c[D]^d}{[A]^a[B]^b}$$

17.5 Finding the overall K for a reaction sequence (682):

$$K_{overall} = K_1 \times K_2 \times K_3 \times \cdots$$

17.6 Finding K of a reaction from K of the reverse reaction (683):

$$K_{fwd} = \frac{1}{K_{rev}}$$

17.7 Finding K of a reaction multiplied by a factor n (684):

$$Q' = Q^n = \left(\frac{[C]^c[D]^d}{[A]^a[B]^b}\right)^n \qquad K' = K^n$$

17.8 Relating K based on pressures to K based on concentrations (687):

$$K_p = K_c(RT)^{\Delta n_{gas}}$$

17.9 Assuming that ignoring the concentration that reacts introduces no significant error (695):

$$[A]_{init} - [A]_{reacting} = [A]_{eq} \approx [A]_{init}$$

17.10 Finding K at one temperature given K at another (van't Hoff equation) (704):

$$\ln\frac{K_2}{K_1} = -\frac{\Delta H°_{rxn}}{R}\left(\frac{1}{T_2} - \frac{1}{T_1}\right)$$

Brief Solutions to Follow-Up Problems

17.1 (a) $Q_c = \dfrac{[NO]^4[H_2O]^6}{[NH_3]^4[O_2]^5}$ (b) $Q_c = \dfrac{[N_2O][NO_2]}{[NO]^3}$

17.2 $H_2(g) + Br_2(g) \rightleftharpoons 2HBr(g)$;

$$Q_{c(overall)} = \frac{[HBr]^2}{[H_2][Br_2]}$$

$$Q_{c(overall)} = Q_{c1} \times Q_{c2} \times Q_{c3}$$

$$= \frac{\cancel{[Br]^2}}{[Br_2]} \times \frac{[HBr]\cancel{[H]}}{\cancel{[Br]}[H_2]} \times \frac{[HBr]}{\cancel{[H]}\cancel{[Br]}} = \frac{[HBr]^2}{[H_2][Br_2]}$$

17.3 (a) $K_c = K^{1/2}_{c(ref)} = 2.8\times10^4$

(b) $K_c = \left(\dfrac{1}{K_{c(ref)}}\right)^{2/3} = 1.2\times10^{-6}$

17.4 $K_p = K_c(RT)^{-1} = 1.67\left(0.0821\ \dfrac{\text{atm}\cdot\text{L}}{\text{mol}\cdot\text{K}} \times 500.\ \text{K}\right)^{-1}$

$= 4.07\times10^{-2}$

17.5 $K_c = \dfrac{[Y]}{[X]} = 1.4$

1. $Q = 0.33$, right 2. $Q = 1.4$, no net change 3. $Q = 2.0$, left

17.6 $Q_p = \dfrac{(P_{CH_3Cl})(P_{HCl})}{(P_{CH_4})(P_{Cl_2})} = \dfrac{(0.24)(0.47)}{(0.13)(0.035)} = 25;$

$Q_p < K_p$, so CH_3Cl is forming.

17.7 From the reaction table for $2NO + O_2 \rightleftharpoons 2NO_2$,

$P_{O_2} = 1.000\ \text{atm} - x = 0.506\ \text{atm} \qquad x = 0.494\ \text{atm}$

Also, $P_{NO} = 0.012$ atm and $P_{NO_2} = 0.988$ atm, so

$$K_p = \frac{0.988^2}{0.012^2(0.506)} = 1.3\times10^4$$

17.8 Since $\Delta n_{gas} = 0$, $K_p = K_c = 2.3\times10^{30} = \dfrac{(0.781)(0.209)}{P^2_{NO}}$

Thus, $P_{NO} = 2.7\times10^{-16}$ atm

17.9 From the reaction table, $[H_2] = [I_2] = x$; $[HI] = 0.242 - 2x$.

Thus, $$K_c = 1.26\times10^{-3} = \frac{x^2}{(0.242 - 2x)^2}$$

Taking the square root of both sides, ignoring the negative root, and solving gives $x = [H_2] = 8.02\times10^{-3}\ M$.

17.10 (a) Based on the reaction table, and assuming that $0.20\ M - x \approx 0.20\ M$,

$$K_c = 2.94\times10^{-10} \approx \frac{4x^2}{0.20} \qquad x \approx 3.8\times10^{-6}$$

Error $= 1.9\times10^{-3}\%$, so assumption is justified; therefore, at equilibrium, $[I_2] = 0.20\ M$ and $[I] = 7.6\times10^{-6}\ M$.

(b) Based on the same reaction table and assumption, $x \approx 0.10$; error is 50%, so assumption is *not* justified. Solve equation:

$$4x^2 + 0.209x - 0.042 = 0 \qquad x = 0.080\ M$$

Therefore, at equilibrium, $[I_2] = 0.12\ M$ and $[I] = 0.16\ M$.

17.11 (a) $$Q_c = \frac{(0.0900)(0.0900)}{0.2100} = 3.86\times10^{-2}$$

$Q_c < K_c$, so reaction proceeds to the right.

(b) From the reaction table,

$$[PCl_5] = 0.2100\ M - x = 0.2065\ M \qquad \text{so} \qquad x = 0.0035\ M$$

Thus, $[Cl_2] = [PCl_3] = 0.0900\ M + x = 0.0935\ M$.

17.12 (a) $[SiF_4]$ increases; (b) decreases; (c) decreases; (d) no effect.

17.13 (a) Decrease P; (b) increase P; (c) increase P.

17.14 (a) P_{H_2} will decrease; K will increase; (b) P_{N_2} will increase; K will decrease; (c) P_{PCl_5} will increase; K will increase.

17.15 (a) Since $P = \frac{n}{V}RT$ and, in this case, V, R, and T cancel,

$$K_p = \frac{n_{CD}^2}{n_{C_2}\times n_{D_2}} = \frac{16}{(2)(2)} = 4$$

(b) Scene 2, to the left; scene 3, to the right. (c) There are 2 mol of gas on each side of the balanced equation, so increasing T has no effect on total moles of gas.

PROBLEMS

Problems with **colored** numbers are answered in Appendix E and worked in detail in the Student Solutions Manual. Problem sections match those in the text and provide the numbers of relevant sample problems. Most offer Concept Review Questions, Skill-Building Exercises (grouped in pairs covering the same concept), and Problems in Context. The Comprehensive Problems are based on material from any section or previous chapter.

The Equilibrium State and the Equilibrium Constant

Concept Review Questions

17.1 A change in reaction conditions increases the rate of a certain forward reaction more than that of the reverse reaction. What is the effect on the equilibrium constant and on the concentrations of reactants and products at equilibrium?

17.2 When a chemical company employs a new reaction to manufacture a product, the chemists consider its rate (kinetics) and yield (equilibrium). How do each of these affect the usefulness of a manufacturing process?

17.3 If there is no change in concentrations, why is the equilibrium state considered dynamic?

17.4 Is K very large or very small for a reaction that goes essentially to completion? Explain.

17.5 White phosphorus, P_4, is produced by the reduction of phosphate rock, $Ca_3(PO_4)_2$. If exposed to oxygen, the waxy, white solid smokes, bursts into flames, and releases a large quantity of heat:

$$P_4(g) + 5O_2(g) \rightleftharpoons P_4O_{10}(s) + heat$$

Does this reaction have a large or small equilibrium constant? Explain.

The Reaction Quotient and the Equilibrium Constant

(Sample Problems 17.1 to 17.3)

Concept Review Questions

17.6 For a given reaction at a given temperature, the value of K is constant. Is the value of Q also constant? Explain.

17.7 In a study of the thermal decomposition of lithium peroxide,

$$2Li_2O_2(s) \rightleftharpoons 2Li_2O(s) + O_2(g)$$

a chemist finds that, as long as some Li_2O_2 is present at the end of the experiment, the amount of O_2 obtained in a given container at a given T is the same. Explain.

17.8 In a study of the formation of HI from its elements,

$$H_2(g) + I_2(g) \rightleftharpoons 2HI(g)$$

equal amounts of H_2 and I_2 were placed in a container, which was then sealed and heated.

(a) On one set of axes, sketch concentration vs. time curves for H_2 and HI, and explain how Q changes as a function of time.

(b) Is the value of Q different if $[I_2]$ is plotted instead of $[H_2]$?

17.9 Explain the difference between a heterogeneous and a homogeneous equilibrium. Give an example of each.

17.10 Does Q for the formation of 1 mol of NO from its elements differ from Q for the decomposition of 1 mol of NO to its elements? Explain and give the relationship between the two Q's.

17.11 Does Q for the formation of 1 mol of NH_3 from H_2 and N_2 differ from Q for the formation of NH_3 from H_2 and 1 mol of N_2? Explain and give the relationship between the two Q's.

Skill-Building Exercises (grouped in similar pairs)

17.12 Balance each reaction and write its reaction quotient, Q_c:
(a) $NO(g) + O_2(g) \rightleftharpoons N_2O_3(g)$
(b) $SF_6(g) + SO_3(g) \rightleftharpoons SO_2F_2(g)$
(c) $SClF_5(g) + H_2(g) \rightleftharpoons S_2F_{10}(g) + HCl(g)$

17.13 Balance each reaction and write its reaction quotient, Q_c:
(a) $C_2H_6(g) + O_2(g) \rightleftharpoons CO_2(g) + H_2O(g)$
(b) $CH_4(g) + F_2(g) \rightleftharpoons CF_4(g) + HF(g)$
(c) $SO_3(g) \rightleftharpoons SO_2(g) + O_2(g)$

17.14 Balance each reaction and write its reaction quotient, Q_c:
(a) $NO_2Cl(g) \rightleftharpoons NO_2(g) + Cl_2(g)$
(b) $POCl_3(g) \rightleftharpoons PCl_3(g) + O_2(g)$
(c) $NH_3(g) + O_2(g) \rightleftharpoons N_2(g) + H_2O(g)$

17.15 Balance each reaction and write its reaction quotient, Q_c:
(a) $O_2(g) \rightleftharpoons O_3(g)$
(b) $NO(g) + O_3(g) \rightleftharpoons NO_2(g) + O_2(g)$
(c) $N_2O(g) + H_2(g) \rightleftharpoons NH_3(g) + H_2O(g)$

17.16 At a particular temperature, $K_c = 1.6\times10^{-2}$ for

$$2H_2S(g) \rightleftharpoons 2H_2(g) + S_2(g)$$

Calculate K_c for each of the following reactions:
(a) $\frac{1}{2}S_2(g) + H_2(g) \rightleftharpoons H_2S(g)$
(b) $5H_2S(g) \rightleftharpoons 5H_2(g) + \frac{5}{2}S_2(g)$

17.17 At a particular temperature, $K_c = 6.5\times10^{2}$ for

$$2NO(g) + 2H_2(g) \rightleftharpoons N_2(g) + 2H_2O(g)$$

Calculate K_c for each of the following reactions:
(a) $NO(g) + H_2(g) \rightleftharpoons \frac{1}{2}N_2(g) + H_2O(g)$
(b) $2N_2(g) + 4H_2O(g) \rightleftharpoons 4NO(g) + 4H_2(g)$

17.18 Balance each of the following examples of heterogeneous equilibria and write each reaction quotient, Q_c:
(a) $Na_2O_2(s) + CO_2(g) \rightleftharpoons Na_2CO_3(s) + O_2(g)$
(b) $H_2O(l) \rightleftharpoons H_2O(g)$
(c) $NH_4Cl(s) \rightleftharpoons NH_3(g) + HCl(g)$

17.19 Balance each of the following examples of heterogeneous equilibria and write each reaction quotient, Q_c:
(a) $H_2O(l) + SO_3(g) \rightleftharpoons H_2SO_4(aq)$
(b) $KNO_3(s) \rightleftharpoons KNO_2(s) + O_2(g)$
(c) $S_8(s) + F_2(g) \rightleftharpoons SF_6(g)$

17.20 Balance each of the following examples of heterogeneous equilibria and write each reaction quotient, Q_c:
(a) $NaHCO_3(s) \rightleftharpoons Na_2CO_3(s) + CO_2(g) + H_2O(g)$
(b) $SnO_2(s) + H_2(g) \rightleftharpoons Sn(s) + H_2O(g)$
(c) $H_2SO_4(l) + SO_3(g) \rightleftharpoons H_2S_2O_7(l)$

17.21 Balance each of the following examples of heterogeneous equilibria and write each reaction quotient, Q_c:
(a) $Al(s) + NaOH(aq) + H_2O(l) \rightleftharpoons Na[Al(OH)_4](aq) + H_2(g)$
(b) $CO_2(s) \rightleftharpoons CO_2(g)$
(c) $N_2O_5(s) \rightleftharpoons NO_2(g) + O_2(g)$

Problems in Context

17.22 Write Q_c for each of the following:
(a) Hydrogen chloride gas reacts with oxygen gas to produce chlorine gas and water vapor.
(b) Solid diarsenic trioxide reacts with fluorine gas to produce liquid arsenic pentafluoride and oxygen gas.
(c) Gaseous sulfur tetrafluoride reacts with liquid water to produce gaseous sulfur dioxide and hydrogen fluoride gas.
(d) Solid molybdenum(VI) oxide reacts with gaseous xenon difluoride to form liquid molybdenum(VI) fluoride, xenon gas, and oxygen gas.

17.23 The interhalogen ClF_3 is prepared in a two-step fluorination of chlorine gas:

$$Cl_2(g) + F_2(g) \rightleftharpoons ClF(g)$$
$$ClF(g) + F_2(g) \rightleftharpoons ClF_3(g)$$

(a) Balance each step and write the overall equation.
(b) Show that the overall Q_c equals the product of the Q_c's for the individual steps.

Expressing Equilibria with Pressure Terms: Relation Between K_c and K_p

(Sample Problem 17.4)

Concept Review Questions

17.24 Guldberg and Waage proposed the definition of the equilibrium constant as a certain ratio of *concentrations*. What relationship allows us to use a particular ratio of *partial pressures* (for a gaseous reaction) to express an equilibrium constant? Explain.

17.25 When are K_c and K_p equal, and when are they not?

17.26 A certain reaction at equilibrium has more moles of gaseous products than of gaseous reactants.
(a) Is K_c larger or smaller than K_p?
(b) Write a statement about the relative sizes of K_c and K_p for any gaseous equilibrium.

Skill-Building Exercises (grouped in similar pairs)

17.27 Determine Δn_{gas} for each of the following reactions:
(a) $2KClO_3(s) \rightleftharpoons 2KCl(s) + 3O_2(g)$
(b) $2PbO(s) + O_2(g) \rightleftharpoons 2PbO_2(s)$
(c) $I_2(s) + 3XeF_2(s) \rightleftharpoons 2IF_3(s) + 3Xe(g)$

17.28 Determine Δn_{gas} for each of the following reactions:
(a) $MgCO_3(s) \rightleftharpoons MgO(s) + CO_2(g)$
(b) $2H_2(g) + O_2(g) \rightleftharpoons 2H_2O(l)$
(c) $HNO_3(l) + ClF(g) \rightleftharpoons ClONO_2(g) + HF(g)$

17.29 Calculate K_c for each of the following equilibria:
(a) $CO(g) + Cl_2(g) \rightleftharpoons COCl_2(g)$; $K_p = 3.9\times10^{-2}$ at 1000. K
(b) $S_2(g) + C(s) \rightleftharpoons CS_2(g)$; $K_p = 28.5$ at 500. K

17.30 Calculate K_c for each of the following equilibria:
(a) $H_2(g) + I_2(g) \rightleftharpoons 2HI(g)$; $K_p = 49$ at 730. K
(b) $2SO_2(g) + O_2(g) \rightleftharpoons 2SO_3(g)$; $K_p = 2.5\times10^{10}$ at 500. K

17.31 Calculate K_p for each of the following equilibria:
(a) $N_2O_4(g) \rightleftharpoons 2NO_2(g)$; $K_c = 6.1\times10^{-3}$ at 298 K
(b) $N_2(g) + 3H_2(g) \rightleftharpoons 2NH_3(g)$; $K_c = 2.4\times10^{-3}$ at 1000. K

17.32 Calculate K_p for each of the following equilibria:
(a) $H_2(g) + CO_2(g) \rightleftharpoons H_2O(g) + CO(g)$; $K_c = 0.77$ at 1020. K
(b) $3O_2(g) \rightleftharpoons 2O_3(g)$; $K_c = 1.8\times10^{-56}$ at 570. K

Comparing Q and K to Determine Reaction Direction

(Sample Problems 17.5 and 17.6)

Concept Review Questions

17.33 When the numerical value of Q is less than K, in which direction does the reaction proceed to reach equilibrium? Explain.

17.34 The following molecular scenes depict the aqueous reaction $2D \rightleftharpoons E$, with D *red* and E *blue*. Each sphere represents 0.0100 mol, but the volume is 1.00 L in scene A, whereas in scenes B and C, it is 0.500 L.

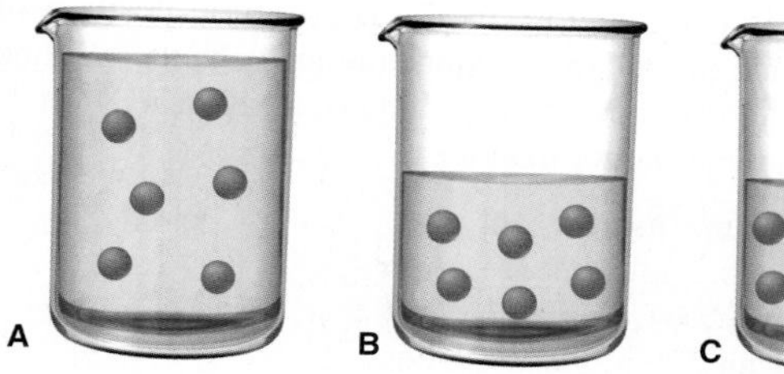

(a) If the reaction in scene A is at equilibrium, calculate K_c.
(b) Are the reactions in scenes B and C at equilibrium? Which, if either, is not, and in which direction will it proceed?

Skill-Building Exercises (grouped in similar pairs)

17.35 At 425°C, $K_p = 4.18\times10^{-9}$ for the reaction

$$2HBr(g) \rightleftharpoons H_2(g) + Br_2(g)$$

In one experiment, 0.20 atm of HBr(*g*), 0.010 atm of $H_2(g)$, and 0.010 atm of $Br_2(g)$ are introduced into a container. Is the reaction at equilibrium? If not, in which direction will it proceed?

17.36 At 100°C, $K_p = 60.6$ for the reaction

$$2NOBr(g) \rightleftharpoons 2NO(g) + Br_2(g)$$

In a given experiment, 0.10 atm of each component is placed in a container. Is the system at equilibrium? If not, in which direction will the reaction proceed?

Problems in Context

17.37 The water-gas shift reaction plays a central role in the chemical methods for obtaining cleaner fuels from coal:

$$CO(g) + H_2O(g) \rightleftharpoons CO_2(g) + H_2(g)$$

At a given temperature, $K_p = 2.7$. If 0.13 mol of CO, 0.56 mol of H_2O, 0.62 mol of CO_2, and 0.43 mol of H_2 are put in a 2.0-L flask, in which direction does the reaction proceed?

How to Solve Equilibrium Problems

(Sample Problems 17.7 to 17.11)

Concept Review Questions

17.38 In the 1980s, CFC-11 was one of the most heavily produced chlorofluorocarbons. The last step in its formation is

$$CCl_4(g) + HF(g) \rightleftharpoons CFCl_3(g) + HCl(g)$$

If you start the reaction with equal concentrations of CCl_4 and HF, you obtain equal concentrations of $CFCl_3$ and HCl at equilibrium. Are the final concentrations of $CFCl_3$ and HCl equal if you start with unequal concentrations of CCl_4 and HF? Explain.

17.39 For a problem involving the catalyzed reaction of methane and steam, the following reaction table was prepared:

Pressure (atm)	$CH_4(g)$ +	$2H_2O(g)$ ⇌	$CO_2(g)$ +	$4H_2(g)$
Initial	0.30	0.40	0	0
Change	$-x$	$-2x$	$+x$	$+4x$
Equilibrium	$0.30 - x$	$0.40 - 2x$	x	$4x$

Explain the entries in the "Change" and "Equilibrium" rows.

17.40 (a) What is the basis of the approximation that avoids using the quadratic formula to find an equilibrium concentration?
(b) When should this approximation *not* be made?

Skill-Building Exercises (grouped in similar pairs)

17.41 In an experiment to study the formation of HI(g),

$$H_2(g) + I_2(g) \rightleftharpoons 2HI(g)$$

$H_2(g)$ and $I_2(g)$ were placed in a sealed container at a certain temperature. At equilibrium, $[H_2] = 6.50\times10^{-5}\ M$, $[I_2] = 1.06\times10^{-3}\ M$, and $[HI] = 1.87\times10^{-3}\ M$. Calculate K_c for the reaction at this temperature.

17.42 Gaseous ammonia was introduced into a sealed container and heated to a certain temperature:

$$2NH_3(g) \rightleftharpoons N_2(g) + 3H_2(g)$$

At equilibrium, $[NH_3] = 0.0225\ M$, $[N_2] = 0.114\ M$, and $[H_2] = 0.342\ M$. Calculate K_c for the reaction at this temperature.

17.43 Gaseous PCl_5 decomposes according to the reaction

$$PCl_5(g) \rightleftharpoons PCl_3(g) + Cl_2(g)$$

In one experiment, 0.15 mol of $PCl_5(g)$ was introduced into a 2.0-L container. Construct the reaction table for this process.

17.44 Hydrogen fluoride, HF, can be made from the reaction

$$H_2(g) + F_2(g) \rightleftharpoons 2HF(g)$$

In one experiment, 0.10 mol of $H_2(g)$ and 0.050 mol of $F_2(g)$ are added to a 0.50-L flask. Write a reaction table for this process.

17.45 For the following reaction, $K_p = 6.5\times10^4$ at 308 K:

$$2NO(g) + Cl_2(g) \rightleftharpoons 2NOCl(g)$$

At equilibrium, $P_{NO} = 0.35$ atm and $P_{Cl_2} = 0.10$ atm. What is the equilibrium partial pressure of NOCl(*g*)?

17.46 For the following reaction, $K_p = 0.262$ at 1000°C:

$$C(s) + 2H_2(g) \rightleftharpoons CH_4(g)$$

At equilibrium, P_{H_2} is 1.22 atm. What is the equilibrium partial pressure of $CH_4(g)$?

17.47 Ammonium hydrogen sulfide decomposes according to the following reaction, for which $K_p = 0.11$ at 250°C:

$$NH_4HS(s) \rightleftharpoons H_2S(g) + NH_3(g)$$

If 55.0 g of $NH_4HS(s)$ is placed in a sealed 5.0-L container, what is the partial pressure of $NH_3(g)$ at equilibrium?

17.48 Hydrogen sulfide decomposes according to the following reaction, for which $K_c = 9.30\times10^{-8}$ at 700°C:

$$2H_2S(g) \rightleftharpoons 2H_2(g) + S_2(g)$$

If 0.45 mol of H_2S is placed in a 3.0-L container, what is the equilibrium concentration of $H_2(g)$ at 700°C?

17.49 Even at high *T*, the formation of NO is not favored:

$$N_2(g) + O_2(g) \rightleftharpoons 2NO(g) \quad K_c = 4.10\times10^{-4} \text{ at } 2000^\circ C$$

What is [NO] when a mixture of 0.20 mol of $N_2(g)$ and 0.15 mol of $O_2(g)$ reach equilibrium in a 1.0-L container at 2000°C?

17.50 Nitrogen dioxide decomposes according to the reaction

$$2NO_2(g) \rightleftharpoons 2NO(g) + O_2(g)$$

where $K_p = 4.48\times10^{-13}$ at a certain temperature. If 0.75 atm of NO_2 is added to a container and allowed to come to equilibrium, what are the equilibrium partial pressures of NO(*g*) and $O_2(g)$?

17.51 Hydrogen iodide decomposes according to the reaction

$$2HI(g) \rightleftharpoons H_2(g) + I_2(g)$$

A sealed 1.50-L container initially holds 0.00623 mol of H_2, 0.00414 mol of I_2, and 0.0244 mol of HI at 703 K. When equilibrium is reached, the concentration of $H_2(g)$ is 0.00467 *M*. What are the concentrations of HI(*g*) and $I_2(g)$?

17.52 Compound A decomposes according to the equation

$$A(g) \rightleftharpoons 2B(g) + C(g)$$

A sealed 1.00-L container initially contains 1.75×10^{-3} mol of A(*g*), 1.25×10^{-3} mol of B(*g*), and 6.50×10^{-4} mol of C(*g*) at 100°C. At equilibrium, [A] is 2.15×10^{-3} *M*. Find [B] and [C].

Problems in Context

17.53 In an analysis of interhalogen reactivity, 0.500 mol of ICl was placed in a 5.00-L flask, where it decomposed at a high *T*: $2ICl(g) \rightleftharpoons I_2(g) + Cl_2(g)$. Calculate the equilibrium concentrations of I_2, Cl_2, and ICl ($K_c = 0.110$ at this temperature).

17.54 A toxicologist studying mustard gas, $S(CH_2CH_2Cl)_2$, a blistering agent, prepares a mixture of 0.675 *M* SCl_2 and 0.973 *M* C_2H_4 and allows it to react at room temperature (20.0°C):

$$SCl_2(g) + 2C_2H_4(g) \rightleftharpoons S(CH_2CH_2Cl)_2(g)$$

At equilibrium, $[S(CH_2CH_2Cl)_2] = 0.350\ M$. Calculate K_p.

17.55 The first step in HNO_3 production is the catalyzed oxidation of NH_3. Without a catalyst, a different reaction predominates:

$$4NH_3(g) + 3O_2(g) \rightleftharpoons 2N_2(g) + 6H_2O(g)$$

When 0.0150 mol of $NH_3(g)$ and 0.0150 mol of $O_2(g)$ are placed in a 1.00-L container at a certain temperature, the N_2 concentration at equilibrium is 1.96×10^{-3} *M*. Calculate K_c.

17.56 A key step in the extraction of iron from its ore is

$$FeO(s) + CO(g) \rightleftharpoons Fe(s) + CO_2(g) \quad K_p = 0.403 \text{ at } 1000°C$$

This step occurs in the 700°C to 1200°C zone within a blast furnace. What are the equilibrium partial pressures of CO(*g*) and $CO_2(g)$ when 1.00 atm of CO(*g*) and excess FeO(*s*) react in a sealed container at 1000°C?

Reaction Conditions and Equilibrium: Le Châtelier's Principle

(Sample Problems 17.12 to 17.15)

Concept Review Questions

17.57 What does "disturbance" mean in Le Châtelier's principle?

17.58 What is the difference between the equilibrium position and the equilibrium constant of a reaction? Which changes as a result of a change in reactant concentration?

17.59 Scenes A, B, and C below depict the following reaction at three temperatures:

$$NH_4Cl(s) \rightleftharpoons NH_3(g) + HCl(g) \qquad \Delta H^\circ_{rxn} = 176 \text{ kJ}$$

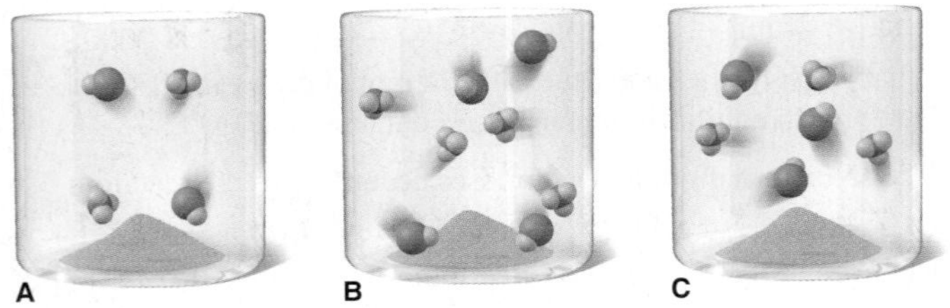

A B C

(a) Which best represents the reaction mixture at the highest temperature? Explain. (b) Which best represents the reaction mixture at the lowest temperature? Explain.

17.60 What is implied by the word "constant" in the term *equilibrium constant?* Give two reaction parameters that can be changed without changing the value of an equilibrium constant.

17.61 Le Châtelier's principle is related ultimately to the rates of the forward and reverse steps in a reaction. Explain (a) why an increase in reactant concentration shifts the equilibrium position to the right but does not change *K;* (b) why a decrease in *V* shifts the equilibrium position toward fewer moles of gas but does not change *K*; (c) why a rise in *T* shifts the equilibrium position of an exothermic reaction toward reactants and also changes *K;* and (d) why a rise in temperature of an endothermic reaction from T_1 to T_2 results in K_2 being larger than K_1.

17.62 An equilibrium mixture of two solids and a gas, in the reaction $XY(s) \rightleftharpoons X(g) + Y(s)$, is depicted at right (X is *green* and Y is *black*). Does scene A, B, or C best represent the system at equilibrium after two formula units of Y(*s*) is added? Explain.

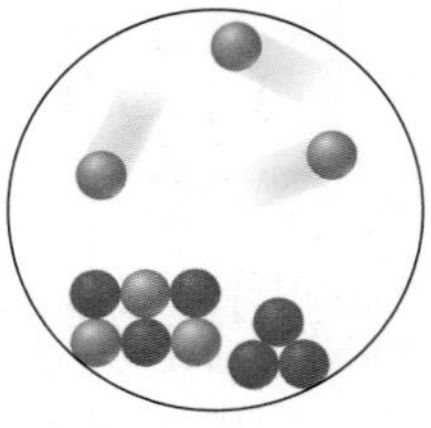

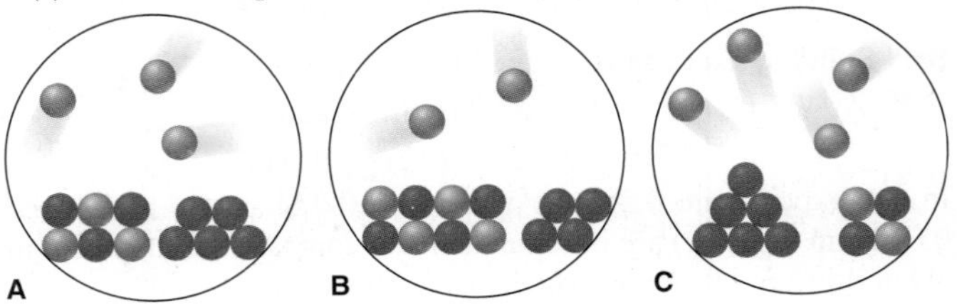

A B C

Skill-Building Exercises (grouped in similar pairs)

17.63 Consider this equilibrium system:

$$CO(g) + Fe_3O_4(s) \rightleftharpoons CO_2(g) + 3FeO(s)$$

How does the equilibrium position shift as a result of each of the following disturbances? (a) CO is added. (b) CO_2 is removed by adding solid NaOH. (c) Additional $Fe_3O_4(s)$ is added to the system. (d) Dry ice is added at constant temperature.

17.64 Sodium bicarbonate undergoes thermal decomposition according to the reaction

$$2NaHCO_3(s) \rightleftharpoons Na_2CO_3(s) + CO_2(g) + H_2O(g)$$

How does the equilibrium position shift as a result of each of the following disturbances? (a) 0.20 atm of argon gas is added. (b) $NaHCO_3(s)$ is added. (c) $Mg(ClO_4)_2(s)$ is added as a drying agent to remove H_2O. (d) Dry ice is added at constant *T*.

17.65 Predict the effect of *increasing* the container volume on the amounts of each reactant and product in the following reactions:
(a) $F_2(g) \rightleftharpoons 2F(g)$
(b) $2CH_4(g) \rightleftharpoons C_2H_2(g) + 3H_2(g)$

17.66 Predict the effect of *increasing* the container volume on the amounts of each reactant and product in the following reactions:
(a) $CH_3OH(l) \rightleftharpoons CH_3OH(g)$
(b) $CH_4(g) + NH_3(g) \rightleftharpoons HCN(g) + 3H_2(g)$

17.67 Predict the effect of *decreasing* the container volume on the amounts of each reactant and product in the following reactions:
(a) $H_2(g) + Cl_2(g) \rightleftharpoons 2HCl(g)$
(b) $2H_2(g) + O_2(g) \rightleftharpoons 2H_2O(l)$

17.68 Predict the effect of *decreasing* the container volume on the amounts of each reactant and product in the following reactions:
(a) $C_3H_8(g) + 5O_2(g) \rightleftharpoons 3CO_2(g) + 4H_2O(l)$
(b) $4NH_3(g) + 3O_2(g) \rightleftharpoons 2N_2(g) + 6H_2O(g)$

17.69 How would you adjust the *volume* of the container in order to maximize product yield in each of the following reactions?
(a) $Fe_3O_4(s) + 4H_2(g) \rightleftharpoons 3Fe(s) + 4H_2O(g)$
(b) $2C(s) + O_2(g) \rightleftharpoons 2CO(g)$

17.70 How would you adjust the *volume* of the container in order to maximize product yield in each of the following reactions?
(a) $Na_2O_2(s) \rightleftharpoons 2Na(l) + O_2(g)$
(b) $C_2H_2(g) + 2H_2(g) \rightleftharpoons C_2H_6(g)$

17.71 Predict the effect of *increasing* the temperature on the amounts of products in the following reactions:
(a) $CO(g) + 2H_2(g) \rightleftharpoons CH_3OH(g)$ $\Delta H^\circ_{rxn} = -90.7$ kJ
(b) $C(s) + H_2O(g) \rightleftharpoons CO(g) + H_2(g)$ $\Delta H^\circ_{rxn} = 131$ kJ
(c) $2NO_2(g) \rightleftharpoons 2NO(g) + O_2(g)$ (endothermic)
(d) $2C(s) + O_2(g) \rightleftharpoons 2CO(g)$ (exothermic)

17.72 Predict the effect of *decreasing* the temperature on the amounts of reactants in the following reactions:
(a) $C_2H_2(g) + H_2O(g) \rightleftharpoons CH_3CHO(g)$ $\Delta H^\circ_{rxn} = -151$ kJ
(b) $CH_3CH_2OH(l) + O_2(g) \rightleftharpoons CH_3CO_2H(l) + H_2O(g)$
$\Delta H^\circ_{rxn} = -451$ kJ
(c) $2C_2H_4(g) + O_2(g) \rightleftharpoons 2CH_3CHO(g)$ (exothermic)
(d) $N_2O_4(g) \rightleftharpoons 2NO_2(g)$ (endothermic)

17.73 The molecule D_2 (where D, deuterium, is ^{2}H) undergoes a reaction with ordinary H_2 that leads to isotopic equilibrium:

$$D_2(g) + H_2(g) \rightleftharpoons 2DH(g) \quad K_p = 1.80 \text{ at } 298\text{ K}$$

If ΔH°_{rxn} is 0.32 kJ/mol DH, calculate K_p at 500. K.

17.74 The formation of methanol is important to the processing of new fuels. At 298 K, $K_p = 2.25\times10^4$ for the reaction

$$CO(g) + 2H_2(g) \rightleftharpoons CH_3OH(l)$$

If $\Delta H^\circ_{rxn} = -128$ kJ/mol CH_3OH, calculate K_p at 0°C.

Problems in Context

17.75 The minerals hematite (Fe_2O_3) and magnetite (Fe_3O_4) exist in equilibrium with atmospheric oxygen:

$$4Fe_3O_4(s) + O_2(g) \rightleftharpoons 6Fe_2O_3(s) \quad K_p = 2.5\times10^{87} \text{ at } 298\text{ K}$$

(a) Determine P_{O_2} at equilibrium. (b) Given that P_{O_2} in air is 0.21 atm, in which direction will the reaction proceed to reach equilibrium? (c) Calculate K_c at 298 K.

17.76 The oxidation of SO_2 is the key step in H_2SO_4 production:

$$SO_2(g) + \tfrac{1}{2}O_2(g) \rightleftharpoons SO_3(g) \quad \Delta H^\circ_{rxn} = -99.2\text{ kJ}$$

(a) What qualitative combination of T and P maximizes SO_3 yield?
(b) How does addition of O_2 affect Q? K?
(c) Why is catalysis used for this reaction?

17.77 A mixture of 3.00 volumes of H_2 and 1.00 volume of N_2 reacts at 344°C to form ammonia. The equilibrium mixture at 110. atm contains 41.49% NH_3 by volume. Calculate K_p for the reaction, assuming that the gases behave ideally.

17.78 You are a member of a research team of chemists discussing plans for a plant to produce ammonia:

$$N_2(g) + 3H_2(g) \rightleftharpoons 2NH_3(g)$$

(a) The plant will operate at close to 700 K, at which K_p is 1.00×10^{-4}, and employs the stoichiometric 1/3 ratio of N_2/H_2. At equilibrium, the partial pressure of NH_3 is 50. atm. Calculate the partial pressures of each reactant and P_{total}.
(b) One member of the team suggests the following: since the partial pressure of H_2 is cubed in the reaction quotient, the plant could produce the same amount of NH_3 if the reactants were in a 1/6 ratio of N_2/H_2 and could do so at a lower pressure, which would cut operating costs. Calculate the partial pressure of each reactant and P_{total} under these conditions, assuming an unchanged partial pressure of 50. atm for NH_3. Is the suggestion valid?

Comprehensive Problems

17.79 For the following equilibrium system, which of the changes will form more $CaCO_3$?

$$CO_2(g) + Ca(OH)_2(s) \rightleftharpoons CaCO_3(s) + H_2O(l) \quad \Delta H^\circ = -113\text{ kJ}$$

(a) Decrease temperature at constant pressure (no phase change)
(b) Increase volume at constant temperature
(c) Increase partial pressure of CO_2
(d) Remove one-half of the initial $CaCO_3$

17.80 The "filmstrip" represents five molecular scenes of a gaseous mixture as it reaches equilibrium over time:

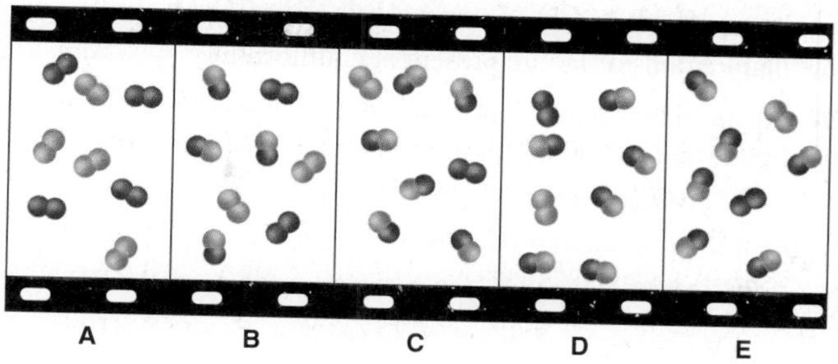

X is *purple* and Y is *orange:* $X_2(g) + Y_2(g) \rightleftharpoons 2XY(g)$.
(a) Write the reaction quotient, Q, for this reaction.
(b) If each particle represents 0.1 mol, find Q for each scene.
(c) If $K > 1$, is time progressing to the right or to the left? Explain.
(d) Calculate K at this temperature.
(e) If $\Delta H^\circ_{rxn} < 0$, which scene, if any, best represents the mixture at a higher temperature? Explain.
(f) Which scene, if any, best represents the mixture at a higher pressure (lower volume)? Explain.

17.81 Ammonium carbamate (NH_2COONH_4) is a salt of carbamic acid that is found in the blood and urine of mammals. At 250.°C, $K_c = 1.58\times10^{-8}$ for the following equilibrium:

$$NH_2COONH_4(s) \rightleftharpoons 2NH_3(g) + CO_2(g)$$

If 7.80 g of NH_2COONH_4 is put into a 0.500-L evacuated container, what is the total pressure at equilibrium?

17.82 Isolation of Group 8B(10) elements, used as industrial catalysts, involves a series of steps. For nickel, the sulfide ore is roasted in air: $Ni_3S_2(s) + O_2(g) \rightleftharpoons NiO(s) + SO_2(g)$. The metal oxide is reduced by the H_2 in water gas ($CO + H_2$) to impure Ni: $NiO(s) + H_2(g) \rightleftharpoons Ni(s) + H_2O(g)$. The CO in water gas then reacts with the metal in the Mond process to form gaseous nickel carbonyl, $Ni(s) + CO(g) \rightleftharpoons Ni(CO)_4(g)$, which is subsequently decomposed to the metal. (a) Balance each of the three steps, and obtain an overall balanced equation for the conversion of Ni_3S_2 to $Ni(CO)_4$. (b) Show that the overall Q_c is the product of the Q_c's for the individual reactions.

17.83 Consider the formation of ammonia in two experiments.
(a) To a 1.00-L container at 727°C, 1.30 mol of N_2 and 1.65 mol of H_2 are added. At equilibrium, 0.100 mol of NH_3 is present. Calculate the equilibrium concentrations of N_2 and H_2, and find K_c for the reaction: $2NH_3(g) \rightleftharpoons N_2(g) + 3H_2(g)$.
(b) In a different 1.00-L container at the same temperature, equilibrium is established with 8.34×10^{-2} mol of NH_3, 1.50 mol of N_2, and 1.25 mol of H_2 present. Calculate K_c for the reaction:

$$NH_3(g) \rightleftharpoons \tfrac{1}{2}N_2(g) + \tfrac{3}{2}H_2(g)$$

(c) What is the relationship between the K_c values in parts (a) and (b)? Why aren't these values the same?

17.84 An important industrial source of ethanol is the reaction, catalyzed by H_3PO_4, of steam with ethylene derived from oil:

$$C_2H_4(g) + H_2O(g) \rightleftharpoons C_2H_5OH(g)$$

$$\Delta H^\circ_{rxn} = -47.8\text{ kJ} \quad K_c = 9\times10^3 \text{ at } 600.\text{ K}$$

(a) At equilibrium, $P_{C_2H_5OH} = 200.$ atm and $P_{H_2O} = 400.$ atm. Calculate $P_{C_2H_4}$. (b) Is the highest yield of ethanol obtained at high or low P? High or low T? (c) Calculate K_c at 450. K. (d) In NH_3 manufacture, the yield is increased by condensing the NH_3 to a liquid and removing it. Would condensing the C_2H_5OH have the same effect in ethanol production? Explain.

17.85 An industrial chemist introduces 2.0 atm of H_2 and 2.0 atm of CO_2 into a 1.00-L container at 25.0°C and then raises the temperature to 700.°C, at which $K_c = 0.534$:

$$H_2(g) + CO_2(g) \rightleftharpoons H_2O(g) + CO(g)$$

How many grams of H_2 are present at equilibrium?

17.86 As an EPA scientist studying catalytic converters and urban smog, you want to find K_c for the following reaction:

$$2NO_2(g) \rightleftharpoons N_2(g) + 2O_2(g) \qquad K_c = ?$$

Use the following data to find the unknown K_c:

$$\tfrac{1}{2}N_2(g) + \tfrac{1}{2}O_2(g) \rightleftharpoons NO(g) \qquad K_c = 4.8\times10^{-10}$$

$$2NO_2(g) \rightleftharpoons 2NO(g) + O_2(g) \qquad K_c = 1.1\times10^{-5}$$

17.87 An engineer examining the oxidation of SO_2 in the manufacture of sulfuric acid determines that $K_c = 1.7\times10^8$ at 600. K:

$$2SO_2(g) + O_2(g) \rightleftharpoons 2SO_3(g)$$

(a) At equilibrium, $P_{SO_3} = 300.$ atm and $P_{O_2} = 100.$ atm. Calculate P_{SO_2}. (b) The engineer places a mixture of 0.0040 mol of $SO_2(g)$ and 0.0028 mol of $O_2(g)$ in a 1.0-L container and raises the temperature to 1000 K. At equilibrium, 0.0020 mol of $SO_3(g)$ is present. Calculate K_c and P_{SO_2} for this reaction at 1000. K.

17.88 Phosgene ($COCl_2$) is a toxic substance that forms readily from carbon monoxide and chlorine at elevated temperatures:

$$CO(g) + Cl_2(g) \rightleftharpoons COCl_2(g)$$

If 0.350 mol of each reactant is placed in a 0.500-L flask at 600 K, what are the concentrations of all three substances at equilibrium ($K_c = 4.95$ at this temperature)?

17.89 When 0.100 mol of $CaCO_3(s)$ and 0.100 mol of $CaO(s)$ are placed in an evacuated sealed 10.0-L container and heated to 385 K, $P_{CO_2} = 0.220$ atm after equilibrium is established:

$$CaCO_3(s) \rightleftharpoons CaO(s) + CO_2(g)$$

An additional 0.300 atm of $CO_2(g)$ is pumped in. What is the total mass (in g) of $CaCO_3$ after equilibrium is re-established?

17.90 Use each of the following reaction quotients to write the balanced equation:

(a) $Q = \dfrac{[CO_2]^2[H_2O]^2}{[C_2H_4][O_2]^3}$ (b) $Q = \dfrac{[NH_3]^4[O_2]^7}{[NO_2]^4[H_2O]^6}$

17.91 Hydrogenation of carbon-carbon π bonds is important in the petroleum and food industries. The conversion of acetylene to ethylene is a simple example of the process:

$$C_2H_2(g) + H_2(g) \rightleftharpoons C_2H_4(g)$$

The calculated K_c at 2000. K is 2.9×10^8. But the process is run at lower temperatures with the aid of a catalyst to prevent decomposition. Use $\Delta H°$ values to calculate K_c at 300. K.

17.92 For the reaction $M_2 + N_2 \rightleftharpoons 2MN$, scene A represents the mixture at equilibrium, with M *black* and N *orange*. If each molecule represents 0.10 mol and the volume is 1.0 L, how many moles of each substance will be present in scene B when that mixture reaches equilibrium?

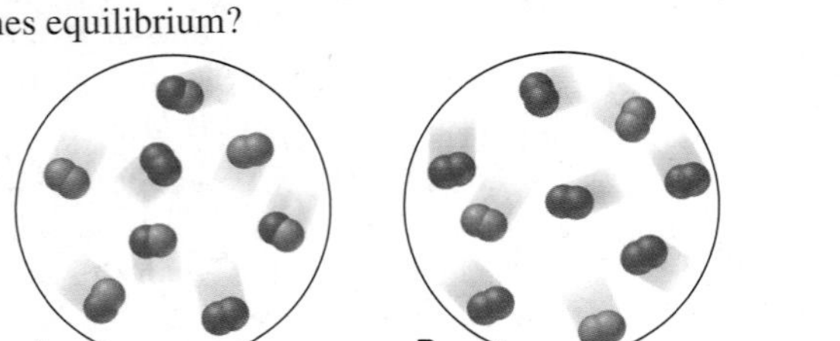

A B

17.93 Highly toxic disulfur decafluoride decomposes by a free-radical process: $S_2F_{10}(g) \rightleftharpoons SF_4(g) + SF_6(g)$. In a study of the decomposition, S_2F_{10} was placed in a 2.0-L flask and heated to 100°C; $[S_2F_{10}]$ was 0.50 *M* at equilibrium. More S_2F_{10} was added, and when equilibrium was reattained, $[S_2F_{10}]$ was 2.5 *M*. How did $[SF_4]$ and $[SF_6]$ change from the original to the new equilibrium position after the addition of more S_2F_{10}?

17.94 A study of the water-gas shift reaction (see Problem 17.37) was made in which equilibrium was reached with $[CO] = [H_2O] = [H_2] = 0.10\ M$ and $[CO_2] = 0.40\ M$. After 0.60 mol of H_2 is added to the 2.0-L container and equilibrium is re-established, what are the new concentrations of all the components?

17.95 A gaseous mixture of 10.0 volumes of CO_2, 1.00 volume of unreacted O_2, and 50.0 volumes of unreacted N_2 leaves an engine at 4.0 atm and 800. K. Assuming that the mixture reaches equilibrium, what are (a) the partial pressure and (b) the concentration (in picograms per liter, pg/L) of CO in this exhaust gas?

$$2CO_2(g) \rightleftharpoons 2CO(g) + O_2(g) \qquad K_p = 1.4\times10^{-28} \text{ at } 800.\ K$$

(The actual concentration of CO in exhaust gas is much higher because the gases do *not* reach equilibrium in the short transit time through the engine and exhaust system.)

17.96 When ammonia is made industrially, the mixture of N_2, H_2, and NH_3 that emerges from the reaction chamber is far from equilibrium. Why does the plant supervisor use reaction conditions that produce less than the maximum yield of ammonia?

17.97 The following reaction can be used to make H_2 for the synthesis of ammonia from the greenhouse gases carbon dioxide and methane:

$$CH_4(g) + CO_2(g) \rightleftharpoons 2CO(g) + 2H_2(g)$$

(a) What is the percent yield of H_2 when an equimolar mixture of CH_4 and CO_2 with a total pressure of 20.0 atm reaches equilibrium at 1200. K, at which $K_p = 3.548\times10^6$?
(b) What is the percent yield of H_2 for this system at 1300. K, at which $K_p = 2.626\times10^7$?
(c) Use the van't Hoff equation to find $\Delta H°_{rxn}$.

17.98 The methane used to obtain H_2 for NH_3 manufacture is impure and usually contains other hydrocarbons, such as propane, C_3H_8. Imagine the reaction of propane occurring in two steps:

$$C_3H_8(g) + 3H_2O(g) \rightleftharpoons 3CO(g) + 7H_2(g)$$
$$K_p = 8.175\times10^{15} \text{ at } 1200.\ K$$

$$CO(g) + H_2O(g) \rightleftharpoons CO_2(g) + H_2(g)$$
$$K_p = 0.6944 \text{ at } 1200.\ K$$

(a) Write the overall equation for the reaction of propane and steam to produce carbon dioxide and hydrogen.
(b) Calculate K_p for the overall process at 1200. K.
(c) When 1.00 volume of C_3H_8 and 4.00 volumes of H_2O, each at 1200. K and 5.0 atm, are mixed in a container, what is the final pressure? Assume the total volume remains constant, that the reaction is essentially complete, and that the gases behave ideally.
(d) What percentage of the C_3H_8 remains unreacted?

17.99 Using CH_4 and steam as a source of H_2 for NH_3 synthesis requires high temperatures. Rather than burning CH_4 separately to heat the mixture, it is more efficient to inject some O_2 into the reaction mixture. All of the H_2 is thus released for the synthesis, and the heat of reaction for the combustion of CH_4 helps maintain the required temperature. Imagine the reaction occurring in two steps:

$$2CH_4(g) + O_2(g) \rightleftharpoons 2CO(g) + 4H_2(g)$$
$$K_p = 9.34\times10^{28} \text{ at } 1000.\ K$$

$$CO(g) + H_2O(g) \rightleftharpoons CO_2(g) + H_2(g)$$
$$K_p = 1.374 \text{ at } 1000. \text{ K}$$

(a) Write the overall equation for the reaction of methane, steam, and oxygen to form carbon dioxide and hydrogen.
(b) What is K_p for the overall reaction?
(c) What is K_c for the overall reaction?
(d) A mixture of 2.0 mol of CH_4, 1.0 mol of O_2, and 2.0 mol of steam with a total pressure of 30. atm reacts at 1000. K at constant volume. Assuming that the reaction is complete and the ideal gas law is a valid approximation, what is the final pressure?

17.100 One mechanism for the synthesis of ammonia proposes that N_2 and H_2 molecules catalytically dissociate into atoms:

$$N_2(g) \rightleftharpoons 2N(g) \qquad \log K_p = -43.10$$
$$H_2(g) \rightleftharpoons 2H(g) \qquad \log K_p = -17.30$$

(a) Find the partial pressure of N in N_2 at 1000. K and 200. atm.
(b) Find the partial pressure of H in H_2 at 1000. K and 600. atm.
(c) How many N atoms and H atoms are present per liter?
(d) Based on these answers, which of the following is a more reasonable step to continue the mechanism after the catalytic dissociation? Explain.

$$N(g) + H(g) \longrightarrow NH(g)$$
$$N_2(g) + H(g) \longrightarrow NH(g) + N(g)$$

17.101 The molecular scenes below depict the reaction $Y \rightleftharpoons 2Z$ at four different times, out of sequence, as it reaches equilibrium. Each sphere (Y is *red* and Z is *green*) represents 0.025 mol, and the volume is 0.40 L. (a) Which scene(s) represent(s) equilibrium? (b) List the scenes in the correct sequence. (c) Calculate K_c.

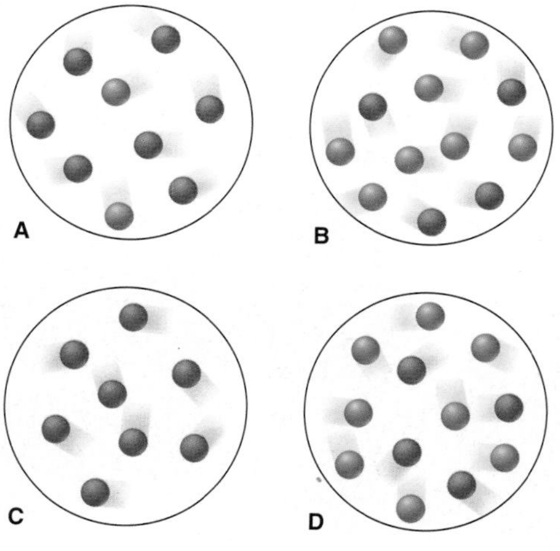

17.102 For the equilibrium

$$H_2S(g) \rightleftharpoons 2H_2(g) + S_2(g) \qquad K_c = 9.0\times10^{-8} \text{ at } 700°C$$

the initial concentrations of the three gases are 0.300 M H_2S, 0.300 M H_2, and 0.150 M S_2. Determine the equilibrium concentrations of the gases.

17.103 The two most abundant atmospheric gases react to a tiny extent at 298 K in the presence of a catalyst:

$$N_2(g) + O_2(g) \rightleftharpoons 2NO(g) \qquad K_p = 4.35\times10^{-31}$$

(a) What are the equilibrium pressures of the three gases when the atmospheric partial pressures of O_2 (0.210 atm) and of N_2 (0.780 atm) are put into an evacuated 1.00-L flask at 298 K with the catalyst? (b) What is P_{total} in the container? (c) Find K_c at 298 K.

17.104 The oxidation of nitrogen monoxide is favored at 457 K:

$$2NO(g) + O_2(g) \rightleftharpoons 2NO_2(g) \qquad K_p = 1.3\times10^4$$

(a) Calculate K_c at 457 K. (b) Find ΔH°_{rxn} from standard heats of formation. (c) At what temperature does $K_c = 6.4\times10^9$?

17.105 The kinetics and equilibrium of the decomposition of hydrogen iodide have been studied extensively:

$$2HI(g) \rightleftharpoons H_2(g) + I_2(g)$$

(a) At 298 K, $K_c = 1.26\times10^{-3}$ for this reaction. Calculate K_p.
(b) Calculate K_c for the *formation* of HI at 298 K.
(c) Calculate ΔH°_{rxn} for HI decomposition from ΔH°_f values.
(d) At 729 K, $K_c = 2.0\times10^{-2}$ for HI decomposition. Calculate ΔH_{rxn} for this reaction from the van't Hoff equation.

17.106 Isopentyl alcohol reacts with pure acetic acid to form isopentyl acetate, the essence of banana oil:

$$C_5H_{11}OH + CH_3COOH \rightleftharpoons CH_3COOC_5H_{11} + H_2O$$

A student adds a drying agent to remove H_2O and thus increase the yield of banana oil. Is this approach reasonable? Explain.

17.107 Isomers Q (*blue*) and R (*yellow*) interconvert. They are depicted in an equilibrium mixture in scene A. Scene B represents the mixture after addition of more Q. How many molecules of each isomer are present when the mixture in scene B attains equilibrium again?

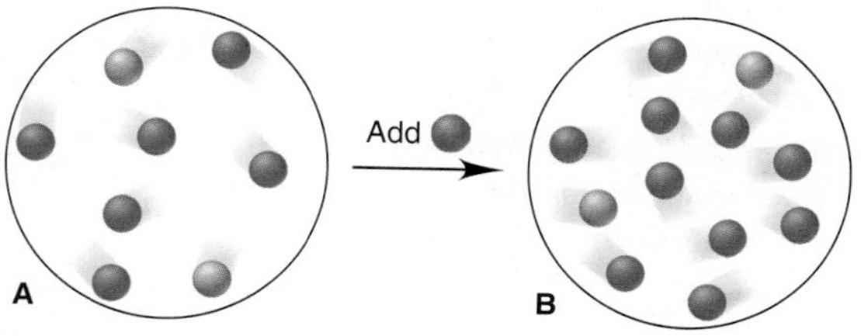

17.108 Glauber's salt, $Na_2SO_4\cdot10H_2O$, was used by J. R. Glauber in the 17th century as a medicinal agent. At 25°C, $K_p = 4.08\times10^{-25}$ for the loss of waters of hydration from Glauber's salt:

$$Na_2SO_4\cdot10H_2O(s) \rightleftharpoons Na_2SO_4(s) + 10H_2O(g)$$

(a) What is the vapor pressure of water at 25°C in a closed container holding a sample of $Na_2SO_4\cdot10H_2O(s)$?
(b) How do the following changes affect the ratio (higher, lower, same) of hydrated form to anhydrous form for the system above?
(1) Add more $Na_2SO_4(s)$ (2) Reduce the container volume
(3) Add more water vapor (4) Add N_2 gas

17.109 In a study of synthetic fuels, 0.100 mol of CO and 0.100 mol of water vapor are added to a 20.00-L container at 900.°C, and they react to form CO_2 and H_2. At equilibrium, [CO] is 2.24×10^{-3} M. (a) Calculate K_c at this temperature. (b) Calculate P_{total} in the flask at equilibrium. (c) How many moles of CO must be added to double this pressure? (d) After P_{total} is doubled and the system reattains equilibrium, what is $[CO]_{eq}$?

17.110 Synthetic diamonds are made under conditions of high temperature (2000 K) and high pressure (10^{10} Pa; 10^5 atm) in the presence of catalysts. Carbon's phase diagram is useful for finding the conditions for formation of natural and synthetic diamonds. Along the diamond-graphite line, the two allotropes are in equilibrium. (a) At point A, what is the sign of ΔH for the formation of diamond from graphite? Explain. (b) Which allotrope is denser? Explain.

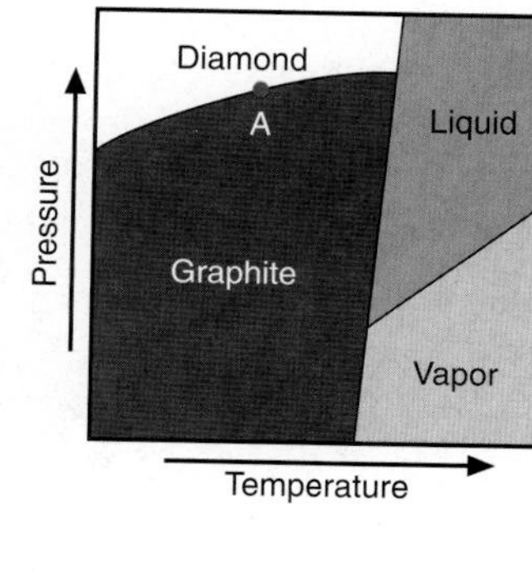

Acid-Base Equilibria

18.1 Acids and Bases in Water
- Arrhenius Acid-Base Definition
- Acid-Dissociation Constant (K_a)
- Relative Strengths of Acids and Bases

18.2 Autoionization of Water and the pH Scale
- Autoionization and K_w
- The pH Scale

18.3 Proton Transfer and the Brønsted-Lowry Acid-Base Definition
- Conjugate Acid-Base Pairs
- Net Direction of Acid-Base Reactions

18.4 Solving Problems Involving Weak-Acid Equilibria
- Finding K_a Given Concentrations
- Finding Concentrations Given K_a
- Extent of Acid Dissociation
- Polyprotic Acids

18.5 Weak Bases and Their Relation to Weak Acids
- Ammonia and the Amines
- Anions of Weak Acids
- Relation Between K_a and K_b

18.6 Molecular Properties and Acid Strength
- Nonmetal Hydrides
- Oxoacids
- Hydrated Metal Ions

18.7 Acid-Base Properties of Salt Solutions
- Salts That Yield Neutral Solutions
- Salts That Yield Acidic Solutions
- Salts That Yield Basic Solutions
- Salts of Weakly Acidic Cations and Weakly Basic Anions
- Salts of Amphiprotic Anions

18.8 Generalizing the Brønsted-Lowry Concept: The Leveling Effect

18.9 Electron-Pair Donation and the Lewis Acid-Base Definition
- Molecules as Lewis Acids
- Metal Cations as Lewis Acids
- Overview of Acid-Base Definitions

18

Concepts and skills to review before you study this chapter

- role of water as solvent (Section 4.1)
- writing ionic equations (Section 4.2)
- acids, bases, and acid-base reactions (Section 4.4)
- proton transfer in acid-base reactions (Section 4.4)
- properties of an equilibrium constant (Section 17.2)
- solving equilibrium problems (Section 17.5)

Acids and bases played a central role in the alchemists' labs, and they remain indispensable, not only in modern academic and industrial research, but in many consumer products (Table 18.1), and even in a classic seafood dish.

The slice of lemon (citric acid) on the plate, and the vinegar (acetic acid) in the salad have a sour taste. In fact, sourness was a defining property since the 17th century: an acid was any substance that had a sour taste; reacted with active metals, such as aluminum and zinc, to produce hydrogen gas; and turned certain organic compounds specific colors. (We discuss *indicators* in this chapter and Chapter 19.) Similarly, a base (like the amines in fish) was any substance that had a bitter taste and slippery feel and turned the same organic compounds different colors. Moreover, it was known that *when acids and bases react, each cancels the properties of the other in a process called neutralization.* Although these early definitions described distinctive properties, they gave way to others based on molecular behavior. As science progresses, limited definitions are replaced by broader ones that explain more phenomena.

Table 18.1 Some Common Acids and Bases and Their Household Uses

Substance	Use
Acids	
Acetic acid, CH_3COOH	Flavoring, preservative
Citric acid, $H_3C_6H_5O_7$	Flavoring
Ascorbic acid, $H_2C_6H_6O_6$	Vitamin C; nutritional supplement
Aluminum salts, $NaAl(SO_4)_2 \cdot 12H_2O$	In baking powder, with sodium hydrogen carbonate
Bases	
Sodium hydroxide (lye), NaOH	Oven and drain cleaners
Ammonia, NH_3	Household cleaner
Sodium carbonate, Na_2CO_3	Water softener, grease remover
Sodium hydrogen carbonate, $NaHCO_3$	Fire extinguisher, rising agent in cake mixes (baking soda), mild antacid
Sodium phosphate, Na_3PO_4	Cleaner for surfaces before painting or wallpapering

IN THIS CHAPTER . . . We develop three definitions of acids and bases that explain an expanded range of reactions, and we apply equilibrium principles to understand acid-base behavior.

- We begin with the *Arrhenius* acid-base definition, which relies on formulas and behavior in water.
- We examine acid dissociation to see how acid variation in strength is expressed by a new equilibrium constant.
- We introduce the pH scale to measure the acidity of aqueous solutions.
- We discuss proton transfer in the *Brønsted-Lowry* acid-base definition, which expands the meaning of "base," along with the scope of acid-base reactions.
- We apply a systematic approach to solving acid-base equilibrium problems.
- We examine weak bases and their interdependence with weak acids.

- We examine the molecular structures of acids to rationalize their relative strengths.
- We determine the relative acidity of salts from the reactions of their cations and anions with water.
- We see that the designations "acid" and "base" depend on the substances' relative strengths *and* on the solvent.
- We discuss the *Lewis* acid-base definition, which greatly expands the meanings of "acid" and "acid-base reaction."

18.1 • ACIDS AND BASES IN WATER

Most laboratory work with acids and bases involves water, as do most environmental, biological, and industrial applications. Recall from our discussion in Chapter 4 that *water is **the** product in all reactions between strong acids and strong bases,* which the net ionic equation for any such reaction shows:

$$HX(aq) + MOH(aq) \longrightarrow MX(aq) + H_2O(l) \qquad \text{[molecular]}$$

And

$$H^+(aq) + OH^-(aq) \longrightarrow H_2O(l) \qquad \text{[net ionic]}$$

Furthermore, whenever an acid dissociates in water, solvent molecules participate in the reaction:

$$HA(g \text{ or } l) + H_2O(l) \longrightarrow A^-(aq) + H_3O^+(aq)$$

Water molecules surround the proton to form H-bonded species with the general formula $H(H_2O)_n{}^+$. The proton's charge density is so high that it attracts water especially strongly. The proton bonds covalently to one of the lone electron pairs of a water molecule's O atom to form a **hydronium ion, H_3O^+,** which forms H bonds to several other water molecules (see Figure 4.7, p. 147). To emphasize the active role of water and the proton-water interaction, the hydrated proton is usually shown in the text as $H_3O^+(aq)$ [although, for simplicity, we sometimes show it as $H^+(aq)$].

Release of H^+ or OH^- and the Arrhenius Acid-Base Definition

The earliest definition that highlighted the molecular nature of acids and bases is the **Arrhenius acid-base definition,** which classifies these substances in terms of their formulas and behavior *in water:*

- An *acid* is a substance with H in its formula that dissociates in water to yield H_3O^+.
- A *base* is a substance with OH in its formula that dissociates in water to yield OH^-.

Some typical Arrhenius acids are HCl, HNO_3, and HCN, and some typical bases are NaOH, KOH, and $Ba(OH)_2$. While Arrhenius bases contain discrete OH^- ions in their structures, Arrhenius acids *never* contain discrete H^+ ions. Instead, they contain *covalently bonded H atoms that ionize when the molecule dissolves in water.*

When an acid and a base react, they undergo **neutralization.** The meaning of this term has changed, as we'll see, but in the Arrhenius sense, neutralization occurs when *the H^+ from the acid and the OH^- from the base form H_2O.* A key point about neutralization that Arrhenius was able to explain is that no matter which strong acid and strong base react, and no matter which salt results, ΔH°_{rxn} is -55.9 kJ per mole of water formed. Arrhenius suggested that the enthalpy change is always the same because the reaction is always the same—a hydrogen ion and a hydroxide ion form water:

$$H^+(aq) + OH^-(aq) \longrightarrow H_2O(l) \qquad \Delta H^\circ_{rxn} = -55.9 \text{ kJ}$$

The dissolved salt that is present, for example, NaCl in the reaction of sodium hydroxide with hydrochloric acid,

$$Na^+(aq) + OH^-(aq) + H^+(aq) + Cl^-(aq) \longrightarrow Na^+(aq) + Cl^-(aq) + H_2O(l)$$

exists as hydrated spectator ions and does not affect ΔH°_{rxn}.

Despite its importance at the time, limitations in the Arrhenius definition soon became apparent. Arrhenius and many others realized that even though some substances do *not* have discrete OH^- ions, they still behave as bases. For example, NH_3 and K_2CO_3 also yield OH^- in water. As you'll see shortly, broader acid-base definitions are required to include these species.

Variation in Acid Strength: The Acid-Dissociation Constant (K_a)

Acids (and bases) are classified by their *strength,* the amount of H_3O^+ (or OH^-) produced per mole of substance dissolved, in other words, by the extent of their dissociation into ions (see Table 4.2, p. 146). Because acids and bases are electrolytes, their strength correlates with electrolyte strength: *strong electrolytes dissociate completely, and weak electrolytes dissociate slightly.*

1. *Strong acids dissociate* **completely** *into ions in water* (Figure 18.1A):

$$HA(g \text{ or } l) + H_2O(l) \longrightarrow H_3O^+(aq) + A^-(aq)$$

In a dilute solution of a strong acid, *HA molecules are no longer present:* $[H_3O^+] \approx [HA]_{init}$. In other words, $[HA]_{eq} \approx 0$, so the value of K_c is extremely large:

$$Q_c = \frac{[H_3O^+][A^-]}{[HA][H_2O]} \quad \text{(at equilibrium, } Q_c = K_c >> 1)$$

Because the reaction is essentially complete, we usually don't express it as an equilibrium process. In dilute aqueous nitric acid, for example, there are virtually no undissociated nitric acid molecules:

$$HNO_3(l) + H_2O(l) \longrightarrow H_3O^+(aq) + NO_3^-(aq)$$

2. *Weak acids dissociate* **slightly** *into ions in water* (Figure 18.1B):

$$HA(aq) + H_2O(l) \rightleftharpoons H_3O^+(aq) + A^-(aq)$$

In a dilute solution of a weak acid, *the great majority of HA molecules are undissociated.* Thus, $[H_3O^+] << [HA]_{init}$, and $[HA]_{eq} \approx [HA]_{init}$, so K_c is very small. Hydrocyanic acid is an example of a weak acid:

$$HCN(aq) + H_2O(l) \rightleftharpoons H_3O^+(aq) + CN^-(aq)$$

$$Q_c = \frac{[H_3O^+][CN^-]}{[HCN][H_2O]} \quad \text{(at equilibrium, } Q_c = K_c << 1)$$

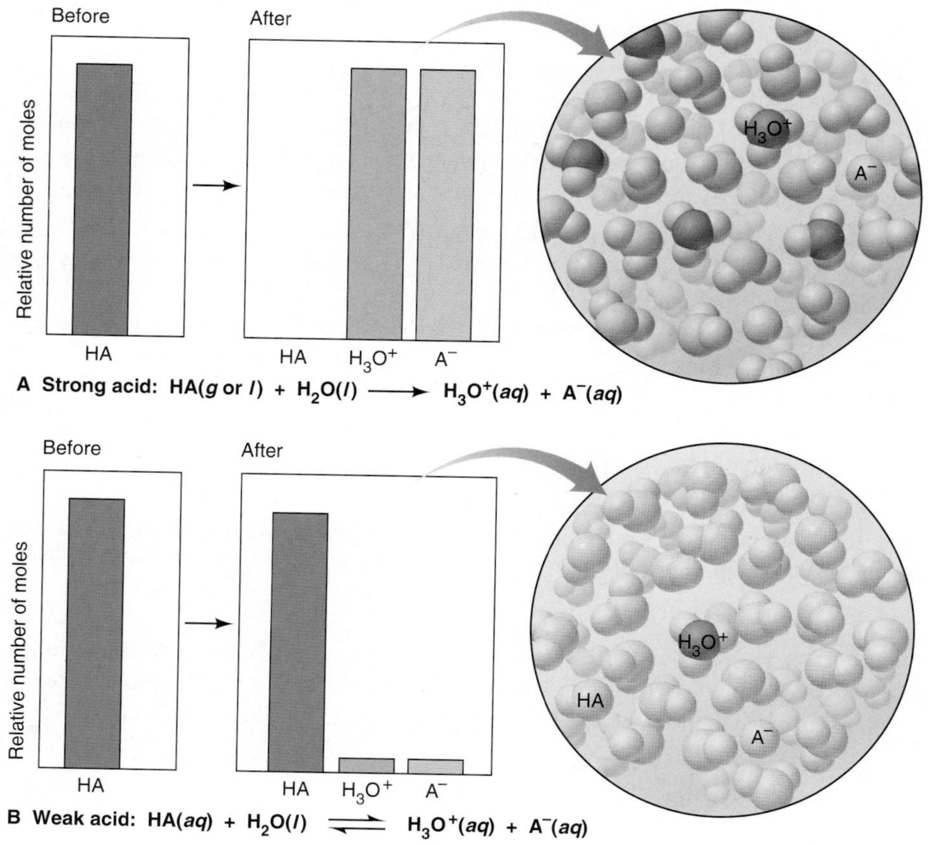

Figure 18.1 The extent of dissociation for strong acids and weak acids. The bar graphs show the relative numbers of moles of species before (*left*) and after (*right*) acid dissociation. **A,** A strong acid dissociates completely; virtually no HA molecules are present. **B,** A weak acid dissociates very little, remaining mostly as intact HA molecules.

Figure 18.2 Reaction of zinc with a strong acid (*left*) and a weak acid (*right*).

(As in Chapter 17, brackets with no subscript mean molar concentration *at equilibrium;* that is, [X] means $[X]_{eq}$. In this chapter, we are dealing with systems *at equilibrium,* so instead of writing Q and stating that Q equals K at equilibrium, we'll express K directly as a collection of equilibrium concentration terms.)

The difference in $[H_3O^+]$ causes a much higher rate for the reaction of a strong acid with an active metal like zinc than for the same reaction of a weak acid (Figure 18.2):

$$Zn(s) + 2H_3O^+(aq) \longrightarrow Zn^{2+}(aq) + 2H_2O(l) + H_2(g)$$

In a strong acid, with its much higher $[H_3O^+]$, zinc reacts rapidly, forming bubbles of H_2 vigorously. In a weak acid, $[H_3O^+]$ is much lower, so zinc reacts slowly.

The Meaning of K_a We write a *specific* equilibrium constant for acid dissociation that only includes species whose concentrations change to any significant extent. The equilibrium expression for the dissociation of a general *weak acid,* HA, in water is

$$K_c = \frac{[H_3O^+][A^-]}{[HA][H_2O]}$$

The concentration of water ($[H_2O] = \frac{1000\ g}{18.02\ g/mol} = 55.5\ M$) is typically several orders of magnitude larger than [HA]. Therefore, $[H_2O]$ is essentially constant when HA dissociates. As you saw for pure liquids and solids (Section 17.2), we simplify the equilibrium expression by multiplying K_c by $[H_2O]$ to define a new equilibrium constant, the **acid-dissociation constant** (or **acid-ionization constant**), K_a**:**

$$K_c[H_2O] = K_a = \frac{[H_3O^+][A^-]}{[HA]} \quad (18.1)$$

Like any equilibrium constant, K_a is a number whose magnitude is temperature dependent and tells how far to the right the reaction has proceeded to reach equilibrium. Thus, *the stronger the acid, the higher $[H_3O^+]$ is at equilibrium, and the larger the K_a:*

Stronger acid $\Longrightarrow$ higher $[H_3O^+]$ $\Longrightarrow$ larger K_a

The Range of K_a Values Acid-dissociation constants of weak acids range over many orders of magnitude. Some benchmark K_a values for typical weak acids give an idea of the fraction of HA molecules that dissociate into ions:

- For a weak acid with a relatively high K_a ($\sim10^{-2}$), a 1 M solution has ~10% of the HA molecules dissociated. The K_a of chlorous acid ($HClO_2$) is 1.1×10^{-2}, and 1 M $HClO_2$ is 10.% dissociated.
- For a weak acid with a moderate K_a ($\sim10^{-5}$), a 1 M solution has ~0.3% of the HA molecules dissociated. The K_a of acetic acid (CH_3COOH) is 1.8×10^{-5}, and 1 M CH_3COOH is 0.42% dissociated.
- For a weak acid with a relatively low K_a ($\sim10^{-10}$), a 1 M solution has ~0.001% of the HA molecules dissociated. The K_a of HCN is 6.2×10^{-10}, and 1 M HCN is 0.0025% dissociated.

Thus, for solutions of the same initial HA concentration, *the smaller the K_a, the lower the percent dissociation of HA:*

Weaker acid $\Longrightarrow$ lower % dissociation of HA $\Longrightarrow$ smaller K_a

Table 18.2 lists K_a values of some weak *monoprotic* acids, those with one ionizable proton. (A more extensive list is in Appendix C.) Note that the ionizable proton in organic acids is bound to the O in —COOH; H atoms bonded to C do *not* ionize.

Table 18.2 K_a Values for Some Monoprotic Acids at 25°C

Name (Formula)	Lewis Structure*	K_a
Chlorous acid ($HClO_2$)	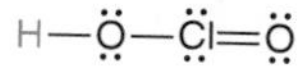	1.1×10^{-2}
Nitrous acid (HNO_2)	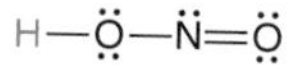	7.1×10^{-4}
Hydrofluoric acid (HF)	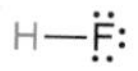	6.8×10^{-4}
Formic acid (HCOOH)	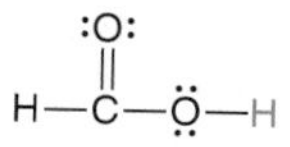	1.8×10^{-4}
Acetic acid (CH_3COOH)	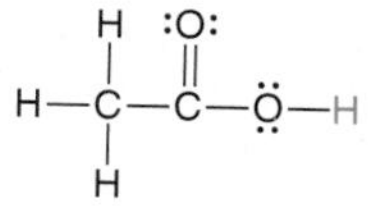	1.8×10^{-5}
Propanoic acid (CH_3CH_2COOH)	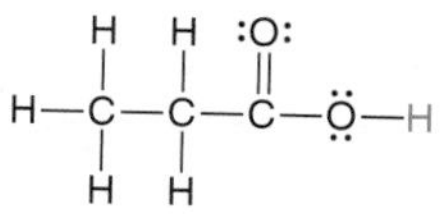	1.3×10^{-5}
Hypochlorous acid (HClO)	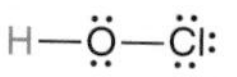	2.9×10^{-8}
Hydrocyanic acid (HCN)	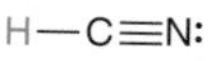	6.2×10^{-10}

* Red type indicates the ionizable proton; all atoms have zero formal charge.

Classifying the Relative Strengths of Acids and Bases

Using a table of K_a values is the surest way to quantify strengths of weak acids, but you can classify acids and bases qualitatively as strong or weak from their formulas:

- *Strong acids.* Two types of strong acids, with examples *you should memorize,* are
  1. The hydrohalic acids HCl, HBr, and HI
  2. Oxoacids in which the number of O atoms exceeds the number of ionizable protons by two or more, such as HNO_3, H_2SO_4, and $HClO_4$; for example, in the case of H_2SO_4, 4 O's − 2 H's = 2
- *Weak acids.* There are many *more* weak acids than strong ones. Four types are
  1. The hydrohalic acid HF
  2. Acids in which H is not bonded to O or to a halogen, such as HCN and H_2S
  3. Oxoacids in which the number of O atoms equals or exceeds by one the number of ionizable protons, such as HClO, HNO_2, and H_3PO_4
  4. Carboxylic acids (general formula RCOOH, with the ionizable proton shown in red), such as CH_3COOH and C_6H_5COOH
- *Strong bases.* Water-soluble compounds containing O^{2-} or OH^- ions are strong bases. The cations are usually those of the most active metals:
  1. M_2O or MOH, where M = Group 1A(1) metal (Li, Na, K, Rb, Cs)
  2. MO or $M(OH)_2$, where M = Group 2A(2) metal (Ca, Sr, Ba)
     [MgO and $Mg(OH)_2$ are only slightly soluble in water, but the soluble portion dissociates completely.]
- *Weak bases.* Many compounds with an electron-rich nitrogen atom are weak bases (none is an Arrhenius base). The common structural feature is an N atom with a lone electron pair (shown in blue):
  1. Ammonia ($\ddot{N}H_3$)
  2. Amines (general formula $R\ddot{N}H_2$, $R_2\ddot{N}H$, or $R_3\ddot{N}$), such as $CH_3CH_2\ddot{N}H_2$, $(CH_3)_2\ddot{N}H$, and $(C_3H_7)_3\ddot{N}$

Sample Problem 18.1 **Classifying Acid and Base Strength from the Chemical Formula**

Problem Classify each of the following compounds as a strong acid, weak acid, strong base, or weak base:
(a) KOH **(b)** $(CH_3)_2CHCOOH$
(c) H_2SeO_4 **(d)** $(CH_3)_2CHNH_2$

Plan We examine the formula and classify each acid or base, using the text descriptions. Particular points to note for acids are the numbers of O atoms relative to ionizable H atoms and the presence of the —COOH group. For bases, note the nature of the cation or the presence of an N atom that has a lone pair.

Solution **(a)** Strong base: KOH is one of the Group 1A(1) hydroxides.
(b) Weak acid: $(CH_3)_2CHCOOH$ is a carboxylic acid, as indicated by the —COOH group.
(c) Strong acid: H_2SeO_4 is an oxoacid in which the number of O atoms exceeds the number of ionizable protons by two.
(d) Weak base: $(CH_3)_2CHNH_2$ has a lone pair on the N and is an amine.

Follow-Up Problem 18.1 Which member of each pair is the stronger acid or base?
(a) HClO or $HClO_3$ **(b)** HCl or CH_3COOH **(c)** NaOH or CH_3NH_2

Summary of Section 18.1

- In aqueous solution, water binds the proton released from an acid to form a hydrated species represented by $H_3O^+(aq)$.
- By the Arrhenius definition, acids contain H and yield H_3O^+ in water, bases contain OH and yield OH^- in water, and an acid-base reaction (neutralization) is the reaction of H^+ and OH^- to form H_2O.
- Acid strength depends on $[H_3O^+]$ relative to [HA] in aqueous solution. Strong acids dissociate completely and weak acids slightly.
- The extent of dissociation is expressed by the acid-dissociation constant, K_a. Weak acids have K_a values ranging from about 10^{-1} to 10^{-12}.
- Many acids and bases can be classified as strong or weak based on their formulas.

18.2 • AUTOIONIZATION OF WATER AND THE pH SCALE

Before we discuss the next major acid-base definition, let's examine a crucial property of water that enables us to quantify $[H_3O^+]$: *water dissociates very slightly into ions* in an equilibrium process known as **autoionization** (or self-ionization):

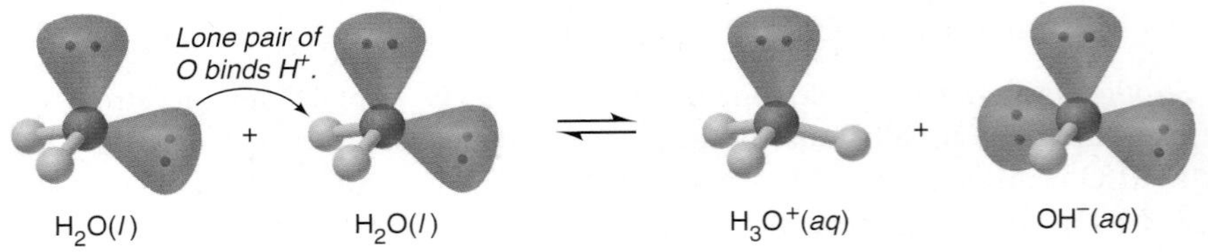

The Equilibrium Nature of Autoionization: The Ion-Product Constant for Water (K_w)

Like any equilibrium process, the autoionization of water is described quantitatively by an equilibrium constant:

$$K_c = \frac{[H_3O^+][OH^-]}{[H_2O]^2}$$

Because the concentration of H_2O (55.5 *M*) remains essentially constant, we multiply K_c by $[H_2O]^2$ to obtain a new equilibrium constant, the **ion-product constant for water, K_w:**

$$K_c[H_2O]^2 = K_w = [H_3O^+][OH^-] = 1.0\times10^{-14} \text{ (at 25°C)} \quad (18.2)$$

Notice that *one H_3O^+ ion and one OH^- ion form for each H_2O molecule that dissociates.* Therefore, in pure water, we find that

$$[H_3O^+] = [OH^-] = \sqrt{1.0\times10^{-14}} = 1.0\times10^{-7}\ M \text{ (at 25°C)}$$

Since pure water has a concentration of about 55.5 *M*, these equilibrium concentrations are attained when only 1 in 555 million water molecules dissociates reversibly into ions!

Autoionization of water affects aqueous acid-base chemistry in two major ways:

1. *A change in $[H_3O^+]$ causes an inverse change in $[OH^-]$,* and vice versa:

Higher $[H_3O^+] \Longrightarrow$ lower $[OH^-]$ and Higher $[OH^-] \Longrightarrow$ lower $[H_3O^+]$

Recall from Le Châtelier's principle (Section 17.6) that a change in concentration shifts the equilibrium position but does *not* change the equilibrium constant. Therefore, if some acid is added, $[H_3O^+]$ increases and $[OH^-]$ decreases as the ions react to form water; similarly, if some base is added, $[OH^-]$ increases and $[H_3O^+]$ decreases. In both cases, as long as the temperature is constant, the value of K_w is constant.

2. *Both ions are present in all aqueous systems.* Thus, all acidic solutions contain a low $[OH^-]$, and all basic solutions contain a low $[H_3O^+]$. The equilibrium nature of autoionization allows us to define "acidic" and "basic" solutions in terms of relative magnitudes of $[H_3O^+]$ and $[OH^-]$:

In an *acidic* solution, $[H_3O^+] > [OH^-]$
In a *neutral* solution, $[H_3O^+] = [OH^-]$
In a *basic* solution, $[H_3O^+] < [OH^-]$

Figure 18.3 summarizes these relationships. Moreover, if you know the value of K_w at a particular temperature and the concentration of one of the two ions, you can find the concentration of the other:

$$[H_3O^+] = \frac{K_w}{[OH^-]} \quad \text{or} \quad [OH^-] = \frac{K_w}{[H_3O^+]}$$

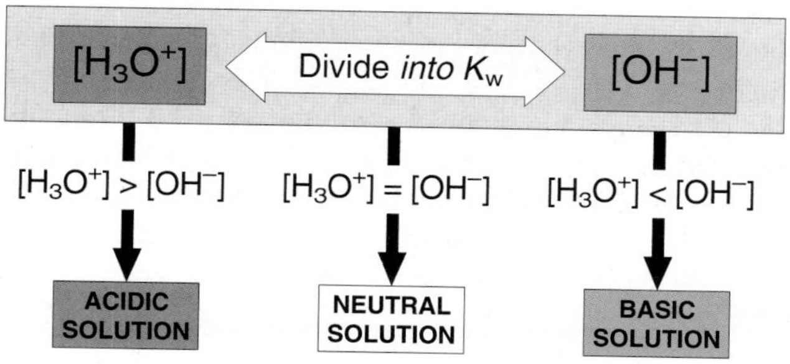

Figure 18.3 The relationship between $[H_3O^+]$ and $[OH^-]$ and the relative acidity of solutions.

Sample Problem 18.2 Calculating $[H_3O^+]$ or $[OH^-]$ in Aqueous Solution

Problem A research chemist adds a measured amount of HCl gas to pure water at 25°C and obtains a solution with $[H_3O^+] = 3.0\times10^{-4}\ M$. Calculate $[OH^-]$. Is the solution neutral, acidic, or basic?

Plan We use the known value of K_w at 25°C (1.0×10^{-14}) and the given $[H_3O^+]$ ($3.0\times10^{-4}\ M$) to solve for $[OH^-]$. Then we compare $[H_3O^+]$ with $[OH^-]$ to determine whether the solution is acidic, basic, or neutral (see Figure 18.3).

Solution Calculating $[OH^-]$:

$$[OH^-] = \frac{K_w}{[H_3O^+]} = \frac{1.0\times10^{-14}}{3.0\times10^{-4}}$$
$$= 3.3\times10^{-11}\ M$$

Because $[H_3O^+] > [OH^-]$, the solution is acidic.

Check It makes sense that adding an acid to water results in an acidic solution. Also, since $[H_3O^+]$ is greater than $10^{-7}\ M$, $[OH^-]$ must be less than $10^{-7}\ M$ to give a constant K_w.

Follow-Up Problem 18.2 Calculate $[H_3O^+]$ in a solution that has $[OH^-] = 6.7\times10^{-2}\ M$ at 25°C. Is the solution neutral, acidic, or basic?

Expressing the Hydronium Ion Concentration: The pH Scale

In aqueous solutions, $[H_3O^+]$ can vary from about 10 *M* to $10^{-15}\ M$. To handle numbers with negative exponents more conveniently in calculations, we convert them to positive numbers using a numerical system called a *p-scale,* the negative of the common (base-10) logarithm of the number. Applying this numerical system to $[H_3O^+]$ gives **pH,** the negative logarithm of $[H^+]$ (or $[H_3O^+]$):

$$\text{pH} = -\log\,[H_3O^+] \qquad (18.3)$$

What is the pH of $10^{-12}\ M\ H_3O^+$ solution?

$$\text{pH} = -\log\,[H_3O^+] = -\log 10^{-12} = (-1)(-12) = 12$$

Similarly, a $10^{-3}\ M\ H_3O^+$ solution has a pH of 3, and a $5.4\times10^{-4}\ M\ H_3O^+$ solution has a pH of 3.27:

$$\text{pH} = -\log\,[H_3O^+] = (-1)(\log 5.4 + \log 10^{-4}) = 3.27$$

As with any measurement, the number of significant figures in a pH value reflects the precision with which the concentration is known. However, a pH value is a logarithm, so the number of significant figures in the concentration equals the number of digits *to the right of the decimal point in the pH value* (see Appendix A). In the preceding example, $5.4\times10^{-4}\ M$ has two significant figures, so its negative logarithm, 3.27, has two digits to the right of the decimal point.

Note in particular that *the higher the pH, the lower the $[H_3O^+]$.* Therefore, *an acidic solution has a lower pH (higher $[H_3O^+]$) than a basic solution.* At 25°C in pure water, $[H_3O^+]$ is $1.0\times10^{-7}\ M$, so

pH of an acidic solution	< 7.00
pH of a neutral solution	$= 7.00$
pH of a basic solution	> 7.00

Figure 18.4 shows that the pH values of some familiar aqueous solutions fall within a range of 0 to 14.

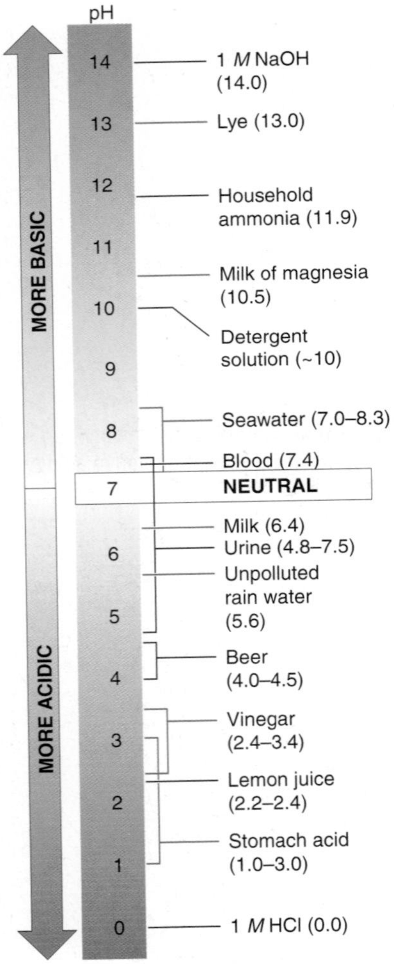

Figure 18.4 The pH values of some familiar aqueous solutions.

Because the pH scale is logarithmic, a solution of pH 1.0 has an $[H_3O^+]$ that is 10 times higher than that of a pH 2.0 solution, 100 times higher than that of a pH 3.0 solution, and so forth. To find the $[H_3O^+]$ from the pH, you perform the opposite arithmetic process; that is, you find the negative antilog of pH:

$$[H_3O^+] = 10^{-\text{pH}}$$

A p-scale is used to express other quantities as well:

- Hydroxide ion concentration can be expressed as pOH:
$$\text{pOH} = -\log\,[OH^-]$$
Acidic solutions have a higher pOH (lower $[OH^-]$) than basic solutions.
- Equilibrium constants can be expressed as p*K*:
$$\text{p}K = -\log K$$
A low pK corresponds to a high K. A reaction that reaches equilibrium with mostly products present (proceeds far to the right) has a low p*K* (high *K*), whereas one that has mostly reactants present at equilibrium has a high p*K* (low *K*). Table 18.3 shows this relationship for aqueous equilibria of some weak acids.

The Relations Among pH, pOH, and pK_w Taking the negative log of both sides of the K_w expression gives a very useful relationship among pK_w, pH, and pOH:

$$K_w = [H_3O^+][OH^-] = 1.0\times10^{-14}\ (\text{at } 25°\text{C})$$
$$-\log K_w = (-\log\,[H_3O^+]) + (-\log\,[OH^-]) = -\log\,(1.0\times10^{-14})$$

$$\text{p}K_w = \text{pH} + \text{pOH} = 14.00 \quad (\text{at } 25°\text{C}) \qquad (18.4)$$

Table 18.3 The Relationship Between K_a and pK_a

Acid Name (Formula)	K_a at 25°C	pK_a
Hydrogen sulfate ion (HSO_4^-)	1.0×10^{-2}	1.99
Nitrous acid (HNO_2)	7.1×10^{-4}	3.15
Acetic acid (CH_3COOH)	1.8×10^{-5}	4.75
Hypobromous acid (HBrO)	2.3×10^{-9}	8.64
Phenol (C_6H_5OH)	1.0×10^{-10}	10.00

Note these important points:

1. The sum of pH and pOH is pK_w for any aqueous solution at any temperature, and pK_w equals 14.00 at 25°C.
2. Because K_w is constant, pH, pOH, $[H_3O^+]$, and $[OH^-]$ are interrelated:
   - $[H_3O^+]$ and $[OH^-]$ change in opposite directions.
   - pH and pOH also change in opposite directions.
   - At 25°C, the product of $[H_3O^+]$ and $[OH^-]$ is 1.0×10^{-14}, and the sum of pH and pOH is 14.00 (Figure 18.5).

		$[H_3O^+]$	pH	$[OH^-]$	pOH
MORE BASIC		1.0×10^{-15}	15.00	1.0×10^{1}	−1.00
		1.0×10^{-14}	14.00	1.0×10^{0}	0.00
		1.0×10^{-13}	13.00	1.0×10^{-1}	1.00
	BASIC	1.0×10^{-12}	12.00	1.0×10^{-2}	2.00
		1.0×10^{-11}	11.00	1.0×10^{-3}	3.00
		1.0×10^{-10}	10.00	1.0×10^{-4}	4.00
		1.0×10^{-9}	9.00	1.0×10^{-5}	5.00
		1.0×10^{-8}	8.00	1.0×10^{-6}	6.00
	NEUTRAL	1.0×10^{-7}	7.00	1.0×10^{-7}	7.00
MORE ACIDIC		1.0×10^{-6}	6.00	1.0×10^{-8}	8.00
		1.0×10^{-5}	5.00	1.0×10^{-9}	9.00
		1.0×10^{-4}	4.00	1.0×10^{-10}	10.00
	ACIDIC	1.0×10^{-3}	3.00	1.0×10^{-11}	11.00
		1.0×10^{-2}	2.00	1.0×10^{-12}	12.00
		1.0×10^{-1}	1.00	1.0×10^{-13}	13.00
		1.0×10^{0}	0.00	1.0×10^{-14}	14.00
		1.0×10^{1}	−1.00	1.0×10^{-15}	15.00

Figure 18.5 The relations among $[H_3O^+]$, pH, $[OH^-]$, and pOH.

Sample Problem 18.3 Calculating $[H_3O^+]$, pH, $[OH^-]$, and pOH

Problem In an art restoration project, a conservator prepares copper-plate etching solutions by diluting concentrated HNO_3 to 2.0 *M*, 0.30 *M*, and 0.0063 *M* HNO_3. Calculate $[H_3O^+]$, pH, $[OH^-]$, and pOH of the three solutions at 25°C.

Plan We know from its formula that HNO_3 is a strong acid, so it dissociates completely; thus, $[H_3O^+] = [HNO_3]_{init}$. We use the given concentrations and the value of K_w at 25°C (1.0×10^{-14}) to find $[H_3O^+]$ and $[OH^-]$ and then use them to calculate pH and pOH.

Solution Calculating the values for 2.0 *M* HNO_3:

$$[H_3O^+] = 2.0\ M$$

$$\text{pH} = -\log[H_3O^+] = -\log 2.0 = -0.30$$

$$[OH^-] = \frac{K_w}{[H_3O^+]} = \frac{1.0\times10^{-14}}{2.0} = 5.0\times10^{-15}\ M$$

$$\text{pOH} = -\log(5.0\times10^{-15}) = 14.30$$

Calculating the values for 0.30 *M* HNO_3:

$$[H_3O^+] = 0.30\ M$$
$$pH = -\log [H_3O^+] = -\log 0.30 = 0.52$$
$$[OH^-] = \frac{K_w}{[H_3O^+]} = \frac{1.0\times10^{-14}}{0.30} = 3.3\times10^{-14}\ M$$
$$pOH = -\log (3.3\times10^{-14}) = 13.48$$

Calculating the values for 0.0063 *M* HNO_3:

$$[H_3O^+] = 6.3\times10^{-3}\ M$$
$$pH = -\log [H_3O^+] = -\log (6.3\times10^{-3}) = 2.20$$
$$[OH^-] = \frac{K_w}{[H_3O^+]} = \frac{1.0\times10^{-14}}{6.3\times10^{-3}} = 1.6\times10^{-12}\ M$$
$$pOH = -\log (1.6\times10^{-12}) = 11.80$$

Check As the solution becomes more dilute, $[H_3O^+]$ decreases, so pH increases, as we expect. An $[H_3O^+] > 1.0\ M$, as in 2.0 *M* HNO_3, gives a positive log, so it results in a negative pH. The arithmetic seems correct because pH + pOH = 14.00 in each case.

Comment On most calculators, finding the pH requires several keystrokes. For example, to find the pH of 6.3×10^{-3} *M* HNO_3 solution, you enter: 6.3, EXP, 3, +/−, log, +/−.

Follow-Up Problem 18.3 A solution of NaOH has a pH of 9.52. What is its pOH, $[H_3O^+]$, and $[OH^-]$ at 25°C?

Measuring pH In the laboratory, pH values are usually obtained in two ways:

1. **Acid-base indicators** are organic molecules whose colors depend on the acidity of the solution in which they are dissolved. A pH can be estimated quickly with *pH paper,* a paper strip impregnated with one or a mixture of indicators. A drop of solution is placed on the strip, and the color is compared with a chart (Figure 18.6A).

2. A *pH meter* measures $[H_3O^+]$ by means of two electrodes immersed in the test solution. One electrode supplies a reference system; the other consists of a very thin glass membrane that separates a known internal $[H_3O^+]$ from the unknown external $[H_3O^+]$. The difference in $[H_3O^+]$ creates a voltage difference across the membrane, which is displayed in pH units (Figure 18.6B). We examine this device in Chapter 21.

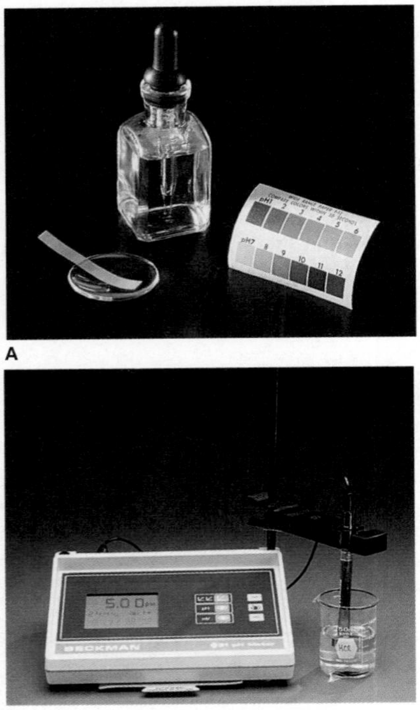

Figure 18.6 Methods for measuring the pH of an aqueous solution. **A,** pH paper. **B,** pH meter.

Summary of Section 18.2

- Pure water has a low conductivity because it autoionizes to a small extent in a process whose equilibrium constant is the ion-product constant for water, K_w (1.0×10^{-14} at 25°C).
- $[H_3O^+]$ and $[OH^-]$ are inversely related: in acidic solution, $[H_3O^+]$ is greater than $[OH^-]$; the reverse is true in basic solution; and the two are equal in neutral solution.
- To express small values of $[H_3O^+]$, we use the pH scale ($pH = -\log [H_3O^+]$). Similarly, $pOH = -\log [OH^-]$, and $pK = -\log K$.
- A high pH represents a low $[H_3O^+]$. In acidic solutions, pH < 7.00; in basic solutions, pH > 7.00; and in neutral solutions, pH = 7.00. The sum of pH and pOH equals pK_w (14.00 at 25°C).
- A pH is typically measured with either an acid-base indicator or a pH meter.

18.3 • PROTON TRANSFER AND THE BRØNSTED-LOWRY ACID-BASE DEFINITION

Earlier we noted one limitation of the Arrhenius definition: many substances that yield OH^- ions in water do not contain OH in their formulas. Examples include ammonia, the amines, and many salts of weak acids, such as NaF. Another limitation is that water had to be the solvent for acid-base reactions. In the early 20th century, J. N. Brønsted and T. M. Lowry suggested definitions that remove these limitations. (We introduced some of these ideas in Section 4.4.)

According to the **Brønsted-Lowry acid-base definition,**

- *An acid is a* ***proton donor,*** *any species that donates an* H^+ *ion.* An acid must contain H in its formula; HNO_3 and $H_2PO_4^-$ are two of many examples. All Arrhenius acids are Brønsted-Lowry acids.
- *A base is a* ***proton acceptor,*** *any species that accepts an* H^+ *ion.* A base must contain a lone pair of electrons to bind H^+; a few examples are NH_3, CO_3^{2-}, and F^-, as well as OH^- itself. Brønsted-Lowry bases are not Arrhenius bases, but all Arrhenius bases contain the Brønsted-Lowry base OH^-.

From this perspective, an acid-base reaction occurs when *one species donates a proton and another species simultaneously accepts it: an acid-base reaction is thus a proton-transfer process.* Acid-base reactions can occur between gases, in nonaqueous solutions, and in heterogeneous mixtures, as well as in aqueous solutions.

According to this definition, an acid-base reaction occurs even when an acid (or a base) just dissolves in water, because water acts as the proton acceptor (or donor):

1. *Acid donates a proton to water* (Figure 18.7A). When HCl dissolves in water, an H^+ ion (a proton) is transferred from HCl to H_2O, where it becomes attached to a lone pair of electrons on the O atom, forming H_3O^+. Thus, HCl (the acid) has *donated* the H^+, and H_2O (the base) has *accepted* it:

$$HCl(g) + H_2\ddot{\underset{\cdot\cdot}{O}}(l) \longrightarrow Cl^-(aq) + H_3\ddot{O}^+(aq)$$

2. *Base accepts a proton from water* (Figure 18.7B). When ammonia dissolves in water, an H^+ from H_2O is transferred to the lone pair of N, forming NH_4^+, and the H_2O becomes an OH^- ion:

$$\ddot{N}H_3(aq) + H_2O(l) \rightleftharpoons NH_4^+(aq) + OH^-(aq)$$

In this case, H_2O (the acid) has *donated* the H^+, and NH_3 (the base) has *accepted* it.

Note that H_2O is *amphiprotic:* it acts as a base (accepts an H^+) in one case and as an acid (donates an H^+) in the other. Many other species are amphiprotic as well.

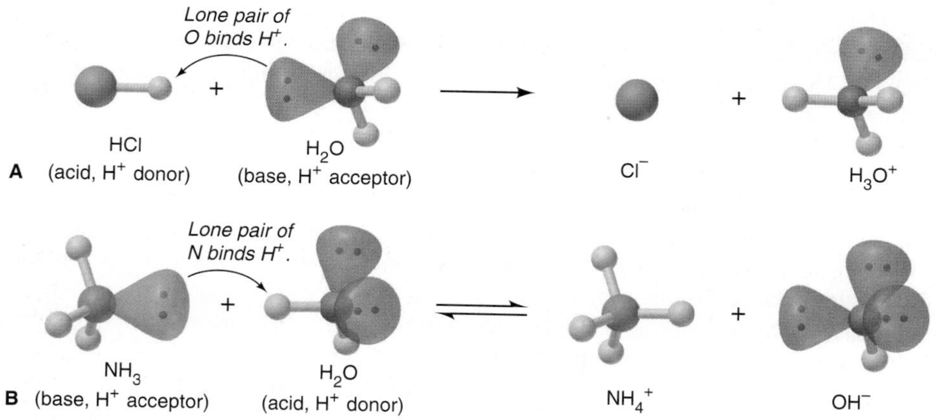

Figure 18.7 Dissolving of an acid or base in water as a Brønsted-Lowry acid-base reaction. **A,** The acid HCl dissolving in the base water. **B,** The base NH_3 dissolving in the acid water.

Conjugate Acid-Base Pairs

The Brønsted-Lowry definition provides a new way to look at these reactions because it focuses on the reactants *and* the products as acids and bases. For example, let's examine the reaction between hydrogen sulfide and ammonia:

$$H_2S + NH_3 \rightleftharpoons HS^- + NH_4^+$$

In the forward reaction, H_2S acts as an acid by donating an H^+ to NH_3, which acts as a base by accepting it. In the reverse reaction, the ammonium ion, NH_4^+, acts as an acid by donating an H^+ to the hydrogen sulfide ion, HS^-, which acts as a base. Notice that the acid, H_2S, becomes a base, HS^-, and the base, NH_3, becomes an acid, NH_4^+.

In Brønsted-Lowry terminology, H_2S and HS^- are a **conjugate acid-base pair:** HS^- is the conjugate base of the acid H_2S. Similarly, NH_3 and NH_4^+ are a conjugate acid-base pair: NH_4^+ is the conjugate acid of the base NH_3. *Every acid has a conjugate base, and every base has a conjugate acid.* For any conjugate acid-base pair,

- The conjugate base has one *fewer* H and one *more* minus charge than the acid.
- The conjugate acid has one *more* H and one *fewer* minus charge than the base.

A Brønsted-Lowry acid-base reaction occurs when *an acid and a base react to form their conjugate base and conjugate acid, respectively:*

$$\text{acid}_1 + \text{base}_2 \rightleftharpoons \text{base}_1 + \text{acid}_2$$

Table 18.4 shows some Brønsted-Lowry acid-base reactions. Note these points:

- Each reaction has an acid and a base as reactants *and* as products, comprising two conjugate acid-base pairs.
- Acids and bases can be neutral, cationic, or anionic.
- The same species can be an acid or a base (amphiprotic), depending on the other species reacting. Water behaves this way in reactions 1 and 4, and HPO_4^{2-} does so in reactions 4 and 6.

Table 18.4 The Conjugate Pairs in Some Acid-Base Reactions

(Conjugate Pair: Acid (left) / Base (right); Conjugate Pair: Base (left) / Base (right))

	Acid	+	Base	⇌	Base	+	Acid
Reaction 1	HF	+	H_2O		F^-	+	H_3O^+
Reaction 2	$HCOOH$	+	CN^-		$HCOO^-$	+	HCN
Reaction 3	NH_4^+	+	CO_3^{2-}		NH_3	+	HCO_3^-
Reaction 4	$H_2PO_4^-$	+	OH^-		HPO_4^{2-}	+	H_2O
Reaction 5	H_2SO_4	+	$N_2H_5^+$		HSO_4^-	+	$N_2H_6^{2+}$
Reaction 6	HPO_4^{2-}	+	SO_3^{2-}		PO_4^{3-}	+	HSO_3^-

Sample Problem 18.4 Identifying Conjugate Acid-Base Pairs

Problem The following reactions are important environmental processes. Identify the conjugate acid-base pairs.

(a) $H_2PO_4^-(aq) + CO_3^{2-}(aq) \rightleftharpoons HCO_3^-(aq) + HPO_4^{2-}(aq)$

(b) $H_2O(l) + SO_3^{2-}(aq) \rightleftharpoons OH^-(aq) + HSO_3^-(aq)$

Plan To find the conjugate pairs, we find the species that donated an H^+ (acid) and the species that accepted it (base). The acid (or base) on the left becomes its conjugate base (or conjugate acid) on the right. Remember, the conjugate acid has one more H and one fewer minus charge than its conjugate base.

Solution (a) $H_2PO_4^-$ has one more H^+ than HPO_4^{2-}; CO_3^{2-} has one fewer H^+ than HCO_3^-. Therefore, $H_2PO_4^-$ and HCO_3^- are the acids, and HPO_4^{2-} and CO_3^{2-} are the bases. The conjugate acid-base pairs are $H_2PO_4^-/HPO_4^{2-}$ and HCO_3^-/CO_3^{2-}.

(b) H_2O has one more H^+ than OH^-; SO_3^{2-} has one fewer H^+ than HSO_3^-. The acids are H_2O and HSO_3^-; the bases are OH^- and SO_3^{2-}. The conjugate acid-base pairs are H_2O/OH^- and HSO_3^-/SO_3^{2-}.

Follow-Up Problem 18.4 Identify the conjugate acid-base pairs:

(a) $CH_3COOH(aq) + H_2O(l) \rightleftharpoons CH_3COO^-(aq) + H_3O^+(aq)$

(b) $H_2O(l) + F^-(aq) \rightleftharpoons OH^-(aq) + HF(aq)$

Relative Acid-Base Strength and the Net Direction of Reaction

The *net* direction of an acid-base reaction depends on relative acid and base strengths: *A reaction proceeds to the greater extent in the direction in which a stronger acid and stronger base form a weaker acid and weaker base.*

Competition for the Proton The net direction of the reaction of H_2S and NH_3 is to the right ($K_c > 1$) because H_2S is a stronger acid than NH_4^+, the other acid present, and NH_3 is a stronger base than HS^-, the other base:

$$\underset{\text{stronger acid}}{H_2S} + \underset{\text{stronger base}}{NH_3} \rightleftharpoons \underset{\text{weaker base}}{HS^-} + \underset{\text{weaker acid}}{NH_4^+}$$

You might think of the process as *a competition for the proton between the two bases,* NH_3 and HS^-, in which NH_3 wins.

The extent of acid (HA) dissociation in water depends on a competition for the proton between the two bases, A^- and H_2O. Strong and weak acids give different results:

1. *Strong acids.* When the strong acid HNO_3 dissolves, it completely transfers an H^+ to the base, H_2O, forming the conjugate base NO_3^- and the conjugate acid H_3O^+:

$$\underset{\text{stronger acid}}{HNO_3} + \underset{\text{stronger base}}{H_2O} \rightleftharpoons \underset{\text{weaker base}}{NO_3^-} + \underset{\text{weaker acid}}{H_3O^+}$$

Even though we show an equilibrium arrow here, the net direction is so far to the right that $K_c >> 1$ and the reaction is essentially complete. HNO_3 is a stronger acid than H_3O^+, and H_2O is a stronger base than NO_3^-. Thus, with a strong HA, H_2O wins the competition for the proton because A^- is a *much* weaker base. In fact, *the only acidic species that remains in strong-acid solutions is H_3O^+.*

2. *Weak acids.* On the other hand, with weak acids such as HF, the A^- (F^-) wins the competition because it is a stronger base than H_2O ($K_c < 1$):

$$\underset{\text{weaker acid}}{HF} + \underset{\text{weaker base}}{H_2O} \rightleftharpoons \underset{\text{stronger base}}{F^-} + \underset{\text{stronger acid}}{H_3O^+}$$

Ranking Conjugate Pairs Based on evidence from many such reactions, we can rank conjugate pairs in terms of the ability of the acid to transfer its proton (Figure 18.8). Note

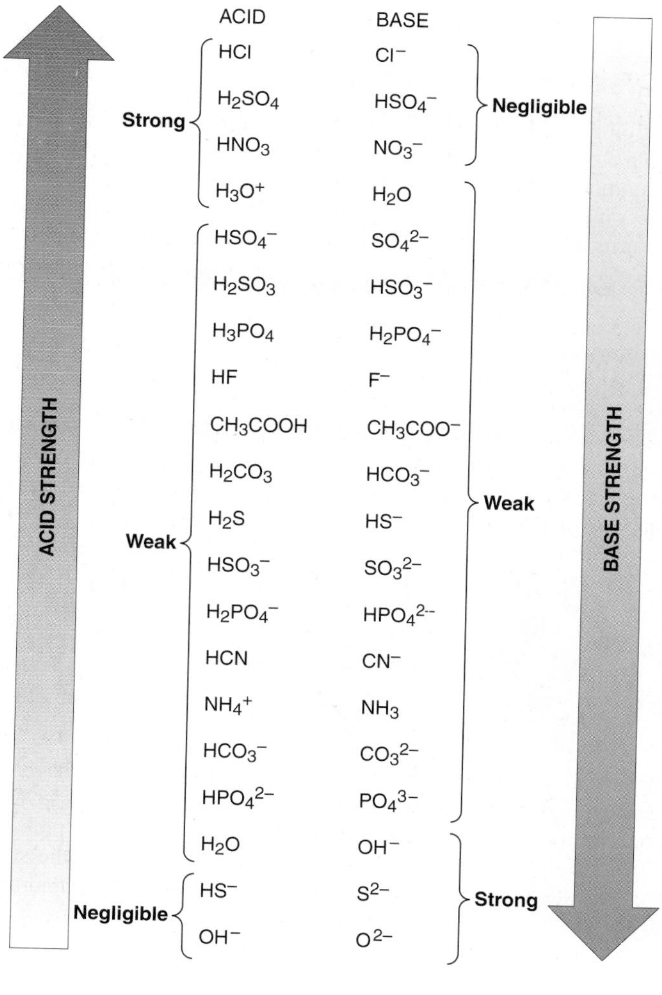

Figure 18.8 Strengths of conjugate acid-base pairs. The stronger the acid is, the weaker its conjugate base. The strongest acid is at top left and the strongest base at bottom right. When an acid reacts with a base farther down the list, the reaction proceeds to the right ($K_c > 1$).

that *a weaker acid has a stronger conjugate base:* the acid can't give up its proton very readily because its conjugate base is holding it too strongly.

We use Figure 18.8 to predict the net direction of a reaction between any two pairs, that is, whether the equilibrium position lies to the right ($K_c > 1$) or to the left ($K_c < 1$). *A reaction proceeds to the right if an acid reacts with a base lower on the list.* Here are two sample problems that demonstrate this key idea.

Sample Problem 18.5 Predicting the Net Direction of an Acid-Base Reaction

Problem Predict the net direction and whether K_c is greater or less than 1 for each of the following reactions (assume equal initial concentrations of all species):

(a) $H_2PO_4^-(aq) + NH_3(aq) \rightleftharpoons NH_4^+(aq) + HPO_4^{2-}(aq)$

(b) $H_2O(l) + HS^-(aq) \rightleftharpoons OH^-(aq) + H_2S(aq)$

Plan We identify the conjugate acid-base pairs and consult Figure 18.8 to see which acid and base are stronger. The reaction proceeds in the direction that the stronger acid and base form the weaker acid and base. If the reaction *as written* proceeds to the right, then [products] is higher than [reactants], so $K_c > 1$.

Solution (a) The conjugate pairs are $H_2PO_4^-/HPO_4^{2-}$ and NH_4^+/NH_3. Since $H_2PO_4^-$ is higher on the list of acids, it is stronger than NH_4^+; since NH_3 is lower on the list of bases, it is stronger than HPO_4^{2-}. Therefore,

$$\underset{\text{stronger acid}}{H_2PO_4^-(aq)} + \underset{\text{stronger base}}{NH_3(aq)} \rightleftharpoons \underset{\text{weaker base}}{HPO_4^{2-}(aq)} + \underset{\text{weaker acid}}{NH_4^+(aq)}$$

stronger acid + stronger base ⟶ weaker base + weaker acid

The net direction is to the right, so $K_c > 1$.

(b) The conjugate pairs are H_2O/OH^- and H_2S/HS^-. Since H_2S is higher on the list of acids, and OH^- is lower on the list of bases, we have

$$\underset{\text{weaker acid}}{H_2O(l)} + \underset{\text{weaker base}}{HS^-(aq)} \rightleftharpoons \underset{\text{stronger base}}{OH^-(aq)} + \underset{\text{stronger acid}}{H_2S(aq)}$$

weaker acid + weaker base ⟵ stronger base + stronger acid

The net direction is to the left, so $K_c < 1$.

Follow-Up Problem 18.5 Use balanced equations that show the net direction of the reaction to explain each of the following observations:

(a) You smell ammonia when NH_3 dissolves in water.

(b) The odor goes away when you add an excess of HCl to the solution in part (a).

(c) The odor returns when you add an excess of NaOH to the solution in part (b).

Sample Problem 18.6 Using Molecular Scenes to Predict the Net Direction of an Acid-Base Reaction

Problem Given that 0.10 *M* HX *(blue and green)* has a pH of 2.88, and 0.10 *M* HY *(blue and orange)* has a pH of 3.52, which scene best represents the final mixture after equimolar solutions of HX and Y^- are mixed?

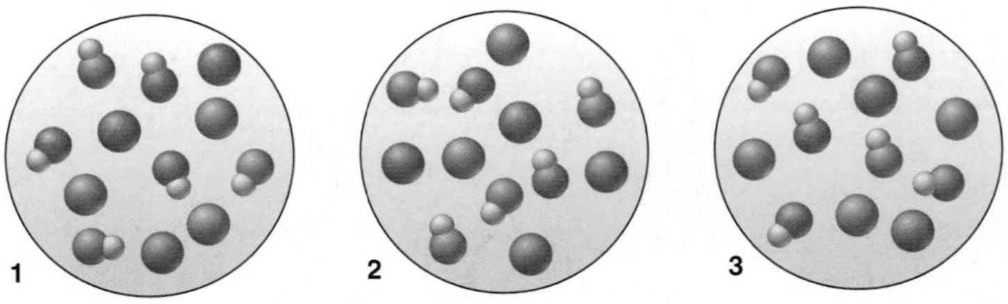

Plan A stronger acid and base yield a weaker acid and base, so we have to determine the relative acid strengths of HX and HY in order to choose the correct molecular scene. The concentrations of the acid solutions are equal, so we can pick the stronger acid directly from the pH values of the two acid solutions. Because the stronger acid reacts to a greater extent, fewer molecules of it will be in the scene than molecules of the weaker acid.

Solution The HX solution has a lower pH (2.88) than the HY solution (3.52), so we know right away that HX is the stronger acid and Y^- is the stronger base. Therefore, the reaction of HX and Y^- has a $K_c > 1$, which means the equilibrium mixture will have more HY than HX. Scene 1 has equal numbers of HX and HY, which would occur if the acids were of equal strength, and scene 2 shows fewer HY than HX, which would occur if HY were stronger. Therefore, only scene 3 is consistent with the relative acid strengths.

Follow-Up Problem 18.6 The scene below represents the equilibrium mixture after 0.10 *M* solutions of HA *(blue and red)* and B^- *(black)* react: Does their reaction have a K_c greater or less than 1? Which acid is stronger, HA or HB?

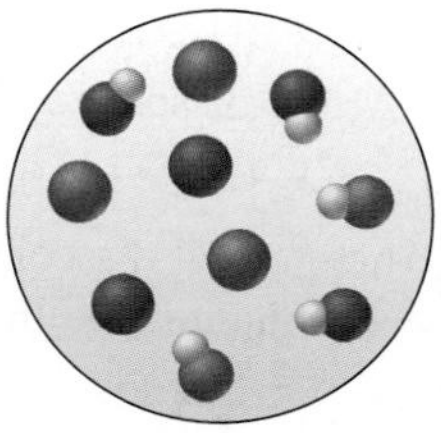

Summary of Section 18.3

- The Brønsted-Lowry acid-base definition does not require that bases contain OH in their formula or that acid-base reactions occur in aqueous solution.
- An acid is a species that donates a proton and a base is one that accepts it, so an acid-base reaction is a proton-transfer process.
- When an acid donates a proton, it becomes the conjugate base; when a base accepts a proton, it becomes the conjugate acid. In an acid-base reaction, acids and bases form their conjugates. A stronger acid has a weaker conjugate base, and vice versa.
- An acid-base reaction proceeds to the greater extent in the direction in which a stronger acid and base form a weaker base and acid.

18.4 • SOLVING PROBLEMS INVOLVING WEAK-ACID EQUILIBRIA

Just as you saw in Chapter 17 for equilibrium problems in general, there are two general types of equilibrium problems involving weak acids and their conjugate bases:

1. Given equilibrium concentrations, find K_a.
2. Given K_a and some concentrations, find other equilibrium concentrations.

For all of these problems, we'll apply the same problem-solving approach, notation system, and assumptions:

- *The problem-solving approach.* Start with what is given in the problem and move toward what you want to find. Make a habit of applying the following steps:
  1. Write the balanced equation and K_a expression; these tell you what to find.
  2. Define x as the unknown change in concentration that occurs during the reaction. Frequently, $x = [HA]_{dissoc}$, the concentration of HA that dissociates, which, through the use of certain assumptions, also equals $[H_3O^+]$ and $[A^-]$ at equilibrium.
  3. Construct a reaction table (for most problems) that incorporates x.
  4. Make assumptions (usually that x is very small relative to the initial concentration; see below) that simplify the calculations.
  5. Substitute the values into the K_a expression, and solve for x.
  6. Check that the assumptions are justified with the 5% test first used in Sample Problem 17.10, pp. 695–696. If they are not justified, use the quadratic formula to find x.

- *The notation system.* As always, molar concentration is indicated with brackets. A subscript refers to where the species comes from or when it occurs in the reaction process. For example, $[H_3O^+]_{\text{from HA}}$ is the molar concentration of H_3O^+ that comes from the dissociation of HA; $[HA]_{\text{init}}$ is the initial molar concentration of HA, that is, before dissociation; $[HA]_{\text{dissoc}}$ is the molar concentration of HA that dissociates; and so forth. A bracketed formula with *no* subscript represents the molar concentration of the species *at equilibrium.*

- *The assumptions.* We make two assumptions to simplify the arithmetic:
  1. $[H_3O^+]$ from the autoionization of water is negligible. It is so much smaller than the $[H_3O^+]$ from the dissociation of HA that we can neglect it in these problems:
  $$[H_3O^+] = [H_3O^+]_{\text{from HA}} + [H_3O^+]_{\text{from } H_2O} \approx [H_3O^+]_{\text{from HA}}$$
  Note that each molecule of HA that dissociates forms one H_3O^+ and one A^-:
  $$[HA]_{\text{dissoc}} = [H_3O^+] = [A^-]$$
  2. A weak acid has a small K_a. Therefore, it dissociates to such a small extent that we can neglect the change in its concentration to find its equilibrium concentration:
  $$[HA] = [HA]_{\text{init}} - [HA]_{\text{dissoc}} \approx [HA]_{\text{init}}$$

Finding K_a Given Concentrations

This type of problem involves finding K_a of a weak acid from the concentration of one of the species in solution, usually $[H_3O^+]$ from a given pH:

$$HA(aq) + H_2O(l) \rightleftharpoons H_3O^+(aq) + A^-(aq)$$
$$K_a = \frac{[H_3O^+][A^-]}{[HA]}$$

You prepare an aqueous solution of HA and measure its pH. Thus, you know $[HA]_{\text{init}}$, can calculate $[H_3O^+]$ from the pH, and then determine $[A^-]$ and [HA] at equilibrium. You substitute these values into the K_a expression and solve for K_a. Let's go through the approach in Sample Problem 18.7.

Sample Problem 18.7 Finding K_a of a Weak Acid from the Solution pH

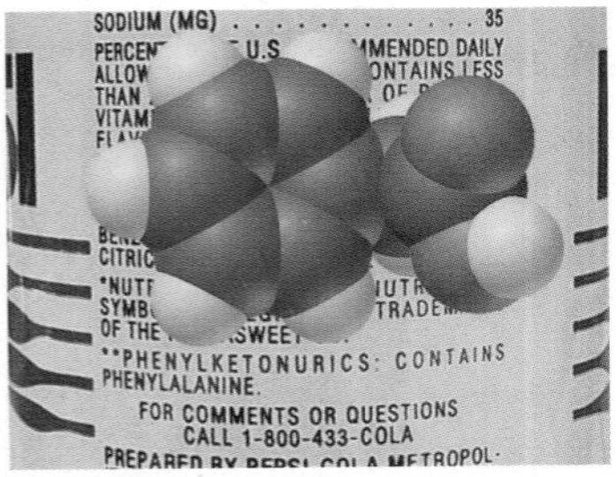

Phenylalanine, one of the amino acids that make up aspartame, is metabolized to phenylacetic acid (model).

Problem Phenylacetic acid ($C_6H_5CH_2COOH$, simplified here to HPAc; *see model*) builds up in the blood of persons with phenylketonuria, an inherited disorder that, if untreated, causes mental retardation and death. A study of the acid shows that the pH of 0.12 *M* HPAc is 2.62. What is the K_a of phenylacetic acid?

Plan We are given $[HPAc]_{\text{init}}$ (0.12 *M*) and the pH (2.62) and must find K_a. As always, we first write the equation for HPAc dissociation and the expression for K_a to see which values we need. We assume $[H_3O^+]_{\text{from } H_2O}$ is negligible, so we can use the given pH to find $[H_3O^+]$, which equals $[PAc^-]$ and $[HPAc]_{\text{dissoc}}$. To find [HPAc], we assume that, because it is a weak acid, very little dissociates, so $[HPAc]_{\text{init}} - [HPAc]_{\text{dissoc}} = [HPAc] \approx [HPAc]_{\text{init}}$. We make these assumptions, substitute the equilibrium values, solve for K_a, and then check the assumptions. Note that we *don't* need a reaction table here because the pH will give us $[HPAc]_{\text{dissoc}}$.

Solution Writing the dissociation equation and K_a expression:

$$HPAc(aq) + H_2O(l) \rightleftharpoons H_3O^+(aq) + PAc^-(aq) \qquad K_a = \frac{[H_3O^+][PAc^-]}{[HPAc]}$$

Calculating $[H_3O^+]$:

$$[H_3O^+] = 10^{-pH} = 10^{-2.62} = 2.4\times10^{-3}\ M$$

Making the assumptions:
1. The calculated $[H_3O^+]$ (2.4×10^{-3} *M*) >> $[H_3O^+]_{\text{from } H_2O}$ (1.0×10^{-7} *M*), so we assume that $[H_3O^+] \approx [H_3O^+]_{\text{from HPAc}} = [PAc^-] = x$ (the change in [HPAc], or $[HPAc]_{\text{dissoc}}$).
2. HPAc is a weak acid, so we assume that $[HPAc] = 0.12\ M - x \approx 0.12\ M$.

Solving for the equilibrium concentrations:

$$x \approx [H_3O^+] = [PAc^-] = 2.4\times10^{-3}\ M$$

$$[HPAc] = 0.12\ M - x = 0.12\ M - (2.4\times10^{-3}\ M) \approx 0.12\ M \text{ (to 2 sf)}$$

Substituting these values into K_a:

$$K_a = \frac{[H_3O^+][PAc^-]}{[HPAc]} \approx \frac{(2.4\times10^{-3})(2.4\times10^{-3})}{0.12} = 4.8\times10^{-5}$$

Checking the assumptions by finding the percent error in concentration:

1. For $[H_3O^+]_{\text{from } H_2O}$: $\frac{1\times10^{-7}\ M}{2.4\times10^{-3}\ M} \times 100 = 4\times10^{-3}\%$ (<5%; assumption is justified).

2. For $[HPAc]_{dissoc}$: $\frac{2.4\times10^{-3}\ M}{0.12\ M} \times 100 = 2.0\%$ (< 5%; assumption is justified).

Check The $[H_3O^+]$ makes sense: pH 2.62 should give $[H_3O^+]$ between 10^{-2} and 10^{-3} M. The K_a calculation also seems in the correct range: $(10^{-3})^2/10^{-1} = 10^{-5}$, and this value seems reasonable for a weak acid.

Follow-Up Problem 18.7 The conjugate acid of ammonia is the weak acid NH_4^+. If a 0.2 M NH_4Cl solution has a pH of 5.0, what is the K_a of NH_4^+?

Finding Concentrations Given K_a

The second type of equilibrium problem gives some concentration data and K_a and asks for the equilibrium concentration of some component. Such problems are very similar to those we solved in Chapter 17 in which a substance with a given initial concentration reacted to an unknown extent (see Sample Problems 17.9 to 17.11). We *will* use a reaction table in these problems to find the values, and, as we just found, $[H_3O^+]_{\text{from } H_2O}$ is so small relative to $[H_3O^+]_{\text{from HA}}$ that we will neglect it and enter the initial $[H_3O^+]$ in all reaction tables as zero.

Sample Problem 18.8 Determining Concentration from K_a and Initial [HA]

Problem Propanoic acid (CH_3CH_2COOH, which we simplify as HPr) is a carboxylic acid whose salts are used to retard mold growth in foods. What is the $[H_3O^+]$ of 0.10 M HPr ($K_a = 1.3\times10^{-5}$)?

Plan We know the initial concentration (0.10 M) and K_a (1.3×10^{-5}) of HPr, and we need to find $[H_3O^+]$. First, we write the balanced equation and the expression for K_a. We know $[HPr]_{init}$ but not [HPr] (that is, the concentration at equilibrium). If we let $x = [HPr]_{dissoc}$, x is also $[H_3O^+]_{\text{from HPr}}$ and $[Pr^-]$ because each HPr dissociates into one H_3O^+ and one Pr^-. With this information, we set up a reaction table. We assume that, because HPr has a small K_a, it dissociates very little. After solving for x, we check the assumption.

Solution Writing the balanced equation and expression for K_a:

$$HPr(aq) + H_2O(l) \rightleftharpoons H_3O^+(aq) + Pr^-(aq) \qquad K_a = \frac{[H_3O^+][Pr^-]}{[HPr]} = 1.3\times10^{-5}$$

Setting up a reaction table, with $x = [HPr]_{dissoc} = [Pr^-] = [H_3O^+]$:

Concentration (M)	$HPr(aq)$	+	$H_2O(l)$	$\rightleftharpoons$	$H_3O^+(aq)$	+	$Pr^-(aq)$
Initial	0.10		—		0		0
Change	$-x$		—		$+x$		$+x$
Equilibrium	$0.10 - x$		—		x		x

Making the assumption: K_a is small, so x is small compared with $[HPr]_{init}$; therefore, $[HPr]_{init} - x = [HPr] \approx [HPr]_{init}$, or $0.10\ M - x \approx 0.10\ M$. Substituting into the K_a expression and solving for x:

$$K_a = \frac{[H_3O^+][Pr^-]}{[HPr]} = 1.3\times10^{-5} \approx \frac{(x)(x)}{0.10}$$

$$x \approx \sqrt{(0.10)(1.3\times10^{-5})} = 1.1\times10^{-3}\ M = [H_3O^+]$$

Checking the assumption:

For $[HPr]_{dissoc}$: $\frac{1.1\times10^{-3}\ M}{0.10\ M} \times 100 = 1.1\%$ (<5%; assumption is justified).

Check The $[H_3O^+]$ seems reasonable for a dilute solution of a weak acid with a moderate K_a. By reversing the calculation, we can check the math: $(1.1\times10^{-3})^2/0.10 = 1.2\times10^{-5}$, which is within rounding of the given K_a.

Comment In Chapter 17 we introduced a benchmark, aside from the 5% rule, to see if the assumption is justified (see the discussion following Sample Problem 17.10):

- If $\frac{[HA]_{init}}{K_a} > 400$, the assumption is justified: neglecting x introduces an error <5%.
- If $\frac{[HA]_{init}}{K_a} < 400$, the assumption is *not* justified; neglecting x introduces an error >5%, so we solve a quadratic equation to find x.

In this sample problem, we have $\frac{0.10}{1.3\times10^{-5}} = 7.7\times10^3$, which is greater than 400. The alternative situation occurs in the follow-up problem.

Follow-Up Problem 18.8 Cyanic acid (HOCN) is an extremely acrid, unstable substance. What is the $[H_3O^+]$ of 0.10 M HOCN ($K_a = 3.5\times10^{-4}$)?

The Effect of Concentration on the Extent of Acid Dissociation

If we repeat the calculation in Sample Problem 18.8, but start with a lower [HPr], we observe a very interesting fact about the extent of dissociation of a weak acid. Suppose the initial concentration of HPr is one-tenth as much, 0.010 M rather than 0.10 M. After filling in the reaction table and making the same assumptions, we find that

$$x = [H_3O^+] = [HPr]_{dissoc} = 3.6\times10^{-4}\ M$$

Now, let's compare the percentages of HPr molecules dissociated at the two different initial acid concentrations, using the relationship

$$\text{Percent HA dissociated} = \frac{[HA]_{dissoc}}{[HA]_{init}} \times 100 \qquad (18.5)$$

Case 1: $[HPr]_{init} = 0.10\ M$

$$\text{Percent HPr dissociated} = \frac{1.1\times10^{-3}\ M}{1.0\times10^{-1}\ M} \times 100 = 1.1\%$$

Case 2: $[HPr]_{init} = 0.010\ M$

$$\text{Percent HPr dissociated} = \frac{3.6\times10^{-4}\ M}{1.0\times10^{-2}\ M} \times 100 = 3.6\%$$

As the initial acid concentration decreases, the percent dissociation of the acid increases. Don't confuse the *concentration* of HA dissociated with the *percent* HA dissociated. The concentration, $[HA]_{dissoc}$, is lower in the diluted HA solution because the actual *number* of dissociated HA molecules is smaller. It is the *fraction* (or the *percent*) of dissociated HA molecules that increases with dilution.

This phenomenon is analogous to a change in container volume (pressure) for gases at equilibrium (Section 17.6). In the case of gases, an increase in volume shifts the equilibrium position to favor more moles of gas. In the case of HA dissociation, a lower HA concentration, which is the same as an increase in volume, shifts the equilibrium position to favor more moles of ions. Sample Problem 18.9 uses molecular scenes to highlight this idea. (Note that, in order to depict the scenes practically, the acid has a much higher percent dissociation than any real weak acid does.)

Sample Problem 18.9 Using Molecular Scenes to Determine the Extent of HA Dissociation

Problem A 0.15 M solution of HA *(blue and green)* is 33% dissociated. Which scene represents a sample of that solution after it is diluted with water?

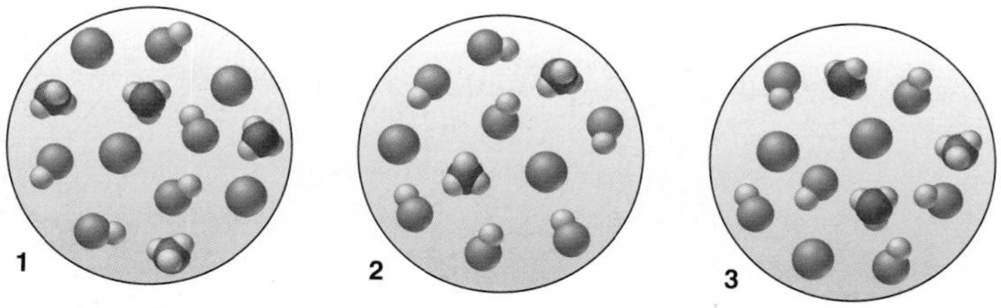

Plan We are given the percent dissociation of the original HA solution (33%), and we know that the percent dissociation increases as the acid is diluted. Thus, we calculate the percent dissociation of each diluted sample and see which is greater than 33%. To determine percent dissociation, we apply Equation 18.5, with HA_{dissoc} equal to the number of H_3O^+ (or A^-) and HA_{init} equal to the number of HA *plus* the number of H_3O^+ (or A^-).

Solution Calculating the percent dissociation of each diluted solution with Equation 18.5:

Solution 1. Percent dissociated = $4/(5 + 4) \times 100 = 44\%$
Solution 2. Percent dissociated = $2/(7 + 2) \times 100 = 22\%$
Solution 3. Percent dissociated = $3/(6 + 3) \times 100 = 33\%$

Therefore, scene 1 represents the diluted solution.

Check Let's confirm our choice by examining the other scenes: in scene 2, HA is *less* dissociated than originally, so that scene must represent a more concentrated HA solution; scene 3 represents another solution with the same percent dissociation as the original.

Follow-Up Problem 18.9 The scene shown in the margin represents a sample of a weak acid HB *(blue and purple)* dissolved in water. Draw a scene that represents the same volume after the solution has been diluted with water.

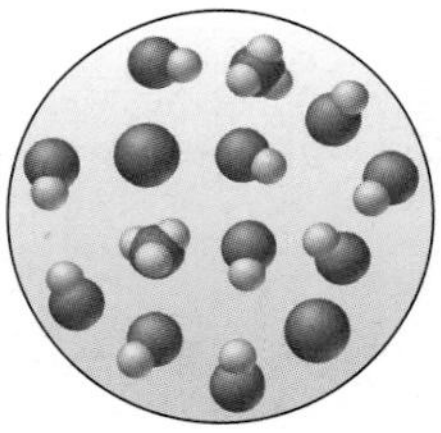

The Behavior of Polyprotic Acids

Acids with more than one ionizable proton are **polyprotic acids.** In solution, each dissociation step has a different K_a. For example, phosphoric acid is a triprotic acid (three ionizable protons), so it has three K_a values:

$$H_3PO_4(aq) + H_2O(l) \rightleftharpoons H_2PO_4^-(aq) + H_3O^+(aq)$$

$$K_{a1} = \frac{[H_2PO_4^-][H_3O^+]}{[H_3PO_4]} = 7.2\times10^{-3}$$

$$H_2PO_4^-(aq) + H_2O(l) \rightleftharpoons HPO_4^{2-}(aq) + H_3O^+(aq)$$

$$K_{a2} = \frac{[HPO_4^{2-}][H_3O^+]}{[H_2PO_4^-]} = 6.3\times10^{-8}$$

$$HPO_4^{2-}(aq) + H_2O(l) \rightleftharpoons PO_4^{3-}(aq) + H_3O^+(aq)$$

$$K_{a3} = \frac{[PO_4^{3-}][H_3O^+]}{[HPO_4^{2-}]} = 4.2\times10^{-13}$$

The relative K_a values show that H_3PO_4 is a much stronger acid than $H_2PO_4^-$, which is much stronger than HPO_4^{2-}.

Table 18.5 Successive K_a Values for Some Polyprotic Acids at 25°C

Name (Formula)	Lewis Structure*	K_{a1}	K_{a2}	K_{a3}
Oxalic acid ($H_2C_2O_4$)	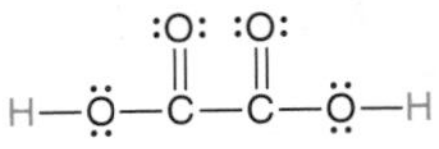	5.6×10^{-2}	5.4×10^{-5}	
Sulfurous acid (H_2SO_3)	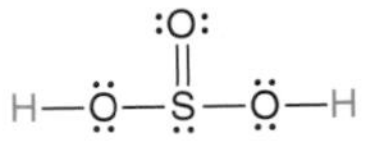	1.4×10^{-2}	6.5×10^{-8}	
Phosphoric acid (H_3PO_4)	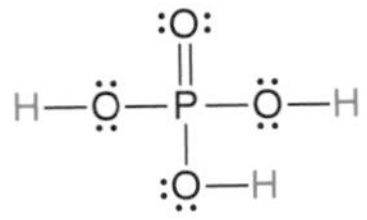	7.2×10^{-3}	6.3×10^{-8}	4.2×10^{-13}
Arsenic acid (H_3AsO_4)	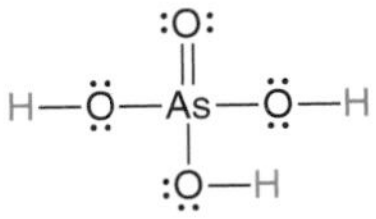	6×10^{-3}	1.1×10^{-7}	3×10^{-12}
Carbonic acid (H_2CO_3)	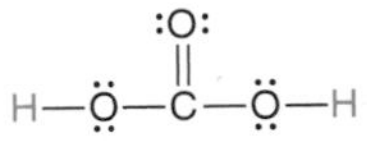	4.5×10^{-7}	4.7×10^{-11}	
Hydrosulfuric acid (H_2S)	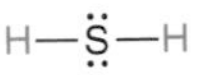	9×10^{-8}	1×10^{-17}	

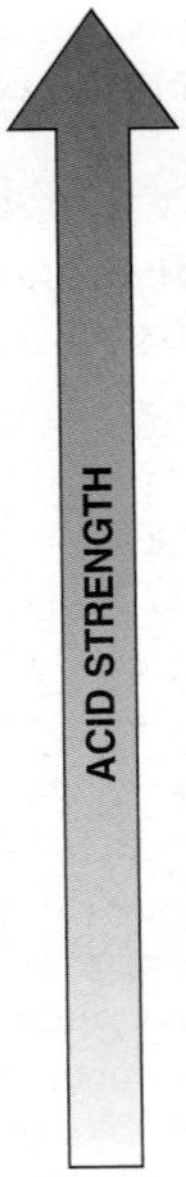

*Red type indicates the ionizable protons.

Table 18.5 lists some common polyprotic acids and their K_a values. (More are listed in Appendix C.) Note that the general pattern seen for H_3PO_4 occurs for all polyprotic acids:

$$K_{a1} >> K_{a2} >> K_{a3}$$

This trend occurs because it is more difficult for an H^+ ion to leave a singly charged anion (such as $H_2PO_4^-$) than to leave a neutral molecule (such as H_3PO_4), and more difficult still for it to leave a doubly charged anion (such as HPO_4^{2-}). Successive K_a values typically differ by several orders of magnitude. This fact simplifies calculations because *we usually neglect the H_3O^+ coming from the subsequent dissociations.*

Sample Problem 18.10 Calculating Equilibrium Concentrations for a Polyprotic Acid

Problem Ascorbic acid ($H_2C_6H_6O_6$; H_2Asc for this problem), known as vitamin C, is a diprotic acid ($K_{a1} = 1.0\times10^{-5}$ and $K_{a2} = 5\times10^{-12}$) found in citrus fruit. Calculate $[HAsc^-]$, $[Asc^{2-}]$, and the pH of 0.050 M H_2Asc.

Plan We know the initial concentration (0.050 M) and both K_a's for H_2Asc, and we have to calculate the equilibrium concentrations of all species and convert $[H_3O^+]$ to pH. We first write the equations and K_a expressions. Because $K_{a1} >> K_{a2}$, we can assume that the first dissociation produces almost all the H_3O^+: $[H_3O^+]_{\text{from } H_2Asc} >> [H_3O^+]_{\text{from } HAsc^-}$. Also, because K_{a1} is small, the amount of H_2Asc that dissociates can be neglected. We set up a reaction table for the first dissociation, with x equal to $[H_2Asc]_{dissoc}$, and then we solve for $[H_3O^+]$ and $[HAsc^-]$. Because the second dissociation occurs to a much lesser extent, we can substitute values from the first dissociation directly to find $[Asc^{2-}]$ from the second.

Solution Writing the equations and K_a expressions:

$$H_2Asc(aq) + H_2O(l) \rightleftharpoons HAsc^-(aq) + H_3O^+(aq)$$

$$K_{a1} = \frac{[HAsc^-][H_3O^+]}{[H_2Asc]} = 1.0\times10^{-5}$$

$$HAsc^-(aq) + H_2O(l) \rightleftharpoons Asc^{2-}(aq) + H_3O^+(aq)$$

$$K_{a2} = \frac{[Asc^{2-}][H_3O^+]}{[HAsc^-]} = 5\times10^{-12}$$

Setting up a reaction table with $x = [H_2Asc]_{dissoc} = [HAsc^-] \approx [H_3O^+]$:

Concentration (*M*)	$H_2Asc(aq)$	+	$H_2O(l)$	$\rightleftharpoons$	$H_3O^+(aq)$	+	$HAsc^-(aq)$
Initial	0.050		—		0		0
Change	$-x$		—		$+x$		$+x$
Equilibrium	$0.050 - x$		—		x		x

Making the assumptions:

1. Because $K_{a2} << K_{a1}$, $[H_3O^+]_{\text{from HAsc}^-} << [H_3O^+]_{\text{from H}_2\text{Asc}}$. Therefore,

$$[H_3O^+]_{\text{from H}_2\text{Asc}} \approx [H_3O^+]$$

2. Because K_{a1} is small, $[H_2Asc]_{init} - x = [H_2Asc] \approx [H_2Asc]_{init}$. Thus,

$$[H_2Asc] = 0.050\ M - x \approx 0.050\ M$$

Substituting into the expression for K_{a1} and solving for x:

$$K_{a1} = \frac{[H_3O^+][HAsc^-]}{[H_2Asc]} = 1.0\times10^{-5} = \frac{x^2}{0.050 - x} \approx \frac{x^2}{0.050}$$

$$x = [HAsc^-] \approx [H_3O^+] \approx 7.1\times10^{-4}\ M$$

$$pH = -\log[H_3O^+] = -\log(7.1\times10^{-4}) = 3.15$$

Checking the assumptions:

1. $[H_3O^+]_{\text{from HAsc}^-} << [H_3O^+]_{\text{from H}_2\text{Asc}}$: For any second dissociation that does occur,

$$[H_3O^+]_{\text{from HAsc}^-} \approx \sqrt{[HAsc^-](K_{a2})} = \sqrt{(7.1\times10^{-4})(5\times10^{-12})} = 6\times10^{-8}\ M$$

This is even less than $[H_3O^+]_{\text{from H}_2\text{O}}$, so the assumption is justified.

2. $[H_2Asc]_{dissoc} << [H_2Asc]_{init}$: $\dfrac{7.1\times10^{-4}\ M}{0.050\ M} \times 100 = 1.4\%$ (<5%; assumption is justified).

Also, note that

$$\frac{[H_2Asc]_{init}}{K_{a1}} = \frac{0.050}{1.0\times10^{-5}} = 5000 > 400$$

Using the equilibrium concentrations from the first dissociation to calculate $[Asc^{2-}]$:

$$K_{a2} = \frac{[H_3O^+][Asc^{2-}]}{[HAsc^-]} \quad \text{and} \quad [Asc^{2-}] = \frac{(K_{a2})[HAsc^-]}{[H_3O^+]}$$

$$[Asc^{2-}] = \frac{(5\times10^{-12})(7.1\times10^{-4})}{7.1\times10^{-4}} = 5\times10^{-12}\ M$$

Check $K_{a1} >> K_{a2}$, so it makes sense that $[HAsc^-] >> [Asc^{2-}]$ because Asc^{2-} is produced only in the second (much weaker) dissociation. Both K_a's are small, so all concentrations except $[H_2Asc]$ should be much lower than the original 0.050 *M*.

Follow-Up Problem 18.10 Oxalic acid (HOOC—COOH, or $H_2C_2O_4$) is the simplest diprotic carboxylic acid. Its commercial uses include bleaching straw and leather and removing rust and ink stains. Calculate the equilibrium values of $[H_2C_2O_4]$, $[HC_2O_4^-]$, and $[C_2O_4^{2-}]$, and find the pH of a 0.150 *M* $H_2C_2O_4$ solution. Use K_a values from Appendix C. (*Hint:* First check whether you need the quadratic equation to find x.)

Summary of Section 18.4

- Two common types of weak-acid equilibrium problems involve finding K_a from a given concentration and finding a concentration from a given K_a.
- We simplify the arithmetic by assuming (1) that $[H_3O^+]_{from\ H_2O}$ is much smaller than $[H_3O^+]_{from\ HA}$ and can be neglected and (2) that weak acids dissociate so little that $[HA]_{init} \approx [HA]$ at equilibrium.
- The *fraction* of weak acid molecules that dissociates is greater in a more dilute solution, even though the total $[H_3O^+]$ is lower.
- Polyprotic acids have more than one ionizable proton, but we assume that the first dissociation provides virtually all the H_3O^+.

18.5 • WEAK BASES AND THEIR RELATION TO WEAK ACIDS

The Brønsted-Lowry concept expands the definition of a base to encompass a host of species that the Arrhenius definition excludes: *to accept a proton, a base needs only a lone electron pair.*

Let's examine the equilibrium system of a weak base (B) as it dissolves in water: B accepts a proton from H_2O, which acts as an acid, leaving behind an OH^- ion:

$$B(aq) + H_2O(l) \rightleftharpoons BH^+(aq) + OH^-(aq)$$

This general reaction for a base in water is described by the equilibrium expression

$$K_c = \frac{[BH^+][OH^-]}{[B][H_2O]}$$

Based on our earlier reasoning, we incorporate $[H_2O]$ in the value of K_c and obtain the **base-dissociation constant** (or **base-ionization constant**), $\boldsymbol{K_b}$**:**

$$K_b = \frac{[BH^+][OH^-]}{[B]} \qquad (18.6)$$

Despite the name "base-dissociation constant," *no base dissociates in the process.*

As in the relation between pK_a and K_a, we know that a lower pK_b indicates a higher K_b, that is, a stronger base. In aqueous solution, the two large classes of weak bases are (1) the molecules ammonia and the amines and (2) the anions of weak acids.

Molecules as Weak Bases: Ammonia and the Amines

Ammonia is the simplest N-containing compound that acts as a weak base in water:

$$NH_3(aq) + H_2O(l) \rightleftharpoons NH_4^+(aq) + OH^-(aq) \qquad K_b = 1.76\times10^{-5} \text{ (at 25°C)}$$

Despite labels on reagent bottles that read "ammonium hydroxide," an aqueous solution of ammonia consists largely of water and *unprotonated* NH_3 molecules, as its small K_b indicates. In a 1.0 M NH_3 solution, for example, $[OH^-] = [NH_4^+] = 4.2\times10^{-3}$ M, so about 99.6% of the NH_3 is not protonated. Table 18.6 shows the K_b values for a few molecular bases. (A more extensive list appears in Appendix C.)

If one or more of the H atoms in ammonia is replaced by an organic group (designated as R), an *amine* results: RNH_2, R_2NH, or R_3N (Section 15.4; see Figure 15.17). The key structural feature of these organic compounds, as in all Brønsted-Lowry bases, is *a lone pair of electrons that can bind the proton donated by the acid.* Figure 18.9 depicts this process for methylamine, the simplest amine.

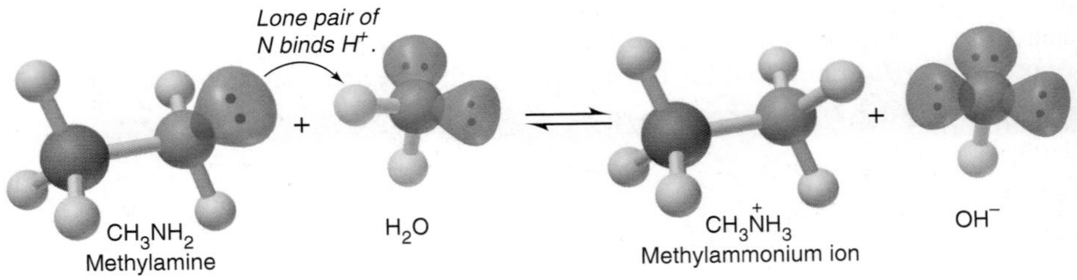

Figure 18.9 Abstraction of a proton from water by the base methylamine.

Table 18.6 K_b Values for Some Molecular (Amine) Bases at 25°C

Name (Formula)	Lewis Structure*	K_b
Diethylamine [$(CH_3CH_2)_2NH$]	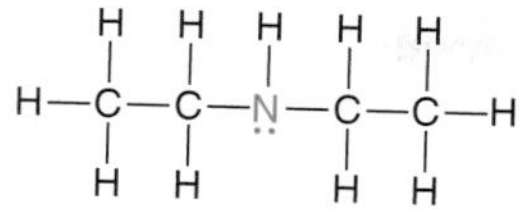	8.6×10^{-4}
Dimethylamine [$(CH_3)_2NH$]	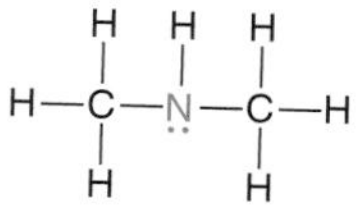	5.9×10^{-4}
Methylamine (CH_3NH_2)	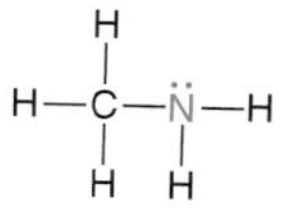	4.4×10^{-4}
Ammonia (NH_3)	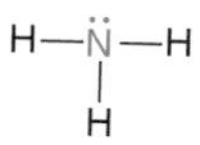	1.76×10^{-5}
Pyridine (C_5H_5N)		1.7×10^{-9}
Aniline ($C_6H_5NH_2$)	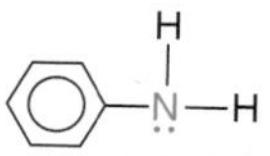	4.0×10^{-10}

*Blue type indicates the basic nitrogen and its lone pair.

To find the pH of a solution of a molecular weak base, we use an approach very similar to that for a weak acid: write the equilibrium expression, set up a reaction table to find $[B]_{reacting}$, make the usual assumptions, and then solve for $[OH^-]$. The only additional step is to convert $[OH^-]$ to $[H_3O^+]$ in order to calculate pH.

Sample Problem 18.11 Determining pH from K_b and Initial [B]

Dimethylamine

Problem Dimethylamine, $(CH_3)_2NH$ (*see margin*), a key intermediate in detergent manufacture, has a K_b of 5.9×10^{-4}. What is the pH of 1.5 *M* $(CH_3)_2NH$?

Plan We know the initial concentration (1.5 *M*) and K_b (5.9×10^{-4}) of $(CH_3)_2NH$ and have to find the pH. The amine reacts with water to form OH^-, so we have to find $[OH^-]$ and then calculate $[H_3O^+]$ and pH. We first write the balanced equation and K_b expression. Because $K_b >> K_w$, the $[OH^-]$ from the autoionization of water is negligible, so we disregard it and assume that all the $[OH^-]$ comes from the base reacting with water. Because K_b is small, we assume that the amount of amine reacting, $[(CH_3)_2NH]_{reacting}$, can be neglected. We set up a reaction table, make the assumption, and solve for x. Then we check the assumption and convert $[OH^-]$ to $[H_3O^+]$ using K_w; finally, we calculate pH.

Solution Writing the balanced equation and K_b expression:

$$(CH_3)_2NH(aq) + H_2O(l) \rightleftharpoons (CH_3)_2NH_2^+(aq) + OH^-(aq)$$

$$K_b = \frac{[(CH_3)_2NH_2^+][OH^-]}{[(CH_3)_2NH]}$$

Setting up the reaction table, with $x = [(CH_3)_2NH]_{reacting} = [(CH_3)_2NH_2^+] = [OH^-]$:

Concentration (*M*)	$(CH_3)_2NH(aq)$	+ $H_2O(l)$	$\rightleftharpoons$ $(CH_3)_2NH_2^+(aq)$	+ $OH^-(aq)$
Initial	1.5	—	0	0
Change	$-x$	—	$+x$	$+x$
Equilibrium	$1.5 - x$	—	x	x

Making the assumption:
K_b is small, so $[(CH_3)_2NH]_{init} - [(CH_3)_2NH]_{reacting} = [(CH_3)_2NH] \approx [(CH_3)_2NH]_{init}$;
thus, $1.5\ M - x \approx 1.5\ M$.
Substituting into the K_b expression and solving for x:

$$K_b = \frac{[(CH_3)_2NH_2^+][OH^-]}{[(CH_3)_2NH]} = 5.9\times10^{-4} \approx \frac{x^2}{1.5}$$

$$x = [OH^-] \approx 3.0\times10^{-2}\ M$$

Checking the assumption:

$$\frac{3.0\times10^{-2}\ M}{1.5\ M} \times 100 = 2.0\%\ (<5\%;\ \text{assumption is justified})$$

Note that the Comment in Sample Problem 18.8 applies in these cases as well:

$$\frac{[B]_{init}}{K_b} = \frac{1.5}{5.9\times10^{-4}} = 2.5\times10^{3} > 400$$

Calculating pH:

$$[H_3O^+] = \frac{K_w}{[OH^-]} = \frac{1.0\times10^{-14}}{3.0\times10^{-2}} = 3.3\times10^{-13}\ M$$

$$pH = -\log(3.3\times10^{-13}) = 12.48$$

Check The value of x seems reasonable: $\sqrt{(\sim6\times10^{-4})(1.5)} = \sqrt{9\times10^{-4}} = 3\times10^{-2}$. Because $(CH_3)_2NH$ is a weak base, the pH should be several pH units above 7.

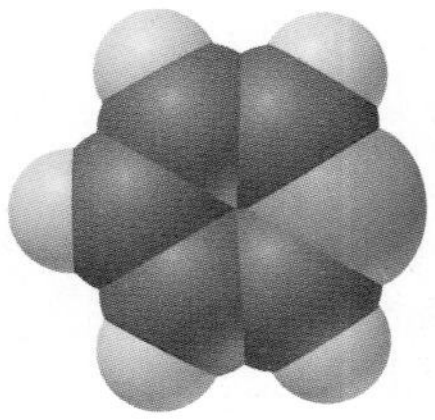
Pyridine

Follow-Up Problem 18.11 Pyridine (C_5H_5N, *see margin*) serves as a solvent *and* base in many organic syntheses. It has a pK_b of 8.77. What is the pH of 0.10 M pyridine?

Anions of Weak Acids as Weak Bases

The other large group of Brønsted-Lowry bases consists of anions of weak acids:*

$$A^-(aq) + H_2O(l) \rightleftharpoons HA(aq) + OH^-(aq) \qquad K_b = \frac{[HA][OH^-]}{[A^-]}$$

For example, F^-, the anion of the weak acid HF, is a weak base:

$$F^-(aq) + H_2O(l) \rightleftharpoons HF(aq) + OH^-(aq) \qquad K_b = \frac{[HF][OH^-]}{[F^-]}$$

Why is a solution of HA acidic and a solution of A^- basic? We'll find the answer from relative concentrations of species in 1 M HF and in 1 M NaF:

1. *The acidity of HA(aq).* HF is a weak acid, so the equilibrium position of the acid dissolving in water lies far to the left:

$$HF(aq) + H_2O(l) \leftrightharpoons H_3O^+(aq) + F^-(aq)$$

Water also contributes H_3O^+ and OH^-, but their concentrations are extremely small:

$$2H_2O(l) \leftrightharpoons H_3O^+(aq) + OH^-(aq)$$

Of all the species present—HF, H_2O, H_3O^+, F^-, and OH^-—the two that can influence the acidity of the solution are H_3O^+, predominantly from HF, and OH^- from water. Thus, the HF solution is acidic because $[H_3O^+]_{from\ HF} >> [OH^-]_{from\ H_2O}$.

2. *The basicity of $A^-(aq)$.* Now, consider the species present in 1 M NaF. The salt dissociates completely to yield 1 M Na^+ and 1 M F^-. The Na^+ behaves as a spectator ion, while some F^- reacts as a weak base to produce small amounts of HF and OH^-:

$$F^-(aq) + H_2O(l) \leftrightharpoons HF(aq) + OH^-(aq)$$

*This equation and equilibrium expression are sometimes referred to as a *hydrolysis reaction* and a *hydrolysis constant,* K_h, because water is dissociated (hydrolyzed). Actually, except for the charge on the base, this process is the same as the proton-abstraction process by ammonia and amines. That is, K_h is just another symbol for K_b, so we'll use K_b throughout.

As before, water dissociation contributes minute amounts of H_3O^+ and OH^-. Thus, in addition to the Na^+ ion, the species present are the same as in the HF solution: HF, H_2O, H_3O^+, F^-, and OH^-. The two species that affect the acidity are OH^-, predominantly from F^- reacting with water, and H_3O^+ from water. In this case, $[OH^-]_{\text{from } F^-} >> [H_3O^+]_{\text{from } H_2O}$, so the solution is basic.

To summarize,

- In an HA solution, $[HA] >> [A^-]$ and $[H_3O^+]_{\text{from HA}} >> [OH^-]_{\text{from } H_2O}$, so the solution is acidic.
- In an A^- solution, $[A^-] >> [HA]$ and $[OH^-]_{\text{from } A^-} >> [H_3O^+]_{\text{from } H_2O}$, so the solution is basic.

The Relation Between K_a and K_b of a Conjugate Acid-Base Pair

A key relationship exists between the K_a of HA and the K_b of A^-, which we can see by writing the two reactions as a reaction sequence and adding them:

$$\begin{array}{r} \cancel{HA} + H_2O \rightleftharpoons H_3O^+ + \cancel{A^-} \\ \cancel{A^-} + H_2O \rightleftharpoons \cancel{HA} + OH^- \\ \hline 2H_2O \rightleftharpoons H_3O^+ + OH^- \end{array}$$

The sum of the two dissociation reactions is the autoionization of water. Recall from Chapter 17 that, for a reaction that is the *sum* of two or more reactions, the overall equilibrium constant is the *product* of the individual equilibrium constants. Therefore, writing the equilibrium expressions for each reaction gives

$$\frac{[H_3O^+]\cancel{[A^-]}}{\cancel{[HA]}} \times \frac{\cancel{[HA]}[OH^-]}{\cancel{[A^-]}} = [H_3O^+][OH^-]$$

or

$$K_a \times K_b = K_w \qquad (18.7)$$

This relationship allows us to find K_a of the acid in a conjugate pair given K_b of the base, and vice versa. Reference tables typically have K_a and K_b values for *molecular species only*. The K_b for F^- and the K_a for $CH_3NH_3^+$, for example, do not appear in standard tables, but you can calculate them by looking up the value for the molecular conjugate species and relating it to K_w. To find the K_b value for F^-, for instance, we look up the K_a value for HF and apply Equation 18.7:

$$K_a \text{ of HF} = 6.8\times10^{-4} \text{ (from Appendix C)}$$

So, we have

$$K_a \text{ of HF} \times K_b \text{ of } F^- = K_w$$

or

$$K_b \text{ of } F^- = \frac{K_w}{K_a \text{ of HF}} = \frac{1.0\times10^{-14}}{6.8\times10^{-4}} = 1.5\times10^{-11}$$

Sample Problem 18.12 Determining the pH of a Solution of A^-

Problem Sodium acetate (CH_3COONa, or NaAc for this problem) is used in textile dyeing. What is the pH of 0.25 *M* NaAc at 25°C? K_a of acetic acid (HAc) is 1.8×10^{-5}.

Plan We know the initial concentration of Ac^- (0.25 *M*) and the K_a of HAc (1.8×10^{-5}), and we have to find the pH of the Ac^- solution, which acts as a base in water. We write the base dissociation equation and K_b expression. If we can find $[OH^-]$, we can use K_w to find $[H_3O^+]$ and convert it to pH. To solve for $[OH^-]$, we need the K_b of Ac^-, which we obtain from the K_a of HAc by applying Equation 18.7. We set up a reaction table to find $[OH^-]$ and make the usual assumption that K_b is small, so $[Ac^-]_{init} \approx [Ac^-]$.

Solution Writing the base dissociation equation and K_b expression:

$$Ac^-(aq) + H_2O(l) \rightleftharpoons HAc(aq) + OH^-(aq) \qquad K_b = \frac{[HAc][OH^-]}{[Ac^-]}$$

Setting up the reaction table, with $x = [\text{Ac}^-]_{\text{reacting}} = [\text{HAc}] = [\text{OH}^-]$:

Concentration (*M*)	$Ac^-(aq)$	+	$H_2O(l)$	⇌	$HAc(aq)$	+	$OH^-(aq)$
Initial	0.25		—		0		0
Change	$-x$		—		$+x$		$+x$
Equilibrium	$0.25 - x$		—		x		x

Solving for K_b of Ac^-:

$$K_b = \frac{K_w}{K_a} = \frac{1.0\times10^{-14}}{1.8\times10^{-5}} = 5.6\times10^{-10}$$

Making the assumption: Because K_b is small, $0.25\ M - x \approx 0.25\ M$.
Substituting into the expression for K_b and solving for x:

$$K_b = \frac{[\text{HAc}][\text{OH}^-]}{[\text{Ac}^-]} = 5.6\times10^{-10} \approx \frac{x^2}{0.25} \qquad x = [\text{OH}^-] \approx 1.2\times10^{-5}\ M$$

Checking the assumption:

$$\frac{1.2\times10^{-5}\ M}{0.25\ M} \times 100 = 4.8\times10^{-3}\% \text{ (<5\%; assumption is justified)}$$

Also note that

$$\frac{0.25}{5.6\times10^{-10}} = 4.5\times10^{8} > 400$$

Solving for pH:

$$[\text{H}_3\text{O}^+] = \frac{K_w}{[\text{OH}^-]} = \frac{1.0\times10^{-14}}{1.2\times10^{-5}} = 8.3\times10^{-10}\ M$$

$$\text{pH} = -\log(8.3\times10^{-10}) = 9.08$$

Check The K_b calculation seems reasonable: $\sim10\times10^{-15}/2\times10^{-5} = 5\times10^{-10}$. Because Ac^- is a weak base, $[OH^-] > [H_3O^+]$; thus, pH > 7, which makes sense.

Follow-Up Problem 18.12 Sodium hypochlorite (NaClO) is the active ingredient in household laundry bleach. What is the pH of 0.20 *M* NaClO?

Summary of Section 18.5

- The extent to which a weak base accepts a proton from water to form OH^- is expressed by a base-dissociation constant, K_b.
- Brønsted-Lowry bases include NH_3 and amines and the anions of weak acids. All produce basic solutions by accepting H^+ from water, which yields OH^-, thus making $[H_3O^+] < [OH^-]$.
- A solution of HA is acidic because $[HA] >> [A^-]$, so $[H_3O^+] > [OH^-]$. A solution of A^- is basic because $[A^-] >> [HA]$, so $[OH^-] > [H_3O^+]$.
- By multiplying the expressions for K_a of HA and K_b of A^-, we obtain K_w. This relationship allows us to calculate either K_a of BH^+ or K_b of A^-.

18.6 • MOLECULAR PROPERTIES AND ACID STRENGTH

The strength of an acid depends on its ability to donate a proton, which depends in turn on the strength of the bond to the acidic proton. In this section, we apply trends in atomic and bond properties to determine the trends in acid strength of nonmetal hydrides and oxoacids and then discuss the acidity of hydrated metal ions.

Acid Strength of Nonmetal Hydrides

Two factors determine how easily a proton is released from a nonmetal hydride:

- The electronegativity of the central nonmetal (E)
- The strength of the E—H bond

Figure 18.10 displays two periodic trends among the nonmetal hydrides:

1. *Across a period, acid strength increases.* The electronegativity of the nonmetal E determines the trend. From left to right, as E becomes more electronegative, it withdraws electron density from H, and the E—H bond becomes more polar. As a result, H^+ is pulled away more easily by an O atom of a water molecule. In aqueous solution, the hydrides of Groups 3A(13) to 5A(15) do not behave as acids, but an increase in acid strength is seen from Group 6A(16) to 7A(17).

2. *Down a group, acid strength increases.* E—H bond strength determines the trend. As E becomes larger, the E—H bond becomes longer and weaker, so H^+ comes off more easily.* For example, the hydrohalic acid strength increases down the group:

$$HF \ll HCl < HBr < HI$$

(This trend is not seen in aqueous solution, where HCl, HBr, and HI are all equally strong; we discuss how it *is* observed in Section 18.8.)

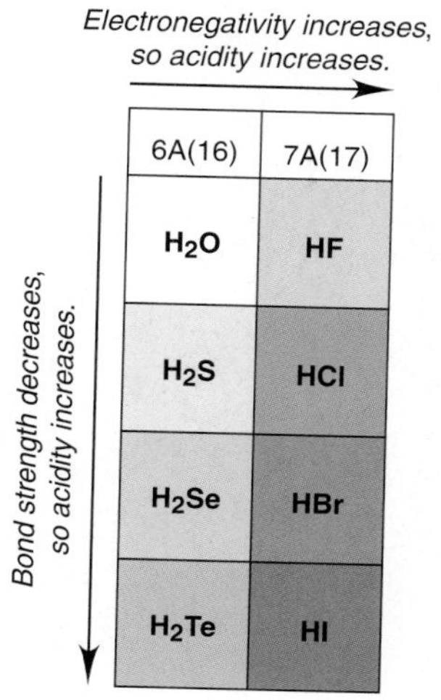

Figure 18.10 The effect of atomic and molecular properties on nonmetal hydride acidity.

Acid Strength of Oxoacids

All oxoacids have the acidic H atom bonded to an O atom, so bond length is not involved. Two other factors determine the acid strength of oxoacids (Section 14.8):

- The electronegativity of the central nonmetal (E)
- The number of O atoms around E (O.N. of E)

Figure 18.11 summarizes these trends:

1. *For oxoacids with the* ***same*** *number of O atoms, acid strength increases with the electronegativity of E.* Consider the hypohalous acids (HOE, where E is a halogen atom). The more electronegative E is, the more polar the O—H bond becomes and the more easily H^+ is lost (Figure 18.11A). Electronegativity decreases down a group, as does acid strength:

K_a of $HOCl = 2.9\times10^{-8}$ K_a of $HOBr = 2.3\times10^{-9}$ K_a of $HOI = 2.3\times10^{-11}$

Similarly, in Group 6A(16), H_2SO_4 is stronger than H_2SeO_4; in Group 5A(15), H_3PO_4 is stronger than H_3AsO_4, and so forth.

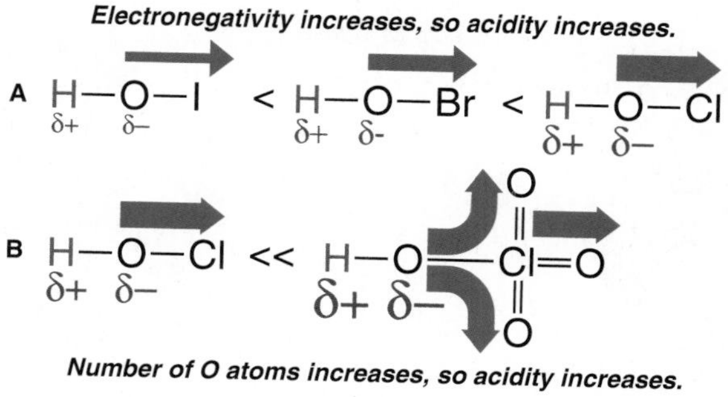

Figure 18.11 The relative strengths of oxoacids. **A,** Cl withdraws electron density (thickness of green arrow) from the O—H bond most effectively, making that bond most polar (relative size of δ symbols). **B,** Additional O atoms pull more electron density from the O—H bond.

2. *For oxoacids with* ***different*** *numbers of O atoms, acid strength increases with number of O atoms (or O.N. of central nonmetal).* The electronegative O atoms pull electron density away from E, which makes the O—H bond more polar. The more O atoms present, the greater the shift in electron density, and the more easily the H^+ ion comes off (Figure 18.11B). Therefore, the chlorine oxoacids ($HOClO_n$, with n from 0 to 3) increase in strength with the number of O atoms (and O.N. of Cl):

K_a of $HO\overset{+1}{Cl} = 2.9\times10^{-8}$ K_a of $HO\overset{+3}{Cl}O = 1.12\times10^{-2}$ K_a of $HO\overset{+5}{Cl}O_2 \approx 1$ K_a of $HO\overset{+7}{Cl}O_3 > 10^7$

Similarly, HNO_3 is stronger than HNO_2, H_2SO_4 is stronger than H_2SO_3, and so forth.

*Actually, bond energy refers to bond breakage that forms an H atom, whereas acidity refers to bond breakage that forms an H^+ ion. Although these two types of bond breakage are not the same, the trends in bond energy and acid strength are opposite each other.

Acidity of Hydrated Metal Ions

The aqueous solutions of certain metal ions are acidic because the *hydrated* metal ion transfers an H^+ ion to water. Consider a general metal nitrate, $M(NO_3)_n$, as it dissolves in water. The ions separate and the metal ion becomes bonded to some number of H_2O molecules. This equation shows the hydration of the cation (M^{n+}) with H_2O molecules and (aq); hydration of the anion (NO_3^-) is indicated by just (aq):

$$M(NO_3)_n(s) + xH_2O(l) \longrightarrow M(H_2O)_x^{n+}(aq) + nNO_3^-(aq)$$

If the metal ion, M^{n+}, is *small and highly charged,* its high charge density withdraws sufficient electron density from the O—H bonds of the bound water molecules for an H^+ to be released. Thus, the hydrated cation, $M(H_2O)_x^{n+}$, is a typical Brønsted-Lowry acid. The bound H_2O that releases the H^+ becomes a bound OH^- ion:

$$M(H_2O)_x^{n+}(aq) + H_2O(l) \rightleftharpoons M(H_2O)_{x-1}OH^{(n-1)+}(aq) + H_3O^+(aq)$$

Salts of most M^{2+} and M^{3+} ions yield acidic aqueous solutions. The K_a values for some acidic hydrated metal ions appear in Appendix C.

Consider the small, highly charged Al^{3+} ion. When an aluminum salt, such as $Al(NO_3)_3$, dissolves in water, the following steps occur:

$$Al(NO_3)_3(s) + 6H_2O(l) \longrightarrow Al(H_2O)_6^{3+}(aq) + 3NO_3^-(aq)$$
[dissolution and hydration]

$$Al(H_2O)_6^{3+}(aq) + H_2O(l) \rightleftharpoons Al(H_2O)_5OH^{2+}(aq) + H_3O^+(aq)$$
[dissociation of weak acid]

Note the formulas of the hydrated metal ions in the last step. When H^+ is released, the number of bound H_2O molecules decreases by 1 (from 6 to 5) and the number of bound OH^- ions increases by 1 (from 0 to 1), which reduces the ion's positive charge by 1 (from 3 to 2) (Figure 18.12). This pattern of changes in the formula of the hydrated metal ion before and after it loses a proton appears for any highly charged metal ion in water.

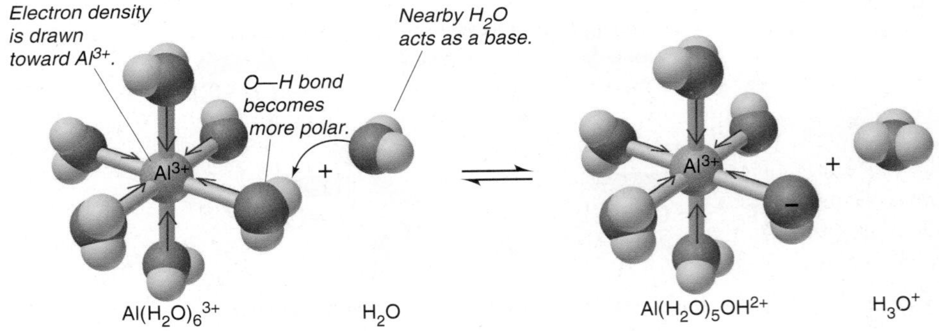

Figure 18.12 The acidic behavior of the hydrated Al^{3+} ion. The hydrated Al^{3+} ion is small and multiply charged and pulls electron density from the O—H bonds, so an H^+ ion can be transferred to a nearby water molecule.

Summary of Section 18.6

- For nonmetal hydrides, acid strength increases across a period, with the electronegativity of the nonmetal (E), and down a group, with the length of the E—H bond.
- For oxoacids with the same number of O atoms, acid strength increases with electronegativity of E; for oxoacids with the same E, acid strength increases with number of O atoms (or O.N. of E).
- Small, highly charged metal ions are acidic in water because they withdraw electron density from the O—H bonds of bound H_2O molecules, releasing an H^+ ion to the solution.

18.7 • ACID-BASE PROPERTIES OF SALT SOLUTIONS

In many cases, when a salt dissolves, one or both of its ions may react with water and affect the pH of the solution. You've seen that cations of weak bases (such as NH_4^+) are acidic, anions of weak acids (such as CN^-) are basic, and small, highly charged metal cations (such as Al^{3+}) are acidic. In addition, certain ions (such as $H_2PO_4^-$ and HCO_3^-) can act as an acid or a base. In this section, we classify the acid-base behavior of the various types of salt solutions.

Salts That Yield Neutral Solutions

A salt consisting of the anion of a strong acid and the cation of a strong base yields a neutral solution because the ions do not react with water. When a strong acid such as HNO_3 dissolves, the reaction goes essentially to completion because *the anion of a strong acid is a much weaker base than water.* The anion is hydrated, but *it does not react with water:*

$$HNO_3(l) + H_2O(l) \longrightarrow NO_3^-(aq) + H_3O^+(aq) \qquad \text{[dissolution and hydration]}$$

Similarly, a strong base, such as NaOH, dissolves completely. The cation, in this case Na^+, is hydrated, but *it is not small and charged enough to react with water:*

$$NaOH(s) \xrightarrow{H_2O} Na^+(aq) + OH^-(aq) \qquad \text{[dissolution and hydration]}$$

The anions of strong acids are the halide ions (except F^-) and ions of strong oxoacids, such as NO_3^- and ClO_4^-. The cations of strong bases are Group 1A(1) and Ca^{2+}, Sr^{2+}, and Ba^{2+} Group 2A(2). *Salts containing only these ions yield neutral solutions.*

Salts That Yield Acidic Solutions

There are two types of these salts:

1. *A salt consisting of the cation of a weak base and the anion of a strong acid yields an acidic solution because the cation acts as a weak acid,* and the anion does not react. For example, NH_4Cl yields an acidic solution because NH_4^+, the cation of the weak base NH_3, is a weak acid; Cl^-, the anion of the strong HCl, does not react:

$$NH_4Cl(s) \xrightarrow{H_2O} NH_4^+(aq) + Cl^-(aq) \qquad \text{[dissolution and hydration]}$$

$$NH_4^+(aq) + H_2O(l) \rightleftharpoons NH_3(aq) + H_3O^+(aq) \qquad \text{[dissociation of weak acid]}$$

2. *A salt consisting of a small, highly charged metal cation and the anion of a strong acid yields an acidic solution because the cation acts as a weak acid,* and the anion does not react. For example, $Fe(NO_3)_3$ yields an acidic solution because the hydrated Fe^{3+} ion is a weak acid; NO_3^-, the anion of the strong HNO_3, does not react:

$$Fe(NO_3)_3(s) + 6H_2O(l) \xrightarrow{H_2O} Fe(H_2O)_6^{3+}(aq) + 3NO_3^-(aq) \qquad \text{[dissolution and hydration]}$$

$$Fe(H_2O)_6^{3+}(aq) + H_2O(l) \rightleftharpoons Fe(H_2O)_5OH^{2+}(aq) + H_3O^+(aq)$$

$$\text{[dissociation of weak acid]}$$

Salts That Yield Basic Solutions

A salt consisting of the anion of a weak acid and the cation of a strong base yields a basic solution because the anion acts as a weak base, and the cation does not react. Sodium acetate, for example, yields a basic solution because the CH_3COO^- ion, the anion of the weak acid CH_3COOH, acts as a weak base; Na^+, the cation of the strong base NaOH, does not react:

$$CH_3COONa(s) \xrightarrow{H_2O} Na^+(aq) + CH_3COO^-(aq) \qquad \text{[dissolution and hydration]}$$

$$CH_3COO^-(aq) + H_2O(l) \rightleftharpoons CH_3COOH(aq) + OH^-(aq) \qquad \text{[reaction of weak base]}$$

Sample Problem 18.13 Predicting Relative Acidity of Salt Solutions from Reactions of the Ions with Water

Problem Predict whether aqueous solutions of the following salts are acidic, basic, or neutral, and write an equation for the reaction of any ion with water:
(a) Potassium perchlorate, $KClO_4$ **(b)** Sodium benzoate, C_6H_5COONa
(c) Chromium(III) nitrate, $Cr(NO_3)_3$

Plan The formula shows the cation and anion. Depending on an ion's ability to react with water, the solution will be neutral (strong-acid anion and strong-base cation), acidic (weak-base cation or highly charged metal cation with strong-acid anion), or basic (weak-acid anion and strong-base cation).

Solution (a) Neutral. The ions are K^+ and ClO_4^-. The K^+ is from the strong base KOH, and the ClO_4^- is from the strong acid $HClO_4$. Neither ion reacts with water.
(b) Basic. The ions are Na^+ and $C_6H_5COO^-$. The Na^+ is the cation of the strong base NaOH, so it does not react with water. The benzoate ion, $C_6H_5COO^-$, is the anion of the weak acid benzoic acid, so it reacts with water to produce OH^- ion:

$$C_6H_5COO^-(aq) + H_2O(l) \rightleftharpoons C_6H_5COOH(aq) + OH^-(aq)$$

(c) Acidic. The ions are Cr^{3+} and NO_3^-. The NO_3^- is the anion of the strong acid HNO_3, so it does not react with water. Cr^{3+} is a small and highly charged, so the hydrated ion, $Cr(H_2O)_6^{3+}$, reacts with water to produce H_3O^+:

$$Cr(H_2O)_6^{3+}(aq) + H_2O(l) \rightleftharpoons Cr(H_2O)_5OH^{2+}(aq) + H_3O^+(aq)$$

Follow-Up Problem 18.13 Write equations to predict whether solutions of the following salts are acidic, basic, or neutral: **(a)** $KClO_2$; **(b)** $CH_3NH_3NO_3$; **(c)** CsI.

Salts of Weakly Acidic Cations and Weakly Basic Anions

If a salt consists of a cation that is a weak acid *and* an anion that is a weak base, the overall acidity of the solution depends on the relative acid strength (K_a) or base strength (K_b) of the separated ions. Consider a solution of ammonium cyanide, NH_4CN, and the reactions that occur between the separated ions and water. Ammonium ion is the conjugate acid of a weak base, so it is a weak acid:

$$NH_4^+(aq) + H_2O(l) \rightleftharpoons NH_3(aq) + H_3O^+(aq)$$

Cyanide ion is the anion of a weak acid, so it is a weak base:

$$CN^-(aq) + H_2O(l) \rightleftharpoons HCN(aq) + OH^-(aq)$$

The reaction that goes farther to the right determines the pH of the solution, so we compare the K_a of NH_4^+ with the K_b of CN^-. Only molecular compounds are listed in K_a and K_b tables, so we calculate these values for the ions with Equation 18.7:

$$K_a \text{ of } NH_4^+ = \frac{K_w}{K_b \text{ of } NH_3} = \frac{1.0\times10^{-14}}{1.76\times10^{-5}} = 5.7\times10^{-10}$$

$$K_b \text{ of } CN^- = \frac{K_w}{K_a \text{ of } HCN} = \frac{1.0\times10^{-14}}{6.2\times10^{-10}} = 1.6\times10^{-5}$$

Because K_b of $CN^- > K_a$ of NH_4^+, we know that CN^- is a stronger base than NH_4^+ is an acid. Thus, NH_4CN solution is basic.

Salts of Amphiprotic Anions

The only salts left to consider are those in which the the cation comes from a strong base and the anion comes from a polyprotic acid with one or more ionizable protons still attached. These anions are amphiprotic—they can act as an acid and release a proton *to* water or as a base and abstract a proton *from* water. As in the previous case, to determine the overall acidity of their solutions, we compare the magnitudes of K_a and K_b, but here, we compare both the K_a and K_b of the same species, the anion.

For example, Na_2HPO_4 consists of Na^+, the cation of a strong base, which does not react with water, and HPO_4^{2-}, the second anion of the weak polyprotic acid H_3PO_4. In water, the salt undergoes three steps:

1. $Na_2HPO_4(s) \xrightarrow{H_2O} 2Na^+(aq) + HPO_4^{2-}(aq)$ [dissolution and hydration]
2. $HPO_4^{2-}(aq) + H_2O(l) \rightleftharpoons PO_4^{3-}(aq) + H_3O^+(aq)$ [acting as a weak acid]
3. $HPO_4^{2-}(aq) + H_2O(l) \rightleftharpoons H_2PO_4^-(aq) + OH^-(aq)$ [acting as a weak base]

We must decide whether step 2 or step 3 goes farther to the right. Appendix C lists the K_a of HPO_4^{2-} as 4.2×10^{-13}, but the K_b of HPO_4^{2-} is not given, so we find it with Equation 18.7:

$$K_b \text{ of } HPO_4^{2-} = \frac{K_w}{K_a \text{ of } H_2PO_4^-} \quad \text{or} \quad \frac{1.0\times10^{-14}}{6.3\times10^{-8}} = 1.6\times10^{-7}$$

Because K_b $(1.6\times10^{-7}) > K_a$ (4.2×10^{-13}), HPO_4^{2-} is stronger as a base than as an acid, so a solution of Na_2HPO_4 is basic.

Table 18.7 displays the acid-base behavior of the various types of salts in water.

Table 18.7 The Acid-Base Behavior of Salts in Water

Relative Acidity: Examples	pH	Nature of Ions	Ion That Reacts with Water: Examples
Neutral: NaCl, KBr, $Ba(NO_3)_2$	7.0	Cation of strong base Anion of strong acid	None
Acidic: NH_4Cl, NH_4NO_3, CH_3NH_3Br	<7.0	Cation of weak base Anion of strong acid	Cation: $NH_4^+ + H_2O \rightleftharpoons NH_3 + H_3O^+$
Acidic: $Al(NO_3)_3$, $CrBr_3$, $FeCl_3$	<7.0	Small, highly charged cation Anion of strong acid	Cation: $Al(H_2O)_6^{3+} + H_2O \rightleftharpoons Al(H_2O)_5OH^{2+} + H_3O^+$
Acidic/Basic: NH_4ClO_2, NH_4CN, $Pb(CH_3COO)_2$	<7.0 if $K_{a(cation)} > K_{b(anion)}$ >7.0 if $K_{b(anion)} > K_{a(cation)}$	Cation of weak base (or small, highly charged cation) Anion of weak acid	Cation *and* anion: $CH_3NH_3^+ + H_2O \rightleftharpoons CH_3NH_2 + H_3O^+$ $F^- + H_2O \rightleftharpoons HF + OH^-$
Acidic/Basic: NaH_2PO_4, $KHCO_3$, $NaHSO_3$	<7.0 if $K_{a(anion)} > K_{b(anion)}$ >7.0 if $K_{b(anion)} > K_{a(anion)}$	Cation of strong base Anion of polyprotic acid	Anion: $HSO_3^- + H_2O \rightleftharpoons SO_3^{2-} + H_3O^+$ $HSO_3^- + H_2O \rightleftharpoons H_2SO_3 + OH^-$

Sample Problem 18.14 Predicting the Relative Acidity of a Salt Solution from K_a and K_b of the Ions

Problem Determine whether an aqueous solution of zinc formate, $Zn(HCOO)_2$, at 25°C is acidic, basic, or neutral.

Plan The formula consists of the small, highly charged, and therefore weakly acidic, Zn^{2+} cation and the weakly basic $HCOO^-$ anion of the weak acid HCOOH. To determine the relative acidity of the solution, we write equations that show the reactions of the ions with water, and then find K_a of Zn^{2+} (from Appendix C) and calculate K_b of $HCOO^-$ (from K_a of HCOOH in Appendix C) to see which ion reacts with water to a greater extent.

Solution Writing the reactions with water:

$$Zn(H_2O)_6^{2+}(aq) + H_2O(l) \rightleftharpoons Zn(H_2O)_5OH^+(aq) + H_3O^+(aq)$$
$$HCOO^-(aq) + H_2O(l) \rightleftharpoons HCOOH(aq) + OH^-(aq)$$

Obtaining K_a and K_b of the ions: From Appendix C, the K_a of $Zn(H_2O)_6^{2+}(aq)$ is 1×10^{-9}. We obtain K_a of HCOOH and solve for K_b of $HCOO^-$:

$$K_b \text{ of } HCOO^- = \frac{K_w}{K_a \text{ of } HCOOH} = \frac{1.0\times10^{-14}}{1.8\times10^{-4}} = 5.6\times10^{-11}$$

K_a of $Zn(H_2O)_6^{2+} > K_b$ of $HCOO^-$, so the solution is acidic.

Follow-Up Problem 18.14 Determine whether solutions of the following salts are acidic, basic, or neutral at 25°C: **(a)** $Cu(CH_3COO)_2$; **(b)** NH_4F; **(c)** $KHSO_3$.

Summary of Section 18.7

- Salts that yield a neutral solution consist of ions that do not react with water.
- Salts that yield an acidic solution contain an unreactive anion and a cation that releases a proton to water.
- Salts that yield a basic solution contain an unreactive cation and an anion that accepts a proton from water.
- If both cation and anion react with water, the ion that reacts to the greater extent (higher K) determines the acidity or basicity of the salt solution.
- If the anion is amphiprotic (from a polyprotic acid), the strength of the anion as an acid (K_a) or as a base (K_b) determines the acidity of the salt.

18.8 • GENERALIZING THE BRØNSTED-LOWRY CONCEPT: THE LEVELING EFFECT

In general, *an acid yields the cation and a base yields the anion of solvent autoionization.* For example, in H_2O, all Brønsted-Lowry acids yield H_3O^+ and all Brønsted-Lowry bases yield OH^-, which are the ions that form when water autoionizes.

This idea lets us examine a key question: Why are all strong acids and strong bases *equally* strong in water? The answer is that *in water, the strongest acid possible is H_3O^+ and the strongest base possible is OH^-:*

- *For strong acids.* The moment we put gaseous HCl in water, it reacts with the base H_2O to form H_3O^+. The same holds for any strong acid because it dissociates *completely* to form H_3O^+. Thus, we are actually observing the acid strength of H_3O^+.
- *For strong bases.* A strong base, such as $Ba(OH)_2$, dissociates completely in water to yield OH^-. Even strong bases that do not contain hydroxide ions in the solid, such as K_2O, do so. The oxide ion, which is a stronger base than OH^-, immediately takes a proton from water to form OH^-:

$$O^{2-}(aq) + H_2O(l) \longrightarrow 2OH^-(aq)$$

Thus, water exerts a **leveling effect** on any strong acid or base by reacting with it to form the products of water's autoionization. Acting as a base, water levels the strength of all strong acids by making them appear equally strong, and acting as an acid, it levels the strength of all strong bases.

Therefore, to rank the relative strengths of strong acids, we must dissolve them in a solvent that is a *weaker* base than water, so it accepts their protons less readily. For example, the hydrohalic acids increase in strength as the halogen becomes larger, as a result of the longer, weaker H—X bond (see Figure 18.10). But, in water, HF is weak, and HCl, HBr, and HI appear equally strong because they dissociate completely. When we dissolve them in acetic acid, however, *the acetic acid acts as the base* and accepts a proton:

$$\underset{\text{acid}}{HCl(g)} + \underset{\text{base}}{CH_3COOH(l)} \rightleftharpoons \underset{\text{base}}{Cl^-(acet)} + \underset{\text{acid}}{CH_3COOH_2^+(acet)}$$

$$HBr(g) + CH_3COOH(l) \rightleftharpoons Br^-(acet) + CH_3COOH_2^+(acet)$$

$$HI(g) + CH_3COOH(l) \rightleftharpoons I^-(acet) + CH_3COOH_2^+(acet)$$

[The use of (*acet*) instead of (*aq*) indicates solvation by CH_3COOH.] Because acetic acid is a *weaker base* than water, the three acids donate their protons to *different* extents. Measurements show that HI protonates the solvent to a greater extent than HBr, and HBr does so more than HCl; that is, in pure acetic acid, $K_{HI} > K_{HBr} > K_{HCl}$. Similarly, the relative strengths of strong bases are determined in a solvent that is a weaker acid than H_2O, such as liquid NH_3.

Summary of Section 18.8

- Strong acids (or strong bases) dissociate completely to yield H_3O^+ (or OH^-) in water; in effect, water equalizes (levels) their strengths.
- Strong acids show differences in strength when dissolved in a weaker base than water, such as acetic acid.

18.9 • ELECTRON-PAIR DONATION AND THE LEWIS ACID-BASE DEFINITION

The final acid-base concept we consider was developed by Gilbert N. Lewis, whose contribution to understanding valence electron pairs in bonding we discussed in Chapter 9. Whereas the Brønsted-Lowry concept focuses on the proton in defining a species as an acid or a base, the Lewis concept highlights the role of the *electron pair*. The **Lewis acid-base definition** holds that

- A *base* is any species that *donates* an electron pair to form a bond.
- An *acid* is any species that *accepts* an electron pair to form a bond.

The Lewis definition, like the Brønsted-Lowry definition, requires that a base have an electron pair to donate, so it does not expand the classes of bases. However, *it greatly expands the classes of acids*. Many species, such as CO_2 and Cu^{2+}, that do not contain H in their formula (and thus cannot be Brønsted-Lowry acids) are Lewis acids because they accept an electron pair in reactions. Thus, the proton itself is a Lewis acid because it accepts the electron pair donated by a base:

$$\mathrm{B\!:} + \mathrm{H^+} \rightleftharpoons \mathrm{B{-}H^+}$$

Thus, *all Brønsted-Lowry acids donate* H^+, *a Lewis acid.*

The product of a Lewis acid-base reaction is an **adduct,** *a single species that contains a* ***new*** *covalent bond:*

$$\mathrm{A} + \mathrm{:B} \rightleftharpoons \mathrm{A{-}B}\ \text{(adduct)}$$

Thus, the Lewis concept radically broadens the idea of an acid-base reaction:

- To Arrhenius, it is the formation of H_2O from H^+ and OH^-.
- To Brønsted and Lowry, it is H^+ transfer from a stronger acid to a stronger base to form a weaker base and weaker acid.
- To Lewis, it is *the donation and acceptance of an electron pair to form a covalent bond in an adduct.*

By definition, then,

- *A Lewis base must have a lone pair of electrons to donate.*
- *A Lewis acid must have a vacant orbital* (or the ability to rearrange its bonds to form one) to accept a lone pair and form a new bond.

In this section, we discuss molecules and positive ions that act as Lewis acids.

Molecules as Lewis Acids

Many molecules act as Lewis acids. In every case, the atom accepting the electron pair has low electron density due to either an electron deficiency or a polar multiple bond.

Lewis Acids with Electron-Deficient Atoms The most important of the *electron-deficient* Lewis acids are compounds of the Group 3A(13) elements boron and aluminum. Recall from Chapters 10 and 14 that these compounds have fewer than eight electrons around the central atom, so they react to complete that atom's octet. For example, boron trifluoride accepts an electron pair from ammonia to form a covalent bond:

Aluminum chloride dissolves freely in relatively nonpolar diethyl ether when the ether's O atom donates an electron pair to Al to form a covalent bond:

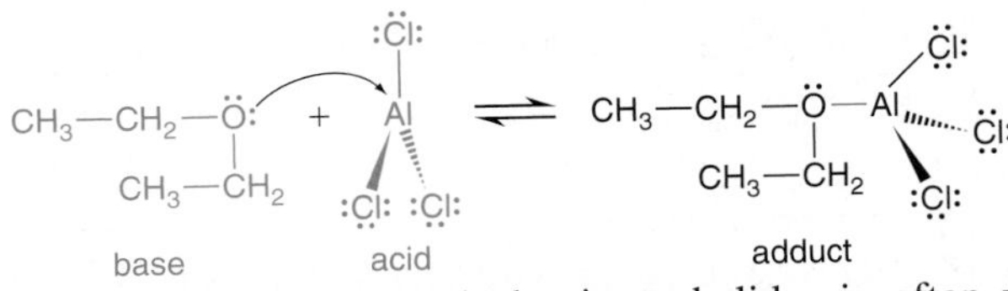

This acidic behavior of boron and aluminum halides is often used in organic syntheses. For example, a methyl group is added to the benzene ring by the action of CH_3Cl in the presence of $AlCl_3$. The Lewis acid $AlCl_3$ abstracts the Lewis base Cl^- from CH_3Cl to form an adduct that has a reactive CH_3^+ group, which then attacks the electron-rich benzene ring:

$$\underset{\text{base}}{CH_3Cl} + \underset{\text{acid}}{AlCl_3} \rightleftharpoons \underset{\text{adduct}}{[CH_3]^+[Cl{-}AlCl_3]^-}$$

$$\underset{\text{benzene}}{C_6H_6} + [CH_3]^+[Cl{-}AlCl_3]^- \rightleftharpoons \underset{\text{toluene}}{C_6H_5CH_3} + AlCl_3 + HCl$$

Lewis Acids with Polar Multiple Bonds Molecules with a polar double bond also function as Lewis acids. An electron pair on the Lewis base approaches the partially positive end of the double bond to form the new bond in the adduct, as the π bond breaks. For example, consider the reaction of SO_2 in water. The electronegative O atoms in SO_2 make the central S partially positive. The O atom of water donates a lone pair to the S, thus forming an S—O bond and breaking one of the π bonds. Then, a proton is transferred from water to the O that was part of the π bond. The resulting adduct is sulfurous acid:

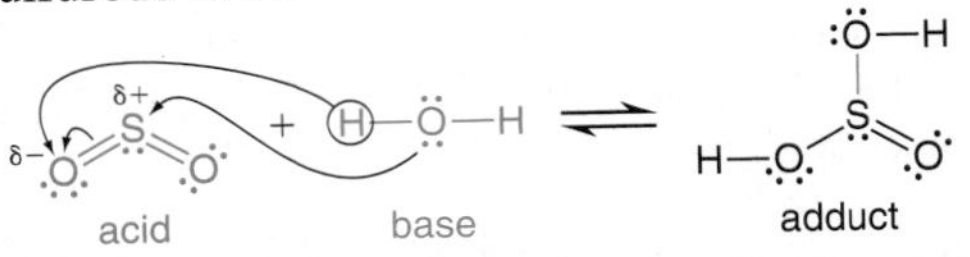

The analogous formation of a carbonate from a metal oxide and carbon dioxide occurs in a nonaqueous system. The O^{2-} ion (shown coming from CaO) donates an electron pair to the partially positive C in CO_2, a π bond breaks, and the CO_3^{2-} ion (shown as part of $CaCO_3$) is the adduct:

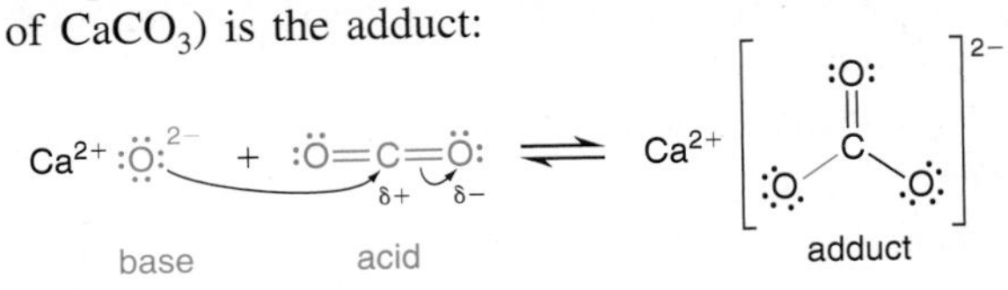

Metal Cations as Lewis Acids

In the Lewis sense, hydration of a metal ion is itself an acid-base reaction. As electron pairs on the O atoms of H_2O molecules form covalent bonds, the hydrated cation is the adduct; thus, *a metal ion acts as a Lewis acid when it dissolves in water:*

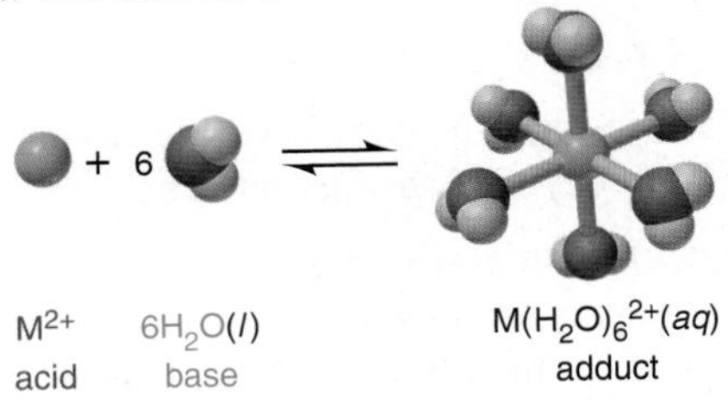

Ammonia is a stronger Lewis base than water because, when it is added to the aqueous solution of the hydrated cation, it displaces H_2O, with $K >> 1$:

$$\underset{\text{hydrated adduct}}{Ni(H_2O)_6^{2+}(aq)} + \underset{\text{base}}{6NH_3(aq)} \rightleftharpoons \underset{\text{ammoniated adduct}}{Ni(NH_3)_6^{2+}(aq)} + 6H_2O(l)$$

We discuss the equilibrium nature of these acid-base reactions in greater detail in Chapter 19, and we investigate the structures of these ions in Chapter 23.

Many biomolecules with central metal ions are Lewis adducts. Most often, O and N atoms of organic groups donate their lone pairs as the Lewis bases. Chlorophyll is a Lewis adduct of a central Mg^{2+} and the four N atoms of a tetrapyrrole (porphin) ring system (Figure 18.13). Vitamin B_{12} has a similar structure with a central Co^{3+}, and so does heme with a central Fe^{2+}. Several other metal ions, such as Zn^{2+}, Mo^{2+}, and Cu^{2+}, are bound at the active sites of enzymes and function as Lewis acids in the catalytic action.

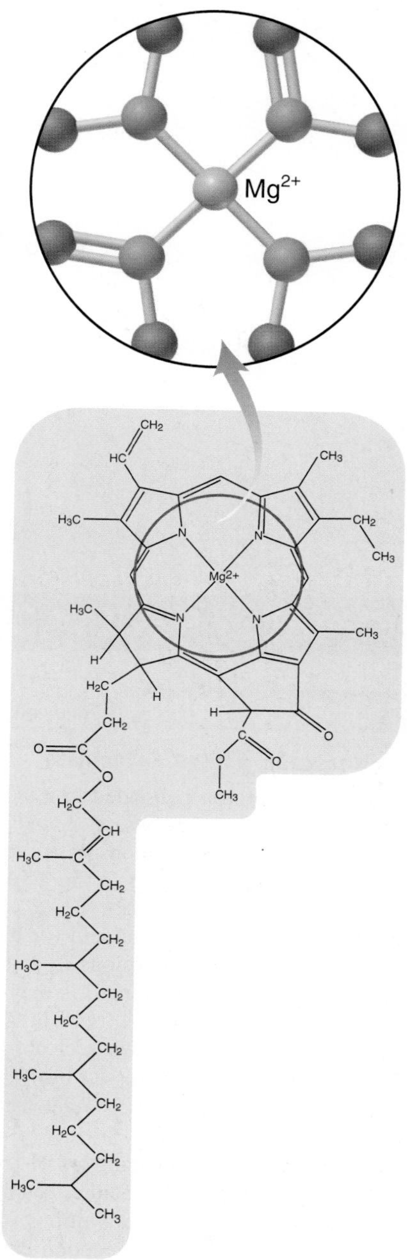

Figure 18.13 The Mg^{2+} ion as a Lewis acid in chlorophyll. Mg^{2+} accepts electron pairs from surrounding N atoms.

Sample Problem 18.15 Identifying Lewis Acids and Bases

Problem Identify the Lewis acids and Lewis bases in the following reactions:
(a) $H^+ + OH^- \rightleftharpoons H_2O$ **(b)** $Cl^- + BCl_3 \rightleftharpoons BCl_4^-$ **(c)** $K^+ + 6H_2O \rightleftharpoons K(H_2O)_6^+$

Plan We examine the formulas to see which species accepts the electron pair (Lewis acid) and which donates it (Lewis base) in forming the adduct.

Solution (a) The H^+ ion accepts an electron pair from the OH^- ion in forming a bond. H^+ is the acid and OH^- is the base.
(b) The Cl^- ion has four lone pairs and uses one to form a new bond to the central B. BCl_3 is the acid and Cl^- is the base.
(c) The K^+ ion does not have any valence electrons to provide, so the bond is formed when electron pairs from O atoms of water enter empty orbitals on K^+. K^+ is the acid and H_2O is the base.

Check The Lewis acids (H^+, BCl_3, and K^+) each have an unfilled valence shell that can accept an electron pair from the Lewis bases (OH^-, Cl^-, and H_2O).

Follow-Up Problem 18.15 Identify the Lewis acids and Lewis bases:
(a) $OH^- + Al(OH)_3 \rightleftharpoons Al(OH)_4^-$ **(b)** $SO_3 + H_2O \rightleftharpoons H_2SO_4$
(c) $Co^{3+} + 6NH_3 \rightleftharpoons Co(NH_3)_6^{3+}$

An Overview of Acid-Base Definitions

From a broader chemical perspective, the diversity of acid-base reactions takes on more unity. Chemists see a common theme in reactions as diverse as a standardized base being used to analyze an unknown fatty acid, baking soda being used in breadmaking, and even oxygen binding to hemoglobin in a blood cell. Let's see how the three acid-base definitions fit together.

1. The *Arrhenius definition,* which was the first attempt at describing acids and bases on the molecular level, is the most limited and narrow of the three. It applies only to species with an H atom or an OH group that is released as an ion when the species dissolves in water. Because relatively few species have these structural prerequisites, Arrhenius acid-base reactions are relatively few in number, and all occur in H_2O and result in the formation of H_2O.

2. The *Brønsted-Lowry definition* sees acid-base reactions as proton-transfer processes that need not occur in water. A Brønsted-Lowry acid, like an Arrhenius acid, must have an H, but a Brønsted-Lowry base is any species with an electron pair available to accept a proton. This definition includes many more species as bases, including OH^-. It defines the acid-base reaction in terms of conjugate acid-base pairs, with an acid and a base on both sides of the reaction. The system reaches equilibrium based on the relative strengths of the acid, the base, and their conjugates.

3. The *Lewis definition* has the widest scope and includes the other two. The defining event of a Lewis acid-base reaction is the donation and acceptance of an electron pair to form a new covalent bond in an adduct. Lewis bases still must have an electron pair to donate, but Lewis acids—the electron-pair acceptors—include many species not encompassed by the other definitions, including molecules with electron-deficient atoms or with polar double bonds, metal ions, and even H^+ itself.

Summary of Section 18.9

- The Lewis acid-base definition focuses on the donation or acceptance of an electron pair to form a new covalent bond in an adduct, the product of an acid-base reaction. Lewis bases donate the electron pair, and Lewis acids accept it.
- Thus, many species that do not contain H are Lewis acids. Molecules with polar double bonds act as Lewis acids, as do those with electron-deficient atoms.
- Metal ions act as Lewis acids when they dissolve in water, which acts as a Lewis base, to form the adduct, a hydrated cation.
- Many metal ions function as Lewis acids in biomolecules.

CHAPTER REVIEW GUIDE

Learning Objectives

Relevant section (§) and/or sample problem (SP) numbers appear in parentheses.

Understand These Concepts

1. Why the proton is bonded to a water molecule, as H_3O^+, in all aqueous acid-base systems (§18.1)
2. The Arrhenius definitions of an acid and a base (§18.1)
3. Why all reactions of a strong acid and a strong base have the same ΔH°_{rxn} (§18.1)
4. How the strength of an acid (or base) relates to the extent of its dissociation into ions in water (§18.1)
5. How relative acid strength is expressed by the acid-dissociation constant K_a (§18.1)
6. Why water is a very weak electrolyte and how its autoionization is expressed by K_w (§18.2)
7. Why $[H_3O^+]$ is inversely related to $[OH^-]$ in any aqueous solution (§18.2)
8. How the relative magnitudes of $[H_3O^+]$ and $[OH^-]$ define whether a solution is acidic, basic, or neutral (§18.2)
9. The Brønsted-Lowry definitions of an acid and a base and how an acid-base reaction can be viewed as a proton-transfer process (§18.3)
10. How water acts as a base (or as an acid) when an acid (or a base) dissolves in it (§18.3)
11. How a conjugate acid-base pair differs by one proton (§18.3)
12. How a Brønsted-Lowry acid-base reaction involves two conjugate acid-base pairs (§18.3)
13. Why a stronger acid and base react ($K_c > 1$) to form a weaker base and acid (§18.3)
14. How the percent dissociation of a weak acid increases as its concentration decreases (§18.4)
15. How a polyprotic acid dissociates in two or more steps and why only the first step supplies significant $[H_3O^+]$ (§18.4)
16. How weak bases in water accept a proton rather than dissociate; the meaning of K_b and pK_b (§18.5)
17. How ammonia, amines, and weak-acid anions act as weak bases in water (§18.5)
18. Why relative concentrations of HA and A^- determine the acidity or basicity of their solution (§18.5)
19. The relationship of the K_a and K_b of a conjugate acid-base pair to K_w (§18.5)
20. The effects of electronegativity, bond polarity, and bond strength on acid strength (§18.6)
21. Why aqueous solutions of small, highly charged metal ions are acidic (§18.6)
22. The various combinations of cations and anions that lead to acidic, basic, or neutral salt solutions (§18.7)
23. Why the strengths of strong acids are leveled in water but differentiated in a less basic solvent (§18.8)
24. The Lewis definitions of an acid and a base and how a Lewis acid-base reaction involves the donation and acceptance of an electron pair to form a covalent bond (§18.9)
25. How molecules with electron-deficient atoms, molecules with polar multiple bonds, and metal cations act as Lewis acids (§18.9)

Master These Skills

1. Classifying strong and weak acids and bases from their formulas (SP 18.1)
2. Using K_w to calculate $[H_3O^+]$ or $[OH^-]$ in an aqueous solution (SP 18.2)
3. Using p-scales to express $[H_3O^+]$, $[OH^-]$, and K (§18.2)
4. Calculating $[H_3O^+]$, pH, $[OH^-]$, and pOH (SP 18.3)
5. Identifying conjugate acid-base pairs (SP 18.4)
6. Using relative acid strengths to predict the net direction of an acid-base reaction (SPs 18.5, 18.6)
7. Calculating K_a of a weak acid from pH (SP 18.7)
8. Calculating $[H_3O^+]$ (and, thus, pH) from K_a and $[HA]_{init}$ (SP 18.8)
9. Applying the quadratic equation to find a concentration (Follow-Up Problem 18.8)

10. Calculating the percent dissociation of a weak acid (§18.4 and SP 18.9)
11. Calculating $[H_3O^+]$ and other concentrations for a polyprotic acid (SP 18.10)
12. Calculating pH from K_b and $[B]_{init}$ (SP 18.11)
13. Finding K_b of A^- from K_a of HA and K_w (§18.5 and SP 18.12)
14. Calculating pH from K_b of A^- and $[A^-]_{init}$ (SP 18.12)
15. Predicting relative acid strengths of nonmetal hydrides and oxoacids (§18.6)
16. Predicting the relative acidity of a salt solution from the nature of the cation and anion (SPs 18.13, 18.14)
17. Identifying Lewis acids and bases (SP 18.15)

Key Terms

Page numbers appear in parentheses.

Section 18.1
hydronium ion, H_3O^+ (720)
Arrhenius acid-base definition (720)
neutralization (720)
acid-dissociation (acid-ionization) constant (K_a) (722)

Section 18.2
autoionization (724)
ion-product constant for water (K_w) (724)
pH (726)
acid-base indicator (728)

Section 18.3
Brønsted-Lowry acid-base definition (729)
proton donor (729)
proton acceptor (729)
conjugate acid-base pair (729)

Section 18.4
polyprotic acid (737)

Section 18.5
base-dissociation (base-ionization) constant (K_b) (740)

Section 18.8
leveling effect (750)

Section 18.9
Lewis acid-base definition (751)
adduct (751)

Key Equations and Relationships

Page numbers appear in parentheses.

18.1 Defining the acid-dissociation constant (722):

$$K_a = \frac{[H_3O^+][A^-]}{[HA]}$$

18.2 Defining the ion-product constant for water (724):

$$K_w = [H_3O^+][OH^-] = 1.0\times10^{-14} \text{ (at 25°C)}$$

18.3 Defining pH (726):

$$pH = -\log [H_3O^+]$$

18.4 Relating pK_w to pH and pOH (726):

$$pK_w = pH + pOH = 14.00 \text{ (at 25°C)}$$

18.5 Finding the percent dissociation of HA (736):

$$\text{Percent HA dissociated} = \frac{[HA]_{dissoc}}{[HA]_{init}} \times 100$$

18.6 Defining the base-dissociation constant (740):

$$K_b = \frac{[BH^+][OH^-]}{[B]}$$

18.7 Expressing the relationship among K_a, K_b, and K_w (743):

$$K_a \times K_b = K_w$$

Brief Solutions to Follow-Up Problems

18.1 (a) $HClO_3$; (b) HCl; (c) NaOH

18.2 $[H_3O^+] = \dfrac{1.0\times10^{-14}}{6.7\times10^{-2}} = 1.5\times10^{-13}$ *M*; basic

18.3 pOH = 14.00 − 9.52 = 4.48
$[H_3O^+] = 10^{-9.52} = 3.0\times10^{-10}$ *M*
$[OH^-] = \dfrac{1.0\times10^{-14}}{3.0\times10^{-10}} = 3.3\times10^{-5}$ *M*

18.4 (a) CH_3COOH/CH_3COO^- and H_3O^+/H_2O
(b) H_2O/OH^- and HF/F^-

18.5 (a) $NH_3(g) + H_2O(l) \rightleftharpoons NH_4^+(aq) + OH^-(aq)$
(b) $NH_3(g) + H_3O^+(aq\text{; from HCl}) \longrightarrow NH_4^+(aq) + H_2O(l)$
(c) $NH_4^+(aq) + OH^-(aq\text{; from NaOH}) \longrightarrow NH_3(g) + H_2O(l)$

18.6 There are more HB molecules than HA, so $K_c > 1$ and HA is the stronger acid.

18.7 $NH_4^+(aq) + H_2O(l) \rightleftharpoons NH_3(aq) + H_3O^+(aq)$
$[H_3O^+] = 10^{-pH} = 10^{-5.0} = 1\times10^{-5}\ M = [NH_3]$
And, $[NH_4^+] = 0.2\ M - (1\times10^{-5}\ M) = 0.2\ M$

$$K_a = \frac{[NH_3][H_3O^+]}{[NH_4^+]} \approx \frac{(1\times10^{-5})^2}{0.2} = 5\times10^{-10}$$

18.8 $K_a = \dfrac{[H_3O^+][OCN^-]}{[HOCN]} = \dfrac{(x)(x)}{0.10 - x} = 3.5\times10^{-4}$

Since $\dfrac{[HOCN]_{init}}{K_a} = \dfrac{0.10}{3.5\times10^{-4}} = 286 < 400$, you must solve a quadratic equation: $x^2 + (3.5\times10^{-4})x - (3.5\times10^{-5}) = 0$
$x = [H_3O^+] = 5.7\times10^{-3}$ *M*

Brief Solutions to Follow-Up Problems (continued)

18.9 There is no single correct scene: any scene in which the total number of HB + H_3O^+ (or HB + B^-) is less than in the original solution, yet the number of HB dissociated is greater, would be correct, for example:

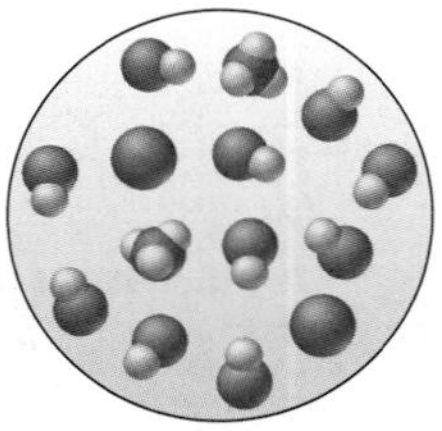

18.10 $K_{a1} = \frac{[HC_2O_4^-][H_3O^+]}{[H_2C_2O_4]} = \frac{x^2}{0.150 - x} = 5.6\times10^{-2}$ Since $\frac{[H_2C_2O_4]_{init}}{K_{a1}} < 400$, you must solve a quadratic equation:

$x^2 + (5.6\times10^{-2})x - (8.4\times10^{-3}) = 0$

$x = [H_3O^+] = 0.068\ M$; pH = 1.17

$x = [HC_2O_4^-] = 0.068\ M$; $[H_2C_2O_4] = 0.150\ M - x = 0.082\ M$

$$[C_2O_4^{2-}] = \frac{(K_{a2})[HC_2O_4^-]}{[H_3O^+]} = \frac{(5.4\times10^{-5})(0.068)}{0.068}$$

$$= 5.4\times10^{-5}\ M$$

18.11 $K_b = \frac{[C_5H_5NH^+][OH^-]}{[C_5H_5N]} = 10^{-8.77} = 1.7\times10^{-9}$

Assuming $0.10\ M - x \approx 0.10\ M$, $K_b = 1.7\times10^{-9} \approx \frac{(x)(x)}{0.10}$;

$x = [OH^-] \approx 1.3\times10^{-5}\ M$; $[H_3O^+] = 7.7\times10^{-10}\ M$;
pH = 9.11

18.12 K_b of $ClO^- = \frac{K_w}{K_a \text{ of } HClO} = \frac{1.0\times10^{-14}}{2.9\times10^{-8}} = 3.4\times10^{-7}$

Assuming $0.20\ M - x \approx 0.20\ M$,

$K_b = 3.4\times10^{27} = \frac{[HClO][OH^-]}{[ClO^-]} \approx \frac{x^2}{0.20}$;

$x = [OH^-] \approx 2.6\times10^{-4}\ M$; $[H_3O^+] = 3.8\times10^{-11}\ M$;

pH = 10.42

18.13 (a) Basic:

$$ClO_2^-(aq) + H_2O(l) \rightleftharpoons HClO(aq) + OH^-(aq)$$

K^+ is from the strong base KOH.
(b) Acidic:

$$CH_3NH_3^+(aq) + H_2O(l) \rightleftharpoons CH_3NH_2(aq) + H_3O^+(aq)$$

NO_3^- is from the strong acid HNO_3.
(c) Neutral: Cs^+ is from the strong base CsOH; I^- is from the strong acid HI.

18.14 (a) K_a of $Cu(H_2O)_6^{2+} = 3\times10^{-8}$

K_b of $CH_3COO^- = \frac{K_w}{K_a \text{ of } CH_3COOH} = 5.6\times10^{-10}$

Since $K_a > K_b$, $Cu(CH_3COO)_2(aq)$ is acidic.

(b) K_a of $NH_4^+ = \frac{K_w}{K_b \text{ of } NH_3} = 5.7\times10^{-10}$

K_b of $F^- = \frac{K_w}{K_a \text{ of HF}} = 1.5\times10^{-11}$

Because $K_a > K_b$, $NH_4F(aq)$ is acidic.
(c) From Appendix C, K_a of $HSO_3^- = 6.5\times10^{-8}$

K_b of $HSO_3^- = \frac{K_w}{K_a \text{ of } H_2SO_3} = 7.1\times10^{-13}$

Because $K_a > K_b$, $KHSO_3(aq)$ is acidic.

18.15 (a) OH^- is the Lewis base; $Al(OH)_3$ is the Lewis acid.
(b) H_2O is the Lewis base; SO_3 is the Lewis acid.
(c) NH_3 is the Lewis base; Co^{3+} is the Lewis acid.

PROBLEMS

Problems with **colored** numbers are answered in Appendix E and worked in detail in the Student Solutions Manual. Problem sections match those in the text and provide the numbers of relevant sample problems. Most offer Concept Review Questions, Skill-Building Exercises (grouped in pairs covering the same concept), and Problems in Context. The Comprehensive Problems are based on material from any section or previous chapter.

Note: Unless stated otherwise, all problems refer to aqueous solutions at 298 K (25°C).

Acids and Bases in Water

(Sample Problem 18.1)

Concept Review Questions

18.1 What is the role of water in the Arrhenius acid-base definition?

18.2 What do Arrhenius acids have in common? What do Arrhenius bases have in common? Explain neutralization in terms of the Arrhenius acid-base definition. What data led Arrhenius to propose this idea of neutralization?

18.3 Why is the Arrhenius acid-base definition too limited? Give an example for which the Arrhenius definition does not apply.

18.4 What do "strong" and "weak" mean for acids and bases? K_a values of weak acids vary over more than 10 orders of magnitude. What do the acids have in common that makes them "weak"?

Skill-Building Exercises (grouped in similar pairs)

18.5 Which of the following are Arrhenius acids?
(a) H_2O (b) $Ca(OH)_2$ (c) H_3PO_3 (d) HI

18.6 Which of the following are Arrhenius acids?
(a) $NaHSO_4$ (b) CH_4 (c) NaH (d) H_3N

18.7 Which of the following are Arrhenius bases?
(a) H_3AsO_4 (b) $Ba(OH)_2$ (c) HClO (d) KOH

18.8 Which of the following are Arrhenius bases?
(a) CH_3COOH (b) HOH (c) CH_3OH (d) H_2NNH_2

18.9 Write the K_a expression for each of the following in water:
(a) HCN (b) HCO_3^- (c) HCOOH

18.10 Write the K_a expression for each of the following in water:
(a) $CH_3NH_3^+$ (b) HClO (c) H_2S

18.11 Write the K_a expression for each of the following in water:
(a) HNO_2 (b) CH_3COOH (c) $HBrO_2$

18.12 Write the K_a expression for each of the following in water:
(a) $H_2PO_4^-$ (b) H_3PO_2 (c) HSO_4^-

18.13 Use Appendix C to rank the following in order of *increasing* acid strength: HIO_3, HI, CH_3COOH, HF.

18.14 Use Appendix C to rank the following in order of *decreasing* acid strength: HClO, HCl, HCN, HNO_2.

18.15 Classify each as a strong or weak acid or base:
(a) H_3AsO_4 (b) $Sr(OH)_2$ (c) HIO (d) $HClO_4$

18.16 Classify each as a strong or weak acid or base:
(a) CH_3NH_2 (b) K_2O (c) HI (d) HCOOH

18.17 Classify each as a strong or weak acid or base:
(a) RbOH (b) HBr (c) H_2Te (d) HClO

18.18 Classify each as a strong or weak acid or base:
(a) $HOCH_2CH_2NH_2$ (b) H_2SeO_4 (c) HS^- (d) $B(OH)_3$

Autoionization of Water and the pH Scale

(Sample Problems 18.2 and 18.3)

Concept Review Questions

18.19 What is an autoionization reaction? Write equations for the autoionization reactions of H_2O and of H_2SO_4.

18.20 What is the difference between K_c and K_w for the autoionization of water?

18.21 (a) What is the change in pH when $[OH^-]$ increases by a factor of 10? (b) What is the change in $[H_3O^+]$ when the pH decreases by 3 units?

18.22 Which solution has the higher pH? Explain.
(a) A 0.1 *M* solution of an acid with $K_a = 1\times10^{-4}$ or one with $K_a = 4\times10^{-5}$
(b) A 0.1 *M* solution of an acid with $pK_a = 3.0$ or one with $pK_a = 3.5$
(c) A 0.1 *M* solution or a 0.01 *M* solution of a weak acid
(d) A 0.1 *M* solution of a weak acid or a 0.1 *M* solution of a strong acid
(e) A 0.1 *M* solution of an acid or a 0.01 *M* solution of a base
(f) A solution of pOH 6.0 or one of pOH 8.0

Skill-Building Exercises (grouped in similar pairs)

18.23 (a) What is the pH of 0.0111 *M* NaOH? Is the solution neutral, acidic, or basic? (b) What is the pOH of 1.35×10^{-3} *M* HCl? Is the solution neutral, acidic, or basic?

18.24 (a) What is the pH of 0.0333 *M* HNO_3? Is the solution neutral, acidic, or basic? (b) What is the pOH of 0.0347 *M* KOH? Is the solution neutral, acidic, or basic?

18.25 (a) What is the pH of 6.14×10^{-3} *M* HI? Is the solution neutral, acidic, or basic? (b) What is the pOH of 2.55 *M* $Ba(OH)_2$? Is the solution neutral, acidic, or basic?

18.26 (a) What is the pH of 7.52×10^{-4} *M* CsOH? Is the solution neutral, acidic, or basic? (b) What is the pOH of 1.59×10^{-3} *M* $HClO_4$? Is the solution neutral, acidic, or basic?

18.27 (a) What are $[H_3O^+]$, $[OH^-]$, and pOH in a solution with a pH of 9.85? (b) What are $[H_3O^+]$, $[OH^-]$, and pH in a solution with a pOH of 9.43?

18.28 (a) What are $[H_3O^+]$, $[OH^-]$, and pOH in a solution with a pH of 3.47? (b) What are $[H_3O^+]$, $[OH^-]$, and pH in a solution with a pOH of 4.33?

18.29 (a) What are $[H_3O^+]$, $[OH^-]$, and pOH in a solution with a pH of 4.77? (b) What are $[H_3O^+]$, $[OH^-]$, and pH in a solution with a pOH of 5.65?

18.30 (a) What are $[H_3O^+]$, $[OH^-]$, and pOH in a solution with a pH of 8.97? (b) What are $[H_3O^+]$, $[OH^-]$, and pH in a solution with a pOH of 11.27?

18.31 How many moles of H_3O^+ or OH^- must you add per liter of HA solution to adjust its pH from 3.15 to 3.65? Assume a negligible volume change.

18.32 How many moles of H_3O^+ or OH^- must you add per liter of HA solution to adjust its pH from 9.33 to 9.07? Assume a negligible volume change.

18.33 How many moles of H_3O^+ or OH^- must you add to 5.6 L of HA solution to adjust its pH from 4.52 to 5.25? Assume a negligible volume change.

18.34 How many moles of H_3O^+ or OH^- must you add to 87.5 mL of HA solution to adjust its pH from 8.92 to 6.33? Assume a negligible volume change.

Problems in Context

18.35 The two molecular scenes below depict the relative concentrations of H_3O^+ *(purple)* in solutions of the same volume (with counter ions and solvent molecules omitted for clarity). If the pH in scene A is 4.8, what is the pH in scene B?

18.36 Like any equilibrium constant, K_w changes with temperature. (a) Given that autoionization is endothermic, how does K_w change with rising *T*? Explain with a reaction that includes heat as reactant or product. (b) In many medical applications, the value of K_w at 37°C (body temperature) may be more appropriate than the value at 25°C, 1.0×10^{-14}. The pH of pure water at 37°C is 6.80. Calculate K_w, pOH, and $[OH^-]$ at this temperature.

Proton Transfer and the Brønsted-Lowry Acid-Base Definition

(Sample Problems 18.4 to 18.6)

Concept Review Questions

18.37 How are the Arrhenius and Brønsted-Lowry acid-base definitions different? How are they similar? Name two Brønsted-Lowry bases that are not Arrhenius bases. Can you do the same for acids? Explain.

18.38 What is a conjugate acid-base pair? What is the relationship between the two members of the pair?

18.39 (a) A Brønsted-Lowry acid-base reaction proceeds in the net direction in which a stronger acid and stronger base form a weaker acid and weaker base. Explain.
(b) The molecular scene at right depicts an aqueous solution of two conjugate acid-base pairs: HA/A^- and HB/B^-. The base in the first pair is represented by red spheres and the base in the second pair by green spheres; solvent molecules are omitted for clarity. Which is the stronger acid? Stronger base? Explain.

18.40 What is an amphiprotic species? Name one and write balanced equations that show why it is amphiprotic.

Skill-Building Exercises (grouped in similar pairs)

18.41 Write balanced equations and K_a expressions for these Brønsted-Lowry acids in water:
(a) H_3PO_4 (b) C_6H_5COOH (c) HSO_4^-

18.42 Write balanced equations and K_a expressions for these Brønsted-Lowry acids in water:
(a) HCOOH (b) $HClO_3$ (c) $H_2AsO_4^-$

18.43 Give the formula of the conjugate base:
(a) HCl (b) H_2CO_3 (c) H_2O

18.44 Give the formula of the conjugate base:
(a) HPO_4^{2-} (b) NH_4^+ (c) HS^-

18.45 Give the formula of the conjugate acid:
(a) NH_3 (b) NH_2^- (c) nicotine, $C_{10}H_{14}N_2$

18.46 Give the formula of the conjugate acid:
(a) O^{2-} (b) SO_4^{2-} (c) H_2O

18.47 In each equation, label the acids, bases, and conjugate pairs:
(a) $HCl + H_2O \rightleftharpoons Cl^- + H_3O^+$
(b) $HClO_4 + H_2SO_4 \rightleftharpoons ClO_4^- + H_3SO_4^+$
(c) $HPO_4^{2-} + H_2SO_4 \rightleftharpoons H_2PO_4^- + HSO_4^-$

18.48 In each equation, label the acids, bases, and conjugate pairs:
(a) $NH_3 + HNO_3 \rightleftharpoons NH_4^+ + NO_3^-$
(b) $O^{2-} + H_2O \rightleftharpoons OH^- + OH^-$
(c) $NH_4^+ + BrO_3^- \rightleftharpoons NH_3 + HBrO_3$

18.49 In each equation, label the acids, bases, and conjugate pairs:
(a) $NH_3 + H_3PO_4 \rightleftharpoons NH_4^+ + H_2PO_4^-$
(b) $CH_3O^- + NH_3 \rightleftharpoons CH_3OH + NH_2^-$
(c) $HPO_4^{2-} + HSO_4^- \rightleftharpoons H_2PO_4^- + SO_4^{2-}$

18.50 In each equation, label the acids, bases, and conjugate pairs:
(a) $NH_4^+ + CN^- \rightleftharpoons NH_3 + HCN$
(b) $H_2O + HS^- \rightleftharpoons OH^- + H_2S$
(c) $HSO_3^- + CH_3NH_2 \rightleftharpoons SO_3^{2-} + CH_3NH_3^+$

18.51 Write balanced net ionic equations for the following reactions, and label the conjugate acid-base pairs:
(a) $NaOH(aq) + NaH_2PO_4(aq) \rightleftharpoons H_2O(l) + Na_2HPO_4(aq)$
(b) $KHSO_4(aq) + K_2CO_3(aq) \rightleftharpoons K_2SO_4(aq) + KHCO_3(aq)$

18.52 Write balanced net ionic equations for the following reactions, and label the conjugate acid-base pairs:
(a) $HNO_3(aq) + Li_2CO_3(aq) \rightleftharpoons LiNO_3(aq) + LiHCO_3(aq)$
(b) $2NH_4Cl(aq) + Ba(OH)_2(aq) \rightleftharpoons 2H_2O(l) + BaCl_2(aq) + 2NH_3(aq)$

18.53 The following aqueous species constitute two conjugate acid-base pairs. Use them to write one acid-base reaction with $K_c > 1$ and another with $K_c < 1$: HS^-, Cl^-, HCl, H_2S.

18.54 The following aqueous species constitute two conjugate acid-base pairs. Use them to write one acid-base reaction with $K_c > 1$ and another with $K_c < 1$: NO_3^-, F^-, HF, HNO_3.

18.55 Use Figure 18.8 (p. 745) to determine whether $K_c > 1$ for
(a) $HCl + NH_3 \rightleftharpoons NH_4^+ + Cl^-$
(b) $H_2SO_3 + NH_3 \rightleftharpoons HSO_3^- + NH_4^+$

18.56 Use Figure 18.8 (p. 745) to determine whether $K_c > 1$ for
(a) $OH^- + HS^- \rightleftharpoons H_2O + S^{2-}$
(b) $HCN + HCO_3^- \rightleftharpoons H_2CO_3 + CN^-$

18.57 Use Figure 18.8 (p. 745) to determine whether $K_c < 1$ for
(a) $NH_4^+ + HPO_4^{2-} \rightleftharpoons NH_3 + H_2PO_4^-$
(b) $HSO_3^- + HS^- \rightleftharpoons H_2SO_3 + S^{2-}$

18.58 Use Figure 18.8 (p. 745) to determine whether $K_c < 1$ for
(a) $H_2PO_4^- + F^- \rightleftharpoons HPO_4^{2-} + HF$
(b) $CH_3COO^- + HSO_4^- \rightleftharpoons CH_3COOH + SO_4^{2-}$

Solving Problems Involving Weak-Acid Equilibria
(Sample Problems 18.7 to 18.10)

Concept Review Questions

18.59 In each of the following cases, is the concentration of acid before and after dissociation nearly the same or very different? Explain your reasoning: (a) a concentrated solution of a strong acid; (b) a concentrated solution of a weak acid; (c) a dilute solution of a weak acid; (d) a dilute solution of a strong acid.

18.60 A sample of 0.0001 *M* HCl has $[H_3O^+]$ close to that of a sample of 0.1 *M* CH_3COOH. Are acetic acid and hydrochloric acid equally strong in these samples? Explain.

18.61 In which of the following solutions will $[H_3O^+]$ be approximately equal to $[CH_3COO^-]$: (a) 0.1 *M* CH_3COOH; (b) 1×10^{-7} *M* CH_3COOH; (c) a solution containing both 0.1 *M* CH_3COOH and 0.1 *M* CH_3COONa? Explain.

18.62 Why do successive K_a's decrease for all polyprotic acids?

Skill-Building Exercises (grouped in similar pairs)

18.63 A 0.15 *M* solution of butanoic acid, $CH_3CH_2CH_2COOH$, contains 1.51×10^{-3} *M* H_3O^+. What is the K_a of butanoic acid?

18.64 A 0.035 *M* solution of a weak acid (HA) has a pH of 4.88. What is the K_a of the acid?

18.65 Nitrous acid, HNO_2, has a K_a of 7.1×10^{-4}. What are $[H_3O^+]$, $[NO_2^-]$, and $[OH^-]$ in 0.60 *M* HNO_2?

18.66 Hydrofluoric acid, HF, has a K_a of 6.8×10^{-4}. What are $[H_3O^+]$, $[F^-]$, and $[OH^-]$ in 0.75 *M* HF?

18.67 Chloroacetic acid, $ClCH_2COOH$, has a pK_a of 2.87. What are $[H_3O^+]$, pH, $[ClCH_2COO^-]$, and $[ClCH_2COOH]$ in 1.25 *M* $ClCH_2COOH$?

18.68 Hypochlorous acid, HClO, has a pK_a of 7.54. What are $[H_3O^+]$, pH, $[ClO^-]$, and [HClO] in 0.115 *M* HClO?

18.69 In a 0.20 *M* solution, a weak acid is 3.0% dissociated.
(a) Calculate the $[H_3O^+]$, pH, $[OH^-]$, and pOH of the solution.
(b) Calculate K_a of the acid.

18.70 In a 0.735 M solution, a weak acid is 12.5% dissociated. (a) Calculate the $[H_3O^+]$, pH, $[OH^-]$, and pOH of the solution. (b) Calculate K_a of the acid.

18.71 A 0.250-mol sample of HX is dissolved in enough H_2O to form 655 mL of solution. If the pH of the solution is 3.54, what is the K_a of HX?

18.72 A 4.85×10^{-3}-mol sample of HY is dissolved in enough H_2O to form 0.095 L of solution. If the pH of the solution is 2.68, what is the K_a of HY?

18.73 The weak acid HZ has a K_a of 2.55×10^{-4}.
(a) Calculate the pH of 0.075 M HZ.
(b) Calculate the pOH of 0.045 M HZ.

18.74 The weak acid HQ has a pK_a of 4.89.
(a) Calculate the $[H_3O^+]$ of 3.5×10^{-2} M HQ.
(b) Calculate the $[OH^-]$ of 0.65 M HQ.

18.75 (a) Calculate the pH of 0.175 M HY, if $K_a = 1.50\times10^{-4}$.
(b) Calculate the pOH of 0.175 M HX, if $K_a = 2.00\times10^{-2}$.

18.76 (a) Calculate the pH of 0.55 M HCN, if $K_a = 6.2\times10^{-10}$.
(b) Calculate the pOH of 0.044 M HIO_3, if $K_a = 0.16$.

18.77 Use Appendix C to calculate the percent dissociation of 0.55 M benzoic acid, C_6H_5COOH.

18.78 Use Appendix C to calculate the percent dissociation of 0.050 M CH_3COOH.

18.79 Use Appendix C to calculate $[H_2S]$, $[HS^-]$, $[S^{2-}]$, $[H_3O^+]$, pH, $[OH^-]$, and pOH in a 0.10 M solution of the diprotic acid hydrosulfuric acid.

18.80 Use Appendix C to calculate $[H_2C_3H_2O_4]$, $[HC_3H_2O_4^-]$, $[C_3H_2O_4^{2-}]$, $[H_3O^+]$, pH, $[OH^-]$, and pOH in a 0.200 M solution of the diprotic acid malonic acid.

Problems in Context

18.81 Acetylsalicylic acid (aspirin), $HC_9H_7O_4$, is the most widely used pain reliever and fever reducer. Find the pH of 0.018 M aqueous aspirin at body temperature (K_a at 37°C = 3.6×10^{-4}).

18.82 Formic acid, HCOOH, the simplest carboxylic acid, is used in the textile and rubber industries and is secreted as a defense by many species of ants (family *Formicidae*). Calculate the percent dissociation of 0.75 M HCOOH.

Weak Bases and Their Relation to Weak Acids

(Sample Problems 18.11 and 18.12)

Concept Review Questions

18.83 What is the key structural feature of all Brønsted-Lowry bases? How does this feature function in an acid-base reaction?

18.84 Why are most anions basic in H_2O? Give formulas of four anions that are not basic.

18.85 Except for the Na^+ spectator ion, aqueous solutions of CH_3COOH and CH_3COONa contain the same species. (a) What are the species (other than H_2O)? (b) Why is 0.1 M CH_3COOH acidic and 0.1 M CH_3COONa basic?

Skill-Building Exercises (grouped in similar pairs)

18.86 Write balanced equations and K_b expressions for these Brønsted-Lowry bases in water:
(a) Pyridine, C_5H_5N (b) CO_3^{2-}

18.87 Write balanced equations and K_b expressions for these Brønsted-Lowry bases in water:
(a) Benzoate ion, $C_6H_5COO^-$ (b) $(CH_3)_3N$

18.88 Write balanced equations and K_b expressions for these Brønsted-Lowry bases in water:
(a) Hydroxylamine, HO—NH_2 (b) HPO_4^{2-}

18.89 Write balanced equations and K_b expressions for these Brønsted-Lowry bases in water:
(a) Guanidine, $(H_2N)_2C{=}NH$ (double-bonded N is most basic)
(b) Acetylide ion, $HC{\equiv}C^-$

18.90 What is the pH of 0.070 M dimethylamine?

18.91 What is the pH of 0.12 M diethylamine?

18.92 What is the pH of 0.25 M ethanolamine?

18.93 What is the pH of 0.26 M aniline?

18.94 (a) What is the K_b of the acetate ion?
(b) What is the K_a of the anilinium ion, $C_6H_5NH_3^+$?

18.95 (a) What is the K_b of the benzoate ion, $C_6H_5COO^-$?
(b) What is the K_a of the 2-hydroxyethylammonium ion, $HOCH_2CH_2NH_3^+$ (pK_b of $HOCH_2CH_2NH_2 = 4.49$)?

18.96 (a) What is the pK_b of ClO_2^-?
(b) What is the pK_a of the dimethylammonium ion, $(CH_3)_2NH_2^+$?

18.97 (a) What is the pK_b of NO_2^-?
(b) What is the pK_a of the hydrazinium ion, $H_2N{-}NH_3^+$ (K_b of hydrazine = 8.5×10^{-7})?

18.98 (a) What is the pH of 0.150 M KCN?
(b) What is the pH of 0.40 M triethylammonium chloride, $(CH_3CH_2)_3NHCl$?

18.99 (a) What is the pH of 0.100 M sodium phenolate, C_6H_5ONa, the sodium salt of phenol?
(b) What is the pH of 0.15 M methylammonium bromide, CH_3NH_3Br (K_b of $CH_3NH_2 = 4.4\times10^{-4}$)?

18.100 (a) What is the pH of 0.65 M potassium formate, HCOOK?
(b) What is the pH of 0.85 M NH_4Br?

18.101 (a) What is the pH of 0.75 M NaF?
(b) What is the pH of 0.88 M pyridinium chloride, C_5H_5NHCl?

Problems in Context

18.102 Sodium hypochlorite solution, sold as chlorine bleach, is potentially dangerous because of the basicity of ClO^-, the active bleaching ingredient. What is $[OH^-]$ in an aqueous solution that is 6.5% NaClO by mass? What is the pH of the solution? (Assume d of solution = 1.0 g/mL.)

18.103 Codeine ($C_{18}H_{21}NO_3$) is a narcotic pain reliever that forms a salt with HCl. What is the pH of 0.050 M codeine hydrochloride (pK_b of codeine = 5.80)?

Molecular Properties and Acid Strength

Concept Review Questions

18.104 Across a period, how does the electronegativity of a nonmetal affect the acidity of its binary hydride?

18.105 How does the atomic size of a nonmetal affect the acidity of its binary hydride?

18.106 A strong acid has a weak bond to its acidic proton, whereas a weak acid has a strong bond to its acidic proton. Explain.

18.107 Perchloric acid, $HClO_4$, is the strongest of the halogen oxoacids, and hypoiodous acid, HIO, is the weakest. What two factors govern this difference in acid strength?

Skill-Building Exercises (grouped in similar pairs)

18.108 Choose the *stronger* acid in each of the following pairs:
(a) H_2SeO_3 or H_2SeO_4 (b) H_3PO_4 or H_3AsO_4 (c) H_2S or H_2Te

18.109 Choose the *weaker* acid in each of the following pairs:
(a) HBr or H_2Se (b) $HClO_4$ or H_2SO_4 (c) H_2SO_3 or H_2SO_4

18.110 Choose the *stronger* acid in each of the following pairs:
(a) H_2Se or H_3As (b) $B(OH)_3$ or $Al(OH)_3$ (c) $HBrO_2$ or HBrO

18.111 Choose the *weaker* acid in each of the following pairs:
(a) HI or HBr (b) H_3AsO_4 or H_2SeO_4 (c) HNO_3 or HNO_2

18.112 Use Appendix C to choose the solution with the *lower* pH:
(a) 0.5 *M* $CuBr_2$ or 0.5 *M* $AlBr_3$
(b) 0.3 *M* $ZnCl_2$ or 0.3 *M* $SnCl_2$

18.113 Use Appendix C to choose the solution with the *lower* pH:
(a) 0.1 *M* $FeCl_3$ or 0.1 *M* $AlCl_3$
(b) 0.1 *M* $BeCl_2$ or 0.1 *M* $CaCl_2$

18.114 Use Appendix C to choose the solution with the *higher* pH:
(a) 0.2 *M* $Ni(NO_3)_2$ or 0.2 *M* $Co(NO_3)_2$
(b) 0.35 *M* $Al(NO_3)_3$ or 0.35 *M* $Cr(NO_3)_3$

18.115 Use Appendix C to choose the solution with the *higher* pH:
(a) 0.1 *M* $NiCl_2$ or 0.1 *M* NaCl
(b) 0.1 *M* $Sn(NO_3)_2$ or 0.1 *M* $Co(NO_3)_2$

Acid-Base Properties of Salt Solutions

(Sample Problems 18.13 and 18.14)

Concept Review Questions

18.116 What determines whether an aqueous solution of a salt will be acidic, basic, or neutral? Give an example of each type of salt.

18.117 Why is aqueous NaF basic but aqueous NaCl neutral?

18.118 The NH_4^+ ion forms acidic solutions, and the CH_3COO^- ion forms basic solutions. However, a solution of ammonium acetate is almost neutral. Do all of the ammonium salts of weak acids form neutral solutions? Explain your answer.

Skill-Building Exercises (grouped in similar pairs)

18.119 Explain with equations and calculations, when necessary, whether an aqueous solution of each of these salts is acidic, basic, or neutral: (a) KBr; (b) NH_4I; (c) KCN.

18.120 Explain with equations and calculations, when necessary, whether an aqueous solution of each of these salts is acidic, basic, or neutral: (a) $Cr(NO_3)_3$; (b) NaHS; (c) $Zn(CH_3COO)_2$.

18.121 Explain with equations and calculations, when necessary, whether an aqueous solution of each of these salts is acidic, basic, or neutral: (a) Na_2CO_3; (b) $CaCl_2$; (c) $Cu(NO_3)_2$.

18.122 Explain with equations and calculations, when necessary, whether an aqueous solution of each of these salts is acidic, basic, or neutral: (a) CH_3NH_3Cl; (b) $KClO_4$; (c) CoF_2.

18.123 Explain with equations and calculations, when necessary, whether an aqueous solution of each of these salts is acidic, basic, or neutral: (a) $SrBr_2$; (b) $Ba(CH_3COO)_2$; (c) $(CH_3)_2NH_2Br$.

18.124 Explain with equations and calculations, when necessary, whether an aqueous solution of each of these salts is acidic, basic, or neutral: (a) $Fe(HCOO)_3$; (b) $KHCO_3$; (c) K_2S.

18.125 Explain with equations and calculations, when necessary, whether an aqueous solution of each of these salts is acidic, basic, or neutral: (a) $(NH_4)_3PO_4$; (b) Na_2SO_4; (c) LiClO.

18.126 Explain with equations and calculations, when necessary, whether an aqueous solution of each of these salts is acidic, basic, or neutral: (a) $Pb(CH_3COO)_2$; (b) $Cr(NO_2)_3$; (c) CsI.

18.127 Rank the following salts in order of *increasing* pH of their 0.1 *M* aqueous solutions:
(a) KNO_3, K_2SO_3, K_2S, $Fe(NO_3)_2$
(b) NH_4NO_3, $NaHSO_4$, $NaHCO_3$, Na_2CO_3

18.128 Rank the following salts in order of *decreasing* pH of their 0.1 *M* aqueous solutions:
(a) $FeCl_2$, $FeCl_3$, $MgCl_2$, $KClO_2$
(b) NH_4Br, $NaBrO_2$, NaBr, $NaClO_2$

Generalizing the Brønsted-Lowry Concept: The Leveling Effect

Concept Review Questions

18.129 Methoxide ion, CH_3O^-, and amide ion, NH_2^-, are very strong bases that are "leveled" by water. What does this mean? Write the reactions that occur in the leveling process. What species do the two leveled solutions have in common?

18.130 Explain the differing extents of dissociation of H_2SO_4 in CH_3COOH, H_2O, and NH_3.

18.131 In H_2O, HF is weak and the other hydrohalic acids are equally strong. In NH_3, however, all the hydrohalic acids are equally strong. Explain.

Electron-Pair Donation and the Lewis Acid-Base Definition

(Sample Problem 18.15)

Concept Review Questions

18.132 What feature must a molecule or ion have for it to act as a Lewis base? A Lewis acid? Explain the roles of these features.

18.133 How do Lewis acids differ from Brønsted-Lowry acids? How are they similar? Do Lewis bases differ from Brønsted-Lowry bases? Explain.

18.134 (a) Is a weak Brønsted-Lowry base necessarily a weak Lewis base? Explain with an example.
(b) Identify the Lewis bases in the following reaction:

$$Cu(H_2O)_4^{2+}(aq) + 4CN^-(aq) \rightleftharpoons Cu(CN)_4^{2-}(aq) + 4H_2O(l)$$

(c) Given that $K_c > 1$ for the reaction in part (b), which Lewis base is stronger?

18.135 In which of the three acid-base concepts can water be a product of an acid-base reaction? In which is it the only product?

18.136 (a) Give an example of a *substance* that is a base in two of the three acid-base definitions, but not in the third.
(b) Give an example of a *substance* that is an acid in one of the three acid-base definitions, but not in the other two.

Skill-Building Exercises (grouped in similar pairs)

18.137 Which are Lewis acids and which are Lewis bases?
(a) Cu^{2+} (b) Cl^- (c) $SnCl_2$ (d) OF_2

18.138 Which are Lewis acids and which are Lewis bases?
(a) Na^+ (b) NH_3 (c) CN^- (d) BF_3

18.139 Which are Lewis acids and which are Lewis bases?
(a) BF_3 (b) S^{2-} (c) SO_3^{2-} (d) SO_3

18.140 Which are Lewis acids and which are Lewis bases?
(a) Mg^{2+} (b) OH^- (c) SiF_4 (d) $BeCl_2$

18.141 Identify the Lewis acid and Lewis base in each equation:
(a) $Na^+ + 6H_2O \rightleftharpoons Na(H_2O)_6{}^+$
(b) $CO_2 + H_2O \rightleftharpoons H_2CO_3$
(c) $F^- + BF_3 \rightleftharpoons BF_4{}^-$

18.142 Identify the Lewis acid and Lewis base in each equation:
(a) $Fe^{3+} + 2H_2O \rightleftharpoons FeOH^{2+} + H_3O^+$
(b) $H_2O + H^- \rightleftharpoons OH^- + H_2$
(c) $4CO + Ni \rightleftharpoons Ni(CO)_4$

18.143 Classify the following as Arrhenius, Brønsted-Lowry, or Lewis acid-base reactions. A reaction may fit all, two, one, or none of the categories:
(a) $Ag^+ + 2NH_3 \rightleftharpoons Ag(NH_3)_2{}^+$
(b) $H_2SO_4 + NH_3 \rightleftharpoons HSO_4{}^- + NH_4{}^+$
(c) $2HCl \rightleftharpoons H_2 + Cl_2$
(d) $AlCl_3 + Cl^- \rightleftharpoons AlCl_4{}^-$

18.144 Classify the following as Arrhenius, Brønsted-Lowry, or Lewis acid-base reactions. A reaction may fit all, two, one, or none of the categories:
(a) $Cu^{2+} + 4Cl^- \rightleftharpoons CuCl_4{}^{2-}$
(b) $Al(OH)_3 + 3HNO_3 \rightleftharpoons Al^{3+} + 3H_2O + 3NO_3{}^-$
(c) $N_2 + 3H_2 \rightleftharpoons 2NH_3$
(d) $CN^- + H_2O \rightleftharpoons HCN + OH^-$

Comprehensive Problems

18.145 Chloral ($Cl_3C{-}CH{=}O$) forms a monohydrate, chloral hydrate, the sleep-inducing depressant called "knockout drops" in old movies. (a) Write two possible structures for chloral hydrate, one involving hydrogen bonding and one that is a Lewis adduct. (b) What spectroscopic method could be used to identify the real structure? Explain.

18.146 In humans, blood pH is maintained within a narrow range: *acidosis* occurs if the blood pH is below 7.35, and *alkalosis* occurs if the pH is above 7.45. Given that the pK_w of blood is 13.63 at 37°C (body temperature), what is the normal range of $[H_3O^+]$ and of $[OH^-]$ in blood?

18.147 The disinfectant phenol, C_6H_5OH, has a pK_a of 10.0 in water, but 14.4 in methanol. (a) Why are the values different? (b) Is methanol a stronger or weaker base than water? (c) Write the dissociation reaction of phenol in methanol. (d) Write an expression for the autoionization constant of methanol.

18.148 When carbon dioxide dissolves in water, it undergoes a multistep equilibrium process, with $K_{overall} = 4.5\times10^{-7}$, which is simplified to the following:

$$CO_2(g) + H_2O(l) \rightleftharpoons H_2CO_3(aq)$$
$$H_2CO_3(aq) + H_2O(l) \rightleftharpoons HCO_3{}^-(aq) + H_3O^+(aq)$$

(a) Classify each step as a Lewis or a Brønsted-Lowry reaction.
(b) What is the pH of nonpolluted rainwater in equilibrium with clean air (P_{CO_2} in clean air $= 3.2\times10^{-4}$ atm; Henry's law constant for CO_2 at 25°C is 0.033 mol/L·atm)?
(c) What is $[CO_3{}^{2-}]$ in rainwater (K_a of $HCO_3{}^- = 4.7\times10^{-11}$)?
(d) If the partial pressure of CO_2 in clean air doubles in the next few decades, what will the pH of rainwater become?

18.149 Seashells are mostly calcium carbonate, which reacts with H_3O^+ according to the equation

$$CaCO_3(s) + H_3O^+(aq) \rightleftharpoons Ca^{2+}(aq) + HCO_3{}^-(aq) + H_2O(l)$$

If K_w increases at higher pressure, will seashells dissolve more rapidly near the surface of the ocean or at great depths? Explain.

18.150 Many molecules with central atoms from Period 3 or higher take part in Lewis acid-base reactions in which the central atom expands its valence shell. $SnCl_4$ reacts with $(CH_3)_3N$ as follows:

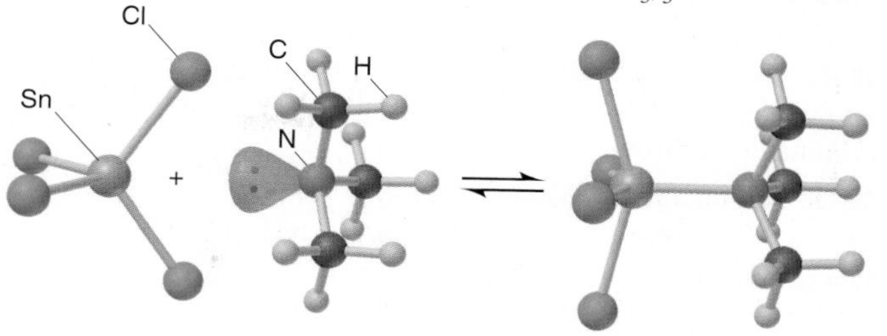

(a) Identify the Lewis acid and the Lewis base in the reaction.
(b) Give the *nl* designation of the sublevel of the central atom in the acid before it accepts the lone pair.

18.151 A chemist makes four successive ten-fold dilutions of 1.0×10^{-5} *M* HCl. Calculate the pH of the original solution and of each diluted solution (through 1.0×10^{-9} *M* HCl).

18.152 Chlorobenzene, C_6H_5Cl, is a key intermediate in the manufacture of dyes and pesticides. It is made by the chlorination of benzene, catalyzed by $FeCl_3$, in this series of steps:
(1) $Cl_2 + FeCl_3 \rightleftharpoons FeCl_5$ (or $Cl^+FeCl_4{}^-$)
(2) $C_6H_6 + Cl^+FeCl_4{}^- \rightleftharpoons C_6H_6Cl^+ + FeCl_4{}^-$
(3) $C_6H_6Cl^+ \rightleftharpoons C_6H_5Cl + H^+$
(4) $H^+ + FeCl_4{}^- \rightleftharpoons HCl + FeCl_3$
(a) Which of the step(s) is (are) Lewis acid-base reactions?
(b) Identify the Lewis acids and bases in each of those steps.

18.153 The beakers shown contain 0.300 L of aqueous solutions of a moderately weak acid HY. Each particle represents 0.010 mol; solvent molecules are omitted for clarity. (a) The reaction in beaker A is at equilibrium. Calculate *Q* for B, C, and D to determine which, if any, is also at equilibrium. (b) For any not at equilibrium, in which direction does the reaction proceed? (c) Does dilution affect the extent of dissociation of a weak acid? Explain.

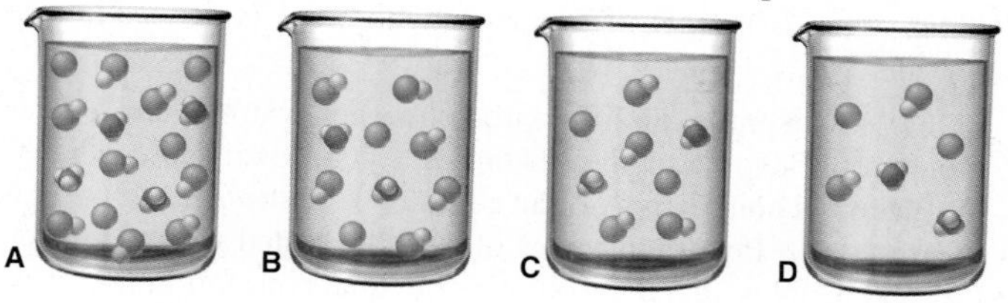

18.154 The strength of an acid or base is related to its strength as an electrolyte. (a) Is the electrical conductivity of 0.1 *M* HCl higher, lower, or the same as that of 0.1 *M* CH_3COOH? Explain.
(b) Is the electrical conductivity of 1×10^{-7} *M* HCl higher, lower, or the same as that of 1×10^{-7} *M* CH_3COOH? Explain.

18.155 Esters, RCOOR′, are formed by the reaction of carboxylic acids, RCOOH, and alcohols, R′OH, where R and R′ are hydrocarbon groups. Many esters are responsible for the odors of fruit and, thus, have important uses in the food and cosmetics industries. The first two steps in the mechanism of ester formation are

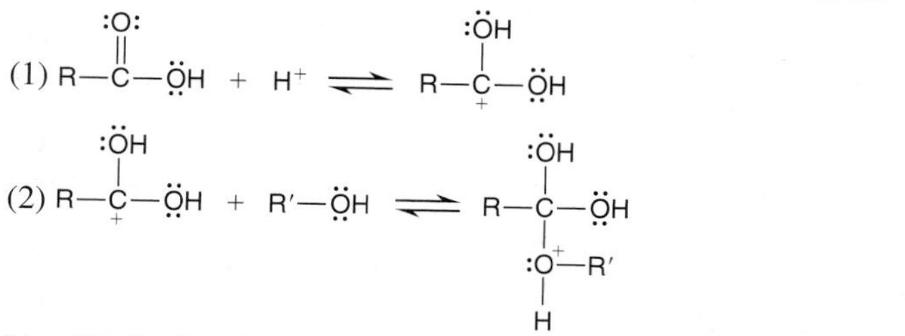

Identify the Lewis acids and Lewis bases in these two steps.

18.156 Three beakers contain 100. mL of 0.10 *M* HCl, $HClO_2$, and HClO, respectively. (a) Find the pH of each. (b) Describe quantitatively how to make the pH equal in the beakers through the addition of water only.

18.157 Human urine has a normal pH of 6.2. If a person eliminates an average of 1250. mL of urine per day, how many H^+ ions are eliminated per week?

18.158 Liquid ammonia autoionizes like water:

$$2NH_3(l) \longrightarrow NH_4^+(am) + NH_2^-(am)$$

where (*am*) represents solvation by NH_3.
(a) Write the ion-product constant expression, K_{am}.
(b) What are the strongest acid and base that can exist in $NH_3(l)$?
(c) HNO_3 and HCOOH are leveled in $NH_3(l)$. Explain with equations.
(d) At the boiling point (−33°C), $K_{am} = 5.1\times10^{-27}$. Calculate $[NH_4^+]$ at this temperature.
(e) Pure sulfuric acid also autoionizes. Write the ion-product constant expression, K_{sulf}, and find the concentration of the conjugate base at 20°C ($K_{sulf} = 2.7\times10^{-4}$ at 20°C).

18.159 Thiamine hydrochloride ($C_{12}H_{18}ON_4SCl_2$) is a water-soluble form of thiamine (vitamin B_1; $K_a = 3.37\times10^{-7}$). How many grams of the hydrochloride must be dissolved in 10.00 mL of water to give a pH of 3.50?

18.160 Tris(hydroxymethyl)aminomethane, known as TRIS or THAM, is a water-soluble base used to synthesize surfactants and pharmaceuticals, as an emulsifying agent in cosmetics, and in cleaning mixtures for textiles and leather. In biomedical research, solutions of TRIS are used to maintain nearly constant pH for the study of enzymes and other cellular components. Given that the pK_b is 5.91, calculate the pH of 0.075 *M* TRIS.

18.161 When an Fe^{3+} salt is dissolved in water, the solution becomes acidic due to formation of $Fe(H_2O)_5OH^{2+}$ and H_3O^+. The overall process involves both Lewis and Brønsted-Lowry acid-base reactions. Write the equations for the process.

18.162 What is the pH of a vinegar with 5.0% (w/v) acetic acid in water?

18.163 How would you differentiate between a strong and a weak monoprotic acid from the results of the following procedures? (a) Electrical conductivity of an equimolar solution of each acid is measured. (b) Equal molarities of each are tested with pH paper. (c) Zinc metal is added to solutions of equal concentration.

18.164 The catalytic efficiency of an enzyme is called its *activity* and refers to the rate at which it catalyzes the reaction. Most enzymes have optimum activity over a relatively narrow pH range, which is related to the pH of the local cellular fluid. The pH profiles of three digestive enzymes are shown.

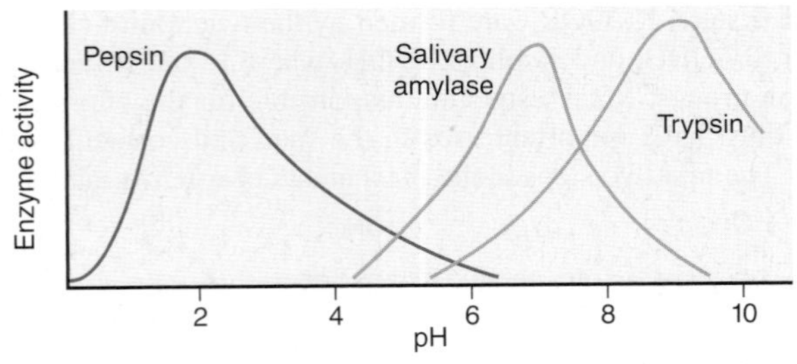

Salivary amylase begins digestion of starches in the mouth and has optimum activity at a pH of 6.8; pepsin begins protein digestion in the stomach and has optimum activity at a pH of 2.0; and trypsin, released in pancreatic juices, continues protein digestion in the small intestine and has optimum activity at a pH of 9.5. Calculate $[H_3O^+]$ in the local cellular fluid for each enzyme.

18.165 Acetic acid has a K_a of 1.8×10^{-5}, and ammonia has a K_b of 1.8×10^{-5}. Find $[H_3O^+]$, $[OH^-]$, pH, and pOH for (a) 0.240 *M* acetic acid and (b) 0.240 *M* ammonia.

18.166 The uses of sodium phosphate include clarifying crude sugar, manufacturing paper, removing boiler scale, and washing concrete. What is the pH of a solution containing 33 g of Na_3PO_4 per liter? What is $[OH^-]$ of this solution?

18.167 The Group 5A(15) hydrides react with boron trihalides in a reversible Lewis acid-base reaction. When 0.15 mol of $PH_3BCl_3(s)$ is introduced into a 3.0-L container at a certain temperature, 8.4×10^{-3} mol of PH_3 is present at equilibrium: $PH_3BCl_3(s) \rightleftharpoons PH_3(g) + BCl_3(g)$. (a) Find K_c for the reaction at this temperature. (b) Draw a Lewis structure for the reactant.

18.168 A 1.000 *m* solution of chloroacetic acid ($ClCH_2COOH$) freezes at −1.93°C. Find the K_a of chloroacetic acid. (Assume the molarities equal the molalities.)

18.169 Sodium stearate ($C_{17}H_{35}COONa$) is a major component of bar soap. The K_a of the stearic acid is 1.3×10^{-5}. What is the pH of 10.0 mL of a solution containing 0.42 g of sodium stearate?

18.170 Calcium propionate [$Ca(CH_3CH_2COO)_2$; calcium propanoate] is a mold inhibitor used in food, tobacco, and pharmaceuticals. (a) Use balanced equations to show whether aqueous calcium propionate is acidic, basic, or neutral. (b) Use Appendix C to find the resulting pH when 8.75 g of $Ca(CH_3CH_2COO)_2$ dissolves in enough water to give 0.500 L of solution.

18.171 A site in Pennsylvania receives a total annual deposition of 2.688 g/m^2 of sulfate from fertilizer and acid rain. The ratio by mass of ammonium sulfate/ammonium bisulfate/sulfuric acid is 3.0/5.5/1.0. (a) How much acid, expressed as kg of sulfuric acid, is deposited over an area of 10. km^2? (b) How many pounds of $CaCO_3$ are needed to neutralize this acid? (c) If 10. km^2 is the area of an unpolluted lake 3 m deep and there is no loss of acid, what pH would be attained in the year? (Assume constant volume.)

18.172 (a) If $K_w = 1.139\times10^{-15}$ at 0°C and 5.474×10^{-14} at 50°C, find $[H_3O^+]$ and pH of water at 0°C and 50°C.
(b) The autoionization constant for heavy water (deuterium oxide, D_2O) is 3.64×10^{-16} at 0°C and 7.89×10^{-15} at 50°C. Find $[D_3O^+]$ and pD of heavy water at 0°C and 50°C.
(c) Suggest a reason for these differences.

18.173 HX ($\mathcal{M}$ = 150. g/mol) and HY ($\mathcal{M}$ = 50.0 g/mol) are weak acids. A solution of 12.0 g/L of HX has the same pH as one containing 6.00 g/L of HY. Which is the stronger acid? Why?

18.174 The beakers below depict the aqueous dissociations of weak acids HA *(blue and green)* and HB *(blue and yellow)*; solvent molecules are omitted for clarity. If the HA solution is 0.50 L, and the HB solution is 0.25 L, and each particle represents 0.010 mol, find the K_a of each acid. Which acid, if either, is stronger?

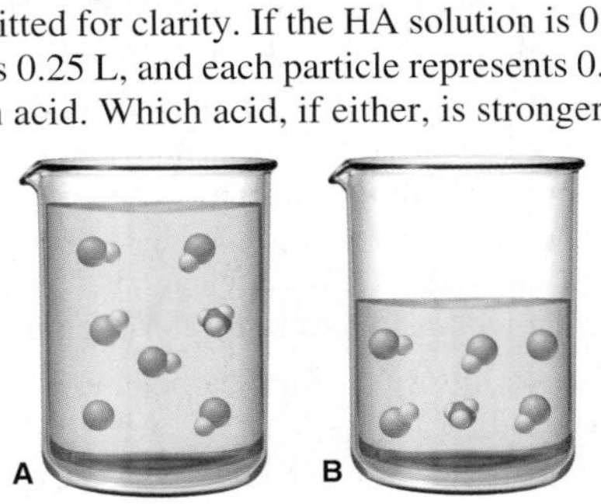

18.175 In his acid-base studies, Arrhenius discovered an important fact involving reactions like the following:

$$KOH(aq) + HNO_3(aq) \longrightarrow ?$$
$$NaOH(aq) + HCl(aq) \longrightarrow ?$$

(a) Complete the reactions and use the data for the individual ions in Appendix B to calculate each ΔH°_{rxn}.
(b) Explain your results and use them to predict ΔH°_{rxn} for

$$KOH(aq) + HCl(aq) \longrightarrow ?$$

18.176 Putrescine [$NH_2(CH_2)_4NH_2$], found in rotting animal tissue, is now known to be in all cells and essential for normal and abnormal (cancerous) growth. It also plays a key role in the formation of GABA, a neurotransmitter. A 0.10 *M* aqueous solution of putrescine has $[OH^-] = 2.1\times10^{-3}$. What is the K_b?

18.177 The molecular scene depicts the relative concentrations of H_3O^+ *(purple)* and OH^- *(green)* in an aqueous solution at 25°C. (Counter ions and solvent molecules are omitted for clarity.) (a) Calculate the pH. (b) How many H_3O^+ ions would you have to draw for every OH^- ion to depict a solution of pH 4?

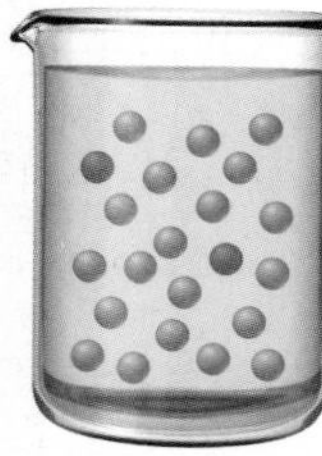

18.178 Polymers are not very soluble in water, but their solubility increases if they have charged groups. (a) Casein, a milk protein, contains many $-COO^-$ groups on its side chains. How does the solubility of casein vary with pH? (b) Histones are proteins essential to the function of DNA. They are weakly basic due to the presence of side chains with $-NH_2$ and $=NH$ groups. How does the solubility of a histone vary with pH?

18.179 Hemoglobin (Hb) transports oxygen in the blood:

$$HbH^+(aq) + O_2(aq) + H_2O(l) \longrightarrow HbO_2(aq) + H_3O^+(aq)$$

In blood, $[H_3O^+]$ is held nearly constant at 4×10^{-8} *M*.
(a) How does the equilibrium position change in the lungs?
(b) How does it change in O_2-deficient cells?
(c) Excessive vomiting may lead to metabolic *alkalosis,* in which $[H_3O^+]$ in blood *decreases.* How does this condition affect the ability of Hb to transport O_2?
(d) Diabetes mellitus may lead to metabolic *acidosis,* in which $[H_3O^+]$ in blood *increases.* How does this condition affect the ability of Hb to transport O_2?

18.180 Nitrogen is discharged from wastewater treatment facilities into rivers and streams, usually as NH_3 and NH_4^+:

$$NH_3(aq) + H_2O(l) \rightleftharpoons NH_4^+(aq) + OH^-(aq) \quad K_b = 1.76\times10^{-5}$$

One strategy for removing it is to raise the pH and "strip" the NH_3 from solution by bubbling air through the water. (a) At pH 7.00, what fraction of the total nitrogen in solution is NH_3, defined as $[NH_3]/([NH_3] + [NH_4^+])$? (b) What is the fraction at pH 10.00? (c) Explain the basis of ammonia stripping.

18.181 A solution of propanoic acid (CH_3CH_2COOH), made by dissolving 7.500 g in sufficient water to make 100.0 mL, has a freezing point of −1.890°C.
(a) Calculate the molarity of the solution.
(b) Calculate the molarity of the propanoate ion. (Assume the molarity of the solution equals the molality.)
(c) Calculate the percent dissociation of propanoic acid.

18.182 The antimalarial properties of quinine ($C_{20}H_{24}N_2O_2$) saved thousands of lives during construction of the Panama Canal. This substance is a classic example of the medicinal wealth of tropical forests. Both N atoms are basic, but the N (colored) of the 3° amine group is far more basic ($pK_b = 5.1$) than the N within the aromatic ring system ($pK_b = 9.7$). (a) A saturated solution of quinine in water is only 1.6×10^{-3} *M*. What is the pH of this solution?

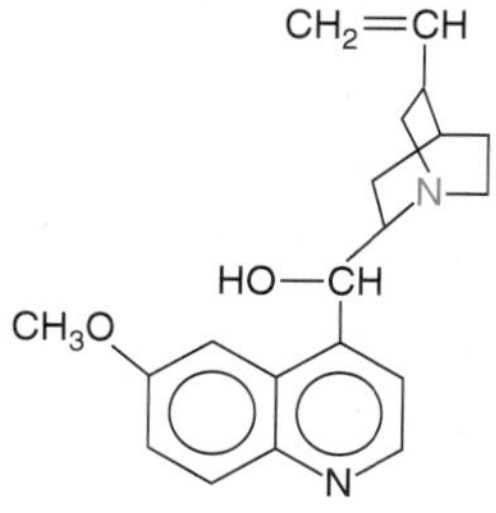

(b) Show that the aromatic N contributes negligibly to the pH of the solution.
(c) Because of its low solubility, quinine is given as the salt quinine hydrochloride ($C_{20}H_{24}N_2O_2\cdot HCl$), which is 120 times more soluble than quinine. What is the pH of 0.33 *M* quinine hydrochloride?
(d) An antimalarial concentration in water is 1.5% quinine hydrochloride by mass (*d* = 1.0 g/mL). What is the pH?

18.183 Drinking water is often disinfected with Cl_2, which hydrolyzes to form HClO, a weak acid but powerful disinfectant:

$$Cl_2(aq) + 2H_2O(l) \longrightarrow HClO(aq) + H_3O^+(aq) + Cl^-(aq)$$

The fraction of HClO in solution is defined as

$$\frac{[HClO]}{[HClO] + [ClO^-]}$$

(a) What is the fraction of HClO at pH 7.00 (K_a of HClO $= 2.9\times10^{-8}$)? (b) What is the fraction at pH 10.00?

18.184 The following scenes represent three weak acids HA (where A = X, Y, or Z) dissolved in water (H_2O is not shown):

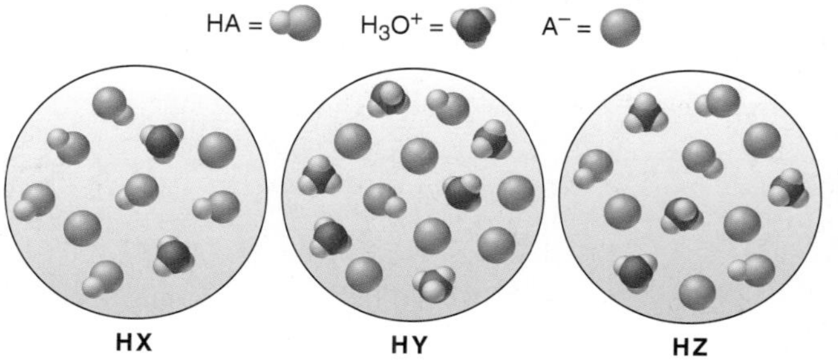

(a) Rank the acids in order of increasing K_a. (b) Rank the acids in order of increasing pK_a. (c) Rank the conjugate bases in order of increasing pK_b. (d) What is the percent dissociation of HX? (e) If equimolar amounts of the sodium salts of the acids (NaX, NaY, and NaZ) were dissolved in water, which solution would have the highest pOH? The lowest pH?

Ionic Equilibria in Aqueous Systems

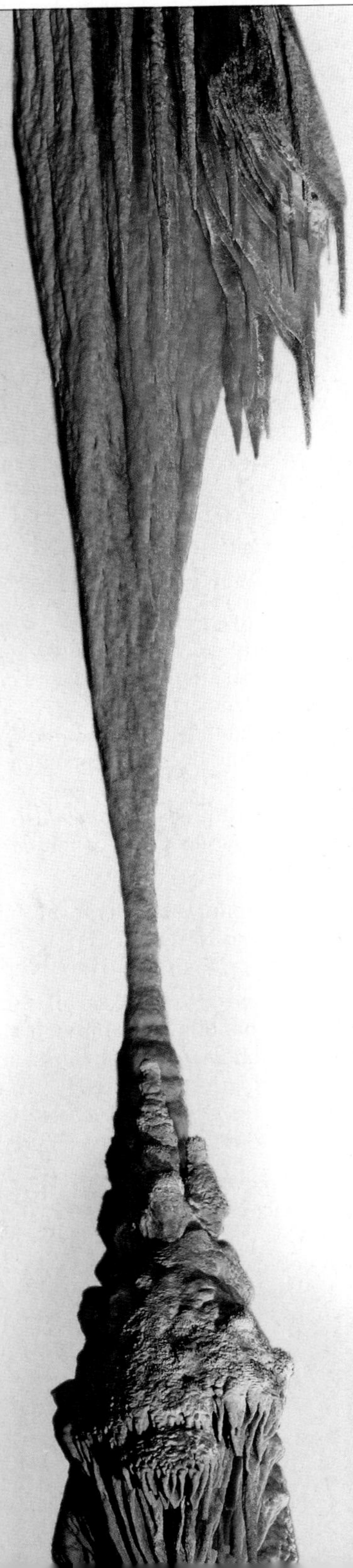

19

Concepts and skills to review before you study this chapter

- solubility rules for ionic compounds (Section 4.3)
- effect of concentration on equilibrium position (Section 17.6)
- conjugate acid-base pairs (Section 18.3)
- calculations for weak-acid and weak-base equilibria (Sections 18.4 and 18.5)
- acid-base properties of salt solutions (Section 18.7)
- Lewis acids and bases (Section 18.9)

Expanding our view of the universal nature of equilibrium, we now examine aqueous ionic systems. The unique formations in limestone caves (*photo*) and the vast expanses of oceanic coral reefs arise from subtle shifts in carbonate solubility equilibria. Similar interactions prevent acidification of lakes. Organisms survive by maintaining cellular pH within narrow limits through complex carbonate and phosphate equilibria. In soils, equilibria involving clays control the availability of ionic nutrients for plants. In industrial settings, the same principles govern the softening of water and the purification of products by precipitation of unwanted ions. And they even explain how the weak acids in wine and vinegar influence the delicate taste of a fine sauce.

IN THIS CHAPTER . . . We define and quantify three aqueous ionic equilibrium systems—acid-base buffers, slightly soluble salts, and complex ions.

- We introduce the common-ion effect to explain how buffers work, and see why buffers are important and how to prepare them.
- We describe several types of acid-base titrations and the role of buffers in them.
- We see that slightly soluble salts have their own equilibrium constant and learn how a common ion and pH influence the solubility of these compounds.
- We use concepts of aqueous ionic equilibria to understand how a cave forms.
- We investigate how complex ions form and change from one type to another.

19.1 • EQUILIBRIA OF ACID-BASE BUFFERS

Why do some lakes become acidic when showered by acid rain, while others remain unaffected? How does blood maintain a constant pH in contact with countless cellular acid-base reactions? How can a chemist sustain a nearly constant $[H_3O^+]$ in reactions that consume or produce H_3O^+ or OH^-? The answer in each case depends on the action of a buffer, and in this section we discuss how buffers work and how to prepare them.

What a Buffer Is and How It Works: The Common-Ion Effect

In everyday language, a buffer is something that lessens the impact of an external force. An **acid-base buffer** is a solution that *lessens the impact on pH from the addition of acid or base*. Add a small amount of H_3O^+ or OH^- to an unbuffered solution, and the pH changes by several units, thus, $[H_3O^+]$ changes by *several orders of magnitude* (Figure 19.1).

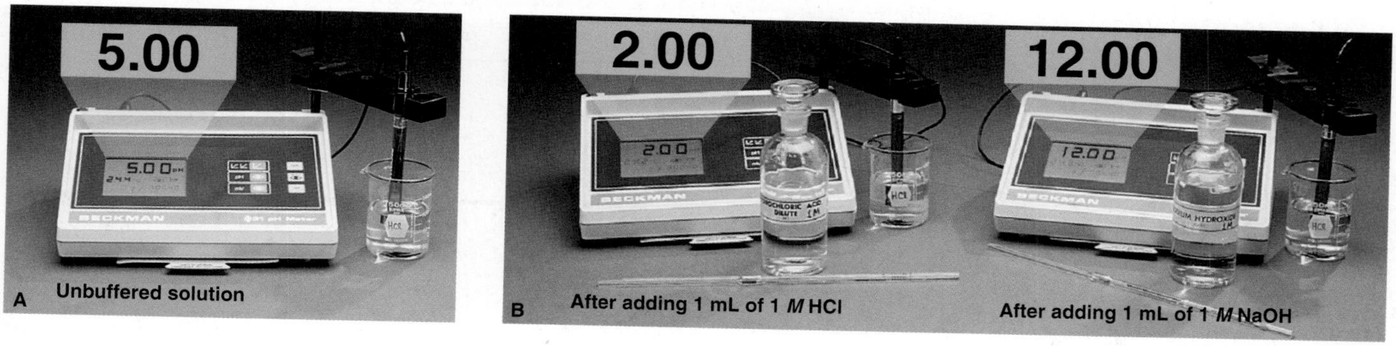

Figure 19.1 The effect of adding acid or base to an unbuffered solution. **A,** A 100-mL sample of dilute HCl is adjusted to pH 5.00 (*left*). **B,** Adding 1 mL of strong acid (*left*) or of strong base (*right*) changes the pH by several units.

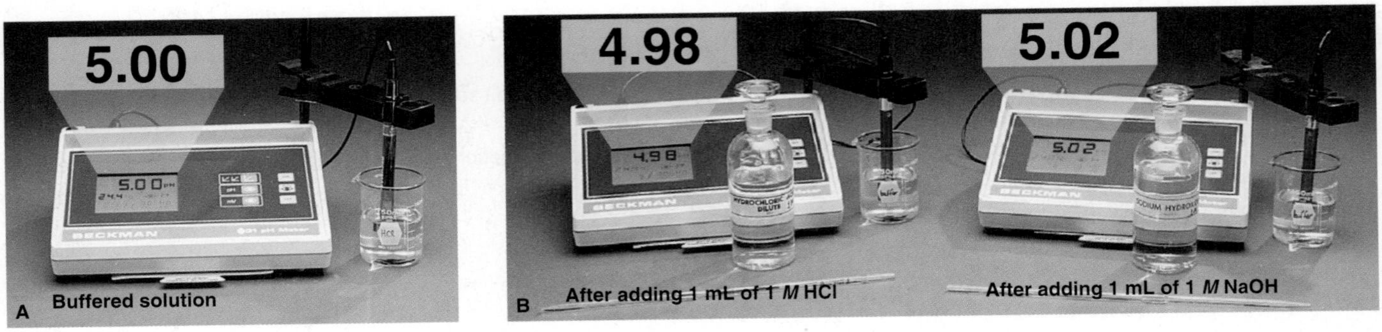

Figure 19.2 The effect of adding acid or base to a buffered solution. **A,** A 100-mL sample of an acetate buffer, which was made by mixing 1 *M* CH_3COOH with 1 *M* CH_3COONa, is adjusted to pH 5.00. **B,** Adding 1 mL of strong acid (*left*) or of strong base (*right*) changes the pH negligibly.

The same addition of strong acid or strong base to a buffered solution causes only a minor change in pH (Figure 19.2). To withstand these additions, a buffer must have an acidic component that reacts with the added OH^- *and* a basic component that reacts with the added H_3O^+. However, these components can't be any acid and base because they would neutralize each other. Most often, *the components of a buffer are a conjugate acid-base pair* (weak acid and conjugate base or weak base and conjugate acid). The buffer in Figure 19.2, for example, is a mixture of acetic acid (CH_3COOH) and acetate ion (CH_3COO^-).

Presence of a Common Ion Buffers work through the **common-ion effect.** When you dissolve acetic acid in water, the acid dissociates slightly:

$$CH_3COOH(aq) + H_2O(l) \rightleftharpoons H_3O^+(aq) + CH_3COO^-(aq)$$

What happens if you now introduce acetate ion by adding the soluble salt sodium acetate? From Le Châtelier's principle (Section 17.6), we know that adding CH_3COO^- ion will shift the equilibrium position to the left; thus, $[H_3O^+]$ decreases, in effect lowering the extent of acid dissociation:

$$CH_3COOH(aq) + H_2O(l) \overset{\longleftarrow}{\rightleftharpoons} H_3O^+(aq) + CH_3COO^-(aq;\text{ added})$$

We get the same result when we add acetic acid to a sodium acetate solution instead of water. The acetate ion already present suppresses the acid from dissociating as much as it does in water, thus keeping the $[H_3O^+]$ lower. In either case, the effect is less acid dissociation. Acetate ion is called *the common ion* because it is "common" to both the acetic acid and sodium acetate solutions. *The common-ion effect occurs when a given ion is added to an equilibrium mixture that already contains that ion, and the position of equilibrium shifts away from forming it.*

Table 19.1 shows that the percent dissociation (and the $[H_3O^+]$) of an acetic acid solution decreases as the concentration of acetate ion (supplied by dissolving sodium acetate) increases. Thus, the *common ion, A^-, suppresses the dissociation of HA,* which makes the solution less acidic (higher pH).

Table 19.1 The Effect of Added Acetate Ion on the Dissociation of Acetic Acid

$[CH_3COOH]_{init}$	$[CH_3COO^-]_{added}$	% Dissociation*	H_3O^+	pH
0.10	0.00	1.3	1.3×10^{-3}	2.89
0.10	0.050	0.036	3.6×10^{-5}	4.44
0.10	0.10	0.018	1.8×10^{-5}	4.74
0.10	0.15	0.012	1.2×10^{-5}	4.92

$$\text{*\% Dissociation} = \frac{[CH_3COOH]_{dissoc}}{[CH_3COOH]_{init}} \times 100$$

Relative Concentrations of Buffer Components A buffer works because *large amounts of the acidic (HA) and basic (A^-) components consume small amounts of added OH^- or H_3O^+, respectively*. Consider what happens in a solution containing high $[CH_3COOH]$ and high $[CH_3COO^-]$ when we add small amounts of strong acid or base. The equilibrium expression for HA dissociation is

$$K_a = \frac{[CH_3COO^-][H_3O^+]}{[CH_3COOH]}$$

Solving for $[H_3O^+]$ gives

$$[H_3O^+] = K_a \times \frac{[CH_3COOH]}{[CH_3COO^-]}$$

Since K_a is constant, *the $[H_3O^+]$ of the solution depends on the buffer-component concentration ratio,* $\frac{[CH_3COOH]}{[CH_3COO^-]}$:

- If the ratio $[HA]/[A^-]$ goes up, $[H_3O^+]$ goes up.
- If the ratio $[HA]/[A^-]$ goes down, $[H_3O^+]$ goes down.

Let's track this ratio as we add strong acid or strong base to a buffer in which $[HA] = [A^-]$ (Figure 19.3, *middle*):

1. *Strong acid*. When we add a small amount of strong acid, the H_3O^+ ions react with an *equal (stoichiometric) amount* of acetate ion from the buffer to form more acetic acid:

$$H_3O^+(aq;\ \text{added}) + CH_3COO^-(aq;\ \text{from buffer}) \longrightarrow CH_3COOH(aq) + H_2O(l)$$

As a result, $[CH_3COO^-]$ goes down by that small amount and $[CH_3COOH]$ goes up by that amount, which increases the buffer-component concentration ratio (Figure 19.3, *to the left*). The $[H_3O^+]$ increases *very* slightly.

2. *Strong base*. The addition of a small amount of strong base produces the opposite result. The OH^- ions react with an *equal (stoichiometric) amount* of CH_3COOH from the buffer to form that much more CH_3COO^- (Figure 19.3, *to the right*):

$$CH_3COOH(aq;\ \text{from buffer}) + OH^-(aq;\ \text{added}) \longrightarrow CH_3COO^-(aq) + H_2O(l)$$

This time, the buffer-component concentration ratio decreases, which decreases $[H_3O^+]$ *very* slightly.

Thus, the buffer components consume *nearly all* the added H_3O^+ or OH^-. To reiterate, as long as the amount of added H_3O^+ or OH^- is small compared with the

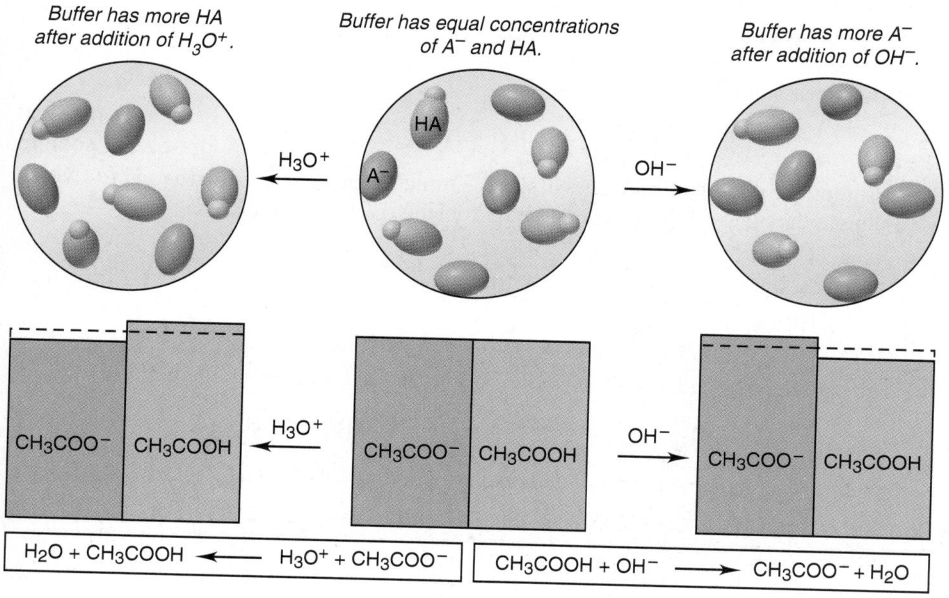

Figure 19.3 How a buffer works. The relative concentrations of the buffer components, acetic acid (CH_3COOH, *red*) and acetate ion (CH_3COO^-, *blue*) are indicated by the heights of the bars.

amounts of the buffer components, *the conversion of one component into the other produces a small change in the buffer-component concentration ratio and, consequently, a small change in [H_3O^+] and in pH.* Sample Problem 19.1 demonstrates how small these pH changes typically are. Note that the latter two parts of the problem combine a stoichiometry portion, like the problems in Chapter 3, and a weak-acid dissociation portion, like those in Chapter 18.

Sample Problem 19.1 Calculating the Effect of Added H_3O^+ or OH^- on Buffer pH

Problem Calculate the pH:
(a) Of a buffer solution consisting of 0.50 *M* CH_3COOH and 0.50 *M* CH_3COONa
(b) After adding 0.020 mol of solid NaOH to 1.0 L of the buffer solution in part (a)
(c) After adding 0.020 mol of HCl to 1.0 L of the buffer solution in part (a)
K_a of $CH_3COOH = 1.8\times10^{-5}$. (Assume the additions cause negligible volume changes.)

Plan For each part, we know, or can find, $[CH_3COOH]_{init}$ and $[CH_3COO^-]_{init}$. We know the K_a of CH_3COOH (1.8×10^{-5}) and need to find [H_3O^+] at equilibrium and convert it to pH. **(a)** We use the given concentrations of buffer components (each 0.50 *M*) as the initial values. As in earlier problems, we assume that x, the [CH_3COOH] that dissociates, which equals [H_3O^+], is so small relative to $[CH_3COOH]_{init}$ that it can be neglected. We set up a reaction table, solve for x, and check the assumption. **(b)** and **(c)** We assume that the added OH^- or H_3O^+ reacts completely with the buffer components to yield new $[CH_3COOH]_{init}$ and $[CH_3COO^-]_{init}$, and then the acid dissociates to an unknown extent. We set up two reaction tables. The first summarizes the stoichiometry of adding strong base (0.020 mol) or acid (0.020 mol). The second summarizes the dissociation of the new $[CH_3COOH]_{init}$, and we proceed as in part (a) to find the new [H_3O^+].

Solution (a) The original pH: [H_3O^+] in the original buffer. Setting up a reaction table with $x = [CH_3COOH]_{dissoc} = [H_3O^+]$ (as in Chapter 18, we assume that [H_3O^+] from H_2O is negligible and disregard it):

Concentration (*M*)	$CH_3COOH(aq)$	+ $H_2O(l)$	$\rightleftharpoons$ $CH_3COO^-(aq)$	+ $H_3O^+(aq)$
Initial	0.50	—	0.50	0
Change	$-x$	—	$+x$	$+x$
Equilibrium	$0.50 - x$	—	$0.50 + x$	x

Making the assumption and finding the equilibrium [CH_3COOH] and [CH_3COO^-]: With K_a small, x is small, so we assume

$$[CH_3COOH] = 0.50\ M - x \approx 0.50\ M \quad \text{and} \quad [CH_3COO^-] = 0.50\ M + x \approx 0.50\ M$$

Solving for x ([H_3O^+] at equilibrium):

$$x = [H_3O^+] = K_a \times \frac{[CH_3COOH]}{[CH_3COO^-]} \approx (1.8\times10^{-5}) \times \frac{0.50}{0.50} = 1.8\times10^{-5}\ M$$

Checking the assumption:

$$\frac{1.8\times10^{-5}\ M}{0.50\ M} \times 100 = 3.6\times10^{-3}\% < 5\%$$

The assumption is justified, and we will use the same assumption in parts (b) and (c). Also, according to the other criterion (see Sample Problems 17.10 and 18.8),

$$\frac{[HA]_{init}}{K_a} = \frac{0.50}{1.8\times10^{-5}} = 2.8\times10^{4} > 400$$

Calculating pH:

$$pH = -\log[H_3O^+] = -\log(1.8\times10^{-5}) = 4.74$$

(b) The pH after adding base (0.020 mol of NaOH to 1.0 L of buffer). Finding $[OH^-]_{added}$:

$$[OH^-]_{added} = \frac{0.020\ \text{mol}\ OH^-}{1.0\ \text{L soln}} = 0.020\ M\ OH^-$$

Setting up a reaction table for the *stoichiometry* of adding OH^- to CH_3COOH:

Concentration (*M*)	$CH_3COOH(aq)$	+ $OH^-(aq)$	$\longrightarrow$ $CH_3COO^-(aq)$	+ $H_2O(l)$
Initial	0.50	0.020	0.50	—
Change	−0.020	−0.020	+0.020	—
Final	0.48	0	0.52	—

Setting up a reaction table for the *acid dissociation,* using these new initial concentrations. As in part (a), $x = [CH_3COOH]_{dissoc} = [H_3O^+]$:

Concentration (*M*)	$CH_3COOH(aq)$ +	$H_2O(l)$ ⇌	$CH_3COO^-(aq)$ +	$H_3O^+(aq)$
Initial	0.48	—	0.52	0
Change	$-x$	—	$+x$	$+x$
Equilibrium	$0.48 - x$	—	$0.52 + x$	x

Making the assumption that x is small, and solving for x:

$$[CH_3COOH] = 0.48\ M - x \approx 0.48\ M \quad \text{and} \quad [CH_3COO^-] = 0.52\ M + x \approx 0.52\ M$$

$$x = [H_3O^+] = K_a \times \frac{[CH_3COOH]}{[CH_3COO^-]} \approx (1.8\times10^{-5}) \times \frac{0.48}{0.52} = 1.7\times10^{-5}\ M$$

Calculating the pH:

$$pH = -\log [H_3O^+] = -\log (1.7\times10^{-5}) = 4.77$$

The addition of strong base increased the concentration of the basic buffer component at the expense of the acidic buffer component. Note especially that the pH *increased only slightly,* from 4.74 to 4.77.

(c) The pH after adding acid (0.020 mol of HCl to 1.0 L of buffer). Finding $[H_3O^+]_{added}$:

$$[H_3O^+]_{added} = \frac{0.020\ \text{mol}\ H_3O^+}{1.0\ \text{L soln}} = 0.020\ M\ H_3O^+$$

Now we proceed as in part (b), by first setting up a reaction table for the *stoichiometry* of adding H_3O^+ to CH_3COO^-:

Concentration (*M*)	$CH_3COO^-(aq)$ +	$H_3O^+(aq)$ ⟶	$CH_3COOH(aq)$ +	$H_2O(l)$
Initial	0.50	0.020	0.50	—
Change	−0.020	−0.020	+0.020	—
Final	0.48	0	0.52	—

The reaction table for the *acid dissociation,* with $x = [CH_3COOH]_{dissoc} = [H_3O^+]$ is

Concentration (*M*)	$CH_3COOH(aq)$ +	$H_2O(l)$ ⇌	$CH_3COO^-(aq)$ +	$H_3O^+(aq)$
Initial	0.52	—	0.48	0
Change	$-x$	—	$+x$	$+x$
Equilibrium	$0.52 - x$	—	$0.48 + x$	x

Making the assumption that x is small, and solving for x:

$$[CH_3COOH] = 0.52\ M - x \approx 0.52\ M \quad \text{and} \quad [CH_3COO^-] = 0.48\ M + x \approx 0.48\ M$$

$$x = [H_3O^+] = K_a \times \frac{[CH_3COOH]}{[CH_3COO^-]} \approx (1.8\times10^{-5}) \times \frac{0.52}{0.48} = 2.0\times10^{-5}\ M$$

Calculating the pH:

$$pH = -\log [H_3O^+] = -\log (2.0\times10^{-5}) = 4.70$$

The addition of strong acid increased the concentration of the acidic buffer component at the expense of the basic buffer component and *lowered* the pH only slightly, from 4.74 to 4.70.

Check The changes in $[CH_3COOH]$ and $[CH_3COO^-]$ occur in opposite directions in parts (b) and (c), which makes sense. The additions were of equal amounts, so the pH increase in (b) should equal the pH decrease in (c), within rounding.

Comment In part (a), we justified our assumption that x can be neglected. Therefore, in parts (b) and (c), we could have used the "Final" values from the last line of the stoichiometry reaction tables directly for the ratio of buffer components; that would have allowed us to dispense with a reaction table for the acid dissociation. In subsequent problems in this chapter, we will follow this more straightforward approach.

Follow-Up Problem 19.1 Calculate the pH of a buffer consisting of 0.50 *M* HF and 0.45 *M* F^- **(a)** before and **(b)** after addition of 0.40 g of NaOH to 1.0 L of the buffer (K_a of HF $= 6.8\times10^{-4}$).

The Henderson-Hasselbalch Equation

For any weak acid, HA, the dissociation equation and K_a expression are

$$HA + H_2O \rightleftharpoons H_3O^+ + A^-$$

$$K_a = \frac{[H_3O^+][A^-]}{[HA]}$$

The key variable that determines $[H_3O^+]$ is the concentration *ratio* of acid species to base species, so, as before, rearranging to isolate $[H_3O^+]$ gives

$$[H_3O^+] = K_a \times \frac{[HA]}{[A^-]}$$

Taking the negative common (base 10) logarithm of both sides gives

$$-\log [H_3O^+] = -\log K_a - \log\left(\frac{[HA]}{[A^-]}\right)$$

from which definitions give $\text{pH} = \text{p}K_a - \log \frac{[HA]}{[A^-]}$

Then, because of the nature of logarithms, when we invert the buffer-component concentration ratio, the sign of the logarithm changes, to give $\text{pH} = \text{p}K_a + \log\left(\frac{[A^-]}{[HA]}\right)$.

Generalizing the previous equation for any conjugate acid-base pair gives the **Henderson-Hasselbalch equation:**

$$\text{pH} = \text{p}K_a + \log\left(\frac{[\text{base}]}{[\text{acid}]}\right) \quad (19.1)$$

This relationship allows us to solve directly for pH instead of having to calculate $[H_3O^+]$ first. For instance, using the Henderson-Hasselbalch equation in part (b) of Sample Problem 19.1, the pH of the buffer after the addition of NaOH is

$$\text{pH} = \text{p}K_a + \log\left(\frac{[CH_3COO^-]}{[CH_3COOH]}\right) = 4.74 + \log\left(\frac{0.52}{0.48}\right) = 4.77$$

Buffer Capacity and Buffer Range

Let's consider two key aspects of a buffer—its capacity and the closely related range.

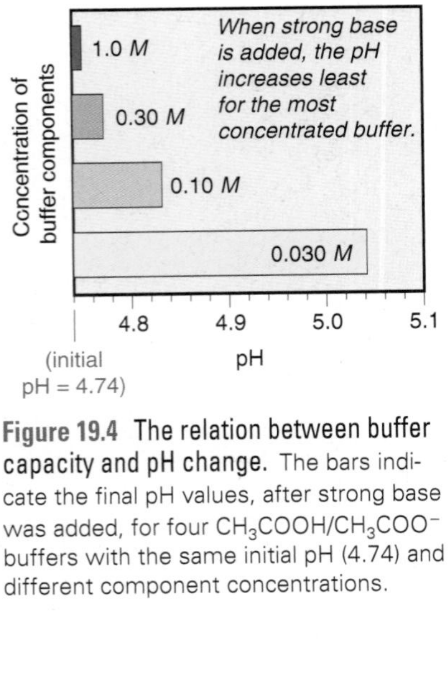

Figure 19.4 The relation between buffer capacity and pH change. The bars indicate the final pH values, after strong base was added, for four CH_3COOH/CH_3COO^- buffers with the same initial pH (4.74) and different component concentrations.

Buffer Capacity **Buffer capacity** is a measure of the "strength" of the buffer, its ability to maintain the pH following addition of strong acid or base. Capacity depends ultimately on component concentrations, both the absolute and relative concentrations:

1. In terms of *absolute* concentrations, *the more concentrated the buffer components, the greater the capacity.* Thus, for a given amount of added H_3O^+ or OH^-, the pH of a higher capacity buffer changes less than the pH of a lower capacity buffer (Figure 19.4). Note that *buffer pH is independent of buffer capacity.* A buffer made of equal volumes of 1.0 M CH_3COOH and 1.0 M CH_3COO^- has the same pH (4.74) as a buffer made of equal volumes of 0.10 M CH_3COOH and 0.10 M CH_3COO^-, but the more concentrated buffer has a greater capacity.

2. In terms of *relative* concentrations, *the closer the component concentrations are to each other, the greater the capacity.* As a buffer functions, the concentration of one component increases relative to the other. Because the concentration ratio determines the pH, the less the ratio changes, the less the pH changes. Let's compare the percent change in component concentration ratio for a buffer at two different initial ratios:

- Add 0.010 mol of OH^- to 1.00 L of buffer with initial concentrations $[HA] = [A^-] = 1.000\ M$: $[A^-]$ becomes 1.010 M and $[HA]$ becomes 0.990 M,

$$\frac{[A^-]_{init}}{[HA]_{init}} = \frac{1.000\ M}{1.000\ M} = 1.000 \qquad \frac{[A^-]_{final}}{[HA]_{final}} = \frac{1.010\ M}{0.990\ M} = 1.02$$

$$\text{Percent change} = \frac{1.02 - 1.000}{1.000} \times 100 = 2\%$$

- Add 0.010 mol of OH^- to 1.00 L of buffer with initial concentrations [HA] = 0.250 *M* and $[A^-]$ = 1.750 *M*: $[A^-]$ becomes 1.760 *M* and [HA] becomes 0.240 *M*,

$$\frac{[A^-]_{init}}{[HA]_{init}} = \frac{1.750\ M}{0.250\ M} = 7.00 \qquad \frac{[A^-]_{final}}{[HA]_{final}} = \frac{1.760\ M}{0.240\ M} = 7.33$$

$$\text{Percent change} = \frac{7.33 - 7.00}{7.00} \times 100 = 4.7\%$$

Note that the change in the concentration ratio is more than twice as large when the initial component concentrations are different than when they are the same. Thus, *a buffer has the highest capacity when the component concentrations are equal.* In the Henderson-Hasselbalch equation, when $[A^-] = [HA]$, their ratio is 1, the log term is 0, and so pH = pK_a:

$$pH = pK_a + \log\left(\frac{[A^-]}{[HA]}\right) = pK_a + \log 1 = pK_a + 0 = pK_a$$

Therefore, *a buffer whose pH is equal to or near the pK_a of its acid component has the highest capacity* for a given concentration.

Buffer Range **Buffer range** is the pH range over which the buffer is effective and is also related to the *relative* buffer-component concentrations. The further the concentration ratio is from 1, the less effective the buffer (the lower the buffer capacity). In practice, if the $[A^-]/[HA]$ ratio is greater than 10 or less than 0.1—that is, if one component concentration is more than 10 times the other—buffering action is poor. Since log 10 = +1 and log 0.1 = −1, *buffers have a usable range within ±1 pH unit of the pK_a of the acid component:*

$$pH = pK_a + \log\left(\frac{10}{1}\right) = pK_a + 1 \qquad \text{and} \qquad pH = pK_a + \log\left(\frac{1}{10}\right) = pK_a - 1$$

Sample Problem 19.2 Using Molecular Scenes to Examine Buffers

Problem The molecular scenes below represent samples of four HA/A^- buffers. (HA is blue and green, A^- is green, and other ions and water are not shown.)

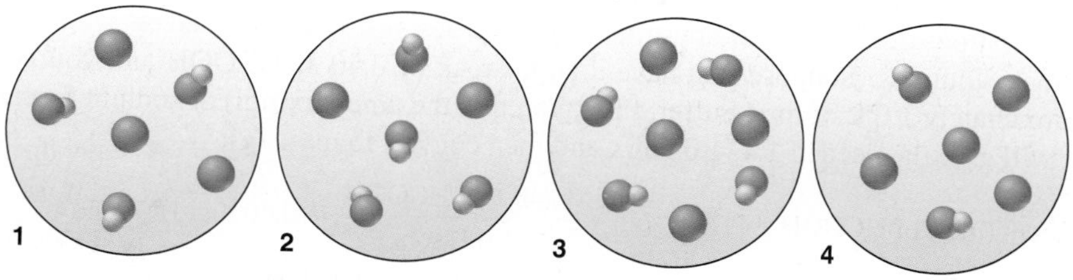

(a) Which buffer has the highest pH?
(b) Which buffer has the greatest capacity?
(c) Should we add a small amount of concentrated strong acid or strong base to convert sample 1 to sample 2 (assuming no volume change)?

Plan The molecular scenes show varying numbers of weak acid molecules (HA) and the conjugate base (A^-). Because the volumes are equal, the scenes represent molarities as well as numbers. **(a)** As the pH rises, more HA loses its H^+ and becomes A^-, so the $[A^-]/[HA]$ ratio will increase. We examine the scenes to see which has the highest ratio. **(b)** Buffer capacity depends on buffer-component concentration *and* ratio. We examine the scenes to see which has a high concentration and a ratio close to 1. **(c)** Adding strong acid converts some A^- to HA, and adding strong base does the opposite. Comparing the $[A^-]/[HA]$ ratios in samples 1 and 2 tells us which to add.

Solution **(a)** The $[A^-]/[HA]$ ratios are as follows: For sample 1, $[A^-]/[HA] = 3/3 = 1$. Similarly, sample 2 = 0.5; sample 3 = 1; sample 4 = 2. Sample 4 has the highest pH because it has the highest $[A^-]/[HA]$ ratio.
(b) Samples 1 and 3 have a $[A^-]/[HA]$ ratio of 1, but sample 3 has the greater capacity because it has a higher concentration.
(c) Sample 2 has a lower $[A^-]/[HA]$ ratio than sample 1, so we would add strong acid to sample 1 to convert some A^- to HA.

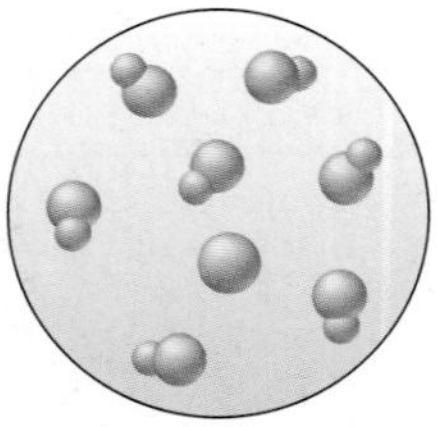

Follow-Up Problem 19.2 The molecular scene (*see margin*) shows a sample of an HB/B^- buffer. (HB is blue and yellow, B^- is yellow, and other ions and water are not shown.)
(a) Would you add a small amount of concentrated strong acid or strong base to increase the buffer capacity?
(b) Assuming no volume change, draw a scene that represents the buffer with the highest possible capacity after the addition in part (a).

Preparing a Buffer

Even though chemical supply-houses offer buffers in a variety of pH values and concentrations, you may have to prepare a specific one, for example, in an environmental or biomedical application. Several steps are required to prepare a buffer:

1. *Choose the conjugate acid-base pair.* Deciding on the chemical composition is based to a large extent on the desired pH. Suppose that, for a biochemical experiment, you need a buffer whose pH is 3.90. Therefore, to maximize the capacity, the pK_a of the acid component should be close to 3.90; or $K_a = 10^{-3.90} = 1.3\times10^{-4}$. A table of K_a values (see Appendix C) shows that lactic acid (pK_a = 3.86), glycolic acid (pK_a = 3.83), and formic acid (pK_a = 3.74) are possibilities. To avoid substances that are common in biochemical systems, you choose formic acid, HCOOH, and formate ion, $HCOO^-$, supplied by a soluble salt, such as sodium formate, HCOONa, as the basic component.

2. *Calculate the ratio of buffer component concentrations.* To find the ratio $[A^-]/[HA]$ that gives the desired pH, we have

$$\text{pH} = \text{p}K_a + \log\left(\frac{[A^-]}{[HA]}\right) \quad \text{or} \quad 3.90 = 3.74 + \log\left(\frac{[HCOO^-]}{[HCOOH]}\right)$$

$$\log\left(\frac{[HCOO^-]}{[HCOOH]}\right) = 0.16 \quad \text{so} \quad \left(\frac{[HCOO^-]}{[HCOOH]}\right) = 10^{0.16} = 1.4$$

Thus, for every 1.0 mol of HCOOH in a given volume of solution, you need 1.4 mol of HCOONa.

3. *Determine the buffer concentration.* For most laboratory-scale applications, concentrations of about 0.5 *M* are suitable, but the decision is often based on availability of stock solutions. Suppose you have a large stock of 0.40 *M* HCOOH and you need approximately 1.0 L of final buffer. First, you find the amount (mol) of sodium formate that will give the needed 1.4/1.0 ratio, and then convert to mass (g):

$$\text{Amount (mol) of HCOOH} = 1.0\text{ L soln} \times \frac{0.40\text{ mol HCOOH}}{1.0\text{ L soln}} = 0.40\text{ mol HCOOH}$$

$$\text{Amount (mol) of HCOONa} = 0.40\text{ mol HCOOH} \times \frac{1.4\text{ mol HCOONa}}{1.0\text{ mol HCOOH}} = 0.56\text{ mol HCOONa}$$

$$\text{Mass (g) of HCOONa} = 0.56\text{ mol HCOONa} \times \frac{68.01\text{ g HCOONa}}{1\text{ mol HCOONa}} = 38\text{ g HCOONa}$$

4. *Mix the solution and correct the pH.* You dissolve 38 g of sodium formate in the stock 0.40 *M* HCOOH to a total volume of 1.0 L. Because of nonideal behavior (Section 13.6), the buffer may vary slightly from the desired pH, so you add strong acid or strong base dropwise, while monitoring the solution with a pH meter.

Sample Problem 19.3 Preparing a Buffer

Problem An environmental chemist needs a carbonate buffer of pH 10.00 to study the effects of acid rain on limestone-rich soils. How many grams of Na_2CO_3 must she add to 1.5 L of 0.20 *M* $NaHCO_3$ to make the buffer? K_a of HCO_3^- is 4.7×10^{-11}.

Plan The conjugate pair is HCO_3^- (acid) and CO_3^{2-} (base), and we know the buffer volume (1.5 L) and the concentration (0.20 *M*) of HCO_3^-, so we need the buffer-component concentration ratio that gives pH 10.00 and the mass of Na_2CO_3 to dissolve.

We convert pH to $[H_3O^+]$ and use the K_a expression to solve for $[CO_3^{2-}]$. Multiplying by the volume of solution gives the amount (mol) of CO_3^{2-} needed, which we convert to mass (g) of Na_2CO_3.

Solution Calculating $[H_3O^+]$: $[H_3O^+] = 10^{-pH} = 10^{-10.00} = 1.0\times10^{-10}\ M$
Solving for $[CO_3^{2-}]$ in the concentration ratio:

$$HCO_3^-(aq) + H_2O(l) \rightleftharpoons H_3O^+(aq) + CO_3^{2-}(aq) \qquad K_a = \frac{[H_3O^+][CO_3^{2-}]}{[HCO_3^-]}$$

So
$$[CO_3^{2-}] = \frac{K_a[HCO_3^-]}{[H_3O^+]} = \frac{(4.7\times10^{-11})(0.20)}{1.0\times10^{-10}} = 0.094\ M$$

Calculating the amount (mol) of CO_3^{2-} needed for the given volume:

$$\text{Amount (mol) of } CO_3^{2-} = 1.5\text{ L soln} \times \frac{0.094\text{ mol } CO_3^{2-}}{1\text{ L soln}} = 0.14\text{ mol } CO_3^{2-}$$

Calculating the mass (g) of Na_2CO_3 needed:

$$\text{Mass (g) of } Na_2CO_3 = 0.14\text{ mol } Na_2CO_3 \times \frac{105.99\text{ g } Na_2CO_3}{1\text{ mol } Na_2CO_3} = 15\text{ g } Na_2CO_3$$

The chemist should dissolve 15 g of Na_2CO_3 into about 1.3 L of 0.20 M $NaHCO_3$ and add more 0.20 M $NaHCO_3$ to make 1.5 L. Using a pH meter, she can then adjust the pH to 10.00 by dropwise addition of concentrated strong acid or base.

Check For a useful buffer range, the concentration of the acidic component, $[HCO_3^-]$, must be within a factor of 10 of the concentration of the basic component, $[CO_3^{2-}]$. And we have (1.5 L)(0.20 M HCO_3^-), or 0.30 mol of HCO_3^-, and 0.14 mol of CO_3^{2-}; 0.30/0.14 = 2.1. Make sure the relative amounts of components are reasonable: we want a pH below the pK_a of HCO_3^- (10.33), so we want more of the acidic than the basic species.

Follow-Up Problem 19.3 How would you prepare a benzoic acid/benzoate buffer with pH = 4.25, starting with 5.0 L of 0.050 M sodium benzoate (C_6H_5COONa) solution and adding the acidic component? K_a of benzoic acid (C_6H_5COOH) is 6.3×10^{-5}.

Another way to prepare a buffer is to form one of the components by *partial neutralization* of the other. For example, you can prepare an $HCOOH/HCOO^-$ buffer by mixing aqueous solutions of HCOOH and NaOH. As OH^- reacts with HCOOH, neutralization of some of the HCOOH produces the $HCOO^-$ needed:

$$HCOOH\text{ (HA total)} + OH^-\text{(amt added)} \longrightarrow$$
$$HCOOH\text{ (HA total} - OH^-\text{amt added)} + HCOO^-(OH^-\text{amt added}) + H_2O$$

This method is based on the same chemical process that occurs when a weak acid is titrated with a strong base, as you'll see in Section 19.2.

Summary of Section 19.1

- The pH of a buffered solution changes much less than the pH of an unbuffered solution when H_3O^+ or OH^- is added.
- A buffer consists of a weak acid and its conjugate base (or a weak base and its conjugate acid). To be effective, the amounts of the components must be *much* greater than the amount of H_3O^+ or OH^- added.
- The buffer-component concentration ratio determines the pH; the ratio and the pH are related by the Henderson-Hasselbalch equation.
- When H_3O^+ or OH^- is added to a buffer, one component reacts to form the other; thus, $[H_3O^+]$ (and pH) changes only slightly.
- A concentrated (higher capacity) buffer undergoes smaller changes in pH than a dilute buffer. When the buffer pH equals the pK_a of the acid component, the buffer has its highest capacity.
- A buffer has an effective pH range of $pK_a \pm 1$ pH unit.
- To prepare a buffer, choose the conjugate acid-base pair, calculate the ratio of components, determine the buffer concentration, and adjust the final solution to the desired pH.

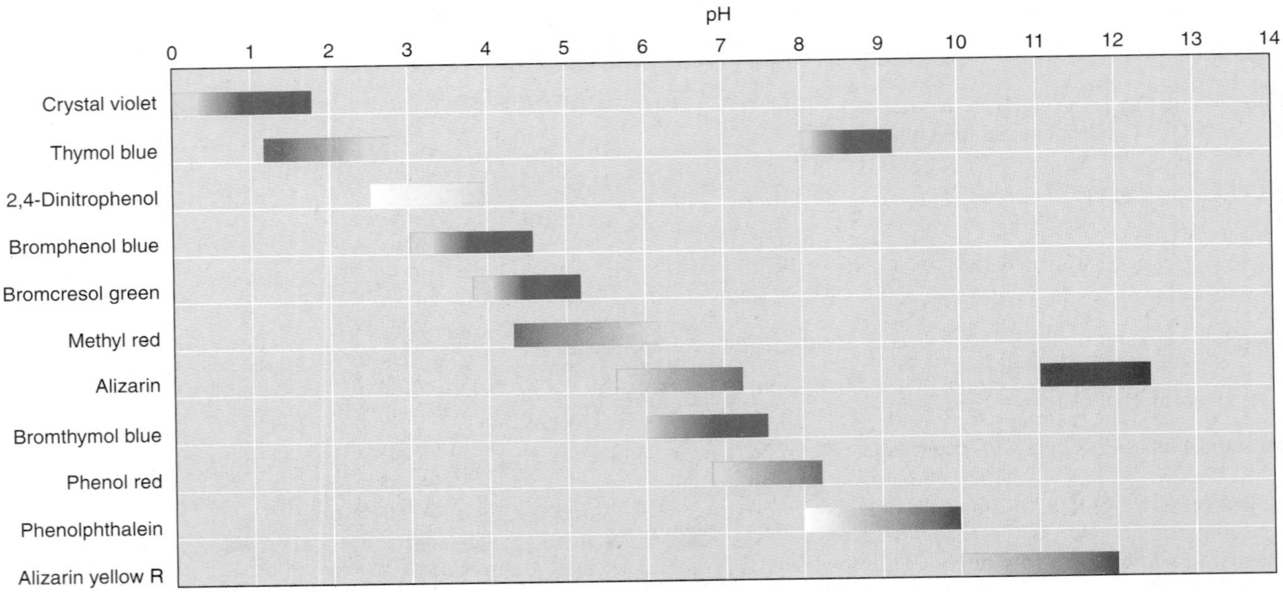

Figure 19.5 Colors and approximate pH ranges of some common acid-base indicators.

19.2 • ACID-BASE TITRATION CURVES

In Chapter 4, we used titrations to quantify acid-base (and redox) reactions. In this section, we focus on the **acid-base titration curve,** a plot of pH vs. volume of titrant added. We discuss curves for strong acid–strong base, weak acid–strong base, weak base–strong acid, and polyprotic acid–strong base titrations. Running a titration is an exercise for the lab, but understanding the role of acid-base indicators and seeing how salt solutions (Section 18.7) and buffers are involved applies key principles of acid-base equilibria.

Monitoring pH with Acid-Base Indicators

An *acid-base indicator* is a weak organic acid (denoted here as HIn) whose color differs from the color of its conjugate base (In^-) and whose color change occurs over a specific, narrow pH range. Typically, one or both forms are intensely colored, so only a tiny amount of indicator is needed, far too little to affect the pH during the titration.

Figure 19.5 shows the color change(s) and pH range(s) of some acid-base indicators. To select an indicator, you must know the approximate pH of the titration end point, which means you know the ionic species present. Because the indicator is a weak acid, the $[HIn]/[In^-]$ ratio is governed by the $[H_3O^+]$ of the solution:

$$HIn(aq) + H_2O(l) \rightleftharpoons H_3O^+(aq) + In^-(aq) \qquad K_a \text{ of HIn} = \frac{[H_3O^+][In^-]}{[HIn]}$$

Therefore,

$$\frac{[HIn]}{[In^-]} = \frac{[H_3O^+]}{K_a}$$

An indicator's color reflects the concentration ratio:

- We see the HIn color if the $[HIn]/[In^-]$ ratio is 10/1 or greater.
- We see the In^- color if the $[HIn]/[In^-]$ ratio is 1/10 or less.
- Between these extremes, the two colors merge into an intermediate hue.

Thus, an indicator has a *color range* equal to a 10^2-fold range in the [HIn]/[In] ratio: an *indicator changes color over a range of about 2 pH units.* For example, bromthymol blue has a pH range of about 6.0 to 7.6. As Figure 19.6 shows, it is yellow below that range (*left*), blue above it (*right*), and greenish in between (*center*).

Figure 19.6 The color change of the indicator bromthymol blue.

Strong Acid–Strong Base Titration Curves

Figure 19.7 shows a typical curve for the titration of a strong acid with a strong base, the data used to construct it, and molecular views of the key species in solution at various points during the titration.

Features of the Curve There are three distinct regions of the titration curve, which correspond to three major changes in slope:

1. *The pH starts out low,* reflecting the high [H_3O^+] of the strong acid, and increases slowly as acid is gradually neutralized by the added base.
2. *The pH rises 6 to 8 units very rapidly.* This steep increase begins when the amount (mol) of OH^- added nearly equals the amount (mol) of H_3O^+ originally present in the acid. One or two more drops of base neutralize the remaining tiny excess of acid and introduce a tiny excess of base.
3. *The pH increases slowly* beyond the steep rise as more base is added.

Let's distinguish between the *equivalence point* and the *end point,* both of which occur on the steep portion of the curve:

- The **equivalence point** occurs when the *number of moles of added* OH^- *equals the number of moles of* H_3O^+ originally present. *The solution consists of the anion of the strong acid and the cation of the strong base.* Recall from Chapter 18 that *these ions do not react with water, so the solution is neutral: pH = 7.00.*

Volume of NaOH added (mL)	pH
00.00	1.00
10.00	1.22
20.00	1.48
30.00	1.85
35.00	2.18
39.00	2.89
39.50	3.20
39.75	3.50
39.90	3.90
39.95	4.20
39.99	4.90
40.00	7.00
40.01	9.10
40.05	9.80
40.10	10.10
40.25	10.50
40.50	10.79
41.00	11.09
45.00	11.76
50.00	12.05
60.00	12.30
70.00	12.43
80.00	12.52

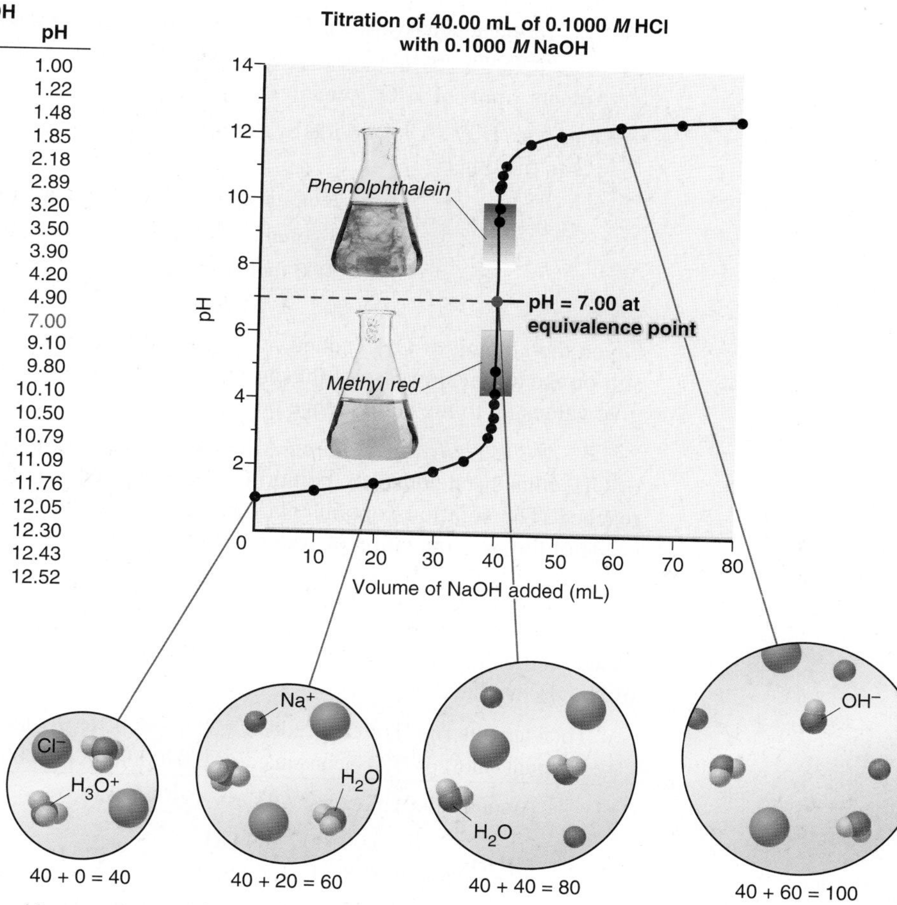

Figure 19.7 Curve for a strong acid–strong base titration. Data (*at left*) for the titration of 40.00 mL of 0.1000 *M* HCl with 0.1000 *M* NaOH. In the titration, pH increases gradually, then rapidly near and at the equivalence point, and then gradually again. In a strong acid–strong base titration, pH = 7.00 at the equivalence point. Each molecular view shows the relative numbers of species, other than solvent, in a portion of the solution at one point during the titration. The circles increase in size in proportion to the increase in the solution's total volume.

- The **end point** occurs when the indicator, which we added before the titration, changes color. *We choose an indicator with a color change close to the pH of the equivalence point.* Figure 19.5 includes two indicators suitable for a strong acid–strong base titration. Methyl red changes from red at pH 4.2 to yellow at pH 6.3, and phenolphthalein changes from colorless at pH 8.3 to pink at pH 10.0. Neither change occurs *at* the equivalence point (pH 7.00), but both occur on the vertical portion of the curve. Therefore, when methyl red turns yellow or phenolphthalein pink, we are within a drop or two of the equivalence point. In practice, then, the *visible* end point signals the *invisible* equivalence point.

Calculating the pH During This Titration By knowing the chemical species present during the titration, we can calculate the pH at various points along the way:

1. *Initial solution of strong HA.* In Figure 19.7, 40.00 mL of 0.1000 M HCl is titrated with 0.1000 M NaOH. Because a strong acid is completely dissociated, [HCl] = $[H_3O^+]$ = 0.1000 M. Therefore, the initial pH is*

$$pH = -\log[H_3O^+] = -\log(0.1000) = 1.00$$

2. *Before the equivalence point.* As we start adding base, some acid is neutralized and the volume of solution increases. To find the pH at various points up to the equivalence point, we find the *initial* amount (mol) of H_3O^+ and subtract the amount *reacted, which equals the amount (mol) of OH^- added,* to find the amount (mol) of H_3O^+ remaining. Then, we use the *total* volume to calculate $[H_3O^+]$ and convert to pH. For example, after adding 20.00 mL of 0.1000 M NaOH:

- *Find the amount (mol) of H_3O^+ remaining.*

$$\begin{array}{rcl} \text{Initial amount (mol) of } H_3O^+ &=& 0.04000\text{ L} \times 0.1000\ M = 0.004000\text{ mol } H_3O^+ \\ -\text{Amount (mol) of } OH^- \text{ added} &=& 0.02000\text{ L} \times 0.1000\ M = 0.002000\text{ mol } OH^- \\ \hline \text{Amount (mol) of } H_3O^+ \text{ remaining} &=& 0.002000\text{ mol } H_3O^+ \end{array}$$

- *Calculate $[H_3O^+]$.* We divide by the *total volume* because one solution dilutes the ions in the other:

$$[H_3O^+] = \frac{\text{amount (mol) of } H_3O^+ \text{ remaining}}{\text{original volume of acid + volume of added base}}$$

$$= \frac{0.002000\text{ mol } H_3O^+}{0.04000\text{ L} + 0.02000\text{ L}} = 0.03333\ M \qquad pH = 1.48$$

Given the amount of OH^- added, we are halfway to the equivalence point; but we are still on the initial slow rise of the curve, so the pH is still very low. Similar calculations give values up to the equivalence point.

3. *At the equivalence point.* After 40.00 mL of 0.1000 M NaOH (0.004000 mol of OH^-) has been added to the initial 0.004000 mol of H_3O^+, the equivalence point is reached. The solution contains Na^+ and Cl^-, neither of which reacts with water. Because of the autoionization of water, however,

$$[H_3O^+] = 1.0\times10^{-7}\ M \qquad pH = 7.00$$

4. *After the equivalence point.* From the equivalence point on, the pH calculation is based on the amount (mol) of *excess* OH^- present. For example, after adding 50.00 mL of NaOH, we have

$$\begin{array}{rcl} \text{Total amount (mol) of } OH^- \text{ added} &=& 0.05000\text{ L} \times 0.1000\ M = 0.005000\text{ mol } OH^- \\ -\text{Amount (mol) of } H_3O^+ \text{ consumed} &=& 0.04000\text{ L} \times 0.1000\ M = 0.004000\text{ mol } H_3O^+ \\ \hline \text{Amount (mol) of excess } OH^- &=& 0.001000\text{ mol } OH^- \end{array}$$

$$[OH^-] = \frac{0.001000\text{ mol } OH^-}{0.04000\text{ L} + 0.05000\text{ L}} = 0.01111\ M \qquad pOH = 1.95$$

$$pH = pK_w - pOH = 14.00 - 1.95 = 12.05$$

*In acid-base titrations, volumes and concentrations are usually known to four significant figures, but pH is reported to no more than two digits to the right of the decimal point.

Weak Acid–Strong Base Titration Curves

Figure 19.8 shows a curve for the titration of a weak acid with strong base: 40.00 mL of 0.1000 *M* propanoic acid ($K_a = 1.3\times10^{-5}$) titrated with 0.1000 *M* NaOH. (We abbreviate the acid, CH_3CH_2COOH, as HPr and the conjugate base, $CH_3CH_2COO^-$, as Pr^-.)

Features of the Curve The dotted portion of the curve in Figure 19.8 corresponds to the bottom half of the strong acid–strong base curve (Figure 19.7). There are four key points to note for the weak acid curve, and the first three differ from the strong acid curve:

1. *The initial pH is higher.* Because the weak acid (HPr) dissociates slightly, much less H_3O^+ is present than with the strong acid.
2. *The curve rises gradually in the so-called buffer region before the steep rise to the equivalence point.* As HPr reacts with strong base, more Pr^- forms, which creates an HPr/Pr^- buffer. At the midpoint of the buffer region, half the initial HPr has reacted (that is, half of the OH^- needed to reach the equivalence point has been added), so $[HPr] = [Pr^-]$, or $[Pr^-]/[HPr] = 1$. Therefore, *the pH equals the* pK_a*:*

   $$\text{Middle of buffer region: pH} = pK_a + \log\left(\frac{[Pr^-]}{[HPr]}\right) = pK_a + \log 1 = pK_a + 0 = pK_a$$

   The pH observed at this point is used to estimate the pK_a of an unknown acid.
3. *The pH at the equivalence point is above 7.00.* The solution contains the strong-base cation Na^+, which does not react with water, and the weak-acid anion Pr^-, which acts as a weak base to accept a proton from H_2O and yield OH^-.
4. *The pH increases slowly* beyond the equivalence point as excess OH^- is added.

The choice of indicator here is more limited than for a strong acid–strong base titration because the steep rise occurs over a smaller pH range. Phenolphthalein will work because it changes color within this range. But methyl red will not because its color change requires about 30 mL of titrant, rather than just a drop or two.

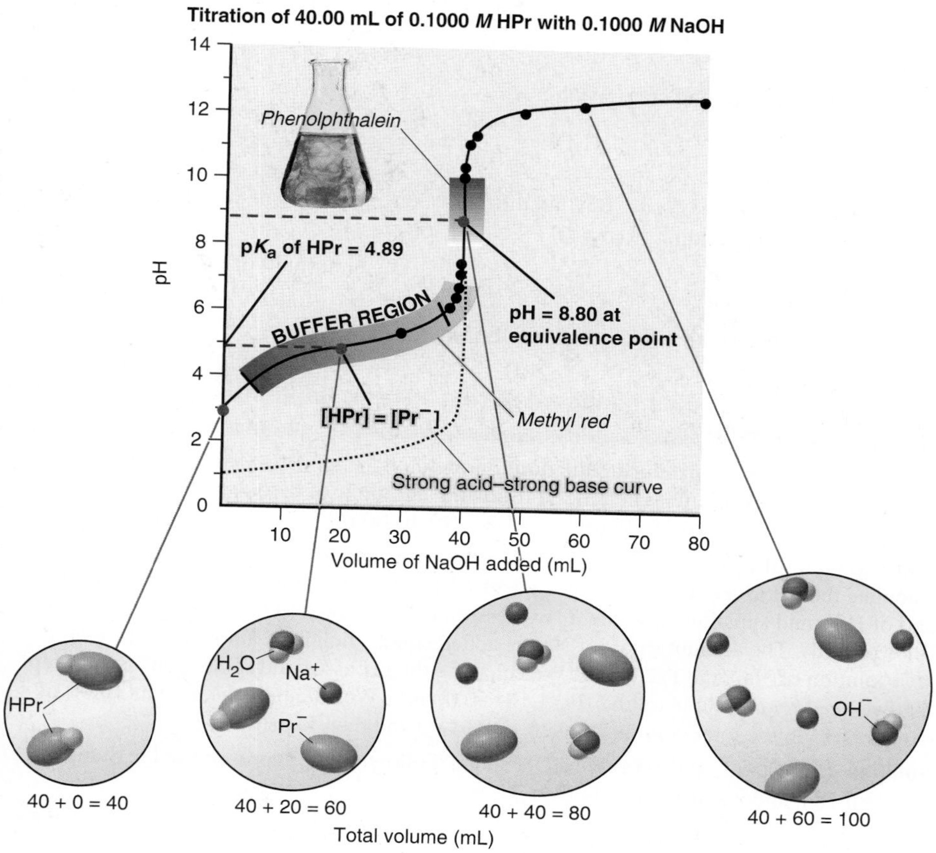

Figure 19.8 Curve for a weak acid–strong base titration.

Calculating the pH During This Titration During the weak acid–strong base titration we must take into account the partial dissociation of the weak acid, the presence of the buffer, and the reaction of the conjugate base with water. Thus, each of four regions of the curve requires its own calculation to find $[H_3O^+]$:

1. *Initial HA solution.* Before base is added, a weak acid dissociates, so we find $[H_3O^+]$ as in Section 18.4: we set up a reaction table with $x = [HPr]_{dissoc}$, assume $[H_3O^+]$ (and $[Pr^-]$) $= [HPr]_{dissoc} << [HPr]_{init}$, and solve for x:

$$K_a = \frac{[H_3O^+][Pr^-]}{[HPr]} \approx \frac{x^2}{[HPr]_{init}} \qquad \text{therefore,} \qquad x = [H_3O^+] \approx \sqrt{K_a \times [HPr]_{init}}$$

2. *Solution of HA and added base.* As we add NaOH, HPr forms Pr^-. Thus, for much of the titration up to the equivalence point, we have an HPr/Pr^- buffer. Therefore, we find $[H_3O^+]$ from

$$[H_3O^+] = K_a \times \frac{[HPr]}{[Pr^-]}$$

(Or, we can find pH directly with the Henderson-Hasselbalch equation.) Because *volumes cancel in the concentration ratio,* that is, $[HPr]/[Pr^-]$ = amount (mol) of HPr/amount (mol) of Pr^-, we don't need volumes or have to calculate concentrations.

3. *Equivalent amounts of HA and added base.* At the equivalence point, all of the HPr has reacted, so the solution contains Pr^-, which reacts with water to form OH^-:

$$Pr^-(aq) + H_2O(l) \rightleftharpoons HPr(aq) + OH^-(aq)$$

This explains why, in a weak acid–strong base titration, the pH > 7.00 at the equivalence point. To calculate $[H_3O^+]$ (see Section 18.5), we first find K_b of Pr^- from K_a of HPr, set up a reaction table (assume $[Pr^-] >> [Pr^-]_{reacting}$), and solve for $[OH^-]$. Since we use a single concentration, $[Pr^-]$, to solve for $[OH^-]$, we *do* need the total volume. Then, we convert $[OH^-]$ to $[H_3O^+]$. These two steps are

$$(1)\ [OH^-] \approx \sqrt{K_b \times [Pr^-]}, \quad \text{where} \quad K_b = \frac{K_w}{K_a} \quad \text{and} \quad [Pr^-] = \frac{\text{amount (mol) of } HPr_{init}}{\text{total volume}}$$

$$(2)\ [H_3O^+] = \frac{K_w}{[OH^-]}$$

Combining them into one step gives

$$[H_3O^+] \approx \frac{K_w}{\sqrt{K_b \times [Pr^-]}}$$

4. *Solution of excess base.* Beyond the equivalence point, as in the strong acid–strong base titration, we are adding excess OH^-:

$$[H_3O^+] = \frac{K_w}{[OH^-]} \qquad \text{where} \qquad [OH^-] = \frac{\text{amount (mol) of excess } OH^-}{\text{total volume}}$$

Sample Problem 19.4 shows the overall approach.

Sample Problem 19.4 Finding the pH During a Weak Acid–Strong Base Titration

Problem Calculate the pH during the titration of 40.00 mL of 0.1000 *M* propanoic acid (HPr; $K_a = 1.3\times10^{-5}$) after each of the following additions of 0.1000 *M* NaOH:
(a) 0.00 mL **(b)** 30.00 mL **(c)** 40.00 mL **(d)** 50.00 mL

Plan **(a)** 0.00 mL: No base has been added yet, so this is a weak-acid dissociation. We calculate the pH as we did in Section 18.4. **(b)** 30.00 mL: We find the amount (mol) of Pr^- and of HPr, and substitute into the K_a expression to solve for $[H_3O^+]$, and convert to pH. **(c)** 40.00 mL: The amount (mol) of NaOH added equals the initial amount (mol) of HPr, so a solution of Na^+ and Pr^- exists. We calculate the pH as we did in Section 18.5, except that we need *total* volume to find $[Pr^-]$. **(d)** 50.00 mL: We calculate the amount (mol) of excess OH^- in the total volume, convert to $[H_3O^+]$ and then to pH.

Solution **(a)** 0.00 mL of 0.1000 *M* NaOH added. Following the approach used in Sample Problem 18.8 and just described in the text, we obtain

$$[H_3O^+] \approx \sqrt{K_a \times [HPr]_{init}} = \sqrt{(1.3\times10^{-5})(0.1000)} = 1.1\times10^{-3}\,M \quad \text{so} \quad pH = 2.96$$

(b) 30.00 mL of 0.1000 *M* NaOH added. Calculating the ratio of moles of HPr to Pr^-:

Initial amount (mol) of HPr = 0.04000 L × 0.1000 *M* = 0.004000 mol HPr
Amount (mol) of NaOH added = 0.03000 L × 0.1000 *M* = 0.003000 mol OH^-

For every mole of NaOH, 1 mol of Pr^- forms, so we have this stoichiometry reaction table:

Amount (mol)	HPr(*aq*)	+	OH^-(*aq*)	⟶	Pr^+(*aq*)	+	H_2O(*l*)
Initial	0.004000		0.003000		0		—
Change	−0.003000		−0.003000		+0.003000		—
Final	0.001000		0		0.003000		—

The last line of the table gives the new initial amounts of HPr and Pr^- that react to attain a new equilibrium. With *x* very small, we assume that the $[HPr]/[Pr^-]$ ratio at equilibrium is essentially equal to the ratio of these new initial amounts (see Comment in Sample Problem 19.1). Thus,

$$\frac{[HPr]}{[Pr^-]} = \frac{0.001000\ \text{mol}}{0.003000\ \text{mol}} = 0.3333$$

Solving for $[H_3O^+]$: $$[H_3O^+] = K_a \times \frac{[HPr]}{[Pr^-]} = (1.3\times10^{-5})(0.3333) = 4.3\times10^{-6}\ M$$

$$\text{pH} = 5.37$$

(c) 40.00 mL of 0.1000 *M* NaOH added. Calculating $[Pr^-]$ after all HPr has reacted:

$$[Pr^-] = \frac{0.004000\ \text{mol}}{0.04000\ \text{L} + 0.04000\ \text{L}} = 0.05000\ M$$

Calculating K_b using the given K_a (see Sample Problem 18.2 for similar steps):

$$K_b = \frac{K_w}{K_a} = \frac{1.0\times10^{-14}}{1.3\times10^{-5}} = 7.7\times10^{-10}$$

Solving for $[H_3O^+]$ as described above in the text for region 3 of the curve:

$$[H_3O^+] \approx \frac{K_w}{\sqrt{K_b \times [Pr^-]}} = \frac{1.0\times10^{-14}}{\sqrt{(7.7\times10^{-10})(0.05000)}} = 1.6\times10^{-9}\ M$$

$$\text{pH} = 8.80$$

(d) 50.00 mL of 0.1000 *M* NaOH added.

Amount (mol) of excess OH^- = (0.1000 *M*)(0.05000 L − 0.04000 L) = 0.001000 mol

$$[OH^-] = \frac{\text{amount (mol) of excess } OH^-}{\text{total volume}} = \frac{0.001000\ \text{mol}}{0.09000\ \text{L}} = 0.01111\ M$$

$$[H_3O^+] = \frac{K_w}{[OH^-]} = \frac{1.0\times10^{-14}}{0.01111} = 9.0\times10^{-13}\ M$$

$$\text{pH} = 12.05$$

Check As expected, the pH increases through the four regions of the titration. Be sure to round off and check the arithmetic along the way.

Follow-Up Problem 19.4 A chemist titrates 20.00 mL of 0.2000 *M* HBrO ($K_a = 2.3\times10^{-9}$) with 0.1000 *M* NaOH. What is the pH:
(a) Before any base is added?
(b) When $[HBrO] = [BrO^-]$?
(c) At the equivalence point?
(d) When the amount (mol) of OH^- added is twice the amount of HBrO present initially?
(e) Sketch the titration curve; label the pK_a and equivalence point.

Weak Base–Strong Acid Titration Curves

The opposite of a weak acid–strong base titration is the titration of a weak base (NH_3) with a strong acid (HCl). This titration curve, shown in Figure 19.9 on the next page, has the *same shape as the weak acid–strong base curve, but it is inverted.*

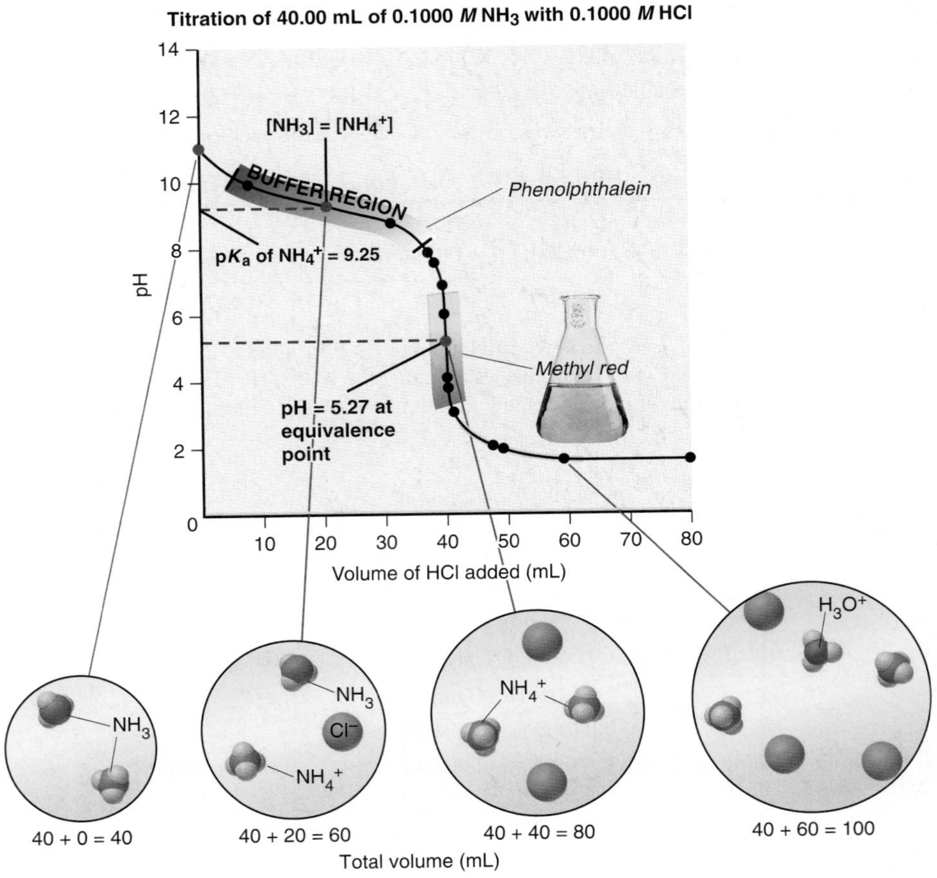

Figure 19.9 Curve for a weak base–strong acid titration.

Thus, we have the same features as the weak acid–strong base curve, but *the pH decreases* throughout the process:

1. *The initial weak-base solution has a pH well above 7.00* (see Sample Problem 18.11).
2. *The pH decreases gradually in the buffer region,* where significant amounts of NH_3 and its conjugate acid, NH_4^+, are present. At the midpoint of this region, *the pH equals the pK_a of NH_4^+.*
3. *The curve drops steeply to the equivalence point.* All the NH_3 has reacted with added HCl, and the solution contains only NH_4^+ and Cl^-. Note that *the pH at the equivalence point is below 7.00* because Cl^- does not react with water and NH_4^+ is acidic:

$$NH_4^+(aq) + H_2O(l) \rightleftharpoons NH_3(aq) + H_3O^+(aq)$$

4. *The pH decreases slowly* beyond the equivalence point as excess H_3O^+ is added.

For this titration, phenolphthalein changes color too slowly, but methyl red's change occurs on the steep portion of the curve and straddles the equivalence point, so it is the perfect choice.

Titration Curves for Polyprotic Acids

Except for sulfuric acid, the common polyprotic acids are all weak. The successive K_a values for a polyprotic acid differ by several orders of magnitude, as these values for sulfurous acid show:

$$H_2SO_3(aq) + H_2O(l) \rightleftharpoons HSO_3^-(aq) + H_3O^+(aq)$$
$$K_{a1} = 1.4\times10^{-2} \quad \text{and} \quad pK_{a1} = 1.85$$

$$HSO_3^-(aq) + H_2O(l) \rightleftharpoons SO_3^{2-}(aq) + H_3O^+(aq)$$
$$K_{a2} = 6.5\times10^{-8} \quad \text{and} \quad pK_{a2} = 7.19$$

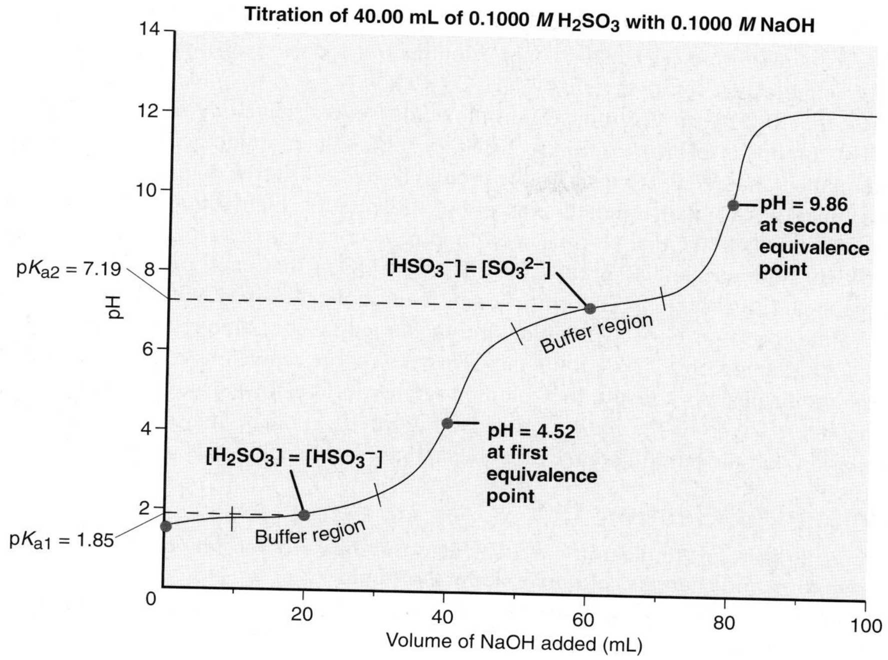

Figure 19.10 **Curve for the titration of a weak polyprotic acid.** Because the K_a values are separated by several orders of magnitude, the titration curve looks like two weak acid–strong base curves joined.

In a titration of a diprotic acid such as H_2SO_3, two OH^- ions are required to react with the two H^+ ions of each acid molecule. Figure 19.10 shows the titration curve for sulfurous acid with strong base. Because of the large difference in K_a values, each mole of H^+ is titrated separately, so H_2SO_3 molecules lose one H^+ before any HSO_3^- ions do:

$$H_2SO_3 \xrightarrow{1\text{ mol }OH^-} HSO_3^- \xrightarrow{1\text{ mol }OH^-} SO_3^{2-}$$

Several features of the curve are

- The same amount of base (0.004000 mol OH^-) is required per mole of H^+.
- There are two equivalence points and two buffer regions. The pH at the midpoint of each buffer region is equal to the pK_a of that acidic species.
- The pH of the first equivalence point is below 7.00, because HSO_3^- is a stronger acid than it is a base (K_a of $HSO_3^- = 6.5\times10^{-8}$; K_b of $HSO_3^- = 7.1\times10^{-13}$).

Amino Acids as Biological Polyprotic Acids

Amino acids have the general formula NH_2—CH(R)—COOH, where R can be one of about 20 different groups (Sections 13.2 and 15.6). In essence, amino acids contain a weak base (—NH_2) and a weak acid (—COOH) on the same molecule. Both the amino and carboxylic acid groups are protonated at low pH: $^+NH_3$—CH(R)—COOH. Thus, in this form, the amino acid behaves like a polyprotic acid. For glycine, the simplest amino acid (R = H), the dissociation reactions and pK_a values are

$$^+NH_3CH_2COOH(aq) + H_2O(l) \rightleftharpoons {}^+NH_3CH_2COO^-(aq) + H_3O^+(aq) \quad pK_{a1} = 2.35$$

$$^+NH_3CH_2COO^-(aq) + H_2O(l) \rightleftharpoons NH_2CH_2COO^-(aq) + H_3O^+(aq) \quad pK_{a2} = 9.78$$

These values show that the —COOH group is *much* more acidic than the —NH_3^+ group. As we saw with H_2SO_3, the protons (*black circles*) are titrated separately, so all the —COOH protons are removed before any —NH_3^+ protons are:

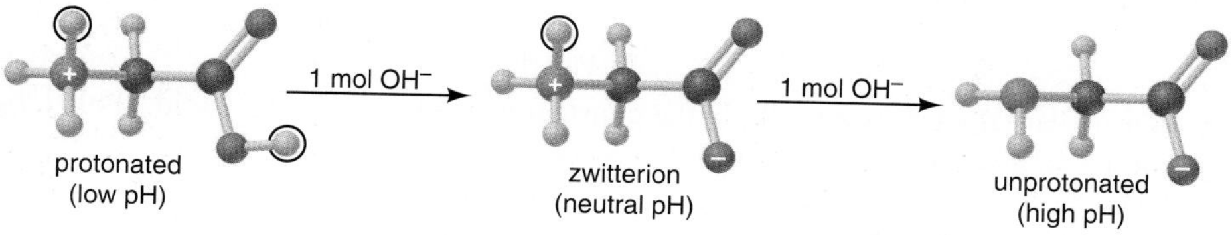

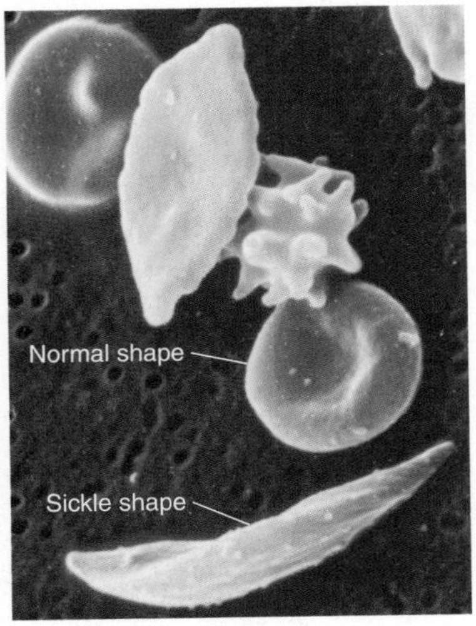

Figure 19.11 Abnormal shape of red blood cells in sickle cell anemia.

Thus, at physiological pH (~7), which is between the two pK_a values, *an amino acid exists as a zwitterion* (German *zwitter,* "double"), a species with opposite charges on the same molecule; for glycine it is $^+NH_3CH_2COO^-$.

Of the 20 different R groups of amino acids, several have *additional* —COO^- or —NH_3^+ groups at pH 7 (see Figure 15.30, p. 609). When amino acids link to form a protein, their charged R groups give the protein its overall charge, which is often related to its function. A widely studied example of this relationship occurs in the hereditary disease sickle cell anemia. Normal red blood cells contain hemoglobin molecules that have two glutamic acid R groups (—$CH_2CH_2COO^-$) that each provide a negative charge at a critical region. Abnormal hemoglobin molecules in sickle cell anemia have two valine R groups (—CH_3), which are uncharged, at the same region. This change in just 2 of hemoglobin's 574 amino acids lowers charge repulsions between the hemoglobin molecules. As a result, they clump together in fiber-like structures, which leads to the sickle shape of the red blood cells (Figure 19.11). The misshapen cells block capillaries, and the painful course of sickle cell anemia usually ends in early death.

Summary of Section 19.2

- An acid-base (pH) indicator is a weak acid that has a differently colored conjugate base form and changes color over about 2 pH units.
- In a strong acid–strong base titration, the pH starts out low, rises slowly, then shoots up near the equivalence point (pH = 7).
- In a weak acid–strong base titration, the pH starts out higher, rises slowly in the buffer region (pH = pK_a at the midpoint), and then rises quickly near the equivalence point (pH > 7).
- A weak base–strong acid titration curve has a shape that is the inverse of the weak acid–strong base case, with the pH decreasing to the equivalence point (pH < 7).
- Polyprotic acids have two or more acidic protons, each with its own K_a value. Because the K_a's differ by several orders of magnitude, each proton is titrated separately.
- Amino acids exist in charged forms that depend on the pH of the solution and determine the overall charge of a protein.

19.3 • EQUILIBRIA OF SLIGHTLY SOLUBLE IONIC COMPOUNDS

In this section, we explore an equilibirum system that involves the solubility of ionic compounds. Recall from Chapter 13 that most solutes, even those called "soluble," have a limited solubility in a particular solvent. In a saturated solution at a particular temperature, equilibrium exists between dissolved and undissolved solute. Slightly soluble ionic compounds, which we've been calling "insoluble," reach equilibrium with very little solute dissolved. In this introductory treatment, we will *assume* that, like a soluble ionic compound, the small amount of a slightly soluble ionic compound that does dissolve dissociates completely into ions.

The Ion-Product Expression (Q_{sp}) and the Solubility-Product Constant (K_{sp})

For a slightly soluble ionic compound, *equilibrium exists between solid solute and aqueous ions.* Thus, for example, for a saturated solution of lead(II) fluoride, we have

$$PbF_2(s) \rightleftharpoons Pb^{2+}(aq) + 2F^-(aq)$$

As for any equilibrium system, we can write a reaction quotient:

$$Q_c = \frac{[Pb^{2+}][F^-]^2}{[PbF_2]}$$

And, as in earlier cases, we multiply the constant concentration of the solid, $[PbF_2]$, by Q_c. Doing so gives a relationship called the *ion-product expression,* Q_{sp}:

$$Q_{sp} = Q_c[PbF_2] = [Pb^{2+}][F^-]^2$$

When the solution is saturated, the numerical value of Q_{sp} attains a constant value called the **solubility-product constant, K_{sp}.** The K_{sp} for PbF_2 at 25°C, for example, is 3.6×10^{-8}. Like other equilibrium constants, K_{sp} depends *only* on the temperature, not on the individual ion concentrations.

Writing the Ion-Product Expression The form of Q_{sp} is identical to that of other reaction quotients: each concentration is raised to an exponent equal to the coefficient in the balanced equation, which in this case also *equals the subscript of each ion in the compound's formula.* At saturation, the concentration terms have their equilibrium values. Thus, in general, for a slightly soluble ionic compound, M_pX_q, composed of the ions M^{n+} and X^{z-}, the ion-product expression at equilibrium is

$$Q_{sp} = [M^{n+}]^p[X^{z-}]^q = K_{sp} \qquad (19.2)$$

We'll write Q_{sp} directly with the symbol K_{sp}.

The Special Case of Metal Sulfides The aqueous equilibria of metal sulfides have a special form of the ion-product expression. The sulfide ion, S^{2-}, is so basic that it reacts completely with water to form the hydrogen sulfide ion (HS^-) and OH^-:

$$S^{2-}(aq) + H_2O(l) \longrightarrow HS^-(aq) + OH^-(aq)$$

Although S^{2-} is not stable in water, we can think of the dissolution process as the sum of two steps, with S^{2-} formed in the first and consumed immediately in the second. Thus, for instance, for manganese(II) sulfide, we have

$$MnS(s) \rightleftharpoons Mn^{2+}(aq) + \cancel{S^{2-}(aq)}$$
$$\cancel{S^{2-}(aq)} + H_2O(l) \longrightarrow HS^-(aq) + OH^-(aq)$$
$$MnS(s) + H_2O(l) \rightleftharpoons Mn^{2+}(aq) + HS^-(aq) + OH^-(aq)$$

Note that we have constant concentrations of water and the solid, so incorporating them into Q_c gives the ion-product expression at equilibrium:

$$Q_c[MnS][H_2O] = K_{sp} = [Mn^{2+}][HS^-][OH^-]$$

Sample Problem 19.5 Writing Ion-Product Expressions

Problem Write the ion-product expression at equilibrium for each compound: **(a)** magnesium carbonate; **(b)** iron(II) hydroxide; **(c)** calcium phosphate; **(d)** silver sulfide.

Plan We write an equation for a saturated solution and then write the ion-product expression at equilibrium, K_{sp} (Equation 19.2), noting the sulfide in part (d).

Solution (a) Magnesium carbonate:

$$MgCO_3(s) \rightleftharpoons Mg^{2+}(aq) + CO_3^{2-}(aq) \qquad K_{sp} = [Mg^{2+}][CO_3^{2-}]$$

(b) Iron(II) hydroxide:

$$Fe(OH)_2(s) \rightleftharpoons Fe^{2+}(aq) + 2OH^-(aq) \qquad K_{sp} = [Fe^{2+}][OH^-]^2$$

(c) Calcium phosphate:

$$Ca_3(PO_4)_2(s) \rightleftharpoons 3Ca^{2+}(aq) + 2PO_4^{3-}(aq) \qquad K_{sp} = [Ca^{2+}]^3[PO_4^{3-}]^2$$

(d) Silver sulfide:

$$Ag_2S(s) \rightleftharpoons 2Ag^+(aq) + \cancel{S^{2-}(aq)}$$
$$\cancel{S^{2-}(aq)} + H_2O(l) \longrightarrow HS^-(aq) + OH^-(aq)$$
$$Ag_2S(s) + H_2O(l) \rightleftharpoons 2Ag^+(aq) + HS^-(aq) + OH^-(aq) \qquad K_{sp} = [Ag^+]^2[HS^-][OH^-]$$

Check Except for part (d), you can check by reversing the process to see if you obtain the formula of the compound from K_{sp}.

Follow-Up Problem 19.5 Write the ion-product expression at equilibrium for each compound: **(a)** calcium sulfate; **(b)** chromium(III) carbonate; **(c)** magnesium hydroxide; **(d)** arsenic(III) sulfide.

Calculations Involving the Solubility-Product Constant

In Chapters 17 and 18, we described two types of equilibrium problems. In one type, we use concentrations (or other quantities) to find K, and in the other, we use K to find concentrations. Here we encounter the same two types.

The Problem with Assuming Complete Dissociation Before we focus on calculations, let's address a complication that affects accuracy and results in approximate answers. Our assumption that the small dissolved amount of these compounds dissociates completely into separate ions is an oversimplification. Many slightly soluble salts have polar covalent metal-nonmetal bonds, and partially dissociated or even undissociated species occur in solution. Here are two of many examples:

- With slightly soluble lead(II) chloride in water, the solution contains not only the separate $Pb^{2+}(aq)$ and $Cl^-(aq)$ ions we expect from complete dissociation, but also undissociated $PbCl_2(aq)$ molecules and $PbCl^+(aq)$ ions.
- In an aqueous solution of $CaSO_4$, undissociated ion pairs, $Ca^{2+}SO_4^{2-}(aq)$, are present.

Table 19.2 Solubility-Product Constants (K_{sp}) of Selected Ionic Compounds at 25°C

Name, Formula	K_{sp}
Aluminum hydroxide, $Al(OH)_3$	3×10^{-34}
Cobalt(II) carbonate, $CoCO_3$	1.0×10^{-10}
Iron(II) hydroxide, $Fe(OH)_2$	4.1×10^{-15}
Lead(II) fluoride, PbF_2	3.6×10^{-8}
Lead(II) sulfate, $PbSO_4$	1.6×10^{-8}
Mercury(I) iodide, Hg_2I_2	4.7×10^{-29}
Silver sulfide, Ag_2S	8×10^{-48}
Zinc iodate, $Zn(IO_3)_2$	3.9×10^{-6}

These partly dissociated and undissociated species increase the *apparent* solubility of a slightly soluble salt above the value obtained by assuming complete dissociation. More advanced courses discuss these factors, but we simply mention them in the Comments of several sample problems. Thus, it is best to view the problem answers as first approximations.

The Meaning of K_{sp} and How to Determine It from Solubility Values The K_{sp} value indicates *how far the dissolution proceeds at equilibrium (saturation).* Table 19.2 presents a few K_{sp} values; Appendix C lists many more. Note that all the values are low, but they range over many orders of magnitude. In Sample Problem 19.6, we find K_{sp} from the solubility of a compound.

Sample Problem 19.6 Determining K_{sp} from Solubility

Problem (a) Lead(II) sulfate ($PbSO_4$) is a key component in lead-acid car batteries. Its solubility in water at 25°C is 4.25×10^{-3} g/100 mL solution. What is the K_{sp} of $PbSO_4$?
(b) When lead(II) fluoride (PbF_2) is shaken with pure water at 25°C, the solubility is found to be 0.64 g/L. Calculate the K_{sp} of PbF_2.

Plan We are given the solubilities in various units and must find K_{sp}. As always, we write a dissolution equation and the ion-product expression for each compound. This tells us the number of moles of each ion. We use the molar mass to convert the solubility of the compound from the given mass units to *molar solubility* (molarity), then use it to find the molarity of each ion, and substitute into the ion-product expression to calculate K_{sp}.

Solution (a) For $PbSO_4$. Writing the equation and ion-product (K_{sp}) expression:

$$PbSO_4(s) \rightleftharpoons Pb^{2+}(aq) + SO_4^{2-}(aq) \qquad K_{sp} = [Pb^{2+}][SO_4^{2-}]$$

Converting solubility to molar solubility:

$$\text{Molar solubility of } PbSO_4 = \frac{0.00425 \text{ g } PbSO_4}{100 \text{ mL soln}} \times \frac{1000 \text{ mL}}{1 \text{ L}} \times \frac{1 \text{ mol } PbSO_4}{303.3 \text{ g } PbSO_4}$$
$$= 1.40 \times 10^{-4}\, M\ PbSO_4$$

Determining molarities of the ions: Because 1 mol of Pb^{2+} and 1 mol of SO_4^{2-} form when 1 mol of $PbSO_4$ dissolves, $[Pb^{2+}] = [SO_4^{2-}] = 1.40 \times 10^{-4}\, M$.
Substituting these values into the ion-product expression to calculate K_{sp}:

$$K_{sp} = [Pb^{2+}][SO_4^{2-}] = (1.40 \times 10^{-4})^2 = 1.96 \times 10^{-8}$$

(b) For PbF_2. Writing the equation and K_{sp} expression:

$$PbF_2(s) \rightleftharpoons Pb^{2+}(aq) + 2F^-(aq) \qquad K_{sp} = [Pb^{2+}][F^-]^2$$

Converting solubility to molar solubility:

$$\text{Molar solubility of } PbF_2 = \frac{0.64 \text{ g } PbF_2}{1 \text{ L soln}} \times \frac{1 \text{ mol } PbF_2}{245.2 \text{ g } PbF_2} = 2.6\times10^{-3}\, M\ PbF_2$$

Determining molarities of the ions: Since 1 mol of Pb^{2+} and 2 mol of F^- form when 1 mol of PbF_2 dissolves, we have

$$[Pb^{2+}] = 2.6\times10^{-3}\, M \quad \text{and} \quad [F^-] = 2(2.6\times10^{-3}\, M) = 5.2\times10^{-3}\, M$$

Substituting these values into the ion-product expression to calculate K_{sp}:

$$K_{sp} = [Pb^{2+}][F^-]^2 = (2.6\times10^{-3})(5.2\times10^{-3})^2 = 7.0\times10^{-8}$$

Check The low solubilities are consistent with K_{sp} values being small. **(a)** The molar solubility seems about right: $\sim \dfrac{4\times10^{-2}\text{ g/L}}{3\times10^{2}\text{ g/mol}} \approx 1.3\times10^{-4}\, M$. Squaring this number gives 1.7×10^{-8}, close to the calculated K_{sp}. **(b)** Let's check the math in the final step as follows: $\sim(3\times10^{-3})(5\times10^{-3})^2 = 7.5\times10^{-8}$, close to the calculated K_{sp}.

Comment **1.** In part (b), the formula PbF_2 means that $[F^-]$ is twice $[Pb^{2+}]$. Then we follow the ion-product expression exactly and square this value of $[F^-]$.
2. The tabulated K_{sp} values for these compounds (Table 19.2) are lower than our calculated values. For PbF_2, for instance, the tabulated value is 3.6×10^{-8}, but we calculated 7.0×10^{-8} from solubility data. The discrepancy arises because we assumed that PbF_2 in solution dissociates completely to Pb^{2+} and F^-. Here is an example of the complication pointed out earlier. Actually, about a third of the PbF_2 dissolves as $PbF^+(aq)$ and a small amount dissolves as undissociated $PbF_2(aq)$. The solubility given in the problem statement (0.64 g/L) is determined experimentally and includes these other species, which we did *not* include in our calculation.

Follow-Up Problem 19.6 When fluorite (CaF_2; *see photo*) is pulverized and shaken in water at 18°C, 10.0 mL of solution contains 1.5×10^{-4} g of solute. Find the K_{sp} of CaF_2 at 18°C.

Fluorite.

Determining Solubility from K_{sp} The reverse of Sample Problem 19.6 involves finding the solubility of a compound based on its formula and K_{sp} value. We'll use an approach similar to the one we used for weak acids in Sample Problem 18.8: we define the unknown amount dissolved—the molar solubility—as S, include ion concentrations in terms of this unknown in a reaction table, and solve for S.

Sample Problem 19.7 Determining Solubility from K_{sp}

Problem Calcium hydroxide (slaked lime) is a major component of mortar, plaster, and cement, and solutions of $Ca(OH)_2$ are used in industry as a strong, inexpensive base. Calculate the molar solubility of $Ca(OH)_2$ in water if K_{sp} is 6.5×10^{-6}.

Plan We write the dissolution equation and the ion-product expression. We know K_{sp} (6.5×10^{-6}), so to find molar solubility (S), we set up a reaction table that expresses $[Ca^{2+}]$ and $[OH^-]$ in terms of S, substitute into the ion-product expression, and solve for S.

Solution Writing the equation and ion-product expression:

$$Ca(OH)_2(s) \rightleftharpoons Ca^{2+}(aq) + 2OH^-(aq) \qquad K_{sp} = [Ca^{2+}][OH^-]^2 = 6.5\times10^{-6}$$

Setting up a reaction table, with S = molar solubility:

Concentration (M)	$Ca(OH)_2(s)$	$\rightleftharpoons$	$Ca^{2+}(aq)$	+	$2OH^-(aq)$
Initial	—		0		0
Change	—		$+S$		$+2S$
Equilibrium	—		S		$2S$

Substituting into the ion-product expression and solving for S:

$$K_{sp} = [Ca^{2+}][OH^-]^2 = (S)(2S)^2 = (S)(4S^2) = 4S^3 = 6.5\times10^{-6}$$

$$S = \sqrt[3]{\frac{6.5\times10^{-6}}{4}} = 1.2\times10^{-2}\ M$$

Check We expect a low solubility from a slightly soluble salt. If we reverse the calculation, we should obtain the given K_{sp}: $4(1.2\times10^{-2})^3 = 6.9\times10^{-6}$, close to 6.5×10^{-6}.

Comment 1. Note that we did not double and *then* square $[OH^-]$. $2S$ *is* the $[OH^-]$, so we just squared it, as the ion-product expression required.

2. Once again, we assumed that the solid dissociates completely. Actually, the solubility is increased to about 2.0×10^{-2} M by the presence of $CaOH^+(aq)$ formed in the reaction $Ca(OH)_2(s) \rightleftharpoons CaOH^+(aq) + OH^-(aq)$. Our calculated answer is only approximate because we did not take this other species into account.

Follow-Up Problem 19.7 Milk of magnesia, a suspension of $Mg(OH)_2$ in water, relieves indigestion by neutralizing stomach acid. What is the molar solubility of $Mg(OH)_2$ ($K_{sp} = 6.3\times10^{-10}$) in water?

Using K_{sp} Values to Compare Solubilities As long as we compare compounds with the *same total number of ions* in their formulas, K_{sp} values indicate *relative* solubility: *the higher the K_{sp}, the greater the solubility* (Table 19.3). Note that for compounds that form three ions, the relationship holds whether the cation/anion ratio is 1/2 or 2/1, because the mathematical expression containing S is the same ($4S^3$) in the calculation (see Sample Problem 19.7).

Table 19.3 Relationship Between K_{sp} and Solubility at 25°C

No. of Ions	Formula	Cation/Anion	K_{sp}	Solubility (M)
2	$MgCO_3$	1/1	3.5×10^{-8}	1.9×10^{-4}
2	$PbSO_4$	1/1	1.6×10^{-8}	1.3×10^{-4}
2	$BaCrO_4$	1/1	2.1×10^{-10}	1.4×10^{-5}
3	$Ca(OH)_2$	1/2	6.5×10^{-6}	1.2×10^{-2}
3	BaF_2	1/2	1.5×10^{-6}	7.2×10^{-3}
3	CaF_2	1/2	3.2×10^{-11}	2.0×10^{-4}
3	Ag_2CrO_4	2/1	2.6×10^{-12}	8.7×10^{-5}

Effect of a Common Ion on Solubility

From Le Châtelier's principle, we know that *adding a common ion decreases the solubility of a slightly soluble ionic compound.* Consider a saturated solution of lead(II) chromate:

$$PbCrO_4(s) \rightleftharpoons Pb^{2+}(aq) + CrO_4^{2-}(aq) \qquad K_{sp} = [Pb^{2+}][CrO_4^{2-}] = 2.3\times10^{-13}$$

At a given temperature, K_{sp} depends on the product of the ion concentrations. If the concentration of either ion goes up, the other goes down to maintain K_{sp}. Suppose we add Na_2CrO_4, a soluble salt, to the saturated $PbCrO_4$ solution. The concentration of the common ion, CrO_4^{2-}, increases, and some of it combines with Pb^{2+} ion to form more solid $PbCrO_4$ (Figure 19.12). That is, the equilibrium position shifts to the left:

$$PbCrO_4(s) \leftleftharpoons Pb^{2+}(aq) + CrO_4^{2-}(aq;\ \text{added})$$

As a result of the addition, $[Pb^{2+}]$ is lower. And, since $[Pb^{2+}]$ defines the solubility of $PbCrO_4$, in effect, the solubility of $PbCrO_4$ has decreased. Note that we would get the same result if Na_2CrO_4 solution were the solvent; that is, $PbCrO_4$ is more soluble in water than in aqueous Na_2CrO_4.

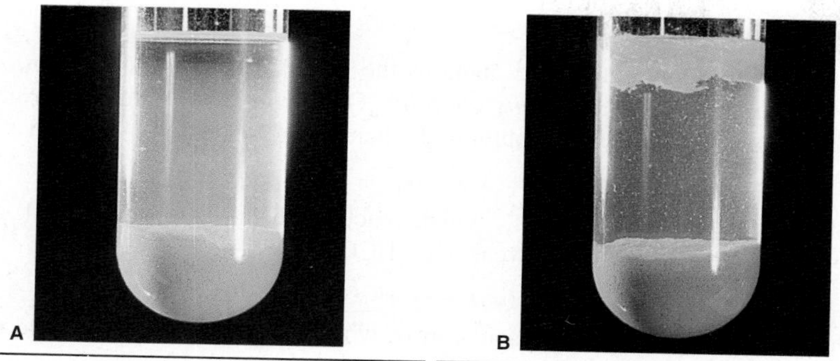

$PbCrO_4(s) \rightleftharpoons Pb^{2+}(aq) + CrO_4^{2-}(aq)$ | $PbCrO_4(s) \rightleftharpoons Pb^{2+}(aq) + CrO_4^{2-}(aq;\ \text{added})$

Figure 19.12 The effect of a common ion on solubility. **A,** Lead(II) chromate, a slightly soluble salt, forms a saturated solution. **B,** When Na_2CrO_4 solution is added, the amount of $PbCrO_4(s)$ increases.

Sample Problem 19.8 Calculating the Effect of a Common Ion on Solubility

Problem In Sample Problem 19.7, we calculated the solubility of $Ca(OH)_2$ in water. What is its solubility in 0.10 *M* $Ca(NO_3)_2$? K_{sp} of $Ca(OH)_2$ is 6.5×10^{-6}.

Plan Addition of Ca^{2+}, the common ion, should lower the solubility. We write the equation and ion-product expression and set up a reaction table, with $[Ca^{2+}]_{init}$ reflecting the 0.10 *M* $Ca(NO_3)_2$ and *S* equal to $[Ca^{2+}]_{from\ Ca(OH)_2}$. To simplify the math, we assume that, because K_{sp} is low, *S* is so small relative to $[Ca^{2+}]_{init}$ that it can be neglected. Then we solve for *S* and check the assumption.

Solution Writing the equation and ion-product expression:

$$Ca(OH)_2(s) \rightleftharpoons Ca^{2+}(aq) + 2OH^-(aq) \qquad K_{sp} = [Ca^{2+}][OH^-]^2 = 6.5\times10^{-6}$$

Setting up the reaction table, with $S = [Ca^{2+}]_{from\ Ca(OH)_2}$:

Concentration (*M*)	$Ca(OH)_2(s)$	$\rightleftharpoons$	$Ca^{2+}(aq)$	+	$2OH^-(aq)$
Initial	—		0.10		0
Change	—		$+S$		$+2S$
Equilibrium	—		$0.10 + S$		$2S$

Making the assumption: K_{sp} is small, so $S << 0.10\ M$; thus, $0.10\ M + S \approx 0.10\ M$. Substituting into the ion-product expression and solving for *S*:

$$K_{sp} = [Ca^{2+}][OH^-]^2 = 6.5\times10^{-6} \approx (0.10)(2S)^2$$

Therefore, $$4S^2 \approx \frac{6.5\times10^{-6}}{0.10} \quad \text{so} \quad S \approx \sqrt{\frac{6.5\times10^{-5}}{4}} = 4.0\times10^{-3}\ M$$

Checking the assumption: $$\frac{4.0\times10^{-3}\ M}{0.10\ M} \times 100 = 4.0\% < 5\%$$

Check In Sample Problem 19.7, the solubility of $Ca(OH)_2$ was 0.012 *M*; here it is 0.0040 *M*, one-third as much. As expected, the solubility *decreased* in the presence of added Ca^{2+}, the common ion.

Follow-Up Problem 19.8 To improve the x-ray image used to diagnose intestinal disorders, a patient drinks an aqueous suspension of $BaSO_4$ before the procedure because Ba^{2+} is opaque to x-rays (*photo*). However, Ba^{2+} is also toxic; thus, $[Ba^{2+}]$ is lowered by adding dilute Na_2SO_4. What is the solubility of $BaSO_4$ ($K_{sp} = 1.1\times10^{-10}$) in **(a)** water and **(b)** 0.10 *M* Na_2SO_4?

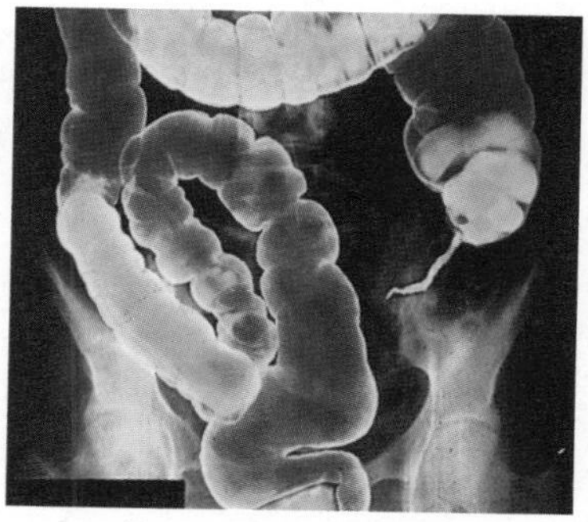

$BaSO_4$ imaging of a large intestine.

Effect of pH on Solubility

If a slightly soluble ionic compound contains the anion of a weak acid, *addition of H_3O^+ (from a strong acid) increases its solubility*. Once again, Le Châtelier's principle explains why. Consider a saturated solution of calcium carbonate:

$$CaCO_3(s) \rightleftharpoons Ca^{2+}(aq) + CO_3^{2-}(aq)$$

Adding strong acid introduces H_3O^+, which reacts with the anion of a weak acid, CO_3^{2-}, to form the anion of another weak acid, HCO_3^-:

$$CO_3^{2-}(aq) + H_3O^+(aq) \longrightarrow HCO_3^-(aq) + H_2O(l)$$

If enough H_3O^+ is added, carbonic acid forms, which decomposes to H_2O and CO_2, and the gas escapes the container:

$$HCO_3^-(aq) + H_3O^+(aq) \longrightarrow [H_2CO_3(aq)] + H_2O(l) \longrightarrow CO_2(g) + 2H_2O(l)$$

The net effect of adding H_3O^+ is a shift in the equilibrium position to the right, and more $CaCO_3$ dissolves:

$$CaCO_3(s) \rightleftharpoons Ca^{2+} + CO_3^{2-} \xrightarrow{H_3O^+} HCO_3^- \xrightarrow{H_3O^+} [H_2CO_3] \longrightarrow CO_2(g) + H_2O + Ca^{2+}$$

In fact, this example illustrates a qualitative field test for carbonate minerals because the CO_2 bubbles vigorously (Figure 19.13).

Figure 19.13 Test for the presence of a carbonate. When a carbonate mineral is treated with HCl, bubbles of CO_2 form.

In contrast, adding H_3O^+ to a saturated solution of a slightly soluble ionic compound with a strong-acid anion, such as AgCl, has no effect on its solubility:

$$AgCl(s) \rightleftharpoons Ag^+(aq) + Cl^-(aq)$$

The Cl^- ion can coexist with high $[H_3O^+]$, so the equilibrium position is not affected.

Sample Problem 19.9 Predicting the Effect on Solubility of Adding Strong Acid

Problem Write balanced equations to explain whether addition of H_3O^+ from a strong acid affects the solubility of each ionic compound:
(a) Lead(II) bromide **(b)** Copper(II) hydroxide **(c)** Iron(II) sulfide

Plan We write the balanced dissolution equation and note the anion:
- Weak-acid anions react with H_3O^+ and increase solubility when strong acid is added.
- Strong-acid anions do not react with H_3O^+, so addition of strong acid has no effect.

Solution (a) $PbBr_2(s) \rightleftharpoons Pb^{2+}(aq) + 2Br^-(aq)$
No effect. Br^- is the anion of HBr, a strong acid, so it does not react with H_3O^+.
(b) $Cu(OH)_2(s) \rightleftharpoons Cu^2(aq) + 2OH^-(aq)$ Increases solubility. OH^- is the anion of H_2O, a very weak acid, so it reacts with the added H_3O^+:

$$OH^-(aq) + H_3O^+(aq) \longrightarrow 2H_2O(l)$$

(c) $FeS(s) + H_2O(l) \rightleftharpoons Fe^{2+}(aq) + HS^-(aq) + OH^-(aq)$ Increases solubility. The S^{2-} ion reacts completely with water to form HS^- and OH^-. The added H_3O^+ reacts with both of these weak-acid anions:

$$HS^-(aq) + H_3O^+(aq) \longrightarrow H_2S(aq) + H_2O(l)$$
$$OH^-(aq) + H_3O^+(aq) \longrightarrow 2H_2O(l)$$

Follow-Up Problem 19.9 Write balanced equations to show how addition of $HNO_3(aq)$ affects the solubility of: **(a)** calcium fluoride; **(b)** zinc sulfide; **(c)** silver iodide.

Applying Ionic Equilibria to the Formation of a Limestone Cave

Limestone caves and the remarkable structures within them provide striking evidence of the results of aqueous ionic equilibria involving carbonate rocks and the carbon dioxide and water that have flowed through them for many hundreds of millennia (Figure 19.14).

The Cave-Forming Reactions Limestone is mostly calcium carbonate ($CaCO_3$; $K_{sp} = 3.3\times10^{-9}$). Two key reactions help us understand how limestone caves form:

1. Gaseous CO_2 in air is in equilibrium with aqueous CO_2 in natural waters:

$$CO_2(g) \xrightleftharpoons{H_2O(l)} CO_2(aq) \qquad \textbf{(equation 1)}$$

The concentration of aqueous CO_2 is proportional to the partial pressure of $CO_2(g)$ in contact with the water (Henry's law; Section 13.4):

$$[CO_2(aq)] \propto P_{CO_2}$$

Due to the continual release of CO_2 from within Earth (outgassing), P_{CO_2} in soil-trapped air is *higher* than P_{CO_2} in the atmosphere.

2. The reaction of CO_2 with water produces H_3O^+:

$$CO_2(aq) + 2H_2O(l) \rightleftharpoons H_3O^+(aq) + HCO_3^-(aq)$$

Thus, since $CaCO_3$ contains the anion of a weak acid, this formation of H_3O^+ increases the solubility of $CaCO_3$:

$$CaCO_3(s) + CO_2(aq) + H_2O(l) \rightleftharpoons Ca^{2+}(aq) + 2HCO_3^-(aq) \qquad \textbf{(equation 2)}$$

Figure 19.14 Limestone cave in Nerja, Málaga, Spain.

The Cave-Forming Process Here is an overview of the process that forms most limestone caves:

1. As surface water trickles through cracks in the ground, it meets soil-trapped air with a high P_{CO_2}. As a result, $[CO_2(aq)]$ increases (equation 1 shifts to the right), and the solution becomes more acidic.
2. When this CO_2-rich water contacts $CaCO_3$, more $CaCO_3$ dissolves (equation 2 shifts to the right). As a result, more rock is carved out, more water flows in, and so on. Centuries pass, and a cave slowly begins to form.
3. Some of the aqueous solution, dilute $Ca(HCO_3)_2$, passes through the ceiling of the growing cave. As it drips, it meets air, which has a lower P_{CO_2} than the soil, so some $CO_2(aq)$ comes out of solution (equation 1 shifts to the left).
4. Consequently, some $CaCO_3$ precipitates on the ceiling and on the floor below, where the drops land (equation 2 shifts to the left). After many decades, the ceiling bears a *stalactite*, while a spike, called a *stalagmite,* grows up from the floor. Eventually, they meet to form a column of precipitated limestone *(see chapter opener).*

The same chemical process can lead to different shapes. Standing pools of $Ca(HCO_3)_2$ solution form limestone "lily pads" or "corals." Cascades of solution form delicate limestone "draperies" on a cave wall, with fabulous colors arising from trace metal ions, such as iron (reddish brown) or copper (bluish green).

Predicting the Formation of a Precipitate: Q_{sp} vs. K_{sp}

As in Chapter 17, here we compare the values of Q_{sp} and K_{sp} to see if a reaction has reached equilibrium and, if not, in which net direction it will move until it does. Using solutions of *soluble* salts that contain the ions of *slightly* soluble salts, we can calculate the ion concentrations and predict the result when we mix the solutions:

- If $Q_{sp} = K_{sp}$, the solution is saturated and no change will occur.
- If $Q_{sp} > K_{sp}$, a precipitate will form until the remaining solution is saturated.
- If $Q_{sp} < K_{sp}$, no precipitate will form because the solution is unsaturated.

Sample Problem 19.10 Predicting Whether a Precipitate Will Form

Problem A common laboratory method for preparing a precipitate is to mix solutions containing the component ions. Does a precipitate form when 0.100 L of 0.30 *M* $Ca(NO_3)_2$ is mixed with 0.200 L of 0.060 *M* NaF?

Plan First, we decide which slightly soluble salt could form, look up its K_{sp} value in Appendix C, and write a dissolution equation and ion-product expression. To see whether mixing these solutions forms the precipitate, we find the initial ion concentrations by calculating the amount (mol) of each ion from its concentration and volume, and dividing by the *total* volume because each solution dilutes the other. Finally, we substitute these concentrations to calculate Q_{sp}, and compare Q_{sp} with K_{sp}.

Precipitation of CaF_2.

Solution The ions present are Ca^{2+}, Na^+, F^-, and NO_3^-. All sodium and all nitrate salts are soluble (Table 4.1, p. 145), so the only possibility is CaF_2 ($K_{sp} = 3.2\times10^{-11}$).
Writing the equation and ion-product expression:

$$CaF_2(s) \rightleftharpoons Ca^{2+}(aq) + 2F^-(aq) \qquad Q_{sp} = [Ca^{2+}][F^-]^2$$

Calculating the ion concentrations:

$$\text{Amount (mol) of } Ca^{2+} = 0.30\ M\ Ca^{2+} \times 0.100\text{ L} = 0.030\text{ mol } Ca^{2+}$$

$$[Ca^{2+}]_{init} = \frac{0.030\text{ mol } Ca^{2+}}{0.100\text{ L} + 0.200\text{ L}} = 0.10\ M\ Ca^{2+}$$

$$\text{Amount (mol) of } F^- = 0.060\ M\ F^- \times 0.200\text{ L} = 0.012\text{ mol } F^-$$

$$[F^-]_{init} = \frac{0.012\text{ mol } F^-}{0.100\text{ L} + 0.200\text{ L}} = 0.040\ M\ F^-$$

Substituting into the ion-product expression and comparing Q_{sp} with K_{sp}:

$$Q_{sp} = [Ca^{2+}]_{init}[F^-]^2_{init} = (0.10)(0.040)^2 = 1.6\times10^{-4}$$

Because $Q_{sp} > K_{sp}$, CaF_2 will precipitate until $Q_{sp} = 3.2\times10^{-11}$.

Check Make sure you round off and quickly check the math. For example, $Q_{sp} = (1\times10^{-1})(4\times10^{-2})^2 = 1.6\times10^{-4}$. With K_{sp} so low, CaF_2 must have a low solubility, and given the sizable concentrations being mixed, we would expect CaF_2 to precipitate.

Follow-Up Problem 19.10 As a result of mineral erosion and biological activity, phosphate ion is common in natural waters, where it often precipitates as insoluble salts such as $Ca_3(PO_4)_2$. If $[Ca^{2+}]_{init} = [PO_4^{3-}]_{init} = 1.0\times10^{-9}\ M$ in a given river, will $Ca_3(PO_4)_2$ precipitate? K_{sp} of $Ca_3(PO_4)_2$ is 1.2×10^{-29}.

Sample Problem 19.11 Using Molecular Scenes to Predict Whether a Precipitate Will Form

Problem These four scenes represent solutions of silver (*gray*) and carbonate (*black and red*) ions above solid silver carbonate. (The solid, other ions, and water are not shown.)

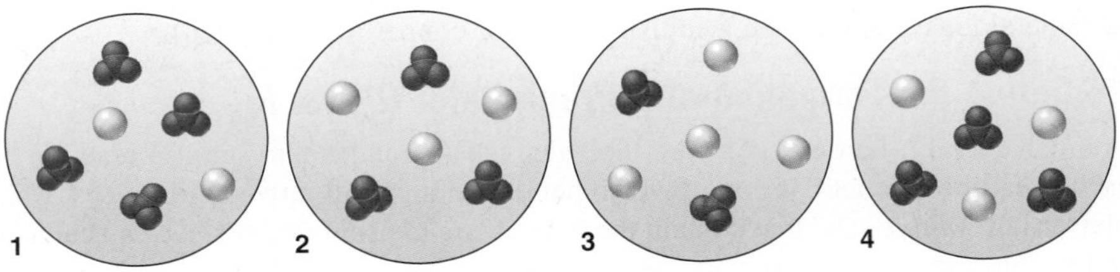

(a) Which scene best represents the solution in equilibrium with the solid?
(b) In which, if any, other scene(s) will additional solid silver carbonate form?
(c) Explain how, if at all, addition of a small volume of concentrated strong acid affects the $[Ag^+]$ in scene 4 and the mass of solid present.

Plan (a) The solution of silver and carbonate ions in equilibrium with the solid (Ag_2CO_3) should have the same relative numbers of cations and anions as in the formula. We examine the scenes to see which has a ratio of 2 Ag^+ to 1 CO_3^{2-}. **(b)** A solid forms if the value of Q_{sp} exceeds the K_{sp}. We write the dissolution equation and Q_{sp} expression. Then we count ions to calculate Q_{sp} in each scene and see which, if any, exceeds the value for the solution from part (a). **(c)** The CO_3^{2-} ion reacts with added H_3O^+, so adding strong acid will shift the equilibrium to the right. We write the equations and determine how a shift to the right affects $[Ag^+]$ and the mass of solid Ag_2CO_3.

Solution (a) Scene 3 is the only one with an Ag^+/CO_3^{2-} ratio of 2/1, as in the solid's formula.

(b) Calculating the ion products:

$$Ag_2CO_3(s) \rightleftharpoons 2Ag^+(aq) + CO_3^{2-}(aq) \qquad Q_{sp} = [Ag^+]^2[CO_3^{2-}]$$

Scene 1: $Q_{sp} = (2)^2(4) = 16$ Scene 2: $Q_{sp} = (3)^2(3) = 27$
Scene 3: $Q_{sp} = (4)^2(2) = 32$ Scene 4: $Q_{sp} = (3)^2(4) = 36$

Therefore, from scene 3, $K_{sp} = 32$; the Q_{sp} value for scene 4 is the only other one that equals or exceeds 32, so a precipitate of Ag_2CO_3 will form there.

(c) Writing the equations:

(1) $$Ag_2CO_3(s) \rightleftharpoons 2Ag^+(aq) + CO_3^{2-}(aq)$$

(2) $$CO_3^{2-}(aq) + 2H_3O^+(aq) \longrightarrow [H_2CO_3(aq)] + 2H_2O(l) \longrightarrow 3H_2O(l) + CO_2(g)$$

The CO_2 leaves as a gas, so adding H_3O^+ shifts the equilibrium position of reaction 2 to the right. This change lowers the $[CO_3^{2-}]$ in reaction 1, thereby causing more CO_3^{2-} to form. As a result, more solid dissolves, which means that the $[Ag^+]$ increases and the mass of Ag_2CO_3 decreases.

Check **(a)** In scene 1, the formula has two CO_3^{2-} per formula unit, not two Ag^+. **(b)** Even though scene 4 has fewer Ag^+ ions than scene 3, its Q_{sp} value is higher and exceeds the K_{sp}.

Follow-Up Problem 19.11 The following scenes represent solutions of nickel(II) (*black*) and hydroxide (*red and blue*) ions that are above solid nickel(II) hydroxide. (For clarity, the solid, other ions, and water are not shown.)

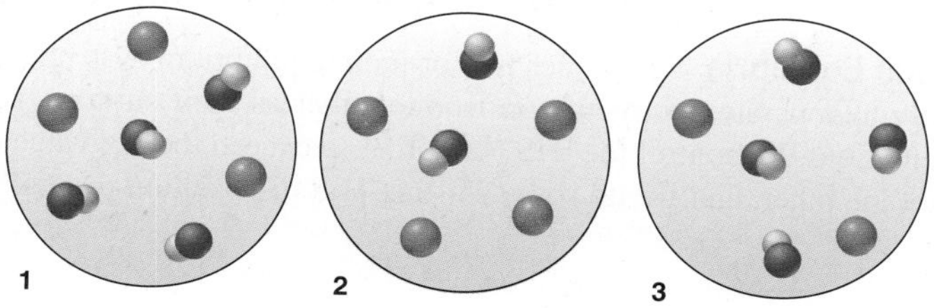

(a) Which scene best depicts the solution at equilibrium with the solid?
(b) In which, if any, other scene(s) will additional solid form?
(c) Will addition of a small amount of concentrated strong acid or strong base affect the mass of solid present in any scene? Explain.

Separating Ions by Selective Precipitation and Simultaneous Equilibria

Let's consider two ways to separate one ion from another by reacting them with a given precipitating ion to form compounds with different solubilities.

Selective Precipitation In the process of **selective precipitation,** a solution of one precipitating ion is added to a solution of two ionic compounds until the Q_{sp} of the *more soluble* compound is almost equal to its K_{sp}. This method ensures that the K_{sp} of the *less soluble* compound is exceeded as much as possible. As a result, the maximum amount of the less soluble compound precipitates, but none of the more soluble compound does.

Sample Problem 19.12 Separating Ions by Selective Precipitation

Problem A solution consists of 0.20 *M* $MgCl_2$ and 0.10 *M* $CuCl_2$. Calculate the $[OH^-]$ that would separate the metal ions. K_{sp} of $Mg(OH)_2$ is 6.3×10^{-10}; K_{sp} of $Cu(OH)_2$ is 2.2×10^{-20}.

Plan Because both compounds have 1/2 ratios of cation/anion (see p. 786), when we compare their K_{sp} values, we find that $Mg(OH)_2$ is about 10^{10} times more soluble than $Cu(OH)_2$; thus, $Cu(OH)_2$ precipitates first. We write the dissolution equations and ion-product expressions. We are given both cation concentrations, so we solve for the $[OH^-]$ that gives a saturated solution of $Mg(OH)_2$, because this $[OH^-]$ will precipitate the most Cu^{2+}. Then, we calculate the $[Cu^{2+}]$ remaining to see if the separation was accomplished.

Solution Writing the equations and ion-product expressions:

$$Mg(OH)_2(s) \rightleftharpoons Mg^{2+}(aq) + 2OH^-(aq) \quad K_{sp} = [Mg^{2+}][OH^-]^2 = 6.3\times10^{-10}$$

$$Cu(OH)_2(s) \rightleftharpoons Cu^{2+}(aq) + 2OH^-(aq) \quad K_{sp} = [Cu^{2+}][OH^-]^2 = 2.2\times10^{-20}$$

Calculating the $[OH^-]$ that gives a saturated $Mg(OH)_2$ solution:

$$[OH^-] = \sqrt{\frac{K_{sp}}{[Mg^{2+}]}} = \sqrt{\frac{6.3\times10^{-10}}{0.20}} = 5.6\times10^{-5}\ M$$

This is the maximum $[OH^-]$ that will *not* precipitate Mg^{2+} ion.
Calculating the $[Cu^{2+}]$ remaining in the solution with this $[OH^-]$:

$$[Cu^{2+}] = \frac{K_{sp}}{[OH^-]^2} = \frac{2.2\times10^{-20}}{(5.6\times10^{-5})^2} = 7.0\times10^{-12}\ M$$

Since the initial $[Cu^{2+}]$ is 0.10 M, virtually all the Cu^{2+} ion is precipitated.

Check Rounding, we find that $[OH^-]$ seems right: $\sim\sqrt{(6\times10^{-10})/0.2} = 5\times10^{-5}$. The $[Cu^{2+}]$ remaining also seems correct: $(200\times10^{-22})/(5\times10^{-5})^2 = 8\times10^{-12}$.

Follow-Up Problem 19.12 A solution is 0.050 M $BaCl_2$ and 0.025 M $CaCl_2$. What concentration of SO_4^{2-} will separate the cations in solution? K_{sp} of $BaSO_4$ is 1.1×10^{-10}, and K_{sp} of $CaSO_4$ is 2.4×10^{-5}.

Simultaneous Equilibria Sometimes two or more equilibrium systems are controlled simultaneously to separate one metal ion from another as their sulfides, using HS^- as the precipitating ion. We control the $[HS^-]$ in order to exceed the K_{sp} value of one metal sulfide but not the other, and we do so by shifting H_2S dissociation through adjustments of $[H_3O^+]$:

$$H_2S(aq) + H_2O(l) \rightleftharpoons H_3O^+(aq) + HS^-(aq)$$

These interactions are controlled in the following way:

- If we add strong acid, the high $[H_3O^+]$ shifts H_2S dissociation to the left, which decreases $[HS^-]$, so the *less* soluble sulfide precipitates.
- If we add strong base, the low $[H_3O^+]$ shifts H_2S dissociation to the right, which increases $[HS^-]$, so the *more* soluble sulfide precipitates.

Thus, we shift one equilibrium system (H_2S dissociation) by adjusting a second (H_2O ionization) to control a third (metal sulfide solubility).

As the Chemical Connections essay demonstrates, the principles of ionic equilibria often help us understand the chemical basis of complex environmental problems and may provide ways to solve them.

Summary of Section 19.3

- Only as a first approximation does the dissolved portion of a slightly soluble salt dissociate completely into ions.
- In a saturated solution, dissolved ions and the undissolved solid salt are in equilibrium. The product of the ion concentrations, each raised to the power of its subscript in the formula, has a constant value ($Q_{sp} = K_{sp}$).
- The value of K_{sp} can be obtained from the solubility, and vice versa.
- Adding a common ion lowers a compound's solubility.
- Adding H_3O^+ (lowering pH) increases a compound's solubility if the anion of the compound is also that of a weak acid.
- Limestone caves result from shifts in the $CaCO_3/CO_2$ equilibrium system.
- An ionic solid forms if $Q_{sp} > K_{sp}$ when solutions that each contain one of the ions are mixed.
- Ions are precipitated selectively from a solution of two compounds by adding a precipitating ion until the K_{sp} of one compound is exceeded as much as possible without exceeding the K_{sp} of the other. An extension of this approach uses simultaneous control of three equilibrium systems to separate metal ions as their sulfides.
- Lakes bounded by limestone-rich soils form buffer systems that prevent acidification.

CHEMICAL CONNECTIONS TO ENVIRONMENTAL SCIENCE | The Acid-Rain Problem

Acid rain, the deposition of acids in wet form as rain, snow, or fog or in dry form as solid particles, is a global environmental problem. It has been observed in the United States, Canada, Mexico, the Amazon basin, Europe, Russia, many parts of Asia, and even at the North and South Poles. Let's see how it arises and how to prevent some of its harmful effects.

Origins of Acid Rain

The strong acids H_2SO_4 and HNO_3 cause the greatest concern, so let's see how they form (Figure B19.1):

1. *Sulfuric acid.* Sulfur dioxide (SO_2), formed mostly by the burning of high-sulfur coal, forms sulfurous acid (H_2SO_3) in contact with water. The atmospheric pollutants hydrogen peroxide (H_2O_2) and ozone (O_3) dissolve in the water in clouds and oxidize the sulfurous acid to sulfuric acid:

$$H_2O_2(aq) + H_2SO_3(aq) \longrightarrow H_2SO_4(aq) + H_2O(l)$$

Alternatively, SO_2 is oxidized by atmospheric hydroxyl radicals ($HO\cdot$) to sulfur trioxide (SO_3), which forms H_2SO_4 with water.

2. *Nitric acid.* Nitrogen oxides (NO_x) form from N_2 and O_2 during high-temperature combustion in car and truck engines and electric power plants. Once formed, NO forms NO_2 and HNO_3 in a process that creates smog (p. 547). At night, NO_x is converted to N_2O_5, which reacts with water to form HNO_3:

$$N_2O_5(g) + H_2O(l) \longrightarrow 2HNO_3(aq)$$

Ammonium salts, deposited as NH_4HSO_4 or NH_4NO_3, produce HNO_3 in soil through biochemical oxidation.

The pH of Acid Rain

Normal rainwater is weakly acidic from the reaction of atmospheric CO_2 with water (see Problem 19.142):

$$CO_2(g) + 2H_2O(l) \rightleftharpoons H_3O^+(aq) + HCO_3^-(aq)$$

Yet, as long ago as 1984, rainfall in the United States had already reached an average pH of 4.2, an increase of about 25 times as much H_3O^+. Rain in Wheeling, West Virginia, has had a pH of 1.8, lower than the pH of lemon juice. And rain in industrial parts of Sweden once had a pH of 2.7, about the same as vinegar.

Effects of Acid Rain

Some fish and shellfish die at pH values between 4.5 and 5.0. The young of most species are generally more vulnerable. At pH 5, most fish eggs cannot hatch. With tens of thousands of rivers and lakes around the world becoming or already acidified, the loss of freshwater fish became a major concern long ago.

In addition, acres of forest have been harmed by the acid, which removes nutrients and releases toxic substances from the soil. The aluminosilicates that make up most soils are extremely insoluble in water. Through a complex series of simultaneous equilibria, contact with water at pH < 5 causes these materials to release some bound Al^{3+}, which is toxic to fish and plants. At the

(continued)

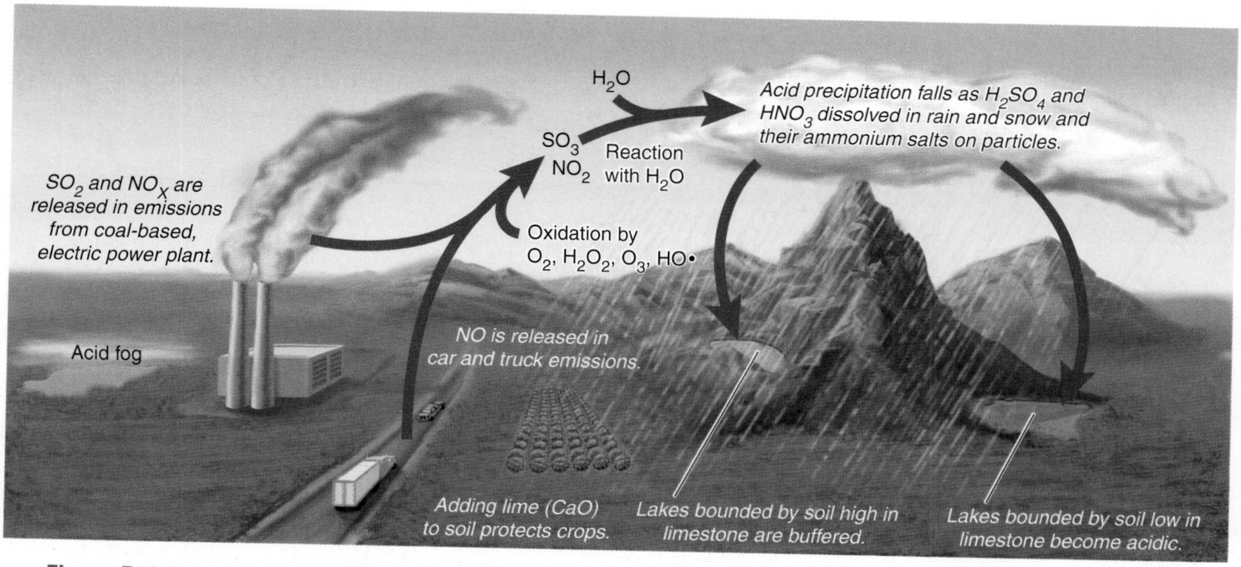

Figure B19.1 Formation of acidic precipitation. A complex interplay of human activities, atmospheric chemistry, and environmental distribution leads to acidic precipitation and its harmful effects.

same time, acid rain dissolves Ca^{2+} and Mg^{2+} ions from the soil, which are nutrients for plants and animals.

Marble and limestone (both primarily $CaCO_3$) in buildings and monuments react with sulfuric acid to form gypsum ($CaSO_4 \cdot 2H_2O$), which flakes off. Ironically, the same process that destroys these structures rescues lakes that are bounded by limestone-rich soil. Limestone dissolves sufficiently in lake water to form an HCO_3^-/CO_3^{2-} buffer capable of absorbing the incoming H_3O^+ and maintaining a mildly basic pH:

$$CO_3^{2-}(aq) + H_3O^+(aq) \rightleftharpoons HCO_3^-(aq) + H_2O(l)$$

Acidified lakes and rivers that are in contact with granite and other weathering-resistant bedrock can be remediated by *liming* (treating with limestone). This approach is expensive and only a stopgap because the lakes are acidic again within several years.

Preventing Acid Rain

Effective prevention of acid rain has to address the sources of the sulfur and nitrogen pollutants:

1. *Sulfur pollutants.* As was pointed out earlier (Chemical Connections, p. 249), the principal means of minimizing sulfur dioxide release is by "scrubbing" power-plant emissions with limestone in both dry and wet form. Another method reduces SO_2 with methane, coal, or H_2S, and the mixture is converted catalytically to sulfur, which is sold as a byproduct:

$$16H_2S(g) + 8SO_2(g) \xrightarrow{\text{catalyst}} 3S_8(s) + 16H_2O(l)$$

Although low-sulfur coal is rare and expensive to mine, coal can be converted into gaseous and liquid low-sulfur fuels. The sulfur is removed (as H_2S) in an acid-gas scrubber after gasification.

2. *Nitrogen pollutants.* Through the use of a catalytic converter in an auto exhaust system, NO_x species are reduced to N_2. In power plant emissions, NO_x is decreased by adjusting conditions and by treating hot stack gases with ammonia in the presence of a heterogeneous catalyst:

$$4NO(g) + 4NH_3(g) + O_2(g) \xrightarrow{\text{catalyst}} 4N_2(g) + 6H_2O(g)$$

Reducing power-plant emissions in North America and Europe has increased the pH of rainfall and some surface waters. Lime (CaO) is routinely used to react with acid rain falling on croplands. Further progress is expected under current legislation, but, in much of eastern North America and northern Europe, additional measures are needed for full recovery.

Problems

B19.1 An environmental technician collects a sample of rainwater. Back in the lab, her pH meter isn't working, so she uses indicator solutions to estimate the pH. A piece of litmus paper turns red, indicating acidity, so she divides the sample into thirds and obtains the following results: thymol blue turns yellow; bromphenol blue turns green; and methyl red turns red. Estimate the pH of the rainwater.

B19.2 A lake that has a surface area of 10.0 acres (1 acre = 4.840×10^3 yd^2) receives 1.00 in. of rain of pH 4.20. (Assume that the acidity of the rain is due to a strong, monoprotic acid.)
(a) How many moles of H_3O^+ are in the rain falling on the lake?
(b) If the lake is unbuffered and its average depth is 10.0 ft before the rain, find the pH after the rain has been mixed with lake water. (Assume the initial pH is 7.00, and ignore runoff from the surrounding land.)
(c) If the lake contains hydrogen carbonate ions (HCO_3^-), what mass of HCO_3^- would neutralize the acid in the rain?

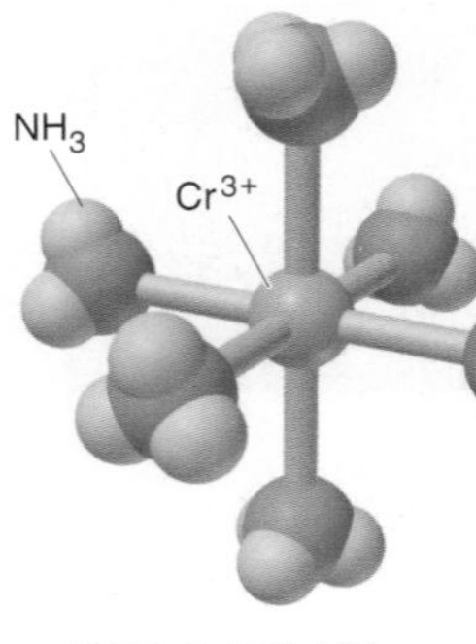

Figure 19.15 $Cr(NH_3)_6^{3+}$, a typical complex ion.

19.4 • EQUILIBRIA INVOLVING COMPLEX IONS

A third kind of aqueous ionic equilibrium involves a type of ion we mentioned briefly in Section 18.9. A *simple ion,* such as Na^+ or CH_3COO^-, consists of one or a few bonded atoms, with an excess or deficit of electrons. A **complex ion** consists of a central metal ion covalently bonded to two or more anions or molecules, called **ligands.** Hydroxide, chloride, and cyanide ions are examples of ionic ligands; water, carbon monoxide, and ammonia are some molecular ligands. In the complex ion $Cr(NH_3)_6^{3+}$, for example, the central Cr^{3+} is surrounded by six NH_3 ligands (Figure 19.15). Hydrated metal ions are complex ions with water as ligands (Section 18.6). In Chapter 23, we discuss the transition metals and the structures and properties of the numerous complex ions they form. Here, we focus on equilibria of hydrated ions with ligands other than water.

Formation of Complex Ions

When a salt dissolves in water, a complex ion forms, with water as ligands around the metal ion. In many cases, when we treat this hydrated cation with a solution of another ligand, the bound water molecules are replaced by the other ligand. For example, a hydrated M^{2+} ion, $M(H_2O)_4^{2+}$, forms the ammoniated ion, $M(NH_3)_4^{2+}$, in aqueous NH_3:

$$M(H_2O)_4^{2+}(aq) + 4NH_3(aq) \rightleftharpoons M(NH_3)_4^{2+}(aq) + 4H_2O(l)$$

At equilibrium, this system is expressed by a ratio of concentration terms whose form follows that of any other equilibrium expression:

$$K_c = \frac{[M(NH_3)_4^{2+}][H_2O]^4}{[M(H_2O)_4^{2+}][NH_3]^4}$$

Once again, because the concentration of water is essentially constant in aqueous reactions, we incorporate it into K_c and obtain the expression for a new equilibrium constant called the **formation constant, K_f:**

$$K_f = \frac{K_c}{[H_2O]^4} = \frac{[M(NH_3)_4^{2+}]}{[M(H_2O)_4^{2+}][NH_3]^4}$$

At the molecular level, depicted in Figure 19.16, the actual process is stepwise, with ammonia molecules replacing water molecules one at a time. This process yields a series of intermediate species, each with its own formation constant:

$$M(H_2O)_4^{2+}(aq) + NH_3(aq) \rightleftharpoons M(H_2O)_3(NH_3)^{2+}(aq) + H_2O(l)$$

$$K_{f1} = \frac{[M(H_2O)_3(NH_3)^{2+}]}{[M(H_2O)_4^{2+}][NH_3]}$$

$$M(H_2O)_3(NH_3)^{2+}(aq) + NH_3(aq) \rightleftharpoons M(H_2O)_2(NH_3)_2^{2+}(aq) + H_2O(l)$$

$$K_{f2} = \frac{[M(H_2O)_2(NH_3)_2^{2+}]}{[M(H_2O)_3(NH_3)^{2+}][NH_3]}$$

$$M(H_2O)_2(NH_3)_2^{2+}(aq) + NH_3(aq) \rightleftharpoons M(H_2O)(NH_3)_3^{2+}(aq) + H_2O(l)$$

$$K_{f3} = \frac{[M(H_2O)(NH_3)_3^{2+}]}{[M(H_2O)_2(NH_3)_2^{2+}][NH_3]}$$

$$M(H_2O)(NH_3)_3^{2+}(aq) + NH_3(aq) \rightleftharpoons M(NH_3)_4^{2+}(aq) + H_2O(l)$$

$$K_{f4} = \frac{[M(NH_3)_4^{2+}]}{[M(H_2O)(NH_3)_3^{2+}][NH_3]}$$

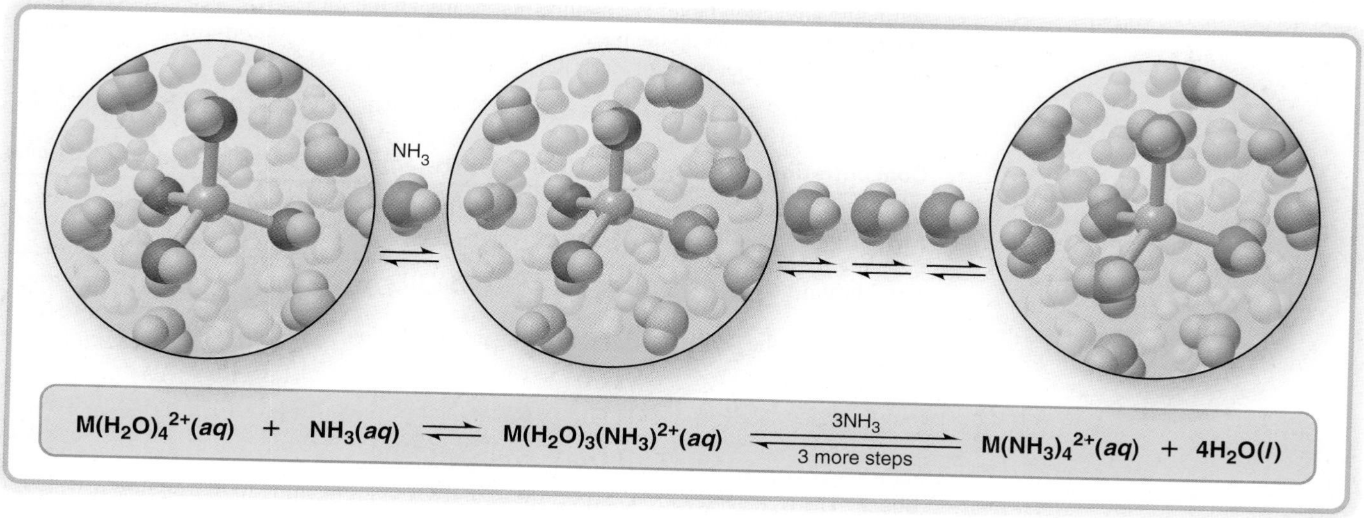

Figure 19.16 The stepwise exchange of NH_3 for H_2O in $M(H_2O)_4^{2+}$. The molecular views show the first exchange and the fully ammoniated ion.

Table 19.4 Formation Constants (K_f) of Some Complex Ions at 25°C

Complex Ion	K_f
$Ag(CN)_2^-$	3.0×10^{20}
$Ag(NH_3)_2^+$	1.7×10^{7}
$Ag(S_2O_3)_2^{3-}$	4.7×10^{13}
AlF_6^{3-}	$4\ \times10^{19}$
$Al(OH)_4^-$	$3\ \times10^{33}$
$Be(OH)_4^{2-}$	$4\ \times10^{18}$
CdI_4^{2-}	$1\ \times10^{6}$
$Co(OH)_4^{2-}$	$5\ \times10^{9}$
$Cr(OH)_4^-$	8.0×10^{29}
$Cu(NH_3)_4^{2+}$	5.6×10^{11}
$Fe(CN)_6^{4-}$	$3\ \times10^{35}$
$Fe(CN)_6^{3-}$	4.0×10^{43}
$Hg(CN)_4^{2-}$	9.3×10^{38}
$Ni(NH_3)_6^{2+}$	2.0×10^{8}
$Pb(OH)_3^-$	$8\ \times10^{13}$
$Sn(OH)_3^-$	$3\ \times10^{25}$
$Zn(CN)_4^{2-}$	4.2×10^{19}
$Zn(NH_3)_4^{2+}$	7.8×10^{8}
$Zn(OH)_4^{2-}$	$3\ \times10^{15}$

The *sum* of the equations gives the overall equation, so the *product* of the individual formation constants gives the overall formation constant:

$$K_f = K_{f1} \times K_{f2} \times K_{f3} \times K_{f4}$$

Recall that *all complex ions are Lewis adducts* (Section 18.9). The metal ion acts as a Lewis acid (accepts an electron pair), and the ligand acts as a Lewis base (donates an electron pair). In the formation of $M(NH_3)_4^{2+}$, the K_f for each step is much larger than 1 because ammonia is a stronger Lewis base than water. Therefore, if we add excess ammonia to the $M(H_2O)_4^{2+}$ solution, nearly all the M^{2+} ions exist as $M(NH_3)_4^{2+}(aq)$.

Table 19.4 (and Appendix C) shows K_f values of some complex ions. Notice that they are all 10^6 or greater, which means that these ions form readily from the hydrated ion. Because of this behavior, some uses of complex-ion formation are to retrieve a metal from its ore, eliminate a toxic or unwanted metal ion from a solution, or convert a metal ion to a different form, as Sample Problem 19.13 shows for the zinc ion.

Sample Problem 19.13 Calculating the Concentration of a Complex Ion

Problem An industrial chemist converts $Zn(H_2O)_4^{2+}$ to the more stable $Zn(NH_3)_4^{2+}$ by mixing 50.0 L of 0.0020 *M* $Zn(H_2O)_4^{2+}$ and 25.0 L of 0.15 *M* NH_3. What is the $[Zn(H_2O)_4^{2+}]$ at equilibrium? K_f of $Zn(NH_3)_4^{2+}$ is 7.8×10^8.

Plan We write the equation and the K_f expression and use a reaction table to calculate the equilibrium concentrations. To set up the table, we must first find $[Zn(H_2O)_4^{2+}]_{init}$ and $[NH_3]_{init}$. We are given the individual volumes and molar concentrations, so we find the number of moles and divide by the *total* volume because the solutions are mixed. With the large excess of NH_3 and the high K_f, we assume that almost all the $Zn(H_2O)_4^{2+}$ is converted to $Zn(NH_3)_4^{2+}$. Because $[Zn(H_2O)_4^{2+}]$ at equilibrium is very small, we use *x* to represent it.

Solution Writing the equation and the K_f expression:

$$Zn(H_2O)_4^{2+}(aq) + 4NH_3(aq) \rightleftharpoons Zn(NH_3)_4^{2+}(aq) + 4H_2O(l)$$

$$K_f = \frac{[Zn(NH_3)_4^{2+}]}{[Zn(H_2O)_4^{2+}][NH_3]^4}$$

Finding the initial reactant concentrations:

$$[Zn(H_2O)_4^{2+}]_{init} = \frac{50.0\ \text{L} \times 0.0020\ M}{50.0\ \text{L} + 25.0\ \text{L}} = 1.3\times10^{-3}\ M$$

$$[NH_3]_{init} = \frac{25.0\ \text{L} \times 0.15\ M}{50.0\ \text{L} + 25.0\ \text{L}} = 5.0\times10^{-2}\ M$$

Setting up a reaction table: We assume that nearly all the $Zn(H_2O)_4^{2+}$ is converted to $Zn(NH_3)_4^{2+}$, so we set up the table with $x = [Zn(H_2O)_4^{2+}]$ at equilibrium. Because 4 mol of NH_3 is needed per mole of $Zn(H_2O)_4^{2+}$, the change in $[NH_3]$ is

$$[NH_3]_{reacted} \approx 4(1.3\times10^{-3}\ M) = 5.2\times10^{-3}\ M \quad \text{and} \quad [Zn(NH_3)_4^{2+}] \approx 1.3\times10^{-3}\ M$$

Concentration (*M*)	$Zn(H_2O)_4^{2+}(aq)$	+ $4NH_3(aq)$	$\rightleftharpoons$ $Zn(NH_3)_4^{2+}(aq)$	+ $4H_2O(l)$
Initial	1.3×10^{-3}	5.0×10^{-2}	0	—
Change	$\sim(-1.3\times10^{-3})$	$\sim(-5.2\times10^{-3})$	$\sim(+1.3\times10^{-3})$	—
Equilibrium	*x*	4.5×10^{-2}	1.3×10^{-3}	—

Solving for *x*, the $[Zn(H_2O)_4^{2+}]$ remaining at equilibrium:

$$K_f = \frac{[Zn(NH_3)_4^{2+}]}{[Zn(H_2O)_4^{2+}][NH_3]^4} = 7.8\times10^8 \approx \frac{1.3\times10^{-3}}{x(4.5\times10^{-2})^4}$$

$$x = [Zn(H_2O)_4^{2+}] \approx 4.1\times10^{-7}\ M$$

Check The K_f is large, so we expect the $[Zn(H_2O)_4^{2+}]$ remaining to be very low.

Follow-Up Problem 19.13 Cyanide ion is toxic because it forms stable complex ions with the Fe^{3+} ion in certain proteins involved in cellular energy production. To study this effect, a biochemist mixes 25.5 mL of 3.1×10^{-2} *M* $Fe(H_2O)_6^{3+}$ with 35.0 mL of 1.5 *M* NaCN. What is the final $[Fe(H_2O)_6^{3+}]$? K_f of $Fe(CN)_6^{3-}$ is 4.0×10^{43}.

Complex Ions and the Solubility of Precipitates

In Section 19.3, you saw that H_3O^+ increases the solubility of a slightly soluble ionic compound if its anion is that of a weak acid. Similarly, *a ligand increases the solubility of a slightly soluble ionic compound if it forms a complex ion with the cation.* For example, iron(II) sulfide is very slightly soluble:

$$FeS(s) + H_2O(l) \rightleftharpoons Fe^{2+}(aq) + HS^-(aq) + OH^-(aq) \qquad K_{sp} = 8\times10^{-16}$$

When we add some 1.0 *M* NaCN, the CN^- ions act as ligands and react with the small amount of $Fe^{2+}(aq)$ to form the complex ion $Fe(CN)_6^{4-}$:

$$Fe^{2+}(aq) + 6CN^-(aq) \rightleftharpoons Fe(CN)_6^{4-}(aq) \qquad K_f = 3\times10^{35}$$

To see the effect of complex-ion formation on the solubility of FeS, we add the equations and, therefore, multiply their equilibrium constants:

$$FeS(s) + 6CN^-(aq) + H_2O(l) \rightleftharpoons Fe(CN)_6^{4-}(aq) + HS^-(aq) + OH^-(aq)$$

$$K_{overall} = K_{sp} \times K_f = (8\times10^{-16})(3\times10^{35}) = 2\times10^{20}$$

The overall dissociation of FeS into ions increased by more than a factor of 10^{35} in the presence of the ligand.

Sample Problem 19.14 Calculating the Effect of Complex-Ion Formation on Solubility

Problem In black-and-white film developing *(see photo)*, excess AgBr is removed from a film negative with "hypo," an aqueous solution of sodium thiosulfate ($Na_2S_2O_3$), which forms the complex ion $Ag(S_2O_3)_2^{3-}$. Calculate the solubility of AgBr in **(a)** H_2O; **(b)** 1.0 *M* hypo. K_f of $Ag(S_2O_3)_2^{3-}$ is 4.7×10^{13} and K_{sp} of AgBr is 5.0×10^{-13}.

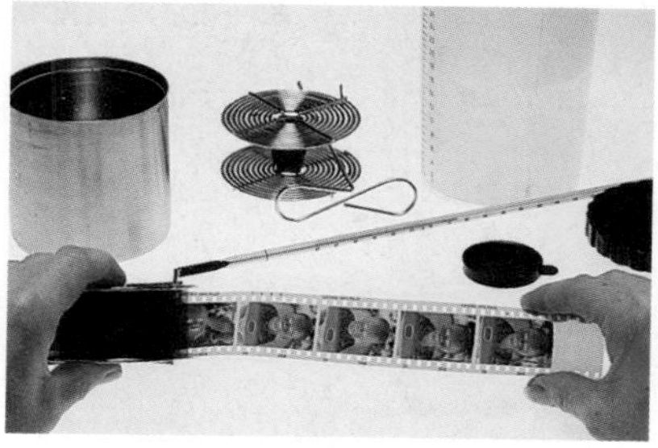

Developing an image in "hypo."

Plan (a) After writing the equation and the ion-product expression, we use the given K_{sp} to solve for *S*, the molar solubility of AgBr. **(b)** In hypo, Ag^+ forms a complex ion with $S_2O_3^{2-}$, which shifts the equilibrium and dissolves more AgBr. We write the complex-ion equation and add it to the equation for dissolving AgBr to obtain the overall equation for dissolving AgBr in hypo. We multiply K_{sp} by K_f to find $K_{overall}$. To find the solubility of AgBr in hypo, we set up a reaction table, with $S = [Ag(S_2O_3)_2^{3-}]$, substitute into the expression for $K_{overall}$, and solve for *S*.

Solution (a) Solubility in water. Writing the equation for the saturated solution and the ion-product expression:

$$AgBr(s) \rightleftharpoons Ag^+(aq) + Br^-(aq) \qquad K_{sp} = [Ag^+][Br^-]$$

Solving for solubility (*S*) directly from the equation: We know that

$$S = [AgBr]_{dissolved} = [Ag^+] = [Br^-]$$

Thus,

$$K_{sp} = [Ag^+][Br^-] = S^2 = 5.0\times10^{-13}$$

so

$$S = 7.1\times10^{-7}\ M$$

(b) Solubility in 1.0 *M* hypo. Writing the overall equation:

$$AgBr(s) \rightleftharpoons \cancel{Ag^+(aq)} + Br^-(aq)$$

$$\cancel{Ag^+(aq)} + 2S_2O_3^{2-}(aq) \rightleftharpoons Ag(S_2O_3)_2^{3-}(aq)$$

$$AgBr(s) + 2S_2O_3^{2-}(aq) \rightleftharpoons Ag(S_2O_3)_2^{3-}(aq) + Br^-(aq)$$

Calculating $K_{overall}$:

$$K_{overall} = \frac{[Ag(S_2O_3)_2^{3-}][Br^-]}{[S_2O_3^{2-}]^2} = K_{sp} \times K_f = (5.0\times10^{-13})(4.7\times10^{13}) = 24$$

Setting up a reaction table, with $S = [AgBr]_{dissolved} = [Ag(S_2O_3)_2^{3-}]$:

Concentration (*M*)	$AgBr(s)$ +	$2S_2O_3^{2-}(aq)$ ⇌	$Ag(S_2O_3)_2^{3-}(aq)$ +	$Br^-(aq)$
Initial	—	1.0	0	0
Change	—	$-2S$	$+S$	$+S$
Equilibrium	—	$1.0 - 2S$	S	S

Substituting the values into the expression for $K_{overall}$ and solving for S:

$$K_{overall} = \frac{[Ag(S_2O_3)_2^{3-}][Br^-]}{[S_2O_3^{2-}]^2} = \frac{S^2}{(1.0\ M - 2S)^2} = 24$$

Taking the square root of both sides gives

$$\frac{S}{1.0\ M - 2S} = \sqrt{24} = 4.9 \quad \text{so} \quad S = 4.9\ M - 9.8S \quad \text{and} \quad 10.8S = 4.9\ M$$

$$[Ag(S_2O_3)_2^{3-}] = S = 0.45\ M$$

Check **(a)** From the number of ions in the formula of AgBr, we know that $S = \sqrt{K_{sp}}$, so the order of magnitude seems right: $\sim\sqrt{10^{-14}} \approx 10^{-7}$. **(b)** The $K_{overall}$ seems correct: the exponents cancel, and $5 \times 5 = 25$. Most importantly, the answer makes sense because the photographic process requires the remaining AgBr to be washed off the film and the large $K_{overall}$ confirms that. We can check S by rounding and working backward to find $K_{overall}$: from the reaction table, we find that

$$[(S_2O_3)^{2-}] = 1.0\ M - 2S = 1.0\ M - 2(0.45\ M) = 1.0\ M - 0.90\ M = 0.1\ M$$

so $K_{overall} \approx (0.45)^2/(0.1)^2 = 20$, within rounding of the calculated value.

Follow-Up Problem 19.14 How does the solubility of AgBr in 1.0 *M* NH_3 compare with its solubility in 1.0 *M* hypo? K_f of $Ag(NH_3)_2^+$ is 1.7×10^7.

Complex Ions of Amphoteric Hydroxides

Many of the same metals that form amphoteric oxides (Chapter 8, p. 316) also form slightly soluble *amphoteric hydroxides*. These compounds dissolve very little in water, but they dissolve to a much greater extent in both acidic and basic solutions. Aluminum hydroxide is one of several examples:

$$Al(OH)_3(s) \rightleftharpoons Al^{3+}(aq) + 3OH^-(aq)$$

It is insoluble in water ($K_{sp} = 3\times10^{-34}$), but

- It dissolves in acid because H_3O^+ reacts with the OH^- anion (Sample Problem 19.9b),

$$3H_3O^+(aq) + 3OH^-(aq) \longrightarrow 6H_2O(l)$$

  giving the overall equation

$$Al(OH)_3(s) + 3H_3O^+(aq) \longrightarrow Al^{3+}(aq) + 6H_2O(l)$$

- It dissolves in base through the formation of a complex ion:

$$Al(OH)_3(s) + OH^-(aq) \longrightarrow Al(OH)_4^-(aq)$$

Let's look more closely at this behavior. When we dissolve a soluble aluminum salt, such as $Al(NO_3)_3$, in water and then slowly add a strong base, a white precipitate first forms and then dissolves as more base is added. What reactions are occurring? The formula for the hydrated Al^{3+} ion is $Al(H_2O)_6^{3+}(aq)$. It acts as a weak polyprotic acid and reacts with added OH^- ions in a stepwise manner. In each step, one of the bound H_2O molecules loses a proton and becomes a bound OH^- ion, so the number of bound H_2O molecules is reduced by 1:

$$Al(H_2O)_6^{3+}(aq) + OH^-(aq) \rightleftharpoons Al(H_2O)_5OH^{2+}(aq) + H_2O(l)$$

$$Al(H_2O)_5OH^{2+}(aq) + OH^-(aq) \rightleftharpoons Al(H_2O)_4(OH)_2^+(aq) + H_2O(l)$$

$$Al(H_2O)_4(OH)_2^+(aq) + OH^-(aq) \rightleftharpoons Al(H_2O)_3(OH)_3(s) + H_2O(l)$$

After three protons have been removed from each $Al(H_2O)_6^{3+}$, the white precipitate has formed, which is the insoluble hydroxide $Al(H_2O)_3(OH)_3(s)$, often written more simply as $Al(OH)_3(s)$. Now you can see that the precipitate actually consists of the hydrated Al^{3+} ion with an H^+ removed from each of three bound H_2O molecules (Figure 19.17, *center*). Addition of H_3O^+ protonates the OH^- ions and re-forms the hydrated Al^{3+} ion (Figure 19.17, *left*).

Further addition of OH^- removes a fourth H^+ and the precipitate dissolves as the soluble ion $Al(H_2O)_2(OH)_4^-(aq)$ forms (Figure 19.17, *right*), which we usually write with the formula $Al(OH)_4^-(aq)$:

$$Al(H_2O)_3(OH)_3(s) + OH^-(aq) \rightleftharpoons Al(H_2O)_2(OH)_4^-(aq) + H_2O(l)$$

In other words, this complex ion is not created by ligands substituting for bound water molecules but through an acid-base reaction in which added OH^- ions titrate bound water molecules.

Several other slightly soluble hydroxides, including those of cadmium, chromium(III), cobalt(III), lead(II), tin(II), and zinc, are amphoteric and exhibit similar reactions:

$$Zn(H_2O)_2(OH)_2(s) + OH^-(aq) \rightleftharpoons Zn(H_2O)(OH)_3^-(aq) + H_2O(l)$$

In contrast, the slightly soluble hydroxides of iron(II), iron(III), and calcium dissolve in acid, but do *not* dissolve in base, because the three remaining bound water molecules are not acidic enough to lose any of their protons:

$$Fe(H_2O)_3(OH)_3(s) + 3H_3O^+(aq) \longrightarrow Fe(H_2O)_6^{3+}(aq) + 3H_2O(l)$$

$$Fe(H_2O)_3(OH)_3(s) + OH^-(aq) \longrightarrow \text{no reaction}$$

This difference in solubility in base between $Al(OH)_3$ and $Fe(OH)_3$ is the key to an important separation step in the production of aluminum metal, so we'll consider it again in Section 22.4.

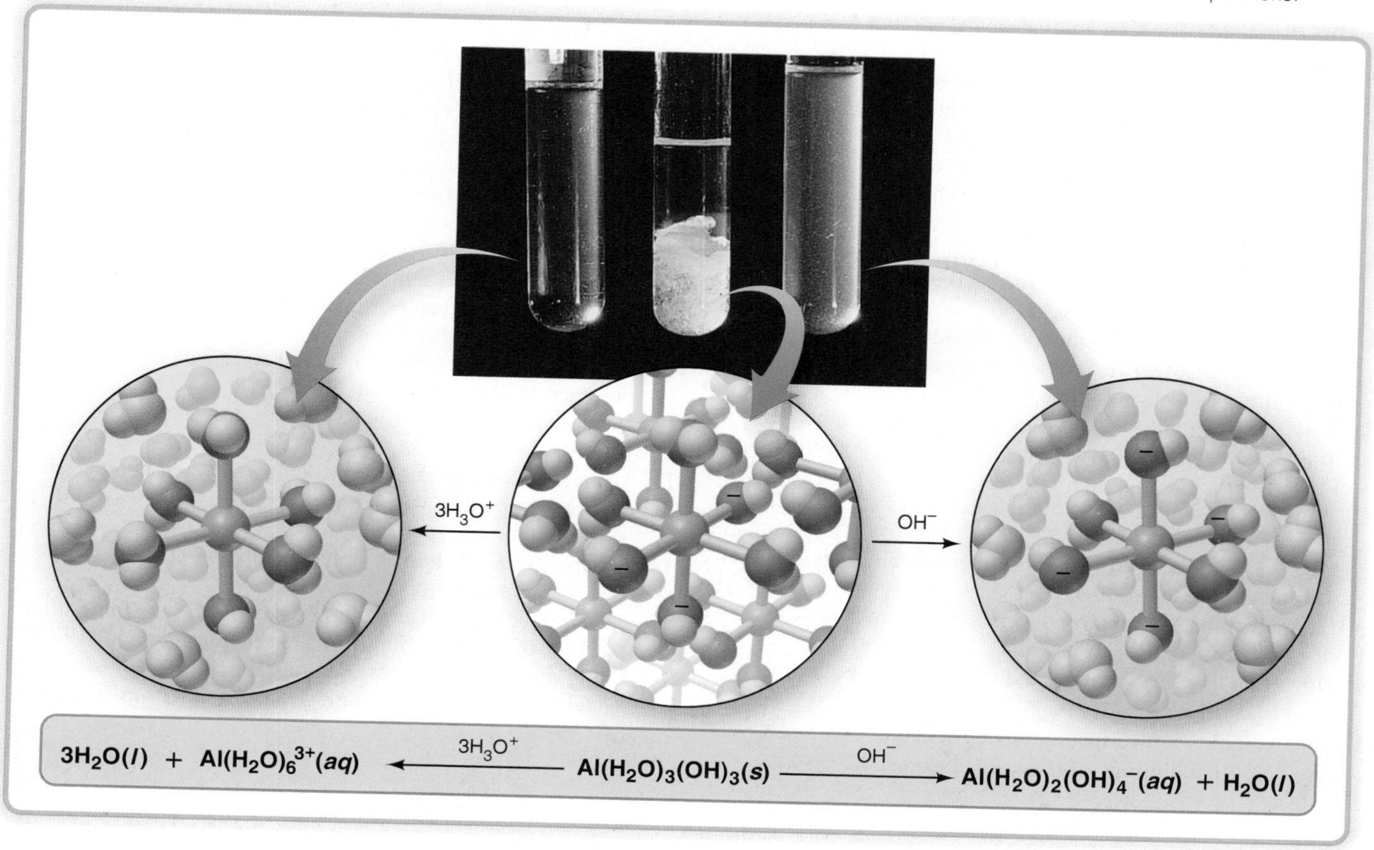

Figure 19.17 The amphoteric behavior of aluminum hydroxide. When solid $Al(OH)_3$ is treated with H_3O^+ (*left*) or with OH^- (*right*), it dissolves as a result of the formation of soluble complex ions.

Summary of Section 19.4

- A complex ion consists of a central metal ion covalently bonded to two or more negatively charged or neutral ligands. Its formation is described by a formation constant, K_f.
- A hydrated metal ion is a complex ion with water molecules as ligands. Other ligands (stronger Lewis bases) can displace the water in a stepwise process. In most cases, the K_f value of each step is large, so the fully substituted complex ion forms almost completely with excess ligand.
- Adding a solution containing a ligand increases the solubility of an ionic precipitate if the cation forms a complex ion with the ligand.
- Amphoteric metal hydroxides dissolve in acid and base due to reactions that involve complex ions.

CHAPTER REVIEW GUIDE

Learning Objectives

Relevant section (§) and/or sample problem (SP) numbers appear in parentheses.

Understand These Concepts

1. How the presence of a common ion suppresses a reaction that forms it (§19.1)
2. Why the concentrations of buffer components must be high to minimize the change in pH from addition of small amounts of H_3O^+ or OH^- (§19.1)
3. How buffer capacity depends on buffer concentration and on the pK_a of the acid component; why buffer range is within ±1 pH unit of the pK_a (§19.1)
4. The nature of an acid-base indicator as a conjugate acid-base pair with differently colored acidic and basic forms (§19.2)
5. The distinction between equivalence point and end point in an acid-base titration (§19.2)
6. Why the shapes of strong acid–strong base, weak acid–strong base, and weak base–strong acid titration curves differ (§19.2)
7. How the pH at the equivalence point is determined by the species present; why the pH at the midpoint of the buffer region equals the pK_a of the acid (§19.2)
8. How the titration curve of a polyprotic acid has a buffer region and equivalence point for each ionizable proton (§19.2)
9. How a slightly soluble ionic compound reaches equilibrium in water, expressed by an equilibrium (solubility-product) constant, K_{sp} (§19.3)
10. Why incomplete dissociation of an ionic compound leads to approximate calculated values for K_{sp} and solubility (§19.3)
11. Why a common ion in a solution decreases the solubility of its compounds (§19.3)
12. How pH affects the solubility of a compound that contains a weak-acid anion (§19.3)
13. How precipitate formation depends on the relative values of Q_{sp} and K_{sp} (§19.3)
14. How selective precipitation and simultaneous equilibria are used to separate ions (§19.3)
15. How complex-ion formation is stepwise and expressed by an overall equilibrium (formation) constant, K_f (§19.4)
16. Why addition of a ligand increases the solubility of a compound whose metal ion forms a complex ion (§19.4)
17. How the aqueous chemistry of amphoteric hydroxides involves precipitation, complex-ion formation, and acid-base equilibria (§19.4)

Master These Skills

1. Using stoichiometry and equilibrium problem-solving techniques to calculate the effect of added H_3O^+ or OH^- on buffer pH (SP 19.1)
2. Using the Henderson-Hasselbalch equation to calculate buffer pH (§19.1)
3. Using molecular scenes to depict buffers (SP 19.2)
4. Choosing the components of a buffer with a given pH and calculating their quantities (SP 19.3)
5. Calculating the pH at any point in an acid-base titration (§19.2 and SP 19.4)
6. Choosing an appropriate indicator based on the pH at various points in a titration (§19.2)
7. Writing K_{sp} expressions for slightly soluble ionic compounds (SP 19.5)
8. Using K_{sp} values to compare solubilities for compounds with the same total number of ions (§19.3)
9. Calculating a K_{sp} value from solubility data (SP 19.6)
10. Calculating solubility from a K_{sp} value (SP 19.7)
11. Calculating the decrease in solubility caused by the presence of a common ion (SP 19.8)
12. Predicting the effect of added H_3O^+ on solubility (SP 19.9)
13. Using ion concentrations to calculate Q_{sp} and compare it with K_{sp} to predict whether a precipitate forms (SPs 19.10, 19.11)
14. Comparing K_{sp} values in order to separate ions by selective precipitation (SP 19.12)
15. Calculating the concentration of metal ion remaining after addition of excess ligand forms a complex ion (SP 19.13)
16. Using an overall equilibrium constant ($K_{sp} \times K_f$) to calculate the effect of complex-ion formation on solubility (SP 19.14)

Key Terms

Page numbers appear in parentheses.

Section 19.1
acid-base buffer (765)
common-ion effect (766)
Henderson-Hasselbalch equation (770)
buffer capacity (770)
buffer range (771)

Section 19.2
acid-base titration curve (774)
equivalence point (775)
end point (776)

Section 19.3
solubility-product constant (K_{sp}) (783)
selective precipitation (791)

Section 19.4
complex ion (794)
ligand (794)
formation constant (K_f) (795)

Key Equations and Relationships

Page numbers appear in parentheses.

19.1 Finding the pH from known concentrations of a conjugate acid-base pair (Henderson-Hasselbalch equation) (770):

$$pH = pK_a + \log\left(\frac{[\text{base}]}{[\text{acid}]}\right)$$

19.2 Defining the equilibrium condition for a saturated solution of a slightly soluble compound, M_pX_q, composed of M^{n+} and X^{z-} ions (783):

$$Q_{sp} = [M^{n+}]^p[X^{z-}]^q = K_{sp}$$

Brief Solutions to Follow-Up Problems

19.1 (a) Before addition:
Assuming x is small enough to be neglected,

$$[HF] = 0.50\ M \quad \text{and} \quad [F^-] = 0.45\ M$$

$$[H_3O^+] = K_a \times \frac{[HF]}{[F^-]} \approx (6.8\times10^{-4})\left(\frac{0.50}{0.45}\right) = 7.6\times10^{-4}\ M$$

$$pH = 3.12$$

(b) After addition of 0.40 g of NaOH (0.010 mol of NaOH) to 1.0 L of buffer,

$$[HF] = 0.49\ M \quad \text{and} \quad [F^-] = 0.46\ M$$

$$[H_3O^+] \approx (6.8\times10^{-4})\left(\frac{0.49}{0.46}\right) = 7.2\times10^{-4}\ M;\ pH = 3.14$$

19.2 (a) Strong base would convert HB to B^-, thereby making the ratio closer to 1.
(b)

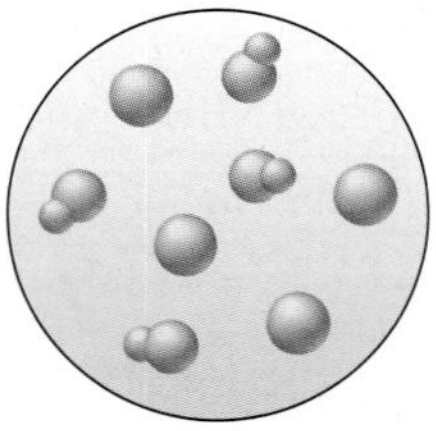

19.3 $[H_3O^+] = 10^{-pH} = 10^{-4.25} = 5.6\times10^{-5}$

$$[C_6H_5COOH] = \frac{[H_3O^+][C_6H_5COO^-]}{K_a} = \frac{(5.6\times10^{-5})(0.050)}{6.3\times10^{-5}} = 0.044\ M$$

Mass (g) of C_6H_5COOH

$$= 5.0\ \text{L soln} \times \frac{0.044\ \text{mol}\ C_6H_5COOH}{1\ \text{L soln}} \times \frac{122.12\ \text{g}\ C_6H_5COOH}{1\ \text{mol}\ C_6H_5COOH}$$
$$= 27\ \text{g}\ C_6H_5COOH$$

Dissolve 27 g of C_6H_5COOH in 4.9 L of 0.050 M C_6H_5COONa and add solution to make 5.0 L. Adjust pH to 4.25 with strong acid or base.

19.4 (a) $[H_3O^+] \approx \sqrt{(2.3\times10^{-9})(0.2000)} = 2.1\times10^{-5}\ M$

$$pH = 4.68$$

(b) $[H_3O^+] = K_a \times \dfrac{[HBrO]}{[BrO^-]} = (2.3\times10^{-9})(1) = 2.3\times10^{-9}\ M$

$$pH = 8.64$$

(c)

$$[BrO^-] = \frac{\text{amount (mol) of } BrO^-}{\text{total volume (L)}} = \frac{0.004000\ \text{mol}}{0.06000\ \text{L}} = 0.06667\ M$$

$$K_b \text{ of } BrO^- = \frac{K_w}{K_a \text{ of } HBrO} = 4.3\times10^{-6}$$

$$[H_3O^+] = \frac{K_w}{\sqrt{K_b \times [BrO^-]}} \approx \frac{1.0\times10^{-14}}{\sqrt{(4.3\times10^{-6})(0.06667)}} = 1.9\times10^{-11}\ M$$

$$pH = 10.72$$

Brief Solutions to Follow-Up Problems (continued)

(d) Amount (mol) of OH^- added = 0.008000 mol
Volume (L) of OH^- soln = 0.08000 L

$$[OH^-] = \frac{\text{amount (mol) of } OH^- \text{ unreacted}}{\text{total volume (L)}}$$

$$= \frac{0.008000 \text{ mol} - 0.004000 \text{ mol}}{(0.02000 + 0.08000) \text{ L}} = 0.04000\ M$$

$$[H_3O^+] = \frac{K_w}{[OH^-]} = 2.5\times10^{-13}$$

$$\text{pH} = 12.60$$

(e)

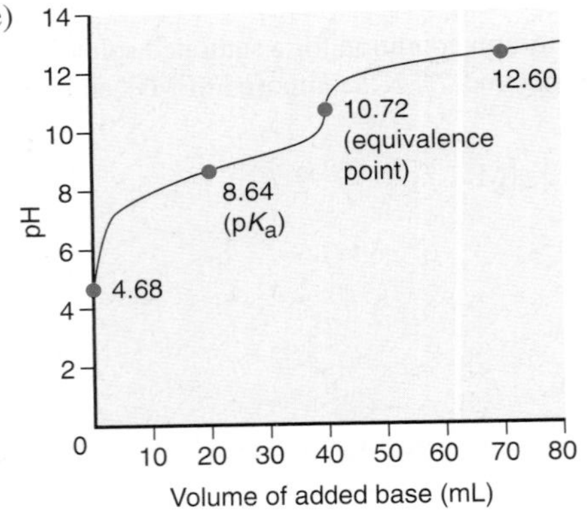

19.5 (a) $K_{sp} = [Ca^{2+}][SO_4^{2-}]$
(b) $K_{sp} = [Cr^{3+}]^2[CO_3^{2-}]^3$
(c) $K_{sp} = [Mg^{2+}][OH^-]^2$
(d) $K_{sp} = [As^{3+}]^2[HS^-]^3[OH^-]^3$

19.6 $$[CaF_2] = \frac{1.5\times10^{-4} \text{ g } CaF_2}{10.0 \text{ mL soln}} \times \frac{1000 \text{ mL}}{1 \text{ L}} \times \frac{1 \text{ mol } CaF_2}{78.08 \text{ g } CaF_2}$$

$$= 1.9\times10^{-4}\ M$$

$CaF_2(s) \rightleftharpoons Ca^{2+}(aq) + 2F^-(aq)$
$[Ca^{2+}] = 1.9\times10^{-4}\ M$ and $[F^-] = 3.8\times10^{-4}\ M$
$K_{sp} = [Ca^{2+}][F^-]^2 = (1.9\times10^{-4})(3.8\times10^{-4})^2 = 2.7\times10^{-11}$

19.7 From the reaction table, $[Mg^{2+}] = S$ and $[OH^-] = 2S$
$K_{sp} = [Mg^{2+}][OH^-]^2 = 4S^3 = 6.3\times10^{-10}$; $S = 5.4\times10^{-4}\ M$

19.8 (a) In water: $K_{sp} = [Ba^{2+}][SO_4^{2-}] = S^2 = 1.1\times10^{-10}$
$S = 1.0\times10^{-5}$
(b) In 0.10 M Na_2SO_4: $[SO_4^{2-}] = 0.10\ M$
$K_{sp} = 1.1\times10^{-10} \approx S \times 0.10$; $S = 1.1\times10^{-9}\ M$
S decreases in presence of the common ion SO_4^{2-}.

19.9 (a) Increases solubility.

$$CaF_2(s) \rightleftharpoons Ca^{2+}(aq) + 2F^-(aq)$$

$$F^-(aq) + H_3O^+(aq) \longrightarrow HF(aq) + H_2O(l)$$

(b) Increases solubility.

$$ZnS(s) + H_2O(l) \rightleftharpoons Zn^{2+}(aq) + HS^-(aq) + OH^-(aq)$$

$$HS^-(aq) + H_3O^+(aq) \longrightarrow H_2S(aq) + H_2O(l)$$

$$OH^-(aq) + H_3O^+(aq) \longrightarrow 2H_2O(l)$$

(c) No effect. $I^-(aq)$ is the conjugate base of strong acid HI.

19.10 $Ca_3(PO_4)_2(s) \rightleftharpoons 3Ca^{2+}(aq) + 2PO_4^{3-}(aq)$
$Q_{sp} = [Ca^{2+}]^3[PO_4^{3-}]^2 = (1.0\times10^{-9})^5 = 1.0\times10^{-45}$
$Q_{sp} < K_{sp}$, so $Ca_3(PO_4)_2$ will not precipitate.

19.11 (a) Scene 3 has the same relative numbers of ions as in the formula.
(b) Based on $Ni(OH)_2(s) \rightleftharpoons Ni^{2+}(aq) + 2OH^-(aq)$ and $Q_{sp} = [Ni^{2+}][OH^-]^2$, the ion products are $(3)(4)^2 = 48$ in scene 1; $(4)(2)^2 = 16$ in scene 2; and $(2)(4)^2 = 32 = K_{sp}$ in scene 3.
Q_{sp} of scene 1 exceeds K_{sp} of scene 3.
(c) Addition of acid will decrease mass of $Ni(OH)_2(s)$ by reacting with OH^-, thereby causing more solid to dissolve; addition of base will increase mass of $Ni(OH)_2(s)$ due to common-ion effect.

19.12 Both are 1/1 salts, and K_{sp} values show $CaSO_4$ is more soluble:

$$[SO_4^{2-}] = \frac{K_{sp}}{[Ca^{2+}]} = \frac{2.4\times10^{-5}}{0.025} = 9.6\times10^{-4}\ M$$

19.13 $$[Fe(H_2O)_6^{3+}]_{init} = \frac{(0.0255 \text{ L})(3.1\times10^{-2}\ M)}{0.0255 \text{ L} + 0.0350 \text{ L}}$$

$$= 1.3\times10^{-2}\ M$$

Similarly, $[CN^-]_{init} = 0.87\ M$. From the reaction table,

$$K_f = \frac{[Fe(CN)_6^{3-}]}{[Fe(H_2O)_6^{3+}][CN^-]^6} = 4.0\times10^{43} \approx \frac{1.3\times10^{-2}}{x(0.79)^6}$$

$x = [Fe(H_2O)_6^{3+}] \approx 1.3\times10^{-45}$

19.14 $AgBr(s) + 2NH_3(aq) \rightleftharpoons Ag(NH_3)_2^+(aq) + Br^-(aq)$
$K_{overall} = K_{sp}$ of AgBr $\times$ K_f of $Ag(NH_3)_2^+$
$= 8.5\times10^{-6}$

From the reaction table, $\dfrac{S}{1.0 - 2S} = \sqrt{8.5\times10^{-6}} = 2.9\times10^{-3}$

$S = [Ag(NH_3)_2^+] = 2.9\times10^{-3}\ M$
Solubility is greater in 1.0 M hypo than in 1.0 M NH_3.

PROBLEMS

Problems with **colored** numbers are answered in Appendix E and worked in detail in the Student Solutions Manual. Problem sections match those in the text and provide the numbers of relevant sample problems. Most offer Concept Review Questions, Skill-Building Exercises (grouped in pairs covering the same concept), and Problems in Context. The Comprehensive Problems are based on material from any section or previous chapter.

Note: Unless stated otherwise, all of the problems for this chapter refer to aqueous solutions at 298 K (25°C).

Equilibria of Acid-Base Buffer Systems

(Sample Problems 19.1 to 19.3)

Concept Review Questions

19.1 What is the purpose of an acid-base buffer?

19.2 How do the acid and base components of a buffer function? Why are they often a conjugate acid-base pair of a weak acid?

19.3 What is the common-ion effect? How is it related to Le Châtelier's principle? Explain with equations that include HF and NaF.

19.4 The scenes below depict solutions of the same HA/A^- buffer (with counterions and water molecules omitted for clarity). (a) Which solution has the greatest buffer capacity? (b) Explain how the pH ranges of the buffers compare. (c) Which solution can react with the largest amount of added strong acid?

19.5 What is the difference between buffers with high and low capacities? Will adding 0.01 mol of HCl produce a greater pH change in a buffer with a high or a low capacity? Explain.

19.6 Which of these factors influence buffer capacity? How?
(a) Conjugate acid-base pair
(b) pH of the buffer
(c) Concentration of buffer components
(d) Buffer range
(e) pK_a of the acid component

19.7 What is the relationship between the buffer range and the buffer-component concentration ratio?

19.8 A chemist needs a pH 3.5 buffer. Should she use NaOH with formic acid ($K_a = 1.8\times10^{-4}$) or with acetic acid ($K_a = 1.8\times10^{-5}$)? Why? What is the disadvantage of choosing the other acid? What is the role of the NaOH?

19.9 State and explain the relative change in the pH and in the buffer-component concentration ratio, [NaA]/[HA], for each of the following additions:
(a) Add 0.1 *M* NaOH to the buffer
(b) Add 0.1 *M* HCl to the buffer
(c) Dissolve pure NaA in the buffer
(d) Dissolve pure HA in the buffer

19.10 Does the pH increase or decrease, and does it do so to a large or small extent, with each of the following additions?
(a) 5 drops of 0.1 *M* NaOH to 100 mL of 0.5 *M* acetate buffer
(b) 5 drops of 0.1 *M* HCl to 100 mL of 0.5 *M* acetate buffer
(c) 5 drops of 0.1 *M* NaOH to 100 mL of 0.5 *M* HCl
(d) 5 drops of 0.1 *M* NaOH to distilled water

Skill-Building Exercises (grouped in similar pairs)

19.11 What are the $[H_3O^+]$ and the pH of a propanoic acid–propanoate buffer that consists of 0.35 *M* CH_3CH_2COONa and 0.15 *M* CH_3CH_2COOH (K_a of propanoic acid $= 1.3\times10^{-5}$)?

19.12 What are the $[H_3O^+]$ and the pH of a benzoic acid–benzoate buffer that consists of 0.33 *M* C_6H_5COOH and 0.28 *M* C_6H_5COONa (K_a of benzoic acid $= 6.3\times10^{-5}$)?

19.13 What are the $[H_3O^+]$ and the pH of a buffer that consists of 0.55 *M* HNO_2 and 0.75 *M* KNO_2 (K_a of $HNO_2 = 7.1\times10^{-4}$)?

19.14 What are the $[H_3O^+]$ and the pH of a buffer that consists of 0.20 *M* HF and 0.25 *M* KF (K_a of HF $= 6.8\times10^{-4}$)?

19.15 Find the pH of a buffer that consists of 0.45 *M* HCOOH and 0.63 *M* HCOONa (pK_a of HCOOH = 3.74).

19.16 Find the pH of a buffer that consists of 0.95 *M* HBrO and 0.68 *M* KBrO (pK_a of HBrO = 8.64).

19.17 Find the pH of a buffer that consists of 1.3 *M* sodium phenolate (C_6H_5ONa) and 1.2 *M* phenol (C_6H_5OH) (pK_a of phenol = 10.00).

19.18 Find the pH of a buffer that consists of 0.12 *M* boric acid (H_3BO_3) and 0.82 *M* sodium borate (NaH_2BO_3) (pK_a of boric acid = 9.24).

19.19 Find the pH of a buffer that consists of 0.25 *M* NH_3 and 0.15 *M* NH_4Cl (pK_b of NH_3 = 4.75).

19.20 Find the pH of a buffer that consists of 0.50 *M* methylamine (CH_3NH_2) and 0.60 *M* CH_3NH_3Cl (pK_b of CH_3NH_2 = 3.35).

19.21 A buffer consists of 0.22 *M* $KHCO_3$ and 0.37 *M* K_2CO_3. Carbonic acid is a diprotic acid with $K_{a1} = 4.5\times10^{-7}$ and $K_{a2} = 4.7\times10^{-11}$. (a) Which K_a value is more important to this buffer? (b) What is the buffer pH?

19.22 A buffer consists of 0.50 *M* NaH_2PO_4 and 0.40 *M* Na_2HPO_4. Phosphoric acid is a triprotic acid ($K_{a1} = 7.2\times10^{-3}$, $K_{a2} = 6.3\times10^{-8}$, and $K_{a3} = 4.2\times10^{-13}$). (a) Which K_a value is most important to this buffer? (b) What is the buffer pH?

19.23 What is the component concentration ratio, $[Pr^-]/[HPr]$, of a buffer that has a pH of 5.44 (K_a of HPr $= 1.3\times10^{-5}$)?

19.24 What is the component concentration ratio, $[NO_2^-]/[HNO_2]$, of a buffer that has a pH of 2.95 (K_a of $HNO_2 = 7.1\times10^{-4}$)?

19.25 What is the component concentration ratio, $[BrO^-]/[HBrO]$, of a buffer that has a pH of 7.95 (K_a of HBrO $= 2.3\times10^{-9}$)?

19.26 What is the component concentration ratio, $[CH_3COO^-]/[CH_3COOH]$, of a buffer that has a pH of 4.39 (K_a of $CH_3COOH = 1.8\times10^{-5}$)?

19.27 A buffer containing 0.2000 *M* of acid, HA, and 0.1500 *M* of its conjugate base, A^-, has a pH of 3.35. What is the pH after 0.0015 mol of NaOH is added to 0.5000 L of this solution?

19.28 A buffer that contains 0.40 *M* base, B, and 0.25 *M* of its conjugate acid, BH^+, has a pH of 8.88. What is the pH after 0.0020 mol of HCl is added to 0.25 L of this solution?

19.29 A buffer that contains 0.110 *M* HY and 0.220 *M* Y^- has a pH of 8.77. What is the pH after 0.0015 mol of $Ba(OH)_2$ is added to 0.350 L of this solution?

19.30 A buffer that contains 1.05 *M* B and 0.750 *M* BH^+ has a pH of 9.50. What is the pH after 0.0050 mol of HCl is added to 0.500 L of this solution?

19.31 A buffer is prepared by mixing 204 mL of 0.452 *M* HCl and 0.500 L of 0.400 M sodium acetate. (See Appendix C.) (a) What is the pH? (b) How many grams of KOH must be added to 0.500 L of the buffer to change the pH by 0.15 units?

19.32 A buffer is prepared by mixing 50.0 mL of 0.050 M sodium bicarbonate and 10.7 mL of 0.10 M NaOH. (See Appendix C.) (a) What is the pH? (b) How many grams of HCl must be added to 25.0 mL of the buffer to change the pH by 0.07 units?

19.33 Choose specific acid-base conjugate pairs to make the following buffers: (a) pH $\approx$ 4.5; (b) pH $\approx$ 7.0. (See Appendix C.)

19.34 Choose specific acid-base conjugate pairs to make the following buffers: (a) $[H_3O^+] \approx 1\times10^{-9}$ *M*; (b) $[OH^-] \approx 3\times10^{-5}$ *M*. (See Appendix C.)

19.35 Choose specific acid-base conjugate pairs to make the following buffers: (a) pH $\approx$ 3.5; (b) pH $\approx$ 5.5. (See Appendix C.)

19.36 Choose specific acid-base conjugate pairs to make the following buffers: (a) $[OH^-] \approx 1\times10^{-6}$ *M*; (b) $[H_3O^+] \approx 4\times10^{-4}$ *M*. (See Appendix C.)

Problems in Context

19.37 An industrial chemist studying bleaching and sterilizing prepares several hypochlorite buffers. Find the pH of (a) 0.100 *M* HClO and 0.100 *M* NaClO; (b) 0.100 *M* HClO and 0.150 *M* NaClO; (c) 0.150 *M* HClO and 0.100 *M* NaClO; (d) 1.0 L of the solution in part (a) after 0.0050 mol of NaOH has been added.

19.38 Oxoanions of phosphorus are buffer components in blood. For a KH_2PO_4/Na_2HPO_4 solution with pH = 7.40 (pH of normal arterial blood), what is the buffer-component concentration ratio?

Acid-Base Titration Curves

(Sample Problem 19.4)

Concept Review Questions

19.39 How can you estimate the pH range of an indicator's color change? Why do some indicators have two separate pH ranges?

19.40 Why does the color change of an indicator take place over a range of about 2 pH units?

19.41 Why doesn't the addition of an acid-base indicator affect the pH of the test solution?

19.42 What is the difference between the end point of a titration and the equivalence point? Is the equivalence point always reached first? Explain.

19.43 The scenes below depict the relative concentrations of H_3PO_4, $H_2PO_4^-$, and HPO_4^{2-} during a titration with aqueous NaOH, but they are out of order. (Phosphate groups are purple, hydrogens are blue, and Na^+ ions and water molecules are not shown.) (a) List the scenes in the correct order. (b) What is the pH in the correctly ordered second scene (see Appendix C)? (c) If it requires 10.00 mL of the NaOH solution to reach this scene, how much more is needed to reach the last scene?

19.44 Explain how strong acid–strong base, weak acid–strong base, and weak base–strong acid titrations using the same concentrations differ in terms of (a) the initial pH and (b) the pH at the equivalence point. (The component in italics is in the flask.)

19.45 What species are in the buffer region of a weak acid–strong base titration? How are they different from the species at the equivalence point? How are they different from the species in the buffer region of a weak base–strong acid titration?

19.46 Why is the center of the buffer region of a weak acid–strong base titration significant?

19.47 How does the titration curve of a monoprotic acid differ from that of a diprotic acid?

Skill-Building Exercises (grouped in similar pairs)

19.48 The indicator cresol red has $K_a = 3.5\times10^{-9}$. Over what approximate pH range does it change color?

19.49 The indicator ethyl red has $K_a = 3.8\times10^{-6}$. Over what approximate pH range does it change color?

19.50 Use Figure 19.5 to find an indicator for these titrations:
(a) 0.10 *M* HCl with 0.10 *M* NaOH
(b) 0.10 *M* HCOOH (Appendix C) with 0.10 *M* NaOH

19.51 Use Figure 19.5 to find an indicator for these titrations:
(a) 0.10 *M* CH_3NH_2 (Appendix C) with 0.10 *M* HCl
(b) 0.50 *M* HI with 0.10 *M* KOH

19.52 Use Figure 19.5 to find an indicator for these titrations:
(a) 0.5 *M* $(CH_3)_2NH$ (Appendix C) with 0.5 *M* HBr
(b) 0.2 *M* KOH with 0.2 *M* HNO_3

19.53 Use Figure 19.5 to find an indicator for these titrations:
(a) 0.25 *M* C_6H_5COOH (Appendix C) with 0.25 *M* KOH
(b) 0.50 *M* NH_4Cl (Appendix C) with 0.50 *M* NaOH

19.54 Calculate the pH during the titration of 40.00 mL of 0.1000 *M* HCl with 0.1000 *M* NaOH solution after the following additions of base:
(a) 0 mL (b) 25.00 mL (c) 39.00 mL (d) 39.90 mL
(e) 40.00 mL (f) 40.10 mL (g) 50.00 mL

19.55 Calculate the pH during the titration of 30.00 mL of 0.1000 *M* KOH with 0.1000 *M* HBr solution after the following additions of acid:
(a) 0 mL (b) 15.00 mL (c) 29.00 mL (d) 29.90 mL
(e) 30.00 mL (f) 30.10 mL (g) 40.00 mL

19.56 Find the pH during the titration of 20.00 mL of 0.1000 *M* butanoic acid, $CH_3CH_2CH_2COOH$ ($K_a = 1.54\times10^{-5}$),

with 0.1000 M NaOH solution after the following additions of titrant:
(a) 0 mL (b) 10.00 mL (c) 15.00 mL (d) 19.00 mL
(e) 19.95 mL (f) 20.00 mL (g) 20.05 mL (h) 25.00 mL

19.57 Find the pH during the titration of 20.00 mL of 0.1000 M triethylamine, $(CH_3CH_2)_3N$ ($K_b = 5.2\times10^{-4}$), with 0.1000 M HCl solution after the following additions of titrant:
(a) 0 mL (b) 10.00 mL (c) 15.00 mL (d) 19.00 mL
(e) 19.95 mL (f) 20.00 mL (g) 20.05 mL (h) 25.00 mL

19.58 Find the pH of the equivalence point(s) and the volume (mL) of 0.0372 M NaOH needed to reach the point(s) in titrations of
(a) 42.2 mL of 0.0520 M CH_3COOH
(b) 28.9 mL of 0.0850 M H_2SO_3 (two equivalence points)

19.59 Find the pH of the equivalence point(s) and the volume (mL) of 0.0588 M KOH needed to reach the point(s) in titrations of
(a) 23.4 mL of 0.0390 M HNO_2
(b) 17.3 mL of 0.130 M H_2CO_3 (two equivalence points)

19.60 Find the pH of the equivalence point(s) and the volume (mL) of 0.125 M HCl needed to reach the point(s) in titrations of
(a) 65.5 mL of 0.234 M NH_3
(b) 21.8 mL of 1.11 M CH_3NH_2

19.61 Find the pH of the equivalence point(s) and the volume (mL) of 0.447 M HNO_3 needed to reach the point(s) in titrations of
(a) 2.65 L of 0.0750 M pyridine (C_5H_5N)
(b) 0.188 L of 0.250 M ethylenediamine ($H_2NCH_2CH_2NH_2$)

Equilibria of Slightly Soluble Ionic Compounds

(Sample Problems 19.5 to 19.12)

Concept Review Questions

19.62 The molar solubility (S) of M_2X is 5×10^{-5} M. Find S of each ion. How do you set up the calculation to find K_{sp}? What assumption must you make about the dissociation of M_2X into ions? Why is the calculated K_{sp} higher than the actual value?

19.63 Why does pH affect the solubility of BaF_2 but not of $BaCl_2$?

19.64 A list of K_{sp} values like that in Appendix C can be used to compare the solubility of silver chloride directly with that of silver bromide but not with that of silver chromate. Explain.

19.65 In a gaseous equilibrium, the reverse reaction occurs when $Q_c > K_c$. What occurs in aqueous solution when $Q_{sp} > K_{sp}$?

Skill-Building Exercises (grouped in similar pairs)

19.66 Write the ion-product expressions for (a) silver carbonate; (b) barium fluoride; (c) copper(II) sulfide.

19.67 Write the ion-product expressions for (a) iron(III) hydroxide; (b) barium phosphate; (c) tin(II) sulfide.

19.68 Write the ion-product expressions for (a) calcium chromate; (b) silver cyanide; (c) nickel(II) sulfide.

19.69 Write the ion-product expressions for (a) lead(II) iodide; (b) strontium sulfate; (c) cadmium sulfide.

19.70 The solubility of silver carbonate is 0.032 M at 20°C. Calculate its K_{sp}.

19.71 The solubility of zinc oxalate is 7.9×10^{-3} M at 18°C. Calculate its K_{sp}.

19.72 The solubility of silver dichromate at 15°C is 8.3×10^{-3} g/100 mL solution. Calculate its K_{sp}.

19.73 The solubility of calcium sulfate at 30°C is 0.209 g/100 mL solution. Calculate its K_{sp}.

19.74 Find the molar solubility of $SrCO_3$ ($K_{sp} = 5.4\times10^{-10}$) in (a) pure water and (b) 0.13 M $Sr(NO_3)_2$.

19.75 Find the molar solubility of $BaCrO_4$ ($K_{sp} = 2.1\times10^{-10}$) in (a) pure water and (b) 1.5×10^{-3} M Na_2CrO_4.

19.76 Calculate the molar solubility of $Ca(IO_3)_2$ in (a) 0.060 M $Ca(NO_3)_2$ and (b) 0.060 M $NaIO_3$. (See Appendix C.)

19.77 Calculate the molar solubility of Ag_2SO_4 in (a) 0.22 M $AgNO_3$ and (b) 0.22 M Na_2SO_4. (See Appendix C.)

19.78 Which compound in each pair is more soluble in water?
(a) Magnesium hydroxide or nickel(II) hydroxide
(b) Lead(II) sulfide or copper(II) sulfide
(c) Silver sulfate or magnesium fluoride

19.79 Which compound in each pair is more soluble in water?
(a) Strontium sulfate or barium chromate
(b) Calcium carbonate or copper(II) carbonate
(c) Barium iodate or silver chromate

19.80 Which compound in each pair is more soluble in water?
(a) Barium sulfate or calcium sulfate
(b) Calcium phosphate or magnesium phosphate
(c) Silver chloride or lead(II) sulfate

19.81 Which compound in each pair is more soluble in water?
(a) Manganese(II) hydroxide or calcium iodate
(b) Strontium carbonate or cadmium sulfide
(c) Silver cyanide or copper(I) iodide

19.82 Write equations to show whether the solubility of either of the following is affected by pH: (a) AgCl; (b) $SrCO_3$.

19.83 Write equations to show whether the solubility of either of the following is affected by pH: (a) CuBr; (b) $Ca_3(PO_4)_2$.

19.84 Write equations to show whether the solubility of either of the following is affected by pH: (a) $Fe(OH)_2$; (b) CuS.

19.85 Write equations to show whether the solubility of either of the following is affected by pH: (a) PbI_2; (b) $Hg_2(CN)_2$.

19.86 Does any solid $Cu(OH)_2$ form when 0.075 g of KOH is dissolved in 1.0 L of 1.0×10^{-3} M $Cu(NO_3)_2$?

19.87 Does any solid $PbCl_2$ form when 3.5 mg of NaCl is dissolved in 0.250 L of 0.12 M $Pb(NO_3)_2$?

19.88 Does any solid $Ba(IO_3)_2$ form when 7.5 mg of $BaCl_2$ is dissolved in 500. mL of 0.023 M $NaIO_3$?

19.89 Does any solid Ag_2CrO_4 form when 2.7×10^{-5} g of $AgNO_3$ is dissolved in 15.0 mL of 4.0×10^{-4} M K_2CrO_4?

Problems in Context

19.90 When blood is donated, sodium oxalate solution is used to precipitate Ca^{2+}, which triggers clotting. A 104-mL sample of blood contains 9.7×10^{-5} g Ca^{2+}/mL. A technologist treats the sample with 100.0 mL of 0.1550 M $Na_2C_2O_4$. Calculate $[Ca^{2+}]$ after the treatment. (See Appendix C for K_{sp} of $CaC_2O_4{\cdot}H_2O$.)

19.91 A 50.0-mL volume of 0.50 M $Fe(NO_3)_3$ is mixed with 125 mL of 0.25 M $Cd(NO_3)_2$.
(a) If aqueous NaOH is added, which ion precipitates first? (See Appendix C.)
(b) Describe how the metal ions can be separated using NaOH.
(c) Calculate the $[OH^-]$ that will accomplish the separation.

Equilibria Involving Complex Ions
(Sample Problems 19.13 and 19.14)

Concept Review Questions

19.92 How can a metal cation be at the center of a complex anion?

19.93 Write equations to show the stepwise reaction of $Cd(H_2O)_4^{2+}$ in an aqueous solution of KI to form CdI_4^{-2}. Show that $K_{f(overall)} = K_{f1} \times K_{f2} \times K_{f3} \times K_{f4}$.

19.94 Consider the dissolution of PbS in water:

$$PbS(s) + H_2O(l) \rightleftharpoons Pb^{2+}(aq) + HS^-(aq) + OH^-(aq)$$

Adding aqueous NaOH causes more PbS to dissolve. Does this violate Le Châtelier's principle? Explain.

Skill-Building Exercises (grouped in similar pairs)

19.95 Write a balanced equation for the reaction of $Hg(H_2O)_4^{2+}$ in aqueous KCN.

19.96 Write a balanced equation for the reaction of $Zn(H_2O)_4^{2+}$ in aqueous NaCN.

19.97 Write a balanced equation for the reaction of $Ag(H_2O)_2^+$ in aqueous $Na_2S_2O_3$.

19.98 Write a balanced equation for the reaction of $Al(H_2O)_6^{3+}$ in aqueous KF.

19.99 What is $[Ag^+]$ when 25.0 mL each of 0.044 M $AgNO_3$ and 0.57 M $Na_2S_2O_3$ are mixed [K_f of $Ag(S_2O_3)_2^{3-} = 4.7\times10^{13}$]?

19.100 Potassium thiocyanate, KSCN, is often used to detect the presence of Fe^{3+} ions in solution through the formation of the red $Fe(H_2O)_5SCN^{2+}$ (or, more simply, $FeSCN^{2+}$). What is $[Fe^{3+}]$ when 0.50 L each of 0.0015 M $Fe(NO_3)_3$ and 0.20 M KSCN are mixed? K_f of $FeSCN^{2+} = 8.9\times10^2$.

19.101 Find the solubility of $Cr(OH)_3$ in a buffer of pH 13.0 [K_{sp} of $Cr(OH)_3 = 6.3\times10^{-31}$; K_f of $Cr(OH)_4^- = 8.0\times10^{29}$].

19.102 Find the solubility of AgI in 2.5 M NH_3 [K_{sp} of AgI $= 8.3\times10^{-17}$; K_f of $Ag(NH_3)_2^+ = 1.7\times10^7$].

19.103 When 0.84 g of $ZnCl_2$ is dissolved in 245 mL of 0.150 M NaCN, what are $[Zn^{2+}]$, $[Zn(CN)_4^{2-}]$, and $[CN^-]$[K_f of $Zn(CN)_4^{2-} = 4.2\times10^{19}$]?

19.104 When 2.4 g of $Co(NO_3)_2$ is dissolved in 0.350 L of 0.22 M KOH, what are $[Co^{2+}]$, $[Co(OH)_4^{2-}]$, and $[OH^-]$ [K_f of $Co(OH)_4^{2-} = 5\times10^9$]?

Comprehensive Problems

19.105 What volumes of 0.200 M HCOOH and 2.00 M NaOH would make 500. mL of a buffer with the pH of one made from 475 mL of 0.200 M benzoic acid and 25 mL of 2.00 M NaOH?

19.106 A microbiologist is preparing a medium on which to culture *E. coli* bacteria. She buffers the medium at pH 7.00 to minimize the effect of acid-producing fermentation. What volumes of equimolar aqueous solutions of K_2HPO_4 and KH_2PO_4 must she combine to make 100. mL of the pH 7.00 buffer?

19.107 As an FDA physiologist, you need 0.700 L of formic acid–formate buffer with a pH of 3.74. (a) What is the required buffer-component concentration ratio? (b) How do you prepare this solution from stock solutions of 1.0 M HCOOH and 1.0 M NaOH? (c) What is the final concentration of HCOOH in this solution?

19.108 Tris(hydroxymethyl)aminomethane $[(HOCH_2)_3CNH_2]$, known as TRIS, is a weak base used in biochemical experiments to make buffer solutions in the pH range of 7 to 9. A certain TRIS buffer has a pH of 8.10 at 25°C and a pH of 7.80 at 37°C. Why does the pH change with temperature?

19.109 Water flowing through pipes of carbon steel must be kept at pH 5 or greater to limit corrosion. If an 8.0×10^3 lb/hr water stream contains 10 ppm sulfuric acid and 0.015% acetic acid, how many pounds per hour of sodium acetate trihydrate must be added to maintain that pH?

19.110 Gout is caused by an error in metabolism that leads to a buildup of uric acid in body fluids, which is deposited as slightly soluble sodium urate ($C_5H_3N_4O_3Na$) in the joints. If the extracellular $[Na^+]$ is 0.15 M and the solubility of sodium urate is 0.085 g/100. mL, what is the minimum urate ion concentration (abbreviated $[Ur^-]$) that will cause a deposit of sodium urate?

19.111 In the process of cave formation (p. 788), the dissolution of CO_2 (equation 1) has a K_{eq} of 3.1×10^{-2}, and the formation of aqueous $Ca(HCO_3)_2$ (equation 2) has a K_{eq} of 1×10^{-12}. The fraction by volume of atmospheric CO_2 is 3×10^{-4}. (a) Find $[CO_2(aq)]$ in equilibrium with atmospheric CO_2. (b) Determine $[Ca^{2+}]$ arising from (equation 2) given current levels of atmospheric CO_2. (c) Calculate $[Ca^{2+}]$ if atmospheric CO_2 doubles.

19.112 Phosphate systems form essential buffers in organisms. Calculate the pH of a buffer made by dissolving 0.80 mol of NaOH in 0.50 L of 1.0 M H_3PO_4.

19.113 The solubility of KCl is 3.7 M at 20°C. Two beakers contain 100. mL of saturated KCl solution: 100. mL of 6.0 M HCl is added to the first beaker and 100. mL of 12 M HCl to the second. (a) Find the ion-product constant of KCl at 20°C. (b) What mass, if any, of KCl will precipitate from each beaker?

19.114 It is possible to detect NH_3 gas over 10^{-2} M NH_3. To what pH must 0.15 M NH_4Cl be raised to form detectable NH_3?

19.115 Manganese(II) sulfide is one of the compounds found in the nodules on the ocean floor that may eventually be a primary source of many transition metals. The solubility of MnS is 4.7×10^{-4} g/100 mL solution. Estimate the K_{sp} of MnS.

19.116 The normal pH of blood is 7.40 ± 0.05 and is controlled in part by the H_2CO_3/HCO_3^- buffer system.
(a) Assuming that the K_a value for carbonic acid at 25°C applies to blood, what is the $[H_2CO_3]/[HCO_3^-]$ ratio in normal blood?
(b) In a condition called *acidosis*, the blood is too acidic. What is the $[H_2CO_3]/[HCO_3^-]$ ratio in a patient whose blood pH is 7.20?

19.117 A bioengineer preparing cells for cloning bathes a small piece of rat epithelial tissue in a TRIS buffer (see Problem 19.108). The buffer is made by dissolving 43.0 g of TRIS ($pK_b = 5.91$) in enough 0.095 M HCl to make 1.00 L of solution. What is the molarity of TRIS and the pH of the buffer?

19.118 Sketch a qualitative curve for the titration of ethylenediamine, $H_2NCH_2CH_2NH_2$, with 0.1 M HCl.

19.119 A solution contains 0.10 M $ZnCl_2$ and 0.020 M $MnCl_2$. Given the following information, how would you adjust the pH to separate the ions as their sulfides ($[H_2S]$ of a saturated aqueous solution at 25°C = 0.10 *M*; $K_w = 1.0\times10^{-14}$ at 25°C)?

$$MnS + H_2O \rightleftharpoons Mn^{2+} + HS^- + OH^- \qquad K_{sp} = 3\times10^{-11}$$
$$ZnS + H_2O \rightleftharpoons Zn^{2+} + HS^- + OH^- \qquad K_{sp} = 2\times10^{-22}$$
$$H_2S + H_2O \rightleftharpoons H_3O^+ + HS^- \qquad K_{a1} = 9\times10^{-8}$$

19.120 Amino acids [general formula $NH_2CH(R)COOH$] can be considered polyprotic acids. In many cases, the R group contains additional amine and carboxyl groups.
(a) Can an amino acid dissolved in pure water have a protonated COOH group and an unprotonated NH_2 group (K_a of COOH group = 4.47×10^{-3}; K_b of NH_2 group = 6.03×10^{-5})? Use glycine, NH_2CH_2COOH, to explain why.
(b) Calculate $[^+NH_3CH_2COO^-]/[^+NH_3CH_2COOH]$ at pH 5.5.
(c) The R group of lysine is $—CH_2CH_2CH_2CH_2NH_2$ ($pK_b = 3.47$). Draw the structure of lysine at pH 1, physiological pH (~7), and pH 13.
(d) The R group of glutamic acid is $—CH_2CH_2COOH$ ($pK_a = 4.07$). Of the forms of glutamic acid that are shown below, which predominates at (1) pH 1, (2) physiological pH (~7), and (3) pH 13?

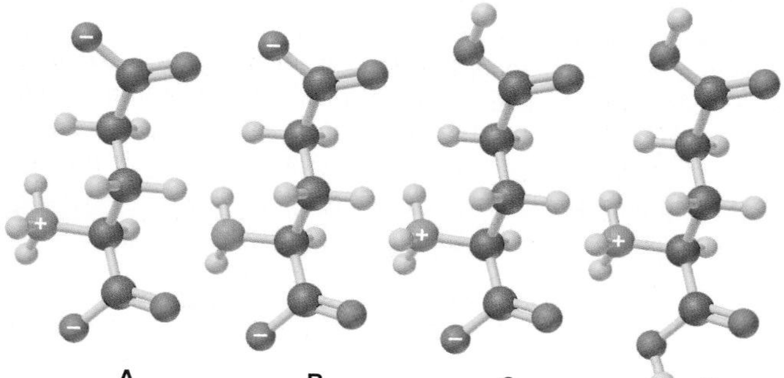

A B C D

19.121 The scene at right depicts a saturated solution of $MCl_2(s)$ in the presence of dilute aqueous NaCl; each sphere represents 1.0×10^{-6} mol of ion, and the volume is 250.0 mL (solid MCl_2 is shown as green chunks; Na^+ ions and water molecules are not shown). (a) Calculate the K_{sp} of MCl_2. (b) If $M(NO_3)_2(s)$ is added, is there an increase, decrease, or no change in the number of Cl^- particles? In K_{sp}? In mass of $MCl_2(s)$?

19.122 Tooth enamel consists of hydroxyapatite, $Ca_5(PO_4)_3OH$ ($K_{sp} = 6.8\times10^{-37}$). Fluoride ion added to drinking water reacts with $Ca_5(PO_4)_3OH$ to form the more tooth decay–resistant fluorapatite, $Ca_5(PO_4)_3F$ ($K_{sp} = 1.0\times10^{-60}$). Fluoridated water has dramatically decreased cavities among children. Calculate the solubility of $Ca_5(PO_4)_3OH$ and of $Ca_5(PO_4)_3F$ in water.

19.123 The acid-base indicator ethyl orange turns from red to yellow over the pH range 3.4 to 4.8. Estimate K_a for ethyl orange.

19.124 Use the values obtained in Problem 19.54 to sketch a curve of $[H_3O^+]$ vs. mL of added titrant. Are there advantages or disadvantages to viewing the results in this form? Explain.

19.125 Instrumental acid-base titrations use a pH meter to monitor the changes in pH and volume. The equivalence point is found from the volume at which the curve has the steepest slope.
(a) Use the data in Figure 19.7 (p. 775) to calculate the slope ($\Delta pH/\Delta V$)for all pairs of adjacent points and to calculate the average volume (V_{avg}) for each interval.
(b) Plot $\Delta pH/\Delta V$ vs. V_{avg} to find the steepest slope, and thus the volume at the equivalence point. (For example, the first pair of points gives $\Delta pH = 0.22$, $\Delta V = 10.00$ mL; hence, $\Delta pH/\Delta V = 0.022\ mL^{-1}$, and $V_{avg} = 5.00$ mL.)

19.126 What is the pH of a solution of 6.5×10^{-9} mol of $Ca(OH)_2$ in 10.0 L of water [K_{sp} of $Ca(OH)_2 = 6.5\times10^{-6}$]?

19.127 Muscle physiologists study the accumulation of lactic acid [$CH_3CH(OH)COOH$] during exercise. Food chemists study its occurrence in sour milk, beer, wine, and fruit. Industrial microbiologists study its formation by various bacterial species from carbohydrates. A biochemist prepares a lactic acid–lactate buffer by mixing 225 mL of 0.85 *M* lactic acid ($K_a = 1.38\times10^{-4}$) with 435 mL of 0.68 *M* sodium lactate. What is the buffer pH?

19.128 A student wants to dissolve the maximum amount of CaF_2 ($K_{sp} = 3.2\times10^{-11}$) to make 1 L of aqueous solution.
(a) Into which of the following solvents should she dissolve the salt?

(I) Pure water (II) 0.01 *M* HF
(III) 0.01 *M* NaOH (IV) 0.01 *M* HCl
(V) 0.01 *M* $Ca(OH)_2$

(b) Which would dissolve the least amount of salt?

19.129 A 500.-mL solution consists of 0.050 mol of solid NaOH and 0.13 mol of hypochlorous acid (HClO; $K_a = 3.0\times10^{-8}$) dissolved in water.
(a) Aside from water, what is the concentration of each species that is present?
(b) What is the pH of the solution?
(c) What is the pH after adding 0.0050 mol of HCl to the flask?

19.130 Calcium ion present in water supplies is easily precipitated as calcite ($CaCO_3$):

$$Ca^{2+}(aq) + CO_3^{2-}(aq) \rightleftharpoons CaCO_3(s)$$

Because the K_{sp} decreases with temperature, heating hard water forms a calcite "scale," which clogs pipes and water heaters. Find the solubility of calcite in water (a) at 10°C ($K_{sp} = 4.4\times10^{-9}$) and (b) at 30°C ($K_{sp} = 3.1\times10^{-9}$).

19.131 Calculate the molar solubility of $Hg_2C_2O_4$ ($K_{sp} = 1.75\times10^{-13}$) in 0.13 *M* $Hg_2(NO_3)_2$.

19.132 Environmental engineers use alkalinity as a measure of the capacity of carbonate buffering systems in water samples:

$$\text{Alkalinity (mol/L)} = [HCO_3^-] + 2[CO_3^{2-}] + [OH^-] - [H^+]$$

Find the alkalinity of a water sample that has a pH of 9.5, 26.0 mg/L CO_3^{2-}, and 65.0 mg/L HCO_3^-.

19.133 Human blood contains one buffer system based on phosphate species and one based on carbonate species. Assuming that blood has a normal pH of 7.4, what are the principal phosphate and carbonate species present? What is the ratio of the two phosphate species? (In the presence of the dissolved ions and other species in blood, K_{a1} of $H_3PO_4 = 1.3\times10^{-2}$, $K_{a2} = 2.3\times10^{-7}$, and $K_{a3} = 6\times10^{-12}$; K_{a1} of $H_2CO_3 = 8\times10^{-7}$ and $K_{a2} = 1.6\times10^{-10}$.)

19.134 A 0.050 *M* H_2S solution contains 0.15 M $NiCl_2$ and 0.35 *M* $Hg(NO_3)_2$. What pH is required to precipitate the maximum amount of HgS but none of the NiS? (See Appendix C.)

19.135 Quantitative analysis of Cl^- ion is often performed by a titration with silver nitrate, using sodium chromate as an indicator. As standardized $AgNO_3$ is added, both white AgCl and red Ag_2CrO_4 precipitate, but so long as some Cl^- remains, the Ag_2CrO_4 redissolves as the mixture is stirred. When the red color is permanent, the equivalence point has been reached.

(a) Calculate the equilibrium constant for the reaction

$$2AgCl(s) + CrO_4^{2-}(aq) \rightleftharpoons Ag_2CrO_4(s) + 2Cl^-(aq)$$

(b) Explain why the silver chromate redissolves.
(c) If 25.00 cm^3 of 0.1000 *M* NaCl is mixed with 25.00 cm^3 of 0.1000 *M* $AgNO_3$, what is the concentration of Ag^+ remaining in solution? Is this sufficient to precipitate any silver chromate?

19.136 An ecobotanist separates the components of a tropical bark extract by chromatography. She discovers a large proportion of quinidine, a dextrorotatory isomer of quinine used for control of arrhythmic heartbeat. Quinidine has two basic nitrogens ($K_{b1} = 4.0\times10^{-6}$ and $K_{b2} = 1.0\times10^{-10}$). To measure the concentration, she carries out a titration. Because of the low solubility of quinidine, she first protonates both nitrogens with excess HCl and titrates the acidified solution with standardized base. A 33.85-mg sample of quinidine ($\mathcal{M}$ = 324.41 g/mol) is acidified with 6.55 mL of 0.150 *M* HCl.
(a) How many milliliters of 0.0133 *M* NaOH are needed to titrate the excess HCl?
(b) How many additional milliliters of titrant are needed to reach the first equivalence point of quinidine dihydrochloride?
(c) What is the pH at the first equivalence point?

19.137 Some kidney stones form by the precipitation of calcium oxalate monohydrate ($CaC_2O_4{\cdot}H_2O$, $K_{sp} = 2.3\times10^{-9}$). The pH of urine varies from 5.5 to 7.0, and the average $[Ca^{2+}]$ in urine is 2.6×10^{-3} *M*.
(a) If the [oxalic acid] in urine is 3.0×10^{-13} *M*, will kidney stones form at pH = 5.5?
(b) At pH = 7.0?
(c) Vegetarians have a urine pH above 7. Are they more or less likely to form kidney stones?

19.138 A biochemist needs a medium for acid-producing bacteria. The pH of the medium must not change by more than 0.05 pH units for every 0.0010 mol of H_3O^+ generated by the organisms per liter of medium. A buffer consisting of 0.10 *M* HA and 0.10 *M* A^- is included in the medium to control its pH. What volume of this buffer must be included in 1.0 L of medium?

19.139 A 35.00-mL solution of 0.2500 *M* HF is titrated with a standardized 0.1532 *M* solution of NaOH at 25°C.
(a) What is the pH of the HF solution before titrant is added?
(b) How many milliliters of titrant are required to reach the equivalence point?
(c) What is the pH at 0.50 mL before the equivalence point?
(d) What is the pH at the equivalence point?
(e) What is the pH at 0.50 mL after the equivalence point?

19.140 Because of the toxicity of mercury compounds, mercury(I) chloride is used in antibacterial salves. The mercury(I) ion (Hg_2^{2+}) consists of two bound Hg^+ ions.
(a) What is the empirical formula of mercury(I) chloride?
(b) Calculate $[Hg_2^{2+}]$ in a saturated solution of mercury(I) chloride ($K_{sp} = 1.5\times10^{-18}$).
(c) A seawater sample contains 0.20 lb of NaCl per gallon. Find $[Hg_2^{2+}]$ if the seawater is saturated with mercury(I) chloride.
(d) How many grams of mercury(I) chloride are needed to saturate 4900 km^3 of pure water (the volume of Lake Michigan)?
(e) How many grams of mercury(I) chloride are needed to saturate 4900 km^3 of seawater?

19.141 A 35.0-mL solution of 0.075 *M* $CaCl_2$ is mixed with 25.0 mL of 0.090 M $BaCl_2$.
(a) If aqueous KF is added, which fluoride precipitates first?
(b) Describe how the metal ions can be separated using KF to form the fluorides.
(c) Calculate the fluoride ion concentration that will accomplish the separation.

19.142 Even before the industrial age, rainwater was slightly acidic due to dissolved CO_2. Use the following data to calculate pH of unpolluted rainwater at 25°C: vol % in air of CO_2 = 0.033 vol %; solubility of CO_2 in pure water at 25°C and 1 atm = 88 mL CO_2/100 mL H_2O; K_{a1} of $H_2CO_3 = 4.5\times10^{-7}$.

19.143 Seawater at the surface has a pH of about 8.5.
(a) Which of the following species has the highest concentration at this pH: H_2CO_3; HCO_3^-; CO_3^{2-}? Explain.
(b) What are the concentration ratios $[CO_3^{2-}]/[HCO_3^-]$ and $[HCO_3^-]/[H_2CO_3]$ at this pH?
(c) In the deep sea, light levels are low, and the pH is around 7.5. Suggest a reason for the lower pH at the greater ocean depth. (*Hint:* Consider the presence or absence of plant and animal life, and the effects on carbon dioxide concentrations.)

19.144 Ethylenediaminetetraacetic acid (abbreviated H_4EDTA) is a tetraprotic acid. Its salts are used to treat toxic metal poisoning by forming soluble complex ions that are then excreted. Because $EDTA^{4-}$ also binds essential calcium ions, it is often administered as the calcium disodium salt. For example, when $Na_2Ca(EDTA)$ is given to a patient, the $[Ca(EDTA)]^{2-}$ ions react with circulating Pb^{2+} ions and the metal ions are exchanged:

$$[Ca(EDTA)]^{2-}(aq) + Pb^{2+}(aq) \rightleftharpoons [Pb(EDTA)]^{2-}(aq) + Ca^{2+}(aq) \qquad K_c = 2.5\times10^7$$

A child has a dangerous blood lead level of 120 μg/100 mL. If the child is administered 100. mL of 0.10 *M* $Na_2Ca(EDTA)$, assuming the exchange reaction and excretion process are 100% efficient, what is the final concentration of Pb^{2+} in μg/100 mL blood? (Total blood volume is 1.5 L.)

19.145 Buffers that are based on 3-morpholinopropanesulfonic acid (MOPS) are often used in RNA analysis. The useful pH range of a MOPS buffer is 6.5 to 7.9. Estimate the K_a of MOPS.

19.146 NaCl is purified by adding HCl to a saturated solution of NaCl (317 g/L). When 28.5 mL of 8.65 *M* HCl is added to 0.100 L of saturated solution, what mass (g) of pure NaCl precipitates?

19.147 Scenes A to D represent tiny portions of 0.10 *M* aqueous solutions of a weak acid HA (red and blue; $K_a = 4.5\times10^{-5}$), its conjugate base A^-(red), or a mixture of the two (only these species are shown):

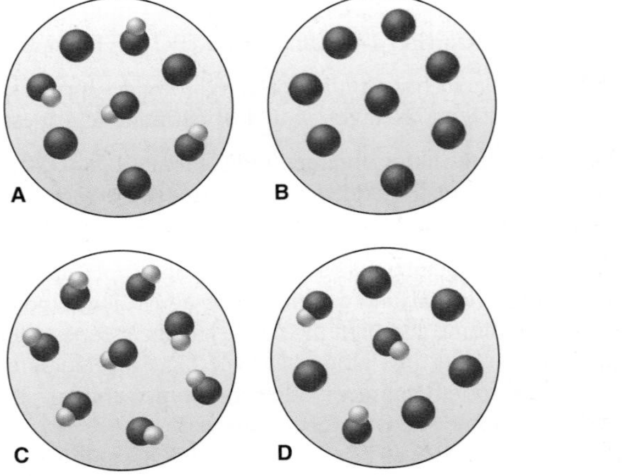

(a) Which scene(s) show(s) a buffer?
(b) What is the pH of each solution?
(c) Arrange the scenes in sequence, assuming that they represent stages in a weak acid–strong base titration.
(d) Which scene represents the titration at its equivalence point?

19.148 Scenes A to C represent aqueous solutions of the slightly soluble salt MZ (only the ions of this salt are shown):

$$MZ(s) \rightleftharpoons M^{2+}(aq) + Z^{2-}(aq)$$

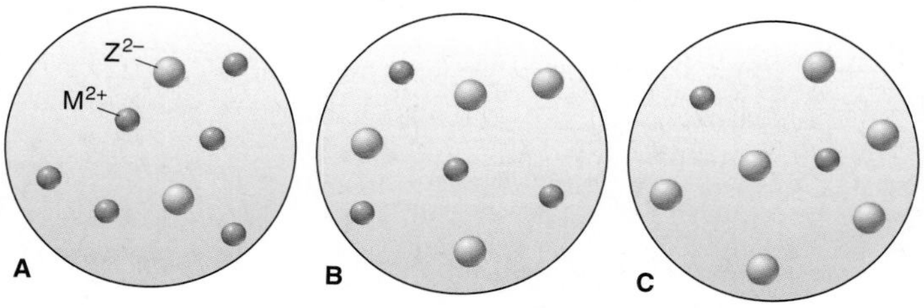

(a) Which scene represents the solution just after solid MZ is stirred thoroughly in distilled water?
(b) If each sphere represents 2.5×10^{-6} *M* of ions, what is the K_{sp} of MZ?
(c) Which scene represents the solution after $Na_2Z(aq)$ has been added?
(d) If Z^{2-} is CO_3^{2-}, which scene represents the solution after the pH has been lowered?

19.149 The solubility of Ag(I) in aqueous solutions containing different concentrations of Cl^- is based on the following equilibria:

$$Ag^+(aq) + Cl^-(aq) \rightleftharpoons AgCl(s) \qquad K_{sp} = 1.8\times10^{-10}$$
$$Ag^+(aq) + 2Cl^-(aq) \rightleftharpoons AgCl_2^-(aq) \qquad K_f = 1.8\times10^{5}$$

When solid AgCl is shaken with a solution containing Cl^-, Ag(I) is present as both Ag^+ and $AgCl_2^-$. The solubility of AgCl is the sum of the concentrations of Ag^+ and $AgCl_2^-$.
(a) Show that $[Ag^+]$ in solution is given by

$$[Ag^+] = 1.8\times10^{-10}/[Cl^-]$$

and that $[AgCl_2^-]$ in solution is given by

$$[AgCl_2^-] = (3.2\times10^{-5})([Cl^-])$$

(b) Find the $[Cl^-]$ at which $[Ag^+] = [AgCl_2^-]$.
(c) Explain the shape of a plot of AgCl solubility vs. $[Cl^-]$.
(d) Find the solubility of AgCl at the $[Cl^-]$ of part (b), which is the minimum solubility of AgCl in the presence of Cl^-.

19.150 EDTA binds metal ions to form complex ions (see Problem 19.144), so it is used to determine the concentrations of metal ions in solution:

$$M^{n+}(aq) + EDTA^{4-}(aq) \longrightarrow MEDTA^{n-4}(aq)$$

A 50.0-mL sample of 0.048 *M* Co^{2+} is titrated with 0.050 *M* $EDTA^{4-}$. Find $[Co^{2+}]$ and $[EDTA^{4-}]$ after (a) 25.0 mL and (b) 75.0 mL of $EDTA^{4-}$ are added ($\log K_f$ of $CoEDTA^{2-} =$ 16.31).

Thermodynamics: Entropy, Free Energy, and the Direction of Chemical Reactions

20

Concepts and skills to review before you study this chapter

- internal energy, heat, and work (Section 6.1)
- state functions (Section 6.1) and standard states (Section 6.6)
- enthalpy, ΔH, and Hess's law (Sections 6.2 and 6.5)
- entropy and solution formation (Section 13.3)
- comparing Q and K to find reaction direction (Section 17.4)

In the last few chapters, we've examined some fundamental questions about change, whether chemical or physical: How fast does it occur? How far does it go toward completion? How are these aspects of the change affected by concentration and temperature? And we've explored these questions in systems ranging from the stratosphere to a limestone cave to the cells of your body.

It's now time to ask the most profound question of all: why does the change occur in the first place? Some changes seem to happen by themselves in one direction but not in the other. A candle burns in air and forms carbon dioxide and water vapor, but those products will never react to form candle wax and oxygen. A new steel shovel left outside slowly rusts, but put a rusty one outside and it won't become shiny. A cube of sugar dissolves in a cup of coffee after a few seconds of stirring, but stir for another millennium and the dissolved sugar won't form the cube again. Chemists speak of these types of changes as being *spontaneous*. Most release energy, but some absorb it.

The principles of thermodynamics were developed almost 200 years ago and soon applied to great new machines based on the steam engine (*photo*). But these principles apply, as far as we know, to every system in the universe and allow us to understand why a spontaneous change occurs.

IN THIS CHAPTER . . . We discuss *why* changes occur and how we can utilize them, by focusing on entropy and free energy and their relation to the direction of a spontaneous change.

- We discuss the need for a criterion to predict the direction of a spontaneous change.
- We review the first law of thermodynamics and see that it accounts for the energy of a change but not the direction.
- We see that the sign of the enthalpy change does not predict direction either.
- We find this criterion for predicting the direction of a spontaneous change in the second law of thermodynamics and its relation to entropy (S), a state function based on the natural tendency of a system's energy to become dispersed.
- We examine entropy changes for exothermic and endothermic changes.
- We develop the concept of free energy as a simplified criterion for spontaneous change and see how it relates to the work a system can do.
- We explore the key relationship between the free energy change of a reaction and its equilibrium constant.

20.1 • THE SECOND LAW OF THERMODYNAMICS: PREDICTING SPONTANEOUS CHANGE

A **spontaneous change** of a system is one that occurs under specified conditions without a continuous input of energy from outside the system. The freezing of water, for example, is spontaneous at 1 atm and $-5°C$. A spontaneous process, such as burning or falling, may need a little "push" to get started—a spark to ignite gasoline vapors in your car's engine, a shove to knock a book off your desk—but once the process begins, it supplies the energy to keep going. In contrast, a *nonspontaneous* change occurs only if the surroundings *continuously* supply the system with an input of energy. Under given conditions, *if a change is spontaneous in one direction, it is* ***not*** *spontaneous in the other.*

The term *spontaneous* does not mean *instantaneous* or reveal anything about how long a process takes to occur; it means that, given enough time, the process will happen by itself. Many processes are spontaneous but slow—ripening, rusting, and aging.

A chemical reaction proceeding toward equilibrium is a spontaneous change. Recall that we can predict the net direction of the reaction—its spontaneous direction—by comparing the reaction quotient (Q) with the equilibrium constant (K). But *why* is there a drive to attain equilibrium? And what determines the value of the equilibrium constant? And, most importantly, can we predict the direction of a spontaneous change in cases that are not as obvious as burning gasoline or falling books?

The First Law of Thermodynamics Does Not Predict Spontaneous Change

Let's see whether energy changes can clarify the criterion for spontaneity. Recall from Chapter 6 that the first law of thermodynamics (law of conservation of energy) states that the internal energy (E) of a system, the sum of the kinetic and potential energies of its particles, changes when heat (q) and/or work (w) are absorbed or released:

$$\Delta E = q + w$$

Whatever is not part of the system (sys) is part of the surroundings (surr); thus, *the change in energy and, therefore, heat and/or work absorbed by the system is released by the surroundings,* and vice versa:

$$\Delta E_{sys} = -\Delta E_{surr} \quad \text{or} \quad (q + w)_{sys} = -(q + w)_{surr}$$

Since the system plus the surroundings is the universe (univ), it follows that *the total energy of the universe is constant, so the change in energy of the universe is zero:**

$$\Delta E_{sys} + \Delta E_{surr} = 0 = \Delta E_{univ}$$

The first law accounts for the energy, but not the direction, of a process. When gasoline burns in a car engine, the first law states that the potential energy difference between the bonds in the fuel mixture and those in the exhaust gases is converted to the kinetic energy of the moving car and its parts plus the heat released to the environment. But, why doesn't the heat released in the engine convert exhaust fumes back into gasoline and oxygen? When an ice cube melts in your hand, the first law tells that energy from your hand is converted to kinetic energy as the solid changes to a liquid. But, why doesn't the pool of water in your cupped hand transfer the heat back to your hand and refreeze? Neither of these events violates the first law—if you measure the work and heat in each case, you find that energy is conserved—but these reverse changes never happen. That is, *the first law by itself does not predict the* ***direction*** *of a spontaneous change.*

The Sign of ΔH Does Not Predict Spontaneous Change

Perhaps the sign of the enthalpy change (ΔH), the heat gained or lost at constant pressure (q_P), is the criterion for spontaneity. If so, we expect exothermic processes ($\Delta H < 0$) to be spontaneous and endothermic processes ($\Delta H > 0$) nonspontaneous. Let's examine some examples to see if this is true.

1. *Spontaneous processes with* $\Delta H < 0$. All freezing and condensing processes are exothermic and spontaneous at certain conditions:

$$H_2O(l) \longrightarrow H_2O(s) \qquad \Delta H^\circ_{rxn} = -\Delta H^\circ_{fus} = -6.02\text{ kJ } (1\text{ atm}; T < 0^\circ\text{C})$$

All combustion reactions are spontaneous and exothermic:

$$CH_4(g) + 2O_2(g) \longrightarrow CO_2(g) + 2H_2O(g) \qquad \Delta H^\circ_{rxn} = -802\text{ kJ}$$

Oxidation of iron and other metals occurs spontaneously and exothermically:

$$2Fe(s) + \tfrac{3}{2}O_2(g) \longrightarrow Fe_2O_3(s) \qquad \Delta H^\circ_{rxn} = -826\text{ kJ}$$

*Any modern statement of conservation of energy must take into account mass-energy equivalence and the processes in stars, which convert enormous amounts of matter into energy. Thus, the total *mass-energy* of the universe is constant.

Ionic compounds form spontaneously and exothermically from their elements:

$$Na(s) + \frac{1}{2}Cl_2(g) \longrightarrow NaCl(s) \qquad \Delta H^\circ_{rxn} = -411\ kJ$$

However, in many cases, an exothermic process occurs spontaneously under one set of conditions, whereas the opposite, endothermic, process occurs spontaneously under another set.

2. *Spontaneous processes with* $\Delta H > 0$. All melting and vaporizing processes are endothermic *and* spontaneous at certain conditions:

$$H_2O(s) \longrightarrow H_2O(l) \qquad \Delta H^\circ_{rxn} = \Delta H^\circ_{fus} = +6.02\ kJ\ (1\ atm;\ T = 0°C)$$

At ordinary pressure water vaporizes spontaneously:

$$H_2O(l) \longrightarrow H_2O(g) \qquad \Delta H^\circ_{rxn} = \Delta H^\circ_{vap} = +44.0\ kJ\ (1\ atm;\ T = 100°C)$$

Most soluble salts dissolve endothermically *and* spontaneously:

$$NaCl(s) \xrightarrow{H_2O} Na^+(aq) + Cl^-(aq) \qquad \Delta H^\circ_{soln} = +3.9\ kJ$$

$$RbClO_3(s) \xrightarrow{H_2O} Rb^+(aq) + ClO_3^-(aq) \qquad \Delta H^\circ_{soln} = +47.7\ kJ$$

$$NH_4NO_3(s) \xrightarrow{H_2O} NH_4^+(aq) + NO_3^-(aq) \qquad \Delta H^\circ_{soln} = +25.7\ kJ$$

Even some endothermic reactions are spontaneous:

$$N_2O_5(s) \longrightarrow 2NO_2(g) + \frac{1}{2}O_2(g) \qquad \Delta H^\circ_{rxn} = +109.5\ kJ$$

$$Ba(OH)_2{\cdot}8H_2O(s) + 2NH_4NO_3(s) \longrightarrow$$
$$Ba^{2+}(aq) + 2NO_3^-(aq) + 2NH_3(aq) + 10H_2O(l) \qquad \Delta H^\circ_{rxn} = +62.3\ kJ$$

In the latter reaction, crystalline solids are mixed (Figure 20.1A) and the release of waters of hydration solvates the ions. The reaction mixture absorbs heat from the surroundings so quickly that the beaker freezes to a wet block (Figure 20.1B).

Given just these few examples, we see that, as for the first law, *the sign of* ΔH *by itself does not predict the* ***direction*** *of a spontaneous change.*

Figure 20.1 A spontaneous endothermic reaction.

Freedom of Particle Motion and Dispersal of Particle Energy

When we look closely at the previous examples of spontaneous *endothermic* processes, they have one major feature in common: in every case, the chemical entities—atoms, molecules, or ions—have more freedom of motion *after* the change. Put another way, after the change, the particles have a wider range of energy of motion (kinetic energy); we say that the energy has become more dispersed, distributed, or spread out:

- The phase changes convert a solid, in which motion is restricted, to a liquid, in which particles have more freedom to move around each other, and then to a gas, in which the particles have much greater freedom of motion. Thus, the energy of motion is more dispersed.
- Dissolving a salt changes a crystalline solid and a pure liquid into separate ions and solvent molecules moving and interacting, so their freedom of motion is greater and their energy of motion more dispersed.
- In the chemical reactions, *fewer* moles of crystalline solids produce *more* moles of gases and/or solvated ions, so once again, the freedom of motion of the particles increases and their energy of motion is more dispersed:

	less freedom of particle motion	⟶	more freedom of particle motion
	localized energy of motion	⟶	dispersed energy of motion
Phase change:	solid ⟶ liquid	⟶	gas
Dissolving of salt:	crystalline solid + liquid	⟶	ions in solution
Chemical change:	crystalline solids	⟶	gases + ions in solution

In thermodynamic terms, a change in the freedom of motion of particles in a system, that is, in the dispersal of their energy of motion, is a key factor affecting the ***direction*** *of a spontaneous process.*

Entropy and the Number of Microstates

Earlier, we discussed the quantized *electronic* energy levels of an atom (Chapter 7) and a molecule (Chapter 11), as well as the quantized *kinetic* energy levels—vibrational, rotational, and translational—of a molecule (see Tools of the Laboratory, p. 343). Now, we'll see that the energy state of a whole system of particles is quantized, too.

Energy Dispersal and the Meaning of Entropy Let's see why freedom of motion and dispersal of energy relate to spontaneous change:

- *Quantization of energy*. Picture a system of, say, 1 mol of N_2 gas and focus on one molecule. At any instant, it is moving through space (translating) at some speed and rotating at some frequency, and its atoms are vibrating at some frequency. In the next instant, the molecule collides with another or with the container, and these motional (kinetic) energy states change to different values. The complete quantum state of the molecule at any instant consists of its electronic states and these translational, rotational, and vibrational states. In this discussion, we focus on the latter three.
- *Number of microstates*. The energy of the other molecules is similarly quantized. Each quantized state of the system of molecules is called a *microstate*, and at any instant, the total energy of the system is dispersed throughout one microstate. In the next instant, it is dispersed throughout a different microstate. The number of microstates possible for a system of 1 mol of molecules is staggering, on the order of $10^{10^{23}}$.
- *Dispersal of energy*. At a given set of conditions, each microstate has the *same* total energy as any other. Therefore, each microstate is equally possible for the system, and the laws of probability say that, over time, all microstates are equally likely. The number of microstates for a system is the number of ways it can disperse (distribute or spread) its kinetic energy among the various motions of all its particles.

In 1877, the Austrian mathematician and physicist Ludwig Boltzmann related the number of microstates (W) to the **entropy (S)** of a system:

$$S = k \ln W \tag{20.1}$$

where k, the *Boltzmann constant*, is the universal gas constant (R) divided by Avogadro's number (N_A), or R/N_A, and equals 1.38×10^{-23} J/K. The term W is the number of microstates, so it has no units; therefore, S has units of joules/kelvin (J/K). Thus,

- A system with fewer microstates (smaller W) has *lower entropy (lower S)*.
- A system with more microstates (larger W) has *higher entropy (higher S)*.

For our earlier examples of endothermic processes,

	lower entropy (fewer microstates)	$\longrightarrow$	higher entropy (more microstates)
Phase change:	solid $\longrightarrow$ liquid	$\longrightarrow$	gas
Dissolving of salt:	crystalline solid + liquid	$\longrightarrow$	ions in solution
Chemical change:	crystalline solids	$\longrightarrow$	gases + ions in solution

(Recall from Chapter 13 that entropy is a factor in the formation of solutions.)

Entropy as a State Function If a change results in a greater number of microstates, there are more ways to disperse the energy of the system and the entropy increases:

$$S_{\text{more microstates}} > S_{\text{fewer microstates}}$$

If a change results in a lower number of microstates, the entropy decreases. Like internal energy (E) and enthalpy (H), *entropy is a state function,* so it depends only on the present state of the system, not on how it arrived at that state (see Chapter 6, p. 234). Therefore, the change in entropy of the system (ΔS_{sys}) depends only on the *difference* between its final and initial values:

$$\Delta S_{sys} = S_{final} - S_{initial}$$

Like any state function, $\Delta S_{sys} > 0$ when its value increases during a change. For example, for the phase change when dry ice sublimes, the entropy increases:

$$CO_2(s) \longrightarrow CO_2(g) \qquad \Delta S_{sys} = S_{final} - S_{initial} = S_{\text{gaseous } CO_2} - S_{\text{solid } CO_2} > 0$$

And, $\Delta S_{sys} < 0$ when the entropy decreases, as when water vapor condenses:

$$H_2O(g) \longrightarrow H_2O(l) \qquad \Delta S_{sys} = S_{liquid\ H_2O} - S_{gaseous\ H_2O} < 0$$

As an example of a reaction during which entropy increases, consider the decomposition of dinitrogen tetraoxide (written as $O_2N—NO_2$):

$$O_2N—NO_2(g) \longrightarrow 2NO_2(g)$$

When the N—N bond in 1 mol of dinitrogen tetraoxide breaks, the 2 mol of NO_2 molecules have many more possible motions; thus, at any instant, the energy of the system is dispersed into any one of a larger number of microstates. Thus, the change in entropy of the system, which is the change in entropy of the reaction (ΔS_{rxn}), goes up:

$$\Delta S_{sys} = \Delta S_{rxn} = S_{final} - S_{initial} = S_{products} - S_{reactants} = 2S_{NO_2} - S_{N_2O_4} > 0$$

Quantitative Meaning of an Entropy Change There are two approaches for quantifying an entropy change, but they give the same result. The first is based on the number of microstates possible for a system, and the second on the heat absorbed (or released) by the system. We'll examine both with a system of 1 mol of a gas expanding from 1 L to 2 L and behaving ideally, much as neon does at 298 K:

$$\text{1 mol neon (initial: 1 L and 298 K)} \longrightarrow \text{1 mol neon (final: 2 L and 298 K)}$$

1. *Quantifying ΔS_{sys} from the number of microstates.* Figure 20.2 shows two flasks connected by a stopcock—the right flask is evacuated, and the left flask contains 1 mol of neon. When we open the stopcock, the gas expands until each flask contains 0.5 mol—but *why*? Opening the stopcock increases the volume, which increases the number of translational energy levels the particles can occupy as they move to more locations. Thus, the number of microstates—and the entropy—increases.

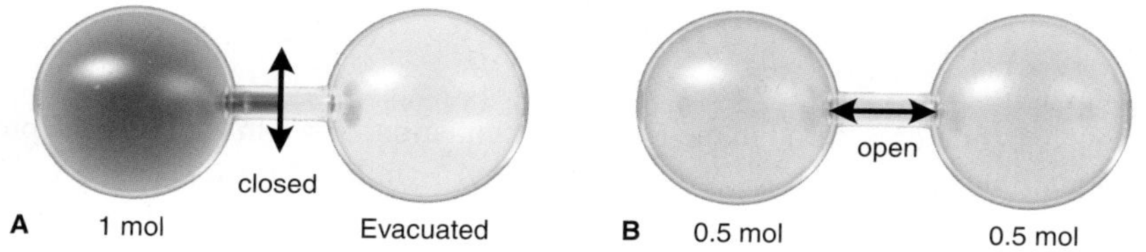

Figure 20.2 Spontaneous expansion of a gas. **A,** With the stopcock closed, the left flask contains 1 mol of Ne. **B,** With the stopcock open, the gas expands and each flask contains 0.5 mol of Ne.

Figure 20.3 presents this idea with particles on energy levels in a box of changeable volume. When the stopcock opens, there are more energy levels, and they are closer together on average, so more distributions of particles are possible.

In Figure 20.4 on the next page, the number of microstates is represented by the placement of particles in the left and/or right flasks:

- *One Ne atom.* At a given instant, an Ne atom in the left flask has its energy in one of some number (W) of microstates. Opening the stopcock increases the volume, which increases the number of possible locations and the number of translational energy levels. Thus, the system has 2^1, or 2, times as many microstates available when the atom moves through both flasks (final state, W_{final}) as when it is confined to the left flask (initial state, $W_{initial}$).
- *Two Ne atoms.* For atoms A and B moving through both flasks, there are 2^2, or 4, times as many microstates as when the atoms were initially in the left flask—some number of microstates with both A and B in the left, that many with A in the left and B in the right or with B in the left and A in the right, and that many with both in the right.
- *Three Ne atoms.* Add another atom, and there are 2^3, or 8, times as many microstates when the stopcock is open.
- *Ten Ne atoms.* With 10 Ne atoms, there are 2^{10}, or 1024, times as many microstates for the atoms in both flasks as there were for the 10 atoms in the left flask.
- *One mole of Ne atoms.* With 1 mol (N_A) of Ne, there are 2^{N_A} times as many microstates for the atoms in the larger volume (W_{final}) than in the smaller ($W_{initial}$):

$$\frac{W_{final}}{W_{initial}} = 2^{N_A}$$

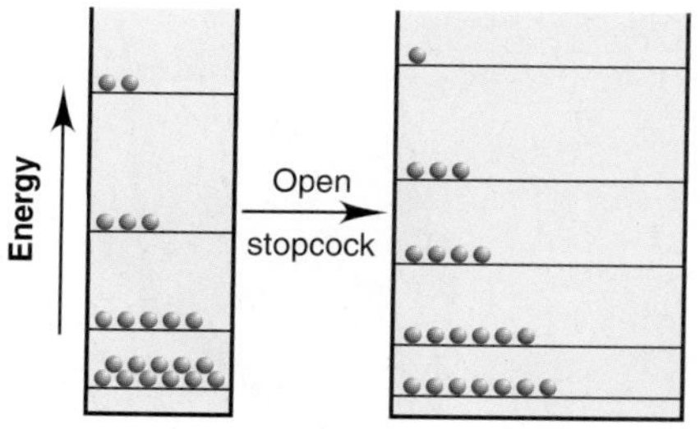

Figure 20.3 The entropy increase due to expansion of a gas. Energy levels are shown as lines in a box of narrow width (*left*). Each distribution of energies for the 21 particles is one microstate. When the stopcock is opened, the box is wider (volume increases, *right*), and the particles have more energy levels available.

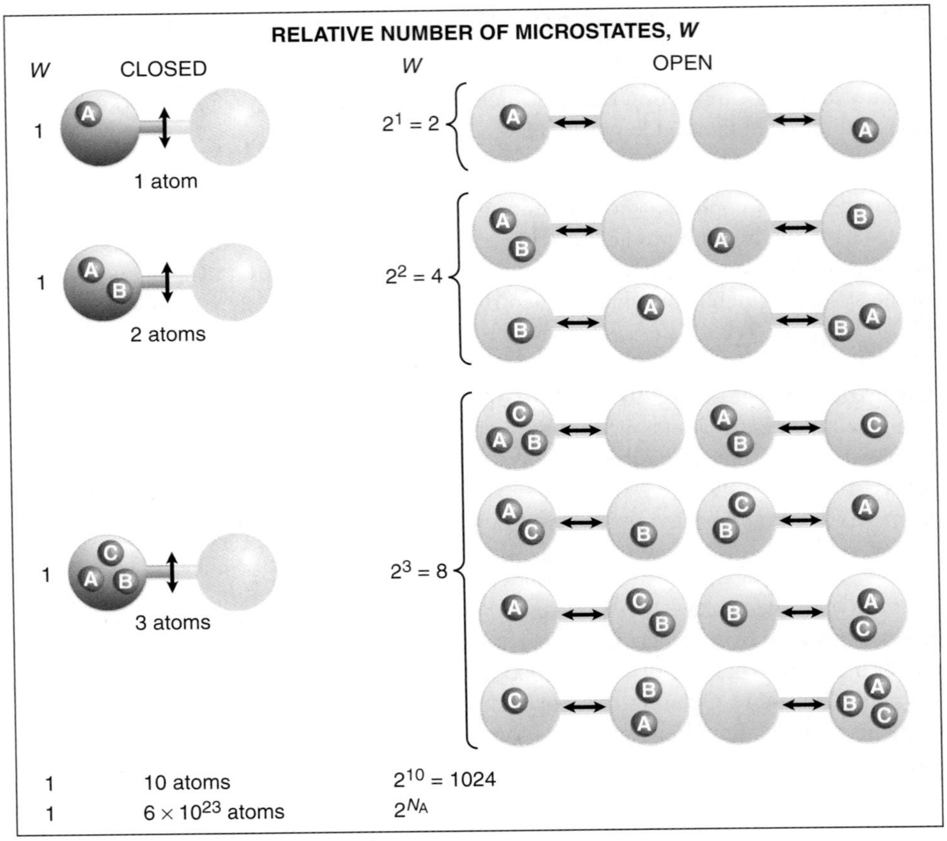

Figure 20.4 **Expansion of a gas and the increase in number of microstates.** Each set of particle locations represents a different microstate. When the volume increases (stopcock opens), the number of microstates is 2^n, where n is the number of particles.

Now let's find ΔS_{sys} through the Boltzmann equation, $S = k \ln W$. From the properties of logarithms (Appendix A), we know that $\ln A - \ln B = \ln A/B$. Thus,

$$\Delta S_{sys} = S_{final} - S_{initial} = k \ln W_{final} - k \ln W_{initial} = k \ln \frac{W_{final}}{W_{initial}} = k \ln 2^{N_A}$$

Also, from Appendix A, $\ln A^y = y \ln A$; thus, with $k = R/N_A$, we have

$$\Delta S_{sys} = \frac{R}{N_A} \ln 2^{N_A} = \left(\frac{R}{N_A}\right) N_A \ln 2 = R \ln 2$$
$$= (8.314 \text{ J/mol·K})(0.693) = 5.76 \text{ J/mol·K}$$

2. *Quantifying ΔS_{sys} from the changes in heat.* Now we compare the ΔS_{sys} we just found for a gas expanding into an evacuated flask with the ΔS_{sys} for a gas that is heated and does work on the surroundings. This approach uses the relationship

$$\Delta S_{sys} = \frac{q_{rev}}{T} \qquad \textbf{(20.2)}$$

where T is the temperature at which the heat change occurs and q is the heat absorbed. The subscript "rev" refers to a *reversible process,* one that occurs in such tiny increments that the system remains at equilibrium and the direction of the change can be reversed by an *infinitesimal* reversal of conditions.

We'll approximate a reversible expansion by placing Ne gas in a piston-cylinder assembly within a heat reservoir (to maintain a constant T of 298 K) and start by confining it to a volume of 1 L by the "pressure" of a beaker of sand on the piston (Figure 20.5). We remove one grain of sand (an "infinitesimal" decrease in pressure) with a pair of tweezers, and the gas expands a tiny amount, raising the piston and doing work, $-w$. Assuming Ne behaves ideally, it absorbs an equivalent tiny increment of heat, q, from the heat reservoir. With each grain of sand removed, the expanding gas absorbs another tiny increment of heat. This process simulates a reversible expansion because we can reverse it by putting back a grain of sand, which causes the surround-

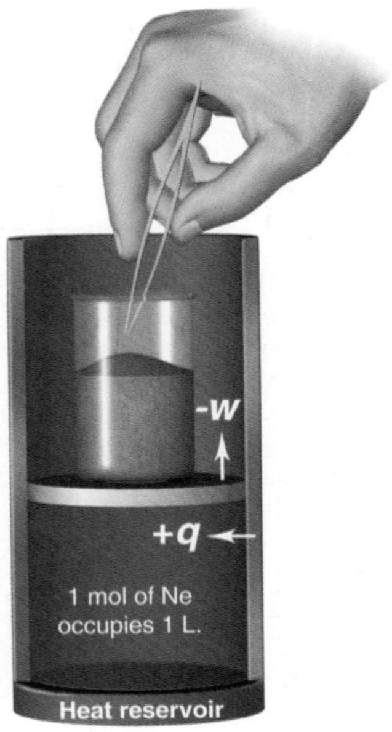

Figure 20.5 Simulating a reversible process.

ings to do a tiny quantity of work compressing the gas, thus releasing a tiny quantity of heat to the reservoir.

If we continue this nearly reversible expansion to 2 L and use calculus to integrate the tiny increments of heat together, q_{rev} is 1718 J. From Equation 20.2,

$$\Delta S_{sys} = \frac{q_{rev}}{T} = \frac{1718\ \text{J}}{298\ \text{K}} = 5.76\ \text{J/K}$$

This is the same value of ΔS_{sys} we obtained based on the number of microstates.

Entropy and the Second Law of Thermodynamics

While it's true that the change in entropy determines the direction of a spontaneous process, we must consider more than the entropy change of the system. After all, some processes, such as ice melting, occur spontaneously and ΔS_{sys} goes up, while others, such as water freezing, occur spontaneously and ΔS_{sys} goes down. But when we consider *both* the system *and* its surroundings, we find that *all real processes occur spontaneously in the direction that increases the entropy of the universe (system plus surroundings).* This is one way to state the **second law of thermodynamics.**

The second law says that *either* the entropy change of the system *or* of the surroundings may be negative. But, for a process to be spontaneous, the *sum* of the two entropy changes must be positive. If the entropy of the system decreases, the entropy of the surroundings must increase even more to offset that decrease, so that the entropy of the universe (system *plus* surroundings) increases. A quantitative statement of the second law is, for any real spontaneous process,

$$\Delta S_{univ} = \Delta S_{sys} + \Delta S_{surr} > 0 \qquad (20.3)$$

Standard Molar Entropies and the Third Law

Entropy and enthalpy are state functions, but their values differ in a fundamental way:

- For *enthalpy,* there is no zero point, so we can measure only *changes.*
- For *entropy,* there *is* a zero point, and we can determine *absolute* values by applying the **third law of thermodynamics:** *a perfect crystal has zero entropy at absolute zero:* $S_{sys} = 0$ at 0 K.

A "perfect" crystal means all the particles are aligned flawlessly. At absolute zero, the particles have minimum energy, so there is only one microstate. Thus, in Equation 20.1,

$$W = 1 \qquad \text{so} \qquad S = k \ln 1 = 0$$

When we warm the crystal to any temperature above 0 K, the total energy increases, so it can be dispersed into more than one microstate. Thus,

$$W > 1 \qquad \text{and} \qquad \ln W > 0 \qquad \text{so} \qquad S > 0$$

In principle, to find S of a substance at a given temperature, we cool it as close to 0 K as possible. Then we heat it in small increments, dividing q by T to get the increase in S for each increment, and add up all the entropy increases to the temperature of interest, usually 298 K. Therefore, S of a substance at a given temperature is an *absolute* value. As with other thermodynamic variables,

- We compare entropy values for substances at the temperature of interest in their *standard states: 1 atm for gases, 1 M for solutions, and the pure substance in its most stable form for solids or liquids.*
- Because entropy is an *extensive* property—one that depends on the amount of substance—we specify the **standard molar entropy ($S°$),** in units of J/mol·K (or J mol^{-1} K^{-1}). ($S°$ values at 298 K for many elements, compounds, and ions appear, with other thermodynamic variables, in Appendix B.)

Predicting Relative $S°$ of a System

Let's see how the standard molar entropy of a substance is affected by several parameters: temperature, physical state, dissolution, and atomic size or molecular complexity. (Unless stated otherwise, the $S°$ values refer to the system at 298 K.)

Temperature Changes Temperature has the most important effect. For any substance, *$S°$ increases as the T rises,* as these values for copper metal show:

T (K):	273	295	298
$S°$:	31.0	32.9	33.2

As heat is absorbed ($q > 0$), temperature, which is a measure of the average kinetic energy of the particles, increases. Recall that the kinetic energies of gas particles are distributed over a range, which becomes wider as T rises (Figure 5.14); liquids and solids behave the same. Thus, at any instant, there are more microstates available in which the energy can be dispersed, so the entropy of the substance goes up. Figure 20.6 presents three ways to view the effect of temperature on entropy.

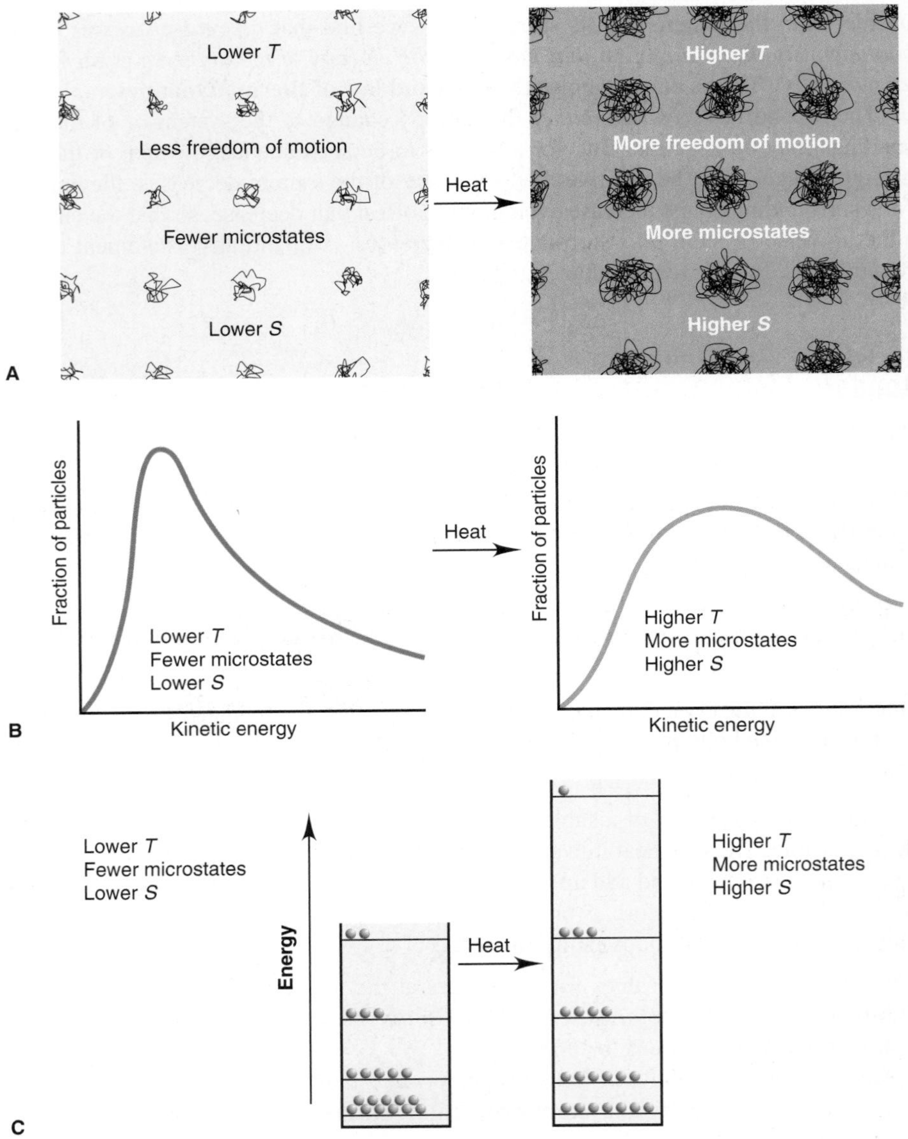

Figure 20.6 Visualizing the effect of temperature on entropy. **A,** Computer simulations show each particle in a crystal moving about its lattice position. Adding heat increases T and the total energy, so the particles have greater freedom of motion, and their energy is more dispersed. Thus, S increases. **B,** At any T, there is a range of occupied energy levels and, thus, a certain number of microstates. Adding heat increases the total energy *(area under curve)*, so the range of occupied energy levels becomes greater, as does the number of microstates (higher S). **C,** A system of 21 particles occupy energy levels *(lines)* in a box whose height represents the total energy. When heat is added, the total energy increases *(box is higher) and* becomes more dispersed *(more lines)*, so S increases.

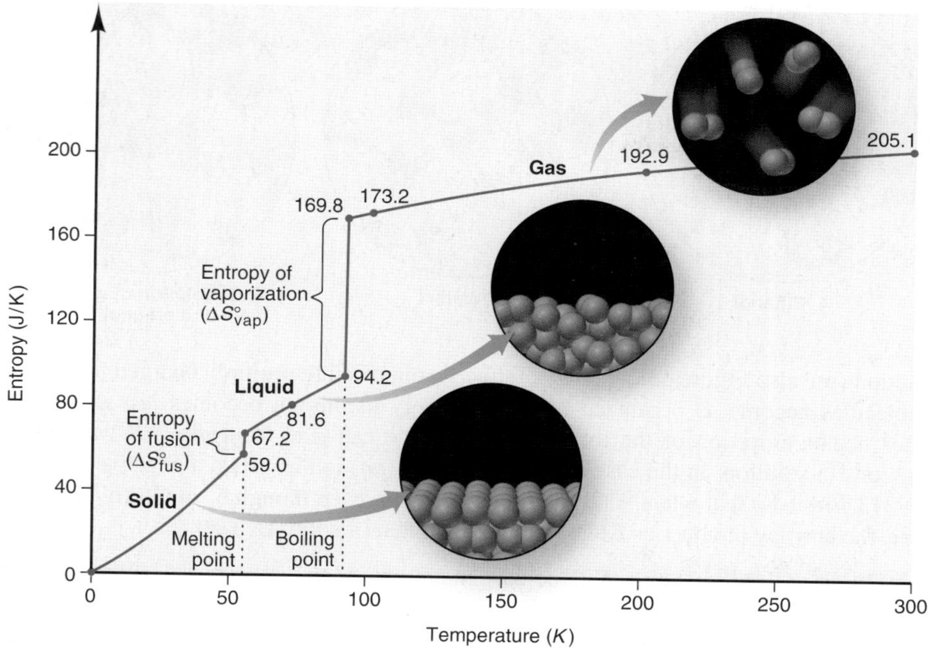

Figure 20.7 The increase in entropy during phase changes from solid to liquid to gas.

Physical States and Phase Changes In melting or vaporizing, heat is absorbed ($q > 0$). The particles have more freedom of motion, and their energy is more dispersed. Thus, S° *increases as the physical state of a substance changes from solid to liquid to gas:*

	Na	H_2O	C(graphite)
S°(*s* or *l*):	51.4(*s*)	69.9(*l*)	5.7(*s*)
S°(*g*):	153.6	188.7	158.0

Figure 20.7 plots entropy versus *T* as solid O_2 is heated and changes to liquid and then to gas, with S° values at various points; this behavior is typical of many substances. At the molecular scale, several stages occur:

- Particles in the solid vibrate about their positions but, on average, remain fixed. The energy of the solid is dispersed least, that is, has the fewest microstates, so the solid has the lowest entropy.
- As *T* rises, the entropy increases gradually as the particles' kinetic energy increases.
- When the solid melts, the particles move much more freely between and around each other, so there is an abrupt increase in entropy (ΔS°_{fus}).
- Further heating of the liquid increases the speed of the particles, and the entropy increases gradually.
- When the liquid vaporizes and becomes a gas, the particles undergo a much larger, abrupt entropy increase (ΔS°_{vap}); *the increase in entropy from liquid to gas is much larger than from solid to liquid:* $\Delta S^\circ_{vap} >> \Delta S^\circ_{fus}$.
- Finally, with further heating of the gas, the entropy increases gradually.

Dissolving a Solid or a Liquid in Water Recall from Chapter 13 that, in general, entropy increases when a solute dissolves in a solvent: $S_{soln} > (S_{solute} + S_{solvent})$. But, when water is the solvent, the entropy may also depend on the nature of solute *and* solvent interactions and includes two opposing events:

	NaCl	$AlCl_3$	CH_3OH
S°(*s* or *l*):	72.1(*s*)	167(*s*)	127(*l*)
S°(*aq*):	115.1	−148	132

1. *For ionic solutes,* when the crystal dissolves in water, the ions have much more freedom of motion and their energy is dispersed into more microstates. That is, the entropy of the ions themselves is greater in the solution. However, some water molecules become arranged around the ions (Figure 20.8), which limits the molecules' freedom of

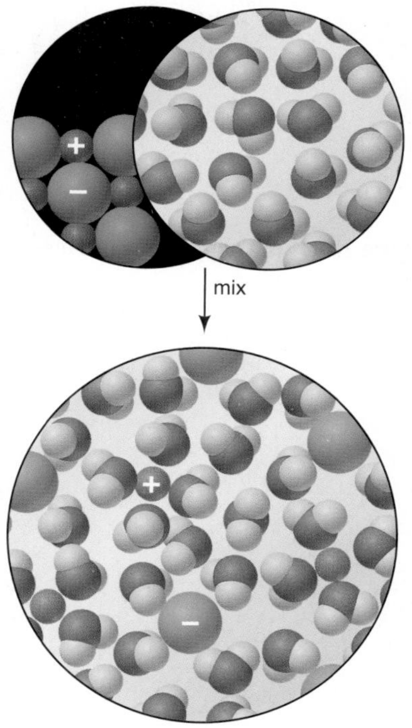

Figure 20.8 The entropy change accompanying the dissolution of a salt. The entropy of a salt solution is usually *greater* than that of the solid and of water, but it is affected by water molecules becoming organized around each ion.

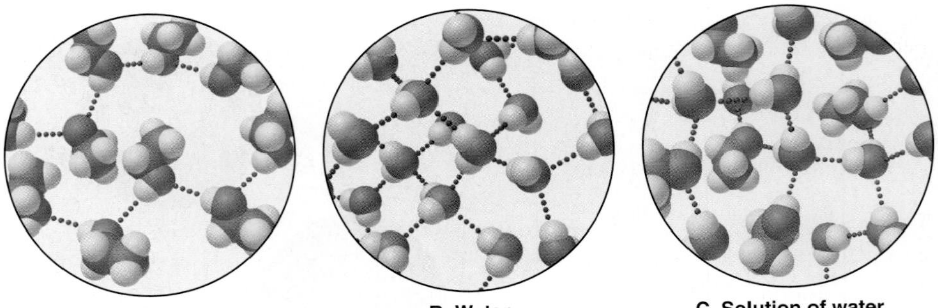

Figure 20.9 The small increase in entropy when ethanol dissolves in water. Ethanol **(A)** and water **(B)** each have many H bonds to themselves. **C,** In solution, they form H bonds to each other, so their freedom of motion does not change significantly.

motion (see also Figure 13.2, p. 479). In fact, around small, multiply charged ions, H_2O molecules become so organized that their energy of motion becomes *less* dispersed. This negative portion of the total entropy change can lead to *negative* $S°$ values for the ions in solution. In the case of $AlCl_3$, the $Al^{3+}(aq)$ ion has such a negative $S°$ value (−313 J/mol·K) that when $AlCl_3$ dissolves in water, even though $S°$ of $Cl^-(aq)$ is positive, the entropy of aqueous $AlCl_3$ is lower than that of solid $AlCl_3$.*

2. *For molecular solutes,* the increase in entropy upon dissolving is typically much smaller than for ionic solutes. After all, for a solid such as glucose, there is no separation into ions, and for a liquid such as methanol or ethanol (Figure 20.9), there is no breakdown of a crystal structure. Furthermore, in these small alcohols and in pure water, the molecules form many H bonds, so there is relatively little change in their freedom of motion either before or after they are mixed.

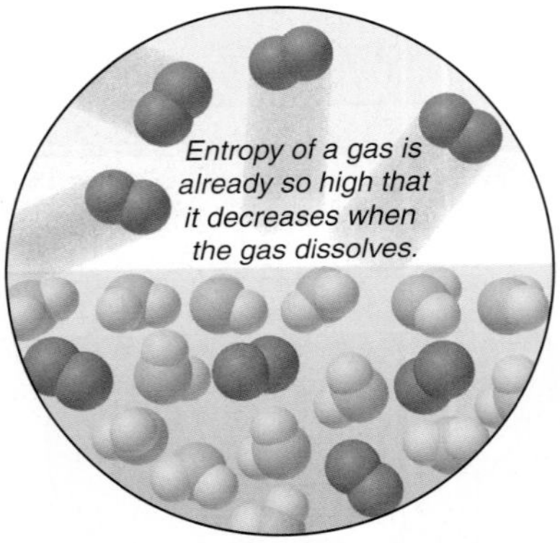

Figure 20.10 The entropy of a gas dissolved in a liquid.

Dissolving a Gas in a Liquid The particles in a gas already have so much freedom of motion—and, thus, such highly dispersed energy—that they lose some when they dissolve in a liquid or solid. Therefore, the entropy of a solution of a gas in a liquid or in a solid is always *less* than the entropy of the gas itself. For instance, when gaseous O_2 [$S°(g)$ = 205.0 J/mol·K] dissolves in water, its entropy decreases considerably [$S°(aq)$ = 110.9 J/mol·K] (Figure 20.10). When a gas dissolves in another gas, however, the entropy increases as a result of the separation and mixing of the molecules.

Atomic Size or Molecular Complexity Differences in $S°$ values for substances in the same phase are usually based on atomic size and molecular complexity.

1. *Within a periodic group,* energy levels become closer together for larger, heavier atoms, so the number of microstates, and thus the molar entropy, increases:

	Li	Na	K	Rb	Cs
Atomic radius (pm):	152	186	227	248	265
Molar mass (g/mol):	6.941	22.99	39.10	85.47	132.9
$S°(s)$:	29.1	51.4	64.7	69.5	85.2

The same trend of increasing entropy holds for similar compounds down a group:

	HF	HCl	HBr	HI
Molar mass (g/mol):	20.01	36.46	80.91	127.9
$S°(g)$:	173.7	186.8	198.6	206.3

2. *For different forms of an element (allotropes),* the entropy is *higher* in the form that allows the atoms more freedom of motion. For example, $S°$ of graphite is 5.69 J/mol·K, whereas $S°$ of diamond is 2.44 J/mol·K. In graphite, covalent bonds extend within a two-dimensional sheet, and the sheets move past each other easily; in diamond, covalent bonds extend in three dimensions, allowing the atoms little movement (Table 12.6, p. 452).

*An $S°$ value for a hydrated ion can be negative because it is relative to the $S°$ value for the hydrated proton, $H^+(aq)$, which is assigned a value of 0. In other words, $Al^{3+}(aq)$ has a lower entropy than $H^+(aq)$.

3. *For compounds,* entropy increases with chemical complexity (that is, with number of atoms in the formula), and this trend holds for ionic and covalent substances:

	NaCl	$AlCl_3$	P_4O_{10}	NO	NO_2	N_2O_4
$S°(s)$:	72.1	167	229			
$S°(g)$:				211	240	304

The trend is also based on the different types of motion. Thus, for example, among the nitrogen oxides listed, the number of different vibrational motions increases with the number of atoms in the molecule (Figure 20.11; see also p. 343).

For larger compounds, we also consider the motion of different parts of a molecule. A long hydrocarbon chain can rotate and vibrate in more ways than a short one, so *entropy increases with chain length.* A ring compound, such as cyclopentane (C_5H_{10}), has lower entropy than the corresponding chain compound, pentene (C_5H_{10}), because the ring structure restricts freedom of motion:

	$CH_4(g)$	$C_2H_6(g)$	$C_3H_8(g)$	$C_4H_{10}(g)$	$C_5H_{10}(g)$	C_5H_{10}(cyclo, g)	$C_2H_5OH(l)$
$S°$:	186	230	270	310	348	293	161

Remember, these trends hold only for *substances in the same physical state.* Gaseous methane (CH_4) has higher entropy than liquid ethanol (C_2H_5OH), even though ethanol molecules are more complex. When gases are compared with liquids, *the effect of physical state dominates the effect of molecular complexity.*

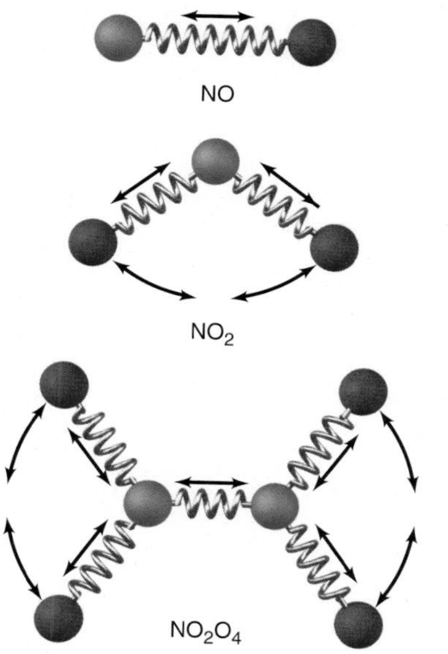

Figure 20.11 Entropy, vibrational motion, and molecular complexity.

Sample Problem 20.1 Predicting Relative Entropy Values

Problem Choose the member with the higher entropy in each of the following pairs, and justify your choice [assume constant temperature, except in part (e)]:
(a) 1 mol of $SO_2(g)$ or 1 mol of $SO_3(g)$
(b) 1 mol of $CO_2(s)$ or 1 mol of $CO_2(g)$
(c) 3 mol of $O_2(g)$ or 2 mol of $O_3(g)$
(d) 1 mol of $KBr(s)$ or 1 mol of $KBr(aq)$
(e) Seawater at 2°C or at 23°C
(f) 1 mol of $CF_4(g)$ or 1 mol of $CCl_4(g)$

Plan In general, particles with more freedom of motion have more microstates in which to disperse their kinetic energy, so they have higher entropy. We know that either raising temperature or having *more* particles increases entropy. We apply the general categories described in the text to choose the member with the higher entropy.

Solution **(a)** 1 mol of $SO_3(g)$. For equal numbers of moles of substances with the same types of atoms in the same physical state, the more atoms in the molecule, the more types of motion available, and thus the higher the entropy.
(b) 1 mol of $CO_2(g)$. For a given substance, entropy increases in the sequence $s < l < g$.
(c) 3 mol of $O_2(g)$. The two samples contain the same number of oxygen atoms but different numbers of molecules. Despite the greater complexity of O_3, the greater number of molecules dominates because there are many more microstates possible for 3 mol of particles than for 2 mol.
(d) 1 mol of $KBr(aq)$. The two samples have the same number of ions, but their motion is more limited and their energy less dispersed in the solid than in the solution.
(e) Seawater at 23°C. Entropy increases with rising temperature.
(f) 1 mol of $CCl_4(g)$. For similar compounds, entropy increases with molar mass.

Follow-Up Problem 20.1 Select the substance with the higher entropy in each of the following pairs, and give the reason for your choice (assume 1 mol of each at the same T):
(a) $PCl_3(g)$ or $PCl_5(g)$
(b) $CaF_2(s)$ or $BaCl_2(s)$
(c) $Br_2(g)$ or $Br_2(l)$

Summary of Section 20.1

- A change is spontaneous under specified conditions if it occurs without a continuous input of energy.
- Neither the first law of thermodynamics nor the sign of ΔH predicts the direction of a spontaneous change.
- Many spontaneous processes involve an increase in the freedom of motion of the system's particles and, thus, in the dispersal of the system's energy of motion.
- Entropy is a state function that measures the extent of energy dispersed into the number of microstates possible for a system. Each microstate consists of the quantized energy levels of the system at a given instant.
- The second law of thermodynamics states that, in a spontaneous process, the entropy of the universe (system plus surroundings) increases.
- Absolute entropy values can be found because perfect crystals have zero entropy at 0 K (third law of thermodynamics).
- Standard molar entropy, S° (J/mol·K), is affected by temperature, phase changes, dissolution, and atomic size or molecular complexity.

20.2 • CALCULATING THE ENTROPY CHANGE OF A REACTION

Chemists are especially interested in learning how to predict the sign *and* calculate the value of the entropy change that occurs during a reaction.

Entropy Changes in the System: Standard Entropy of Reaction (ΔS°_{rxn})

The **standard entropy of reaction, ΔS°_{rxn},** is the entropy change that occurs when all reactants and products are in their standard states.

Predicting the Sign of ΔS°_{rxn} A deciding factor in predicting the sign of ΔS°_{rxn} is a change in the amount (mol) of gas, because gases have such great freedom of motion and, thus, high molar entropies: *if the number of moles of gas increases, ΔS°_{rxn} is positive; if the number decreases, ΔS°_{rxn} is negative.* Here are a few examples:

- *Increase in amount of gas.* When gaseous H_2 reacts with solid I_2 to form gaseous HI, the total number of moles of *substance* stays the same. Nevertheless, the sign of ΔS°_{rxn} is positive (entropy increases) because the number of moles of *gas* increases:

$$H_2(g) + I_2(s) \longrightarrow 2HI(g) \qquad \Delta S^\circ_{rxn} = S^\circ_{products} - S^\circ_{reactants} > 0$$

- *Decrease in amount of gas.* When ammonia forms from its elements, 4 mol of gas produce 2 mol of gas, so ΔS°_{rxn} is negative (entropy decreases):

$$N_2(g) + 3H_2(g) \rightleftharpoons 2NH_3(g) \qquad \Delta S^\circ_{rxn} = S^\circ_{products} - S^\circ_{reactants} < 0$$

- *No change in amount of gas, but change in structure.* When the amount (mol) of gas doesn't change, we *cannot* predict the sign of ΔS°_{rxn}. But, a change in one of the structures can make it easier to predict the sign of ΔS°_{rxn}. For example, when cyclopropane is heated to 500°C, the ring opens and propene forms. The chain has more freedom of motion than the ring, so ΔS°_{rxn} is positive:

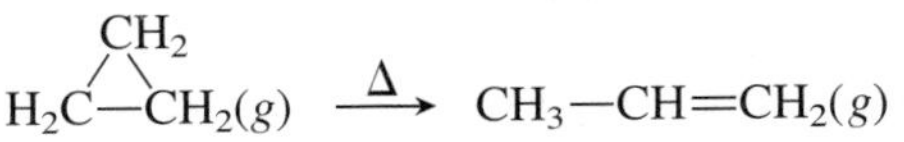

$$\Delta S^\circ = S^\circ_{products} - S^\circ_{reactants} > 0$$

Keep in mind, however, that in general *we cannot predict the sign of the entropy change unless the reaction involves a change in number of moles of gas.*

Calculating ΔS°_{rxn} from S° Values By applying Hess's law (Chapter 6), we combined ΔH°_f values to find ΔH°_{rxn}. Similarly, we combine S° values to find the standard entropy of reaction, ΔS°_{rxn}:

$$\Delta S^\circ_{rxn} = \Sigma m S^\circ_{products} - \Sigma n S^\circ_{reactants} \qquad (20.4)$$

where m and n are the amounts (mol) of products and reactants, respectively, given by the coefficients in the balanced equation. For the formation of ammonia, we have

$$\Delta S^\circ_{rxn} = [(2 \text{ mol } NH_3)(S^\circ \text{ of } NH_3)] - [(1 \text{ mol } N_2)(S^\circ \text{ of } N_2) + (3 \text{ mol } H_2)(S^\circ \text{ of } H_2)]$$

From Appendix B, we find the S° values:

$$\Delta S^\circ_{rxn} = [(2 \text{ mol})(193 \text{ J/mol·K})] - [(1 \text{ mol})(191.5 \text{ J/mol·K}) + (3 \text{ mol})(130.6 \text{ J/mol·K})]$$
$$= -197 \text{ J/K}$$

As we predicted from the decrease in number of moles of gas, $\Delta S^\circ_{rxn} < 0$.

Sample Problem 20.2 Calculating the Standard Entropy of Reaction, ΔS°_{rxn}

Problem Predict the sign of ΔS°_{rxn}, if possible, and calculate its value for the combustion of 1 mol of propane at 25°C:

$$C_3H_8(g) + 5O_2(g) \longrightarrow 3CO_2(g) + 4H_2O(l)$$

Plan From the change in the number of moles of gas (6 mol yields 3 mol), the entropy should decrease ($\Delta S^\circ_{rxn} < 0$). To find ΔS°_{rxn}, we apply Equation 20.4.

Solution Calculating ΔS°_{rxn}. Using Appendix B values,

$$\Delta S^\circ_{rxn} = [(3 \text{ mol } CO_2)(S^\circ \text{ of } CO_2) + (4 \text{ mol } H_2O)(S^\circ \text{ of } H_2O)]$$
$$- [(1 \text{ mol } C_3H_8)(S^\circ \text{ of } C_3H_8) + (5 \text{ mol } O_2)(S^\circ \text{ of } O_2)]$$
$$= [(3 \text{ mol})(213.7 \text{ J/mol·K}) + (4 \text{ mol})(69.9 \text{ J/mol·K})]$$
$$- [(1 \text{ mol})(269.9 \text{ J/mol·K}) + (5 \text{ mol})(205.0 \text{ J/mol·K})]$$
$$= -374 \text{ J/K}$$

Check $\Delta S^\circ < 0$, so our prediction is correct. Rounding gives $[3(200) + 4(70)] - [270 + 5(200)] = 880 - 1270 = -390$, close to the calculated value.

Follow-Up Problem 20.2 Balance the following equations, predict the sign of ΔS°_{rxn} if possible, and calculate its value at 25°C:

(a) $NaOH(s) + CO_2(g) \longrightarrow Na_2CO_3(s) + H_2O(l)$

(b) $Fe(s) + H_2O(g) \longrightarrow Fe_2O_3(s) + H_2(g)$

Entropy Changes in the Surroundings: The Other Part of the Total

In the synthesis of ammonia, the combustion of propane, and many other spontaneous reactions, the entropy of the system decreases ($\Delta S^\circ_{rxn} < 0$). Remember that the second law dictates that, for a spontaneous process, a ***decrease*** *in the entropy of the system is outweighed by an* ***increase*** *in the entropy of the surroundings.* In this section, we examine the influence of the surroundings—in particular, the addition (or removal) of heat and the temperature at which this heat flow occurs—on the *total* entropy change.

The Role of the Surroundings In essence, the surroundings *add heat to or remove heat from the system.* That is, the surroundings function as an enormous heat source or heat sink, one so large that its temperature remains constant, even though its entropy changes. The surroundings participate in the two types of enthalpy changes as follows:

1. *In an exothermic change, heat released by the system is absorbed by the surroundings.* More heat increases the freedom of motion of the particles and makes the energy more dispersed, so the entropy of the surroundings increases:

   For an exothermic change: $q_{sys} < 0$, $q_{surr} > 0$, and $\Delta S_{surr} > 0$

2. *In an endothermic change, heat absorbed by the system is released by the surroundings.* Less heat reduces the freedom of motion of the particles and makes the energy less dispersed, so the entropy of the surroundings decreases:

   For an endothermic change: $q_{sys} > 0$, $q_{surr} < 0$, and $\Delta S_{surr} < 0$

Temperature at Which Heat Is Transferred The *temperature* of the surroundings at the time the heat is transferred also affects ΔS_{surr}. Consider the effect of an exothermic reaction at a low or at a high temperature:

- At a low T, such as 20 K, there is little motion in the surroundings due to little energy. This means there are few energy levels in each microstate and few microstates in which to disperse the energy. Transferring a given quantity of heat to these surroundings causes a relatively large change in how much energy is dispersed.
- At a high T, such as 298 K, the surroundings have a large quantity of energy dispersed. There are more energy levels in each microstate and a greater number of microstates. Transferring the same given quantity of heat to these surroundings causes a relatively small change in how much energy is dispersed.

A Checkbook Analogy for Heating the Surroundings If you have $10 in your checking account, a $10 deposit represents a 100% increase in your net worth; that is, a given change to a low initial state has a large impact. If, however, you have a $1000 balance, a $10 deposit represents only a 1% increase. Thus, the same absolute change to a high initial state has a smaller impact.

In other words, ΔS_{surr} is greater when heat is added at a lower T. Putting these ideas together, *ΔS_{surr} is directly related to an opposite change in the heat of the system (q_{sys}) and inversely related to the temperature at which the heat is transferred:*

$$\Delta S_{surr} = -\frac{q_{sys}}{T}$$

For a process at *constant pressure,* the heat (q_P) is ΔH (Section 6.2), so

$$\Delta S_{surr} = -\frac{\Delta H_{sys}}{T} \quad (20.5)$$

Thus, we find ΔS_{surr} by measuring ΔH_{sys} and T at which the change takes place.

The main point: If a spontaneous reaction has a negative ΔS_{sys} (fewer microstates into which energy is dispersed), ΔS_{surr} must be positive enough (even more microstates into which energy is dispersed) for ΔS_{univ} to be positive (net increase in number of microstates to disperse the energy).

Sample Problem 20.3 Determining Reaction Spontaneity

Problem At 298 K, the formation of ammonia has a negative ΔS°_{sys}:

$$N_2(g) + 3H_2(g) \longrightarrow 2NH_3(g) \qquad \Delta S^\circ_{sys} = -197\ \text{J/K}$$

Calculate ΔS_{univ}, and state whether the reaction occurs spontaneously at this temperature.

Plan For the reaction to occur spontaneously, $\Delta S_{univ} > 0$, so ΔS_{surr} must be greater than +197 J/K. To find ΔS_{surr}, we need ΔH°_{sys}, which is the same as ΔH°_{rxn}. We use ΔH°_f values from Appendix B to find ΔH°_{rxn}. Then, we divide ΔH°_{rxn} by the given T (298 K) to find ΔS_{surr}. To find ΔS_{univ}, we add the calculated ΔS_{surr} to the given ΔS°_{sys} (−197 J/K).

Solution Calculating ΔH°_{sys}:

$$\begin{aligned}\Delta H^\circ_{sys} &= \Delta H^\circ_{rxn}\\ &= [(2\ \text{mol}\ NH_3)(-45.9\ \text{kJ/mol})] - [(3\ \text{mol}\ H_2)(0\ \text{kJ/mol}) + (1\ \text{mol}\ N_2)(0\ \text{kJ/mol})]\\ &= -91.8\ \text{kJ}\end{aligned}$$

Calculating ΔS_{surr}:

$$\Delta S_{surr} = -\frac{\Delta H^\circ_{sys}}{T} = -\frac{-91.8\ \text{kJ} \times \frac{1000\ \text{J}}{1\ \text{kJ}}}{298\ \text{K}} = 308\ \text{J/K}$$

Determining ΔS_{univ}:

$$\Delta S_{univ} = \Delta S^\circ_{sys} + \Delta S_{surr} = -197\ \text{J/K} + 308\ \text{J/K} = 111\ \text{J/K}$$

$\Delta S_{univ} > 0$, so the reaction occurs spontaneously at 298 K (*see margin*).

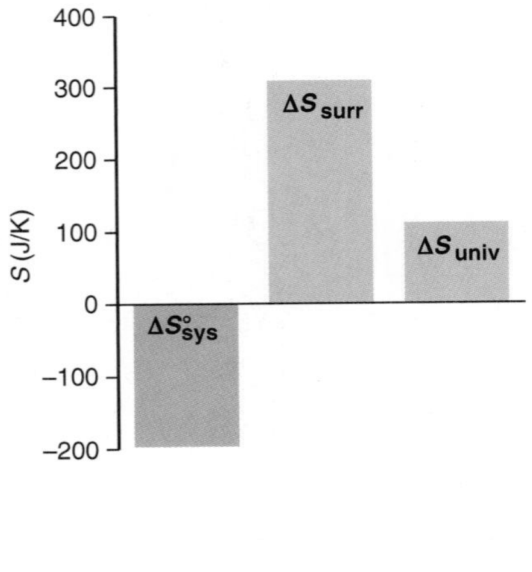

Check Rounding to check the math, we have

$$\begin{aligned}\Delta H^\circ_{rxn} &\approx 2(-45\ \text{kJ}) = -90\ \text{kJ}\\ \Delta S_{surr} &\approx -(-90{,}000\ \text{J})/300\ \text{K} = 300\ \text{J/K}\\ \Delta S_{univ} &\approx -200\ \text{J/K} + 300\ \text{J/K} = 100\ \text{J/K}\end{aligned}$$

Given the negative ΔH°_{rxn}, Le Châtelier's principle says that low T favors NH_3 formation, so the answer is reasonable (see Section 17.6).

Comment **1.** Because $\Delta H°$ has units of kJ, and ΔS has units of J/K, don't forget to convert kJ to J, or you'll introduce a large error.

2. This example highlights the distinction between thermodynamics and kinetics. NH_3 forms spontaneously, but so slowly that catalysts are required to achieve a practical rate.

Follow-Up Problem 20.3 Does the oxidation of FeO(*s*) to $Fe_2O_3(s)$ occur spontaneously at 298 K?

Do Organisms Obey the Laws of Thermodynamics? Taking the surroundings into account is crucial, not only for determining reaction spontaneity, as in Sample Problem 20.3, but also for understanding the relevance of thermodynamics to biology. Let's examine the first and second laws to see if they apply to living systems.

1. *Do organisms comply with the first law?* The chemical bond energy in food and oxygen is converted into the mechanical energy of jumping, flying, crawling, swimming, and countless other movements; the electrical energy of nerve conduction; the thermal energy of warming the body; and so forth. Many experiments have demonstrated that the total energy is conserved in these situations. Some of the earliest were performed by Lavoisier, who showed that "animal heat" was produced by slow, continual combustion. In experiments with guinea pigs, he invented a calorimeter to measure the heat released from intake of food and O_2 and output of CO_2 and water, and he included respiration in his new theory of combustion. Modern, room-sized calorimeters measure these and other variables to confirm the conservation of energy for an exercising human (Figure 20.12).

Figure 20.12 A whole-body calorimeter. In this room-sized apparatus, a person exercises while respiratory gases, energy input and output, and other physiological variables are monitored.

2. *Do organisms comply with the second law?* Mature humans are far more complex than the egg and sperm cells from which they develop, and modern organisms are far more complex than the one-celled ancestral specks from which they evolved. Are the growth of an organism and the evolution of life exceptions to the spontaneous tendency of natural processes to disperse their energy? For an organism to grow or a species to evolve, many moles of oxygen and nutrients—carbohydrates, proteins, and fats—undergo exothermic reactions to form many *more* moles of gaseous CO_2 and H_2O. Formation of these waste gases and the accompanying release of heat result in an enormous *increase* in the entropy of the surroundings. Thus, the localization of energy and synthesis of macromolecular structures required for the growth and evolution of organisms cause a far greater dispersal of energy and freedom of motion of small molecules in the environment. When system *and* surroundings are considered together, the entropy of the universe, as always, increases.

The Entropy Change and the Equilibrium State

For a process approaching equilibrium, $\Delta S_{univ} > 0$. When the process reaches equilibrium, there is no further *net* change, $\Delta S_{univ} = 0$, because any entropy change in the system is balanced by an opposite entropy change in the surroundings:

$$\text{At equilibrium:} \quad \Delta S_{univ} = \Delta S_{sys} + \Delta S_{surr} = 0 \quad \text{so} \quad \Delta S_{sys} = -\Delta S_{surr}$$

As an example, let's calculate ΔS_{univ} for the vaporization-condensation of 1 mol of water at 100°C (373 K),

$$H_2O(l;\ 373\ K) \rightleftharpoons H_2O(g;\ 373\ K)$$

First, we find $\Delta S°_{sys}$ for the forward change (vaporization) of 1 mol of water:

$$\Delta S°_{sys} = \Sigma m S°_{products} - \Sigma n S°_{reactants} = S°\text{ of } H_2O(g;\ 373\ K) - S°\text{ of } H_2O(l;\ 373\ K)$$
$$= 195.9\ J/K - 86.8\ J/K = 109.1\ J/K$$

As we expect, the entropy of the system increases ($\Delta S°_{sys} > 0$) as the liquid absorbs heat and changes to a gas.

For ΔS_{surr} of the vaporization step, we have

$$\Delta S_{surr} = -\frac{\Delta H°_{sys}}{T}$$

where $\Delta H^\circ_{sys} = \Delta H^\circ_{vap}$ at 373 K = 40.7 kJ/mol = 40.7×10³ J/mol. For 1 mol of water, we have

$$\Delta S_{surr} = -\frac{\Delta H^\circ_{vap}}{T} = -\frac{40.7\times10^3\ \text{J}}{373\ \text{K}} = -109\ \text{J/K}$$

The surroundings lose heat, and the negative sign means that the entropy of the surroundings decreases. The two entropy changes have the same magnitude but opposite signs, so they cancel:

$$\Delta S_{univ} = 109\ \text{J/K} + (-109\ \text{J/K}) = 0$$

For the reverse change (condensation), ΔS_{univ} also equals zero, but ΔS°_{sys} and ΔS_{surr} have signs opposite those for vaporization.

A similar treatment of a chemical change shows the same result: the entropy change of the forward reaction is *equal in magnitude but opposite in sign* to the entropy change of the reverse reaction. Thus, *when a system reaches equilibrium, neither the forward nor the reverse reaction is spontaneous,* and so there is no net reaction in either direction.

Spontaneous Exothermic and Endothermic Change

No matter what its *enthalpy* change, a reaction occurs because the total *entropy* of the reacting system *and* its surroundings increases. There are two ways this can happen:

1. *In an exothermic reaction* ($\Delta H_{sys} < 0$), the heat released by the system increases the freedom of motion and dispersal of energy in the surroundings; thus, $\Delta S_{surr} > 0$.

- If the entropy of the products is *more* than that of the reactants ($\Delta S_{sys} > 0$), the total entropy change ($\Delta S_{sys} + \Delta S_{surr}$) will be positive (Figure 20.13A). For example, in the oxidation of glucose, an essential reaction for all higher organisms,

$$C_6H_{12}O_6(s) + 6O_2(g) \longrightarrow 6CO_2(g) + 6H_2O(g) + \textbf{\textit{heat}}$$

6 mol of gas yields 12 mol of gas; thus, $\Delta S_{sys} > 0$, $\Delta S_{surr} > 0$, and $\Delta S_{univ} > 0$.

- If the entropy of the products is *less* than that of the reactants ($\Delta S_{sys} < 0$), the entropy of the surroundings must increase even more ($\Delta S_{surr} >> 0$) to make the total ΔS positive (Figure 20.13B). For example, when calcium oxide and carbon dioxide form calcium carbonate, the amount (mol) of gas decreases from 1 to 0:

$$CaO(s) + CO_2(g) \longrightarrow CaCO_3(s) + \textbf{\textit{heat}}$$

However, even though the system's entropy goes down, the heat released increases the entropy of the surroundings even more; thus, $\Delta S_{sys} < 0$, but $\Delta S_{surr} >> 0$, so $\Delta S_{univ} > 0$.

2. *In an endothermic reaction* ($\Delta H_{sys} > 0$), the heat absorbed by the system decreases molecular freedom of motion and dispersal of energy in the surroundings; thus, $\Delta S_{surr} < 0$. Therefore, the only way an endothermic reaction can occur spontaneously is if ΔS_{sys} is positive and large enough to outweigh the negative ΔS_{surr} (Figure 20.13C).

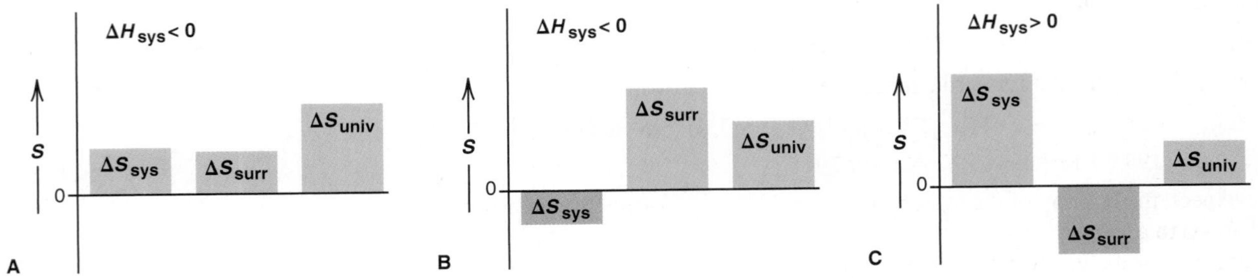

Figure 20.13 Components of ΔS_{univ} for spontaneous reactions. For a reaction to occur spontaneously, ΔS_{univ} must be positive. **A,** An exothermic reaction in which ΔS_{sys} increases; the size of ΔS_{surr} is not important. **B,** An exothermic reaction in which ΔS_{sys} decreases; ΔS_{surr} must be larger than ΔS_{sys}. **C,** An endothermic reaction in which ΔS_{sys} increases; ΔS_{surr} must be smaller than ΔS_{sys}.

- In the solution process for many ionic compounds, heat is absorbed to form the solution, so the entropy of the surroundings decreases ($\Delta S_{surr} < 0$). However, when the crystalline solid becomes freely moving ions, the entropy increase is so large ($\Delta S_{sys} >> 0$) that it outweighs the negative ΔS_{surr}. Thus, ΔS_{univ} is positive.
- Spontaneous endothermic reactions are similar. Recall the reaction between barium hydroxide octahydrate and ammonium nitrate (Figure 20.1, p. 813),

$$\textbf{\textit{heat}} + Ba(OH)_2{\cdot}8H_2O(s) + 2NH_4NO_3(s) \longrightarrow Ba^{2+}(aq) + 2NO_3^-(aq) + 2NH_3(aq) + 10H_2O(l)$$

3 mol of crystalline solids absorb heat from the surroundings ($\Delta S_{surr} < 0$) and yields 15 mol of dissolved ions and molecules, which have much more freedom of motion and, therefore, much greater entropy ($\Delta S_{sys} >> 0$).

Summary of Section 20.2

- The standard entropy of reaction, ΔS°_{rxn}, is calculated from S° values.
- When the amount (mol) of gas increases in a reaction, usually $\Delta S^\circ_{rxn} > 0$.
- ΔS_{surr} is related directly to ΔH°_{sys} and inversely to the T at which a change occurs.
- In a spontaneous change, the entropy of the system can decrease only if the entropy of the surroundings increases even more, so that $\Delta S_{univ} > 0$.
- The second law is obeyed in living systems when we consider system *plus* surroundings.
- For a system at equilibrium, $\Delta S_{univ} = 0$, so $\Delta S^\circ_{sys} = -\Delta S_{surr}$.
- Even if $\Delta S^\circ_{sys} < 0$, an exothermic reaction ($\Delta H^\circ_{rxn} < 0$) is spontaneous ($\Delta S_{univ} > 0$) if $\Delta S_{surr} >> 0$; an endothermic reaction ($\Delta H^\circ_{rxn} > 0$) is spontaneous only if $\Delta S^\circ_{sys} > \Delta S_{surr}$.

20.3 • ENTROPY, FREE ENERGY, AND WORK

By measuring both ΔS_{sys} *and* ΔS_{surr}, we can predict whether a reaction will be spontaneous at a particular temperature. This section introduces *one* criterion for spontaneity that is determined by measuring the system only. The Gibbs free energy, or simply **free energy (*G*)**, combines the system's enthalpy and entropy:

$$G = H - TS$$

One of the greatest, and least recognized, American scientists, Josiah Willard Gibbs (1839–1903), established chemical thermodynamics as well as major principles of equilibrium and electrochemistry. Although the great European scientists of his time, James Clerk Maxwell and Henri Le Châtelier, realized Gibbs's achievements, he was not recognized by his American colleagues until nearly 50 years after his death!

Free Energy Change and Reaction Spontaneity

The free energy change (ΔG) is a measure of the spontaneity of a process and of the useful energy available from it.

Deriving the Gibbs Equation Let's derive ΔG from the second law. By definition, the entropy change of the universe is the sum of the entropy changes of the system and the surroundings:

$$\Delta S_{univ} = \Delta S_{sys} + \Delta S_{surr}$$

At constant pressure,

$$\Delta S_{surr} = -\frac{\Delta H_{sys}}{T}$$

Substituting for ΔS_{surr} gives a relationship that relies solely on the system:

$$\Delta S_{univ} = \Delta S_{sys} - \frac{\Delta H_{sys}}{T}$$

Multiplying both sides by $-T$ gives

$$-T\Delta S_{univ} = \Delta H_{sys} - T\Delta S_{sys}$$

Using the Gibbs free energy relationship, $G = H - TS$, we obtain the *Gibbs equation* for the *change* in the free energy of the system (ΔG_{sys}) at constant T and P:

$$\Delta G_{sys} = \Delta H_{sys} - T\Delta S_{sys} \quad (20.6)$$

Combining Equation 20.6 with the one preceding it shows that

$$-T\Delta S_{univ} = \Delta H_{sys} - T\Delta S_{sys} = \Delta G_{sys}$$

Significance of the Sign of ΔG Let's see how the *sign* of ΔG tells if a reaction is spontaneous. According to the second law,

- $\Delta S_{univ} > 0$ for a spontaneous process
- $\Delta S_{univ} < 0$ for a nonspontaneous process
- $\Delta S_{univ} = 0$ for a process at equilibrium

Since the absolute temperature is always positive, for a spontaneous process,

$$T\Delta S_{univ} > 0 \qquad \text{so} \qquad -T\Delta S_{univ} < 0$$

From our derivation above, $\Delta G = -T\Delta S_{univ}$, so we have

- $\Delta G < 0$ for a spontaneous process
- $\Delta G > 0$ for a nonspontaneous process
- $\Delta G = 0$ for a process at equilibrium

Calculating Standard Free Energy Changes

The *sign* of ΔG reveals *whether* a reaction is spontaneous, but the *magnitude* of ΔG tells *how* spontaneous it is. Because free energy (G) combines three state functions, H, S, and T, it is also a state function. As we do with enthalpy, we focus on the free energy *change* (ΔG). As we do with other thermodynamic variables, to compare the free energy changes of different reactions, we calculate the ***standard* free energy change ($\Delta G°$),** which occurs when all components of the system are in their standard states.

Using the Gibbs Equation to Find $\Delta G°$ One way to calculate $\Delta G°$ is by writing the Gibbs equation (20.6) at standard state conditions and using Appendix B to find $\Delta H°_{sys}$ and $\Delta S°_{sys}$. Adapting the Gibbs equation, we have

$$\Delta G°_{sys} = \Delta H°_{sys} - T\Delta S°_{sys} \quad (20.7)$$

This important relationship is used to find any one of these three variables, given the other two, as in Sample Problem 20.4.

Fireworks explode spontaneously.

Sample Problem 20.4 Calculating $\Delta G°_{rxn}$ from Enthalpy and Entropy Values

Problem Potassium chlorate, a common oxidizing agent in fireworks (*see photo*) and matchheads, undergoes a solid-state disproportionation reaction when heated:

$$\overset{+5}{4KClO_3(s)} \xrightarrow{\Delta} \overset{+7}{3KClO_4(s)} + \overset{-1}{KCl(s)}$$

Use $\Delta H°_f$ and $S°$ values to calculate $\Delta G°_{sys}$ (which is $\Delta G°_{rxn}$) at 25°C for this reaction.

Plan To solve for $\Delta G°$, we need values from Appendix B. We use $\Delta H°_f$ values to calculate $\Delta H°_{rxn}$ ($\Delta H°_{sys}$), use $S°$ values to calculate $\Delta S°_{rxn}$ ($\Delta S°_{sys}$), and then apply Equation 20.7.

Solution Calculating $\Delta H°_{sys}$ from $\Delta H°_f$ values (with Equation 6.9):

$$\begin{aligned}\Delta H°_{sys} = \Delta H°_{rxn} &= \Sigma m\Delta H°_{f(products)} - \Sigma n\Delta H°_{f(reactants)}\\ &= [(3\text{ mol }KClO_4)(\Delta H°_f\text{ of }KClO_4) + (1\text{ mol }KCl)(\Delta H°_f\text{ of }KCl)]\\ &\quad - [(4\text{ mol }KClO_3)(\Delta H°_f\text{ of }KClO_3)]\\ &= [(3\text{ mol})(-432.8\text{ kJ/mol}) + (1\text{ mol})(-436.7\text{ kJ/mol})]\\ &\quad - [(4\text{ mol})(-397.7\text{ kJ/mol})]\\ &= -144\text{ kJ}\end{aligned}$$

Calculating ΔS°_{sys} from S° values (with Equation 20.4):

$$\Delta S^\circ_{sys} = \Delta S^\circ_{rxn} = \Sigma m S^\circ_{products} - \Sigma n S^\circ_{reactants}$$
$$= [(3 \text{ mol } KClO_4)(S^\circ \text{ of } KClO_4) + (1 \text{ mol KCl})(S^\circ \text{ of KCl})] - [(4 \text{ mol } KClO_3)(S^\circ \text{ of } KClO_3)]$$
$$= [(3 \text{ mol})(151.0 \text{ J/mol·K}) + (1 \text{ mol})(82.6 \text{ J/mol·K})] - [(4 \text{ mol})(143.1 \text{ J/mol·K})]$$
$$= -36.8 \text{ J/K}$$

Calculating ΔG°_{sys} at 298 K:

$$\Delta G^\circ_{sys} = \Delta H^\circ_{sys} - T\Delta S^\circ_{sys} = -144 \text{ kJ} - \left[(298 \text{ K})(-36.8 \text{ J/K})\left(\frac{1 \text{ kJ}}{1000 \text{ J}}\right)\right] = -133 \text{ kJ}$$

Check Rounding to check the math:

$$\Delta H^\circ \approx [3(-433 \text{ kJ}) + (-440 \text{ kJ})] - [4(-400 \text{ kJ})] = -1740 \text{ kJ} + 1600 \text{ kJ} = -140 \text{ kJ}$$
$$\Delta S^\circ \approx [3(150 \text{ J/K}) + 85 \text{ J/K}] - [4(145 \text{ J/K})] = 535 \text{ J/K} - 580 \text{ J/K} = -45 \text{ J/K}$$
$$\Delta G^\circ \approx -140 \text{ kJ} - 300 \text{ K}(-0.04 \text{ kJ/K}) = -140 \text{ kJ} + 12 \text{ kJ} = -128 \text{ kJ}$$

Comment Recall from Section 20.1 that reaction spontaneity tells nothing about rate. Even though this reaction is spontaneous, the rate is very low in the solid. When $KClO_3$ is heated slightly above its melting point, the ions can move and the reaction occurs readily.

Follow-Up Problem 20.4 Determine the standard free energy change at 298 K for the reaction $2NO(g) + O_2(g) \longrightarrow 2NO_2(g)$.

Using Standard Free Energies of Formation to Find ΔG°_{rxn} Another way to calculate ΔG°_{rxn} is with values for the **standard free energy of formation (ΔG°_f)** of the components. Analogously to the standard enthalpy of formation, ΔH°_f (Section 6.6), ΔG°_f is the free energy change that occurs when 1 mol of compound is made *from its elements,* with all components in their standard states. Because free energy is a state function, we can apply Hess's law and combine ΔG°_f values of reactants and products to calculate ΔG°_{rxn}, no matter how the reaction takes place:

$$\Delta G^\circ_{rxn} = \Sigma m \Delta G^\circ_{f(products)} - \Sigma n \Delta G^\circ_{f(reactants)} \tag{20.8}$$

ΔG°_f values have properties similar to ΔH°_f values:

- ΔG°_f of an element in its standard state is zero.
- An equation coefficient (*m* or *n* above) multiplies ΔG°_f by that number.
- Reversing a reaction changes the sign of ΔG°_f.

Many ΔG°_f values appear along with those for ΔH°_f and S° in Appendix B.

Sample Problem 20.5 Calculating ΔG°_{rxn} from ΔG°_f Values

Problem Use ΔG°_f values to calculate ΔG°_{rxn} for the reaction in Sample Problem 20.4:

$$4KClO_3(s) \longrightarrow 3KClO_4(s) + KCl(s)$$

Plan We apply Equation 20.8 to calculate ΔG°_{rxn}.

Solution Applying Equation 20.8 with values from Appendix B:

$$\Delta G^\circ_{rxn} = \Sigma m \Delta G^\circ_{f(products)} - \Sigma n \Delta G^\circ_{f(reactants)}$$
$$= [(3 \text{ mol } KClO_4)(\Delta G^\circ_f \text{ of } KClO_4) + (1 \text{ mol KCl})(\Delta G^\circ_f \text{ of KCl})] - [(4 \text{ mol } KClO_3)(\Delta G^\circ_f \text{ of } KClO_3)]$$
$$= [(3 \text{ mol})(-303.2 \text{ kJ/mol}) + (1 \text{ mol})(-409.2 \text{ kJ/mol})] - [(4 \text{ mol})(-296.3 \text{ kJ/mol})] = -134 \text{ kJ}$$

Check Rounding to check the math:

$$\Delta G^\circ_{rxn} \approx [3(-300 \text{ kJ}) + 1(-400 \text{ kJ})] - 4(-300 \text{ kJ})$$
$$= -1300 \text{ kJ} + 1200 \text{ kJ} = -100 \text{ kJ}$$

Comment The slight discrepancy between this answer and the one obtained in Sample Problem 20.4 is due to rounding. As you can see, when ΔG°_f values are available, this method is simpler arithmetically than the approach in Sample Problem 20.4.

Follow-Up Problem 20.5 Use ΔG°_f values to calculate the free energy change at 25°C for each of the following reactions:
(a) $2NO(g) + O_2(g) \longrightarrow 2NO_2(g)$ (from Follow-Up Problem 20.4)
(b) $2C(\text{graphite}) + O_2(g) \longrightarrow 2CO(g)$

ΔG and the Work a System Can Do

Thermodynamics developed after the invention of the steam engine, a major advance that spawned a new generation of machines. Thus, some of the field's key ideas applied the relationships between the free energy change and the work a system can do:

- ΔG is the *maximum useful work* done ***by*** a system during a *spontaneous* process at constant T and P:

$$\Delta G = w_{max} \tag{20.9}$$

- ΔG is the *minimum work* done ***to*** a system to make a *nonspontaneous* process occur at constant T and P.

The free energy change is the maximum work the system can *possibly* do. But the work it *actually* does is always less and depends on how the free energy is released. Let's consider the work done by an expanding gas, a car engine, and a battery.

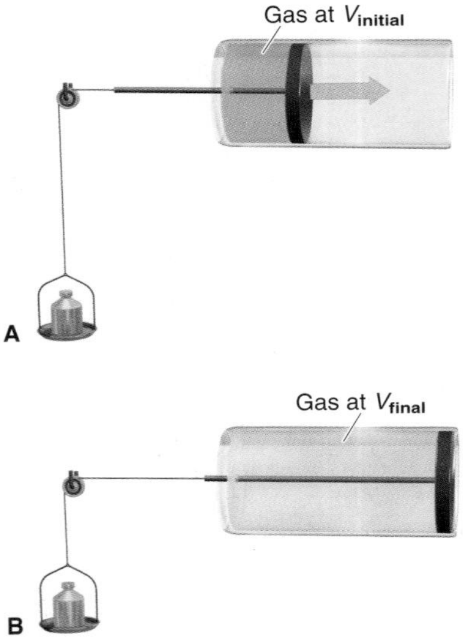

Figure 20.14 An expanding gas lifting a weight.

1. *Work done by an expanding gas.* Suppose a gas at $V_{initial}$ is confined in a cylinder-piston assembly attached to a 1-kg weight (Figure 20.14A). The gas expands to some final volume, V_{final}, lifting the weight in one step and doing a certain quantity of work (Figure 20.14B). The expanding gas can do more work by lifting a 2-kg weight to one-half V_{final} and then lifting a 1-kg weight to V_{final}; that is, doing the work in two steps. Lifting a 3-kg weight to one-third of V_{final}, a 2-kg weight to one-half V_{final}, and a 1-kg weight all the way to V_{final}, that is, in three steps, would do even more work. *As the number of steps increases, the quantity of work done by the gas increases.* Thus, the gas would do *close* to the maximum work if the weight were replaced by a container of sand that could be lifted by removing one grain at a time, that is, in a *very* high number of steps. (We described a similar method for finding the entropy change on p. 816.)

However, the *maximum* work is done by a spontaneous process *only if the work is carried out in an infinite number of steps,* that is, *reversibly.* Of course, in any *real* process, work is performed in a *finite* number of steps, that is, *irreversibly,* so *the maximum work is never done.* Any free energy not used for work is lost to the surroundings as heat. This "unharnessed" energy is a consequence of any real process.

2. *"Useful" work done by a car engine.* When gasoline (represented by octane, C_8H_{18}) is burned in a car engine,

$$C_8H_{18}(l) + \tfrac{25}{2}O_2(g) \longrightarrow 8CO_2(g) + 9H_2O(g)$$

a large amount of energy is released as heat ($\Delta H_{sys} < 0$), and because the number of moles of gas increases, the entropy of the system increases ($\Delta S_{sys} > 0$). Therefore, the reaction is spontaneous ($\Delta G_{sys} < 0$). The free energy released turns the wheels, moves the belts, plays the radio, and so on, all examples of "useful" work. However, only if the free energy is released *reversibly,* that is, in an infinite number of steps, can this reaction do the *maximum* useful work. In reality, the reaction occurs *irreversibly,* and much of the total free energy just warms the engine and the outside air, which increases the freedom of motion of the particles in the universe, in accord with the second law.

3. *"Useful" work done by a battery.* As you'll see in Chapter 21, a battery is essentially a packaged spontaneous redox reaction that releases free energy to the surroundings (flashlight, radio, motor, etc.). If we connect the battery terminals to each other through a short piece of wire, the free energy change is released all at once but does no work—it just heats wire and battery. But, if we connect the terminals to a motor, a significant portion of the free energy runs the motor, but some is still converted to heat. If we connect the battery to a more "efficient" device, one that discharges the free energy still more slowly, more of the energy does work and less is converted to heat. However, as with all systems, only when the battery discharges infinitely slowly can it do the maximum work.

Efficiency can be defined as the percentage of work output relative to the energy input. The range of efficiencies is very large: an incandescent bulb converts <7% of incoming electricity to light, the rest being given off as heat. At the other extreme, an electrical generator converts 95% of the incoming mechanical energy to electricity. Here are the efficiencies of some other devices: home oil furnace, 65%; hand-tool motor, 63%; liquid fuel rocket, 50%; car engine, <30%; compact fluorescent bulb, 18%; solar cell, ~15%.

Therefore, all engineers must face the fact that *no **real** process uses all the available free energy to do work because some is always "wasted" as heat.* Let's summarize the relationship between the free energy change of a reaction and the work it can do:

- A spontaneous reaction ($\Delta G_{sys} < 0$) will do work on the surroundings ($-w$). In any real machine, the actual work done is *always less than the maximum* because some of the ΔG is released as heat.
- A nonspontaneous reaction ($\Delta G_{sys} > 0$) will occur only if the surroundings do work on the system ($+w$). In any real machine, the actual work done on the system is *always more than the minimum* because some of the added free energy is wasted as heat.
- A reaction at equilibrium ($\Delta G_{sys} = 0$) can no longer do any work.

The Effect of Temperature on Reaction Spontaneity

In most cases, the enthalpy contribution (ΔH) to the free energy change (ΔG) is much *larger* than the entropy contribution ($T\Delta S$). In fact, the reason most exothermic reactions are spontaneous is that the large negative ΔH makes ΔG negative. However, the *temperature of a reaction influences the magnitude of the $T\Delta S$ term,* so, for many reactions, the overall spontaneity depends on the temperature. From the signs of ΔH and ΔS, we can predict how the temperature affects the sign of ΔG. (The values we'll use below for the thermodynamic variables are standard state values, but we show them without the degree sign to emphasize that the relationships among ΔG, ΔH, and ΔS are valid at any conditions. Also, we assume that ΔH and ΔS change little with temperature, which is true as long as no phase change occurs.)

Let's examine the four combinations of positive and negative ΔH and ΔS—two that are independent of temperature and two that are dependent on temperature:

- *Temperature-independent cases.* When ΔH and ΔS have *opposite* signs, the reaction occurs spontaneously either at all temperatures or at none (nonspontaneous).
  1. *Reaction is spontaneous at all temperatures: $\Delta H < 0$, $\Delta S > 0$.* Since ΔS is positive, $-T\Delta S$ is negative; thus, both contributions favor a negative ΔG. Most combustion reactions are in this category. The decomposition of hydrogen peroxide, a common disinfectant, is also spontaneous at all temperatures:
  $$2H_2O_2(l) \longrightarrow 2H_2O(l) + O_2(g)$$
  $$\Delta H = -196 \text{ kJ} \quad \text{and} \quad \Delta S = 125 \text{ J/K}$$
  2. *Reaction is nonspontaneous at all temperatures: $\Delta H > 0$, $\Delta S < 0$.* Both contributions oppose spontaneity: ΔH is positive and ΔS is negative, so $-T\Delta S$ is positive; thus, ΔG is always positive. The formation of ozone from oxygen requires a continual energy input, so it is not spontaneous at any temperature:
  $$3O_2(g) \longrightarrow 2O_3(g)$$
  $$\Delta H = 286 \text{ kJ} \quad \text{and} \quad \Delta S = -137 \text{ J/K}$$

- *Temperature-dependent cases.* When ΔH and ΔS have the *same* sign, the relative magnitudes of $-T\Delta S$ and ΔH determine the sign of ΔG. In these cases, the *direction* of the change in T is crucial.
  3. *Reaction becomes spontaneous as temperature increases:* $\Delta H > 0$ *and* $\Delta S > 0$. With a positive ΔH, the reaction will occur spontaneously only when $-T\Delta S$ becomes large enough to make ΔG negative, which will happen as temperatures rise. For example,

$$2N_2O(g) + O_2(g) \longrightarrow 4NO(g)$$
$$\Delta H = 197.1 \text{ kJ} \quad \text{and} \quad \Delta S = 198.2 \text{ J/K}$$

     The oxidation of N_2O occurs spontaneously at any $T > 994$ K.
  4. *Reaction becomes spontaneous as temperature decreases:* $\Delta H < 0$ *and* $\Delta S < 0$. Here, ΔH favors spontaneity, but ΔS does not ($-T\Delta S > 0$). The reaction will occur spontaneously only when $-T\Delta S$ becomes smaller than ΔH, and this happens as temperatures drop. For example,

$$4Fe(s) + 3O_2(g) \longrightarrow 2Fe_2O_3(s)$$
$$\Delta H = -1651 \text{ kJ} \quad \text{and} \quad \Delta S = -549.4 \text{ J/K}$$

     The production of iron(III) oxide occurs spontaneously at any $T < 3005$ K.

Table 20.1 summarizes these four possible combinations of ΔH and ΔS, and Sample Problem 20.6 applies them.

Table 20.1 Reaction Spontaneity and the Signs of ΔH, ΔS, and ΔG

ΔH	ΔS	$-T\Delta S$	ΔG	Description
−	+	−	−	Spontaneous at all T
+	−	+	+	Nonspontaneous at all T
+	+	−	+ or −	Spontaneous at higher T; nonspontaneous at lower T
−	−	+	+ or −	Spontaneous at lower T; nonspontaneous at higher T

Sample Problem 20.6 Using Molecular Scenes to Determine the Signs of ΔH, ΔS, and ΔG

Problem The following scenes represent a familiar phase change for water *(blue spheres)*:

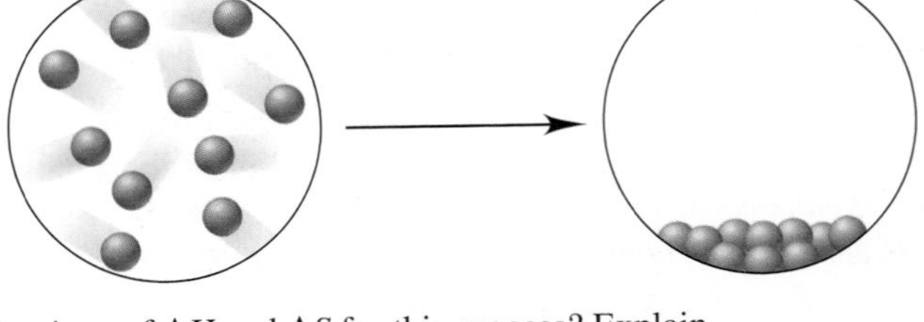

(a) What are the signs of ΔH and ΔS for this process? Explain.
(b) Is the process spontaneous at all T, no T, low T, or high T? Explain.

Plan **(a)** From the scenes, we determine any change in amount of gas, which indicates the sign of ΔS, and any change in the freedom of motion of the particles, which indicates whether heat is absorbed or released, and thus the sign of ΔH. **(b)** The question refers to the sign of ΔG (+ or −) at the different temperature possibilities, so we apply Equation 20.6 and refer to the previous text discussion and Table 20.1.

Solution **(a)** The scene represents the condensation of water vapor, so the amount of gas decreases dramatically, and the separated molecules give up energy as they come closer together. Therefore, $\Delta S < 0$ and $\Delta H < 0$. **(b)** With ΔS negative, the $-T\Delta S$ term is positive. In order for $\Delta G < 0$, the magnitude of T must be small. Therefore, the process is spontaneous at low T.

Check The answer in part (b) seems reasonable based on our analysis in part (a). The answer makes sense because we know from everyday experience that water condenses spontaneously, and it does so at low temperatures.

Follow-Up Problem 20.6 The following molecular scenes represent the gas-phase decomposition of X_2Y_2 to X_2 (*red*) and Y_2 (*blue*):

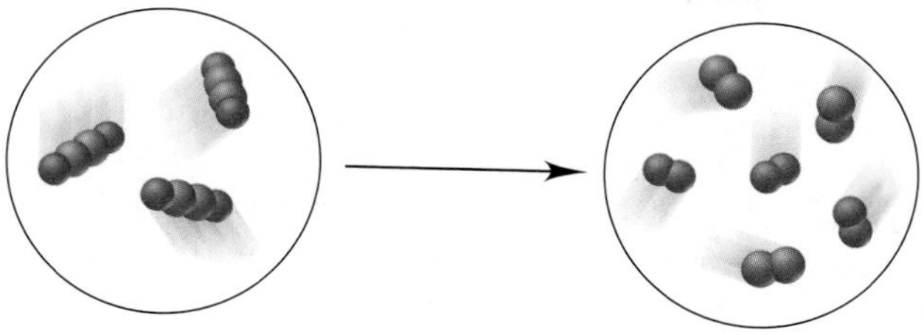

(a) What is the sign of ΔS for the reaction?
(b) If the reaction is spontaneous only above 325°C, what is the sign of ΔH? Explain.

As you saw in Sample Problem 20.4, one way to calculate ΔG is from enthalpy and entropy changes. As long as phase changes don't occur, ΔH and ΔS usually change little with temperature, so we use their values at 298 K in Sample Problem 20.7 to examine the effect of T on ΔG and, thus, on reaction spontaneity.

Sample Problem 20.7 Determining the Effect of Temperature on ΔG

Problem A key step in the production of sulfuric acid is the oxidation of $SO_2(g)$ to $SO_3(g)$:

$$2SO_2(g) + O_2(g) \longrightarrow 2SO_3(g)$$

At 298 K, $\Delta G = -141.6$ kJ; $\Delta H = -198.4$ kJ; and $\Delta S = -187.9$ J/K.
(a) Use the data to decide if this reaction is spontaneous at 25°C, and predict how ΔG will change with increasing T.
(b) Assuming that ΔH and ΔS are constant with T (no phase change occurs), is the reaction spontaneous at 900.°C?

Plan **(a)** We note the sign of ΔG to see if the reaction is spontaneous and the signs of ΔH and ΔS to see the effect of T. **(b)** We use Equation 20.7 to calculate ΔG from the given ΔH and ΔS at the higher T (in K).

Solution **(a)** $\Delta G < 0$, so the reaction is spontaneous at 298 K: SO_2 and O_2 will form SO_3 spontaneously. With $\Delta S < 0$, the term $-T\Delta S > 0$, and this term will become more positive at higher T. Therefore, ΔG will become less negative, and the reaction less spontaneous, with increasing T.
(b) Calculating ΔG at 900.°C ($T = 273 + 900. = 1173$ K):

$$\Delta G = \Delta H - T\Delta S = -198.4 \text{ kJ} - [(1173 \text{ K})(-187.9 \text{ J/K})(1 \text{ kJ}/1000 \text{ J})] = 22.0 \text{ kJ}$$

$\Delta G > 0$, so the reaction is nonspontaneous at the higher T.

Check The answer in part (b) seems reasonable based on our prediction in part (a). The arithmetic seems correct, given considerable rounding:

$$\Delta G \approx -200 \text{ kJ} - [(1200 \text{ K})(-200 \text{ J/K})/1000 \text{ J}] = +40 \text{ kJ}$$

Follow-Up Problem 20.7 A reaction is nonspontaneous at room temperature but *is* spontaneous at −40°C. What can you say about the signs and relative magnitudes of ΔH, ΔS, and $-T\Delta S$?

The Temperature at Which a Reaction Becomes Spontaneous As you've just seen, when the signs are the same for ΔH and ΔS of a reaction, it can be nonspontaneous at one temperature and spontaneous at another. The "crossover" temperature occurs when a positive ΔG switches to a negative ΔG because of the magnitude of the $-T\Delta S$ term. We find this temperature by setting ΔG equal to zero and solving for T:

$$\Delta G = \Delta H - T\Delta S = 0$$

Therefore,

$$\Delta H = T\Delta S \quad \text{and} \quad T = \frac{\Delta H}{\Delta S} \tag{20.10}$$

Consider the reaction of copper(I) oxide with carbon. It does *not* occur at low temperature but does at high temperature and is used to extract copper from one of its ores:

$$Cu_2O(s) + C(s) \xrightarrow{\Delta} 2Cu(s) + CO(g)$$

We predict that this reaction has a positive ΔS because the number of moles of gas increases; in fact, ΔS = 165 J/K. Furthermore, because the reaction is *non*spontaneous at lower temperatures, it must have a positive ΔH; the actual value is 58.1 kJ. As the $-T\Delta S$ term becomes more negative with higher T, it eventually outweighs the positive ΔH term, so ΔG becomes negative and the reaction occurs spontaneously.

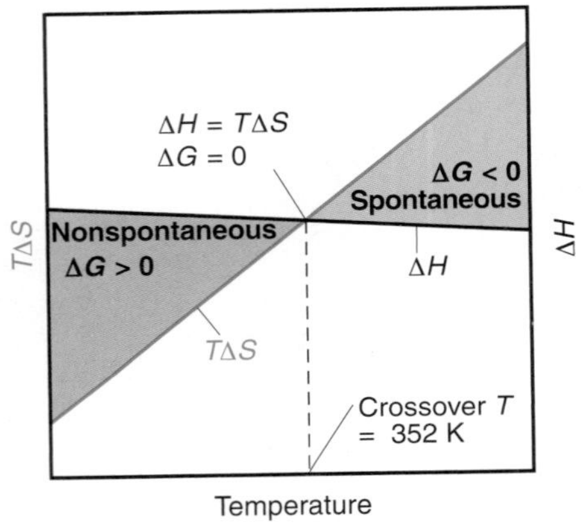

Figure 20.15 The effect of temperature on reaction spontaneity. At low T, $\Delta G > 0$ because ΔH dominates. At 352 K, $\Delta H = T\Delta S$, so $\Delta G = 0$. At any higher T, $\Delta G < 0$ because $-T\Delta S$ dominates.

Sample Problem 20.8 Finding the Temperature at Which a Reaction Becomes Spontaneous

Problem At 25°C (298 K), the reduction of copper(I) oxide to copper is nonspontaneous (ΔG = 8.9kJ). Calculate the temperature at which the reaction becomes spontaneous.

Plan As just discussed, we want the temperature at which ΔG crosses over from a positive to a negative value. We set ΔG equal to zero, and use Equation 20.10 to solve for T, using the ΔH (58.1 kJ) and ΔS (165 J/K) values from the text.

Solution From $\Delta G = \Delta H - T\Delta S = 0$, we have

$$T = \frac{\Delta H}{\Delta S} = \frac{58.1 \text{ kJ} \times \frac{1000 \text{ J}}{1 \text{ kJ}}}{165 \text{ J/K}} = 352 \text{ K}$$

Thus, at any temperature above 352 K (79°C), which is a moderate temperature for extracting a metal from its ore, $\Delta G < 0$, so the reaction becomes spontaneous.

Check Rounding to quickly check the math gives

$$T = \frac{60000 \text{ J}}{150 \text{ J/K}} = 400 \text{ K}$$

which is close to the answer.

Comment Figure 20.15 shows that the line for $T\Delta S$ rises steadily (and thus the $-T\Delta S$ term becomes more negative) with increasing temperature. This line crosses the relatively constant ΔH line at 352 K. At any higher temperature, the $-T\Delta S$ term is greater than the ΔH term, so ΔG is negative.

Follow-Up Problem 20.8 Use Appendix B values to find the temperature at which the following reaction becomes spontaneous (assume ΔH and ΔS are constant with T):

$$CaO(s) + CO_2(g) \longrightarrow CaCO_3(s)$$

Coupling of Reactions to Drive a Nonspontaneous Change

In a complex, multistep reaction, we often see a nonspontaneous step driven by a spontaneous step. In such a **coupling of reactions,** *one step supplies enough free energy for the other to occur,* just as burning gasoline supplies enough free energy to move a car.

Look again at the reduction of copper(I) oxide by carbon. Previously, we found that the *overall* reaction becomes spontaneous at any temperature above 352 K. Dividing the reaction into two steps, however, we find that even at a higher temperature, such as 375 K, copper(I) oxide does not spontaneously decompose to its elements:

$$Cu_2O(s) \longrightarrow 2Cu(s) + \tfrac{1}{2}O_2(g) \qquad \Delta G_{375} = 140.0 \text{ kJ}$$

However, the oxidation of carbon to CO at 375 K is quite spontaneous:

$$C(s) + \tfrac{1}{2}O_2(g) \longrightarrow CO(g) \qquad \Delta G_{375} = -143.8 \text{ kJ}$$

Coupling these reactions means having the carbon in contact with the Cu_2O, which allows the reaction with the larger negative ΔG to "drive" the one with the smaller positive ΔG. Adding the reactions together and canceling the common substance ($\frac{1}{2}O_2$) gives an overall reaction with a negative ΔG:

$$Cu_2O(s) + C(s) \longrightarrow 2Cu(s) + CO(g) \qquad \Delta G_{375} = -3.8\ \text{kJ}$$

Many biochemical reactions are also nonspontaneous, including key steps in the synthesis of proteins and nucleic acids, the formation of fatty acids, the maintenance of ion balance, and the breakdown of nutrients. Driving a nonspontaneous step by coupling it to a spontaneous one is a life-sustaining strategy common to all organisms, as you'll see in the Chemical Connections essay *(next page)*.

Summary of Section 20.3

- The sign of the free energy change, $\Delta G = \Delta H - T\Delta S$, is directly related to reaction spontaneity: a negative ΔG corresponds to a positive ΔS_{univ}.
- We use the standard free energy of formation (ΔG_f°) to calculate ΔG_{rxn}° at 298 K.
- The maximum work a system can do is never obtained from a real (irreversible) process because some free energy is always converted to heat.
- The magnitude of T influences the spontaneity of a temperature-dependent reaction (same signs of ΔH and ΔS) by affecting the size of $T\Delta S$. For such a reaction, the T at which the reaction becomes spontaneous can be found by setting $\Delta G = 0$.
- A nonspontaneous reaction ($\Delta G > 0$) can be coupled to a more spontaneous one ($\Delta G << 0$) to make it occur. For example, in organisms, the hydrolysis of ATP drives many reactions with a positive ΔG.

20.4 • FREE ENERGY, EQUILIBRIUM, AND REACTION DIRECTION

As you know from discussions in earlier chapters, the sign of ΔG is not the only way to predict reaction direction. In Chapter 17, we did so by comparing the values of the reaction quotient (Q) and the equilibrium constant (K). Recall that

- If $Q < K$ ($Q/K < 1$): reaction proceeds spontaneously to the right.
- If $Q > K$ ($Q/K > 1$): reaction proceeds spontaneously to the left.
- If $Q = K$ ($Q/K = 1$): reaction has attained equilibrium and no longer proceeds spontaneously in either direction.

It is easier to see the relation between these two ways to predict reaction spontaneity—the sign of ΔG and the magnitude of Q/K—when we compare the sign of the natural logarithm of Q/K ($\ln Q/K$) with the sign of ΔG (refer to Appendix A if necessary):

- If $Q/K < 1$, then $\ln Q/K < 0$: reaction proceeds spontaneously to the right ($\Delta G < 0$).
- If $Q/K > 1$, then $\ln Q/K > 0$: reaction proceeds spontaneously to the left ($\Delta G > 0$).
- If $Q/K = 1$, then $\ln Q/K = 0$: reaction is at equilibrium ($\Delta G = 0$).

Note that the signs of ΔG and of $\ln Q/K$ are the same for a given direction; in fact, ΔG equals $\ln Q/K$ multiplied by the proportionality constant RT:

$$\Delta G = RT \ln \frac{Q}{K} = RT \ln Q - RT \ln K \qquad (20.11)$$

Q represents the concentrations (or pressures) of a system's components at any time during the reaction, and K represents these quantities at equilibrium. Therefore, Equation 20.11 says that ΔG is a measure of how different the concentrations at any time, Q, are from the concentrations at equilibrium, K:

- If Q and K are very different, the reaction releases (or absorbs) a *lot* of free energy.
- If Q and K are nearly the same, the reaction releases (or absorbs) relatively *little*.

CHEMICAL CONNECTIONS TO BIOLOGICAL ENERGETICS | The Universal Role of ATP

Despite their incredible diversity, virtually all organisms use the same amino acids to make their proteins, the same nucleotides to make their nucleic acids, and the same carbohydrate (glucose) to provide energy.

In addition, *all organisms use the same spontaneous reaction to drive a variety of nonspontaneous ones*. This reaction is the hydrolysis of **adenosine triphosphate (ATP)** to adenosine diphosphate (ADP):*

$$ATP^{4-} + H_2O \rightleftharpoons ADP^{3-} + HPO_4^{2-} + H^+ \qquad \Delta G^{\circ\prime} = -30.5 \text{ kJ}$$

In the metabolic breakdown of glucose, for example, the first step, addition of HPO_4^{2-} to glucose, is nonspontaneous:

$$\text{Glucose} + HPO_4^{2-} + H^+ \rightleftharpoons [\text{glucose phosphate}]^- + H_2O \qquad \Delta G^{\circ\prime} = 13.8 \text{ kJ}$$

Coupling this nonspontaneous reaction to ATP hydrolysis makes the overall process spontaneous. If we add the two reactions, HPO_4^{2-}, H^+, and H_2O cancel:

$$\text{Glucose} + ATP^{4-} \rightleftharpoons [\text{glucose phosphate}]^- + ADP^{3-} \qquad \Delta G^{\circ\prime} = -16.7 \text{ kJ}$$

Coupling cannot occur if reactions are physically separated, so these reactions take place on an enzyme (Section 16.7) that simultaneously binds glucose and ATP, and the phosphate group of ATP that will be transferred lies next to the —OH group of glucose that will bind it (Figure B20.1).

The ADP produced in energy-releasing reactions combines with phosphate to regenerate ATP in energy-absorbing reactions catalyzed by other enzymes. Thus, there is a continuous cycling of ATP to ADP and back to ATP again to supply energy to the cells (Figure B20.2).

*In biochemical systems, the standard-state concentration of H^+ is 10^{-7} *M*, not the usual 1 *M*, and the standard free energy change has the symbol $\Delta G^{\circ\prime}$.

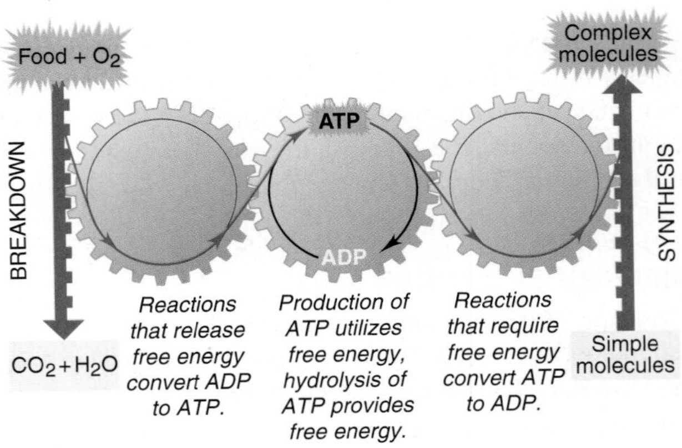

Figure B20.2 The cycling of metabolic free energy.

By examining the phosphate portions of ATP, ADP, and HPO_4^{2-}, we can see two basic chemical reasons why ATP hydrolysis supplies so much free energy (Figure B20.3):

1. *Charge repulsion*. At physiological pH (~7), the triphosphate group of ATP has four negative charges close together. This *high charge repulsion* is reduced in ADP (Figure B20.3, part A).
2. *Electron delocalization*. Once HPO_4^{2-} is free, there is extensive delocalization and resonance stabilization of the π electrons (Figure B20.3, part B).

Thus, greater charge repulsion and less electron delocalization make ATP higher in energy (less stable) than the sum of the energies of ADP and HPO_4^{2-}. When ATP is hydrolyzed, some

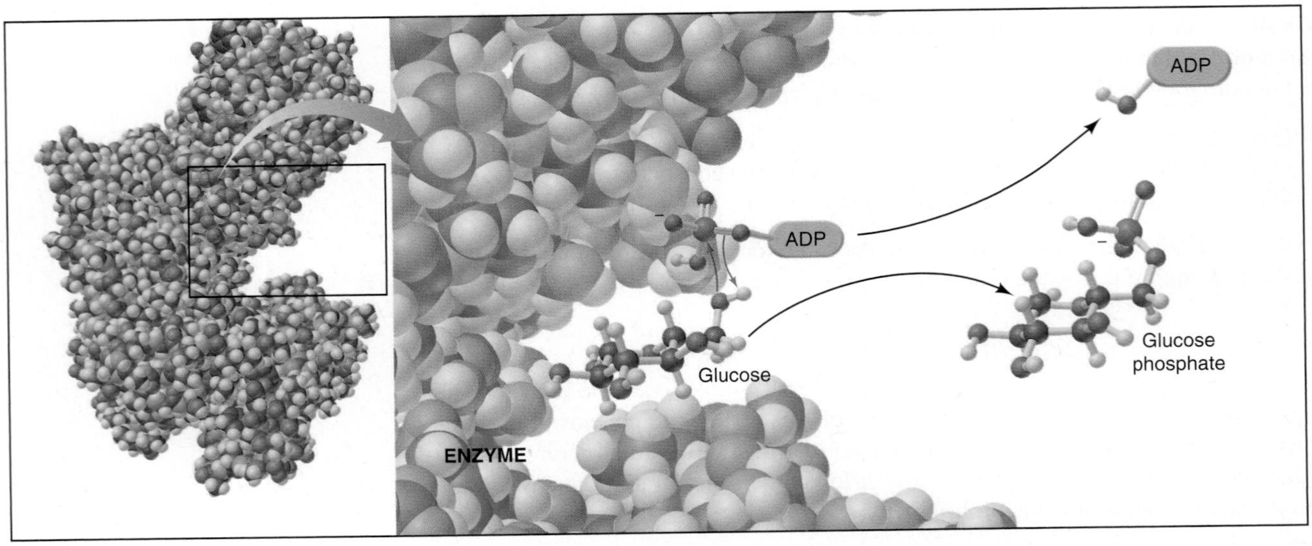

Figure B20.1 The coupling of a nonspontaneous reaction to the hydrolysis of ATP. Glucose lies next to ATP (shown as ADP—O—PO_3H) in the enzyme's active site. ADP (shown as ADP—OH) and glucose phosphate are released.

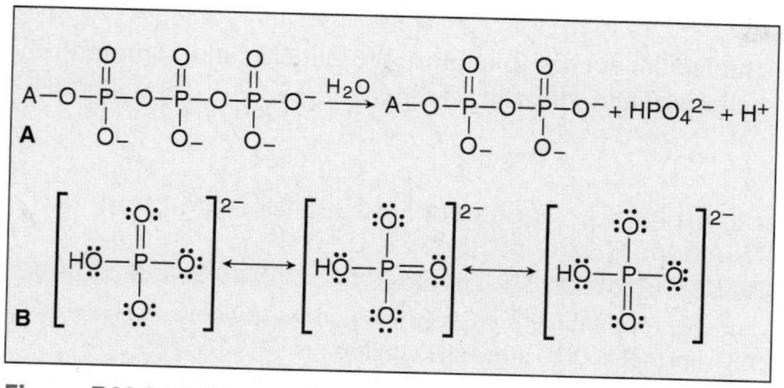

Figure B20.3 ATP is a high-energy molecule.

of this additional energy is released and harnessed by the organism to drive metabolic reactions that could not otherwise take place.

Problems

B20.1 The oxidation of 1 mol of glucose supplies enough metabolic energy to form 36 mol of ATP. Oxidation of 1 mol of a typical dietary fat like tristearin ($C_{57}H_{116}O_6$) yields enough energy to form 458 mol of ATP. How many molecules of ATP can form per gram of (a) glucose; (b) tristearin?

B20.2 Nonspontaneous processes like muscle contraction, protein synthesis, and nerve conduction are coupled to the spontaneous hydrolysis of ATP to ADP. ATP is then regenerated by coupling its synthesis to energy-yielding reactions such as

Creatine phosphate $\longrightarrow$ creatine + phosphate
$\Delta G^{\circ\prime} = -43.1$ kJ/mol

ADP + phosphate $\longrightarrow$ ATP $\Delta G^{\circ\prime} = +30.5$ kJ/mol

Find $\Delta G^{\circ\prime}$ for the overall reaction that regenerates ATP.

The Standard Free Energy Change and the Equilibrium Constant When we choose standard-state values for Q (1 atm for gases, 1 M for solutions, etc.) in Equation 20.11, ΔG becomes, by definition, ΔG° and Q equals 1:

$$\Delta G^\circ = RT \ln 1 - RT \ln K$$

Since $\ln 1 = 0$, the term $RT \ln Q$ drops out, which allows us to find the standard free energy change of a reaction ($\Delta G^\circ_{\text{rxn}}$) from its equilibrium constant, or vice versa:

$$\Delta G^\circ = -RT \ln K \qquad (20.12)$$

Table 20.2 shows that, due to their logarithmic relationship, a small change in ΔG° causes a large change in K. Note just these two examples

- As ΔG° becomes more positive, K becomes smaller: if $\Delta G^\circ = +10$ kJ, K is 0.02, so the product terms are $\frac{1}{50}$ the size of the reactant terms.
- As ΔG° becomes more negative, K becomes larger: if $\Delta G^\circ = -10$ kJ, the product terms are 50 times larger than the reactant terms.

Table 20.2 The Relationship Between ΔG° and K at 298 K

ΔG° (kJ)	K	Significance
200	9×10^{-36}	Essentially no forward reaction; reverse reaction goes to completion
100	3×10^{-18}	
50	2×10^{-9}	
10	2×10^{-2}	
1	7×10^{-1}	
0	1	Forward and reverse reactions proceed to same extent
−1	1.5	
−10	5×10^{1}	
−50	6×10^{8}	
−100	3×10^{17}	
−200	1×10^{35}	Forward reaction goes to completion; essentially no reverse reaction

FORWARD REACTION ↓ / REVERSE REACTION ↑

Finding the Free Energy Change Under Any Conditions In reality, reactions rarely begin with all components in their standard states. By substituting the relationship between $\Delta G°$ and K (Equation 20.12) into the expression for ΔG (Equation 20.11), we obtain a relationship that applies to *any starting concentrations:*

$$\Delta G = \Delta G° + RT \ln Q \tag{20.13}$$

Sample Problem 20.9 uses molecular scenes to explore these ideas, and Sample Problem 20.10 applies them in an important industrial reaction.

Sample Problem 20.9 Using Molecular Scenes to Find ΔG for a Reaction at Nonstandard Conditions

Problem These molecular scenes represent three mixtures in which A_2 (*black*) and B_2 (*green*) are forming AB. Each molecule represents 0.10 atm. The equation is

$$A_2(g) + B_2(g) \rightleftharpoons 2AB(g) \qquad \Delta G° = -3.4 \text{ kJ/mol}$$

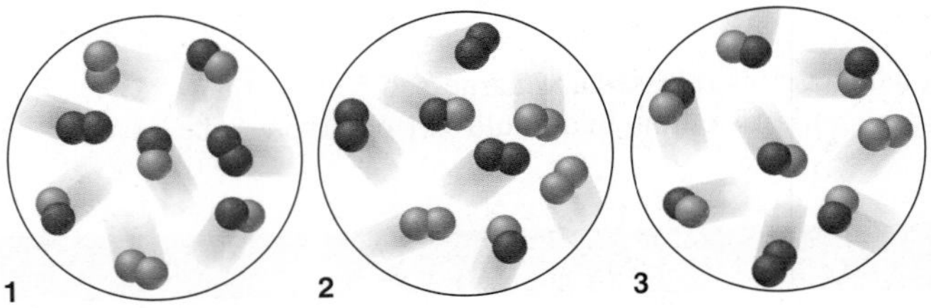

(a) If mixture 1 is at equilibrium, calculate K.
(b) Which mixture has the most negative ΔG, and which has the most positive?
(c) Is the reaction spontaneous at the standard state, that is, $P_{A_2} = P_{B_2} = P_{AB} = 1.0$ atm?

Plan **(a)** Mixture 1 is at equilibrium, so we first write the expression for Q and then find the partial pressure of each substance from the numbers of molecules and calculate K.
(b) To find ΔG, we apply Equation 20.13. We are given $\Delta G°$ (−3.4 kJ/mol) and know R (8.314 J/mol·K) but we still need to find T. We calculate T from Equation 20.12 using K from part (a), and substitute the partial pressure of each substance (by counting particles) to get Q. **(c)** Since 1.0 atm is the standard state, we substitute them into Q in Equation 20.13 and solve for ΔG. Because they are standard state values, ΔG equals $\Delta G°$.

Solution **(a)** Writing the expression for Q and calculating K:

$$A_2(g) + B_2(g) \rightleftharpoons 2AB(g) \qquad Q = \frac{P_{AB}^2}{P_{A_2} \times P_{B_2}} \qquad K = \frac{(0.40)^2}{(0.20)(0.20)} = 4.0$$

(b) Calculating T from Equation 20.12 for use in Equation 20.13:

$$\Delta G° = -RT \ln K = -\frac{3.4 \text{ kJ}}{\text{mol}} = -\left(\frac{8.314 \text{ J}}{\text{mol·K}}\right) T \ln 4.0$$

$$T = \frac{\dfrac{-3.4 \text{ kJ}}{\text{mol}}\left(\dfrac{1000 \text{ J}}{1 \text{ kJ}}\right)}{-\left(\dfrac{8.314 \text{ J}}{\text{mol·K}}\right) \ln 4.0} = 295 \text{ K}$$

Calculating ΔG from Equation 20.13 for each reaction mixture:
Mixture 1:

$$\Delta G = \Delta G° + RT \ln Q = -3.4 \text{ kJ} + RT \ln 4.0$$
$$= -3.4 \text{ kJ}\left(\frac{1000 \text{ J}}{1 \text{ kJ}}\right) + \left(\frac{8.314 \text{ J}}{\text{mol·K}}\right)(295 \text{ K}) \ln 4.0$$
$$= -3400 \text{ J} + 3400 \text{ J} = 0.0 \text{ J}$$

Mixture 2:

$$\Delta G = -3.4 \text{ kJ} + RT \ln \frac{(0.20)^2}{(0.30)(0.30)}$$
$$= -3.4 \text{ kJ}\left(\frac{1000 \text{ J}}{1 \text{ kJ}}\right) + \left(\frac{8.314 \text{ J}}{\text{mol·K}}\right)(295 \text{ K}) \ln 0.44 = -5.4 \times 10^3 \text{ J}$$

Mixture 3:

$$\Delta G = -3.4 \text{ kJ/mol} + RT \ln \frac{(0.60)^2}{(0.10)(0.10)}$$
$$= -3.4 \text{ kJ/mol}\left(\frac{1000 \text{ J}}{1 \text{ kJ}}\right) + \left(\frac{8.314 \text{ J}}{\text{mol·K}}\right)(295 \text{ K}) \ln 36 = 5.4{\times}10^3 \text{ J}$$

Mixture 2 has the most negative ΔG, and mixture 3 has the most positive ΔG.

(c) Finding ΔG when $P_{A_2} = P_{B_2} = P_{AB} = 1.0$ atm:

$$\Delta G = \Delta G^\circ + RT \ln Q = -3.4 \text{ kJ/mol} + RT \ln \frac{(1.0)^2}{(1.0)(1.0)}$$
$$= -3.4 \text{ kJ/mol} + RT \ln 1.0 = -3.4 \text{ kJ/mol}$$

Yes, the reaction is spontaneous when the components are in their standard states.

Check In (b), round to check the arithmetic; for example, for mixture 3, $\Delta G \approx -3000 \text{ J} + (8 \text{ J/mol·K})(300 \text{ K})4 \approx 7000 \text{ J}$, which is in the correct ballpark.

Comment **1.** By using the properties of logarithms, we didn't have to calculate T and ΔG in (b). In mixture 2, $Q < 1$, so $\ln Q$ is negative, which makes ΔG more negative. Also, note that $Q(0.44) < K(4.0)$, so $\Delta G < 0$. In mixture 3, $Q > 1$ (and is greater than it is in mixture 1), so $\ln Q$ is positive, which makes ΔG positive. Also, $Q(36) > K(4.0)$, so $\Delta G > 0$.
2. In (b), the value of zero for ΔG of the equilibrium mixture (mixture 1) makes sense, because a system at equilibrium has released all of its free energy.

Follow-Up Problem 20.9 The scenes below depict mixtures in which X_2 (*tan*) and Y_2 (*blue*) are forming XY_2. Each molecule represents 0.10 mol, and the volume is 1 L. The equation is $X_2(g) + 2Y_2(g) \rightleftharpoons 2XY_2(g)$; $\Delta G^\circ = -1.3$ kJ/mol.

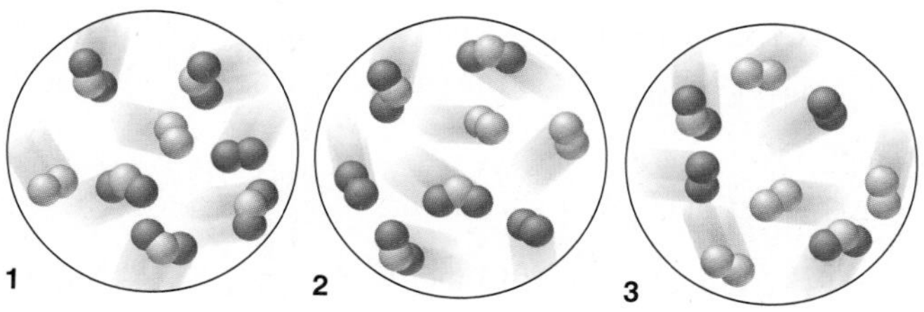

(a) If $K = 2$, which mixture is at equilibrium? **(b)** Rank the three mixtures from the lowest (most negative) ΔG to highest (most positive) ΔG. **(c)** What is the sign of ΔG for the change that occurs as each nonequilibrium mixture approaches equilibrium?

Sample Problem 20.10 Calculating ΔG at Nonstandard Conditions

Problem The oxidation of $SO_2(g)$, $2SO_2(g) + O_2(g) \longrightarrow 2SO_3(g)$, is too slow at 298 K to be useful in the manufacture of sulfuric acid, so the reaction is run at high T.
(a) Calculate K at 298 K and at 973 K. ($\Delta G^\circ_{298} = -141.6$ kJ/mol of reaction as written; using ΔH° and ΔS° values at 973 K, $\Delta G^\circ_{973} = -12.12$ kJ/mol of reaction as written.)
(b) Two containers are filled with 0.500 atm of SO_2, 0.0100 atm of O_2, and 0.100 atm of SO_3; one is kept at 25°C and the other at 700.°C. In which direction, if any, will the reaction proceed to reach equilibrium at each temperature?
(c) Calculate ΔG for the system in part (b) at each temperature.

Plan **(a)** We know ΔG°, T, and R, so we can calculate the K's from Equation 20.12.
(b) To determine if a net reaction will occur, we find Q from the given partial pressures and compare it with each K from part (a). **(c)** These are *not* standard-state pressures, so we find ΔG at each T with Equation 20.13 from the values of ΔG° (given) and Q [from part (b)].

Solution **(a)** Calculating K at the two temperatures:

$$\Delta G^\circ = -RT \ln K$$

so

$$K = e^{-(\Delta G^\circ/RT)}$$

At 298 K, the exponent is

$$-(\Delta G°/RT) = -\left(\frac{-141.6 \text{ kJ/mol} \times \frac{1000 \text{ J}}{1 \text{ kJ}}}{8.314 \text{ J/mol·K} \times 298 \text{ K}}\right) = 57.2$$

so

$$K = e^{-(\Delta G°/RT)} = e^{57.2} = 7\times10^{24}$$

At 973 K, the exponent is

$$-(\Delta G°/RT) = -\left(\frac{-12.12 \text{ kJ/mol} \times \frac{1000 \text{ J}}{1 \text{ kJ}}}{8.314 \text{ J/mol·K} \times 973 \text{ K}}\right) = 1.50$$

so

$$K = e^{-(\Delta G°/RT)} = e^{1.50} = 4.5$$

(b) Calculating the value of Q:

$$Q = \frac{P^2_{SO_3}}{P^2_{SO_2} \times P_{O_2}} = \frac{0.100^2}{0.500^2 \times 0.0100} = 4.00$$

Because $Q < K$ at both temperatures, the denominator will decrease and the numerator will increase—more SO_3 will form—until Q equals K. To reach equilibrium, the reaction will go far to the right at 298 K, and it will go slightly to the right at 973 K.

(c) Calculating ΔG, the nonstandard free energy change, at 298 K:

$$\begin{aligned}\Delta G_{298} &= \Delta G° + RT \ln Q \\ &= -141.6 \text{ kJ/mol} + \left(8.314 \text{ J/mol·K} \times \frac{1 \text{ kJ}}{1000 \text{ J}} \times 298 \text{ K} \times \ln 4.00\right) \\ &= -138.2 \text{ kJ/mol}\end{aligned}$$

Calculating ΔG at 973 K:

$$\begin{aligned}\Delta G_{973} &= \Delta G° + RT \ln Q \\ &= -12.12 \text{ kJ/mol} + \left(8.314 \text{ J/mol·K} \times \frac{1 \text{ kJ}}{1000 \text{ J}} \times 973 \text{ K} \times \ln 4.00\right) \\ &= -0.9 \text{ kJ/mol}\end{aligned}$$

Check Note that in parts (a) and (c), we made the free energy units (kJ) consistent with the units in R (J). For significant figures in addition and subtraction, we retain one digit to the right of the decimal place in part (c).

Comment For these starting gas pressures at 973 K, the process is barely spontaneous ($\Delta G = -0.9$ kJ/mol), so why use a higher temperature? As in the synthesis of NH_3 (Section 17.6), where the *yield* is greater at a lower temperature, this process is carried out at higher temperature *with a catalyst* to attain a higher *rate*. We discuss the details of the industrial production of sulfuric acid in Chapter 22.

Follow-Up Problem 20.10 At 298 K, hypobromous acid (HBrO) dissociates in water with a K_a of 2.3×10^{-9}.
(a) Calculate $\Delta G°$ for the dissociation of HBrO.
(b) Calculate ΔG if $[H_3O^+] = 6.0\times10^{-4}$ *M*, $[BrO^-] = 0.10$ *M*, and $[HBrO] = 0.20$ *M*.

Another Look at the Meaning of Spontaneity At this point, we introduce two terms related to *spontaneous* and *nonspontaneous:*

1. *Product-favored reaction*. For the general reaction

$$A \rightleftharpoons B \qquad K = [B]/[A] > 1$$

and therefore, the reaction proceeds largely from left to right (Figure 20.16A). From pure A to equilibrium, $Q < K$ and the curved *green* arrow in the figure indicates that the

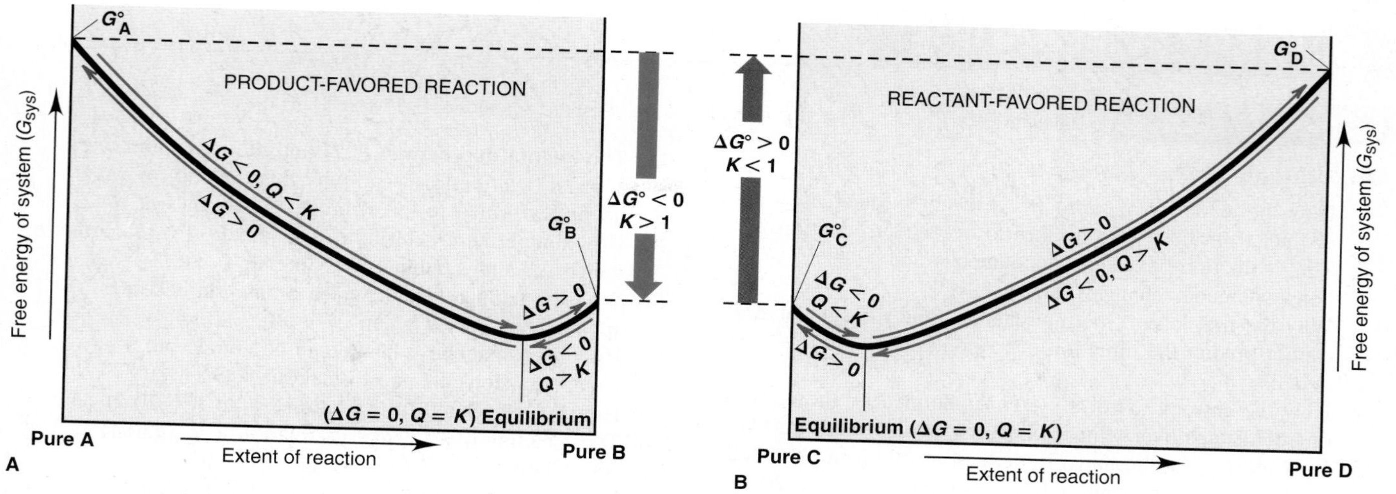

Figure 20.16 Free energy and the extent of reaction. Each reaction proceeds spontaneously (*curved green arrows*) from reactants (A or C) or products (B or D) to the equilibrium mixture, at which point $\Delta G = 0$. After that, the reaction is nonspontaneous (*curved red arrows*). **A,** For the product-favored reaction A $\rightleftharpoons$ B, $G^\circ_A > G^\circ_B$, so $\Delta G^\circ < 0$ and $K > 1$. **B,** For the reactant-favored reaction C $\rightleftharpoons$ D, $G^\circ_D > G^\circ_C$, so $\Delta G^\circ > 0$ and $K < 1$.

reaction is spontaneous ($\Delta G < 0$). From there on, the curved *red* arrow indicates that the reaction is nonspontaneous ($\Delta G > 0$). Similarly, from pure B to equilibrium, $Q > K$ and the reaction is also spontaneous ($\Delta G < 0$), but not thereafter. In either case, *free energy decreases until the reaction reaches a minimum at the equilibrium mixture:* $Q = K$ *and* $\Delta G = 0$. For the overall reaction A $\rightleftharpoons$ B (starting with all components in their standard states), G°_B is smaller than G°_A, so ΔG° is negative, which corresponds to $K > 1$. We call this a *product-favored* reaction because in its final state the system contains mostly product.

2. *Reactant-favored reaction.* For the opposite reaction,

$$C \rightleftharpoons D \qquad K = [D]/[C] < 1$$

and the reaction proceeds slightly from left to right (Figure 20.16B). Here, too, whether we start with pure C or pure D, the reaction is spontaneous ($\Delta G < 0$) until equilibrium. In this case, however, the equilibrium mixture contains mostly C (the reactant), so we say the reaction is *reactant favored.* Here, G°_D is *larger* than G°_C, so ΔG° is *positive,* which corresponds to $K < 1$.

Thus, "*spontaneous*" refers to that *portion* of a reaction in which the free energy decreases—from the starting mixture to the equilibrium mixture. A product-favored reaction goes predominantly, but *not* completely, toward product, and a reactant-favored reaction goes relatively little toward product (see Table 20.2).

Summary of Section 20.4

- Two ways of predicting reaction spontaneity are from the sign of ΔG or the value of Q/K. These variables are related to each other by $\Delta G = RT \ln Q/K$. When $Q = K$, $Q/K = 1$ and $\ln Q/K = 0$. Thus, the system is at equilibrium and can release no more free energy.
- Beginning with Q at the standard state, the free energy change is ΔG° and is related to the equilibrium constant: $\Delta G^\circ = -RT \ln K$.
- Any nonequilibrium mixture of reactants and products moves spontaneously ($\Delta G < 0$) toward the equilibrium mixture.
- A product-favored reaction goes predominantly toward product and, thus, has $K > 1$ and $\Delta G^\circ < 0$; a reactant-favored reaction has $K < 1$ and $\Delta G^\circ > 0$.

CHAPTER REVIEW GUIDE

Learning Objectives

Relevant section (§) and/or sample problem (SP) numbers appear in parentheses.

Understand These Concepts

1. How the tendency of a process to occur by itself is distinct from how long it takes to occur (Introduction)
2. The distinction between a spontaneous and a nonspontaneous change (§20.1)
3. Why the first law of thermodynamics and the sign of ΔH° cannot predict the direction of a spontaneous process (§20.1)
4. How the entropy (S) of a system is defined by the number of microstates over which its energy is dispersed (§20.1)
5. How entropy is alternatively defined by the heat absorbed (or released) at constant T in a reversible process (§20.1)
6. The criterion for spontaneity according to the second law of thermodynamics: that a change increases S_{univ} (§20.1)
7. How absolute values of standard molar entropies (S°) can be obtained because the third law of thermodynamics provides a "zero point" (§20.1)
8. How temperature, physical state, dissolution, atomic size, and molecular complexity influence S° values (§20.1)
9. How ΔS°_{rxn} is based on the difference between the summed S° values for the reactants and those for products (§20.2)
10. How the surroundings add heat to or remove heat from the system and how ΔS_{surr} influences overall ΔS°_{rxn} (§20.2)
11. The relationship between ΔS_{surr} and ΔH_{sys} (§20.2)
12. How reactions proceed spontaneously toward equilibrium ($\Delta S_{univ} > 0$) but proceed no further at equilibrium ($\Delta S_{univ} = 0$) (§20.2)
13. How the free energy change (ΔG) combines a system's entropy and enthalpy changes (§20.3)
14. How the expression for the free energy change is derived from the second law (§20.3)
15. The relationship between ΔG and the maximum work a system can perform and why this quantity of work is never performed in a real process (§20.3)
16. How temperature determines spontaneity for reactions in which ΔS and ΔH have the same sign (§20.3)
17. Why the temperature at which a reaction becomes spontaneous occurs when $\Delta G = 0$ (§20.3)
18. How a spontaneous change can be coupled to a nonspontaneous change to make it occur (§20.3)
19. How ΔG is related to the ratio of Q to K (§20.4)
20. The meaning of ΔG° and its relation to K (§20.4)
21. The relation of ΔG to ΔG° and Q (§20.4)
22. Why G decreases, no matter what the starting concentrations, as the reacting system moves toward equilibrium (§20.4)

Master These Skills

1. Predicting relative S° values of systems (§20.1 and SP 20.1)
2. Calculating ΔS°_{rxn} for a chemical change (SP 20.2)
3. Finding reaction spontaneity from ΔS_{surr} and ΔH°_{sys} (SP 20.3)
4. Calculating ΔG°_{rxn} from ΔH°_f and S° values (SP 20.4)
5. Calculating ΔG°_{rxn} from ΔG°_f values (SP 20.5)
6. Predicting the signs of ΔH, ΔS, and ΔG (SP 20.6)
7. Calculating the effect of temperature on ΔG (SP 20.7)
8. Calculating the temperature at which a reaction becomes spontaneous (§20.3 and SP 20.8)
9. Calculating K from ΔG° (§20.4 and SP 20.10)
10. Using ΔG° and Q to calculate ΔG at any conditions (SPs 20.9, 20.10)

Key Terms

Page numbers appear in parentheses.

Section 20.1
spontaneous change (811)
entropy (S) (814)
second law of thermodynamics (817)
third law of thermodynamics (817)
standard molar entropy (S°) (817)

Section 20.2
standard entropy of reaction (ΔS°_{rxn}) (822)

Section 20.3
free energy (G) (827)
standard free energy change (ΔG°) (828)
standard free energy of formation (ΔG°_f) (829)
coupling of reactions (834)
adenosine triphosphate (ATP) (836)

Key Equations and Relationships

Page numbers appear in parentheses.

20.1 Quantifying entropy in terms of the number of microstates (W) over which the energy of a system can be distributed (814):

$$S = k \ln W$$

20.2 Quantifying the entropy change in terms of heat absorbed (or released) in a reversible process (816):

$$\Delta S_{sys} = \frac{q_{rev}}{T}$$

20.3 Stating the second law of thermodynamics, for a spontaneous process (817):

$$\Delta S_{univ} = \Delta S_{sys} + \Delta S_{surr} > 0$$

20.4 Calculating the standard entropy of reaction from the standard molar entropies of reactants and products (822):

$$\Delta S^\circ_{rxn} = \Sigma m S^\circ_{products} - \Sigma n S^\circ_{reactants}$$

20.5 Relating the entropy change in the surroundings to the enthalpy change of the system and the temperature (824):

$$\Delta S_{surr} = -\frac{\Delta H_{sys}}{T}$$

20.6 Expressing the free energy change of the system in terms of its component enthalpy and entropy changes (Gibbs equation) (828):

$$\Delta G_{sys} = \Delta H_{sys} - T\Delta S_{sys}$$

20.7 Calculating the standard free energy change from standard enthalpy and entropy changes (828):

$$\Delta G^\circ_{sys} = \Delta H^\circ_{sys} - T\Delta S^\circ_{sys}$$

20.8 Calculating the standard free energy change from the standard free energies of formation (829):

$$\Delta G^\circ_{rxn} = \Sigma m\Delta G^\circ_{f(products)} - \Sigma n\Delta G^\circ_{f(reactants)}$$

20.9 Relating the free energy change to the maximum work a process can perform (830):

$$\Delta G = w_{max}$$

20.10 Finding the temperature at which a reaction becomes spontaneous (834):

$$T = \frac{\Delta H}{\Delta S}$$

20.11 Expressing the free energy change in terms of Q and K (835):

$$\Delta G = RT\ln\frac{Q}{K} = RT\ln Q - RT\ln K$$

20.12 Expressing the free energy change when Q is at standard state conditions (837):

$$\Delta G^\circ = -RT\ln K$$

20.13 Expressing the free energy change for nonstandard initial conditions (838):

$$\Delta G = \Delta G^\circ + RT\ln Q$$

Brief Solutions to Follow-Up Problems

20.1 (a) $PCl_5(g)$: higher molar mass and more complex molecule; (b) $BaCl_2(s)$: higher molar mass; (c) $Br_2(g)$: gases have more freedom of motion and dispersal of energy than liquids.

20.2 (a) $2NaOH(s) + CO_2(g) \longrightarrow Na_2CO_3(s) + H_2O(l)$

$\Delta n_{gas} = -1$, so $\Delta S^\circ_{rxn} < 0$

$$\begin{aligned}\Delta S^\circ_{rxn} &= [(1\text{ mol } H_2O)(69.9\text{ J/mol·K}) \\ &\quad + (1\text{ mol } Na_2CO_3)(139\text{ J/mol·K})] \\ &\quad - [(1\text{ mol } CO_2)(213.7\text{ J/mol·K}) \\ &\quad + (2\text{ mol NaOH})(64.5\text{ J/mol·K})] \\ &= -134\text{ J/K}\end{aligned}$$

(b) $2Fe(s) + 3H_2O(g) \longrightarrow Fe_2O_3(s) + 3H_2(g)$

$\Delta n_{gas} = 0$, so cannot predict sign of ΔS°_{rxn}

$$\begin{aligned}\Delta S^\circ_{rxn} &= [(1\text{ mol } Fe_2O_3)(87.4\text{ J/mol·K}) \\ &\quad + (3\text{ mol } H_2)(130.6\text{ J/mol·K})] \\ &\quad - [(2\text{ mol Fe})(27.3\text{ J/mol·K}) \\ &\quad + (3\text{ mol } H_2O)(188.7\text{ J/mol·K})] \\ &= -141.5\text{ J/K}\end{aligned}$$

20.3 $2FeO(s) + \frac{1}{2}O_2(g) \longrightarrow Fe_2O_3(s)$

$$\begin{aligned}\Delta S^\circ_{sys} &= (1\text{ mol } Fe_2O_3)(87.4\text{ J/mol·K}) \\ &\quad - [(2\text{ mol FeO})(60.75\text{ J/mol·K}) \\ &\quad + (\tfrac{1}{2}\text{ mol } O_2)(205.0\text{ J/mol·K})] \\ &= -136.6\text{ J/K}\end{aligned}$$

$$\begin{aligned}\Delta H^\circ_{sys} &= (1\text{ mol } Fe_2O_3)(-825.5\text{ kJ/mol}) \\ &\quad - [(2\text{ mol FeO})(-272.0\text{ kJ/mol}) + (\tfrac{1}{2}\text{ mol } O_2)(0\text{ kJ/mol})] \\ &= -281.5\text{ kJ}\end{aligned}$$

$$\Delta S_{surr} = -\frac{\Delta H^\circ_{sys}}{T} = -\frac{(-281.5\text{ kJ} \times 1000\text{ J/kJ})}{298\text{ K}} = +945\text{ J/K}$$

$$\begin{aligned}\Delta S_{univ} &= \Delta S^\circ_{sys} + \Delta S_{surr} = -136.6\text{ J/K} + 945\text{ J/K} \\ &= 808\text{ J/K; reaction is spontaneous at 298 K.}\end{aligned}$$

20.4 Using ΔH°_f and S° values from Appendix B,

$\Delta H^\circ_{rxn} = -114.2$ kJ and $\Delta S^\circ_{rxn} = -146.5$ J/K

$$\begin{aligned}\Delta G^\circ_{rxn} &= \Delta H^\circ_{rxn} - T\Delta S^\circ_{rxn} \\ &= -114.2\text{ kJ} - [(298\text{ K})(-146.5\text{ J/K})(1\text{ kJ/1000 J})] \\ &= -70.5\text{ kJ}\end{aligned}$$

20.5 (a)
$$\begin{aligned}\Delta G^\circ_{rxn} &= (2\text{ mol } NO_2)(51\text{ kJ/mol}) \\ &\quad - [(2\text{ mol NO})(86.60\text{ kJ/mol}) \\ &\quad + (1\text{ mol } O_2)(0\text{ kJ/mol})] \\ &= -71\text{ kJ}\end{aligned}$$

(b)
$$\begin{aligned}\Delta G^\circ_{rxn} &= (2\text{ mol CO})(-137.2\text{ kJ/mol}) - [(2\text{ mol C})(0\text{ kJ/mol}) \\ &\quad + (1\text{ mol } O_2)(0\text{ kJ/mol})] \\ &= -274.4\text{ kJ}\end{aligned}$$

20.6 (a) More moles of gas are present after the reaction, so $\Delta S > 0$.
(b) The problem says the reaction is spontaneous ($\Delta G < 0$) only above 325°C, which implies high T. If $\Delta S > 0$, $-T\Delta S < 0$, so ΔG will become negative at higher T only if $\Delta H > 0$.

20.7 ΔG becomes negative at lower T, so $\Delta H < 0$, $\Delta S < 0$, and $-T\Delta S > 0$. At lower T, the negative ΔH value becomes larger than the positive $-T\Delta S$ value.

20.8

$$\begin{aligned}\Delta H &= \Delta H^\circ_f\, CaCO_3 - (\Delta H^\circ_f\, CaO + \Delta H^\circ_f\, CO_2) \\ &= -1206.9\text{ kJ} - (-635.1\text{ kJ} - 393.5\text{ kJ}) = -178.3\text{ kJ}\end{aligned}$$

$$\begin{aligned}\Delta S &= S^\circ\, CaCO_3 - (S^\circ\, CaO + S^\circ\, CO_2) \\ &= 92.9\text{ J/K} - (38.2\text{ J/K} + 213.7\text{ J/K}) = -159.0\text{ J/K}\end{aligned}$$

$$T = \frac{\Delta H}{\Delta S} = \frac{-178.3\text{ kJ} \times \dfrac{1000\text{ J}}{1\text{ kJ}}}{-159.0\text{ J/K}} = 1121\text{ K}$$

Reaction becomes spontaneous ($\Delta G < 0$) at any $T < 1121$ K.

20.9 (a) Mixture 2 is at equilibrium.
(b) 3 (most negative) < 2 < 1 (most positive).
(c) Any reaction mixture moves spontaneously toward equilibrium, so both changes have a negative ΔG.

20.10 (a)
$$\begin{aligned}\Delta G^\circ &= -RT\ln K = -8.314\text{ J/mol·K} \times \frac{1\text{ kJ}}{1000\text{ J}} \times 298\text{ K} \\ &\quad \times \ln(2.3\times10^{-9}) \\ &= 49\text{ kJ/mol}\end{aligned}$$

(b)
$$Q = \frac{[H_3O^+][BrO^-]}{[HBrO]} = \frac{(6.0\times10^{-4})(0.10)}{0.20} = 3.0\times10^{-4}$$

$$\begin{aligned}\Delta G &= \Delta G^\circ + RT\ln Q \\ &= 49\text{ kJ/mol} \\ &\quad + \left[8.314\text{ J/mol·K} \times \frac{1\text{ kJ}}{1000\text{ J}} \times 298\text{ K} \times \ln(3.0\times10^{-4})\right] \\ &= 29\text{ kJ/mol}\end{aligned}$$

PROBLEMS

Problems with **colored** numbers are answered in Appendix E and worked in detail in the Student Solutions Manual. Problem sections match those in the text and provide the numbers of relevant sample problems. Most offer Concept Review Questions, Skill-Building Exercises (grouped in pairs covering the same concept), and Problems in Context. The Comprehensive Problems are based on material from any section or previous chapter.

Note: Unless stated otherwise, problems refer to systems at 298 K (25°C). Solving these problems may require values from Appendix B.

The Second Law of Thermodynamics: Predicting Spontaneous Change

(Sample Problem 20.1)

Concept Review Questions

20.1 Distinguish between the terms *spontaneous* and *instantaneous*. Give an example of a process that is spontaneous but very slow, and one that is very fast but not spontaneous.

20.2 Distinguish between the terms *spontaneous* and *nonspontaneous*. Can a nonspontaneous process occur? Explain.

20.3 State the first law of thermodynamics in terms of (a) the energy of the universe; (b) the creation or destruction of energy; (c) the energy change of system and surroundings. Does the first law reveal the direction of spontaneous change? Explain.

20.4 State qualitatively the relationship between entropy and freedom of particle motion. Use this idea to explain why you will probably never (a) be suffocated because all the air near you has moved to the other side of the room; (b) see half the water in your cup of tea freeze while the other half boils.

20.5 Why is ΔS_{vap} of a substance always larger than ΔS_{fus}?

20.6 How does the entropy of the surroundings change during an exothermic reaction? An endothermic reaction? Other than the examples in text, describe a spontaneous endothermic process.

20.7 (a) What is the entropy of a perfect crystal at 0 K?
(b) Does entropy increase or decrease as the temperature rises?
(c) Why is $\Delta H^\circ_f = 0$ but $S^\circ > 0$ for an element?
(d) Why does Appendix B list ΔH°_f values but not ΔS°_f values?

Skill-Building Exercises (grouped in similar pairs)

20.8 Which of the following processes are spontaneous?
(a) Water evaporates from a puddle. (b) A lion chases an antelope.
(c) An isotope undergoes radioactive disintegration.

20.9 Which of the following processes are spontaneous?
(a) Earth moves around the Sun. (b) A boulder rolls up a hill.
(c) Sodium metal and chlorine gas form solid sodium chloride.

20.10 Which of the following processes are spontaneous?
(a) Methane burns in air. (b) A teaspoonful of sugar dissolves in a cup of hot coffee. (c) A soft-boiled egg becomes raw.

20.11 Which of the following processes are spontaneous?
(a) A satellite falls to Earth. (b) Water decomposes to H_2 and O_2 at 298 K and 1 atm. (c) Average car prices increase.

20.12 Predict the sign of ΔS_{sys} for each process: (a) A piece of wax melts. (b) Silver chloride precipitates from solution. (c) Dew forms on a lawn in morning.

20.13 Predict the sign of ΔS_{sys} for each process: (a) Gasoline vapors mix with air in a car engine. (b) Hot air expands. (c) Humidity condenses in cold air.

20.14 Predict the sign of ΔS_{sys} for each process: (a) Alcohol evaporates. (b) A solid explosive converts to a gas. (c) Perfume vapors diffuse through a room.

20.15 Predict the sign of ΔS_{sys} for each process: (a) A pond freezes in winter. (b) Atmospheric CO_2 dissolves in the ocean. (c) An apple tree bears fruit.

20.16 Without using Appendix B, predict the sign of ΔS° for
(a) $2K(s) + F_2(g) \longrightarrow 2KF(s)$
(b) $NH_3(g) + HBr(g) \longrightarrow NH_4Br(s)$
(c) $NaClO_3(s) \longrightarrow Na^+(aq) + ClO_3^-(aq)$

20.17 Without using Appendix B, predict the sign of ΔS° for
(a) $H_2S(g) + \frac{1}{2}O_2(g) \longrightarrow \frac{1}{8}S_8(s) + H_2O(g)$
(b) $HCl(aq) + NaOH(aq) \longrightarrow NaCl(aq) + H_2O(l)$
(c) $2NO_2(g) \longrightarrow N_2O_4(g)$

20.18 Without using Appendix B, predict the sign of ΔS° for
(a) $CaCO_3(s) + 2HCl(aq) \longrightarrow CaCl_2(aq) + H_2O(l) + CO_2(g)$
(b) $2NO(g) + O_2(g) \longrightarrow 2NO_2(g)$
(c) $2KClO_3(s) \longrightarrow 2KCl(s) + 3O_2(g)$

20.19 Without using Appendix B, predict the sign of ΔS° for
(a) $Ag^+(aq) + Cl^-(aq) \longrightarrow AgCl(s)$
(b) $KBr(s) \longrightarrow KBr(aq)$
(c) $CH_3CH{=}CH_2(g) \longrightarrow$ 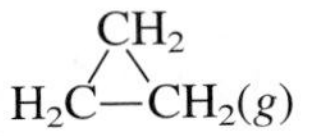

20.20 Predict the sign of ΔS for each process:
(a) $C_2H_5OH(g)$ (350 K and 500 torr) $\longrightarrow$ $C_2H_5OH(g)$ (350 K and 250 torr)
(b) $N_2(g)$ (298 K and 1 atm) $\longrightarrow$ $N_2(aq)$ (298 K and 1 atm)
(c) $O_2(aq)$ (303 K and 1 atm) $\longrightarrow$ $O_2(g)$ (303 K and 1 atm)

20.21 Predict the sign of ΔS for each process:
(a) $O_2(g)$ (1.0 L at 1 atm) $\longrightarrow$ $O_2(g)$ (0.10 L at 10 atm)
(b) $Cu(s)$ (350°C and 2.5 atm) $\longrightarrow$ $Cu(s)$ (450°C and 2.5 atm)
(c) $Cl_2(g)$ (100°C and 1 atm) $\longrightarrow$ $Cl_2(g)$ (10°C and 1 atm)

20.22 Predict which substance has greater molar entropy. Explain.
(a) Butane $CH_3CH_2CH_2CH_3(g)$ or 2-butene $CH_3CH{=}CHCH_3(g)$
(b) $Ne(g)$ or $Xe(g)$ (c) $CH_4(g)$ or $CCl_4(l)$

20.23 Predict which substance has greater molar entropy. Explain.
(a) $NO_2(g)$ or $N_2O_4(g)$ (b) $CH_3OCH_3(l)$ or $CH_3CH_2OH(l)$
(c) $HCl(g)$ or $HBr(g)$

20.24 Predict which substance has greater molar entropy. Explain.
(a) $CH_3OH(l)$ or $C_2H_5OH(l)$ (b) $KClO_3(s)$ or $KClO_3(aq)$
(c) $Na(s)$ or $K(s)$

20.25 Predict which substance has greater molar entropy. Explain.
(a) $P_4(g)$ or $P_2(g)$ (b) $HNO_3(aq)$ or $HNO_3(l)$
(c) $CuSO_4(s)$ or $CuSO_4 \cdot 5H_2O(s)$

20.26 Without consulting Appendix B, arrange each group in order of *increasing* standard molar entropy ($S°$). Explain.
(a) Graphite, diamond, charcoal
(b) Ice, water vapor, liquid water
(c) O_2, O_3, O atoms

20.27 Without consulting Appendix B, arrange each group in order of *increasing* standard molar entropy ($S°$). Explain.
(a) Glucose ($C_6H_{12}O_6$), sucrose ($C_{12}H_{22}O_{11}$), ribose ($C_5H_{10}O_5$)
(b) $CaCO_3$, $Ca + C + \frac{3}{2}O_2$, $CaO + CO_2$
(c) $SF_6(g)$, $SF_4(g)$, $S_2F_{10}(g)$

20.28 Without consulting Appendix B, arrange each group in order of *decreasing* standard molar entropy ($S°$). Explain.
(a) $ClO_4^-(aq)$, $ClO_2^-(aq)$, $ClO_3^-(aq)$
(b) $NO_2(g)$, $NO(g)$, $N_2(g)$
(c) $Fe_2O_3(s)$, $Al_2O_3(s)$, $Fe_3O_4(s)$

20.29 Without consulting Appendix B, arrange each group in order of *decreasing* standard molar entropy ($S°$). Explain.
(a) Mg metal, Ca metal, Ba metal
(b) Hexane (C_6H_{14}), benzene (C_6H_6), cyclohexane (C_6H_{12})
(c) $PF_2Cl_3(g)$, $PF_5(g)$, $PF_3(g)$

Calculating the Entropy Change of a Reaction
(Sample Problems 20.2 and 20.3)

Concept Review Questions

20.30 For the reaction depicted in the molecular scenes, X is red and Y is green.

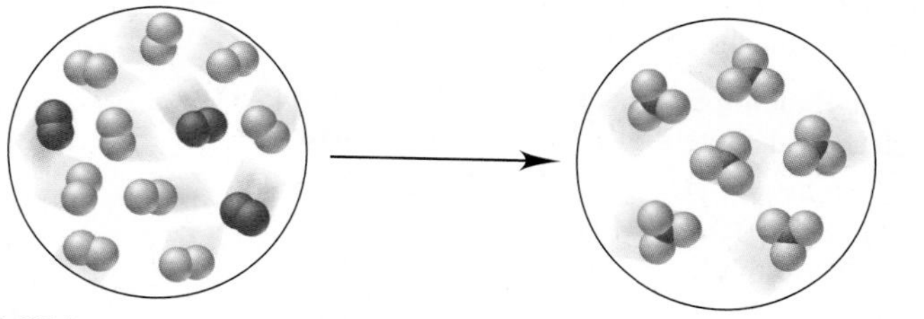

(a) Write a balanced equation.
(b) Determine the sign of ΔS.
(c) Which species has the highest molar entropy?

20.31 Describe the equilibrium condition in terms of the entropy changes of a system and its surroundings. What does this description mean about the entropy change of the universe?

20.32 For the reaction $H_2O(g) + Cl_2O(g) \longrightarrow 2HClO(g)$, you know $\Delta S°_{rxn}$ and $S°$ of $HClO(g)$ and of $H_2O(g)$. Write an expression that can be used to determine $S°$ of $Cl_2O(g)$.

Skill-Building Exercises (grouped in similar pairs)

20.33 For each reaction, predict the sign and find the value of $\Delta S°$:
(a) $3NO(g) \longrightarrow N_2O(g) + NO_2(g)$
(b) $3H_2(g) + Fe_2O_3(s) \longrightarrow 2Fe(s) + 3H_2O(g)$
(c) $P_4(s) + 5O_2(g) \longrightarrow P_4O_{10}(s)$

20.34 For each reaction, predict the sign and find the value of $\Delta S°$:
(a) $3NO_2(g) + H_2O(l) \longrightarrow 2HNO_3(l) + NO(g)$
(b) $N_2(g) + 3F_2(g) \longrightarrow 2NF_3(g)$
(c) $C_6H_{12}O_6(s) + 6O_2(g) \longrightarrow 6CO_2(g) + 6H_2O(g)$

20.35 Find $\Delta S°$ for the combustion of ethane (C_2H_6) to carbon dioxide and gaseous water. Is the sign of $\Delta S°$ as expected?

20.36 Find $\Delta S°$ for the combustion of methane to carbon dioxide and liquid water. Is the sign of $\Delta S°$ as expected?

20.37 Find $\Delta S°$ for the reaction of nitrogen monoxide with hydrogen to form ammonia and water vapor. Is the sign of $\Delta S°$ as expected?

20.38 Find $\Delta S°$ for the combustion of ammonia to nitrogen dioxide and water vapor. Is the sign of $\Delta S°$ as expected?

20.39 Find $\Delta S°$ for the formation of $Cu_2O(s)$ from its elements.

20.40 Find $\Delta S°$ for the formation of $HI(g)$ from its elements.

20.41 Find $\Delta S°$ for the formation of $CH_3OH(l)$ from its elements.

20.42 Find $\Delta S°$ for the formation of $PCl_5(g)$ from its elements.

Problems in Context

20.43 Sulfur dioxide is released in the combustion of coal. Scrubbers use aqueous slurries of calcium hydroxide to remove the SO_2 from flue gases. Write a balanced equation for this reaction and calculate $\Delta S°$ at 298 K [$S°$ of $CaSO_3(s) = 101.4$ J/mol·K].

20.44 Oxyacetylene welding is used to repair metal structures, including bridges, buildings, and even the Statue of Liberty. Calculate $\Delta S°$ for the combustion of 1 mol of acetylene (C_2H_2).

Entropy, Free Energy, and Work
(Sample Problems 20.4 to 20.8)

Concept Review Questions

20.45 What is the advantage of calculating free energy changes rather than entropy changes to determine reaction spontaneity?

20.46 Given that $\Delta G_{sys} = -T\Delta S_{univ}$, explain how the sign of ΔG_{sys} correlates with reaction spontaneity.

20.47 (a) Is an endothermic reaction more likely to be spontaneous at higher temperatures or lower temperatures? Explain.
(b) The change depicted below occurs at constant pressure. Explain your answers to each of the following: (1) What is the sign of ΔH? (2) What is the sign of ΔS? (3) What is the sign of ΔS_{surr}? (4) How does the sign of ΔG vary with temperature?

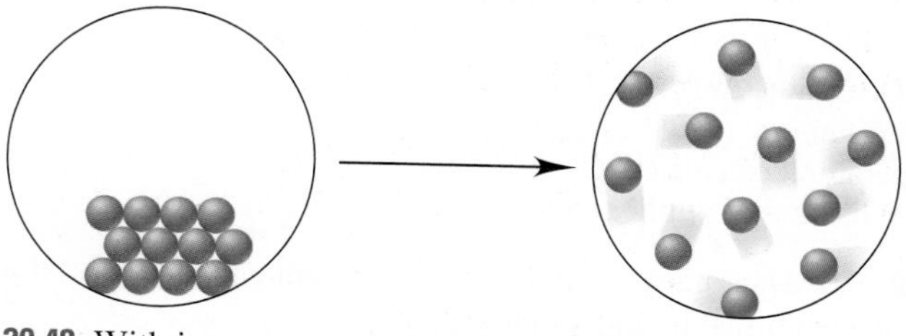

20.48 With its components in their standard states, a certain reaction is spontaneous only at high T. What do you know about the signs of $\Delta H°$ and $\Delta S°$? Describe a process for which this is true.

20.49 How can $\Delta S°$ be relatively independent of T if $S°$ of each reactant and product increases with T?

Skill-Building Exercises (grouped in similar pairs)

20.50 Calculate $\Delta G°$ for each reaction using $\Delta G_f°$ values:
(a) $2Mg(s) + O_2(g) \longrightarrow 2MgO(s)$
(b) $2CH_3OH(g) + 3O_2(g) \longrightarrow 2CO_2(g) + 4H_2O(g)$
(c) $BaO(s) + CO_2(g) \longrightarrow BaCO_3(s)$

20.51 Calculate $\Delta G°$ for each reaction using $\Delta G_f°$ values:
(a) $H_2(g) + I_2(s) \longrightarrow 2HI(g)$
(b) $MnO_2(s) + 2CO(g) \longrightarrow Mn(s) + 2CO_2(g)$
(c) $NH_4Cl(s) \longrightarrow NH_3(g) + HCl(g)$

20.52 Find $\Delta G°$ for the reactions in Problem 20.50 using $\Delta H_f°$ and $S°$ values.

20.53 Find $\Delta G°$ for the reactions in Problem 20.51 using $\Delta H_f°$ and $S°$ values.

20.54 Consider the oxidation of carbon monoxide:

$$CO(g) + \tfrac{1}{2}O_2(g) \longrightarrow CO_2(g)$$

(a) Predict the signs of $\Delta S°$ and $\Delta H°$. Explain.
(b) Calculate $\Delta G°$ by two different methods.

20.55 Consider the combustion of butane gas:

$$C_4H_{10}(g) + \tfrac{13}{2}O_2(g) \longrightarrow 4CO_2(g) + 5H_2O(g)$$

(a) Predict the signs of $\Delta S°$ and $\Delta H°$. Explain.
(b) Calculate $\Delta G°$ by two different methods.

20.56 For the gaseous reaction of xenon and fluorine to form xenon hexafluoride:
(a) Calculate $\Delta S°$ at 298 K ($\Delta H° = -402$ kJ/mol and $\Delta G° = -280.$ kJ/mol).
(b) Assuming that $\Delta S°$ and $\Delta H°$ change little with temperature, calculate $\Delta G°$ at 500. K.

20.57 For the gaseous reaction of carbon monoxide and chlorine to form phosgene ($COCl_2$):
(a) Calculate $\Delta S°$ at 298 K ($\Delta H° = -220.$ kJ/mol and $\Delta G° = -206$ kJ/mol).
(b) Assuming that $\Delta S°$ and $\Delta H°$ change little with temperature, calculate $\Delta G°$ at 450. K.

20.58 One reaction used to produce small quantities of pure H_2 is

$$CH_3OH(g) \rightleftharpoons CO(g) + 2H_2(g)$$

(a) Determine $\Delta H°$ and $\Delta S°$ for the reaction at 298 K.
(b) Assuming that these values are relatively independent of temperature, calculate $\Delta G°$ at 28°C, 128°C, and 228°C.
(c) What is the significance of the different values of $\Delta G°$?

20.59 A reaction that occurs in the internal combustion engine is

$$N_2(g) + O_2(g) \rightleftharpoons 2NO(g)$$

(a) Determine $\Delta H°$ and $\Delta S°$ for the reaction at 298 K.
(b) Assuming that these values are relatively independent of temperature, calculate $\Delta G°$ at 100.°C, 2560.°C, and 3540.°C.
(c) What is the significance of the different values of $\Delta G°$?

20.60 Use $\Delta H°$ and $\Delta S°$ values for the following process at 1 atm to find the normal boiling point of Br_2:

$$Br_2(l) \rightleftharpoons Br_2(g)$$

20.61 Use $\Delta H°$ and $\Delta S°$ values to find the temperature at which these sulfur allotropes reach equilibrium at 1 atm:

$$S(\text{rhombic}) \rightleftharpoons S(\text{monoclinic})$$

Problems in Context

20.62 As a fuel, $H_2(g)$ produces only nonpolluting $H_2O(g)$ when it burns. Moreover, it combines with $O_2(g)$ in a fuel cell (Chapter 21) to provide electrical energy.
(a) Calculate $\Delta H°$, $\Delta S°$, and $\Delta G°$ per mole of H_2 at 298 K.
(b) Is the spontaneity of this reaction dependent on T? Explain.
(c) At what temperature does the reaction become spontaneous?

20.63 The U.S. government requires automobile fuels to contain a renewable component. Fermentation of glucose from corn yields ethanol, which is added to gasoline to fulfill this requirement:

$$C_6H_{12}O_6(s) \longrightarrow 2C_2H_5OH(l) + 2CO_2(g)$$

Calculate $\Delta H°$, $\Delta S°$, and $\Delta G°$ for the reaction at 25°C. Is the spontaneity of this reaction dependent on T? Explain.

Free Energy, Equilibrium, and Reaction Direction

(Sample Problems 20.9 and 20.10)

Concept Review Questions

20.64 (a) If $K << 1$ for a reaction, what do you know about the sign and magnitude of $\Delta G°$? (b) If $\Delta G° << 0$ for a reaction, what do you know about the magnitude of K? Of Q?

20.65 How is the free energy change of a process related to the work that can be obtained from the process? Is this quantity of work obtainable in practice? Explain.

20.66 The scenes and the graph relate to the reaction of $X_2(g)$ (*black*) with $Y_2(g)$ (*orange*) to form $XY(g)$. (a) If reactants and products are in their standard states, what quantity is represented on the graph by x? (b) Which scene represents point 1? Explain. (c) Which scene represents point 2? Explain.

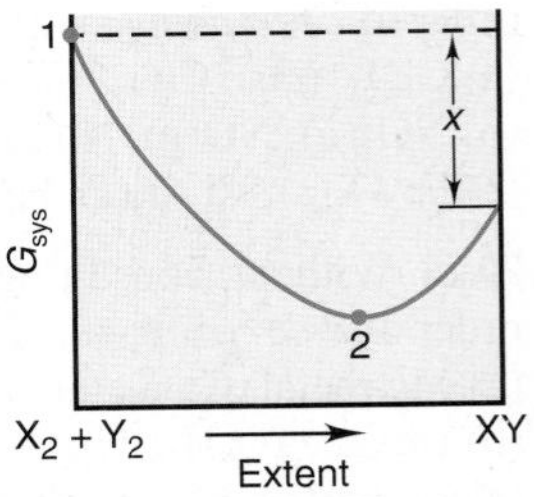

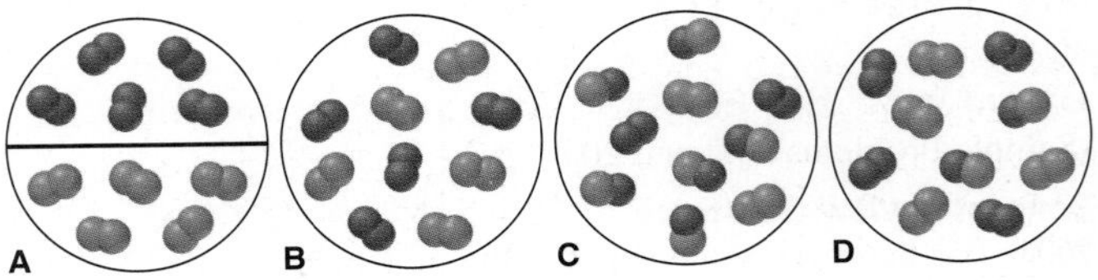

20.67 What is the difference between $\Delta G°$ and ΔG? Under what circumstances does $\Delta G = \Delta G°$?

Skill-Building Exercises (grouped in similar pairs)

20.68 Calculate K at 298 K for each reaction:
(a) $NO(g) + \tfrac{1}{2}O_2(g) \rightleftharpoons NO_2(g)$
(b) $2HCl(g) \rightleftharpoons H_2(g) + Cl_2(g)$
(c) $2C(\text{graphite}) + O_2(g) \rightleftharpoons 2CO(g)$

20.69 Calculate K at 298 K for each reaction:
(a) $MgCO_3(s) \rightleftharpoons Mg^{2+}(aq) + CO_3^{2-}(aq)$
(b) $2HCl(g) + Br_2(l) \rightleftharpoons 2HBr(g) + Cl_2(g)$
(c) $H_2(g) + O_2(g) \rightleftharpoons H_2O_2(l)$

20.70 Calculate K at 298 K for each reaction:
(a) $2H_2S(g) + 3O_2(g) \rightleftharpoons 2H_2O(g) + 2SO_2(g)$
(b) $H_2SO_4(l) \rightleftharpoons H_2O(l) + SO_3(g)$
(c) $HCN(aq) + NaOH(aq) \rightleftharpoons NaCN(aq) + H_2O(l)$

20.71 Calculate K at 298 K for each reaction:
(a) $SrSO_4(s) \rightleftharpoons Sr^{2+}(aq) + SO_4^{2-}(aq)$
(b) $2NO(g) + Cl_2(g) \rightleftharpoons 2NOCl(g)$
(c) $Cu_2S(s) + O_2(g) \rightleftharpoons 2Cu(s) + SO_2(g)$

20.72 Use Appendix B to determine the K_{sp} of Ag_2S.

20.73 Use Appendix B to determine the K_{sp} of CaF_2.

20.74 For the reaction $I_2(g) + Cl_2(g) \rightleftharpoons 2ICl(g)$, calculate K_p at 25°C [$\Delta G_f°$ of $ICl(g) = -6.075$ kJ/mol].

20.75 For the reaction $CaCO_3(s) \rightleftharpoons CaO(s) + CO_2(g)$, calculate the equilibrium P_{CO_2} at 25°C.

20.76 The K_{sp} of $PbCl_2$ is 1.7×10^{-5} at 25°C. What is $\Delta G°$? Is it possible to prepare a solution that contains $Pb^{2+}(aq)$ and $Cl^-(aq)$, at their standard-state concentrations?

20.77 The K_{sp} of ZnF_2 is 3.0×10^{-2} at 25°C. What is $\Delta G°$? Is it possible to prepare a solution that contains $Zn^{2+}(aq)$ and $F^-(aq)$ at their standard-state concentrations?

20.78 The equilibrium constant for the reaction

$$2Fe^{3+}(aq) + Hg_2^{2+}(aq) \rightleftharpoons 2Fe^{2+}(aq) + 2Hg^{2+}(aq)$$

is $K_c = 9.1\times10^{-6}$ at 298 K.
(a) What is $\Delta G°$ at this temperature?
(b) If standard-state concentrations of the reactants and products are mixed, in which direction does the reaction proceed?
(c) Calculate ΔG when $[Fe^{3+}] = 0.20\ M$, $[Hg_2^{2+}] = 0.010\ M$, $[Fe^{2+}] = 0.010\ M$, and $[Hg^{2+}] = 0.025\ M$. In which direction will the reaction proceed to achieve equilibrium?

20.79 The formation constant for the reaction

$$Ni^{2+}(aq) + 6NH_3(aq) \rightleftharpoons Ni(NH_3)_6^{2+}(aq)$$

is $K_f = 5.6\times10^8$ at 25°C.
(a) What is $\Delta G°$ at this temperature?
(b) If standard-state concentrations of the reactants and products are mixed, in which direction does the reaction proceed?
(c) Determine ΔG when $[Ni(NH_3)_6^{2+}] = 0.010\ M$, $[Ni^{2+}] = 0.0010\ M$, and $[NH_3] = 0.0050\ M$. In which direction will the reaction proceed to achieve equilibrium?

Problems in Context

20.80 High levels of ozone (O_3) cause rubber to deteriorate, green plants to turn brown, and many people to have difficulty breathing.
(a) Is the formation of O_3 from O_2 favored at all T, no T, high T, or low T?
(b) Calculate $\Delta G°$ for this reaction at 298 K.
(c) Calculate ΔG at 298 K for this reaction in urban smog where $[O_2] = 0.21$ atm and $[O_3] = 5\times10^{-7}$ atm.

20.81 A $BaSO_4$ slurry is ingested before the gastrointestinal tract is x-rayed because it is opaque to x-rays and defines the contours of the tract. Ba^{2+} ion is toxic, but the compound is nearly insoluble. If $\Delta G°$ at 37°C (body temperature) is 59.1 kJ/mol for the process

$$BaSO_4(s) \rightleftharpoons Ba^{2+}(aq) + SO_4^{2-}(aq)$$

what is $[Ba^{2+}]$ in the intestinal tract? (Assume that the only source of SO_4^{2-} is the ingested slurry.)

Comprehensive Problems

20.82 According to advertisements, "a diamond is forever."
(a) Calculate $\Delta H°$, $\Delta S°$, and $\Delta G°$ at 298 K for the phase change

$$\text{Diamond} \longrightarrow \text{graphite}$$

(b) Given the conditions under which diamond jewelry is normally kept, argue for and against the statement in the ad.
(c) Given the answers in part (a), what would need to be done to make synthetic diamonds from graphite?
(d) Assuming $\Delta H°$ and $\Delta S°$ do not change with temperature, can graphite be converted to diamond spontaneously at 1 atm?

20.83 Replace each question mark with the correct information:

	ΔS_{rxn}	ΔH_{rxn}	ΔG_{rxn}	Comment
(a)	+	−	−	?
(b)	?	0	−	Spontaneous
(c)	−	+	?	Not spontaneous
(d)	0	?	−	Spontaneous
(e)	?	0	+	?
(f)	+	+	?	$T\Delta S > \Delta H$

20.84 Among the many complex ions of cobalt are the following:

$$Co(NH_3)_6^{3+}(aq) + 3en(aq) \rightleftharpoons Co(en)_3^{3+}(aq) + 6NH_3(aq)$$

where "en" stands for ethylenediamine, $H_2NCH_2CH_2NH_2$. Six Co—N bonds are broken and six Co—N bonds are formed in this reaction, so $\Delta H°_{rxn} \approx 0$; yet $K > 1$. What are the signs of $\Delta S°$ and $\Delta G°$? What drives the reaction?

20.85 What is the change in entropy when 0.200 mol of potassium freezes at 63.7°C ($\Delta H_{fus} = 2.39$ kJ/mol)?

20.86 Is each statement true or false? If false, correct it.
(a) All spontaneous reactions occur quickly.
(b) The reverse of a spontaneous reaction is nonspontaneous.
(c) All spontaneous processes release heat.
(d) The boiling of water at 100°C and 1 atm is spontaneous.
(e) If a process increases the freedom of motion of the particles of a system, the entropy of the system decreases.
(f) The energy of the universe is constant; the entropy of the universe decreases toward a minimum.
(g) All systems disperse their energy spontaneously.
(h) Both ΔS_{sys} and ΔS_{surr} equal zero at equilibrium.

20.87 Hemoglobin carries O_2 from the lungs to tissue cells, where the O_2 is released. The protein is represented as Hb in its unoxygenated form and as Hb·O_2 in its oxygenated form. One reason CO is toxic is that it competes with O_2 in binding to Hb:

$$Hb\cdot O_2(aq) + CO(g) \rightleftharpoons Hb\cdot CO(aq) + O_2(g)$$

(a) If $\Delta G° \approx -14$ kJ at 37°C (body temperature), what is the ratio of [Hb·CO] to [Hb·O_2] at 37°C with $[O_2] = [CO]$?
(b) How is Le Châtelier's principle used to treat CO poisoning?

20.88 Magnesia (MgO) is used for fire brick, crucibles, and furnace linings because of its high melting point. It is produced by decomposing magnesite ($MgCO_3$) at around 1200°C.
(a) Write a balanced equation for magnesite decomposition.
(b) Use $\Delta H°$ and S° values to find $\Delta G°$ at 298 K.
(c) Assuming $\Delta H°$ and $S°$ do not change with temperature, find the minimum temperature at which the reaction is spontaneous.
(d) Calculate the equilibrium P_{CO_2} above $MgCO_3$ at 298 K.
(e) Calculate the equilibrium P_{CO_2} above $MgCO_3$ at 1200 K.

20.89 To prepare nuclear fuel, U_3O_8 ("yellow cake") is converted to $UO_2(NO_3)_2$, which is then converted to UO_3 and finally UO_2. The fuel is enriched (the proportion of the ^{235}U is increased) by a two-step conversion of UO_2 into UF_6, a volatile solid, followed by a gaseous-diffusion separation of the ^{235}U and ^{238}U isotopes:

$$UO_2(s) + 4HF(g) \longrightarrow UF_4(s) + 2H_2O(g)$$
$$UF_4(s) + F_2(g) \longrightarrow UF_6(s)$$

Calculate $\Delta G°$ for the overall process at 85°C:

	$\Delta H_f°$ (kJ/mol)	$S°$ (J/mol·K)	$\Delta G_f°$ (kJ/mol)
$UO_2(s)$	−1085	77.0	−1032
$UF_4(s)$	−1921	152	−1830.
$UF_6(s)$	−2197	225	−2068

20.90 Methanol, a major industrial feedstock, is made by several catalyzed reactions, such as $CO(g) + 2H_2(g) \longrightarrow CH_3OH(l)$.
(a) Show that this reaction is thermodynamically feasible.
(b) Is it favored at low or at high temperatures?
(c) One concern about using CH_3OH as an auto fuel is its oxidation in air to yield formaldehyde, $CH_2O(g)$, which poses a health hazard. Calculate $\Delta G°$ at 100.°C for this oxidation.

20.91 (a) Write a balanced equation for the gaseous reaction between N_2O_5 and F_2 to form NF_3 and O_2. (b) Determine $\Delta G°_{rxn}$.

(c) Find ΔG_{rxn} at 298 K if $P_{N_2O_5} = P_{F_2} = 0.20$ atm, $P_{NF_3} = 0.25$ atm, and $P_{O_2} = 0.50$ atm.

20.92 Consider the following reaction:

$$2NOBr(g) \rightleftharpoons 2NO(g) + Br_2(g) \qquad K = 0.42 \text{ at } 373 \text{ K}$$

Given that $S°$ of NOBr(*g*) = 272.6 J/mol·K and that $\Delta S°_{rxn}$ and $\Delta H°_{rxn}$ are constant with temperature, find
(a) $\Delta S°_{rxn}$ at 298 K (b) $\Delta G°_{rxn}$ at 373 K
(c) $\Delta H°_{rxn}$ at 373 K (d) $\Delta H°_f$ of NOBr at 298 K
(e) $\Delta G°_{rxn}$ at 298 K (f) $\Delta G°_f$ of NOBr at 298 K

20.93 Hydrogenation is the addition of H_2 to double (or triple) carbon-carbon bonds. Peanut butter and most commercial baked goods include hydrogenated oils. Find $\Delta H°$, $\Delta S°$, and $\Delta G°$ for the hydrogenation of ethene (C_2H_4) to ethane (C_2H_6) at 25°C.

20.94 Styrene is produced by catalytic dehydrogenation of ethylbenzene at high temperature in the presence of superheated steam.
(a) Find $\Delta H°_{rxn}$, $\Delta G°_{rxn}$, and $\Delta S°_{rxn}$, given these data at 298 K:

Compound	$\Delta H°_f$ (kJ/mol)	$\Delta G°_f$ (kJ/mol)	$S°$ (J/mol·K)
Ethylbenzene, $C_6H_5{-}CH_2CH_3$	−12.5	119.7	255
Styrene, $C_6H_5{-}CH{=}CH_2$	103.8	202.5	238

(b) At what temperature is the reaction spontaneous?
(c) What are $\Delta G°_{rxn}$ and K at 600.°C?
(d) With 5.0 parts steam to 1.0 part ethylbenzene in the reactant mixture and the total pressure kept constant at 1.3 atm, what is ΔG at 50.% conversion, that is, when 50.% of the ethylbenzene has reacted?

20.95 Propylene (propene; $CH_3CH{=}CH_2$) is used to produce polypropylene and many other chemicals. Although most is obtained from the cracking of petroleum, about 2% is produced by catalytic dehydrogenation of propane ($CH_3CH_2CH_3$):

$$CH_3CH_2CH_3 \xrightarrow{Pt/Al_2O_3} CH_3CH{=}CH_2 + H_2$$

Because this reaction is endothermic, heaters are placed between the reactor vessels to maintain the required temperature.
(a) If the molar entropy, $S°$, of propylene is 267.1 J/mol·K, find its entropy of formation, $S°_f$.
(b) Find $\Delta G°_f$ of propylene ($\Delta H°_f$ for propylene = 20.4 kJ/mol).
(c) Calculate $\Delta H°_{rxn}$ and $\Delta G°_{rxn}$ for the dehydrogenation.
(d) What is the theoretical yield of propylene at 580°C if the initial pressure of propane is 1.00 atm?
(e) Would the yield change if the reactor walls were permeable to H_2? Explain.
(f) At what temperature is the dehydrogenation spontaneous, with all substances in the standard state?

Note: Problems 20.96 and 20.97 relate to the thermodynamics of adenosine triphosphate (ATP). Refer to the Chemical Connections essay on pp. 836–837.

20.96 Find K for (a) the hydrolysis of ATP, (b) the dehydration-condensation to form glucose phosphate, and (c) the coupled reaction between ATP and glucose. (d) How does each K change when T changes from 25°C to 37°C?

20.97 Energy from ATP hydrolysis drives many nonspontaneous cell reactions:

$$ATP^{4-}(aq) + H_2O(l) \rightleftharpoons ADP^{3-}(aq) + HPO_4^{2-}(aq) + H^+(aq) \qquad \Delta G°' = -30.5 \text{ kJ}$$

Energy for the reverse process comes ultimately from glucose metabolism:

$$C_6H_{12}O_6(s) + 6O_2(g) \longrightarrow 6CO_2(g) + 6H_2O(l)$$

(a) Find K for the hydrolysis of ATP at 37°C.
(b) Find $\Delta G°'_{rxn}$ for metabolism of 1 mol of glucose.
(c) How many moles of ATP can be produced by metabolism of 1 mol of glucose?
(d) If 36 mol of ATP is formed, what is the actual yield?

20.98 From the following reaction and data, find (a) $S°$ of $SOCl_2$ and (b) T at which the reaction becomes nonspontaneous:

$$SO_3(g) + SCl_2(l) \longrightarrow SOCl_2(l) + SO_2(g) \qquad \Delta G°_{rxn} = -75.2 \text{ kJ}$$

	$SO_3(g)$	$SCl_2(l)$	$SOCl_2(l)$	$SO_2(g)$
$\Delta H°_f$ (kJ/mol)	−396	−50.0	−245.6	−296.8
$S°$ (J/mol·K)	256.7	184	—	248.1

20.99 Write equations for the oxidation of Fe and of Al. Use $\Delta G°_f$ to determine whether either process is spontaneous at 25°C.

20.100 The molecular scene depicts a gaseous equilibrium mixture at 460°C for the reaction of H_2 (*blue*) and I_2 (*purple*) to form HI. Each molecule represents 0.010 mol and the container volume is 1.0 L. (a) Is K_c >, =, or < 1? (b) Is K_p >, =, or < K_c? (c) Calculate $\Delta G°_{rxn}$. (d) How would the value of $\Delta G°_{rxn}$ change if the purple molecules represented H_2 and the blue I_2? Explain.

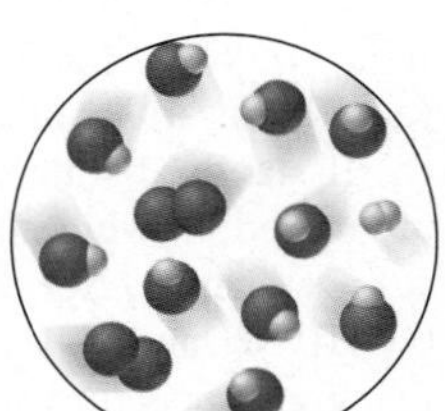

20.101 A key step in the metabolism of glucose for energy is the isomerization of glucose-6-phosphate (G6P) to fructose-6-phosphate (F6P): G6P $\rightleftharpoons$ F6P; $K = 0.510$ at 298 K.
(a) Calculate $\Delta G°$ at 298 K.
(b) Calculate ΔG when Q, the [F6P]/[G6P] ratio, equals 10.0.
(c) Calculate ΔG when $Q = 0.100$.
(d) Calculate Q if $\Delta G = -2.50$ kJ/mol.

20.102 A chemical reaction, such as HI forming from its elements, can reach equilibrium at many temperatures. In contrast, a phase change, such as ice melting, is in equilibrium at a given pressure only at the melting point. Each of the graphs below depicts G_{sys} vs. extent of change. (a) Which graph depicts how G_{sys} changes for the formation of HI? Explain. (b) Which graph depicts how G_{sys} changes as ice melts at 1°C and 1 atm? Explain.

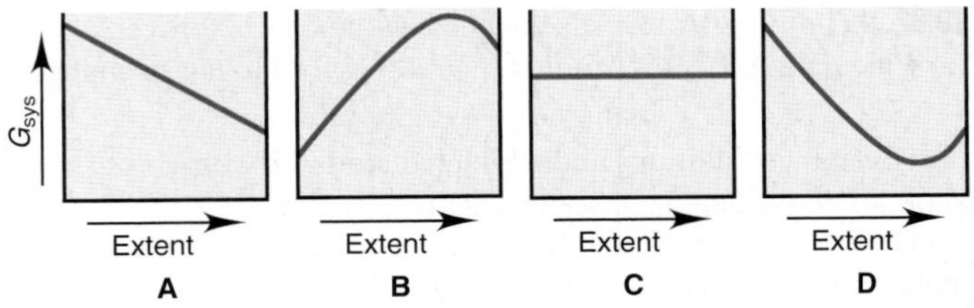

20.103 When heated, the DNA double helix separates into two random-coil single strands. When cooled, the random coils re-form the double helix: double helix $\rightleftharpoons$ 2 random coils.
(a) What is the sign of ΔS for the forward process? Why?
(b) Energy must be added to overcome H bonds and dispersion forces between the strands. What is the sign of ΔG for the forward process when $T\Delta S$ is smaller than ΔH?
(c) Write an expression that shows T in terms of ΔH and ΔS when the reaction is at equilibrium. (This temperature is called the *melting temperature* of the nucleic acid.)

20.104 In the process of respiration, glucose is oxidized completely. In fermentation, O_2 is absent and glucose is broken down to ethanol and CO_2. Ethanol is oxidized to CO_2 and H_2O.
(a) Balance the following equations for these processes:
Respiration: $C_6H_{12}O_6(s) + O_2(g) \longrightarrow CO_2(g) + H_2O(l)$
Fermentation: $C_6H_{12}O_6(s) \longrightarrow C_2H_5OH(l) + CO_2(g)$
Ethanol oxidation: $C_2H_5OH(l) + O_2(g) \longrightarrow CO_2(g) + H_2O(l)$
(b) Calculate ΔG°_{rxn} for respiration of 1.00 g of glucose.
(c) Calculate ΔG°_{rxn} for fermentation of 1.00 g of glucose.
(d) Calculate ΔG°_{rxn} for oxidation of the ethanol from part (c).

20.105 Consider the formation of ammonia:

$$N_2(g) + 3H_2(g) \rightleftharpoons 2NH_3(g)$$

(a) Assuming that ΔH° and ΔS° are constant with temperature, find the temperature at which $K_p = 1.00$.
(b) Find K_p at 400.°C, a typical temperature for NH_3 production.
(c) Given the lower K_p at the higher temperature, why are these conditions used industrially?

20.106 Kyanite, sillimanite, and andalusite all have the formula Al_2SiO_5. Each is stable under different conditions (see the graph at right). At the point where the three phases intersect:

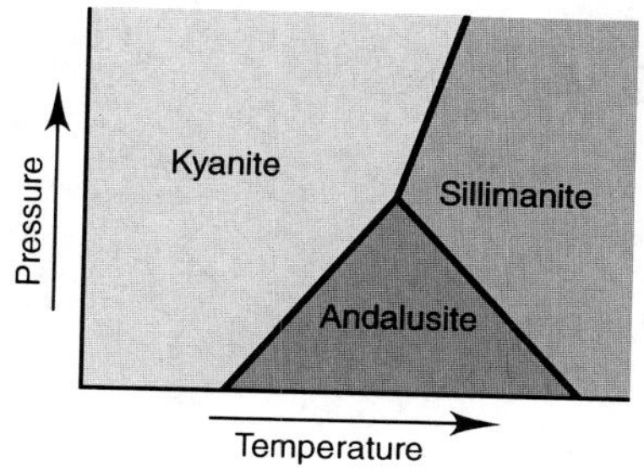

(a) Which mineral, if any, has the lowest free energy?
(b) Which mineral, if any, has the lowest enthalpy?
(c) Which mineral, if any, has the highest entropy?
(d) Which mineral, if any, has the lowest density?

20.107 Acetylene is produced commercially by the partial oxidation of methane. At 1500°C and pressures of 1–10 bar, the yield of acetylene is about 20%. The major side product is carbon monoxide, and some soot and carbon dioxide also form.
(a) At what temperature is the desired reaction spontaneous:

$$2CH_4 + \tfrac{1}{2}O_2 \longrightarrow C_2H_2 + 2H_2 + H_2O$$

(b) Acetylene can also be made by the reaction of its elements, carbon (graphite) and hydrogen. At what temperature is this formation reaction spontaneous?
(c) Why must this reaction mixture be immediately cooled?

20.108 Synthesis gas, a mixture that includes the fuels CO and H_2, is used to produce liquid hydrocarbons and methanol. It is made at pressures up to 100 atm by oxidation of methane followed by the steam re-forming and water-gas shift reactions. Because the process is exothermic, temperatures reach 950–1100°C, and the conditions are such that the amounts of H_2, CO, CO_2, CH_4, and H_2O leaving the reactor are close to the equilibrium amounts for the steam re-forming and water-gas shift reactions:

$$CH_4(g) + H_2O(g) \rightleftharpoons CO(g) + 3H_2(g) \quad \text{(steam re-forming)}$$

$$CO(g) + H_2O(g) \rightleftharpoons CO_2(g) + H_2(g) \quad \text{(water-gas shift)}$$

(a) At 1000.°C, what are ΔG° and ΔH° for the steam re-forming reaction and for the water-gas shift reaction?
(b) By doubling the steam re-forming step and adding it to the water-gas shift step, we obtain the following combined reaction:

$$2CH_4(g) + 3H_2O(g) \rightleftharpoons CO_2(g) + CO(g) + 7H_2(g)$$

Is this reaction spontaneous at 1000.°C in the standard state?
(c) Is it spontaneous at 98 atm and 50.% conversion (when 50.% of the starting materials have reacted)?
(d) Is it spontaneous at 98 atm and 90.% conversion?

Nuclear Reactions and Their Applications

24

Concepts and skills to review before you study this chapter

- discovery of the atomic nucleus (Section 2.4)
- protons, neutrons, mass number, and the $^A_Z X$ notation (Section 2.5)
- half-life and first-order reaction rate (Section 16.4)

You might find it hard to believe that uranium within the fuel pellets used in nuclear power reactors has any measureable behavior in common with ordinary bananas, but both exhibit **radioactivity,** the spontaneous disintegration of an unstable nucleus by emission of radiation. A very small percentage of unstable potassium atoms in a banana are the source of its tiny amount of radioactivity. In fact, as we'll discuss, many everyday materials exhibit radioactivity. For example, the trees that produce Brazil nuts have such deep root systems that the nuts have 1000 times more radium than the next most radioactive food. (Despite these facts, the levels of radioactivity in bananas and Brazil nuts are miniscule and present no health risk.)

Up to this point, we have focused on the atom's electrons, treating the nucleus as their electrostatic anchor and examining the effect of its positive charge on atomic properties and, ultimately, chemical behavior. In this chapter, we *will* focus on the atom's tiny, dense core, which is held together by the strongest force in the universe. Scientists studying the structure and behavior of the nucleus see enormous potential as well as great mystery and wonder.

But society is ambivalent about some applications of nuclear research. The promise of abundant energy and treatments for disease is offset by the threat of nuclear waste contamination, reactor accidents, and unimaginable destruction from nuclear war or terrorism. Can the power of the nucleus be harnessed for our benefit, or are the risks too great? By studying this chapter, you'll learn the principles that can help you consider this vital question knowledgably.

The changes that occur in atomic nuclei differ strikingly from chemical changes. In chemical reactions, electrons are shared or transferred to form *compounds,* while nuclei remain unchanged. In nuclear reactions, the roles are reversed: electrons take part much less often, while nuclei undergo changes that, in nearly every case, form different *elements.* Nuclear reactions are often accompanied by energy changes a million times greater than those for chemical reactions, energy changes so large that changes in mass *are* detectable. Moreover, nuclear reaction yields and rates are *not* subject to the effects of pressure, temperature, and catalysis that chemical reactions are. Table 24.1 summarizes these general differences.

Table 24.1 Comparison of Chemical and Nuclear Reactions

Chemical Reactions	Nuclear Reactions
1. One substance is converted into another, but atoms never change identity.	1. Atoms of one element typically are converted into atoms of another element.
2. Electrons in orbitals are involved as bonds break and form; nuclear particles do not take part.	2. Protons, neutrons, and other nuclear particles are involved; electrons in orbitals take part much less often.
3. Reactions are accompanied by relatively small changes in energy and no measurable changes in mass.	3. Reactions are accompanied by relatively large changes in energy and measurable changes in mass.
4. Reaction rates are influenced by temperature, concentration, catalysts, and the compound in which an element occurs.	4. Reaction rates depend on number of nuclei, but are not affected by temperature, catalysts, or, except on rare occasions, the compound in which an element occurs.

IN THIS CHAPTER . . . We survey the field of nuclear chemistry, examining radioactive nuclei and their decay processes, especially the effects and applications of radioactivity and the interconversion of matter and energy.

- We investigate nuclear stability to determine why some nuclei are stable and others are not and undergo radioactive decay.
- We learn how radioactivity is detected and how the kinetics of decay is applied.
- We see how nuclei synthesized in particle accelerators have extended the periodic table.
- We consider the effects of radioactive emissions on matter, especially living tissue, and focus on some major uses of radioisotopes in science, technology, and medicine.
- We discuss the mass difference that arises when a nucleus forms from its subatomic particles and the energy that is equivalent to this difference.
- We explore current and future attempts to harness the energy released when heavy nuclei split and lighter ones fuse.
- Finally, we look at the nuclear processes in stars that continue to create chemical elements.

24.1 • RADIOACTIVE DECAY AND NUCLEAR STABILITY

A stable nucleus remains intact indefinitely, but *the great majority of nuclei are unstable.* An unstable nucleus exhibits radioactivity, spontaneously decaying by emitting radiation. In Section 24.2, you'll see that each type of unstable nucleus has its own characteristic *rate* of radioactive decay. In this section, we cover important terms and notation for nuclei, discuss some key events in the discovery of radioactivity, define the types of emission, and describe various modes of radioactive decay and how to predict which occurs for a given nucleus.

The Components of the Nucleus: Terms and Notation

Recall from Chapter 2 that the nucleus contains essentially all the atom's mass but is only about 10^{-5} times its radius (or 10^{-15} times its volume), making the nucleus incredibly dense: about 10^{14} g/mL. ● *Protons* and *neutrons,* the elementary particles that make up the nucleus, are called **nucleons.** A **nuclide** is a nucleus with a particular composition, that is, with specific numbers of the two types of nucleons. Most elements occur in nature as a mixture of **isotopes,** atoms with the characteristic number of protons of the element but different numbers of neutrons. Each isotope of an element thus has a different nuclide. For example, oxygen has three naturally occurring isotopes—the most abundant contains eight protons and eight neutrons, whereas the least abundant contains eight protons and nine neutrons.

● **Big Atom, Massive Core** If you could strip the electrons from the atoms in an object and compress the nuclei together, the object would lose only a fraction of a percent of its mass, but it would shrink to 0.0000000000001% (10^{-13}%) of its volume!

The relative mass and charge of a particle—nucleon, elementary particle, or nuclide—is described by the notation ${}^{A}_{Z}\text{X}$, where X is the *symbol* for the particle, *A* is the *mass number,* or the total number of nucleons, and *Z* is the *charge* of the particle; for nuclei, *A* is the *sum of protons and neutrons* and *Z* is the *number of protons* (atomic number). In this notation, the three subatomic elementary particles are

$$ {}^{0}_{-1}\text{e (electron)}, {}^{1}_{1}\text{p (proton), and } {}^{1}_{0}\text{n (neutron)} $$

(A proton is also sometimes represented as ${}^{1}_{1}\text{H}^{+}$.) The number of neutrons (*N*) in a nucleus is the mass number (*A*) minus the atomic number (*Z*): $N = A - Z$. The two naturally occurring stable isotopes of chlorine, for example, have 17 protons ($Z = 17$), but one has 18 neutrons (${}^{35}_{17}\text{Cl}$, also written ${}^{35}\text{Cl}$) and the other has 20 (${}^{37}_{17}\text{Cl}$, or ${}^{37}\text{Cl}$). Nuclides can also be designated with the element name followed by the mass number, for example, chlorine-35 and chlorine-37. In naturally occurring samples of an element or its compounds, *the isotopes of the element are present in specific proportions* that vary only very slightly. Thus, in a sample of sodium chloride (or any Cl-containing substance), 75.77% of the Cl atoms are chlorine-35 and the remaining 24.23% are chlorine-37.

To understand this chapter, it's very important that you are comfortable with nuclear notations, so please take a moment to review Sample Problem 2.4 (pp. 49–50) and Problems 2.39 to 2.46 (p. 76).

The Discovery of Radioactivity and the Types of Emissions

In 1896, the French physicist Antoine-Henri Becquerel accidentally discovered that uranium minerals, even when wrapped in paper and stored in the dark, emit a penetrating radiation that can expose a photographic plate. Becquerel also found that the radiation creates an electric discharge in air, thus providing a means for measuring its intensity.

Two years later, a young doctoral student named Marie Sklodowska Curie began a search for other minerals that behaved in this way. She found that thorium minerals also emit radiation and, most importantly, that *the intensity of the radiation is directly proportional to the concentration of the element in the mineral, not to the formula of the mineral or compound.* Curie named the emissions *radioactivity* and showed that they are *unaffected by temperature, pressure, or other physical and chemical conditions.*

After months of painstaking chemical work, Curie and her husband, physicist Pierre Curie, isolated two new elements from pitchblende, the principal ore of uranium: polonium (Po; $Z = 84$), the most metallic member of Group 6A(16), and radium (Ra; $Z = 88$), the heaviest alkaline earth metal.

Then, starting with several tons of pitchblende residues from which the uranium had been extracted and working arduously for four years, Curie isolated 0.1 g of radium chloride, which she melted and electrolyzed to obtain pure metallic radium. Curie is the only person to have received two Nobel Prizes in science, one in physics for her research into radioactivity, and the other in chemistry for her discoveries of polonium and radium.

During the next few years, Henri Becquerel, the Curies, and P. Villard in France and Ernest Rutherford and his coworkers in England studied the nature of radioactive emissions. A key finding was the observation of Rutherford and his colleague Frederick Soddy that elements other than radium were formed when radium decayed. In 1902, they proposed that radioactive emission results in the change of one element into another. This explanation seemed like a return to alchemy and was met with disbelief and ridicule. We now know it to be true: *when a nuclide of one element decays, it emits radiation and usually changes into a nuclide of a different element.*

There are three natural types of radioactive emission:

- **Alpha particles** (symbolized α, ${}^{4}_{2}\alpha$, or ${}^{4}_{2}He^{2+}$) are identical to helium-4 nuclei.
- **Beta particles** (symbolized β, β^-, or sometimes ${}^{0}_{-1}\beta$) are high-speed electrons. (The emission of electrons from the nucleus may seem strange, but as you'll see shortly, they result from a nuclear reaction.)
- **Gamma rays** (symbolized γ, or sometimes ${}^{0}_{0}\gamma$) are very high-energy photons.

Figure 24.1 illustrates the behavior of these emissions in an electric field: the positively charged α particles curve to a small extent toward the negative plate, the negatively charged β particles curve to a greater extent toward the positive plate (because they have lower mass), and the uncharged γ rays are not affected by the electric field.

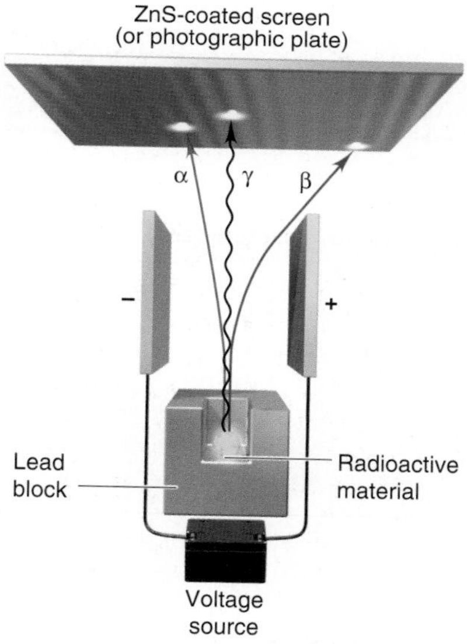

Figure 24.1 How the three types of radioactive emissions behave in an electric field.

Modes of Radioactive Decay; Balancing Nuclear Equations

When a nuclide decays, it forms a nuclide of lower energy, and the excess energy is carried off by the emitted radiation and the recoiling nucleus. The decaying, or reactant, nuclide is called the *parent;* the product nuclide is called the *daughter.* Nuclides can decay in several ways. As each of the major modes of decay is introduced (summarized in Table 24.2 on the next page), we'll show examples of that mode and apply the key principle used to balance nuclear reactions: *the total Z (charge, number of protons) and the total A (sum of protons and neutrons) of the reactants equal those of the products:*

$$\frac{\text{Total } A}{\text{Total } Z}\text{Reactants} = \frac{\text{Total } A}{\text{Total } Z}\text{Products} \qquad (24.1)$$

Table 24.2 Modes of Radioactive Decay*

Mode	Emission	Decay Process	Change in A	Change in Z	Change in N
α Decay	$\alpha(^{4}_{2}He^{2+})$	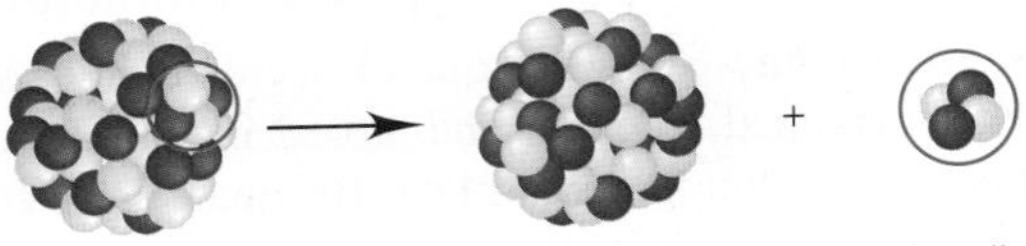 → + α expelled	−4	−2	−2
β^- Decay†	$\beta^-(^{\ 0}_{-1}\beta)$	 nucleus with xp^+ and yn^0 → nucleus with $(x+1)p^+$ and $(y-1)n^0$ + $^{\ 0}_{-1}\beta$ (β^- expelled)	0	+1	−1
	Net:	$^{1}_{0}n$ (in nucleus) → $^{1}_{1}p$ (in nucleus) + $^{\ 0}_{-1}\beta$ (β^- expelled)			
Positron (β^+) emission†	$\beta^+(^{0}_{1}\beta)$	 nucleus with xp^+ and yn^0 → nucleus with $(x-1)p^+$ and $(y+1)n^0$ + $^{0}_{1}\beta$ (β^+ expelled)	0	−1	+1
	Net:	$^{1}_{1}p$ (in nucleus) → $^{1}_{0}n$ (in nucleus) + $^{0}_{1}\beta$ (β^+ expelled)			
Electron (e^-) capture (EC)†	x-ray	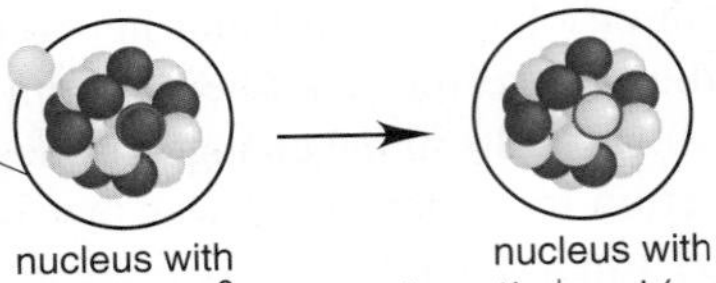 low-energy orbital; nucleus with xp^+ and yn^0 → nucleus with $(x-1)p^+$ and $(y+1)n^0$	0	−1	+1
	Net:	$^{\ 0}_{-1}e$ (absorbed from low-energy orbital) + $^{1}_{1}p$ (in nucleus) → $^{1}_{0}n$ (in nucleus)			
Gamma (γ) emission	γ	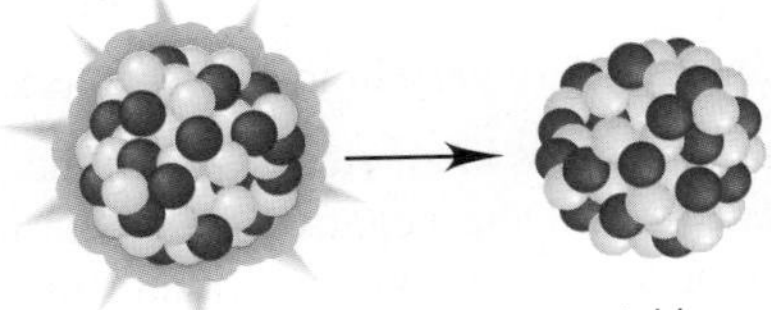 excited nucleus → stable nucleus + γ (γ photon radiated)	0	0	0

*Nuclear chemists consider β^- decay, positron emission, and electron capture to be three decay modes of the more general process known as beta decay (see text).

†Neutrinos (ν) or antineutrinos ($\bar{\nu}$) are also formed during the three modes of beta decay. Although we will not include them in other equations in the chapter, keep in mind that antineutrinos are always expelled during β^- decay, and neutrinos are expelled during β^+ emission and e^- capture.

1. **Alpha (α) decay** involves the loss of an α particle from a nucleus. For each α particle emitted by the parent, *A decreases by 4 and Z decreases by 2* in the daughter. Every element beyond bismuth (Bi; $Z = 83$) is radioactive and exhibits α decay, which is *the most common means for a heavy, unstable nucleus to become more stable*. For example, radium undergoes α decay to yield radon (Rn; $Z = 86$):

$$^{226}_{88}\text{Ra} \longrightarrow ^{222}_{86}\text{Rn} + ^{4}_{2}\alpha$$

Note that the A value for Ra equals the sum of the A values for Rn and α ($226 = 222 + 4$), and that the Z value for Ra equals the sum of the Z values for Rn and α ($88 = 86 + 2$).

2. **Beta (β) decay** is a more general class of radioactive decay that includes three modes: β^- decay, β^+ emission, and electron capture.

- **β^- decay** (or *negatron emission*) occurs through the ejection of a β^- particle from the nucleus. This change does not involve expulsion of a β^- particle that was in the nucleus; rather, *a neutron is converted into a proton, which remains in the nucleus, and a β^- particle, which is expelled immediately:*

$$^{1}_{0}\text{n} \longrightarrow ^{1}_{1}\text{p} + ^{0}_{-1}\beta$$

As always, the totals of the A and the Z values for reactant and products are equal. Radioactive nickel-63 becomes stable copper-63 through β^- decay:

$$^{63}_{28}\text{Ni} \longrightarrow ^{63}_{29}\text{Cu} + ^{0}_{-1}\beta$$

Another example is the β^- decay of carbon-14, used in radiocarbon dating:

$$^{14}_{6}\text{C} \longrightarrow ^{14}_{7}\text{N} + ^{0}_{-1}\beta$$

Note that *β^- decay results in a product nuclide with the same A but with Z one higher (one more proton) than in the reactant nuclide.* In other words, an atom of the element with the next *higher* atomic number is formed. Although equations in this chapter do not include it, a neutral particle called an antineutrino ($\bar{\nu}$) is also emitted during β^- decay. The mass of the antineutrino is thought to be much less than 10^{-4} times that of an electron.

- **Positron (β^+) emission** is the emission of a β^+ particle from the nucleus. A key idea of modern physics is that most fundamental particles have corresponding *antiparticles* with the same mass but opposite charge. The **positron** is the antiparticle of the electron. Positron emission occurs through a process in which *a proton in the nucleus is converted into a neutron, and a positron is expelled:*

$$^{1}_{1}p \longrightarrow ^{1}_{0}n + ^{0}_{1}\beta$$

Also emitted during this process is a *neutrino* (ν), the antiparticle of the antineutrino. In terms of the effect on A and Z, *positron emission has the opposite effect of β^- decay: the daughter has the same A but Z is one lower (one fewer proton) than the parent.* Thus, an atom of the element with the next *lower* atomic number forms. Carbon-11, a synthetic radioisotope, decays to a stable boron isotope through β^+ emission:

$$^{11}_{6}\text{C} \longrightarrow ^{11}_{5}\text{B} + ^{0}_{1}\beta$$

- **Electron (e^-) capture (EC)** occurs when the nucleus interacts with an electron in a low atomic energy level. The net effect is that *a proton is transformed into a neutron:*

$$^{1}_{1}\text{p} + ^{0}_{-1}\text{e} \longrightarrow ^{1}_{0}\text{n}$$

(We use the symbol "e" to distinguish an orbital electron from a beta particle, β.) The orbital vacancy is quickly filled by an electron that moves down from a higher energy level, and that process continues through still higher energy levels, with x-ray photons and neutrinos carrying off the energy difference in each step. Radioactive iron forms stable manganese through electron capture:

$$^{55}_{26}\text{Fe} + ^{0}_{-1}\text{e} \longrightarrow ^{55}_{25}\text{Mn} + h\nu \text{ (x-rays and neutrinos)}$$

Even though the processes are different, *electron capture has the same net effect as positron emission: Z* lower by 1, *A* unchanged.

3. **Gamma (γ) emission** involves the radiation of high-energy γ photons (also called γ rays) from an excited nucleus. Just as an atom in an excited *electronic*

state reduces its energy by emitting photons, usually in the UV and visible ranges (see Section 7.2), a nucleus in an excited state lowers its energy by emitting γ photons, which are of much higher energy (much shorter wavelength) than UV photons. Many nuclear processes leave the nucleus in an excited state, so *γ emission accompanies many other (mostly β) types of decay.* Several γ photons of different energies can be emitted from an excited nucleus as it returns to the ground state. Some of Marie Curie's experiments involved the release of γ rays, such as

$$^{215}_{84}\text{Po} \longrightarrow {}^{211}_{82}\text{Pb} + {}^{4}_{2}\alpha \text{ (several } \gamma \text{ emitted)}$$

Gamma emission often accompanies β^- decay:

$$^{99}_{43}\text{Tc} \longrightarrow {}^{99}_{44}\text{Ru} + {}^{0}_{-1}\beta \text{ (several } \gamma \text{ emitted)}$$

Because γ rays have no mass or charge, *γ emission does not change A or Z.* Two gamma rays are emitted when a particle and an antiparticle annihilate each other. In the medical technique known as *positron-emission tomography* (which we discuss in Section 24.5), a positron and an electron annihilate each other (with all A and Z values shown):

$$^{0}_{1}\beta + {}^{0}_{-1}\text{e} \longrightarrow 2^{0}_{0}\gamma$$

Sample Problem 24.1 Writing Equations for Nuclear Reactions

Problem Write balanced equations for the following nuclear reactions:
(a) Naturally occurring thorium-232 undergoes α decay.
(b) Zirconium-86 undergoes electron capture.

Plan We first write a skeleton equation that includes the mass numbers, atomic numbers, and symbols of all the particles on the correct sides of the equation, showing the unknown product particle as $^{A}_{Z}\text{X}$. Then, because the total of mass numbers and the total of charges on the left side and the right side must be equal, we solve for A and Z, and use Z to determine X from the periodic table.

Solution **(a)** Writing the skeleton equation, with the α particle as a product:

$$^{232}_{90}\text{Th} \longrightarrow {}^{A}_{Z}\text{X} + {}^{4}_{2}\alpha$$

Solving for A and Z and balancing the equation: For A, $232 = A + 4$, so $A = 228$. For Z, $90 = Z + 2$, so $Z = 88$. From the periodic table, we see that the element with $Z = 88$ is radium (Ra). Thus, the balanced equation is

$$^{232}_{90}\text{Th} \longrightarrow {}^{228}_{88}\text{Ra} + {}^{4}_{2}\alpha$$

(b) Writing the skeleton equation, with the captured electron as a reactant:

$$^{86}_{40}\text{Zr} + {}^{0}_{-1}\text{e} \longrightarrow {}^{A}_{Z}\text{X}$$

Solving for A and Z and balancing the equation: For A, $86 + 0 = A$, so $A = 86$. For Z, $40 + (-1) = Z$, so $Z = 39$. The element with $Z = 39$ is yttrium (Y), so we have

$$^{86}_{40}\text{Zr} + {}^{0}_{-1}\text{e} \longrightarrow {}^{86}_{39}\text{Y}$$

Check Always read across superscripts and then across subscripts, with the yield arrow as an equal sign, to check your arithmetic. In part (a), for example, $232 = 228 + 4$, and $90 = 88 + 2$.

Follow-Up Problem 24.1 Write a balanced equation for the reaction in which a nuclide undergoes β^- decay and changes to cesium-133.

Nuclear Stability and the Mode of Decay

Can we predict how, and whether, an unstable nuclide will decay? Our knowledge of the nucleus is much less complete than that of the whole atom, but some patterns emerge by observing naturally occurring nuclides.

The Band of Stability Two key factors determine the stability of a nuclide:

1. The number of neutrons (N), the number of protons (Z), and their ratio (N/Z), which we calculate from $(A - Z)/Z$. This factor relates primarily to nuclides that undergo one of the three modes of β decay.

2. The total mass of the nuclide, which mostly relates to nuclides that undergo α decay.

Figure 24.2A is a plot of number of neutrons vs. number of protons for all stable nuclides. Note the following:

- The points form a narrow **band of stability** that gradually curves above the line for $N = Z$ ($N/Z = 1$).
- The only stable nuclides with $N/Z < 1$ are $^{1}_{1}\text{H}$ and $^{3}_{2}\text{He}$.
- Many lighter nuclides with $N = Z$ are stable, such as $^{4}_{2}\text{He}$, $^{12}_{6}\text{C}$, $^{16}_{8}\text{O}$, and $^{20}_{10}\text{Ne}$; the heaviest of these is $^{40}_{20}\text{Ca}$. Thus, for lighter nuclides, one neutron for each proton ($N = Z$) is enough to provide stability.
- The N/Z ratio of stable nuclides gradually increases as Z increases. For example, for $^{56}_{26}\text{Fe}$, $N/Z = 1.15$; for $^{107}_{47}\text{Ag}$, $N/Z = 1.28$; for $^{184}_{74}\text{W}$, $N/Z = 1.49$, and, finally, for $^{209}_{83}\text{Bi}$, $N/Z = 1.52$. Thus, for heavier stable nuclides, $N > Z$ ($N/Z > 1$), and N increases faster than Z. As we discuss below, and show in Figure 24.2B, if N/Z of a nuclide is either too high (above the band) or not high enough (below the band), the nuclide is unstable and undergoes one of the three modes of beta decay.
- All nuclides with $Z > 83$ are unstable.* This means that all nuclides with a higher Z—the largest members of main groups 1A(1) through 8A(18), actinium and the actinides ($Z = 89$–103), and the other elements of the fourth ($6d$) transition series ($Z = 104$–112)—are radioactive, and, as we point out below, undergo α decay.

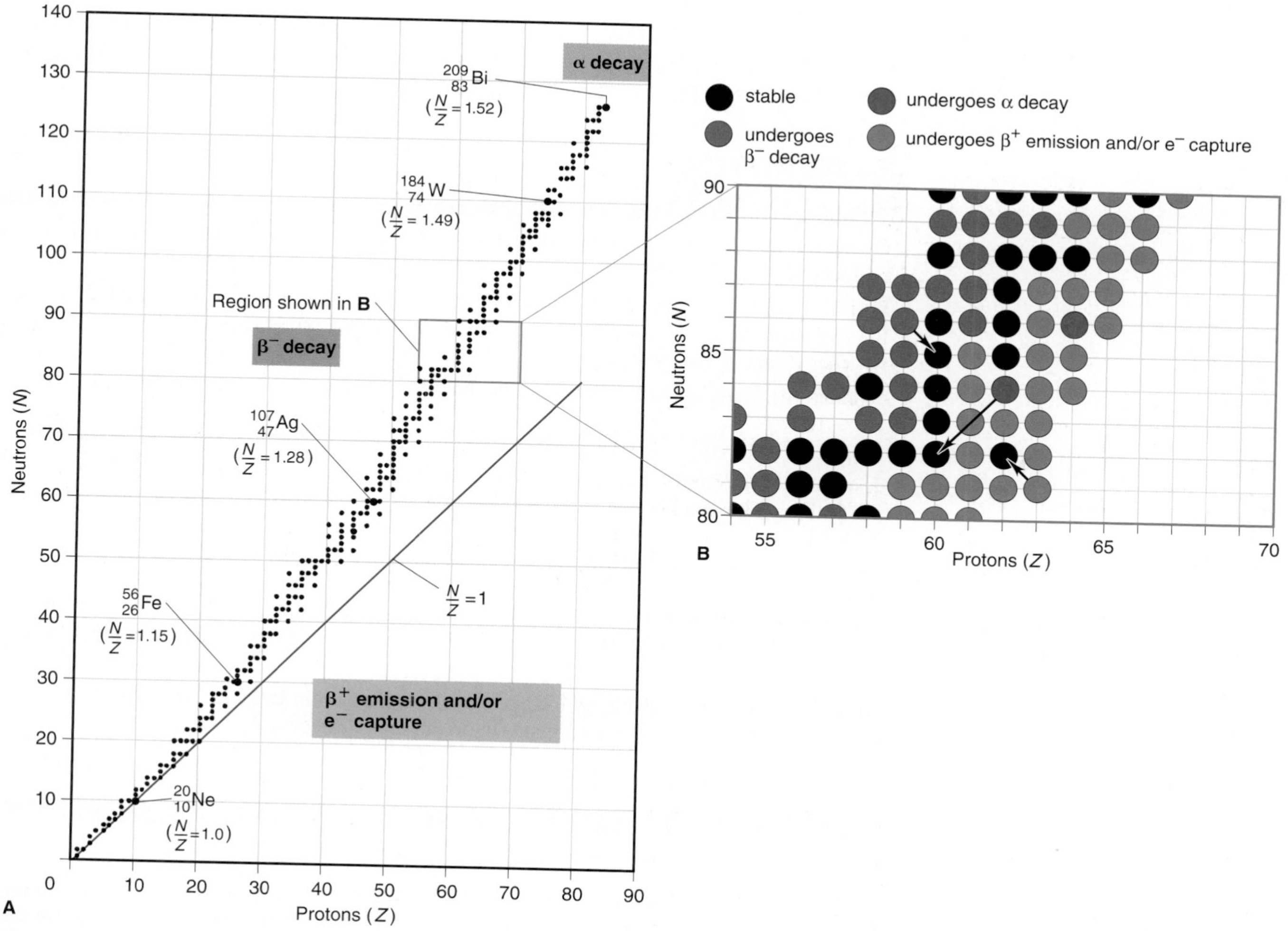

Figure 24.2 A plot of number of neutrons vs. number of protons for the stable nuclides.

Table 24.3 Number of Stable Nuclides for Elements 48 to 54*

Element	Atomic No. (Z)	No. of Nuclides
Cd	**48**	**8**
In	49	2
Sn	**50**	**10**
Sb	51	2
Te	**52**	**8**
I	53	1
Xe	**54**	**9**

*Even Z shown in boldface.

Table 24.4 An Even-Odd Breakdown of the Stable Nuclides

Z	N	No. of Nuclides
Even	Even	157
Even	Odd	53
Odd	Even	50
Odd	Odd	4
	TOTAL	264

Stability and Nuclear Structure Given that protons are positively charged and neutrons are uncharged, the first question to ask is what holds the nucleus together? Nuclear scientists answer this question and explain the importance of N and Z values in terms of two opposing forces: Electrostatic repulsive forces between protons would break the nucleus apart if not for an attractive force called the **strong force,** which exists between all nucleons (protons and neutrons). This force is 137 times stronger than the repulsive force but *operates only over the short distances within the nucleus.* Thus, the *attractive* strong force overwhelms the much weaker *repulsive* electrostatic force and keeps the nucleus together.

The oddness or evenness of N and Z values is related to some important patterns of nuclear stability. Two interesting points become apparent when we classify the known stable nuclides:

1. Elements with an even Z (number of protons) usually have a larger number of stable nuclides than elements with an odd Z. Table 24.3 demonstrates this point for cadmium ($Z = 48$) through xenon ($Z = 54$).
2. Well over half the stable nuclides have *both* even N and even Z (Table 24.4). Only four nuclides with odd N and odd Z are stable: $^{2}_{1}H$, $^{6}_{3}Li$, $^{10}_{5}B$, and $^{14}_{7}N$.

One model of nuclear structure that attempts to explain the stability of even values of N and Z postulates that protons and neutrons lie in *nucleon energy levels,* and that greater stability results from the *pairing of spins* of like nucleons. (Note the analogy to electron energy levels and the stability from pairing of electron spins.)

Just as noble gases—with 2, 10, 18, 36, 54, and 86 electrons—are exceptionally stable because they have filled *electron* levels, nuclides with N or Z values of 2, 8, 20, 28, 50, 82 (and $N = 126$) are exceptionally stable. These so-called *magic numbers* are thought to correspond to the numbers of protons or neutrons in filled *nucleon* levels. A few examples are $^{50}_{22}Ti$ ($N = 28$), $^{88}_{38}Sr$ ($N = 50$), and the ten stable nuclides of tin ($Z = 50$). Some extremely stable nuclides have two magic numbers: $^{4}_{2}He$, $^{16}_{8}O$, $^{40}_{20}Ca$, and $^{208}_{82}Pb$ ($N = 126$).

Sample Problem 24.2 Predicting Nuclear Stability

Problem Which of the following nuclides would you predict to be stable and which radioactive: **(a)** $^{18}_{10}Ne$; **(b)** $^{32}_{16}S$; **(c)** $^{236}_{90}Th$; **(d)** $^{123}_{56}Ba$? Explain.

Plan In order to evaluate the stability of each nuclide, we determine the N and Z values, the N/Z ratio from $(A - Z)/Z$, the value of Z, stable N/Z ratios (from Figure 24.2A), and whether Z and N are even or odd.

Solution (a) Radioactive. This nuclide has $N = 8$ (18 − 10) and $Z = 10$, so $N/Z = \frac{18 - 10}{10} = 0.8$. Except for hydrogen-1 and helium-3, no nuclides with $N < Z$ are stable; despite its even N and Z, this nuclide has too few neutrons to be stable.

(b) Stable. This nuclide has $N = Z = 16$, so $N/Z = 1.0$. With $Z < 20$ and even N and Z, this nuclide is most likely stable.

(c) Radioactive. This nuclide has $Z = 90$, and every nuclide with $Z > 83$ is radioactive.

(d) Radioactive. This nuclide has $N = 67$ and $Z = 56$, so $N/Z = 1.20$. For Z values of 55 to 60, Figure 24.2A shows $N/Z \geq 1.3$, so this nuclide has too few neutrons to be stable.

Check By consulting a table of isotopes, such as the one in the *CRC Handbook of Chemistry and Physics,* we find that our predictions are correct.

Follow-Up Problem 24.2 Why is $^{31}_{15}P$ stable but $^{30}_{15}P$ unstable?

*In 2003, French nuclear physicists discovered that $^{209}_{83}Bi$ actually undergoes α decay, but the half-life is 1.9×10^{19} yr, about a billion times longer than the estimated age of the universe. Bismuth ($Z = 83$) can thus be considered stable.

Predicting the Mode of Decay An unstable nuclide generally decays in a mode that shifts its *N/Z* ratio toward the band of stability. This fact is illustrated in Figure 24.2B, which expands the small region of $Z = 54$ to 70 in Figure 24.2A to show the stable *and* many of the unstable nuclides in that region, as well as their modes of decay. Note the following points:

1. *Neutron-rich nuclides.* Nuclides with too many neutrons for stability (a high *N/Z*) lie above the band of stability. They undergo *β^- decay,* which converts a neutron into a proton, thus reducing the value of *N/Z*.
2. *Proton-rich nuclides.* Nuclides with too many protons for stability (a low *N/Z*) lie below the band. They undergo *β^+ emission* and/or *e^- capture,* both of which convert a proton into a neutron, thus increasing the value of *N/Z*. (The rate of e^- capture increases with *Z*, so β^+ emission is more common among lighter elements and e^- capture more common among heavier elements.)
3. *Heavy nuclides.* Nuclides with $Z > 83$ (shown in Figure 24.2A) are too heavy to be stable and undergo *α decay,* which reduces their *Z* and *N* values by two units per emission.

With the information in Figure 24.2, predicting the mode of decay of an unstable nuclide means just comparing its *N/Z* ratio with those in the nearby region of the band of stability. But, even without Figure 24.2, we can often make an educated guess about mode of decay. The atomic mass of an element is the weighted average of its naturally occurring isotopes. Therefore,

- The mass number *A* of a *stable* nuclide will be relatively close to the atomic mass.
- If an *unstable* nuclide of an element (given *Z*) has an *A* value much higher than the atomic mass, it is neutron rich and will probably decay by β^- emission.
- If, on the other hand, the unstable nuclide has an *A* value much lower than the atomic mass, it is proton rich and will probably decay by β^+ emission and/or e^- capture.

In the next sample problem, we predict the mode of decay of some unstable nuclides.

Sample Problem 24.3 Predicting the Mode of Nuclear Decay

Problem Use the atomic mass of the element to predict the mode(s) of decay of the following radioactive nuclides: **(a)** $^{12}_{5}B$; **(b)** $^{234}_{92}U$; **(c)** $^{81}_{33}As$; **(d)** $^{127}_{57}La$.

Plan If the nuclide is too heavy to be stable ($Z > 83$), it undergoes α decay. For other cases, we use the *Z* value to obtain its atomic mass from the periodic table. If the mass number of the nuclide is higher than the atomic mass, the nuclide has too many neutrons: *N* too high $\Rightarrow$ β^- decay. If the mass number is lower than the atomic mass, the nuclide has too many protons: *Z* too high $\Rightarrow$ β^+ emission and/or e^- capture.

Solution (a) This nuclide has $Z = 5$, which is boron (B), and the atomic mass is 10.81. The nuclide's *A* value of 12 is significantly higher than its atomic mass, so this nuclide is neutron rich. It will probably undergo β^- decay.

(b) This nuclide has $Z = 92$, so it will undergo α decay and decrease its total mass.

(c) This nuclide has $Z = 33$, which is arsenic (As), and the atomic mass is 74.92. The *A* value of 81 is much higher, so this nuclide is neutron rich and will probably undergo β^- decay.

(d) This nuclide has $Z = 57$, which is lanthanum (La), and the atomic mass is 138.9. The *A* value of 127 is much lower, so this nuclide is proton rich and will probably undergo β^+ emission and/or e^- capture.

Check To confirm our predictions in (a), (c), and (d), let's compare each nuclide's *N/Z* ratio to those in the band of stability. **(a)** This nuclide has $N = 7$ and $Z = 5$, so $N/Z = 1.40$, which is too high for this region of the band, so it will undergo β^- decay. **(c)** This nuclide has $N = 48$ and $Z = 33$, so $N/Z = 1.45$, which is too high for this region of the band, so it undergoes β^- decay. **(d)** This nuclide has $N = 70$ and $Z = 57$, so $N/Z = 1.23$, which is too low for this region of the band, so it undergoes β^+ emission and/or e^- capture. Our predictions based on *N/Z values* were the same as those based on atomic mass.

Comment Both possible modes of decay are observed for the nuclide in part (d).

Follow-Up Problem 24.3 Use the A value for the nuclide and the atomic mass in the periodic table to predict the mode of decay of **(a)** $^{61}_{26}Fe$; **(b)** $^{241}_{95}Am$.

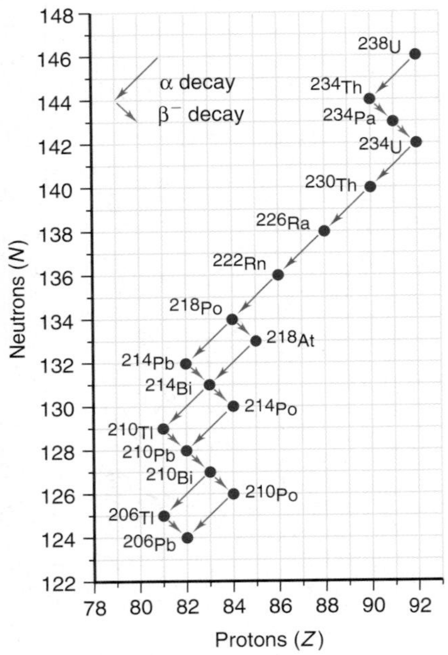

Figure 24.3 The ^{238}U decay series.

Decay Series A parent nuclide may undergo a series of decay steps before a stable daughter nuclide forms. The succession of steps is called a **decay series,** or **disintegration series,** and is typically depicted on a gridlike display. Figure 24.3 shows the decay series from uranium-238 to lead-206. Numbers of neutrons (N) are plotted against numbers of protons (Z) to form the grid, which displays a series of α and β^- decays. The typical zigzag pattern arises because $N > Z$, which means that α decay, which reduces both N and Z by two units, decreases Z slightly more than it does N. Therefore, α decays result in neutron-rich daughters, which undergo β^- decay to gain more stability. Note that a given nuclide can undergo both modes of decay. (Gamma emission accompanies many of these steps but does not affect the type of nuclide.)

The series in Figure 24.3 is one of three that occur in nature. All end with isotopes of lead whose nuclides all have one ($Z = 82$) or two ($N = 126$, $Z = 82$) magic numbers. A second series begins with uranium-235 and ends with lead-207, and a third begins with thorium-232 and ends with lead-208. (Neptunium-237 began a fourth series, but its half-life is so much less than the age of Earth that only traces of it remain today.)

Summary of Section 24.1

- To become more stable, a radioactive nuclide may emit α particles ($^4_2He^{2+}$; helium-4 nuclei), β particles (β^- or $^{0}_{-1}\beta$; high-speed electrons), positrons (β^+ or $^{0}_{1}\beta$), or γ rays (high-energy photons) or may capture an orbital electron ($^{0}_{-1}e$).
- A narrow band of neutron-to-proton ratios (N/Z) includes those of all the stable nuclides.
- Even values of N and Z are associated with stable nuclides, as are certain "magic numbers" of neutrons and protons.
- By comparing a nuclide's mass number with the atomic mass and its N/Z ratio with those in the band of stability, we can predict that, in general, neutron-rich nuclides undergo β^- decay and proton-rich nuclides undergo β^+ emission and/or e^- capture. Heavy nuclides ($Z > 83$) undergo α decay.
- Three naturally occurring decay series all end in isotopes of lead.

24.2 • THE KINETICS OF RADIOACTIVE DECAY

Both chemical and nuclear systems tend toward maximum stability. Just as the concentrations in a chemical system change in a predictable direction to give a stable equilibrium ratio, the type and number of nucleons in an unstable nucleus change in a predictable direction to give a stable N/Z ratio. As you know, however, the tendency of a chemical system to become more stable tells nothing about how long that process will take, and the same holds true for nuclear systems. In this section, we first see how radioactivity is detected and measured and then examine the kinetics of nuclear change; later, we'll examine the energetics of nuclear change.

Detection and Measurement of Radioactivity

Radioactive emissions interact with surrounding atoms. To determine the rate of nuclear decay, we measure radioactivity by observing the effects of these interactions over time. Because these effects can be electrically amplified billions of times, it is

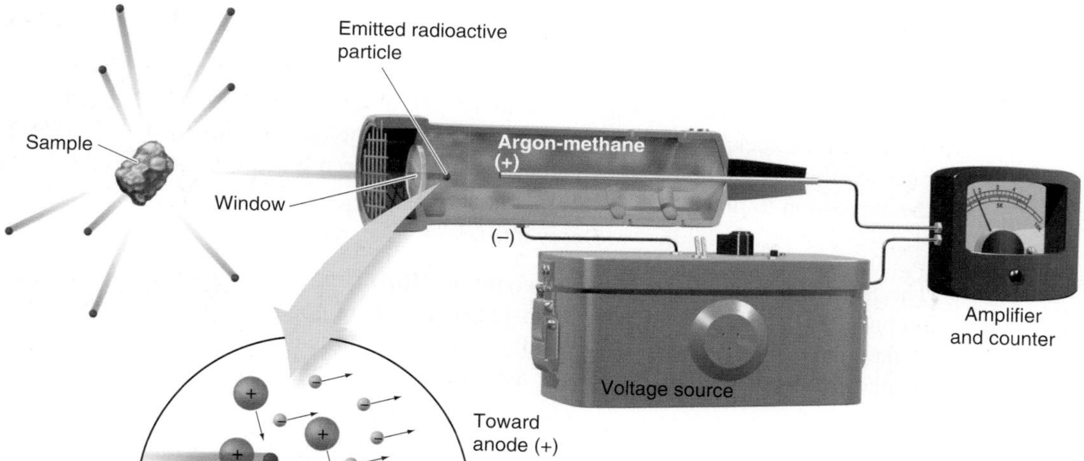
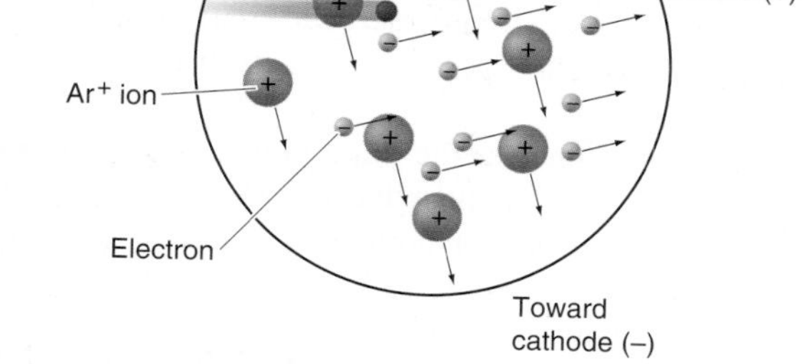

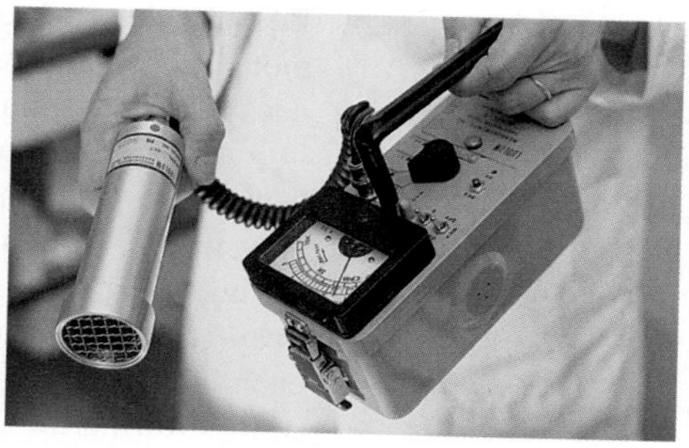

Figure 24.4 Detection of radioactivity by an ionization counter.

possible to detect the decay of a single nucleus. Ionization counters and scintillation counters are two devices used to measure radioactive emissions.

Ionization Counters An *ionization counter* detects radioactive emissions as they ionize a gas. Ionization produces free electrons and gaseous cations, which are attracted to electrodes that conduct a current to a recording device. The most common type of ionization counter is a **Geiger-Müller counter** (Figure 24.4). It consists of a tube filled with an argon-methane mixture; the tube housing acts as the cathode, and a thin wire in the center of the tube acts as the anode. Emissions from the sample enter the tube through a thin window and strike argon atoms, producing Ar^+ ions that migrate toward the cathode and free electrons that are accelerated toward the anode. These electrons collide with other argon atoms and free more electrons in an *avalanche effect.* The current created is amplified and appears as a meter reading and/or an audible click. An initial release of 1 electron can release 10^{10} electrons in a microsecond, giving the Geiger-Müller counter great sensitivity.

Scintillation Counters In a **scintillation counter,** radioactive emissions are detected by their ability to excite atoms and cause them to emit light. The light-emitting substance in the counter, called a *phosphor,* is coated onto part of a *photomultiplier tube,* a device that increases the original electrical signal. Incoming radioactive particles strike the phosphor, which emits photons. Each photon, in turn, strikes a cathode, releasing an electron through the photoelectric effect (Section 7.1). This electron hits other portions of the tube that release increasing numbers of electrons, and the resulting current is recorded. Liquid scintillation counters employ an organic mixture that contains a phosphor and a solvent (Figure 24.5). This "cocktail" dissolves the radioactive sample *and* emits pulses of light when excited by the emission. The number of pulses is proportional to the concentration of the radioactive substance. These counters are often used to measure β^- emissions from dissolved biological samples, particularly those containing compounds of ^3H and ^{14}C.

Figure 24.5 A scintillation "cocktail" in tubes to be placed in the counter.

The Rate of Radioactive Decay

Radioactive nuclei decay at a characteristic rate, regardless of the chemical substance in which they occur. The *decay rate,* or **activity ($\mathcal{A}$),** of a radioactive sample is the change in number of nuclei ($\mathcal{N}$) divided by the change in time (t). As with chemical reaction rates (Section 16.2), because the number of nuclei is *decreasing,* a minus sign precedes the expression to obtain a positive decay rate:

$$\text{Decay rate } (\mathcal{A}) = -\frac{\Delta \mathcal{N}}{\Delta t}$$

The SI unit of radioactivity is the **becquerel (Bq),** defined as one disintegration per second (d/s): 1 Bq = 1 d/s. A much larger and more common unit of radioactivity is the **curie (Ci),** which was originally defined as the number of disintegrations per second in 1 g of radium-226, but is now a fixed quantity:

$$1 \text{ Ci} = 3.70\times 10^{10} \text{ d/s} \quad (24.2)$$

Because the curie is so large, the millicurie (mCi) and microcurie (μCi) are commonly seen. The radioactivity of a sample is often given as a *specific activity,* the decay rate per gram.

An activity is meaningful only when we consider the large number of nuclei in a macroscopic sample. Suppose there are 1×10^{15} radioactive nuclei of a particular type in a sample and they decay at a rate of 10% per hour. Although any particular nucleus in the sample might decay in a microsecond or in a million hours, the *average* of all decays results in 10% of the entire collection of nuclei disintegrating each hour. During the first hour, 10% of the *original* number, or 1×10^{14} nuclei, will decay. During the next hour, 10% of the remaining 9×10^{14} nuclei, or 9×10^{13} nuclei, will decay. During the next hour, 10% of those remaining will decay, and so forth. Thus, for a large collection of radioactive nuclei, *the number decaying per unit time is proportional to the number present:*

$$\text{Decay rate } (\mathcal{A}) \propto \mathcal{N} \quad \text{or} \quad \mathcal{A} = k\mathcal{N}$$

where k is called the **decay constant** and is characteristic of each type of nuclide. The larger the value of k, the higher is the decay rate: larger $k \Rightarrow$ higher $\mathcal{A}$.

Combining the two rate expressions just given, we obtain

$$\mathcal{A} = -\frac{\Delta \mathcal{N}}{\Delta t} = k\mathcal{N} \quad (24.3)$$

Note that the activity depends only on $\mathcal{N}$ raised to the first power (and on the constant value of k). Therefore, *radioactive decay is a first-order process* (Section 16.4), but with respect to the *number* of nuclei rather than their concentration.

Half-Life of Radioactive Decay Decay rates are also commonly expressed in terms of the fraction of nuclei that decay over a given time interval. The **half-life ($t_{1/2}$)** of a nuclide has the same meaning as for a chemical change (Section 16.4) and can be expressed in terms of number of nuclei, mass of radioactive substance, and activity:

- *Number of nuclei.* Half-life is the time it takes for half the nuclei in a sample to decay—*the number of nuclei remaining is halved after each half-life.* Figure 24.6 shows the decay of carbon-14, which has a half-life of 5730 years, in terms of number of ^{14}C nuclei remaining:

$$^{14}_{6}\text{C} \longrightarrow \, ^{14}_{7}\text{N} + \, ^{0}_{-1}\beta$$

- *Mass.* As ^{14}C decays, the mass of ^{14}C decreases while the mass of ^{14}N increases. If we start with 1.0 g of ^{14}C, half that mass of ^{14}C (0.50 g) will be left after 5730 years, half of that mass (0.25 g) after another 5730 years, and so on.
- *Activity.* The activity depends on the number of nuclei, so the activity is halved after each succeeding half-life.

We determine the half-life of a nuclear reaction from its rate constant. Rearranging Equation 24.3 and integrating over time gives an expression for finding the number of nuclei remaining, $\mathcal{N}_t$, after a given time t:

$$\ln \frac{\mathcal{N}_t}{\mathcal{N}_0} = -kt \quad \text{or} \quad \mathcal{N}_t = \mathcal{N}_0 e^{-kt} \quad \text{and} \quad \ln \frac{\mathcal{N}_0}{\mathcal{N}_t} = kt \quad (24.4)$$

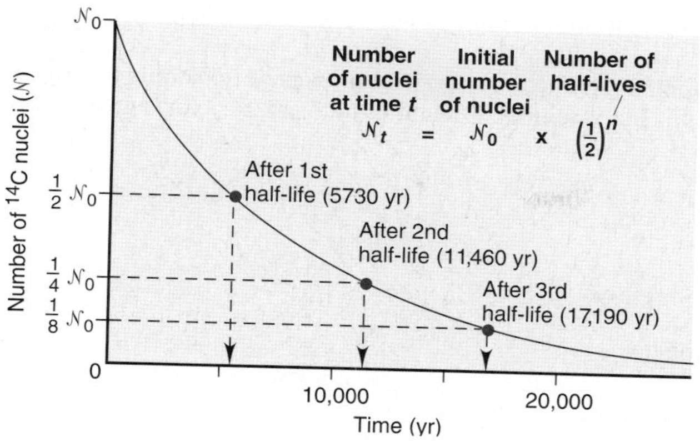

Figure 24.6 Decrease in number of ^{14}C nuclei over time.

where $\mathcal{N}_0$ is the number of nuclei at $t = 0$. (Note the similarity to Equation 16.4, p. 642.) To calculate the half-life ($t_{1/2}$), we set $\mathcal{N}_t$ equal to $\frac{1}{2}\mathcal{N}_0$ and solve for $t_{1/2}$:

$$\ln \frac{\mathcal{N}_0}{\frac{1}{2}\mathcal{N}_0} = kt_{1/2} \quad \text{so} \quad t_{1/2} = \frac{\ln 2}{k} \qquad (24.5)$$

Exactly analogous to the half-life of a first-order chemical change, *this half-life is* ***not*** *dependent on the number of nuclei and is inversely related to the decay constant:*

large $k \Rightarrow$ short $t_{1/2}$ and small $k \Rightarrow$ long $t_{1/2}$

The decay constants and half-lives of radioactive nuclides vary over a very wide range, even for the nuclides of a given element (Table 24.5).

Table 24.5 Decay Constants (k) and Half-Lives ($t_{1/2}$) of Beryllium Isotopes

Nuclide	k	$t_{1/2}$
$^{7}_{4}$Be	1.30×10^{-2}/day	53.3 days
$^{8}_{4}$Be	1.0×10^{16}/s	6.7×10^{-17} s
$^{9}_{4}$Be	Stable	
$^{10}_{4}$Be	4.3×10^{-7}/yr	1.6×10^{6} yr
$^{11}_{4}$Be	5.02×10^{-2}/s	13.8 s

Sample Problem 24.4 Finding the Number of Radioactive Nuclei

Problem Strontium-90 is a radioactive byproduct of nuclear reactors that behaves biologically like calcium, the element above it in Group 2A(2). When ^{90}Sr is ingested by mammals, it is found in their milk and eventually in the bones of those drinking the milk. If a sample of ^{90}Sr has an activity of 1.2×10^{12} d/s, what are the activity and the fraction of nuclei that have decayed after 59 yr ($t_{1/2}$ of ^{90}Sr = 29 yr)?

Plan The fraction of nuclei that have decayed is the change in number of nuclei, expressed as a fraction of the starting number. The activity of the sample ($\mathcal{A}$) is proportional to the number of nuclei ($\mathcal{N}$), so we know that

$$\text{Fraction decayed} = \frac{\mathcal{N}_0 - \mathcal{N}_t}{\mathcal{N}_0} = \frac{\mathcal{A}_0 - \mathcal{A}_t}{\mathcal{A}_0}$$

We are given $\mathcal{A}_0$ (1.2×10^{12} d/s), so we find $\mathcal{A}_t$ from the integrated form of the first-order rate equation (Equation 24.4), in which t is 59 yr. To solve that equation, we first need k, which we can calculate from the given $t_{1/2}$ (29 yr).

Solution Calculating the decay constant k:

$$t_{1/2} = \frac{\ln 2}{k} \quad \text{so} \quad k = \frac{\ln 2}{t_{1/2}} = \frac{0.693}{29\ \text{yr}} = 0.024\ \text{yr}^{-1}$$

Applying Equation 24.4 to calculate $\mathcal{A}_t$, the activity remaining at time t:

$$\ln \frac{\mathcal{N}_0}{\mathcal{N}_t} = \ln \frac{\mathcal{A}_0}{\mathcal{A}_t} = kt \quad \text{or} \quad \ln \mathcal{A}_0 - \ln \mathcal{A}_t = kt$$

So,

$$\ln \mathcal{A}_t = -kt + \ln \mathcal{A}_0 = -(0.024\ \text{yr}^{-1} \times 59\ \text{yr}) + \ln (1.2\times10^{12}\ \text{d/s})$$

$$\ln \mathcal{A}_t = -1.4 + 27.81 = 26.4$$

$$\mathcal{A}_t = 2.9\times10^{11}\ \text{d/s}$$

(All the data contain two significant figures, so we retained two in the answer.)

Calculating the fraction decayed:

$$\text{Fraction decayed} = \frac{\mathcal{A}_0 - \mathcal{A}_t}{\mathcal{A}_0} = \frac{1.2\times10^{12}\ \text{d/s} - 2.9\times10^{11}\ \text{d/s}}{1.2\times10^{12}\ \text{d/s}} = 0.76$$

Check The answer is reasonable: t is about 2 half-lives, so $\mathcal{A}_t$ should be about $\frac{1}{4}\mathcal{A}_0$, or about 0.3×10^{12}; therefore, the activity should have decreased by about $\frac{3}{4}$.

Comment 1. A useful substitution of Equation 24.4 for finding $\mathcal{A}_t$, the activity at time t, is $\mathcal{A}_t = \mathcal{A}_0 e^{-kt}$.

2. Another way to find the fraction of activity (or nuclei) remaining incorporates the number of half-lives ($t/t_{1/2}$). By combining Equations 24.4 and 24.5 and substituting (ln 2)/$t_{1/2}$ for k, we obtain

$$\ln \frac{\mathcal{N}_0}{\mathcal{N}_t} = \left(\frac{\ln 2}{t_{1/2}}\right)t = \frac{t}{t_{1/2}} \ln 2 = \ln 2^{t/t_{1/2}}$$

Inverting the ratio gives
$$\ln \frac{\mathcal{N}_t}{\mathcal{N}_0} = \ln \left(\frac{1}{2}\right)^{t/t_{1/2}}$$

Taking the antilog gives

$$\text{Fraction remaining} = \frac{\mathcal{N}_t}{\mathcal{N}_0} = \left(\frac{1}{2}\right)^{t/t_{1/2}} = \left(\frac{1}{2}\right)^{59/29} = 0.24$$

So,
$$\text{Fraction decayed} = 1.00 - 0.24 = 0.76$$

Follow-Up Problem 24.4 Sodium-24 ($t_{1/2}$ = 15 h) is used to study blood circulation. If a patient is injected with an aqueous solution of ^{24}NaCl whose activity is 2.5×10^9 d/s, how much of the activity is present in the patient's body and excreted fluids after 4.0 days?

Radioisotopic Dating

The historical record fades rapidly with time and virtually disappears for events of more than a few thousand years ago. Much knowledge of prehistory comes from **radioisotopic dating,** which uses **radioisotopes** to determine the ages of objects. This technique supplies data in fields such as art history, archeology, geology, and paleontology.

The technique of *radiocarbon dating,* for which the American chemist Willard F. Libby won the Nobel Prize in chemistry in 1960, is based on measuring the amounts of ^{14}C and ^{12}C in materials of biological origin. The accuracy of the method falls off after about six half-lives of ^{14}C ($t_{1/2}$ = 5730 yr), so it is used to date objects up to about 36,000 years old.

Here is how radiocarbon dating works:

1. High-energy cosmic rays, consisting mainly of protons, enter the atmosphere from outer space and initiate a cascade of nuclear reactions, some of which produce neutrons that bombard ordinary ^{14}N atoms to form ^{14}C:
$$^{14}_{7}\text{N} + ^{1}_{0}\text{n} \longrightarrow ^{14}_{6}\text{C} + ^{1}_{1}\text{p}$$
Through the competing processes of formation and radioactive decay, the amount of ^{14}C in the atmosphere has remained nearly constant.*
2. The ^{14}C atoms combine with O_2, diffuse throughout the lower atmosphere, and enter the total carbon pool as gaseous $^{14}CO_2$ and aqueous $H^{14}CO_3^-$. They mix with ordinary $^{12}CO_2$ and $H^{12}CO_3^-$, reaching a constant ^{12}C/^{14}C ratio of about 10^{12}/1.
3. The CO_2 is taken up by plants during photosynthesis, and then taken up and excreted by animals that eat the plants. Thus, the ^{12}C/^{14}C ratio of a living organism is the same as the ratio in the environment.
4. When an organism dies, it no longer absorbs or releases CO_2, so the ^{12}C/^{14}C ratio steadily increases because *the amount of ^{14}C decreases as it decays:*
$$^{14}_{6}\text{C} \longrightarrow ^{14}_{7}\text{N} + ^{0}_{-1}\beta$$
The difference between the ^{12}C/^{14}C ratio in a dead organism and the ratio in living organisms reflects the time elapsed since the organism died.

*Cosmic ray intensity does vary slightly with time, which affects the amount of atmospheric ^{14}C. From ^{14}C activity in ancient trees, we know the amount fell slightly about 3000 years ago to current levels. Recently, nuclear testing and fossil fuel combustion have also altered the fraction of ^{14}C slightly. Taking these factors into account improves the accuracy of the dating method.

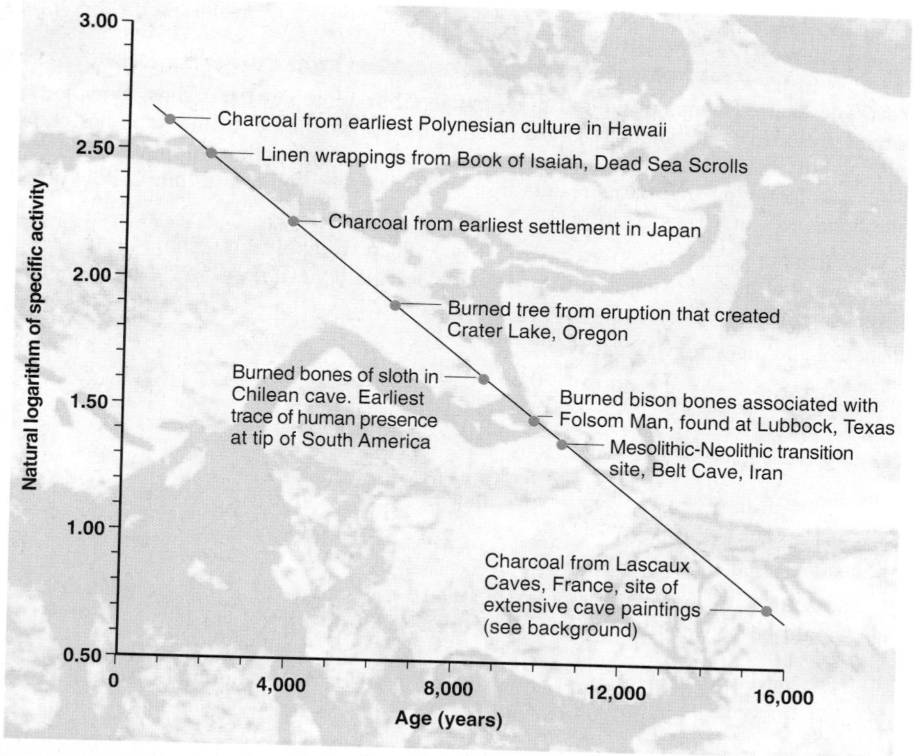

Figure 24.7 Ages of several objects determined by radiocarbon dating.

As you saw in Sample Problem 24.4, the first-order rate equation can be expressed in terms of a ratio of activities:

$$\ln \frac{\mathcal{N}_0}{\mathcal{N}_t} = \ln \frac{\mathcal{A}_0}{\mathcal{A}_t} = kt$$

We use this expression in radiocarbon dating, where $\mathcal{A}_0$ is the activity in a living organism and $\mathcal{A}_t$ is the activity in the object whose age is unknown. Solving for t gives the age of the object:

$$t = \frac{1}{k} \ln \frac{\mathcal{A}_0}{\mathcal{A}_t} \qquad (24.6)$$

A useful graphical method in radioisotopic dating shows a plot of the natural logarithm of the specific activity vs. time, which gives a straight line with a slope of $-k$, the negative of the decay constant. Using such a plot and measuring the ^{14}C specific activity of an object, we can determine its age; several examples appear in Figure 24.7.

One well-known example of the use of radiocarbon dating was in the determination of the age of the Shroud of Turin (*see photo*). One of the holiest Christian relics, the shroud is a piece of linen that bears a faint image of a man's body and was thought to be the burial cloth used to wrap the body of Jesus Christ. However, three labs in Europe and the United States independently measured the $^{12}C/^{14}C$ ratio of a 50-mg piece of the linen and determined that the flax from which the cloth was made was grown between 1260 A.D. and 1390 A.D.

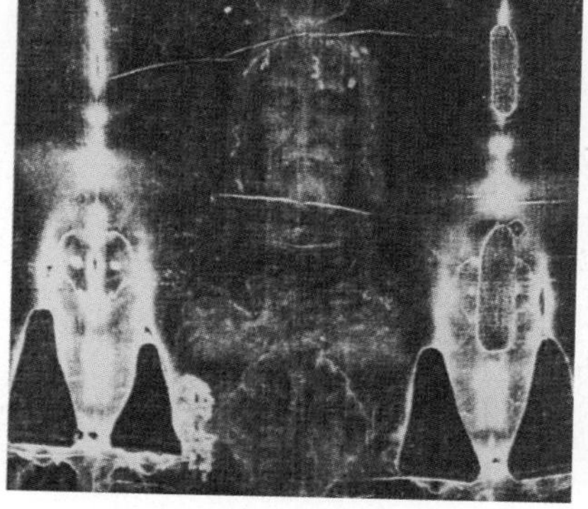

The Shroud of Turin.

To determine the ages of more ancient objects or of objects that do not contain carbon, different radioisotopes are measured. For example, comparing the ratio of ^{238}U ($t_{1/2} = 4.5\times10^9$ yr) to its final decay product, ^{206}Pb, in meteorites gives 4.7 billion years for the age of the Solar System, and therefore Earth. From this and other isotope ratios, such as $^{40}K/^{40}Ar$ ($t_{1/2}$ of $^{40}K = 1.3\times10^9$ yr) and $^{87}Rb/^{87}Sr$ ($t_{1/2}$ of $^{87}Rb = 4.9\times10^{10}$ yr), Moon rocks collected by Apollo astronauts have been dated at 4.2 billion years old.

Sample Problem 24.5 Applying Radiocarbon Dating

Problem The charred bones of a sloth in a cave in Chile represent the earliest evidence of human presence at the southern tip of South America. A sample of the bone has a specific activity of 5.22 disintegrations per minute per gram of carbon (d/min·g). If the $^{12}C/^{14}C$ ratio for living organisms results in a specific activity of 15.3 d/min·g, how old are the bones ($t_{1/2}$ of ^{14}C = 5730 yr)?

Plan We calculate k from the given $t_{1/2}$ (5730 yr). Then we apply Equation 24.6 to find the age (t) of the bones, using the given activities of the bones ($\mathscr{A}_t$ = 5.22 d/min·g) and of a living organism ($\mathscr{A}_0$ = 15.3 d/min·g).

Solution Calculating k for ^{14}C decay:

$$k = \frac{\ln 2}{t_{1/2}} = \frac{0.693}{5730\ \text{yr}} = 1.21\times10^{-4}\ \text{yr}^{-1}$$

Calculating the age (t) of the bones:

$$t = \frac{1}{k}\ln\frac{\mathscr{A}_0}{\mathscr{A}_t} = \frac{1}{1.21\times10^{-4}\ \text{yr}^{-1}}\ln\left(\frac{15.3\ \text{d/min}\cdot\text{g}}{5.22\ \text{d/min}\cdot\text{g}}\right) = 8.89\times10^{3}\ \text{yr}$$

The bones are about 8900 years old.

Check The activity of the bones is between $\frac{1}{2}$ and $\frac{1}{4}$ the activity of a living organism, so the age should be between one and two half-lives (5730 to 11,460 yr).

Follow-Up Problem 24.5 A sample of wood from an Egyptian mummy case has a specific activity of 9.41 d/min·g. How old is the case?

Summary of Section 24.2

- Ionization and scintillation counters measure the number of emissions from a radioactive sample.
- The decay rate (activity) of a sample is proportional to the number of radioactive nuclei. Nuclear decay is a first-order process, so half-life is constant.
- Radioisotopic methods, such as ^{14}C dating, determine the age of an object by measuring the ratio of specific isotopes in it.

24.3 • NUCLEAR TRANSMUTATION: INDUCED CHANGES IN NUCLEI

The alchemists' dream of changing base metals into gold was never realized, but in the early 20th century, nuclear physicists *did* change one element into another. Research into **nuclear transmutation,** the *induced* conversion of the nucleus of one element into the nucleus of another, was closely linked to research into atomic structure and led to the discovery of the neutron and the production of artificial radioisotopes. Later, high-energy bombardment of nuclei in particle accelerators began the ongoing effort to create new nuclides and new elements, and, most recently, to understand fundamental questions of matter and energy.

Early Transmutation Experiments; Nuclear Shorthand Notation

The first recognized transmutation occurred in 1919, when Ernest Rutherford showed that α particles emitted from radium bombarded atmospheric nitrogen to form a proton and oxygen-17:

$$^{14}_{7}\text{N} + {}^{4}_{2}\alpha \longrightarrow {}^{1}_{1}\text{p} + {}^{17}_{8}\text{O}$$

By 1926, experimenters had found that α bombardment transmuted most elements with low atomic numbers to the next higher element, with ejection of a proton.

A shorthand notation used specifically for nuclear transmutation reactions shows the reactant (target) nucleus to the left and the product nucleus to the right of a set of parentheses, within which a comma separates the projectile particle from the ejected particle(s):

reactant nucleus (particle in, particle(s) out) product nucleus **(24.7)**

Using this notation, we write the previous reaction as $^{14}N\ (\alpha,p)\ ^{17}O$.

An unexpected finding in a transmutation experiment led to *the discovery of the neutron.* When lithium, beryllium, and boron were bombarded with α particles, they emitted highly penetrating radiation that could not be deflected by a magnetic or electric field. Unlike γ radiation, these emissions were massive enough to eject protons from the substances they penetrated. In 1932, James Chadwick, a student of Rutherford, proposed that the emissions consisted of neutral particles with a mass similar to that of a proton, which he named *neutrons.* He received the Nobel Prize in physics in 1935 for his discovery.

In 1933, Irene and Frederic Joliot-Curie (*see photo*), daughter and son-in-law of Marie and Pierre Curie, created the first artificial radioisotope, phosphorus-30. When they bombarded aluminum foil with α particles, phosphorus-30 and neutrons were formed:

$$^{27}_{13}\text{Al} + ^{4}_{2}\alpha \longrightarrow ^{1}_{0}\text{n} + ^{37}_{15}\text{P} \quad \text{or} \quad ^{27}\text{Al}(\alpha,\text{n})\ ^{30}\text{P}$$

Since then, other techniques for producing artificial radioisotopes have been developed. In fact, the majority of the nearly 1000 known radionuclides have been produced artificially.

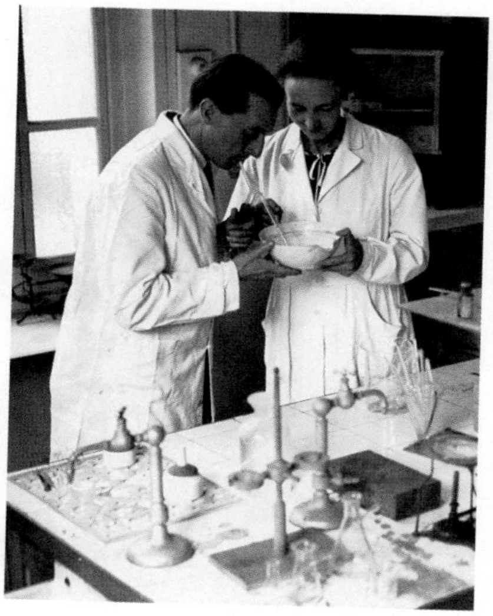

The Joliot-Curies in their laboratory.

Particle Accelerators and the Transuranium Elements

During the 1930s and 1940s, researchers probing the nucleus bombarded elements with neutrons, α particles, protons, and **deuterons** (nuclei of the stable hydrogen isotope deuterium, ^{2}H). Neutrons are especially useful as projectiles because they have no charge and thus are not repelled as they approach a target nucleus. The other particles are all positive, so early researchers found it difficult to give them enough energy to overcome their repulsion by the target nuclei. Beginning in the 1930s, however, **particle accelerators** were invented to impart high kinetic energies to particles by placing them in an electric field, usually in combination with a magnetic field. In the simplest and earliest design, protons are introduced at one end of a tube and attracted to the other end by a potential difference.

Linear Accelerator A major advance was the *linear accelerator,* a series of separated tubes of increasing length that, through a source of alternating voltage, change their charge from positive to negative in synchrony with the movement of the particle through them (Figure 24.8).

A proton, for example, exits the first tube just when that tube becomes positive and the next tube negative. Repelled by the first tube and attracted by the second, the proton accelerates across the gap between them. The process is performed in stages to achieve high particle energies without having to apply a single high voltage. A 40-ft linear accelerator with 46 tubes, built in California after World War II, accelerated protons to speeds several million times faster than earlier accelerators.

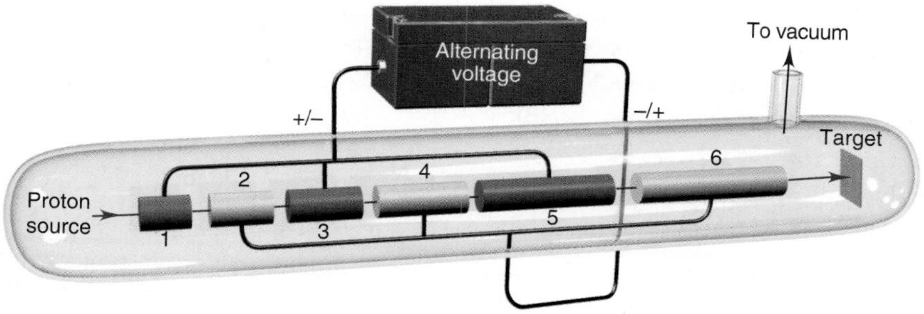

Figure 24.8 Schematic diagram of a linear accelerator.

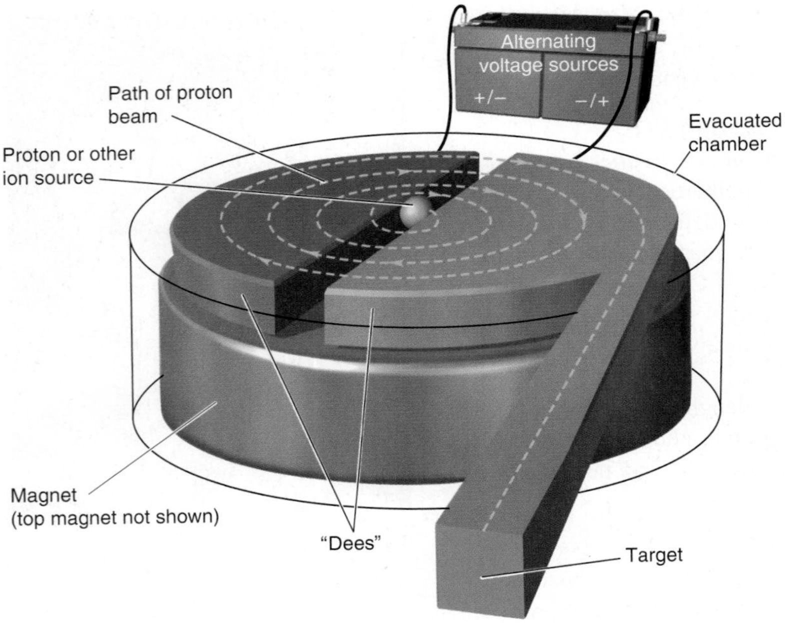

Figure 24.9 Schematic diagram of a cyclotron.

Other Early Particle Accelerators The *cyclotron* (Figure 24.9), invented by E. O. Lawrence in 1930, applies the principle of the linear accelerator but uses electromagnets to give the particle a spiral path to save space. The magnets lie within an evacuated chamber above and below two "dees," open, D-shaped electrodes that act like the tubes in the linear design. The particle is accelerated as it passes from one dee, which is momentarily positive, to the other, which is momentarily negative. Its speed and path radius increase until it is deflected toward the target nucleus.

The *synchrotron* uses a synchronously increasing magnetic field to make the particle's path circular rather than spiral.

Powerful Modern Accelerators Some very powerful accelerators used to study the physics of high-energy particle collisions include both a linear section and a synchrotron section. The *tevatron* at the Fermi Lab near Chicago has a circumference of 3.9 miles and can accelerate particles to an energy slightly less than 1×10^{12} electron volts (1 TeV) before colliding them together.

The world's most powerful accelerator is the Large Hadron Collider (LHC) near Geneva, Switzerland (*photo*). The first successful collision of protons in the LHC was achieved in early 2010. When operating at peak capacity, the LHC will accelerate protons to an energy of 7 TeV as they travel around the main ring at a speed of 11,000 revolutions per second, attaining a final speed about 99.99% of the speed of light before colliding with other protons. Physicists are eager to study the results of these high-energy subatomic collisions for information on the nature of matter and the early universe.

A small section of the Large Hadron Collider.

Synthesis of Transuranium Elements Scientists use accelerators for many applications, from producing radioisotopes used in medical applications to studying the fundamental nature of matter. Perhaps the most specific application for chemists is the synthesis of **transuranium elements,** those with atomic numbers higher than uranium, the heaviest naturally occurring element. Some reactions that were used to form several of these elements appear in Table 24.6. The transuranium elements include the remaining actinides (Z = 93 to 103), in which the 5*f* sublevel is filled, and the elements in the fourth transition series (Z = 104 to 112), in which the 6*d* sublevel is filled, and the remaining elements in the 7*p* sublevel (Z = 113 to 118).

Conflicting claims of discovery by scientists in the United States and the former Soviet Union led to controversies about names for some of the more recently synthesized elements. To provide interim names until the disputes could be settled, the International Union of Pure and Applied Chemistry (IUPAC) adopted a system that

Table 24.6 Formation of Some Transuranium Nuclides*

Reaction							Half-life of Product
$^{239}_{94}\text{Pu}$	+	2^{1}_{0}n	$\longrightarrow$	$^{241}_{95}\text{Am}$	+	$^{0}_{-1}\beta$	432 yr
$^{239}_{94}\text{Pu}$	+	$^{4}_{2}\alpha$	$\longrightarrow$	$^{242}_{96}\text{Cm}$	+	$^{1}_{0}\text{n}$	163 days
$^{241}_{95}\text{Am}$	+	$^{4}_{2}\alpha$	$\longrightarrow$	$^{243}_{97}\text{Bk}$	+	2^{1}_{0}n	4.5 h
$^{242}_{96}\text{Cm}$	+	$^{4}_{2}\alpha$	$\longrightarrow$	$^{245}_{98}\text{Cf}$	+	$^{1}_{0}\text{n}$	45 min
$^{253}_{99}\text{Es}$	+	$^{4}_{2}\alpha$	$\longrightarrow$	$^{256}_{101}\text{Md}$	+	$^{1}_{0}\text{n}$	76 min
$^{243}_{95}\text{Am}$	+	$^{18}_{8}\text{O}$	$\longrightarrow$	$^{256}_{103}\text{Lr}$	+	5^{1}_{0}n	28 s

*Like chemical reactions, nuclear reactions may occur in several steps. For example, the first reaction here is actually an overall process that occurs in three steps:
(1) $^{239}_{94}\text{Pu} + ^{1}_{0}\text{n} \longrightarrow ^{240}_{94}\text{Pu}$ (2) $^{240}_{94}\text{Pu} + ^{1}_{0}\text{n} \longrightarrow ^{241}_{94}\text{Pu}$ (3) $^{241}_{94}\text{Pu} \longrightarrow ^{241}_{95}\text{Am} + ^{0}_{-1}\beta$

uses the atomic number as the basis for a Latin name. Thus, for example, element 104 was named unnilquadium (un = 1, nil = 0, quad = 4, ium = metal suffix), with the symbol Unq. After much compromise, IUPAC has finalized these names: 104, rutherfordium (Rf); 105, dubnium (Db); 106, seaborgium (Sg); 107, bohrium (Bh); 108, hassium (Hs); 109, meitnerium (Mt); 110, darmstadtium (Ds); 111, roentgenium (Rg); and 112, copernicium (Cn). Elements with atomic numbers 113 and higher have not yet been named.

Summary of Section 24.3

- One nucleus can be transmuted to another through bombardment with high-energy particles.
- Accelerators increase the kinetic energy of particles in nuclear bombardment experiments and are used to produce transuranium elements and radioisotopes for medical use.

24.4 • EFFECTS OF NUCLEAR RADIATION ON MATTER

In 1986, an accident at the Chernobyl nuclear facility in the former Soviet Union released radioactivity that, according to the World Health Organization, will cause thousands of cancer deaths. In the same year, isotopes used in medical treatment emitted radioactivity that prevented thousands of cancer deaths. In this section and Section 24.5, we examine radioactivity's harmful and beneficial effects.

The key to both of these effects is that *nuclear changes cause chemical changes in surrounding matter.* In other words, even though the nucleus of an atom may undergo a reaction with little or no involvement of the atom's electrons, the emissions from that reaction *do* affect the electrons of nearby atoms.

Virtually all radioactivity causes **ionization** in surrounding matter, as the emissions collide with atoms and dislodge electrons:

$$\text{Atom} \xrightarrow{\text{ionizing radiation}} \text{ion}^+ + e^-$$

From each ionization event, a cation and a free electron result, and the number of such *cation-electron pairs* produced is directly related to the energy of the incoming **ionizing radiation.**

Many applications of ionizing radiation depend not only on the ionizing event itself, but also on secondary processes. For example, in a Geiger-Müller counter, the free electron of the cation-electron pair often collides with another atom, which ejects a second electron, and in a scintillation counter, the initial ionization eventually results in the emission of light. In nuclear power plants (Section 24.7), the initial process as well as several secondary processes cause the release of heat that makes steam to create electricity.

Effects of Ionizing Radiation on Living Tissue

Ionizing radiation has a destructive effect on living tissue, and if the ionized atom is part of a key biological macromolecule or cell membrane, the results can be devastating to the cell and perhaps the organism.

The danger from a radionuclide depends on three factors: the type of radiation, its half-life, and, most importantly, its biological behavior. For example, both ^{235}U and ^{239}Pu emit α particles and have long half-lives, but uranium is rapidly excreted by the body, whereas plutonium behaves like calcium and, thus, is incorporated into bones and teeth. One of the most dangerous radionuclides is $^{90}Sr^{2+}$ (formed during a nuclear explosion) because it behaves very similarly to Ca^{2+} and is absorbed rapidly by bones. Let's first see how to measure radiation dose and then look in more detail at the damaging power of ionizing radiation.

Units of Radiation Dose and Its Effects To measure the effects of ionizing radiation, we need a unit for radiation dose. Units of radioactive decay, such as the becquerel and curie, measure the number of decay events in a given time but not their energy or absorption by matter. However, the number of cation-electron pairs produced in a given amount of living tissue *is* a measure of the energy absorbed by the tissue. The SI unit for such energy absorption is the **gray (Gy);** it is equal to 1 joule of energy absorbed per kilogram of body tissue: 1 Gy = 1 J/kg. A more widely used unit is the **rad (*r*adiation-*a*bsorbed *d*ose),** which is one-hundredth as much:

$$1 \text{ rad} = 0.01 \text{ J/kg} = 0.01 \text{ Gy}$$

To measure actual tissue damage, we must account for differences in the strength of the radiation, the exposure time, and the type of tissue. To do this, we multiply the number of rads by a *r*elative *b*iological *e*ffectiveness (RBE) factor, which depends on the effect a given type of radiation has on a given tissue or body part. The product is the **rem (*r*oentgen *e*quivalent for *m*an),** the unit of radiation dosage equivalent to a given amount of tissue damage in a human:

$$\text{no. of rems} = \text{no. of rads} \times \text{RBE}$$

Doses are often expressed in millirems (10^{-3} rem). The SI unit for dosage equivalent is the **sievert (Sv).** It is defined in the same way as the rem but with absorbed dose in grays; thus, 1 rem = 0.01 Sv.

Penetrating Power of Emissions The effect on living tissue of a radiation dose depends on the penetrating power *and* ionizing ability of the radiation. Since water is the main component of living tissue, penetrating power is often measured in terms of the depth of water that stops 50% of incoming radiation. In Figure 24.10, the average values of the penetrating distances are shown in actual size for the three common types of emissions. Note, in general, that *penetrating power is inversely related to the mass, charge, and energy of the emission.* In other words, if a particle interacts strongly with matter, it penetrates only slightly, and vice versa:

Figure 24.10 Penetrating power of radioactive emissions.

1. *Alpha particles.* Alpha particles are massive and highly charged, which means that they interact with matter most strongly of the three common emissions. As a result, they penetrate so little that a piece of paper, light clothing, or the outer layer of skin can stop α radiation from an external source. However, if ingested, an α emitter can cause grave localized internal damage through extensive ionization. For example, in the early 20th century, wristwatch and clock dials were painted by hand with paint containing radium so they would glow in the dark. To write numbers clearly, the women who applied the paint "tipped" fine brushes repeatedly between their lips. Small amounts of ingested $^{226}Ra^{2+}$ were incorporated into their bones along with normal Ca^{2+}, which led to numerous cases of bone fracture and jaw cancer.

2. *Beta particles and positrons.* Beta particles (β^-) and positrons (β^+) have less charge and much less mass than α particles, so they interact less strongly with matter. Even though a given particle has less chance of causing ionization, a β^- (or β^+) emitter is a more destructive external source because the particles penetrate deeper. Specialized heavy clothing or a thick (0.5 cm) piece of metal is required to stop these particles. The relative danger from α and β^- emissions is shown by the poisoning of two former Russian intelligence agents. In 1957, an agent was poisoned by thallium-204, a β^- emitter, but he survived because β^- particles do relatively little radiation damage. In contrast, in 2006, another agent was poisoned with polonium-210, an α emitter, and died in three weeks because of the much greater radiation damage.

3. *Gamma rays.* Neutral, massless γ rays interact least with matter and, thus, penetrate most. A block of lead several inches thick is needed to stop them. Therefore, an external γ ray source is the most dangerous because the energy can ionize many layers of living tissue.

The extent of interaction with matter is variable for emitted *neutrons,* which are neutral and massive. Outside a nucleus, neutrons decay with a half-life of 10.6 min into a proton and an electron (and an antineutrino). With energies ranging from very low to very high, they may be scattered or captured by interaction with nuclei.

Molecular Interactions How does the damage take place on the molecular level? When ionizing radiation interacts with molecules, it causes the *loss of an electron from a bond or a lone pair.* The resulting charged species go on to form **free radicals,** molecular or atomic species with one or more unpaired electrons, which, as you know, are very reactive (Section 10.1, p. 370). They form electron pairs by attacking bonds in other molecules, often forming more free radicals.

When γ radiation strikes living tissue, for instance, the most likely molecule to absorb it is water, yielding an electron and a water ion-radical:

$$H_2O + \gamma \longrightarrow H_2O\bullet^+ + e^-$$

The products collide with other water molecules to form more free radicals:

$$H_2O\bullet^+ + H_2O \longrightarrow H_3O^+ + \bullet OH \quad \text{and} \quad e^- + H_2O \longrightarrow H\bullet + OH^-$$

These free radicals attack more H_2O and surrounding biomolecules, whose bonding and structure are intimately connected with their function (Section 15.6).

The double bonds in membrane lipids are highly susceptible to free-radical attack:

$$H\bullet + RCH{=}CHR' \longrightarrow RCH_2{-}\dot{C}HR'$$

In this reaction, one electron of the π bond forms a C—H bond between one of the double-bonded carbons and the H•, and the other electron resides on the other carbon to form a free radical. Changes to lipid structure cause damage that results in leakage through cell membranes and destruction of the protective fatty tissue around organs. Changes to critical bonds in enzymes lead to their malfunction as catalysts of metabolic reactions. Changes in the nucleic acids and proteins that govern the rate of cell division can cause cancer. Genetic damage and mutations may occur when bonds in the DNA of sperm and egg cells are altered by free radicals.

Sources of Ionizing Radiation

We are continuously exposed to ionizing radiation from natural and artificial sources (Table 24.7, *next page*). Indeed, life evolved in the presence of natural ionizing radiation, called **background radiation.** The same radiation that alters bonds in DNA and causes harmful mutations also causes beneficial ones that allow species to evolve.

Background radiation has several natural sources:

- *Cosmic radiation* increases with altitude because of decreased absorption by the atmosphere. Thus, people in Denver absorb twice as much cosmic radiation as people in Los Angeles; even a jet flight involves measurable absorption.
- Thorium and uranium minerals are present in rocks and soil. Radon, the heaviest noble gas [Group 8A(18)], is a radioactive product of uranium and thorium decay. Its concentration in the air we breathe is related to the presence of trace minerals in building materials and to the uranium content of local soil and rocks (Figure 24.11). Once it enters the body, radon poses a serious potential hazard as it decays to radioactive nuclides of Po, Pb, and Bi, through α, β^-, and γ emissions. The emissions damage lung tissue, and the heavy-metal atoms formed aggravate the problem. Recent EPA estimates indicate that radon contributes to 15% of annual lung cancer deaths.
- About 150 g of K^+ ions is dissolved in the water in the tissues of an average adult, and 0.0118% of these ions are radioactive ^{40}K. The presence of these substances and of atmospheric $^{14}CO_2$ makes *all* food (including bananas and Brazil nuts; see beginning of chapter), water, clothing, and building materials slightly radioactive.

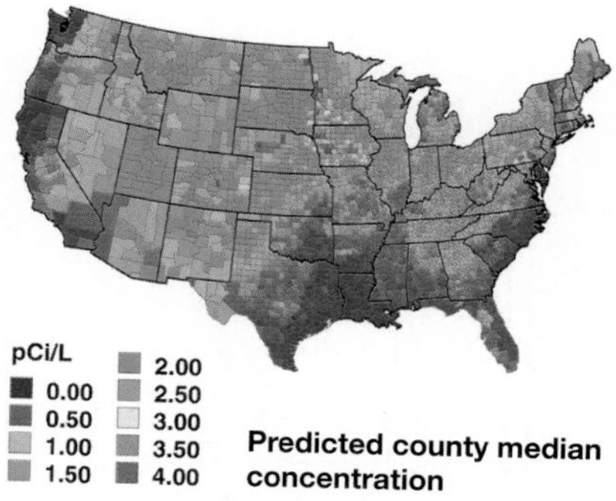

Figure 24.11 U.S. radon distribution.

The largest artificial source of radiation, and the one that is easiest to control, is from medical diagnostic techniques, especially x-rays. The radiation dosage from nuclear testing and radioactive waste disposal is miniscule for most people, but exposures for those living near test sites or disposal areas may be much higher.

Assessing the Risk from Ionizing Radiation

How much radiation is too much? To answer this question, we must ask several others: How strong is the exposure? How long is the exposure? Which tissue is exposed? Are children affected? One reason we lack clear data to answer

Table 24.7 Typical Radiation Doses from Natural and Artificial Sources

Source of Radiation	Average Adult Exposure
Natural	
Cosmic radiation	30–50 mrem/yr
Radiation from the ground	
From clay soil and rocks	~25–170 mrem/yr
In wooden houses	10–20 mrem/yr
In brick houses	60–70 mrem/yr
In concrete (cinder block) houses	60–160 mrem/yr
Radiation from the air (mainly radon)	
Outdoors, average value	20 mrem/yr
In wooden houses	70 mrem/yr
In brick houses	130 mrem/yr
In concrete (cinder block) houses	260 mrem/yr
Internal radiation from minerals in tap water and daily intake of food (^{40}K, ^{14}C, Ra)	~40 mrem/yr
Artificial	
Diagnostic x-ray methods	0.04–0.2 rad/film
Lung (local)	1.5–3 rad/film
Kidney (local)	≤1 rad/film
Dental (dose to the skin)	Locally ≤ 10,000 rad
Therapeutic radiation treatment	
Other sources	
Jet flight (4 h)	~1 mrem
Nuclear testing	<4 mrem/yr
Nuclear power industry	<1 mrem/yr
Total average value	100–200 mrem/yr

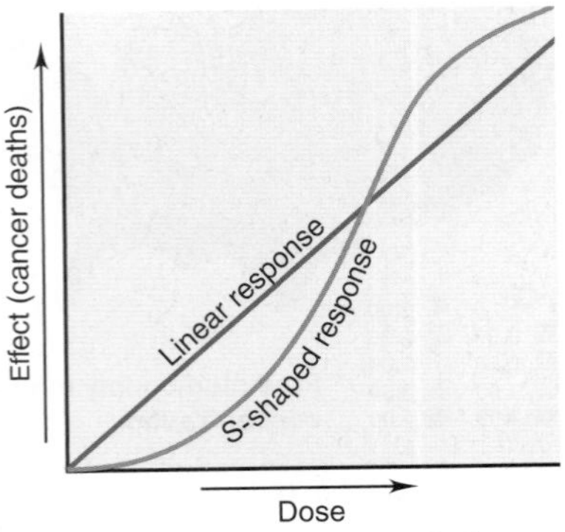

Figure 24.12 Two models of radiation risk.

these questions is that scientific ethical standards forbid the intentional exposure of humans in an experimental setting. However, accidentally exposed radiation workers and Japanese atomic bomb survivors have been studied extensively. Table 24.8 summarizes the immediate effects on humans of an acute single dose of ionizing radiation to the whole body. The severity of the effects increases with dose; a dose of 500 rem will kill about 50% of the exposed population within a month.

Most data come from laboratory animals, whose biological systems may differ greatly from ours. Nevertheless, studies with mice and dogs show that lesions and cancers appear after massive whole-body exposure, with rapidly dividing cells affected first. In an adult animal, these are cells of the bone marrow, organ linings, and reproductive organs, but many other tissues are affected in an immature animal or fetus. Studies in both animals and humans show an increase in the incidence of cancer from either a high, single exposure or a low, chronic exposure.

Two current models of radiation risk are shown in Figure 24.12:

- The *linear response model* proposes that radiation effects, such as cancer risks, accumulate over time regardless of dose and that populations should not be exposed to any radiation above background levels.
- The *S-shaped response model* implies there is a threshhold above which the effects are more significant: very low risk at low dose and high risk at high dose.

Reliable data on genetic effects of radiation are few. Studies on fruit flies show a linear increase in genetic defects with both dose and exposure time. However, in the mouse, whose genetic system is obviously much more similar to ours than is the fruit fly's, a total dose given over a long period created one-third as many genetic defects as the same dose given over a short period. Therefore, rate of exposure is a

Table 24.8 Acute Effects of a Single Dose of Whole-Body Irradiation

Dose (rem)	Effect	Lethal Dose	
		Population (%)	No. of Days
5–20	Possible late effect; possible chromosomal aberrations	—	—
20–100	Temporary reduction in white blood cells	—	—
50+	Temporary sterility in men (100+ rem = 1-yr duration)	—	—
100–200	"Mild radiation sickness": vomiting, diarrhea, tiredness in a few hours Reduction in infection resistance Possible bone growth retardation in children	—	—
300+	Permanent sterility in women	—	—
500	"Serious radiation sickness": marrow/intestine destruction	50–70	30
400–1000	Acute illness, early deaths	60–95	30
3000+	Acute illness, death in hours to days	100	2

key factor. The children of atomic bomb survivors show higher-than-normal childhood cancer rates, implying that their parents' reproductive systems were affected.

Summary of Section 24.4

- All radioactive emissions cause ionization.
- The effect of ionizing radiation on living matter depends on the quantity of energy absorbed and the extent of ionization in a given type of tissue. Radiation dose for the human body is measured in rem.
- Ionization forms free radicals, some of which proliferate and destroy biomolecular function.
- All organisms are exposed to varying quantities of natural ionizing radiation.
- Studies show that either a large acute dose or a chronic small dose is harmful.

24.5 • APPLICATIONS OF RADIOISOTOPES

Radioisotopes are powerful tools for studying processes in biochemistry, medicine, materials science, environmental studies, and many other scientific and industrial fields. Such uses depend on the fact that *isotopes of an element exhibit **very** similar chemical and physical behavior.* In other words, except for having a less stable nucleus, a radioisotope has nearly the same properties as a nonradioactive isotope of that element.* For example, the fact that $^{14}CO_2$ is utilized by a plant in the same way as $^{12}CO_2$ forms the basis of radiocarbon dating.

Radioactive Tracers

Just think how useful it could be to follow a substance through a complex process or from one region of a system to another. A tiny amount of a radioisotope mixed with

*Although this statement is generally correct, differences in isotopic mass *can* influence bond strengths and therefore reaction rates. Such behavior is called a *kinetic isotope effect* and is particularly important for isotopes of hydrogen—^1H, ^2H, and ^3H—because their masses differ by such large proportions. Section 22.4 discussed how the kinetic isotope effect is employed in the industrial production of heavy water, D_2O.

a large amount of the stable isotope can act as a **tracer,** a chemical "beacon" emitting radiation that signals the presence of the substance.

Reaction Pathways Tracers are used to identify simple and complex reaction pathways.

1. *Inorganic systems: the periodate-iodide reaction.* One well-studied example is the reaction between periodate and iodide ions:

$$IO_4^-(aq) + 2I^-(aq) + H_2O(l) \longrightarrow I_2(s) + IO_3^-(aq) + 2OH^-(aq)$$

Is IO_3^- the result of IO_4^- reduction or I^- oxidation? When we add "cold" (nonradioactive) IO_4^- to a solution of I^- that contains some "hot" (radioactive, indicated in red) $^{131}I^-$, we find that the I_2 is radioactive, not the IO_3^-:

$$IO_4^-(aq) + 2\,^{131}I^-(aq) + H_2O(l) \longrightarrow {}^{131}I_2(s) + IO_3^-(aq) + 2OH^-(aq)$$

These results show that IO_3^- forms through the reduction of IO_4^-, and that I_2 forms through the oxidation of I^-. To confirm this pathway, we add IO_4^- containing some $^{131}IO_4^-$ to a solution of I^-. As we expected, the IO_3^- is radioactive, not the I_2:

$$^{131}IO_4^-(aq) + 2I^-(aq) + H_2O(l) \longrightarrow I_2(s) + {}^{131}IO_3^-(aq) + 2OH^-(aq)$$

Thus, tracers act like "handles" we can "hold" to follow the changing reactants.

2. *Biochemical pathways: photosynthesis.* Far more complex pathways can be followed with tracers as well. The photosynthetic pathway, the most essential and widespread metabolic process on Earth, in which energy from sunlight is used to form the chemical bonds of glucose, has an overall reaction that looks quite simple:

$$6CO_2(g) + 6H_2O(l) \xrightarrow[\text{chlorophyll}]{\text{light}} C_6H_{12}O_6(s) + 6O_2(g)$$

However, the actual process is extremely complex: 13 enzyme-catalyzed steps are required to incorporate each C atom from CO_2, so the six CO_2 molecules incorporated to form a molecule of $C_6H_{12}O_6$ require six repetitions of the pathway. Melvin Calvin and his coworkers took seven years to determine the pathway, using ^{14}C in CO_2 as the tracer and chromatography as the means of separating the products formed after different times of light exposure. Calvin won the Nobel Prize in chemistry in 1961 for this remarkable achievement.

Physiological Studies Tracers are used in many studies of physiological function. Some recent studies examine challenges of living in outer space. In an animal study of red blood cell loss during extended space flight, blood plasma volume was measured with ^{125}I-labeled albumin (a blood protein), and red blood cells labeled with ^{51}Cr as a trace substitute for Fe were used to assess survival of blood cells. In another study, blood flow in skin under long periods of microgravity was monitored using injected ^{133}Xe.

Material Flow Tracers are used in studies of solid surfaces and the flow of materials. Metal atoms hundreds of layers deep within a solid have been shown to exchange with metal ions from the surrounding solution within a matter of minutes. Chemists and engineers use tracers to study material movement in semiconductor chips, paint, and metal plating, in detergent action, and in the process of corrosion, to mention just a few of many applications.

Hydrologic engineers use tracers to study the volume and flow of large bodies of water. By following radionuclides that formed during atmospheric nuclear bomb tests (^3H in H_2O, $^{90}Sr^{2+}$, and $^{137}Cs^+$), scientists have mapped the flow of water from land to lakes and streams to oceans. They also use tracers to study the surface and deep ocean currents that circulate around the globe, the mechanisms of hurricane formation, and the mixing of the troposphere and stratosphere. Industries employ tracers to study material flow during manufacturing processes, such as the flow of ore pellets in smelting kilns, the paths of wood chips and bleach in paper mills, the diffusion of fungicide into lumber, and in a particularly important application, the porosity and leakage of oil and gas wells in geological formations.

Activation Analysis Another use of tracers is in *neutron activation analysis* (NAA). In this method, neutrons bombard a nonradioactive sample, converting a small fraction of its atoms to radioisotopes, which exhibit characteristic decay patterns, such as γ-ray spectra, that reveal the elements present. Unlike chemical analysis, NAA leaves the sample virtually intact, so the method can be used to determine the composition of a valuable object or a very small sample. For example, a painting thought to be a 16th-century Dutch masterpiece was shown through NAA to be a 20th-century forgery, because a microgram-sized sample of its pigment contained much less silver and antimony than the pigments used by the Dutch masters. Forensic chemists use NAA to detect traces of ammunition on a suspect's hand or traces of arsenic in the hair of a victim of poisoning.

Automotive engineers employ NAA and γ-ray detectors to measure friction and wear of moving parts without having to take the engine apart. For example, when a steel surface that has been neutron-activated to form some radioactive ^{59}Fe moves against a second steel surface, the amount of radioactivity on the second surface indicates the amount of material rubbing off. The radioactivity appearing in a lubricant placed between the surfaces can demonstrate the lubricant's ability to reduce wear.

Medical Diagnosis The largest use of radioisotopes is in medical science. In fact, over 25% of U.S. hospital admissions are for diagnoses based on data from radioisotopes. Tracers with half-lives of a few minutes to a few days are employed to observe specific organs and body parts. For example, a healthy thyroid gland incorporates dietary I^- into iodine-containing hormones at a known rate. To assess thyroid function, the patient drinks a solution containing a trace amount of $Na^{131}I$; the thyroid gland absorbs $^{131}I^-$ ions, which undergo β^- decay, and the emissions produce an image of the gland (Figure 24.13A). Technetium-99 (Z = 43) is also used for imaging the thyroid (Figure 24.13B), as well as the heart, lungs, and liver. Technetium does not occur naturally, so the radioisotope (actually a metastable form, ^{99m}Tc) is prepared from radioactive molybdenum just before use:

$$^{99}_{42}\text{Mo} \longrightarrow \, ^{99m}_{43}\text{Tc} + \, ^{0}_{-1}\beta$$

Tracers are also used to measure physiological processes, such as blood flow. The rate at which the heart pumps blood, for example, can be observed by injecting ^{59}Fe, which becomes incorporated into the hemoglobin of blood cells. Several radioisotopes used in medical diagnosis are listed in Table 24.9.

Positron-emission tomography (PET) is a powerful imaging method for observing brain structure and function. A biological substance is synthesized with one of its atoms replaced by an isotope that emits positrons. The substance is injected into a patient's bloodstream, from which it is taken up into the brain. The isotope emits positrons, each of which annihilates a nearby electron. In this process, two γ photons are emitted simultaneously 180° from each other:

$$^{0}_{1}\beta + \, ^{0}_{-1}e \longrightarrow 2\,^{0}_{0}\gamma$$

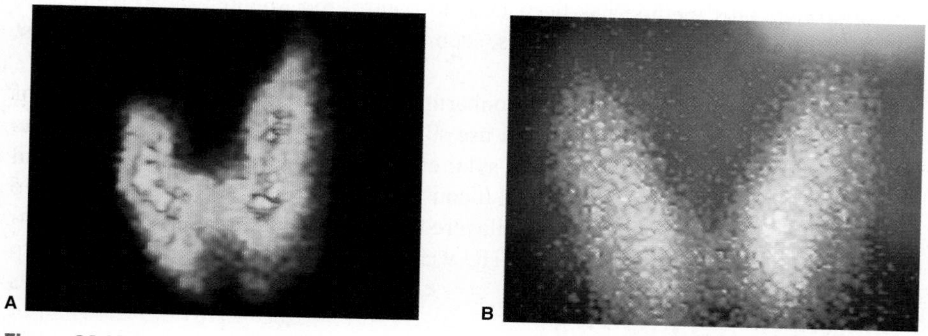

Figure 24.13 The use of radioisotopes to image the thyroid gland. **A,** This ^{131}I scan shows an asymmetric image that is indicative of disease. **B,** A ^{99}Tc scan of a healthy thyroid.

Table 24.9 Some Radioisotopes Used as Medical Tracers

Isotope	Body Part or Process
^{11}C, ^{18}F, ^{13}N, ^{15}O	PET studies of brain, heart
^{60}Co, ^{192}Ir	Cancer therapy
^{64}Cu	Metabolism of copper
^{59}Fe	Blood flow, spleen
^{67}Ga	Tumor imaging
^{123}I, ^{131}I	Thyroid
^{111}In	Brain, colon
^{42}K	Blood flow
^{81m}Kr	Lung
^{99m}Tc	Heart, thyroid, liver, lung, bone
^{201}Tl	Heart muscle
^{90}Y	Cancer, arthritis

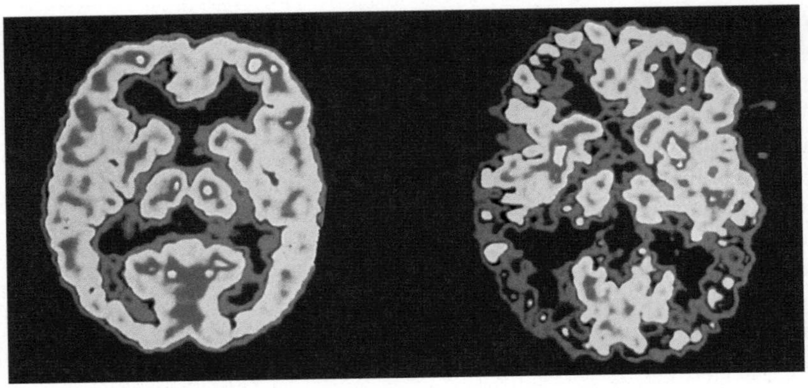

Figure 24.14 PET and brain activity. These PET scans show brain activity in a normal person (*left*) and in a patient with Alzheimer's disease (*right*). Red and yellow indicate relatively high activity within a region.

An array of detectors around the patient's head pinpoints the sites of γ emission, and the image is analyzed by computer. Two of the isotopes used are ^{15}O, injected as $H_2{}^{15}O$ to measure blood flow, and ^{18}F bonded to a glucose analog to measure glucose uptake, which is an indicator of energy metabolism. Among many fascinating PET findings are those that show how changes in blood flow and glucose uptake accompany normal or abnormal brain activity (Figure 24.14). Also, substances incorporating ^{11}C and ^{15}O are being investigated using PET to learn how molecules interact with and move along the surface of a catalyst.

Additional Applications of Ionizing Radiation

Many other uses of radioisotopes involve higher-energy ionizing radiation.

- *Radiation therapy.* Cancer cells divide more rapidly than normal cells, so radioisotopes that interfere with cell division kill more cancer cells than normal ones. Implants of ^{198}Au or of ^{90}Sr, which decays to the γ-emitting ^{90}Y, have been used to destroy pituitary and breast tumor cells, and γ rays from ^{60}Co have been used to destroy tumors of the brain and other body parts.
- *Destruction of microbes.* Irradiation of food increases shelf life by killing microorganisms that cause rotting or spoilage (Figure 24.15), but the practice is controversial. Advocates point to the benefits of preserving fresh foods, grains, and seeds for long periods, whereas opponents suggest that irradiation might lower the food's nutritional content or produce harmful byproducts. Irradiation also provides a way to destroy newer, more resistant bacterial strains that survive the increasing use of the more common antibiotics in animal feed. The United Nations has approved irradiation for potatoes, wheat, chicken, and strawberries, and, in 2003, the U.S. Food and Drug Administration approved it as well.

Figure 24.15 The increased shelf life of irradiated food.

- *Insect control.* Ionizing radiation has been used to control harmful insects. Captured males are sterilized by radiation and released to mate, thereby reducing the number of offspring. This method has been used to control the Mediterranean fruit fly in California and disease-causing insects, such as the tsetse fly and malarial mosquito, in other parts of the world.
- *Power for spacecraft instruments.* A nonharmful use of ionizing radiation relies on its secondary processes. Most spacecraft use solar energy to provide power for instruments. In deep-space missions, when solar energy is too weak, however, a radioisotope heater unit (RHU) has been used. It consists of a $^{238}PuO_2$ fuel pellet the size of a pencil eraser that is clad within a multilayered graphite and metal shell a little smaller than a flashlight battery. The whole RHU weighs only 40 g.

Summary of Section 24.5

- Radioisotopic tracers have been used to study reaction mechanisms, material flow, elemental composition, and medical conditions.
- Ionizing radiation has been used in devices that destroy cancer tissue, kill organisms that spoil food, control insect populations, and power spacecraft instruments.

24.6 • THE INTERCONVERSION OF MASS AND ENERGY

Most of the nuclear processes we've considered so far have involved radioactive decay, in which a nucleus emits one or a few small particles or photons to become a more stable, slightly lighter nucleus. Two other nuclear processes cause much greater mass changes. In nuclear **fission,** a heavy nucleus splits into two much lighter nuclei, emitting several small particles at the same time. In nuclear **fusion,** the opposite process occurs: two lighter nuclei combine to form a heavier one. Both fission and fusion release enormous quantities of energy. Let's take a look at the origins of this energy by first examining the change in mass that accompanies the breakup of a nucleus into its nucleons and then considering the energy that is equivalent to this mass change.

The Mass Difference Between a Nucleus and Its Nucleons

For most of the 20th century, we have known that mass and energy are interconvertible. The separate mass and energy conservation laws are combined to state that *the total quantity of mass-energy in the universe is constant.* Therefore, when *any* reacting system releases or absorbs energy, it also loses or gains mass.

Mass Difference and Chemical Reactions The interconversion of mass and energy is not important for chemical reactions because the energy changes involved in breaking or forming chemical bonds are so small that the mass changes are negligible. For example, when 1 mol of water breaks up into its atoms, heat is absorbed and we have:

$$H_2O(g) \longrightarrow 2H(g) + O(g) \qquad \Delta H^\circ_{rxn} = 2 \times \text{BE of O—H} = 934 \text{ kJ}$$

We find the mass that is equivalent to this energy from *Einstein's equation:*

$$E = mc^2 \quad \text{or} \quad \Delta E = \Delta mc^2 \quad \text{so} \quad \Delta m = \frac{\Delta E}{c^2} \tag{24.8}$$

where Δm is the mass difference between reactants and products:

$$\Delta m = m_{\text{products}} - m_{\text{reactants}}$$

Substituting the enthalpy of reaction (in J/mol) for ΔE and the numerical value for c (2.9979×10^8 m/s), we obtain

$$\Delta m = \frac{9.34\times10^5 \text{ J/mol}}{(2.9979\times10^8 \text{ m/s})^2} = 1.04\times10^{-11} \text{ kg/mol} = 1.04\times10^{-8} \text{ g/mol}$$

(Units of kg/mol are obtained because the joule includes the kilogram: 1 J = 1 kg·m^2/s^2.) The mass of 1 mol of H_2O molecules (reactant) is about 10 ng *less* than the combined masses of 2 mol of H atoms and 1 mol of O atoms (products), a change difficult to measure with even the most sophisticated balance. Such minute mass changes when bonds break or form allow us to assume that, for all practical purposes, mass is conserved in *chemical* reactions.

Mass Difference and Nuclear Reactions The much larger mass change that accompanies a *nuclear* process is related to the enormous energy required to bind the nucleus together from its parts. In an analogy with the calculation above involving the water molecule, consider the change in mass that occurs when one ^{12}C nucleus breaks apart into its nucleons—six protons and six neutrons:

$$^{12}C \longrightarrow 6\,^1_1p + 6\,^1_0n$$

We calculate this mass difference in a special way. By combining the mass of six H *atoms* and six neutrons and then subtracting the mass of one ^{12}C *atom,* the masses of the electrons cancel: six e^- (in six ^1H atoms) cancel six e^- (in one ^{12}C atom). The mass of one ^1H atom is 1.007825 amu, and the mass of one neutron is 1.008665 amu, so

$$\text{Mass of six } ^1\text{H atoms} = 6 \times 1.007825 \text{ amu} = 6.046950 \text{ amu}$$
$$\text{Mass of six neutrons} = 6 \times 1.008665 \text{ amu} = 6.051990 \text{ amu}$$
$$\text{Total mass} = 12.098940 \text{ amu}$$

The mass of the reactant, one ^{12}C atom, is 12 amu (exactly). The mass difference (Δm) we obtain is the total mass of the nucleons minus the mass of the nucleus:

$$\Delta m = 12.098940 \text{ amu} - 12.000000 \text{ amu}$$
$$= 0.098940 \text{ amu}/^{12}\text{C} = 0.098940 \text{ g/mol } ^{12}\text{C}$$

Two key points emerge from these calculations:

- *The mass of the nucleus is* ***less*** *than the combined masses of its nucleons:* there is *always* a mass decrease when nucleons form a nucleus.
- The mass change of this nuclear process (9.89×10^{-2} g/mol) is nearly 10 million times that of the chemical process (10.4×10^{-9} g/mol) we saw earlier and *can* be observed on any laboratory balance.

Nuclear Binding Energy and the Binding Energy per Nucleon

Einstein's equation for the relation between mass and energy allows us to find the energy equivalent of any mass change. For 1 mol of ^{12}C, after converting grams to kilograms, we have

$$\Delta E = \Delta mc^2 = (9.8940\times10^{-5} \text{ kg/mol})(2.9979\times10^{8} \text{ m/s})^2$$
$$= 8.8921\times10^{12} \text{ J/mol} = 8.8921\times10^{9} \text{ kJ/mol}$$

This quantity of energy is called the **nuclear binding energy** for carbon-12, and the positive value means *energy is absorbed.* This is the energy required to break 1 mol of ^{12}C atoms into neutrons and hydrogen atoms. Thus, the *nuclear binding energy* is the energy to *break 1 mol of nuclei into individual nucleons:*

$$\text{Nucleus} + \text{nuclear binding energy} \longrightarrow \text{nucleons}$$

Thus, the nuclear binding energy is qualitatively analogous to the sum of bond energies of a covalent compound or the lattice energy of an ionic compound. But, quantitatively, nuclear binding energies are typically several million times greater.

The Electron Volt as the Unit of Binding Energy We use joules to express the binding energy per mole of nuclei, but the joule is much too large a unit to express the binding energy of a single nucleus. Instead, nuclear scientists use the **electron volt (eV),** the energy an electron acquires when it moves through a potential difference of 1 volt:

$$1 \text{ eV} = 1.602\times10^{-19} \text{ J}$$

Binding energies are commonly expressed in millions of electron volts, that is, in *mega–electron volts* (MeV):

$$1 \text{ MeV} = 10^6 \text{ eV} = 1.602\times10^{-13} \text{ J}$$

A particularly useful factor converts the atomic mass unit to its energy equivalent in electron volts:

$$1 \text{ amu} = 931.5\times10^6 \text{ eV} = 931.5 \text{ MeV} \quad \textbf{(24.9)}$$

Earlier we found the mass change when ^{12}C breaks apart into its nucleons to be 0.098940 amu. The binding energy per ^{12}C nucleus, expressed in MeV, is

$$\frac{\text{Binding energy}}{^{12}\text{C nucleus}} = 0.098940 \text{ amu} \times \frac{931.5 \text{ MeV}}{1 \text{ amu}} = 92.16 \text{ MeV}$$

We can compare the stability of nuclides of different elements by determining the *binding energy per nucleon.* For ^{12}C, we have

$$\text{Binding energy per nucleon} = \frac{\text{binding energy}}{\text{no. of nucleons}} = \frac{92.16 \text{ MeV}}{12 \text{ nucleons}} = 7.680 \text{ MeV/nucleon}$$

Sample Problem 24.6 Calculating the Binding Energy per Nucleon

Problem Iron-56 is an extremely stable nuclide. Compute the binding energy per nucleon for ^{56}Fe and compare it with that for ^{12}C (mass of ^{56}Fe atom = 55.934939 amu; mass of ^{1}H atom = 1.007825 amu; mass of neutron = 1.008665 amu).

Plan Iron-56 has 26 protons and 30 neutrons. We calculate the mass difference, Δm, when the nucleus forms by subtracting the given mass of one ^{56}Fe atom from the sum of the masses of 26 ^{1}H atoms and 30 neutrons. To find the binding energy per nucleon, we multiply Δm by the equivalent in MeV (931.5 MeV/amu) and divide by the number of nucleons (56).

Solution Calculating the mass difference, Δm:

$$\begin{aligned}\text{Mass difference} &= [(26 \times \text{mass }^{1}\text{H atom}) + (30 \times \text{mass neutron})] - \text{mass }^{56}\text{Fe atom}\\ &= [(26)(1.007825\text{ amu}) + (30)(1.008665\text{ amu})] - 55.934939\text{ amu}\\ &= 0.52846\text{ amu}\end{aligned}$$

Calculating the binding energy per nucleon:

$$\text{Binding energy per nucleon} = \frac{0.52846\text{ amu} \times 931.5\text{ MeV/amu}}{56\text{ nucleons}} = 8.790\text{ MeV/nucleon}$$

An ^{56}Fe nucleus would require more energy per nucleon to break up into its nucleons than would ^{12}C (7.680 MeV/nucleon), so ^{56}Fe is more stable than ^{12}C.

Check The answer is consistent with the great stability of ^{56}Fe. Given the number of decimal places in the values, rounding to check the math is useful only to find a *major* error. The number of nucleons (56) is an exact number, so we retain four significant figures.

Follow-Up Problem 24.6 Uranium-235 is an essential component of the fuel in nuclear power plants. Calculate the binding energy per nucleon for ^{235}U. Is this nuclide more or less stable than ^{12}C (mass of ^{235}U atom = 235.043924 amu)?

Fission or Fusion: Means of Increasing the Binding Energy per Nucleon

Calculations similar to those in Sample Problem 24.6 for other nuclides show that the binding energy per nucleon varies considerably. The essential point is that *the greater the binding energy per nucleon, the more stable the nuclide is.*

Figure 24.16 shows a plot of the binding energy per nucleon vs. mass number. It provides information about nuclide stability and the two possible processes nuclides can undergo to form more stable nuclides. Most nuclides with fewer than 10 nucleons have a relatively small binding energy per nucleon. The ^{4}He nucleus is an exception—it is stable enough to be emitted intact as an α particle. Above $A = 12$, the binding energy per nucleon varies from about 7.6 to 8.8 MeV.

The most important observation is that *the binding energy per nucleon peaks at elements with $A \approx 60$.* In other words, nuclides become more stable with increasing mass number up to around 60 nucleons and then become less stable with higher numbers of nucleons. The existence of a peak of stability suggests that there are two ways nuclides can increase their binding energy per nucleon:

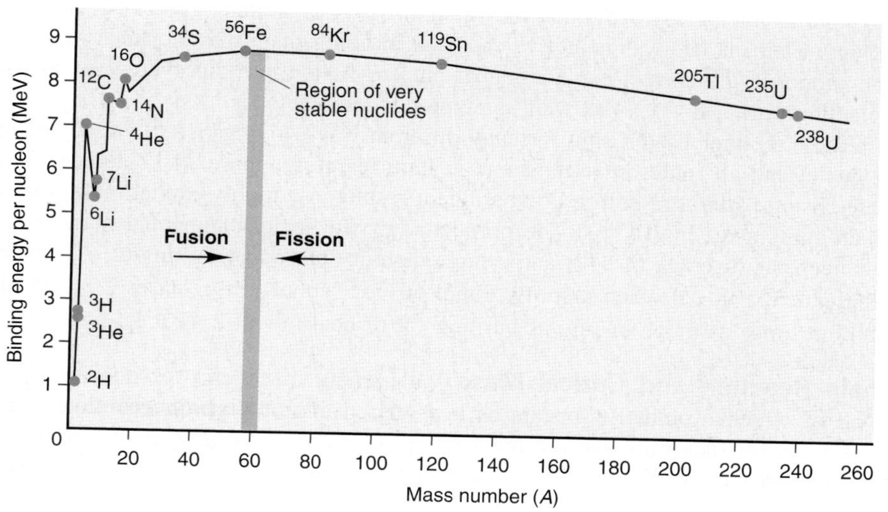

Figure 24.16 The variation in binding energy per nucleon.

- *Fission.* A heavier nucleus can *split into lighter ones (closer to A ≈ 60)* by undergoing fission. The product nuclei have greater binding energy per nucleon (are more stable) than the reactant nucleus, and the difference in *energy is released.* Nuclear power plants generate energy through fission, as do atomic bombs (Section 24.7).
- *Fusion.* Lighter nuclei, on the other hand, can *combine to form a heavier one (closer to A ≈ 60)* by undergoing fusion. Once again, the product is more stable than the reactants, and *energy is released.* The Sun and other stars generate energy through fusion, as do thermonuclear (hydrogen) bombs. In these examples and in all current research efforts for developing fusion as a useful energy source, hydrogen nuclei fuse to form the very stable helium-4 nucleus.

In Section 24.7, we examine fission and fusion and their applications.

Summary of Section 24.6

- The mass of a nucleus is less than the sum of the masses of its nucleons. The energy equivalent to this mass difference is the nuclear binding energy, often expressed in units of MeV.
- The binding energy per nucleon is a measure of nuclide stability and varies with the number of nucleons. Nuclides with $A \approx 60$ are most stable.
- Lighter nuclides join (fusion) or heavier nuclides split (fission) to create more stable products.

24.7 • APPLICATIONS OF FISSION AND FUSION

Of the many beneficial applications of nuclear reactions, the greatest is the potential for abundant quantities of energy, which is based on the multimillion-fold increase in energy yield of nuclear reactions over chemical reactions. Our experience with nuclear energy from power plants in the late 20th century, however, has shown that we must improve ways to tap this energy source safely and economically and deal with the waste generated. In this section, we discuss how fission and fusion occur and how we are applying them.

The Process of Nuclear Fission

During the mid-1930s, Enrico Fermi and coworkers bombarded uranium ($Z = 92$) with neutrons in an attempt to synthesize transuranium elements. Many of the unstable nuclides produced were tentatively identified as having $Z > 92$, but other scientists were skeptical. Four years later, the German chemist Otto Hahn and his associate F. Strassmann showed that one of these unstable nuclides was an isotope of barium ($Z = 56$). The Austrian physicist Lise Meitner, a coworker of Hahn, and her nephew Otto Frisch proposed that barium resulted from the *splitting* of the uranium nucleus into *smaller* nuclei, a process that they called *fission* as an analogy to cell division in biology. Element 109 was named *meitnerium* in honor of this extraordinary physicist who proposed the correct explanation of nuclear fission and discovered the element protactinium (Pa; $Z = 91$) as well as numerous radioisotopes.

The ^{235}U nucleus can split in many different ways, giving rise to various daughter nuclei, but all routes have the same general features. Figure 24.17 depicts one of these fission patterns. Neutron bombardment results in a highly excited ^{236}U nucleus, which splits apart in 10^{-14} s. The products are two nuclei of unequal mass, two to four neutrons (average of 2.4), and a large quantity of energy. A single ^{235}U nucleus releases 3.5×10^{-11} J when it splits; 1 mol of ^{235}U (about $\frac{1}{2}$ lb) releases 2.1×10^{13} J—a billion times as much energy as burning $\frac{1}{2}$ lb of coal (about 2×10^4 J)!

Chain Reaction and Critical Mass We harness the energy of nuclear fission, much of which eventually appears as heat, by means of a **chain reaction** (Figure 24.18): the few neutrons that are released by the fission of one nucleus collide with other fissionable nuclei and cause them to split, releasing more neutrons, and so on,

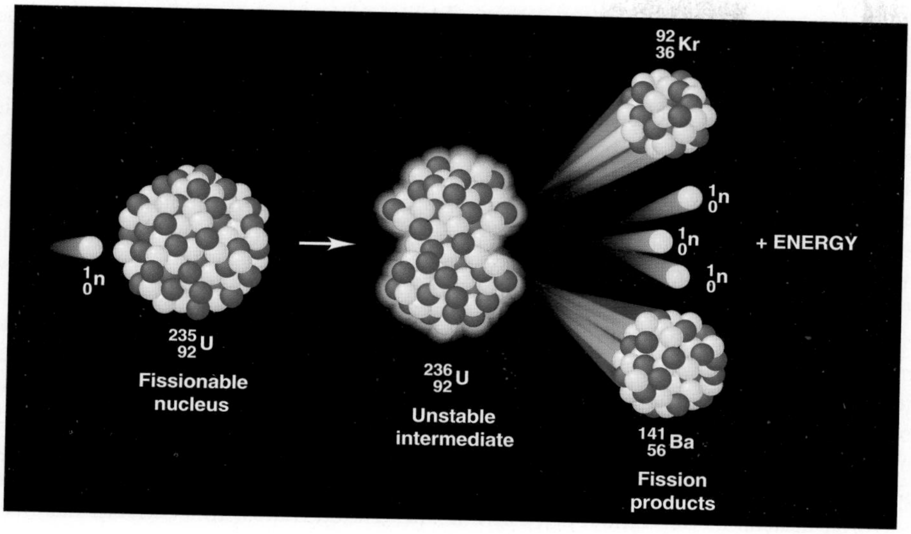

Figure 24.17 Fission of ^{235}U caused by neutron bombardment.

in a self-sustaining process (with each step shown as a vertical dashed line). In this manner, the energy released increases rapidly because each fission event in a chain reaction releases about two-and-a-half times as much energy as the preceding one.

Whether a chain reaction occurs depends on the mass (and thus the volume) of the fissionable sample. If the piece of uranium is large enough, the product neutrons strike another fissionable nucleus *before* flying out of the sample, and a chain reaction takes place. The mass required to achieve a chain reaction is called the **critical mass.** If the sample has less than the critical mass (a *subcritical mass*), too many product neutrons leave the sample before they collide with and cause the fission of another ^{235}U nucleus, and thus a chain reaction does not occur.

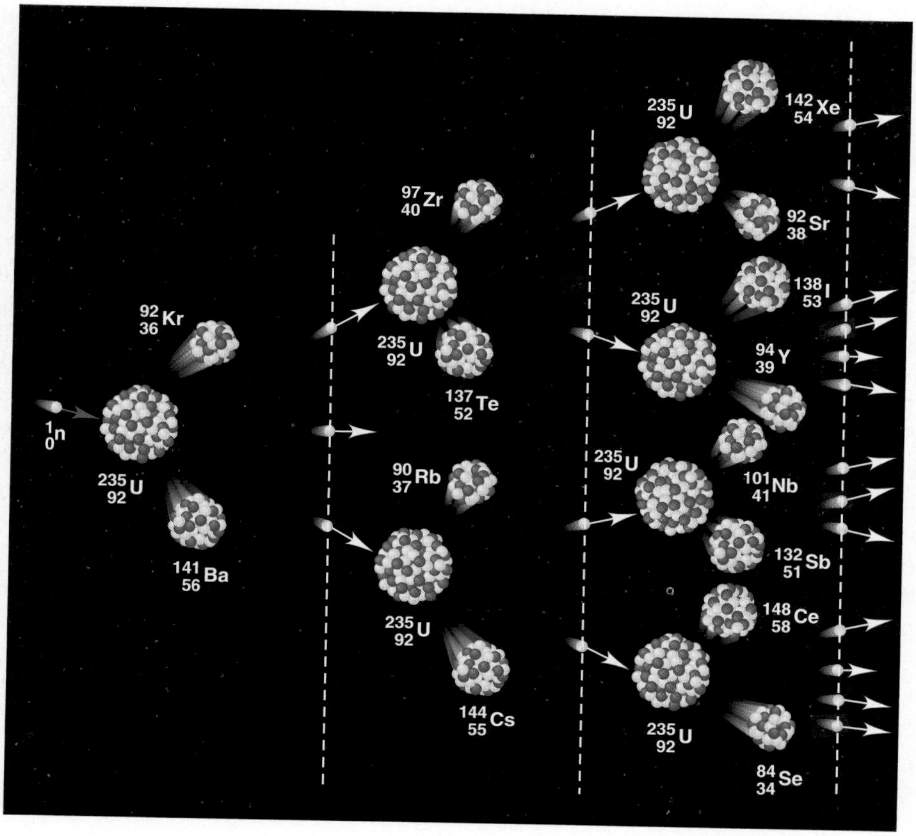

Figure 24.18 A chain reaction involving fission of ^{235}U.

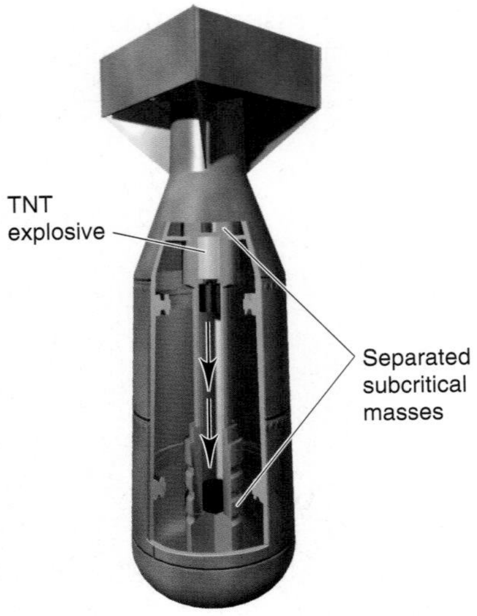

Figure 24.19 An atomic bomb based on ^{235}U.

Uncontrolled Fission: The Atomic Bomb An uncontrolled chain reaction can be adapted to make an extremely powerful explosive, as several of the world's leading atomic physicists hypothesized just prior to World War II. In August 1939, Albert Einstein wrote the president of the United States, Franklin Delano Roosevelt, to this effect, warning of the danger of allowing the Nazi government to develop this power first. It was this concern that led to the Manhattan Project, an enormous scientific effort to develop a bomb based on nuclear fission, which was initiated in 1941.* In August 1945, the United States detonated two atomic bombs over Japan, and the horrible destructive power of these bombs was a major factor in the surrender of the Japanese a few days later.

In an atomic bomb, small explosions of trinitrotoluene (TNT) bring subcritical masses of fissionable material together to exceed the critical mass, and the ensuing chain reaction brings about the explosion (Figure 24.19). The proliferation of nuclear power plants, which use fissionable materials to generate energy for electricity, has increased concern that more countries (and unscrupulous individuals) may have access to such material for making bombs. Since the devastating terrorist attacks of September 11, 2001 in the United States, this concern has been heightened.

Controlled Fission: Nuclear Energy Reactors Like a coal-fired power plant, *a nuclear power plant generates heat to produce steam, which turns a turbine attached to an electric generator.* But a nuclear plant has the potential to produce electric power much more cleanly than by the combustion of coal.

1. *Operation of a nuclear power plant.* Heat generation takes place in the **reactor core** of a nuclear plant (Figure 24.20). The core contains the *fuel rods,* which consist of fuel enclosed in tubes of a corrosion-resistant zirconium alloy. The fuel is uranium(IV) oxide (UO_2) that has been *enriched* from 0.7% ^{235}U, the natural abundance of this fissionable isotope, to the 3% to 4% ^{235}U required to sustain a chain reaction in a practical volume. (Enrichment of nuclear fuel is the most important application of Graham's law, see p. 210.) Sandwiched between the fuel rods are movable *control rods* made of cadmium or boron (or, in nuclear submarines, hafnium), substances that absorb neutrons very efficiently. When the control rods are lowered between the fuel rods, the chain reaction slows because fewer neutrons are available to bombard uranium atoms; when they are raised, the chain reaction speeds up. Neutrons that leave the fuel-rod assembly collide with a *reflector,* usually made of a beryllium alloy, which absorbs very few neutrons. Reflecting the neutrons back to the fuel rods speeds the chain reaction.

Flowing around the fuel and control rods in the reactor core is the *moderator,* a substance that slows the neutrons, making them much better at causing fission than the fast ones emerging directly from the fission event. In most modern reactors, the moderator also acts as the *coolant,* the fluid that transfers the released heat to the steam-producing region. *Light-water reactors* use H_2O as the moderator because ^1H absorbs neutrons to some extent; in heavy-water reactors, D_2O is used. The advantage of D_2O is that it absorbs very few neutrons, leaving more available for fission, so heavy-water reactors can use uranium that has been *less enriched.* As the coolant flows around the encased fuel, pumps circulate it through coils that transfer its heat to the water reservoir. Steam formed in the reservoir turns the turbine that runs the generator. The steam then enters a condenser, where water from a lake or river is used to cool it back to liquid that is returned to the water reservoir. Often (although not shown here), large cooling towers aid in this step (see Figure 13.20, p. 493).

*For an excellent scientific and historical account of the development of the atomic bomb, see R. Rhodes, *The Making of the Atomic Bomb,* New York, Simon and Schuster, 1986.

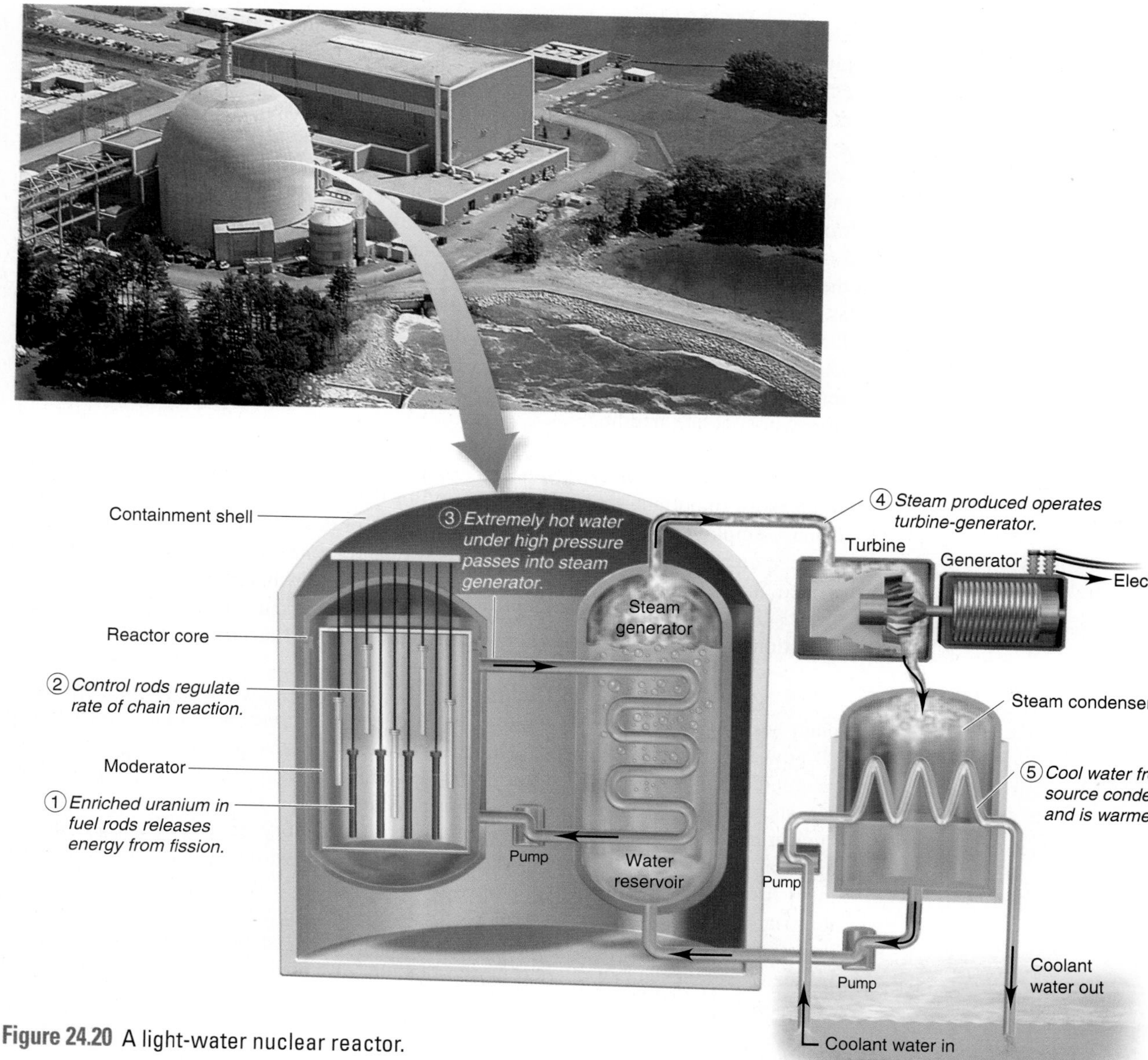

Figure 24.20 A light-water nuclear reactor.

2. *Breeder reactors.* Because ^{235}U is not an abundant isotope, the *breeder reactor* was designed to consume one type of nuclear fuel as it produces another. Outside the moderator, fuel rods are surrounded by natural U_3O_8, which contains 99.3% *nonfissionable* ^{238}U atoms. As neutrons formed during ^{235}U fission escape the fuel rod, they collide with ^{238}U, transmuting it into ^{239}Pu, another fissionable nucleus:

$$^{238}_{92}U + ^{1}_{0}n \longrightarrow ^{239}_{92}U \qquad (t_{1/2} \text{ of } ^{239}_{92}U = 23.5 \text{ min})$$

$$^{239}_{92}U \longrightarrow ^{239}_{93}Np + ^{0}_{-1}\beta \qquad (t_{1/2} \text{ of } ^{239}_{93}Np = 2.35 \text{ days})$$

$$^{239}_{93}Np \longrightarrow ^{239}_{94}Pu + ^{0}_{-1}\beta \qquad (t_{1/2} \text{ of } ^{239}_{94}Pu = 2.4\times10^{4} \text{ yr})$$

Although breeder reactors can make fuel as they operate, they are difficult and expensive to build, and ^{239}Pu is extremely toxic and long lived. Breeder reactors are not used in the United States, although several are operating in Europe and Japan.

3. *Power plant accidents and other concerns.* Some major accidents at nuclear plants have caused decidedly negative public reactions. In 1979, malfunctions of coolant pumps and valves at the Three-Mile Island facility in Pennsylvania led to melting of some of the fuel and damage to the reactor core, but the release of only a very small amount (about 1 Ci) of radioactive gases into the atmosphere. In 1986, a million times as much radioactivity (1 MCi) was released when a cooling system failure at the Chernobyl plant in Ukraine caused a much greater melting of fuel and an uncontrolled reaction. High-pressure steam and ignited graphite moderator rods caused the reactor building to explode and expel radioactive debris. Carried by prevailing winds, the radioactive particles contaminated vegetables and milk in much of Europe. And, as we said earlier, health officials have evidence that thousands of people living near the accident have already developed or may eventually develop cancer from radiation exposure. The design of the Chernobyl plant was particularly unsafe because, unlike reactors in the United States and western Europe, the reactor was not contained in a massive, concrete building.*

4. *Current use of nuclear power.* Despite potential safety problems, nuclear power remains an important source of electricity. In the late 1990s, nearly every European country employed nuclear power, and it is the major power source in some countries—Sweden creates 50% of its electricity this way and France almost 80%. Currently, the United States obtains about 20% of its electricity from nuclear power, and Canada slightly less. As our need for energy grows and climate change from fossil-fuel consumption worsens, safer reactors are being designed and are likely to be built.

5. *Thermal pollution and waste disposal.* However, even a smoothly operating plant has certain inherent problems. The problem of *thermal pollution* is common to all power plants. Water used to condense the steam is several degrees warmer when returned to its source, which can harm aquatic organisms (Section 13.4). A more serious problem is *nuclear waste disposal.* Many of the fission products formed in nuclear reactors have long half-lives, and no satisfactory plan for their permanent disposal has yet been devised. Proposals to place the waste in containers and bury them in deep bedrock cannot possibly be field-tested for the thousands of years the material will remain harmful. Leakage of radioactive material into groundwater is a danger, and earthquakes can occur even in geologically stable regions. It remains to be seen whether we can operate fission reactors *and* dispose of the waste safely and economically.

The Promise of Nuclear Fusion

Nuclear fusion in the Sun is the ultimate source of nearly all the energy—and chemical elements—on Earth. In fact, *all the elements heavier than hydrogen were formed in fusion and decay processes within stars,* as the next Chemical Connections essay describes.

Much research is being devoted to making nuclear fusion a practical, direct source of energy on Earth. To understand the advantages of fusion, let's consider one of the most discussed fusion reactions, in which deuterium and tritium react:

$$^{2}_{1}\text{H} + ^{3}_{1}\text{H} \longrightarrow ^{4}_{2}\text{He} + ^{1}_{0}\text{n}$$

This reaction produces 1.7×10^9 kJ/mol, an enormous quantity of energy with no radioactive byproducts. Moreover, the reactant nuclei are relatively easy to come by.

*An even greater release of radioactivity (1.1 MCi), involving several radionuclides including the extremely dangerous ^{90}Sr, occurred in 1957 in Kyshtym, a town in the South Ural Mountains of Russia. As a result, radioactivity spread globally, but the accident was kept secret by the former Soviet government until 1980.

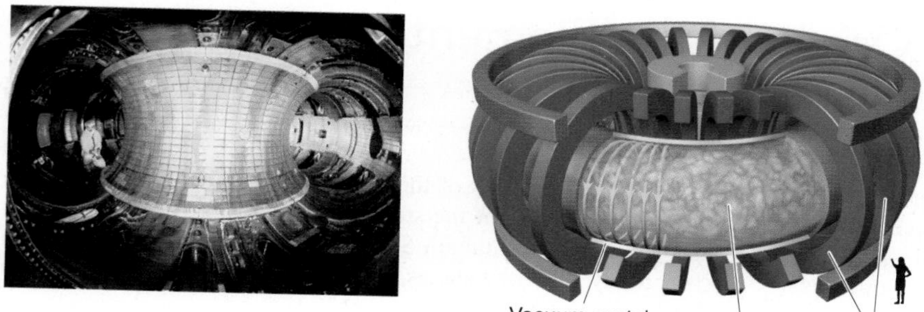

Figure 24.21 The tokamak design for magnetic containment of a fusion plasma.

We obtain deuterium from the electrolysis of water (Section 22.4). In nature, tritium forms through the cosmic (neutron) irradiation of ^{14}N:

$$^{14}_{7}N + ^{1}_{0}n \longrightarrow ^{3}_{1}H + ^{12}_{6}C$$

However, this process results in a natural abundance of only $10^{-7}\%$ ^{3}H. More practically, tritium is produced in nuclear accelerators by bombarding lithium-6 or by surrounding the fusion reactor itself with material containing lithium-6:

$$^{6}_{3}Li + ^{1}_{0}n \longrightarrow ^{3}_{1}H + ^{4}_{2}He$$

Thus, in principle, fusion *seems* promising and may represent an ideal source of power. However, some extremely difficult technical problems remain. Fusion requires enormous energy in the form of heat to give the positively charged nuclei enough kinetic energy to force themselves together. The fusion of deuterium and tritium, for example, occurs at practical rates at about 10^8 K, a temperature hotter than the Sun's core! How can such conditions be achieved? Two current research approaches have promise. In one, atoms are stripped of their electrons at high temperatures, which results in a gaseous *plasma,* a neutral mixture of positive nuclei and electrons. Because of the extreme temperatures needed for fusion, no *material* can contain the plasma. The most successful approach to date has been to enclose the plasma within a magnetic field. The *tokamak* design has a donut-shaped container in which a helical magnetic field confines the plasma and prevents it from contacting the walls (Figure 24.21). Scientists at the Princeton University Plasma Physics facility have achieved some success in generating energy from fusion this way. In another approach, the high temperature is reached by using many focused lasers to compress and heat the fusion reactants. In any event, one or more major breakthroughs are needed before fusion will be a practical, everyday source of energy.

Summary of Section 24.7

- In nuclear fission, neutron bombardment causes a nucleus to split into two smaller nuclei and release neutrons that split other nuclei, giving rise to a chain reaction.
- A nuclear power plant controls the rate of the chain reaction to produce heat that creates steam, which is used to generate electricity.
- Potential hazards, such as radiation leaks, thermal pollution, and disposal of nuclear waste, remain current concerns.
- Nuclear fusion holds great promise as a source of clean abundant energy, but it requires extremely high temperatures and is not yet practical.
- The elements were formed through a complex series of nuclear reactions in evolving stars.

CHEMICAL CONNECTIONS TO COSMOLOGY | Origin of the Elements in the Stars

How did the universe begin? Where did matter come from? How were the elements formed? The most accepted model proposes that a sphere of unimaginable properties—diameter of 10^{-28} cm, density of 10^{96} g/mL (density of a nucleus $\approx 10^{14}$ g/mL), and temperature of 10^{32} K—exploded in a "Big Bang," for reasons not yet known, and distributed its contents through the void of space. Cosmologists consider this moment the beginning of time.

One second later, the universe was an expanding mixture of neutrons, protons, and electrons, denser than rock and hotter than an exploding hydrogen bomb (about 10^{10} K). In the next few minutes, it became a gigantic fusion reactor creating the first atomic nuclei other than ^{1}H: ^{2}H, ^{3}He, and ^{4}He. After 10 min, more than 25% of the mass of the universe existed as ^{4}He, and only about 0.025% as ^{2}H. About 100 million years later, or about 15 billion years ago, gravitational forces pulled this cosmic mixture into primitive, contracting stars.

This account of the origin of the universe is based on the observation of spectra from the Sun, other stars, nearby galaxies, and cosmic (interstellar) dust. Spectral analysis of planets and chemical analysis of Earth and Moon rocks, meteorites, and cosmic-ray particles furnish data about isotope abundance. From these, a model has been developed for **stellar nucleosynthesis,** the creation of the elements in stars. The overall process occurs in several stages during a star's evolution, and the entire sequence of steps occurs only in very massive stars, having 10 to 100 times the mass of the Sun. Each step involves a contraction of the volume of the star that results in higher temperature and yields heavier nuclei. Such events are forming elements in stars today. The key stages in the process are shown in Figure B24.1 and described below:

1. *Hydrogen burning produces He.* The initial contraction of a star heats its core to about 10^7 K, at which point a fusion process called *hydrogen burning* begins. Through three possible reactions (one is shown below), helium nuclei are produced from the abundant protons:

$$4\,^1_1\text{H} \longrightarrow \,^4_2\text{He} + 2\,^0_1\beta + 2\nu + \text{energy}$$

2. *Helium burning produces C, O, Ne, and Mg.* After several billion years of hydrogen burning, about 10% of the ^{1}H is consumed, and the star contracts further. The ^{4}He forms a dense core, hot enough (2×10^8 K) to fuse ^{4}He nuclei. The energy released during *helium burning* expands the remaining ^{1}H into a vast envelope: the star becomes a *red giant,* more than 100 times its original diameter. Within its core, pairs of ^{4}He nuclei (α particles) fuse into unstable ^{8}Be nuclei ($t_{1/2} = 7\times10^{-17}$ s), which play the role of an activated complex in chemical reactions. A ^{8}Be nucleus collides with another ^{4}He to form ^{12}C. Then, further fusion with ^{4}He creates nuclei up to ^{24}Mg:

$$^{12}\text{C} \xrightarrow{\alpha} \,^{16}\text{O} \xrightarrow{\alpha} \,^{20}\text{Ne} \xrightarrow{\alpha} \,^{24}\text{Mg}$$

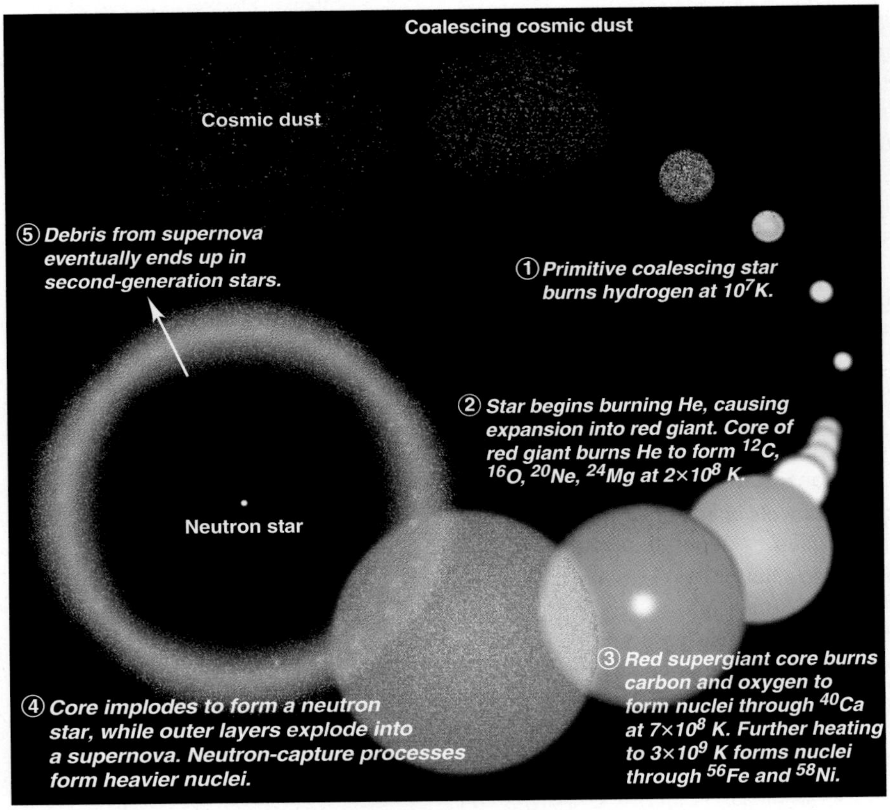

Figure B24.1 Element synthesis in the life cycle of a star.

3. *Elements through Fe and Ni form.* For another 10 million years, ^{4}He is consumed, and the heavier nuclei created form a core. This core contracts and heats, expanding the star into a *supergiant.* Within the hot core (7×10^8 K), *carbon and oxygen burning* occur:

$$^{12}C + {}^{12}C \longrightarrow {}^{23}Na + {}^{1}H$$
$$^{12}C + {}^{16}O \longrightarrow {}^{28}Si + \gamma$$

Absorption of α particles forms nuclei up to ^{40}Ca:

$$^{12}C \xrightarrow{\alpha} {}^{16}O \xrightarrow{\alpha} {}^{20}Ne \xrightarrow{\alpha} {}^{24}Mg \xrightarrow{\alpha} {}^{28}Si \xrightarrow{\alpha} {}^{32}S \xrightarrow{\alpha} {}^{36}Ar \xrightarrow{\alpha} {}^{40}Ca$$

Further contraction and heating to a temperature of 3×10^9 K allow reactions in which nuclei release neutrons, protons, and α particles and then recapture them. As a result, nuclei with lower binding energies supply nucleons to create those with higher binding energies. In stars of moderate mass, less than 10 times the mass of the Sun, this process stops at iron-56 and nickel-58, the nuclei with the highest binding energies.

4. *Heavier elements form.* In very massive stars, the next stage is the most spectacular. With all the fuel consumed, the core collapses within a second. Many Fe and Ni nuclei break down into neutrons and protons. Protons capture electrons to form neutrons, and the entire core forms an incredibly dense *neutron star.* (An Earth-sized star that became a neutron star would fit in the Houston Astrodome!) As the core implodes, the outer layers explode in a *supernova,* which expels material throughout space. A supernova occurs an average of every few hundred years in each galaxy or once every second somewhere in the universe. The heavier elements are formed during supernova events and are found in *second-generation stars,* those that coalesce from interstellar ^{1}H and ^{4}He and the debris of exploded first-generation stars.

Heavier elements form through *neutron-capture* processes. In the *s-process* (*slow* neutron-capture process), a nucleus captures a neutron, sometime over a period of 10 to 1000 years. If the resulting nucleus is unstable, it undergoes β^- decay to form the next element, as in this conversion of ^{68}Zn to ^{70}Ge:

$$^{68}Zn \xrightarrow{n} {}^{69}Zn \xrightarrow{\beta^-} {}^{69}Ga \xrightarrow{n} {}^{70}Ga \xrightarrow{\beta^-} {}^{70}Ge$$

The stable isotopes of most heavy elements up to ^{209}Bi form by the s-process.

Less stable isotopes and those with *A* greater than 230 cannot form by the s-process because their half-lives are too short. These form by the *r-process* (*rapid* neutron-capture process) during the fury of the supernova. Many neutron captures, followed by many β^- decays, occur in a second, as when ^{56}Fe is converted to ^{79}Br:

$$^{56}_{26}Fe + 23\,^{1}_{0}n \longrightarrow {}^{79}_{26}Fe \longrightarrow {}^{79}_{35}Br + 9\,^{0}_{-1}\beta$$

We know from the heavy elements present in the Sun that it is at least a second-generation star presently undergoing hydrogen burning. Together with its planets, it was formed from the dust of exploded stars about 4.6×10^9 years ago. This means that many of the atoms on Earth, including some within you, came from exploded stars and are older than the Solar System itself!

Any theory of element formation must be consistent with the element abundances we observe (Section 22.1). Although local compositions, such as those of Earth and the Sun, differ, and mineral grains in meteorites may have abnormal isotopic compositions, large regions of the universe have, on average, similar compositions. Scientists believe element forming reaches a dynamic equilibrium, resulting in *relatively constant amounts of the isotopes.*

Problems

B24.1 Compare the *s*- and *r*-processes in stellar nucleosynthesis in terms of rate, number of neutrons absorbed, and types of isotopes formed.

B24.2 The overall reaction taking place during hydrogen burning in a young star is

$$4\,^{1}_{1}H \longrightarrow {}^{4}_{2}He + 2\,^{0}_{1}\beta + 2\nu + \text{energy}$$

How much energy (in MeV) is released per He nucleus formed? Per mole of He formed? (Masses of atoms: $^{1}_{1}$H atom = 1.007825 amu; $^{4}_{2}$He atom = 4.00260 amu; mass of positron = 5.48580×10^{-4} amu.)

B24.3 Cosmologists modeling the origin of the elements postulate nuclides with very short half-lives. One of these short-lived nuclides, ^{8}Be ($t_{1/2} = 7\times10^{-17}$ s), is thought to play a key role in stellar nucleosynthesis by fusing with ^{4}He to form ^{12}C. Another model proposes the simultaneous fusion of three ^{4}He nuclei to form ^{12}C. Comment on the validity of this alternative mechanism.

B24.4 The *s*-process produces isotopes of elements up to ^{209}Bi. This process is terminated when ^{209}Bi captures a neutron to produce ^{210}Bi, which subsequently undergoes β^- decay to produce nuclide A, which then decays by emitting an α particle to form nuclide B. This nuclide captures three neutrons to produce nuclide C, which undergoes β^- decay to produce nuclide D, starting the cycle again. Write balanced nuclear equations for the formation of nuclides A through D.

CHAPTER REVIEW GUIDE

Learning Objectives

Relevant section (§) and/or sample problem (SP) numbers appear in parentheses.

Understand These Concepts

1. How nuclear changes differ, in general, from chemical changes (Introduction)
2. The meanings of *radioactivity, nucleon, nuclide,* and *isotope* (§24.1)
3. Characteristics of three types of radioactive emissions: α, β, and γ (§24.1)
4. The various modes of radioactive decay and how each changes the values of A and Z (§24.1)
5. How the N/Z ratio, the even-odd nature of N and Z, and magic numbers correlate with nuclear stability (§24.1)
6. How an unstable nuclide's mass number or N/Z ratio correlates with its mode of decay (§24.1)
7. How a decay series combines numerous decay steps and ends with a stable nuclide (§24.1)
8. How ionization and scintillation counters detect and measure radioactivity (§24.2)
9. Why radioactive decay is a first-order process; the meanings of *decay rate* and *specific activity* (§24.2)
10. The meaning of *half-life* in the context of radioactive decay (§24.2)
11. How the specific activity of an isotope in an object is used to determine the object's age (§24.2)
12. How particle accelerators and reactors are used to synthesize new nuclides (§24.3)
13. The units of radiation dose; the effects on living tissue of various dosage levels; the inverse relationship between the mass and charge of an emission and its penetrating power (§24.4)
14. How ionizing radiation creates free radicals that damage tissue; sources and risks of ionizing radiation (§24.4)
15. How radioisotopes are used in research, analysis, and medical diagnosis (§24.5)
16. Why the mass of a nucleus is less than the total mass of its nucleons and how this mass difference is related to the nuclear binding energy (§24.6)
17. How nuclear stability is related to binding energy per nucleon (§24.6)
18. How heavy nuclides undergo fission and lighter ones undergo fusion to increase the binding energy per nucleon (§24.6)
19. The current application of fission and potential application of fusion to produce energy (§24.7)

Master These Skills

1. Expressing the mass and charge of a particle with the $^{A}_{Z}X$ notation (§24.1; see also §2.5)
2. Using changes in the values of A and Z to write and balance nuclear equations (SP 24.1)
3. Using the N/Z ratio, the even-odd nature of N and Z, and the presence of magic numbers to predict nuclear stability (SP 24.2)
4. Using the atomic mass of the element or the N/Z ratio to predict the mode of decay of an unstable nuclide (SP 24.3)
5. Converting units of radioactivity (§24.2)
6. Calculating specific activity, decay constant, half-life, and number of nuclei (§24.2 and SP 24.4)
7. Estimating the age of an object from the specific activity and half-life of carbon-14 (SP 24.5)
8. Writing notations and balancing equations for nuclear transmutation (§24.3)
9. Calculating radiation dose and converting units (§24.4)
10. Calculating the mass difference between a nucleus and its nucleons and the energy equivalent (§24.6)
11. Calculating the binding energy per nucleon and using it to compare stabilities of nuclides (SP 24.6)

Key Terms

Page numbers appear in parentheses.

radioactivity (977)

Section 24.1
nucleon (978)
nuclide (978)
isotope (978)
alpha (α) particle (979)
beta (β) particle (979)
gamma (γ) ray (979)
alpha (α) decay (981)
beta (β) decay (981)
β^- decay (981)
positron (β^+) emission (981)
positron (981)
electron (e^-) capture (EC) (981)
gamma (γ) emission (982)
band of stability (983)
strong force (984)
decay (disintegration) series (986)

Section 24.2
Geiger-Müller counter (987)
scintillation counter (987)
activity ($\mathscr{A}$) (988)
becquerel (Bq) (988)
curie (Ci) (988)
decay constant (988)
half-life ($t_{1/2}$) (988)
radioisotopic dating (990)
radioisotope (990)

Section 24.3
nuclear transmutation (992)
deuteron (993)
particle accelerator (993)
transuranium element (994)

Section 24.4
ionization (995)
ionizing radiation (995)
gray (Gy) (996)
rad (*r*adiation-*a*bsorbed *d*ose) (996)
rem (*r*oentgen *e*quivalent for *m*an) (996)
sievert (Sv) (996)
free radical (997)
background radiation (997)

Section 24.5
tracer (1000)

Section 24.6
fission (1003)
fusion (1003)
nuclear binding energy (1004)
electron volt (eV) (1004)

Section 24.7
chain reaction (1006)
critical mass (1007)
reactor core (1008)
stellar nucleosynthesis (1012)

Key Equations and Relationships

Page numbers appear in parentheses.

24.1 Balancing a nuclear equation (979):

$$\text{Total } {}^{A}_{Z}\text{Reactants} = \text{Total } {}^{A}_{Z}\text{Products}$$

24.2 Defining the unit of radioactivity (curie, Ci) (988):

$$1 \text{ Ci} = 3.70\times10^{10} \text{ disintegrations per second (d/s)}$$

24.3 Expressing the decay rate (activity) for radioactive nuclei (988):

$$\text{Decay rate } (\mathscr{A}) = -\frac{\Delta \mathscr{N}}{\Delta t} = k\mathscr{N}$$

24.4 Finding the number of nuclei remaining after a given time, $\mathscr{N}_t$ (988):

$$\ln \frac{\mathscr{N}_t}{\mathscr{N}_0} = -kt \quad \text{or} \quad \mathscr{N}_t = \mathscr{N}_0 e^{-kt}$$

24.5 Finding the half-life of a radioactive nuclide (989):

$$t_{1/2} = \frac{\ln 2}{k}$$

24.6 Calculating the time to reach a given specific activity (age of an object in radioisotopic dating) (991):

$$t = \frac{1}{k} \ln \frac{\mathscr{A}_0}{\mathscr{A}_t}$$

24.7 Writing a transmutation in shorthand notation (993):

reactant nucleus (particle in, particle(s) out) product nucleus

24.8 Adapting Einstein's equation to calculate mass difference and/or nuclear binding energy (1003):

$$\Delta m = \frac{\Delta E}{c^2} \quad \text{or} \quad \Delta E = \Delta mc^2$$

24.9 Relating the atomic mass unit to its energy equivalent in MeV (1004):

$$1 \text{ amu} = 931.5\times10^6 \text{ eV} = 931.5 \text{ MeV}$$

Brief Solutions to Follow-Up Problems

24.1 $^{133}_{54}\text{Xe} \longrightarrow {}^{133}_{55}\text{Cs} + {}^{0}_{-1}\beta$

24.2 ^{31}P has an even N (16), but ^{30}P has both N and Z odd. ^{31}P also has a slightly higher N/Z ratio that is closer to the band of stability.

24.3 (a) $Z = 26$ is iron (Fe), and the atomic mass is 55.85. The A value of 61 is higher: β^- decay; (b) $Z > 83$, which is too high for stability: α decay

24.4 $\ln \mathscr{A}_t = -kt + \ln \mathscr{A}_0$

$$= -\left(\frac{\ln 2}{15 \text{ h}} \times 4.0 \text{ days} \times \frac{24 \text{ h}}{1 \text{ day}}\right) + \ln (2.5\times10^9)$$

$$= 17.20$$

$$\mathscr{A} = 3.0\times10^7 \text{ d/s}$$

24.5 $t = \frac{1}{k} \ln \frac{\mathscr{A}_0}{\mathscr{A}_t} = \frac{5730 \text{ yr}}{\ln 2} \ln \left(\frac{15.3 \text{ d/min}\cdot\text{g}}{9.41 \text{ d/min}\cdot\text{g}}\right)$

$$= 4.02\times10^3 \text{ yr}$$

The mummy case is about 4000 years old.

24.6 ^{235}U has 92 $^{1}_{1}$p and 143 $^{1}_{0}$n.

$$\Delta m = [(92 \times 1.007825 \text{ amu}) + (143 \times 1.008665 \text{ amu})] - 235.043924 \text{ amu}$$

$$= 1.9151 \text{ amu}$$

$$\frac{\text{Binding energy}}{\text{nucleon}} = \frac{1.9151 \text{ amu} \times \frac{931.5 \text{ MeV}}{1 \text{ amu}}}{235 \text{ nucleons}}$$

$$= 7.591 \text{ MeV/nucleon}$$

Therefore, ^{235}U is less stable than ^{12}C.

PROBLEMS

Problems with **colored** numbers are answered in Appendix E and worked in detail in the Student Solutions Manual. Problem sections match those in the text and provide the numbers of relevant sample problems. Most offer Concept Review Questions, Skill-Building Exercises (grouped in pairs covering the same concept), and Problems in Context. The Comprehensive Problems are based on material from any section or previous chapter.

Radioactive Decay and Nuclear Stability

(Sample Problems 24.1 to 24.3)

Concept Review Questions

24.1 How do chemical and nuclear reactions differ in
(a) Magnitude of the energy change?
(b) Effect on rate of increasing temperature?
(c) Effect on rate of higher reactant concentration?
(d) Effect on yield of higher reactant concentration?

24.2 Sulfur has four naturally occurring stable isotopes. The one with the lowest mass number is sulfur-32, which is also the most abundant (95.02%).
(a) What percentage of the S atoms in a matchhead are ^{32}S?
(b) The isotopic mass of ^{32}S is 31.972070 amu. Is the atomic mass of S larger, smaller, or equal to this mass? Explain.

24.3 What led Marie Curie to draw the following conclusions?
(a) Radioactivity is a property of the element and not the compound in which it is found. (b) A highly radioactive element, aside from uranium, occurs in pitchblende.

24.4 Which of the following produce an atom of a *different* element: (a) α decay; (b) β^- decay; (c) γ emission; (d) β^+ emission;

(e) e^- capture? Show how Z and N change, if at all, with each process.

24.5 Why is ^3_2He stable, but ^2_2He has never been detected?

24.6 How do the modes of decay differ for a neutron-rich nuclide and a proton-rich nuclide?

24.7 Why might it be difficult to use only a nuclide's N/Z ratio to predict whether it will decay by β^+ emission or by e^- capture? What other factor is important?

Skill-Building Exercises (grouped in similar pairs)

24.8 Write balanced nuclear equations for the following:
(a) Alpha decay of $^{234}_{92}U$
(b) Electron capture by neptunium-232
(c) Positron emission by $^{12}_{7}N$

24.9 Write balanced nuclear equations for the following:
(a) β^- decay of sodium-26
(b) β^- decay of francium-223
(c) Alpha decay of $^{212}_{83}Bi$

24.10 Write balanced nuclear equations for the following:
(a) β^- emission by magnesium-27
(b) β^+ emission by $^{23}_{12}Mg$
(c) Electron capture by $^{103}_{46}Pd$

24.11 Write balanced nuclear equations for the following:
(a) β^- decay of silicon-32
(b) Alpha decay of polonium-218
(c) Electron capture by $^{110}_{49}In$

24.12 Write balanced nuclear equations for the following:
(a) Formation of $^{48}_{22}Ti$ through positron emission
(b) Formation of silver-107 through electron capture
(c) Formation of polonium-206 through α decay

24.13 Write balanced nuclear equations for the following:
(a) Formation of $^{241}_{95}Am$ through β^- decay
(b) Formation of $^{228}_{89}Ac$ through β^- decay
(c) Formation of $^{203}_{83}Bi$ through α decay

24.14 Write balanced nuclear equations for the following:
(a) Formation of ^{186}Ir through electron capture
(b) Formation of francium-221 through α decay
(c) Formation of iodine-129 through β^- decay

24.15 Write balanced nuclear equations for the following:
(a) Formation of ^{52}Mn through positron emission
(b) Formation of polonium-215 through α decay
(c) Formation of ^{81}Kr through electron capture

24.16 Which nuclide(s) would you predict to be stable? Why?
(a) $^{20}_{8}O$ (b) $^{59}_{27}Co$ (c) $^{9}_{3}Li$

24.17 Which nuclide(s) would you predict to be stable? Why?
(a) $^{146}_{60}Nd$ (b) $^{114}_{48}Cd$ (c) $^{88}_{42}Mo$

24.18 Which nuclide(s) would you predict to be stable? Why?
(a) ^{127}I (b) tin-106 (c) ^{68}As

24.19 Which nuclide(s) would you predict to be stable? Why?
(a) ^{48}K (b) ^{79}Br (c) argon-32

24.20 What is the most likely mode of decay for each?
(a) $^{238}_{92}U$ (b) $^{48}_{24}Cr$ (c) $^{50}_{25}Mn$

24.21 What is the most likely mode of decay for each?
(a) $^{111}_{47}Ag$ (b) $^{41}_{17}Cl$ (c) $^{110}_{44}Ru$

24.22 What is the most likely mode of decay for each?
(a) ^{15}C (b) ^{120}Xe (c) ^{224}Th

24.23 What is the most likely mode of decay for each?
(a) ^{106}In (b) ^{141}Eu (c) ^{241}Am

24.24 Why is $^{52}_{24}Cr$ the most stable isotope of chromium?

24.25 Why is $^{40}_{20}Ca$ the most stable isotope of calcium?

Problems in Context

24.26 ^{237}Np is the parent nuclide of a decay series that starts with α emission, followed by β^- emission, and then two more α emissions. Write a balanced nuclear equation for each step.

24.27 Why is helium found in deposits of uranium and thorium ores? What kind of radioactive emission produces it?

24.28 In a natural decay series, how many α and β^- emissions per atom of uranium-235 result in an atom of lead-207?

The Kinetics of Radioactive Decay

(Sample Problems 24.4 and 24.5)

Concept Review Questions

24.29 What electronic process is the basis for detecting radioactivity in (a) a scintillation counter; (b) a Geiger-Müller counter?

24.30 What is the reaction order of radioactive decay? Explain.

24.31 After 1 minute, three radioactive nuclei remain from an original sample of six. Is it valid to conclude that $t_{1/2}$ equals 1 minute? Is this conclusion valid if the original sample contained 6×10^{12} nuclei and 3×10^{12} remain after 1 minute? Explain.

24.32 Radioisotopic dating depends on the constant rate of decay and formation of various nuclides in a sample. How is the proportion of ^{14}C kept relatively constant in living organisms?

Skill-Building Exercises (grouped in similar pairs)

24.33 What is the specific activity (in Ci/g) if 1.65 mg of an isotope emits 1.56×10^6 α particles per second?

24.34 What is the specific activity (in Ci/g) if 2.6 g of an isotope emits 4.13×10^8 β^- particles per hour?

24.35 What is the specific activity (in Bq/g) if 8.58 μg of an isotope emits 7.4×10^4 α particles per minute?

24.36 What is the specific activity (in Bq/g) if 1.07 kg of an isotope emits 3.77×10^7 β^- particles per minute?

24.37 If one-trillionth of the atoms of a radioactive isotope disintegrate each day, what is the decay constant of the process?

24.38 If 2.8×10^{-10}% of the atoms of a radioactive isotope disintegrate in 1.0 yr, what is the decay constant of the process?

24.39 If 1.00×10^{-12} mol of ^{135}Cs emits 1.39×10^5 β^- particles in 1.00 yr, what is the decay constant?

24.40 If 6.40×10^{-9} mol of ^{176}W emits 1.07×10^{15} β^+ particles in 1.00 h, what is the decay constant?

24.41 The isotope $^{212}_{83}Bi$ has a half-life of 1.01 yr. What mass (in mg) of a 2.00-mg sample will remain after 3.75×10^3 h?

24.42 The half-life of radium-226 is 1.60×10^3 yr. How many hours will it take for a 2.50-g sample to decay to the point where 0.185 g of the isotope remains?

24.43 A rock contains 270 μmol of ^{238}U ($t_{1/2}$ = 4.5×10^9 yr) and 110 μmol of ^{206}Pb. Assuming that all the ^{206}Pb comes from decay of the ^{238}U, estimate the rock's age.

24.44 A fabric remnant from a burial site has a $^{14}C/^{12}C$ ratio of 0.735 of the original value. How old is the fabric?

Problems in Context

24.45 Due to decay of ^{40}K, cow's milk has a specific activity of about 6×10^{-11} mCi per milliliter. How many disintegrations of ^{40}K nuclei are there per minute in an 8.0-oz glass of milk?

24.46 Plutonium-239 ($t_{1/2}$ = 2.41×10^4 yr) represents a serious nuclear waste hazard. If seven half-lives are required to reach a tolerable level of radioactivity, how long must ^{239}Pu be stored?

24.47 A rock that contains 3.1×10^{-15} mol of ^{232}Th ($t_{1/2}$ = 1.4×10^{10} yr) has 9.5×10^4 fission tracks, each track representing the fission of one atom of ^{232}Th. How old is the rock?

24.48 A volcanic eruption melts a large chunk of rock, and all gases are expelled. After cooling, $^{40}_{18}Ar$ accumulates from the ongoing decay of $^{40}_{19}K$ in the rock ($t_{1/2}$ = 1.25×10^9 yr). When a piece of rock is analyzed, it is found to contain 1.38 mmol of ^{40}K and 1.14 mmol of ^{40}Ar. How long ago did the rock cool?

Nuclear Transmutation: Induced Changes in Nuclei

Concept Review Questions

24.49 Irene and Frederic Joliot-Curie converted $^{27}_{13}Al$ to $^{30}_{15}P$ in 1933. Why was this transmutation significant?

24.50 Early workers mistakenly thought neutron beams were γ radiation. Why? What evidence led to the correct conclusion?

24.51 Why must the electrical polarity of the tubes in a linear accelerator be reversed at very short time intervals?

24.52 Why does bombardment with protons usually require higher energies than bombardment with neutrons?

Skill-Building Exercises (grouped in similar pairs)

24.53 Determine the missing species in these transmutations, and write a full nuclear equation from the shorthand notation:
(a) ^{10}B (α,n) __
(b) ^{28}Si (d,__) ^{29}P (where d is a deuteron, ^2H)
(c) __ (α,2n) ^{244}Cf

24.54 Name the unidentified species, and write each transmutation process in shorthand notation: (a) gamma irradiation of a nuclide yields a proton, a neutron, and ^{29}Si; (b) bombardment of ^{252}Cf with ^{10}B yields five neutrons and a nuclide; (c) bombardment of ^{238}U with a particle yields three neutrons and ^{239}Pu.

Problems in Context

24.55 Elements 104, 105, and 106 have been named rutherfordium (Rf), dubnium (Db), and seaborgium (Sg), respectively. These elements are synthesized from californium-249 by bombarding with carbon-12, nitrogen-15, and oxygen-18 nuclei, respectively. Four neutrons are formed in each reaction as well. (a) Write balanced nuclear equations for the formation of these elements. (b) Write the equations in shorthand notation.

Effects of Nuclear Radiation on Matter

Concept Review Questions

24.56 The effects on matter of γ rays and α particles differ. Explain.

24.57 What is a cation-electron pair, and how does it form?

24.58 Why is ionizing radiation more harmful to children than adults?

24.59 Why is ·OH more dangerous than OH^- in an organism?

Skill-Building Exercises (grouped in similar pairs)

24.60 A 135-lb person absorbs 3.3×10^{-7} J of energy from radioactive emissions. (a) How many rads does she receive? (b) How many grays (Gy) does she receive?

24.61 A 3.6-kg laboratory animal receives a single dose of 8.92×10^{-4} Gy. (a) How many rads did the animal receive? (b) How many joules did the animal absorb?

24.62 A 70.-kg person exposed to ^{90}Sr absorbs 6.0×10^5 β^- particles, each with an energy of 8.74×10^{-14} J. (a) How many grays does the person receive? (b) If the RBE is 1.0, how many millirems is this? (c) What is the equivalent dose in sieverts (Sv)?

24.63 A laboratory rat weighs 265 g and absorbs 1.77×10^{10} β^- particles, each with an energy of 2.20×10^{-13} J. (a) How many rads does the animal receive? (b) What is this dose in Gy? (c) If the RBE is 0.75, what is the equivalent dose in Sv?

Problems in Context

24.64 If 2.50 pCi [1 pCi (picocurie) = 1×10^{-12} Ci] of radioactivity from ^{239}Pu is emitted in a 95-kg human for 65 h, and each disintegration has an energy of 8.25×10^{-13} J, how many grays does the person receive?

24.65 A small region of a cancer patient's brain is exposed for 24.0 min to 475 Bq of radioactivity from ^{60}Co for treatment of a tumor. If the brain mass exposed is 1.858 g and each β^- particle emitted has an energy of 5.05×10^{-14} J, what is the dose in rads?

Applications of Radioisotopes

Concept Review Questions

24.66 What two ways are radioactive tracers used in organisms?

24.67 Why is neutron activation analysis (NAA) useful to art historians and criminologists?

24.68 Positrons cannot penetrate matter more than a few atomic diameters, but positron emission of radiotracers can be monitored in medical diagnosis. Explain.

24.69 A steel part is treated to form some iron-59. Oil used to lubricate the part emits 298 β^- particles (with the energy characteristic of ^{59}Fe) per minute per milliliter of oil. What other information would you need to calculate the rate of removal of the steel from the part during use?

Problems in Context

24.70 The oxidation of methanol to formaldehyde can be accomplished by reaction with chromic acid:

$$6H^+(aq) + 3CH_3OH(aq) + 2H_2CrO_4(aq) \longrightarrow 3CH_2O(aq) + 2Cr^{3+}(aq) + 8H_2O(l)$$

The reaction can be studied with the stable isotope tracer ^{18}O and mass spectrometry. When a small amount of $CH_3{}^{18}OH$ is present in the alcohol reactant, $CH_2{}^{18}O$ forms. When a small amount of $H_2Cr^{18}O_4$ is present, $H_2{}^{18}O$ forms. Does chromic acid or methanol supply the O atom to the aldehyde? Explain.

The Interconversion of Mass and Energy

(Sample Problem 24.6)

Note: Data for problems in this section: mass of ^1H atom = 1.007825 amu; mass of neutron = 1.008665 amu.

Concept Review Questions

24.71 Many scientists at first reacted skeptically to Einstein's equation, $E = mc^2$. Why?

24.72 How does a change in mass arise when a nuclide forms from nucleons?

24.73 When a nucleus forms from nucleons, is energy absorbed or released? Why?

24.74 What is the binding energy per nucleon? Why is the binding energy per nucleon, rather than per nuclide, used to compare nuclide stability?

Skill-Building Exercises (grouped in similar pairs)

24.75 A ^{3}H nucleus decays with an energy of 0.01861 MeV. Convert this energy into (a) electron volts; (b) joules.

24.76 Arsenic-84 decays with an energy of 1.57×10^{-15} kJ per nucleus. Convert this energy into (a) eV; (b) MeV.

24.77 How many joules are released when 1.5 mol of ^{239}Pu decays, if each nucleus releases 5.243 MeV?

24.78 How many MeV are released per nucleus when 3.2×10^{-3} mol of chromium-49 releases 8.11×10^{5} kJ?

24.79 Oxygen-16 is one of the most stable nuclides. The mass of a ^{16}O atom is 15.994915 amu. Calculate the binding energy (a) per nucleon in MeV; (b) per atom in MeV; (c) per mole in kJ.

24.80 Lead-206 is the end product of ^{238}U decay. One ^{206}Pb atom has a mass of 205.974440 amu. Calculate the binding energy (a) per nucleon in MeV; (b) per atom in MeV; (c) per mole in kJ.

24.81 Cobalt-59 is the only stable isotope of this transition metal. One ^{59}Co atom has a mass of 58.933198 amu. Calculate the binding energy (a) per nucleon in MeV; (b) per atom in MeV; (c) per mole in kJ.

24.82 Iodine-131 is one of the most important isotopes used in the diagnosis of thyroid cancer. One atom has a mass of 130.906114 amu. Calculate the binding energy (a) per nucleon in MeV; (b) per atom in MeV; (c) per mole in kJ.

Problems in Context

24.83 The ^{80}Br nuclide decays either by β^- decay or by electron capture. (a) What is the product of each process? (b) Which process releases more energy? (Masses of atoms: ^{80}Br = 79.918528 amu; ^{80}Kr = 79.916380 amu; ^{80}Se = 79.916520 amu; neglect the mass of electrons involved because these are atomic, not nuclear, masses.)

Applications of Fission and Fusion

Concept Review Questions

24.84 What is the minimum number of neutrons from each fission event that must be absorbed by other nuclei for a chain reaction to be sustained?

24.85 In what main way is fission different from radioactive decay? Are all fission events in a chain reaction identical? Explain.

24.86 What is the purpose of enrichment in the preparation of fuel rods? How is it accomplished?

24.87 Describe the nature and purpose of these components of a nuclear reactor: (a) control rods; (b) moderator; (c) reflector.

24.88 State an advantage and a disadvantage of heavy-water reactors compared to light-water reactors.

24.89 What are the expected advantages of fusion reactors over fission reactors?

24.90 Why is iron the most abundant element in Earth's core?

Problems in Context

24.91 The reaction that will probably power the first commercial fusion reactor is

$$^{3}_{1}H + ^{2}_{1}H \longrightarrow ^{4}_{2}He + ^{1}_{0}n$$

How much energy would be produced per mole of reaction? (Masses of atoms: $^{3}_{1}H$ = 3.01605 amu; $^{2}_{1}H$ = 2.0140 amu; $^{4}_{2}He$ = 4.00260 amu; mass of $^{1}_{0}n$ = 1.008665 amu.)

Comprehensive Problems

24.92 Some $^{243}_{95}Am$ was present when Earth formed, but it all decayed in the next billion years. The first three steps in this decay series are emissions of an α particle, a β^- particle, and another α particle. What other isotopes were present on the young Earth in a rock that contained some $^{243}_{95}Am$?

24.93 Curium-243 undergoes α decay to plutonium-239:

$$^{243}Cm \longrightarrow ^{239}Pu + \alpha$$

(a) Find the change in mass, Δm (in kg). (Masses: ^{243}Cm = 243.0614 amu; ^{239}Pu = 239.0522 amu; ^{4}He = 4.0026 amu; 1 amu = 1.661×10^{-24} g.)
(b) Find the energy released in joules.
(c) Find the energy released in kJ/mol of reaction, and comment on the difference between this value and a typical heat of reaction for a chemical change, which is a few hundred kJ/mol.

24.94 Plutonium "triggers" for nuclear weapons were manufactured at the Rocky Flats plant in Colorado. An 85-kg worker inhaled a dust particle containing 1.00 μg of $^{239}_{94}Pu$, which resided in his body for 16 h ($t_{1/2}$ of ^{239}Pu = 2.41×10^{4} yr; each disintegration released 5.15 MeV). (a) How many rads did he receive? (b) How many grays?

24.95 Archeologists removed some charcoal from a Native American campfire, burned it in O_2, and bubbled the CO_2 formed into $Ca(OH)_2$ solution (limewater). The $CaCO_3$ that precipitated was filtered and dried. If 4.58 g of the $CaCO_3$ had a radioactivity of 3.2 d/min, how long ago was the campfire?

24.96 A 5.4-μg sample of $^{226}RaCl_2$ has a radioactivity of 1.5×10^{5} Bq. Calculate $t_{1/2}$ of ^{226}Ra.

24.97 How many rads does a 65-kg human receive each year from the approximately 10^{-8} g of $^{14}_{6}C$ naturally present in her body ($t_{1/2}$ = 5730 yr; each disintegration releases 0.156 MeV)?

24.98 A sample of AgCl emits 175 nCi/g. A saturated solution prepared from the solid emits 1.25×10^{-2} Bq/mL due to radioactive Ag^+ ions. What is the molar solubility of AgCl?

24.99 The scene below depicts a neutron bombarding ^{235}U:

(a) Is this an example of fission or of fusion? (b) Identify the other nuclide formed. (c) What is the most likely mode of decay of the nuclide with Z = 55?

24.100 What fraction of the ^{235}U ($t_{1/2} = 7.0\times10^8$ yr) created when Earth was formed would remain after 2.8×10^9 yr?

24.101 ^{238}U ($t_{1/2} = 4.5\times10^9$ yr) begins a decay series that ultimately forms ^{206}Pb. The scene below depicts the relative number of ^{238}U atoms (red) and ^{206}Pb atoms (green) in a mineral. If all the Pb comes from ^{238}U, calculate the age of the sample.

24.102 Technetium-99m is a metastable nuclide used in numerous cancer diagnostic and treatment programs. It is prepared just before use because it decays rapidly through γ emission:

$$^{99m}Tc \longrightarrow {}^{99}Tc + \gamma$$

Use the data below to determine (a) the half-life of ^{99m}Tc; (b) the percentage of the isotope that is lost if it takes 2.0 h to prepare and administer the dose.

Time (h)	γ Emission (photons/s)
0	5000.
4	3150.
8	2000.
12	1250.
16	788
20	495

24.103 How many curies are produced by 1.0 mol of ^{40}K ($t_{1/2} = 1.25\times10^9$ yr)? How many becquerels?

24.104 The fraction of a radioactive isotope remaining at time t is $(\frac{1}{2})^{t/t_{1/2}}$, where $t_{1/2}$ is the half-life. If the half-life of carbon-14 is 5730 yr, what fraction of carbon-14 in a piece of charcoal remains after (a) 10.0 yr; (b) 10.0×10^3 yr; (c) 10.0×10^4 yr? (d) Why is radiocarbon dating more reliable for the fraction remaining in part (b) than that in part (a) or in part (c)?

24.105 The isotopic mass of $^{210}_{86}Rn$ is 209.989669 amu. When this nuclide decays by electron capture, it emits 2.368 MeV. What is the isotopic mass of the resulting nuclide?

24.106 Exactly 0.1 of the radioactive nuclei in a sample decay per hour. Thus, after n hours, the fraction of nuclei remaining is $(0.900)^n$. Find the value of n equal to one half-life.

24.107 In neutron activation analysis (NAA), stable isotopes are bombarded with neutrons. Depending on the isotope and the energy of the neutron, various emissions are observed. What are the products when the following neutron-activated species decay? Write an overall equation in shorthand notation for the reaction starting with the stable isotope before neutron activation.

(a) $^{52}_{23}V^* \longrightarrow$ [β^- emission] (b) $^{64}_{29}Cu^* \longrightarrow$ [β^+ emission]
(c) $^{28}_{13}Al^* \longrightarrow$ [β^- emission]

24.108 In the 1950s, radioactive material was spread over the land from aboveground nuclear tests. A woman drinks some contaminated milk and ingests 0.0500 g of ^{90}Sr, which is taken up by bones and teeth and not eliminated. (a) How much ^{90}Sr ($t_{1/2} = 29$ yr) is present in her body after 10 yr? (b) How long will it take for 99.9% of the ^{90}Sr to decay?

24.109 The scene below represents a reaction (with neutrons gray and protons purple) that occurs during the lifetime of a star. (a) Write a balanced nuclear equation for the reaction. (b) If the mass difference is 7.7×10^{-2} amu, find the energy (kJ) released.

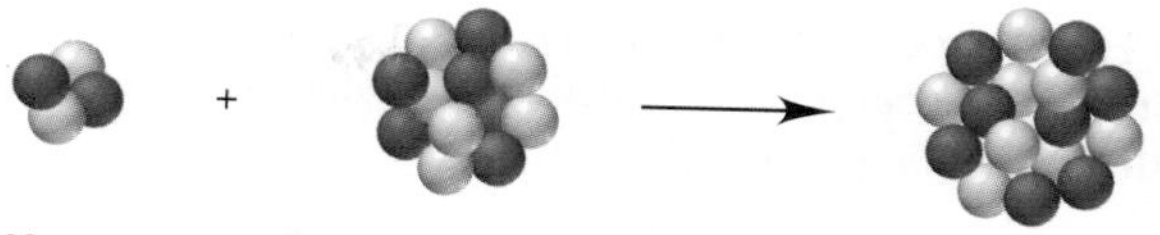

24.110 What volume of radon will be produced per hour at STP from 1.000 g of ^{226}Ra ($t_{1/2} = 1599$ yr; 1 yr = 8766 h; mass of one ^{226}Ra atom = 226.025402 amu)?

24.111 ^{90}Kr ($t_{1/2} = 32$ s) is used to study respiration. How soon after being made must a sample be administered to the patient if the activity must be at least 90% of the original activity?

24.112 Which isotope in each pair is more stable? Why?

(a) $^{140}_{55}Cs$ or $^{133}_{55}Cs$ (b) $^{79}_{35}Br$ or $^{78}_{35}Br$
(c) $^{28}_{12}Mg$ or $^{24}_{12}Mg$ (d) $^{14}_{7}N$ or $^{18}_{7}N$

24.113 A bone sample containing strontium-90 ($t_{1/2} = 29$ yr) emits 7.0×10^4 β^- particles per month. How long will it take for the emission to decrease to 1.0×10^4 particles per month?

24.114 The 23rd-century starship *Enterprise* uses a substance called "dilithium crystals" as its fuel.

(a) Assuming this material is the result of fusion, what is the product of the fusion of two ^{6}Li nuclei?

(b) How much energy is released per kilogram of dilithium formed? (Mass of one ^{6}Li atom is 6.015121 amu.)

(c) When four ^{1}H atoms fuse to form ^{4}He, how many positrons are released?

(d) To determine the energy potential of the fusion processes in parts (b) and (c), compare the changes in mass per kilogram of dilithium and of ^{4}He.

(e) Compare the change in mass per kilogram in part (b) to that for the formation of ^{4}He by the method used in current fusion reactors (see p. 1010). (For masses, see Problem 24.91.)

(f) Using early 21st-century fusion technology, how much tritium can be produced per kilogram of ^{6}Li in the following reaction: $^{6}_{3}Li + ^{1}_{0}n \longrightarrow ^{4}_{2}He + ^{3}_{1}H$? When this amount of tritium is fused with deuterium, what is the change in mass? How does this quantity compare with the use of dilithium in part (b)?

24.115 Uranium and radium are found in many rocky soils throughout the world. Both undergo radioactive decay, and one of the products is radon-222, the heaviest noble gas ($t_{1/2} = 3.82$ days). Inhalation of this gas contributes to many lung cancers. According to Environmental Protection Agency recommendations, the level of radioactivity from radon in homes should not exceed 4.0 pCi/L of air.

(a) What is the safe level of radon in Bq/L of air?

(b) A home has a radon measurement of 41.5 pCi/L. The owner vents the basement in such a way that no more radon enters the living area. What is the activity of the radon remaining in the room air (in Bq/L) after 9.5 days?

(c) How many more days does it take to reach the EPA recommended level?

24.116 Nuclear disarmament could be accomplished if weapons were not "replenished." The tritium in warheads decays to helium with a half-life of 12.26 yr and must be replaced or the weapon is useless. What fraction of the tritium is lost in 5.50 yr?

24.117 A decay series starts with the synthetic isotope $^{239}_{92}U$. The first four steps are emissions of a β^- particle, another β^-, an α particle, and another α. Write a balanced nuclear equation for each step. Which natural series could start by this sequence?

24.118 How long can a 54-lb child be exposed to 1.0 mCi of radiation from ^{222}Rn before accumulating 1.0 mrad if the energy of each disintegration is 5.59 MeV?

24.119 An earthquake in the area of present-day San Francisco is to be dated by measuring the ^{14}C activity ($t_{1/2}$ = 5730 yr) of parts of a tree uprooted during the event. The tree parts have an activity of 12.9 d/min·g C, and a living tree has an activity of 15.3 d/min·g C. How long ago did the earthquake occur?

24.120 Were organisms a billion years ago exposed to more or less ionizing radiation than similar organisms today? Explain.

24.121 Tritium (^3H; $t_{1/2}$ = 12.26 yr) is continually formed in the upper troposphere by interaction of solar particles with nitrogen. As a result, natural waters contain a small amount of tritium. Two samples of wine are analyzed, one known to be made in 1941 and another made earlier. The water in the 1941 wine has 2.23 times as much tritium as the water in the other. When was the other wine produced?

24.122 Even though plutonium-239 ($t_{1/2}$ = 2.41×10^4 yr) is one of the main fission fuels, it is still a radiation hazard present in spent uranium fuel from nuclear power plants. How many years does it take for 99% of the plutonium-239 in spent fuel to decay?

24.123 Carbon from the remains of an extinct Australian marsupial, called *Diprotodon,* has a specific activity of 0.61 pCi/g. Modern carbon has a specific activity of 6.89 pCi/g. How long ago did the *Diprotodon* apparently become extinct?

24.124 The reaction that allows for radiocarbon dating is the continual formation of carbon-14 in the upper atmosphere:

$$^{14}_{7}N + ^{1}_{0}n \longrightarrow ^{14}_{6}C + ^{1}_{1}H$$

What is the energy change associated with this process in eV/reaction and in kJ/mol reaction? (Masses of atoms: $^{14}_{7}N$ = 14.003074 amu; $^{14}_{6}C$ = 14.003241 amu; $^{1}_{1}H$ = 1.007825 amu; mass of $^{1}_{0}n$ = 1.008665 amu.)

24.125 What is the nuclear binding energy of a lithium-7 nucleus in units of kJ/mol and eV/nucleus? (Mass of a lithium-7 atom = 7.016003 amu.)

24.126 Gadolinium-146 undergoes electron capture. Identify the product, and use Figure 24.2 to find the modes of decay and the other two nuclides in the series below:

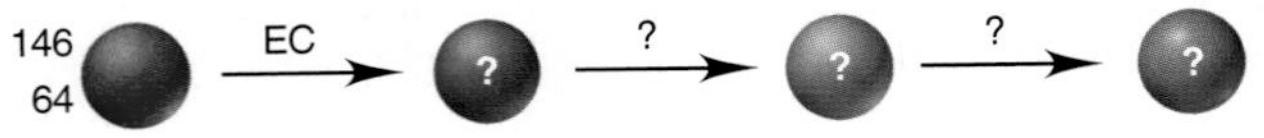

24.127 Using 21st-century technology, hydrogen fusion requires temperatures around 10^8 K. But, lower initial temperatures are used if the hydrogen is compressed. In the late 24th century, the starship *Leinad* uses such methods to fuse hydrogen at 10^6 K.
(a) What is the kinetic energy of an H atom at 1.00×10^6 K?
(b) How many H atoms are heated to 1.00×10^6 K from the energy of one H and one anti-H atom annihilating each other?
(c) If these H atoms fuse into ^4He atoms (with the loss of two positrons per ^4He formed), how much energy (in J) is generated?
(d) How much more energy is generated by the fusion in (c) than by the hydrogen-antihydrogen collision in (b)?
(e) Should the captain of the *Leinad* change the technology and produce ^3He (mass = 3.01603 amu) instead of ^4He?

24.128 A metastable (excited) form of ^{50}Sc changes to its stable form by emitting γ radiation with a wavelength of 8.73 pm. What is the change in mass of 1 mol of the isotope when it undergoes this change?

24.129 A sample of cobalt-60 ($t_{1/2}$ = 5.27 yr), a powerful γ emitter used to treat cancer, was purchased by a hospital on March 1, 2007. The sample must be replaced when its activity reaches 70.% of the original value. On what date must it be replaced?

24.130 Uranium-233 decays to thorium-229 by α decay, but the emissions have different energies and products: 83% emit an α particle with energy of 4.816 MeV and give ^{229}Th in its ground state; 15% emit an α particle of 4.773 MeV and give ^{229}Th in excited state I; and 2% emit a lower energy α particle and give ^{229}Th in the higher excited state II. Excited state II emits a γ ray of 0.060 MeV to reach excited state I. (a) Find the γ-ray energy and wavelength that would convert excited state I to the ground state. (b) Find the energy of the α particle that would convert ^{233}U to excited state II.

24.131 Uranium-238 undergoes a slow decay step ($t_{1/2}$ = 4.5×10^9 yr) followed by a series of fast steps to form the stable isotope ^{206}Pb. Thus, on a time scale of billions of years, ^{238}U effectively decays "directly" to ^{206}Pb, and the relative amounts of these isotopes are used to find the age of some rocks. Two students derive equations relating number of half-lives (n) since the rock formed to the amounts of the isotopes:

Student 1: $\left(\frac{1}{2}\right)^n = \dfrac{^{238}_{92}U}{^{206}_{82}Pb}$

Student 2: $\left(\frac{1}{2}\right)^n = \dfrac{^{238}_{92}U}{^{238}_{92}U + ^{206}_{82}Pb}$

(a) Which equation is correct, and why?
(b) If a rock contains exactly twice as much ^{238}U as ^{206}Pb, what is its age in years?

24.132 In the naturally occurring thorium-232 decay series, the steps emit this sequence of particles: α, β^-, β^-, α, α, α, α, β^-, β^-, and α. Write a balanced equation for each step.

24.133 At death, a nobleman in ancient Egypt was mummified and his body contained 1.4×10^{-3} g of ^{40}K ($t_{1/2}$ = 1.25×10^9 yr), 1.2×10^{-8} g of ^{14}C ($t_{1/2}$ = 5730 yr), and 4.8×10^{-14} g of ^3H ($t_{1/2}$ = 12.26 yr). Which nuclide would give the most accurate estimate of the mummy's age? Explain.

24.134 Assuming that many radioactive nuclides can be considered safe after 20 half-lives, how long will it take for each of the following nuclides to be safe: (a) ^{242}Cm ($t_{1/2}$ = 163 days); (b) ^{214}Po ($t_{1/2}$ = 1.6×10^{-4} s); (c) ^{232}Th ($t_{1/2}$ = 1.39×10^{10} yr)?

24.135 An ancient sword has a blade from the early Roman Empire, around 100 AD, but the wooden handle, inlaid wooden decorations, leather ribbon, and leather sheath have different styles. Given the following activities, estimate the age of each part. Which part was made near the time of the blade ($t_{1/2}$ of ^{14}C = 5730 yr; $\mathcal{A}_0$ = 15.3 d/min·g)?

Part	$\mathcal{A}_t$ **(d/min·g)**
Handle	10.1
Inlaid wood	13.8
Ribbon	12.1
Sheath	15.0

24.136 The starship *Voyager,* like many other vessels of the newly designed 24th-century fleet, uses antimatter as fuel.

(a) How much energy is released when 1.00 kg each of antimatter and matter annihilate each other?
(b) When the antimatter is atomic antihydrogen, a small amount of it is mixed with excess atomic hydrogen (gathered from interstellar space during flight). The annihilation releases so much heat that the remaining hydrogen nuclei fuse to form ^{4}He. If each hydrogen-antihydrogen collision releases enough heat to fuse 1.00×10^5 hydrogen atoms, how much energy (in kJ) is released per kilogram of antihydrogen?
(c) Which produces more energy per kilogram of antihydrogen, the procedure in part (a) or that in part (b)?

24.137 Use Einstein's equation, the mass in grams of 1 amu, and the relation between electron volts and joules to find the energy equivalent (in MeV) of a mass difference of 1 amu.

24.138 Determine the age of a rock containing 0.065 g of uranium-238 ($t_{1/2} = 4.5\times10^9$ yr) and 0.023 g of lead-206. (Assume all the lead-206 came from ^{238}U decay.)

24.139 Plutonium-242 decays to uranium-238 by emission of an α particle with an energy of 4.853 MeV. The ^{238}U that forms is unstable and emits a γ ray ($\lambda = 0.02757$ nm). (a) Write balanced equations for these reactions. (b) What would be the energy of the α particle if ^{242}Pu decayed directly to the more stable ^{238}U?

24.140 Seaborgium-263 (Sg), the first isotope of element 106 synthesized, was made, together with four neutrons, by bombarding californium-249 with oxygen-18. It then underwent a series of decays starting with three α emissions. Write balanced equations for the synthesis and the three α emissions of ^{263}Sg.

24.141 Some nuclear power plants use plutonium-239, which is produced in breeder reactors. The rate-determining step is the second β^- emission. How long does it take to make 1.00 kg of ^{239}Pu if the reaction is complete when the product is 90.% ^{239}Pu?

24.142 A random-number generator can be used to simulate the probability of a given atom decaying over a given time. For example, the formula "=RAND()" in the Excel spreadsheet returns a random number between 0 and 1; thus, for one radioactive atom and a time of one half-life, a number less than 0.5 means the atom decays and a number greater than 0.5 means it doesn't.
(a) Place the "=RAND()" formula in cells A1 to A10 of an Excel spreadsheet. In cell B1, place "=IF(A1<0.5, 0, 1)." This formula returns 0 if A1 is <0.5 (the atom decays) and 1 if A1 is >0.5 (the atom does not decay). Place analogous formulas in cells B2 to B10 (using the "Fill Down" procedure in Excel). To determine the number of atoms remaining after one half-life, sum cells B1 to B10 by placing "=SUM(B1:B10)" in cell B12. To create a new set of random numbers, click on an empty cell (e.g., B13) and hit "Delete." Perform 10 simulations, each time recording the total number of atoms remaining. Do half of the atoms remain after each half-life? If not, why not?
(b) Increase the number of atoms to 100 by placing suitable formulas in cells A1 to A100, B1 to B100, and B102. Perform 10 simulations, and record the number of atoms remaining each time. Are these results more realistic for radioactive decay? Explain.

24.143 In the following Excel-based simulation, the fate of 256 atoms is followed over five half-lives. Set up formulas in columns A and B, as in Problem 24.142, and simulate the fate of the sample of 256 atoms over one half-life. Cells B1 to B256 should contain 1 or 0. In cell C1, enter "=IF(B1=0, 0, RAND())." This returns 0 if the original atom decayed in the previous half-life or a random number between 0 and 1 if it did not. Fill the formula in C1 down to cell C256. Column D should have formulas similar to those in B, but with modified references, as should columns F, H, and J. Columns E, G, and I should have formulas similar to those in C, but with modified references. In cell B258, enter "=SUM(B1:B256)." This records the number of atoms remaining after the first half-life. Put formulas in cells D258, F258, H258, and J258 to record atoms remaining after subsequent half-lives.
(a) Ideally, how many atoms should remain after each half-life?
(b) Make a table of the atoms remaining after each half-life in four separate simulations. Compare these outcomes to the ideal outcome. How would you make the results more realistic?

24.144 Representations of three nuclei (with neutrons gray and protons purple) are shown below. Nucleus 1 is stable, but 2 and 3 are not. (a) Write the symbol for each isotope. (b) What is (are) the most likely mode(s) of decay for 2 and 3?

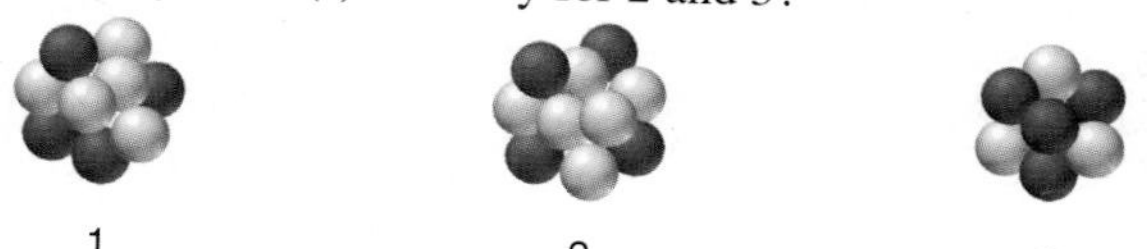

1 2 3

Answers to Selected Problems

Chapter 11

11.1(a) sp^2 (b) sp^3d^2 (c) sp (d) sp^3 (e) sp^3d **11.3** C has only $2s$ and $2p$ atomic orbitals, allowing for a maximum of four hybrid orbitals. Si has $3s$, $3p$, and $3d$ atomic orbitals, allowing it to form more than four hybrid orbitals. **11.5**(a) six, sp^3d^2 (b) four, sp^3 **11.7**(a) sp^2 (b) sp^2 (c) sp^2 **11.9**(a) sp^3 (b) sp^3 (c) sp^3 **11.11**(a) Si: one s and three p atomic orbitals form four sp^3 hybrid orbitals. (b) C: one s and one p atomic orbital forms two sp hybrid orbitals. (c) S: one s, three p, and one d atomic orbital mix to form five sp^3d hybrid orbitals. (d) N: one s and three p atomic orbitals mix to form four sp^3 hybrid orbitals. **11.13**(a) B ($sp^3 \longrightarrow sp^3$) (b) A ($sp^2 \longrightarrow sp^3$)

11.15

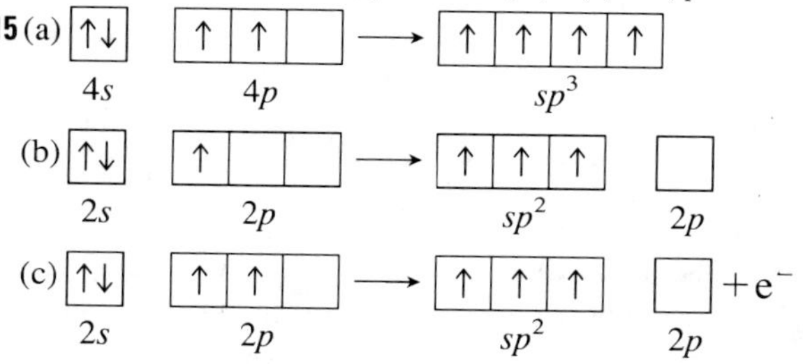

11.17

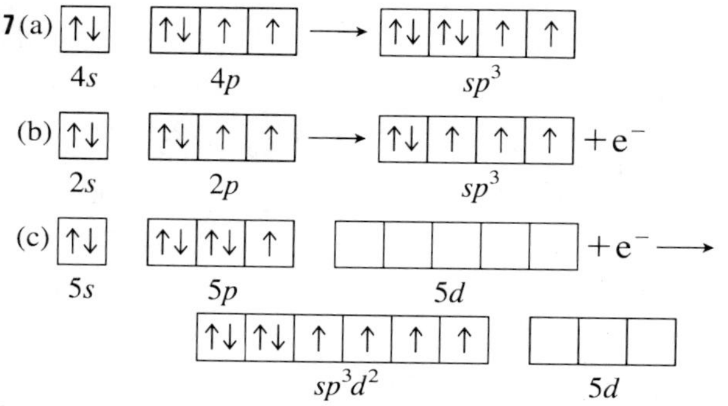

11.20(a) False. A double bond is one σ and one π bond. (b) False. A triple bond consists of one σ and two π bonds. (c) True (d) True (e) False. A π bond consists of a second pair of electrons after a σ bond has been previously formed. (f) False. End-to-end overlap results in a bond with electron density along the bond axis. **11.21**(a) Nitrogen uses sp^2 to form three σ bonds and one π bond. (b) Carbon uses sp to form two σ bonds and two π bonds. (c) Carbon uses sp^2 to form three σ bonds and one π bond.

11.23(a) N: sp^2, forming 2 σ bonds and 1 π bond

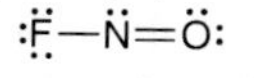

(b) C: sp^2, forming 3 σ bonds and 1 π bond

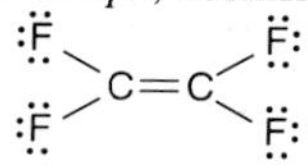

(c) C: sp, forming 2 σ bonds and 2 π bonds

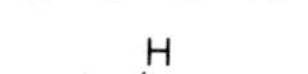

11.25

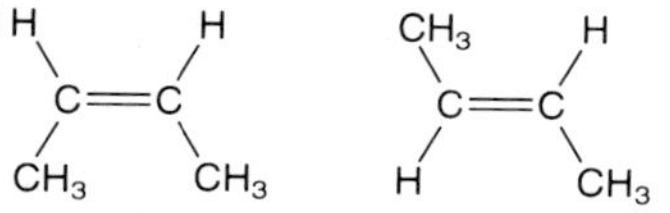

cis *trans*

The single bonds are all σ bonds. The double bond is one σ bond and one π bond. **11.26** Four MOs form from the four p atomic orbitals. The total number of MOs must equal the number of atomic orbitals. **11.28**(a) Bonding MOs have lower energy than antibonding MOs. Lower energy means more stable. (b) Bonding MOs do not have a nodal plane perpendicular to the bond. (c) Bonding MOs have higher electron density between nuclei than antibonding MOs. **11.30**(a) two (b) two (c) four **11.32**(a) A is π^*_{2p}, B is σ_{2p}, C is π_{2p}, and D is σ^*_{2p}. (b) π^*_{2p} (A), σ_{2p} (B), and π_{2p} (C) have at least one electron. (c) π^*_{2p} (A) has only one electron. **11.34**(a) stable (b) paramagnetic (c) $(\sigma_{2s})^2(\sigma^*_{2s})^1$ **11.36**(a) $C_2^+ < C_2 < C_2^-$ (b) $C_2^- < C_2 < C_2^+$ **11.40**(a) C (ring): sp^2; C (all others): sp^3; O (all): sp^3; N: sp^3 (b) 26 (c) 6 **11.42**(a) 17 (b) All carbons are sp^2; the ring N is sp^2, the other N's are sp^3. **11.44**(a) B changes from sp^2 to sp^3. (b) P changes from sp^3 to sp^3d. (c) C changes from sp to sp^2. Two electron groups surround C in C_2H_2, and three electron groups surround C in C_2H_4. (d) Si changes from sp^3 to sp^3d^2. (e) no change for S **11.46** P: tetrahedral, sp^3; N: trigonal pyramid, sp^3; C_1 and C_2: tetrahedral, sp^3; C_3: trigonal planar, sp^2 **11.51**(a) B and D are present. (b) Yes, sp hybrid orbitals. (c) Two sets of sp orbitals, four sets of sp^2 orbitals, and three sets of sp^3 orbitals. **11.52** Through resonance, the C—N bond gains some double bond character, which hinders rotation about that bond.

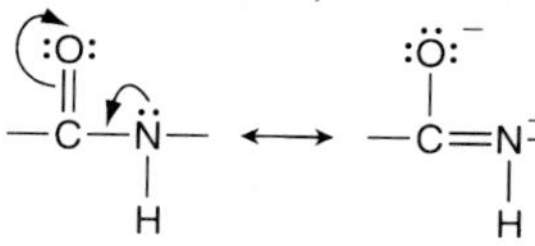

11.55(a) C in —CH_3: sp^3; all other C atoms: sp^2; O in two C—O bonds: sp^3; O in two C=O bonds: sp^2 (b) two (c) eight; one **11.56**(a) four (b) eight

Chapter 5

Answers to Boxed Reading Problems: B5.1 The density of the atmosphere decreases with increasing altitude. High density causes more drag on the aircraft. At high altitudes, low density means that there are relatively few gas particles present to collide with the aircraft. **B5.3** 0.934 %, 7.10 torr

• **5.1**(a) The volume of the liquid remains constant, but the volume of the gas increases to the volume of the larger container. (b) The volume of the container holding the gas sample increases when heated, but the volume of the container holding the liquid sample remains essentially constant when heated. (c) The volume of the liquid remains essentially constant, but the volume of the gas is reduced. **5.6** 990 cmH_2O **5.8**(a) 566 mmHg (b) 1.32 bar (c) 3.60 atm (d) 107 kPa **5.10** 0.9408 atm **5.12** 0.966 atm **5.18** At constant temperature and volume, the pressure of a gas is directly proportional to number of moles of the gas. **5.20**(a) Volume decreases to one-third of the original volume. (b) Volume increases by a factor of 3.0. (c) Volume increases by a factor of 4. **5.22**(a) Volume decreases by a factor of 2. (b) Volume increases by a factor of 1.48. (c) Volume decreases by a factor of 3. **5.24** −144°C **5.26** 35.3 L **5.28** 0.085 mol Cl_2 **5.30** 1.16 g ClF_3 **5.33** yes **5.35** Beaker is inverted for H_2 and upright for CO_2. The molar mass of CO greater than the molar mass of air, which, in turn, has a greater molar mass than H_2. **5.39** 5.86 g/L **5.41** 1.78×10^{-3} mol AsH 3.48 g/L **5.43** 51.1 g/mol **5.45** 1.33 atm **5.47** 39.2 g P_4

5.49 41.2 g PH_3 **5.51** 0.0249 g Al **5.55** C_5H_{12} **5.57**(a) 0.90 mol (b) 6.76 torr **5.58** 286 mL SO_2 **5.60** 0.0997 atm SiF_4 **5.65** At STP, the volume occupied by a mole of any gas is the same. At the same temperature, all gases have the same average kinetic energy, resulting in the same pressure. **5.68**(a) $P_A > P_B > P_C$ (b) $E_A = E_B = E_C$ (c) $rate_A > rate_B > rate_C$ (d) total $E_A >$ total $E_B >$ total E_C (e) $d_A = d_B = d_C$ (f) collision frequency in A > collision frequency in B > collision frequency in C **5.69** 13.21 **5.71**(a) curve 1 (b) curve 1 (c) curve 1; fluorine and argon have about the same molar mass **5.73** 14.9 min **5.75** 4 atoms per molecule **5.78** negative deviations; N_2 < Kr < CO_2 **5.80** At 1 atm; at lower pressures, the gas molecules are farther apart and intermolecular forces are less important. **5.83** 6.81×10^4 g/mol **5.86**(a) 22.1 atm (b) 20.9 atm **5.90**(a) 597 torr N_2; 159 torr O_2; 0.3 torr CO_2; 3.5 torr H_2O (b) 74.9 mol % N_2; 13.7 mol % O_2; 5.3 mol % CO_2; 6.2 mol % H_2O (c) 1.6×10^{21} molecules O_2 **5.92**(a) 4×10^2 mL (b) 0.013 mol N_2 **5.93** 35.7 L NO_2 **5.98** Al_2Cl_6 **5.100** 1.52×10^{-2} mol SO_3 **5.104**(a) 1.95×10^3 g Ni (b) 3.5×10^4 g Ni (c) 63 m^3 CO **5.106**(a) 9 volumes of $O_2(g)$ (b) CH_5N **5.109** The lungs would expand by a factor of 4.86; the diver can safely ascend 52.5 ft to a depth of 73 ft. **5.111** 6.07 g H_2O_2 **5.116** 6.53×10^{-3} g N_2 **5.120**(a) xenon (b) water vapor (c) mercury vapor (d) water vapor **5.124** 17.2 g CO_2; 17.8 g Kr **5.130** Ne, 676 m/s; Ar, 481 m/s; He, 1.52×10^3 m/s **5.132**(a) 0.052 g (b) 1.1 mL **5.139**(a) 16.5 L CO_2 (b) $P_{H_2O} = 48.8$ torr; $P_{O_2} = P_{CO_2} = 3.7\times10^2$ torr **5.144** 332 steps **5.146** 1.4 **5.150** $P_{total} = 245$ torr; $P_{I_2} = 25.2$ torr

Chapter 12

Answer to Boxed Reading Problem: B12.1 1.76×10^{-10} m

• **12.1** In a solid, the energy of attraction of the particles is greater than their energy of motion; in a gas, it is less. Gases have high compressibility and the ability to flow, while solids have neither. **12.4**(a) Because the intermolecular forces are only partially overcome when fusion occurs but need to be totally overcome in vaporization. (b) Because solids have greater intermolecular forces than liquids do. (c) $\Delta H_{vap} = -\Delta H_{cond}$ **12.5**(a) intermolecular (b) intermolecular (c) intramolecular (d) intramolecular **12.7**(a) condensation (b) fusion (c) vaporization **12.9** The gas molecules slow down as the gas is compressed. Therefore, much of the kinetic energy lost by the propane molecules is released to the surroundings. **12.13** At first, the vaporization of liquid molecules from the surface predominates, which increases the number of gas molecules and hence the vapor pressure. As more molecules enter the gas phase, more gas molecules hit the surface of the liquid and "stick" more frequently, so the condensation rate increases. When the vaporization and condensation rates become equal, the vapor pressure becomes constant. **12.14** As intermolecular forces increase, (a) critical temperature increases, (b) boiling point increases, (c) vapor pressure decreases, and (d) heat of vaporization increases. **12.18** because the condensation of the vapor supplies an additional 40.7 kJ/mol **12.19** 7.67×10^3 J **12.21** 0.777 atm **12.23** 2×10^4 J/mol

12.25

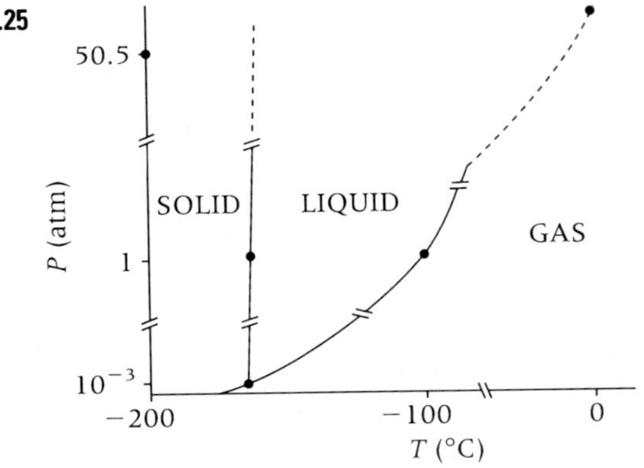

Solid ethylene is more dense than liquid ethylene. **12.28** 32 atm **12.32** O is smaller and more electronegative than Se; so the electron density on O is greater, which attracts H more strongly. **12.34** All particles (atoms and molecules) exhibit dispersion forces, but the total force is weak for small molecules. Dipole-dipole forces between small polar molecules dominate the dispersion forces. **12.37**(a) hydrogen bonding (b) dispersion forces (c) dispersion forces **12.39**(a) dipole-dipole forces (b) dispersion forces (c) hydrogen bonding

12.41(a)

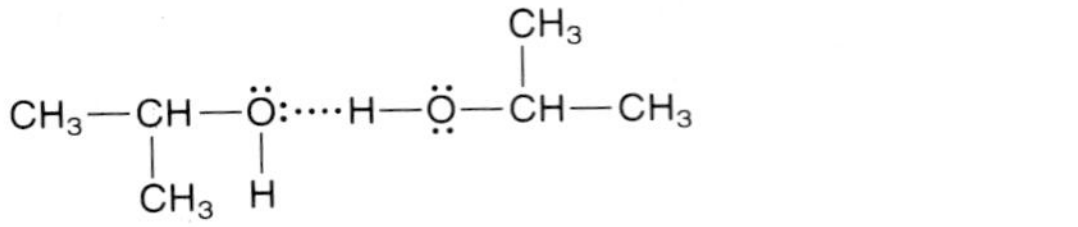

(b)

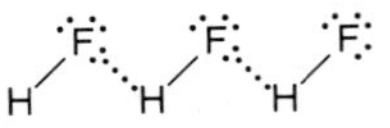

12.43(a) dispersion forces (b) hydrogen bonding (c) dispersion forces **12.45**(a) I^- (b) $CH_2{=}CH_2$ (c) H_2Se. In (a) and (c) the larger particle has the higher polarizability. In (b), the less tightly held π electron clouds are more easily distorted. **12.47**(a) C_2H_6; it is a smaller molecule exhibiting weaker dispersion forces than C_4H_{10}. (b) CH_3CH_2F; it has no H—F bonds, so it exhibits only dipole-dipole forces, which are weaker than the hydrogen bonds of CH_3CH_2OH. (c) PH_3; it has weaker intermolecular forces (dipole-dipole) than NH_3 (hydrogen bonding). **12.49**(a) HCl; it has dipole-dipole forces, and there are stronger ionic bonds in LiCl. (b) PH_3; it has dipole-dipole forces, and there is stronger hydrogen bonding i NH_3. (c) Xe; it exhibits weaker dispersion forces since its smaller size results in lower polarizability than the larger I_2 molecules. **12.51**(a) C_4H_8 (cyclobutane), because it is more

compact than C_4H_{10}. (b) PBr_3; the dipole-dipole forces in PBr_3 are weaker than the ionic bonds in NaBr. (c) HBr; the dipole-dipole forces in HBr are weaker than the hydrogen bonds in water. **12.53** As atomic size decreases and electronegativity increases, the electron density of an atom increases. Thus, the attraction to an H atom on another molecule increases while its bonded H atom becomes more positive. Fluorine is the smallest of the three and the most electronegative, so the H bonds in hydrogen fluoride are the strongest. Oxygen is smaller and more electronegative than nitrogen, so H bonds in water are stronger than H bonds in ammonia. **12.57** The cohesive forces in water and mercury are stronger than the adhesive forces to the nonpolar wax on the floor. Weak adhesive forces result in spherical drops. The adhesive forces overcome the even weaker cohesive forces in the oil, and so the oil drop spreads out. **12.59** Surface tension is defined as the energy needed to increase the surface area by a given amount, so units of energy per area are appropriate. **12.61** $CH_3CH_2CH_2OH <$ $HOCH_2CH_2OH < HOCH_2CH(OH)CH_2OH$.
More hydrogen bonding means more attraction between molecules, so more energy is needed to increase surface area. **12.63** $HOCH_2CH(OH)CH_2OH > HOCH_2CH_2OH >$ $CH_3CH_2CH_2OH$. More hydrogen bonding means more attraction between molecules, so they flow less easily. **12.68** Water is a good solvent for polar and ionic substances and a poor solvent for nonpolar substances. Water is a polar molecule and dissolves polar substances because their intermolecular forces are of similar strength. **12.69** A single water molecule can form four H bonds. The two hydrogen atoms each form one H bond to oxygen atoms on neighboring water molecules. The two lone pairs on the oxygen atom form H bonds with hydrogen atoms on two neighboring molecules. **12.72** Water exhibits strong capillary action, which allows it to be easily absorbed by the plant's roots and transported upward to the leaves.
12.78 simple cubic **12.81** The energy gap is the energy difference between the highest filled energy level (valence band) and the lowest unfilled energy level (conduction band). In conductors and superconductors, the energy gap is zero because the valence band overlaps the conduction band. In semiconductors, the energy gap is small. In insulators, the gap is large. **12.83** atomic mass and atomic radius **12.84**(a) face-centered cubic (b) body-centered cubic (c) face-centered cubic **12.86**(a) The change in unit cell is from a sodium chloride structure in CdO to a zinc blende structure in CdSe. (b) Yes, the coordination number of Cd changes from 6 in CdO to 4 in CdSe. **12.88**(a) Nickel forms a metallic solid since it is a metal whose atoms are held together by metallic bonds. (b) Fluorine forms a molecular solid since the F_2 molecules are held together by dispersion forces. (c) Methanol forms a molecular solid since the CH_3OH molecules are held together by hydrogen bonds. (d) Tin forms a metallic solid since it is a metal whose atoms are held together by metallic bonds. (e) Silicon is in the same group as carbon, so it exhibits similar bonding properties. Since diamond and graphite are both network covalent solids, it makes sense that Si forms a network covalent solid as well. (f) Xe is an atomic solid since its individual atoms are held together by dispersion forces. **12.90** four **12.92**(a) four Se^{2-} ions, four Zn^{2+} ions (b) 577.48 amu

(c) 1.77×10^{-22} cm^3 (d) 5.61×10^{-8} cm **12.94**(a) insulator (b) conductor (c) semiconductor **12.96**(a) Conductivity increases. (b) Conductivity increases. (c) Conductivity decreases. **12.98** 1.68×10^{-8} cm **12.105** A substance whose properties are the same in all directions is isotropic; otherwise, the substance is anisotropic. Liquid crystals have a degree of order only in certain directions, so they are anisotropic. **12.111**(a) n-type semiconductor (b) p-type semiconductor **12.113** $n = 3.4\times10^3$ **12.115** 8.4 pm **12.118**(a) 19.8 torr (b) 0.0485 g **12.124** 259 K **12.126**(a) 2.23×10^{-2} atm (b) 6.23 L
12.129(a) furfuryl alcohol

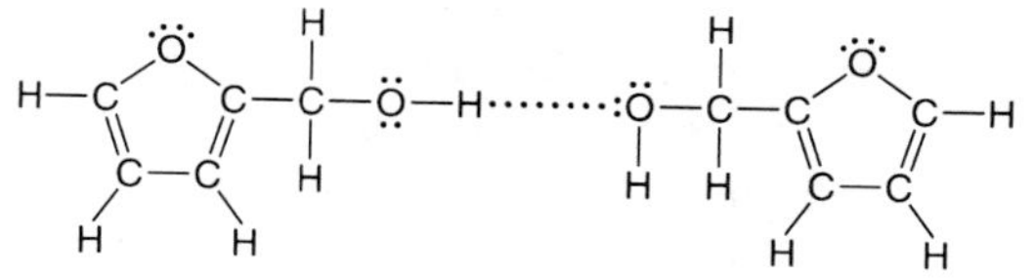

2-furoic acid

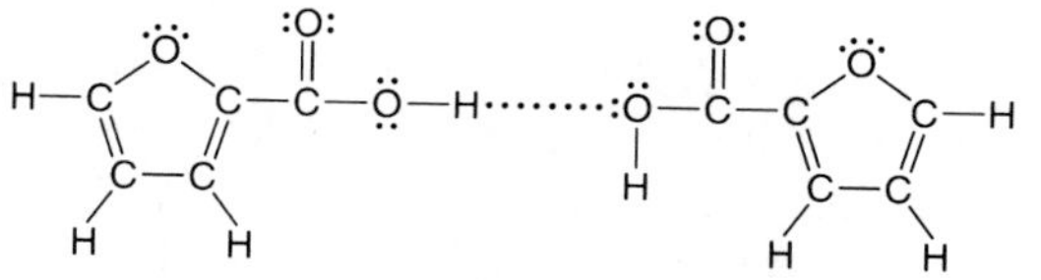

(b) furfuryl alcohol 2-furoic acid

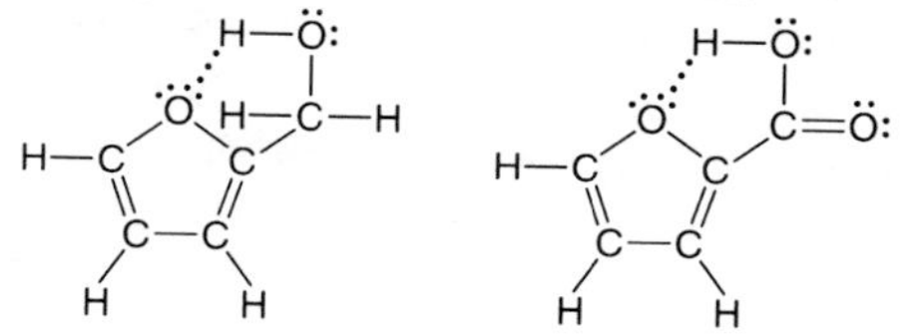

12.130(a) 49.3 metric tons H_2O (b) -1.11×10^8 kJ **12.131** 2.9 g/m^3 **12.136**(a) 1.1 min (b) 10. min
(c)

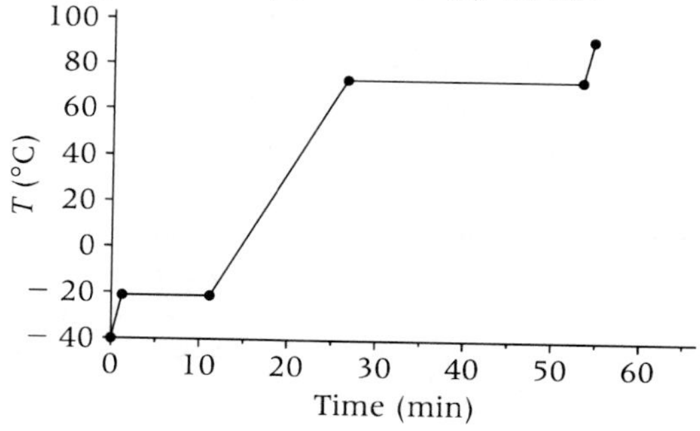

12.137 2.98×10^5 g BN **12.140** 45.98 amu

Chapter 13

Answers to Boxed Reading Problem: B13.1 (a) The colloidal particles in water generally have negatively charged surfaces and so repel each other, slowing the settling process. Cake alum, $Al_2(SO_4)_3$, is added to coagulate the colloids. The Al^{3+} ions neutralize the negative surface charges and allow the particles to aggregate and settle. (b) Water that contains large amounts of divalent cations (such as Ca^{2+}, and Mg^{2+}) is called hard water. During cleaning, these ions combine with the fatty-acid anions in soaps to produce insoluble deposits. (c) In reverse osmosis, a pressure greater than the osmotic pressure is applied to the solution, forcing the water back through the membrane, leaving the ions behind. (d) Chlorine may give the water an unpleasant odor, and can form carcinogenic chlorinated compounds. (e) The high concentration of NaCl displaces the divalent and polyvalent ions from the ion-exchange resin.

• **13.2** When a salt such as NaCl dissolves, ion-dipole forces cause the ions to separate, and many water molecules cluster around each ion in hydration shells. Ion-dipole forces bind the first shell to an ion. The water molecules in that shell form H bonds to others to create the next shell, and so on. **13.4** Sodium stearate is a more effective soap because the hydrocarbon chain in the stearate ion is longer than that in the acetate ion. The longer chain allows for more dispersion forces with grease molecules. **13.7** KNO_3 is an ionic compound and is therefore more soluble in water. **13.9**(a) ion-dipole forces (b) hydrogen bonding (c) dipole–induced dipole forces **13.11**(a) hydrogen bonding (b) dipole–induced dipole forces (c) dispersion forces **13.13**(a) HCl(*g*), because the molecular interactions (dipole-dipole forces) in ether are like those in HCl but not like the ionic bonding in NaCl. (b) $CH_3CHO(l)$, because the molecular interactions with ether (dipole-dipole) can replace those between CH_3CHO, but not the H bonds in water. (c) $CH_3CH_2MgBr(s)$, because the molecular interactions (dipole-dipole and dispersion forces) are greater than between ether and the ions in $MgBr_2$. **13.16** Gluconic acid is soluble in water due to extensive hydrogen bonding by the —OH groups attached to five of its carbons. The dispersion forces in the nonpolar tail of caproic acid are more similar to the dispersion forces in hexane; thus, caproic acid is soluble in hexane. **13.18** The nitrogen-containing bases form H bonds to their complementary bases. The flat, N-containing bases stack above each other, which allows extensive dispersion forces. The exterior negatively charged sugar-phosphate chains form ion-dipole and H bonds with water molecules in the aqueous surroundings, which also stabilizes the structure. **13.21** Dispersion forces are present between the nonpolar tails of the lipid molecules within the bilayer. The polar heads interact with the aqueous surroundings through H bonds and ion-dipole forces. **13.25** The enthalpy changes needed to separate the solvent ($\Delta H_{solvent}$) and to mix the solvent and solute (ΔH_{mix}) combine to give $\Delta H_{solvation}$. **13.29** very soluble, because a decrease in enthalpy and an increase in entropy both favor the formation of a solution

13.30

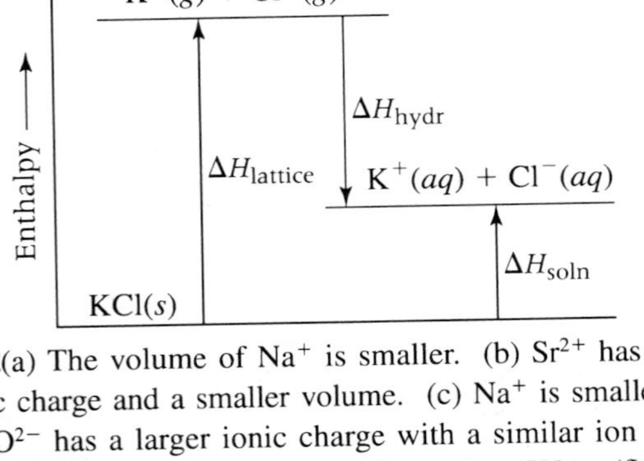

13.32(a) The volume of Na^+ is smaller. (b) Sr^{2+} has a larger ionic charge and a smaller volume. (c) Na^+ is smaller than Cl^-. (d) O^{2-} has a larger ionic charge with a similar ion volume. (e) OH^- has a smaller volume than SH^-. (f) Mg^{2+} has a smaller volume. (g) Mg^{2+} has both a smaller volume and a larger ionic charge. (h) CO_3^{2-} has both a smaller volume and a larger ionic charge. **13.34**(a) Na^+ (b) Sr^{2+} (c) Na^+ (d) O^{2-} (e) OH^- (f) Mg^{2+} (g) Mg^{2+} (h) CO_3^{2-} **13.36**(a) −704 kJ/mol (b) The K^+ ion contributes more because it is smaller and, therefore, has a greater charge density. **13.38**(a) increases (b) decreases (c) increases **13.41** Add a pinch of X to each solution. Addition of a "seec crystal of solute to a supersaturated solution causes the exce solute to crystallize immediately, leaving behind a saturated solution. The solution in which the added X dissolves is the unsaturated solution. The solution in which the added X remains undissolved is the saturated solution. **13.44**(a) incre (b) decrease **13.46**(a) 0.102 g O_2 (b) 0.0214 g O_2 **13.49** 0.20 mol/L **13.52**(a) molarity and % w/v or % v/v (b) parts-by-mass (% w/w) (c) molality **13.54** With just th information, you can convert between molality and molarity but you need to know the molar mass of the solvent to con to mole fraction. **13.56**(a) 0.944 *M* $C_{12}H_{22}O_{11}$ (b) 0.167 *M* $LiNO_3$ **13.58**(a) 0.0749 *M* NaOH (b) 0.36 *M* HNO_3 **13.60**(a) Add 4.25 g KH_2PO_4 to enough water to make 365 of aqueous solution. (b) Add 125 mL of 1.25 *M* NaOH to enough water to make 465 mL of solution. **13.62**(a) Weigh 48.0 g KBr, dissolve it in about 1 L distilled water, and the dilute to 1.40 L with distilled water. (b) Measure 82.7 mL of the 0.264 *M* $LiNO_3$ solution and add distilled water to r a total of 255 mL. **13.64**(a) 0.896 *m* glycine (b) 1.21 *m* gl erol **13.66** 4.48 *m* C_6H_6 **13.68**(a) Add 2.39 g $C_2H_6O_2$ to 308 g H_2O. (b) Add 0.0508 kg of 52.0% HNO_3 by mass to 1.15 kg H_2O to make 1.20 kg of 2.20% HNO_3 by mass. **13.70**(a) 0.29 (b) 58 mass % (c) 23 *m* C_3H_7OH **13.72** 42.6 g CsBr; mole fraction = 7.16×10^{-3}; 7.84% by mass **13.74** 5.11 *m* NH_3; 4.53 *M* NH_3; mole fraction = 0.0843 **13.76** 2.5 ppm Ca^{2+}; 0.56 ppm Mg^{2+} **13.80** It cond a "strong" current. A strong electrolyte dissociates comple into ions in solution. **13.82** The boiling point is higher and freezing point is lower for the solution than for the solvent. **13.85** A dilute solution of an electrolyte behaves mo ideally than a concentrated one. With increasing concentra the effective concentration deviates from the molar concen tion because of ionic attractions. Thus, 0.050 *m* NaF has a boiling point closer to its predicted value. **13.88**(a) strong trolyte (b) strong electrolyte (c) nonelectrolyte (d) weak electrolyte **13.90**(a) 0.6 mol of solute particles (b) 0.13 m (c) 2×10^{-4} mol (d) 0.06 mol **13.92**(a) CH_3OH in H_2O (b) H_2O in CH_3OH solution **13.94**(a) $\Pi_{II} < \Pi_I < \Pi_{III}$ (b) $bp_{II} < bp_I < bp_{III}$ (c) $fp_{III} < fp_I < fp_{II}$ (d) $vp_{III} < vp_I < vp_{II}$ **13.96** 23.4 torr **13.98** −0.467°C **13.100** 79.5°C **13.102** 1.18×10^4 g $C_2H_6O_2$ **13.104**(a) NaCl: 0.173 *m* and *i* 1.84 (b) CH_3COOH: 0.0837 *m* and *i* = 1.02 **13.107** 209 for CH_2Cl_2; 48.1 torr for CCl_4 **13.108** The fluid inside a b rial cell is both a solution and a colloid. It is a solution c and small molecules and a colloid of large molecules (pr and nucleic acids). **13.112** Soap micelles have nonpolar ta pointed inward and anionic heads pointed outward. The l charges on the heads of one micelle repel those on the he of a neighboring micelle. This repulsion between micelles keeps them from coagulating. Soap is more effective in f water than in seawater because the divalent cations in sea combine with the anionic heads to form a precipitate.

13.116 3.4×10^9 L **13.120** 0.0°C: 4.53×10^{-4} M O_2; 20.0°C: 2.83×10^{-4} M O_2; 40.0°C: 2.00×10^{-4} M O_2
13.122(a) 89.9 g/mol (b) C_2H_5O; $C_4H_{10}O_2$
(c) Forms H bonds:

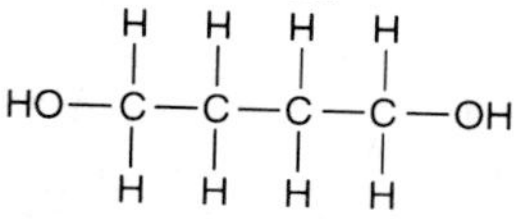

Does not form H bonds:

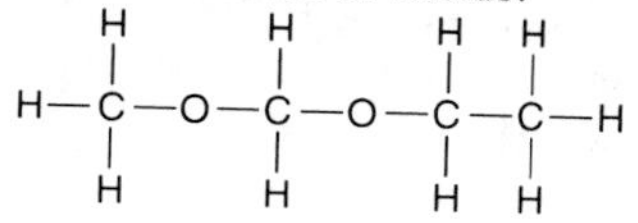

13.126(a) 9.45 g NaF (b) 0.0017 g F^- **13.129**(a) 68 g/mol (b) 2.1×10^2 g/mol (c) The molar mass of CaN_2O_6 is 164.10 g/mol. This value is less than the 2.1×10^2 g/mol calculated when the compound is assumed to be a strong electrolyte and is greater than the 68 g/mol calculated when the compound is assumed to be a nonelectrolyte. Thus, the compound forms a nonideal solution because the ions interact but do not dissociate completely in solution. (d) i = 2.4 **13.133**(a) 1.82×10^4 g/mol (b) 3.41×10^{-5}°C **13.134** 8.2×10^5 **13.138**(a) 0.02 (b) 5×10^{-3} atm·L/mol (c) yes **13.140** Weigh 3.11 g of $NaHCO_3$ and dissolve in 247 g of water. **3.144** M ng/L (kg solvent/L solution) = $m \times d_{\text{solution}}$. Thus, for very dilute solutions, molality × density = molarity. For an aqueous solution, the number of liters of solution is approximately the same as the kg of solvent because the density of water is close to 1 kg/L, so $m = M$. **13.146**(a) 2.5×10^{-3} M SO_2 (b) The base reacts with the sulfur dioxide to produce calcium sulfite. The reaction of sulfur dioxide makes "room" for more sulfur dioxide to dissolve. **13.151**(a) 7.83×10^{-3} mol L·atm (b) 4×10 (c) 3×10^{-6} (d) 1 ppm **13.155**(a) 0.0212 mol/L·atm (b) 8.86 ppm (c) k_H: C_6F_{14} > C_6H_{14} > ethanol > water. To dissolve oxygen in a solvent, the solvent molecules must be moved apart to make room for the gas. The stronger the inter molecular forces in the solvent, the more difficult it is to separate solvent particles and the lower the solubility of the gas. In both C_6F_{14} and C_6H_{14} have weak dispersion forces, with C having the weaker forces due to the electronegative fluorine atoms repelling each other. In both ethanol and water, the molecules are held together by strong hydrogen bonds with those bonds being stronger in water, as the boiling point indicates. **13.157**(a) Yes, the phases of water can still coexist at some temperature and can therefore establish equilibrium. (b) The triple point would occur at a lower pressure and lower temperature because the dissolved air would lower the vapor pressure of the solvent. (c) Yes, this is possible because the gas-solid phase boundary exists below the new triple point. (d) No; at both temperatures, the presence of the solute lowers the vapor pressure of the liquid. **13.159**(a) 2.8×10^{-4} g/mL (b) 81 mL

Chapter 16

Answers to Boxed Reading Problems:

B16.2 (a)
Step 1 $\cancel{NO(g)} + O_3(g) \longrightarrow \cancel{NO_2(g)} + O_2(g)$
Step 2 $\cancel{NO_2(g)} + O(g) \longrightarrow \cancel{NO(g)} + O_2(g)$
Overall $O_3(g) + O(g) \longrightarrow 2O_2(g)$

(b) rate = 3×10^7 molecule/s

B16.3 (a) Step 1 with Cl will have the higher value for the p factor. Since Cl is a single atom, no matter how it collides with the ozone molecule, the two particles should react, if the collision has enough energy. NO is a molecule. If the O_3 molecule collides with the N atom in the NO molecule, reaction can occur as a bond can form between N and O; if the O_3 molecule collides with the O atom in the NO molecule, reaction will not occur as the bond between N and O cannot form. The probability of a successful collision is smaller with NO.

(b) 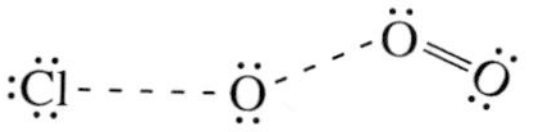

• **16.2** Reaction rate is proportional to concentration. An increase in pressure will increase the concentration, resulting in an increased rate. **16.3** The addition of water will lower the concentrations of all dissolved solutes, and the rate will decrease. **16.5** An increase in temperature increases the rate by increasing the number of collisions between particles, but more importantly, it increases the energy of collisions. **16.8**(a) The instantaneous rate is the rate at one point in time during the reaction. The average rate is the average over a period of time. On a graph of reactant concentration vs. time, the instantaneous rate is the slope of the tangent to the curve at any point. The average rate is the slope of the line connecting two points on the curve. The closer together the two points (the shorter the time interval), the closer the average rate is to the instantaneous rate. (b) The initial rate is the instantaneous rate at the point on the graph where t = 0, that is, when reactants are mixed.

16.10

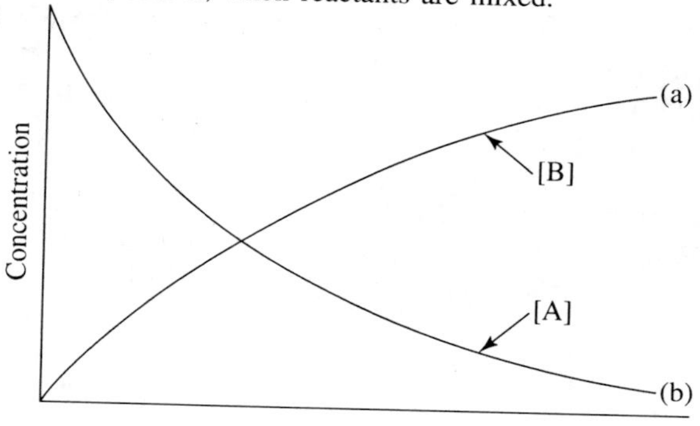

(a) $\text{rate} = -\left(\frac{1}{2}\right)\frac{\Delta[AX_2]}{\Delta t}$

$= -\left(\frac{1}{2}\right)\frac{(0.0088\ M - 0.0500\ M)}{(20.0\ \text{s} - 0\ \text{s})}$

$= 0.0010\ M/\text{s}$

(b)

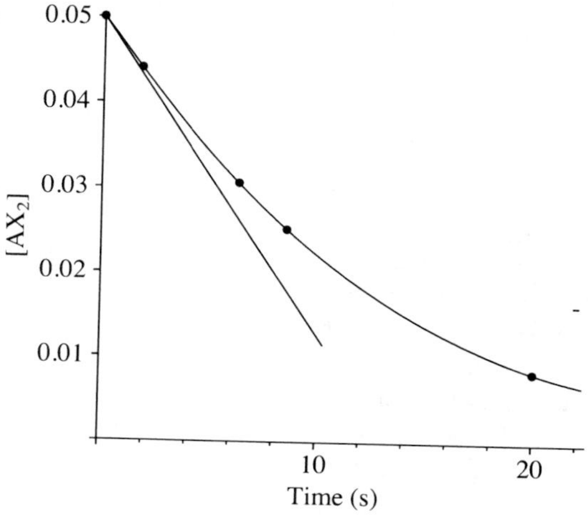

The initial rate is higher than the average rate because the rate decreases as reactant concentration decreases.

16.14 rate $= -\frac{1}{2}\frac{\Delta[A]}{\Delta t} = \frac{\Delta[B]}{\Delta t} = \frac{\Delta[C]}{\Delta t}$; 4 mol/L·s

16.16 rate $= -\frac{\Delta[A]}{\Delta t} = -\frac{1}{2}\frac{\Delta[B]}{\Delta t} = \frac{\Delta[C]}{\Delta t}$; 0.2 mol/L·s

16.18 $2N_2O_5(g) \longrightarrow 4NO_2(g) + O_2(g)$

16.21 rate $= -\frac{\Delta[N_2]}{\Delta t} = -\frac{1}{3}\frac{\Delta[H_2]}{\Delta t} = \frac{1}{2}\frac{\Delta[NH_3]}{\Delta t}$

16.22(a) rate $= -\frac{1}{3}\frac{\Delta[O_2]}{\Delta t} = \frac{1}{2}\frac{[\Delta O_3]}{\Delta t}$

(b) 1.45×10^{-5} mol/L·s

16.23(a) k is the rate constant, the proportionality constant in the rate law; it is reaction and temperature specific. (b) m represents the order of the reaction with respect to [A], and n represents the order of the reaction with respect to [B]. The order of a reactant does not necessarily equal its stoichiometric coefficient in the balanced equation. (c) L^2/mol^2·min **16.25**(a) Rate doubles. (b) Rate decreases by a factor of 4. (c) Rate increases by a factor of 9. **16.26** first order in BrO_3^-; first order in Br^-; second order in H^+; fourth order overall **16.28**(a) Rate doubles. (b) Rate is halved. (c) The rate increases by a factor of 16. **16.30** second order in NO_2; first order in Cl; third order overall **16.32**(a) Rate increases by a factor of 9. (b) Rate increases by a factor of 8. (c) Rate is halved. **16.34**(a) second order in A; first order in B (b) rate = $k[A]^2[B]$ (c) 5.00×10^3 L^2/mol^2·min **16.36**(a) $time^{-1}$ (b) L/mol·time (c) L^2/mol^2·time (d) $L^{3/2}/mol^{3/2}$·time **16.39**(a) first order (b) second order (c) zero order **16.41** 7 s **16.43**(a) $k = 0.0660\ min^{-1}$ (b) 21.0 min

16.45(a)

x-axis (time, s)	$[NH_3]$	y-axis (ln $[NH_3]$)
0	4.000 *M*	1.38629
1.000	3.986 *M*	1.38279
2.000	3.974 *M*	1.37977

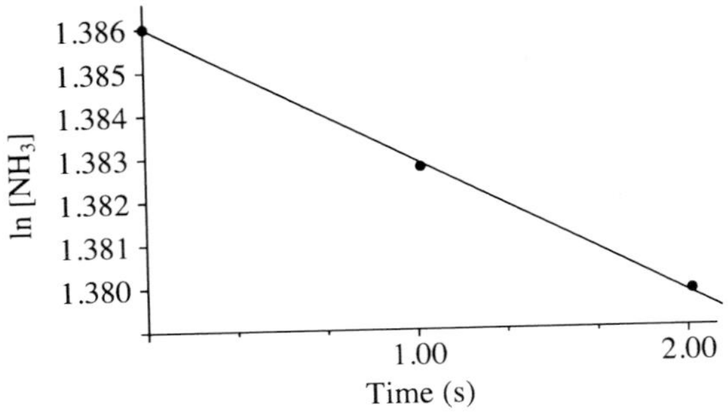

$k = 3\times10^{-3}\ s^{-1}$

(b) $t_{1/2} = 2\times10^2$ s

16.47 No, other factors that affect the rate are the energy and orientation of the collisions. **16.50** Measure the rate constant at a series of temperatures and plot ln k versus $1/T$. The slope of the line equals $-E_a/R$. **16.53** No, reaction is reversible and will eventually reach a state where the forward and reverse rates are equal. When this occurs, there are no concentrations equal to zero. Since some reactants are reformed from EF, the amount of EF will be less than 4×10^{-5} mol. **16.54** At the same temperature, both reaction mixtures have the same average kinetic energy, but the reactant molecules do not have the same average velocity. The trimethylamine molecule has greater mass than the ammonia molecule, so trimethylamine molecules will collide less often with HCl. Moreover, the bulky groups bonded to nitrogen in trimethylamine mean that collisions with HCl having the correct orientation occur less frequently. Therefore, the rate of the reaction between NH_3 and HCl is higher. **16.55** 12 unique collisions **16.57** 2.96×10^{-18} **16.59** 0.033 s^{-1}

16.61(a)

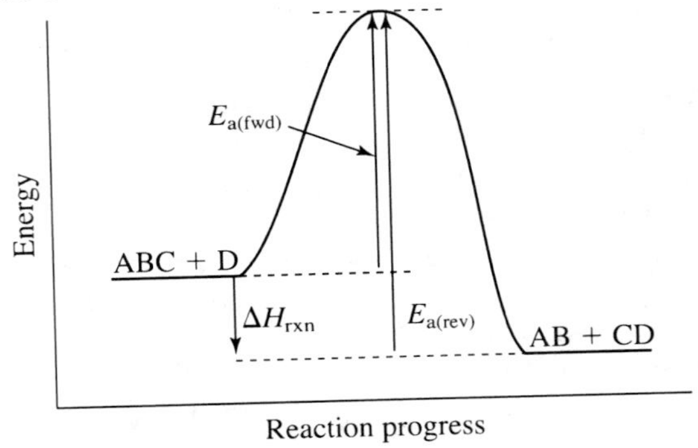

(b) 2.70×10^2 kJ/mol

(c)

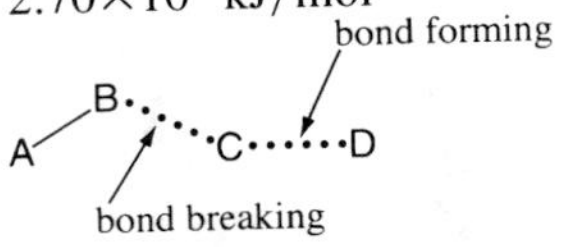

16.64(a) Because the enthalpy change is positive, the reaction is endothermic.

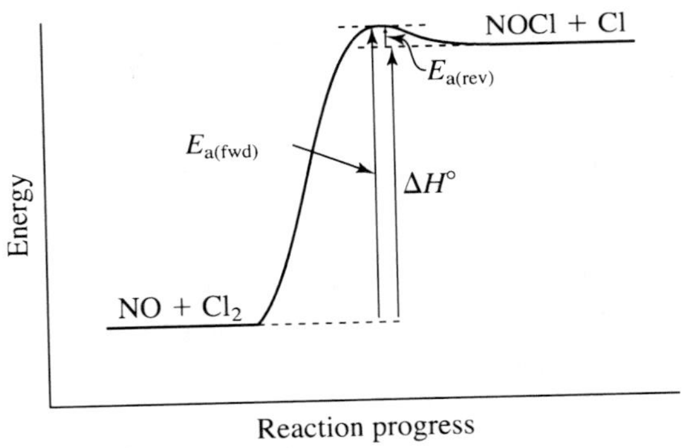

(b) 3 kJ (c)

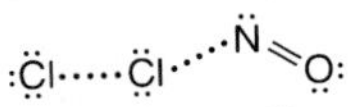

16.65 The rate of an overall reaction depends on the rate of the slowest step. The rate of the overall reaction will be lower than the average of the individual rates because the average includes higher rates as well. **16.69** The probability of three particles colliding with one another with the proper energy and orientation is much less than the probability for two particles. **16.70** No, the overall rate law must contain only reactants (no intermediates), and the overall rate is determined by the slow step.

16.72(a) $A(g) + B(g) + C(g) \longrightarrow D(g)$

(b) X and Y are intermediates.

(c)

Step	Molecularity	Rate Law
$A(g) + B(g) \rightleftharpoons X(g)$	bimolecular	$rate_1 = k_1[A][B]$
$X(g) + C(g) \longrightarrow Y(g)$	bimolecular	$rate_2 = k_2[X][C]$
$Y(g) \longrightarrow D(g)$	unimolecular	$rate_3 = k_3[Y]$

(d) yes (e) yes **16.74** The proposed mechanism is valid because the individual steps are chemically reasonable, they add to give the overall equation, and the rate law for the mechanism matches the observed rate law. **16.77** No. A catalyst changes the mechanism of a reaction to one with lower activation energy. Lower activation energy means a faster reaction. An increase in temperature does not influence the activation energy, but increases the fraction of collisions with sufficient energy to equal or exceed the activation energy. **16.78**(a) No. The spark provides energy that is absorbed by the H_2 and O_2 molecules to achieve the activation energy. (b) Yes. The powdered metal acts as a heterogeneous catalyst, providing a surface on which the oxygen-hydrogen reaction can proceed with a lower activation energy.
16.83(a) Water does not appear as a reactant in the rate-determining step.
(b) Step 1: $\text{rate}_1 = k_1[(CH_3)_3CBr]$
Step 2: $\text{rate}_2 = k_2[(CH_3)_3C^+]$
Step 3: $\text{rate}_3 = k_3[(CH_3)_3COH_2^+]$
(c) $(CH_3)_3C^+$ and $(CH_3)_3COH_2^+$
(d) The rate-determining step is step 1. The rate law for this step agrees with the rate law observed with $k = k_1$.
16.85 4.61×10^4 J/mol **16.89**(a) Rate increases 2.5 times. (b) Rate is halved. (c) Rate decreases by a factor of 0.01. (d) Rate does not change. **16.90** second order **16.93** 57 yr
16.96(a) 0.21 h^{-1}; 3.3 h (b) 6.6 h (c) If the concentration of sucrose is relatively low, the concentration of water remains nearly constant even with small changes in the amount of water. This gives an apparent zero-order reaction with respect to water. Thus, the reaction is first order overall because the rate does not change with changes in the amount of water.
16.99(a) 0.68 M (b) 0.57 **16.102** 71 kPa **16.106** 7.3×10^3 J/mol
16.108(a) 2.4×10^{-15} M (b) 2.4×10^{-11} mol/L·s **16.111**(a) 2.8 days (b) 7.4 days (c) 4.5 mol/m^3 **6.114**(a) $\text{rate}_1 = 1.7\times10^{-5}\ M\ s^{-1}$; $\text{rate}_2 = 3.4\times10^{-5}\ M\ s^{-1}$; $\text{rate}_3 = 3.4\times10^{-5}\ M\ s^{-1}$ (b) zero order with respect to $S_2O_8^{2-}$; first order with respect to I^- (c) $4.3\times10^{-4}\ s^{-1}$ (d) rate $= (4.3\times10^{-4}\ s^{-1})[KI]$
16.117(a) 7×10^4 cells/L (b) 2.0×10^1 min **16.120**(a) Use the Monod equation.

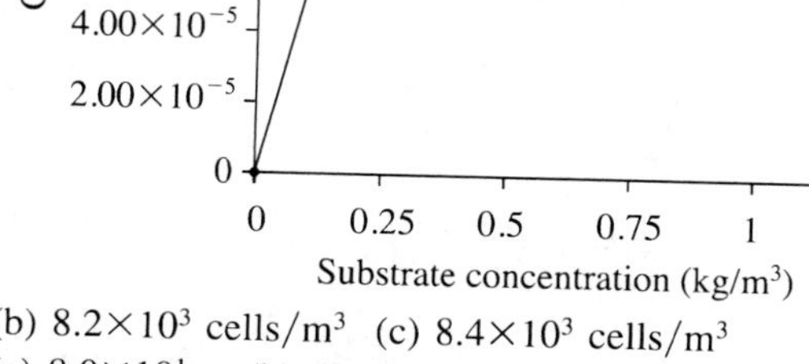

(b) 8.2×10^3 cells/m^3 (c) 8.4×10^3 cells/m^3
16.125(a) 8.0×10^1 s (b) 59 s (c) 2.6×10^2 s

Chapter 17

Answers to Boxed Reading Problem: B17.1 (a) Enzyme 3 (d) If F inhibited enzyme 6, then the second branch would not take place when enough F was made.

• **17.1** If the change is one of concentrations, it results temporarily in more products and less reactants. After equilibrium is re-established, K_c remains unchanged because the ratio of products and reactants remains the same. **17.7** The equilibrium constant expression is $K = [O_2]$. If the temperature remains constant, K remains constant. If the initial amount of Li_2O_2 present is sufficient to reach equilibrium, the amount of O_2 obtained will be constant.

17.8(a) $Q = \dfrac{[HI]^2}{[H_2][I_2]}$

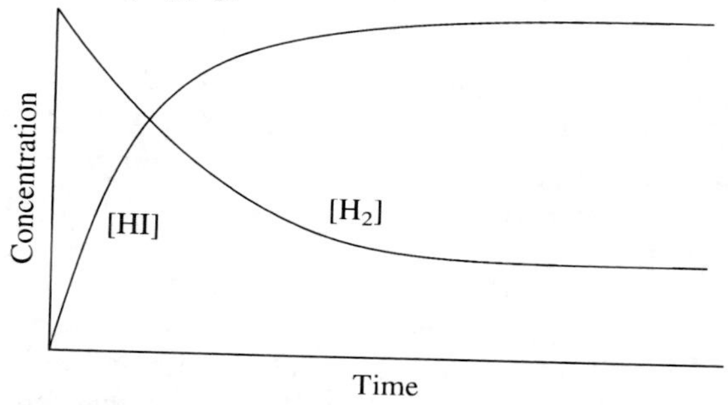

The value of Q increases as a function of time until it reaches the value of K. (b) no **17.11** Yes. If Q_1 is for the formation of 1 mol NH_3 from H_2 and N_2, and Q_2 is for the formation of NH_3 from H_2 and 1 mol of N_2, then $Q_2 = Q_1^2$.
17.12(a) $4NO(g) + O_2(g) \rightleftharpoons 2N_2O_3(g)$;

$$Q_c = \frac{[N_2O_3]^2}{[NO]^4[O_2]}$$

(b) $SF_6(g) + 2SO_3(g) \rightleftharpoons 3SO_2F_2(g)$;

$$Q_c = \frac{[SO_2F_2]^3}{[SF_6][SO_3]^2}$$

(c) $2SClF_5(g) + H_2(g) \rightleftharpoons S_2F_{10}(g) + 2HCl(g)$;

$$Q_c = \frac{[S_2F_{10}][HCl]^2}{[SClF_5]^2[H_2]}$$

17.14(a) $2NO_2Cl(g) \rightleftharpoons 2NO_2(g) + Cl_2(g)$;

$$Q_c = \frac{[NO_2]^2[Cl_2]}{[NO_2Cl]^2}$$

(b) $2POCl_3(g) \rightleftharpoons 2PCl_3(g) + O_2(g)$;

$$Q_c = \frac{[PCl_3]^2[O_2]}{[POCl_3]^2}$$

(c) $4NH_3(g) + 3O_2(g) \rightleftharpoons 2N_2(g) + 6H_2O(g)$;

$$Q_c = \frac{[N_2]^2[H_2O]^6}{[NH_3]^4[O_2]^3}$$

17.16(a) 7.9 (b) 3.2×10^{-5}
17.18(a) $2Na_2O_2(s) + 2CO_2(g) \rightleftharpoons 2Na_2CO_3(s) + O_2(g)$;

$$Q_c = \frac{[O_2]}{[CO_2]^2}$$

(b) $H_2O(l) \rightleftharpoons H_2O(g)$; $Q_c = [H_2O(g)]$
(c) $NH_4Cl(s) \rightleftharpoons NH_3(g) + HCl(g)$; $Q_c = [NH_3][HCl]$

17.20(a) $2NaHCO_3(s) \rightleftharpoons Na_2CO_3(s) + CO_2(g) + H_2O(g)$;
$Q_c = [CO_2][H_2O]$
(b) $SnO_2(s) + 2H_2(g) \rightleftharpoons Sn(s) + 2H_2O(g)$;
$$Q_c = \frac{[H_2O]^2}{[H_2]^2}$$
(c) $H_2SO_4(l) + SO_3(g) \rightleftharpoons H_2S_2O_7(l)$;
$$Q_c = \frac{1}{[SO_3]}$$
17.23(a)

(1)	$Cl_2(g) + F_2(g) \rightleftharpoons 2ClF(g)$	
(2)	$2ClF(g) + 2F_2(g) \rightleftharpoons 2ClF_3(g)$	
overall:	$Cl_2(g) + 3F_2(g) \rightleftharpoons 2ClF_3(g)$	

(b) $$Q_{overall} = Q_1Q_2 = \frac{\cancel{[ClF]^2}}{[Cl_2][F_2]} \times \frac{[ClF_3]^2}{\cancel{[ClF]^2}[F_2]^2} = \frac{[ClF_3]^2}{[Cl_2][F_2]^3}$$
17.25 K_c and K_p are equal when $\Delta n_{gas} = 0$. **17.26**(a) smaller (b) Assuming that $RT > 1$ ($T > 12.2$ K), $K_p > K_c$ if there are more moles of products than reactants at equilibrium, and $K_p < K_c$ if there are more moles of reactants than products. **17.27**(a) 3 (b) −1 (c) 3 **17.29**(a) 3.2 (b) 28.5 **17.31**(a) 0.15 (b) 3.6×10^{-7} **17.33** The reaction quotient (Q) and equilibrium constant (K) are determined by the ratio [products]/[reactants]. When $Q < K$, the reaction proceeds to the right to form more products. **17.35** no; to the left **17.38** At equilibrium, equal concentrations of $CFCl_3$ and HCl exist, regardless of starting reactant concentrations, because the product coefficients are equal. **17.40**(a) The approximation applies when the change in concentration from initial concentration to equilibrium concentration is so small that it is insignificant; this occurs when K is small and initial concentration is large. (b) This approximation should not be used when the change in concentration is greater than 5%. This can occur when $[\text{reactant}]_{initial}$ is very small or when change in [reactant] is relatively large due to a large K. **17.41** 50.8

17.43 Concentration (*M*)	$PCl_5(g)$	$\rightleftharpoons$	$PCl_3(g)$ +	$Cl_2(g)$
Initial	0.075		0	0
Change	$-x$		$+x$	$+x$
Equilibrium	$0.075 - x$		x	x

17.45 28 atm **17.47** 0.33 atm **17.49** 3.5×10^{-3} M **17.51** [HI] = 0.0152 M; $[I_2]$ = 0.00328 M **17.53** $[I_2]_{eq} = [Cl_2]_{eq} = 0.0199$ M; $[ICl]_{eq} = 0.0601$ M **17.55** 6.01×10^{-6} **17.58** Equilibrium position refers to the specific concentrations or pressures of reactants and products that exist at equilibrium, whereas equilibrium constant is the overall ratio of equilibrium concentrations or pressures. Equilibrium position changes as a result of a change in reactant and product concentrations. **17.59**(a) B, because the amount of product increases with temperature (b) A, because the lowest temperature will give the least product **17.63**(a) shifts toward products (b) shifts toward products (c) does not shift (d) shifts toward reactants **17.65**(a) more F and less F_2 (b) more C_2H_2 and H_2 and less CH_4 **17.67**(a) no effect (b) less H_2 and O_2 and more H_2O **17.69**(a) no change (b) increase volume **17.71**(a) amount decreases (b) amounts increase (c) amounts increase (d) amount decreases **17.73** 2.0 **17.76**(a) lower temperature, higher pressure (b) Q decreases; no change in K (c) Reaction rates are lower at lower temperatures, so a catalyst is used to speed up the reaction. **17.78**(a) P_{N_2} = 31 atm P_{H_2} = 93 atm; P_{total} = 174 atm (b) P_{N_2} = 18 atm; P_{H_2} = 111 atm; P_{total} = 179 atm; not a valid argument **17.81** 0.204 atm **17.84**(a) 3×10^{-3} atm (b) high pressure; low temperature (c) 2×10^5 (d) No, because water condenses at a higher temperature. **17.87**(a) 0.016 atm (b) $K_c = 5.6\times10^2$ P_{O_2} = 0.16 atm **17.89** 12.5 g $CaCO_3$ **17.93** Both concentrations increased by a factor of 2.2. **17.95**(a) 3.0×10^{-14} atm (b) 0.013 pg CO/L **17.97**(a) 98.0% (b) 99.0% (c) 2.60×10^5 J/mol **17.99**(a) $2CH_4(g) + O_2(g) + 2H_2O(g) \rightleftharpoons 2CO_2(g) + 6H_2(g)$ (b) 1.76×10^{29} (c) 3.19×10^{23} (d) 48 atm **17.100**(a) 4.0×10^{-21} atm (b) 5.5×10^{-8} atm (c) 29 N atoms/L; 4.0×10^{14} H atoms/L (d) The more reasonable step is $N_2(g) + H(g) \longrightarrow NH(g) + N(g)$. With only 29 N atoms in 1.0 L, the first reaction would produce virtually no NH(g) molecules. There are orders of magnitude more N_2 molecules than N atoms, so the second reaction is the more reasonable step. **17.103**(a) P_{N_2} = 0.780 atm; P_{O_2} = 0.210 atm $P_{NO} = 2.67\times10^{-16}$ atm (b) 0.990 atm (c) $K_c = K_p = 4.35\times10^{-31}$ **17.105**(a) 1.26×10^{-3} (b) 794 (c) −51.8 kJ (d) 1.2×10^4 J/mol **17.109**(a) 1.52 (b) 0.9626 atm (c) 0.2000 mol CO (d) 0.01097 M

Chapter 18

18.2 All Arrhenius acids have H in their formula and produce hydronium ion (H_3O^+) in aqueous solution. All Arrhenius bases have OH in their formula and produce hydroxide ion (OH^-) in aqueous solution. Neutralization occurs when each H_3O^+ ion combines with an OH^- ion to form two molecules of H_2O. Chemists found the reaction of any strong base with any strong acid always had a ΔH of −56 kJ/mol H_2O produced.
18.4 Strong acids and bases dissociate completely into ions when dissolved in water. Weak acids and bases dissociate only partially. The characteristic property of all weak acids is that a great majority of the acid molecules are undissociated.
18.5 a, c, and d
18.7 b and d

18.9(a) $$K_a = \frac{[CN^-][H_3O^+]}{[HCN]}$$
(b) $$K_a = \frac{[CO_3^{2-}][H_3O^+]}{[HCO_3^-]}$$
(c) $$K_a = \frac{[HCOO^-][H_3O^+]}{[HCOOH]}$$
18.11(a) $$K_a = \frac{[NO_2^-][H_3O^+]}{[HNO_2]}$$
(b) $$K_a = \frac{[CH_3COO^-][H_3O^+]}{[CH_3COOH]}$$
(c) $$K_a = \frac{[BrO_2^-][H_3O^+]}{[HBrO_2]}$$

18.13 $CH_3COOH < HF < HIO_3 < HI$ **18.15**(a) weak acid (b) strong base (c) weak acid (d) strong acid **18.17**(a) strong base (b) strong acid (c) weak acid (d) weak acid
18.22(a) The acid with the smaller K_a (4×10^{-5}) has the higher pH, because less dissociation yields fewer hydronium ions. (b) The acid with the larger pK_a (3.5) has the higher pH, because it has a smaller K_a and, thus, lower $[H_3O^+]$. (c) Lower concentration (0.01 *M*) contains fewer hydronium ions. (d) A 0.1 *M* weak acid solution contains fewer hydronium ions. (e) The 0.01 *M* base solution contains more hydroxide ions, so fewer hydronium ions. (f) The solution that has pOH = 6.0 has the higher pH: pH = 14.0 − 6.0 = 8.0.
18.23(a) 12.05; basic (b) 11.13; acidic **18.25**(a) 2.212; acidic (b) −0.708; basic
18.27(a) $[H_3O^+] = 1.4\times10^{-10}\ M$, $[OH^-] = 7.1\times10^{-5}\ M$, pOH = 4.15
(b) $[H_3O^+] = 2.7\times10^{-5}\ M$, $[OH^-] = 3.7\times10^{-10}\ M$, pH = 4.57
18.29(a) $[H_3O^+] = 1.7\times10^{-5}\ M$, $[OH^-] = 5.9\times10^{-10}\ M$, pOH = 9.23
(b) $[H_3O^+] = 4.5\times10^{-9}\ M$, $[OH^-] = 2.2\times10^{-6}\ M$, pH = 8.36
18.31 4.8×10^{-4} mol OH^-/L **18.33** 1.4×10^{-4} mol OH^-
18.36(a) Rising temperature increases the value of K_w. (b) $K_w = 2.5\times10^{-14}$; pOH = 6.80; $[OH^-] = 1.6\times10^{-7}\ M$
18.37 The Brønsted-Lowry theory defines acids as proton donors and bases as proton acceptors, while the Arrhenius definition looks at acids as containing ionizable hydrogen atoms and at bases as containing hydroxide ions. In both definitions, an acid produces H_3O^+ ions and a base produces OH^- ions when added to water. Ammonia and carbonate ion are two Brønsted-Lowry bases that are not Arrhenius bases because they do not contain OH^- ions. Brønsted-Lowry acids must contain an ionizable hydrogen atom in order to be proton donors, so a Brønsted-Lowry acid is also an Arrhenius acid. **18.40** An amphiprotic species is one that can lose a proton to act as an acid or gain a proton to act as a base. The dihydrogen phosphate ion, $H_2PO_4^-$, is an example.

$$H_2PO_4^-(aq) + OH^-(aq) \longrightarrow H_2O(l) + HPO_4^{2-}(aq)$$
$$H_2PO_4^-(aq) + HCl(aq) \longrightarrow H_3PO_4(aq) + Cl^-(aq)$$

18.41(a) $H_3PO_4(aq) + H_2O(l) \rightleftharpoons H_2PO_4^-(aq) + H_3O^+(aq)$

$$K_a = \frac{[H_3O^+][H_2PO_4^-]}{[H_3PO_4]}$$

(b) $C_6H_5COOH(aq) + H_2O(l) \rightleftharpoons C_6H_5COO^-(aq) + H_3O^+(aq)$

$$K_a = \frac{[H_3O^+][C_6H_5COO^-]}{[C_6H_5COOH]}$$

(c) $HSO_4^-(aq) + H_2O(l) \rightleftharpoons SO_4^{2-}(aq) + H_3O^+(aq)$

$$K_a = \frac{[H_3O^+][SO_4^{2-}]}{[HSO_4^-]}$$

18.43(a) Cl^- (b) HCO_3^- (c) OH^- **18.45**(a) NH_4^+ (b) NH_3 (c) $C_{10}H_{14}N_2H^+$

18.47(a) $HCl + H_2O \rightleftharpoons Cl^- + H_3O^+$
acid base base acid
Conjugate acid-base pairs: HCl/Cl^- and H_3O^+/H_2O
(b) $HClO_4 + H_2SO_4 \rightleftharpoons ClO_4^- + H_3SO_4^+$
acid base base acid
Conjugate acid-base pairs: $HClO_4/ClO_4^-$ and $H_3SO_4^+/H_2SO_4$
(c) $HPO_4^{2-} + H_2SO_4 \rightleftharpoons H_2PO_4^- + HSO_4^-$
base acid acid base
Conjugate acid-base pairs: H_2SO_4/HSO_4^- and $H_2PO_4^-/HPO_4^{2-}$
18.49(a) $NH_3 + H_3PO_4 \rightleftharpoons NH_4^+ + H_2PO_4^-$
base acid acid base
Conjugate acid-base pairs: $H_3PO_4/H_2PO_4^-$ and NH_4^+/NH_3
(b) $CH_3O^- + NH_3 \rightleftharpoons CH_3OH + NH_2^-$
base acid acid base
Conjugate acid-base pairs: NH_3/NH_2^- and CH_3OH/CH_3O^-
(c) $HPO_4^{2-} + HSO_4^- \rightleftharpoons H_2PO_4^- + SO_4^{2-}$
base acid acid base
Conjugate acid-base pairs: HSO_4^-/SO_4^{2-} and $H_2PO_4^-/HPO_4^{2-}$
18.51(a) $OH^-(aq) + H_2PO_4^-(aq) \rightleftharpoons H_2O(l) + HPO_4^{2-}(aq)$
Conjugate acid-base pairs: $H_2PO_4^-/HPO_4^{2-}$ and H_2O/OH^-
(b) $HSO_4^-(aq) + CO_3^{2-}(aq) \rightleftharpoons SO_4^{2-}(aq) + HCO_3^-(aq)$
Conjugate acid-base pairs: HSO_4^-/SO_4^{2-} and HCO_3^-/CO_3^{2-}
18.53 $K_c > 1$: $HS^- + HCl \rightleftharpoons H_2S + Cl^-$
$K_c < 1$: $H_2S + Cl^- \rightleftharpoons HS^- + HCl$
18.55 $K_c > 1$ for both a and b **18.57** $K_c < 1$ for both a and b
18.59(a) A strong acid is 100% dissociated, so the acid concentration will be very different after dissociation. (b) A weak acid dissociates to a very small extent, so the acid concentration before and after dissociation is nearly the same. (c) same as b, but with the extent of dissociation greater (d) same as a
18.60 No. HCl is a strong acid and dissociates to a greater extent than the weak acid CH_3COOH. The K_a of the acid, not the concentration of H_3O^+, determines the strength of the acid. **18.63** 1.5×10^{-5} **18.65** $[H_3O^+] = [NO_2^-] = 2.1\times10^{-2}\ M$; $[OH^-] = 4.8\times10^{-13}\ M$ **18.67** $[H_3O^+] = [ClCH_2COO^-] = 0.041\ M$; $[ClCH_2COOH] = 1.21\ M$; pH = 1.39
18.69(a) $[H_3O^+] = 6.0\times10^{-3}\ M$; pH = 2.22; $[OH^-] = 1.7\times10^{-12}\ M$; pOH = 11.78 (b) 1.9×10^{-4} **18.71** 2.2×10^{-7}
18.73(a) 2.37 (b) 11.53 **18.75**(a) 2.290 (b) 12.699 **18.77** 1.1%
18.79 $[H_3O^+] = [HS^-] = 9\times10^{-5}\ M$; pH = 4.0; $[OH^-] = 1\times10^{-10}\ M$; pOH = 10.0; $[H_2S] = 0.10\ M$; $[S^{2-}] = 1\times10^{-17}\ M$ **18.82** 1.5% **18.83** All Brønsted-Lowry bases contain at least one lone pair of electrons, which binds an H^+ and allows the base to act as a proton acceptor.
18.86(a) $C_5H_5N(aq) + H_2O(l) \rightleftharpoons OH^-(aq) + C_5H_5NH^+(aq)$

$$K_b = \frac{[C_5H_5NH^+][OH^-]}{[C_5H_5N]}$$

(b) $CO_3^{2-}(aq) + H_2O(l) \rightleftharpoons OH^-(aq) + HCO_3^-(aq)$

$$K_b = \frac{[HCO_3^-][OH^-]}{[CO_3^{2-}]}$$

18.88(a) $HONH_2(aq) + H_2O(l) \rightleftharpoons OH^-(aq) + HONH_3^+(aq)$

$$K_b = \frac{[HONH_3^+][OH^-]}{[HONH_2]}$$

(b) $HPO_4^{2-}(aq) + H_2O(l) \rightleftharpoons H_2PO_4^-(aq) + OH^-(aq)$

$$K_b = \frac{[H_2PO_4^-][OH^-]}{[HPO_4^{2-}]}$$

18.90 11.79 **18.92** 11.45 **18.94**(a) 5.6×10^{-10} (b) 2.5×10^{-5} **18.96**(a) 12.04 (b) 10.77 **18.98**(a) 11.19 (b) 5.56 **18.100**(a) 8.78 (b) 4.66 **18.102** $[OH^-] = 5.5\times10^{-4}$ *M*; pH = 10.74 **18.104** As a nonmetal becomes more electronegative, the acidity of its binary hydride increases. The electronegative nonmetal attracts the electrons more strongly in the polar bond, shifting the electron density away from H, thus making H^+ more easily transferred to a water molecule to form H_3O^+. **18.107** Chlorine is more electronegative than iodine, and $HClO_4$ has more oxygen atoms than HIO. **18.108**(a) H_2SeO_4 (b) H_3PO_4 (c) H_2Te **18.110**(a) H_2Se (b) $B(OH)_3$ (c) $HBrO_2$ **18.112**(a) 0.5 *M* $AlBr_3$ (b) 0.3 *M* $SnCl_2$ **18.114**(a) 0.2 *M* $Ni(NO_3)_2$ (b) 0.35 *M* $Al(NO_3)_3$ **18.117** NaF contains the anion of the weak acid HF, so F^- acts as a base. NaCl contains the anion of the strong acid HCl.

18.119(a) $KBr(s) \xrightarrow{H_2O} K^+(aq) + Br^-(aq)$; neutral

(b) $NH_4I(s) \xrightarrow{H_2O} NH_4^+(aq) + I^-(aq)$

$NH_4^+(aq) + H_2O(l) \rightleftharpoons NH_3(aq) + H_3O^+(aq)$; acidic

(c) $KCN(s) \xrightarrow{H_2O} K^+(aq) + CN^-(aq)$

$CN^-(aq) + H_2O(l) \rightleftharpoons HCN(aq) + OH^-(aq)$; basic

18.121(a) $Na_2CO_3(s) \xrightarrow{H_2O} 2Na^+(aq) + CO_3^{2-}(aq)$

$CO_3^{2-}(aq) + H_2O(l) \rightleftharpoons HCO_3^-(aq) + OH^-(aq)$; basic

(b) $CaCl_2(s) \xrightarrow{H_2O} Ca^{2+}(aq) + 2Cl^-(aq)$; neutral

(c) $Cu(NO_3)_2(s) \xrightarrow{H_2O} Cu^{2+}(aq) + 2NO_3^-(aq)$

$Cu(H_2O)_6^{2+}(aq) + H_2O(l) \rightleftharpoons Cu(H_2O)_5OH^+(aq) + H_3O^+(aq)$; acidic

18.123(a) $SrBr_2(s) \xrightarrow{H_2O} Sr^{2+}(aq) + 2Br^-(aq)$; neutral

(b) $Ba(CH_3COO)_2(s) \xrightarrow{H_2O} Ba^{2+}(aq) + 2CH_3COO^-(aq)$

$CH_3COO^-(aq) + H_2O(l) \rightleftharpoons CH_3COOH(aq) + OH^-(aq)$; basic

(c) $(CH_3)_2NH_2Br(s) \xrightarrow{H_2O} (CH_3)_2NH_2^+(aq) + Br^-(aq)$

$(CH_3)_2NH_2^+(aq) + H_2O(l) \rightleftharpoons (CH_3)_2NH(aq) + H_3O^+(aq)$; acidic

18.125(a) $NH_4^+(aq) + H_2O(l) \rightleftharpoons NH_3(aq) + H_3O^+(aq)$

$PO_4^{3-}(aq) + H_2O(l) \rightleftharpoons HPO_4^{2-}(aq) + OH^-(aq)$;

$K_b > K_a$; basic

(b) $SO_4^{2-}(aq) + H_2O(l) \rightleftharpoons HSO_4^-(aq) + OH^-(aq)$;

Na^+ gives no reaction; basic

(c) $ClO^-(aq) + H_2O(l) \rightleftharpoons HClO(aq) + OH^-(aq)$;

Li^+ gives no reaction; basic

18.127(a) $Fe(NO_3)_2 < KNO_3 < K_2SO_3 < K_2S$

(b) $NaHSO_4 < NH_4NO_3 < NaHCO_3 < Na_2CO_3$

18.129 Since both bases produce OH^- ions in water, both bases appear equally strong. $CH_3O^-(aq) + H_2O(l) \longrightarrow OH^-(aq) + CH_3OH(aq)$ and $NH_2^-(aq) + H_2O(l) \longrightarrow OH^-(aq) + NH_3(aq)$. **18.131** Ammonia, NH_3, is a more basic solvent than H_2O. In a more basic solvent, weak acids such as HF act like strong acids and are 100% dissociated. **18.133** A Lewis acid is an electron-pair acceptor while a Brønsted-Lowry acid is a proton donor. The proton of a Brønsted-Lowry acid is a Lewis acid because it accepts an electron pair when it bonds with a base. All Lewis acids are not Brønsted-Lowry acids. A Lewis base is an electron-pair donor and a Brønsted-Lowry base is a proton acceptor. All Brønsted-Lowry bases are Lewis bases, and vice versa. **18.134**(a) No,

$Zn(H_2O)_6^{2+}(aq) + 6NH_3(aq) \rightleftharpoons Zn(NH_3)_6^{2+} + 6H_2O(l)$;

NH_3 is a weak Brønsted-Lowry base, but a strong Lewis base. (b) cyanide ion and water (c) cyanide ion **18.137**(a) Lewis acid (b) Lewis base (c) Lewis acid (d) Lewis base **18.139**(a) Lewis acid (b) Lewis base (c) Lewis base (d) Lewis acid **18.141**(a) Lewis acid: Na^+; Lewis base: H_2O (b) Lewis acid: CO_2; Lewis base: H_2O (c) Lewis acid: BF_3; Lewis base: F^- **18.143**(a) Lewis (b) Brønsted-Lowry and Lewis (c) none (d) Lewis **18.146** 3.5×10^{-8} to 4.5×10^{-8} *M* H_3O^+; 5.2×10^{-7} to 6.6×10^{-7} *M* OH^- **18.147**(a) Acids vary in the extent of dissociation depending on the acid-base character of the solvent. (b) Methanol is a weaker base than water since phenol dissociates less in methanol than in water.

(c) $C_6H_5OH(solvated) + CH_3OH(l) \rightleftharpoons CH_3OH_2^+(solvated) + C_6H_5O^-(solvated)$

(d) $CH_3OH(l) + CH_3OH(l) \rightleftharpoons CH_3O^-(solvated) + CH_3OH_2^+(solvated)$; $K = [CH_3O^-][CH_3OH_2^+]$

18.120(a) $SnCl_4$ is the Lewis acid; $(CH_3)_3N$ is the Lewis base (b) 5*d* **18.151** pH = 5.00, 6.00, 6.79, 6.98, 7.00 **18.157** 3×10^{18} **18.160** 10.48 **18.162** 2.41 **18.164** amylase, 2×10^{-7} *M*; pepsin, 1×10^{-2} *M*; trypsin, 3×10^{-10} *M* **18.168** 1.47×10^{-3} **18.170**(a) Ca^{2+} does not react with water; $CH_3CH_2COO^-(aq) + H_2O(l) \rightleftharpoons CH_3CH_2COOH(aq) + OH^-(aq)$; basic (b) 9.08 **18.176** 4.5×10^{-5} **18.179**(a) The concentration of oxygen is higher in the lungs, so the equilibrium shifts to the right. (b) In an oxygen-deficient environment, the equilibrium shifts to the left to release oxygen. (c) A decrease in $[H_3O^+]$ shifts the equilibrium to the right. More oxygen is absorbed, but it will be more difficult to remove the O_2. (d) An increase in $[H_3O^+]$ shifts the equilibrium to the left. Less oxygen is bound to Hb, but it will be easier to remove it. **18.181**(a) 1.012 *M* (b) 0.004 *M* (c) 0.4% **18.182**(a) 10.0 (b) The pK_b for the 3° amine group is much smaller than that for the aromatic ring, thus the K_b is significantly larger (yielding a much greater amount of OH^-). (c) 4.7 (d) 5.1

Chapter 19

Answers to Boxed Reading Problem: B19.2 (a) 65 mol (b) 6.28 (c) 4.0×10^3 g HCO_3^-

• **19.2** The acid component neutralizes added base, and the base component neutralizes added acid, so the pH of the buffer solution remains relatively constant. The components of a buffer do not neutralize one another because they are a conjugate acid-base pair. **19.7** The buffer range, the pH over which the buffer acts effectively, is greatest when the buffer-component concentration ratio is 1; the range decreases as this ratio deviates from 1. **19.9**(a) Ratio and pH increase; added OH^- reacts with HA. (b) Ratio and pH decrease; added H^+ reacts with A^-. (c) Ratio and pH increase; added A^- increases $[A^-]$. (d) Ratio and pH decrease; added HA increases [HA]. **19.11** $[H_3O^+] = 5.6\times10^{-6}$ *M*; pH = 5.25 **19.13** $[H_3O^+] = 5.2\times10^{-4}$ *M*; pH = 3.28 **19.15** 3.89 **19.17** 10.03 **19.19** 9.47 **19.21**(a) K_{a2} (b) 10.55 **19.23** 3.6 **19.25** 0.20 **19.27** 3.37 **19.29** 8.82 **19.31**(a) 4.81 (b) 0.66 g KOH **19.33**(a) $HOOC(CH_2)_4COOH/HOOC(CH_2)_4COO^-$ or $C_6H_5NH_3^+/C_6H_5NH_2$ (b) $H_2PO_4^-/HPO_4^{2-}$ or $H_2AsO_4^-/HAsO_4^{2-}$ **19.35**(a) $HOCH_2CH(OH)COOH/HOCH_2CH(OH)COO^-$ or $CH_3COOC_6H_4COOH/CH_3COOC_6H_4COO^-$ (b) $C_5H_5NH^+/C_5H_5N$ **19.38** 1.6 **19.40** To see a distinct color in a mixture of two colors, you need one to have about 10 times the intensity of the other. For this to be the case, the concentration ratio $[HIn]/[In^-]$ has to be greater than 10/1 or less than 1/10. This occurs when pH = $pK_a - 1$ or pH = $pK_a + 1$, respectively, giving a pH range of about 2 units. **19.42** The equivalence point in a titration is the point at which the number of moles of base is stoichiometrically equivalent to the number of moles of acid. The endpoint is the point at which the added indicator changes color. If an appropriate indicator is selected, the endpoint is close to the equivalence point, but they are not usually the same. The pH at the endpoint, or color change, may precede or follow the pH at the equivalence point, depending on the indicator chosen. **19.44**(a) initial pH: *strong acid*–strong base < *weak acid*–strong base < *weak base*–strong acid (b) pH at equivalence point: *weak base*–strong acid < *strong acid*–strong base < *weak acid*–strong base **19.46** At the center of the buffer region, the concentrations of weak acid and conjugate base are equal, so the pH = pK_a of the acid. **19.48** pH range from 7.5 to 9.5 **19.50**(a) bromthymol blue (b) thymol blue or phenolphthalein **19.52**(a) methyl red (b) bromthymol blue **19.54**(a) 1.0000 (b) 1.6368 (c) 2.898 (d) 3.903 (e) 7.00 (f) 10.10 (g) 12.05 **19.56**(a) 2.91 (b) 4.81 (c) 5.29 (d) 6.09 (e) 7.41 (f) 8.76 (g) 10.10 (h) 12.05 **19.58**(a) 59.0 mL and 8.54 (b) 66.0 mL and 7.13, total 132.1 mL and 9.69 **19.60**(a) 123 mL and 5.17 (b) 194 mL and 5.80 **19.63** Fluoride ion is the conjugate base of a weak acid and reacts with H_2O: $F^-(aq) + H_2O(l) \rightleftharpoons HF(aq) + OH^-(aq)$. As the pH increases, the equilibrium shifts to the left and $[F^-]$ increases. As the pH decreases, the equilibrium shifts to the right and $[F^-]$ decreases. The changes in $[F^-]$ influence the solubility of BaF_2. Chloride ion is the conjugate base of a strong acid, so it does not react with water and its concentration is not influenced by pH. **19.65** The compound precipitates. **19.66**(a) $K_{sp} = [Ag^+]^2[CO_3^{2-}]$ (b) $K_{sp} = [Ba^{2+}][F^-]^2$ (c) $K_{sp} = [Cu^{2+}][HS^-][OH^-]$ **19.68**(a) $K_{sp} = [Ca^{2+}][CrO_4^{2-}]$ (b) $K_{sp} = [Ag^+][CN^-]$ (c) $K_{sp} = [Ni^{2+}][HS^-][OH^-]$ **19.70** 1.3×10^{-4} **19.72** 2.8×10^{-11} **19.74**(a) 2.3×10^{-5} *M* (b) 4.2×10^{-9} *M* **19.76**(a) 1.7×10^{-3} *M* (b) 2.0×10^{-4} *M* **19.78**(a) $Mg(OH)_2$ (b) PbS (c) Ag_2SO_4 **19.80**(a) $CaSO_4$ (b) $Mg_3(PO_4)_2$ (c) $PbSO_4$ **19.82**(a) $AgCl(s) \rightleftharpoons Ag^+(aq) + Cl^-(aq)$. The chloride ion is the anion of a strong acid, so it does not react with H_3O^+. No change with pH.
(b) $SrCO_3(s) \rightleftharpoons Sr^{2+}(aq) + CO_3^{2-}(aq)$. The strontium ion is the cation of a strong base, so pH will not affect its solubility. The carbonate ion acts as a base:
$CO_3^{2-}(aq) + H_2O(l) \rightleftharpoons HCO_3^-(aq) + OH^-(aq)$; also $CO_2(g)$ forms and escapes: $CO_3^{2-}(aq) + 2H_3O^+(aq) \longrightarrow CO_2(g) + 3H_2O(l)$. Therefore, the solubility of $SrCO_3$ will increase with addition of H_3O^+ (decreasing pH). **19.84**(a) $Fe(OH)_2(s) \rightleftharpoons Fe^{2+}(aq) + 2OH^-(aq)$. The OH^- ion reacts with added H_3O^+: $OH^-(aq) + H_3O^+(aq) \longrightarrow 2H_2O(l)$. The added H_3O^+ consumes the OH^-, driving the equilibrium toward the right to dissolve more $Fe(OH)_2$. Solubility increases with addition of H_3O^+ (decreasing pH).
(b) $CuS(s) + H_2O(l) \rightleftharpoons Cu^{2+}(aq) + HS^-(aq) + OH^-(aq)$. Both HS^- and OH^- are anions of weak acids, so both ions react with added H_3O^+. Solubility increases with addition of H_3O^+ (decreasing pH). **19.86** yes **19.88** yes **19.91**(a) $Fe(OH)_3$ (b) The two metal ions are separated by adding just enough NaOH to precipitate iron(III) hydroxide. (c) 2.0×10^{-7} *M* **19.94** No, because it indicates that a complex ion forms between the lead ion and hydroxide ions:

$$Pb^{2+}(aq) + nOH^-(aq) \rightleftharpoons Pb(OH)_n^{2-n}(aq)$$

19.95 $Hg(H_2O)_4^{2+}(aq) + 4CN^-(aq) \rightleftharpoons Hg(CN)_4^{2-}(aq) + 4H_2O(l)$

19.97 $Ag(H_2O)_2^+(aq) + 2S_2O_3^{2-}(aq) \rightleftharpoons Ag(S_2O_3)_2^{3-}(aq) + 2H_2O(l)$

19.99 8.1×10^{-15} *M* **19.101** 0.05 *M* **19.103** 1.0×10^{-16} *M* Zn^{2+}; 0.025 *M* $Zn(CN)_4^{2-}$; 0.049 *M* CN^- **19.105** 0.035 L of 2.00 *M* NaOH and 0.465 L of 0.200 *M* HCOOH **19.107**(a) 0.99 (b) assuming the volumes are additive: 0.468 L of 1.0 *M* HCOOH and 0.232 L of 1.0 *M* NaOH (c) 0.34 *M* **19.110** 1.3×10^{-4} *M* **19.113**(a) 14 (b) 1 g from the second beaker **19.116**(a) 0.088 (b) 0.14 **19.117** 0.260 *M* TRIS; pH = 8.53 **19.119** Lower the pH below 6.6 **19.123** 8×10^{-5}
19.125(a)

V (mL)	pH	$\Delta pH/\Delta V$	V_{avg} (mL)
0.00	1.00		
10.00	1.22	0.022	5.00
20.00	1.48	0.026	15.00
30.00	1.85	0.037	25.00
35.00	2.18	0.066	32.50
39.00	2.89	0.18	37.00
39.50	3.20	0.62	39.25
39.75	3.50	1.2	39.63
39.90	3.90	2.7	39.83
39.95	4.20	6	39.93
39.99	4.90	18	39.97

V (mL)	pH	ΔpH/ΔV	V_{avg} (mL)
40.00	7.00	200	40.00
40.01	9.40	200	40.01
40.05	9.80	10	40.03
40.10	10.40	10	40.08
40.25	10.50	0.67	40.18
40.50	10.79	1.2	40.38
41.00	11.09	0.60	40.75
45.00	11.76	0.17	43.00
50.00	12.05	0.058	47.50
60.00	12.30	0.025	55.00
70.00	12.43	0.013	65.00
80.00	12.52	0.009	75.00

(b)
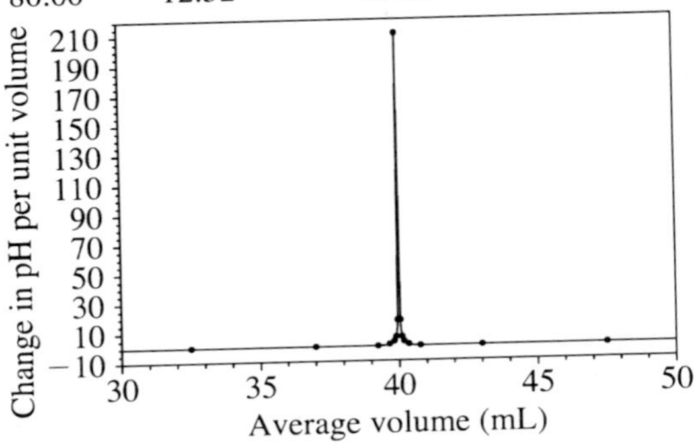

Maximum slope (equivalence point) is at V_{avg} = 40.00 mL. **19.127** 4.05 **19.133** H_2CO_3/HCO_3^- and $H_2PO_4^-/HPO_4^{2-}$; $[HPO_4^{2-}]/[H_2PO_4^-]$ = 5.8 **19.134** 3.8 **19.136**(a) 58.2 mL (b) 7.85 mL (c) 6.30 **19.138** 170 mL **19.142** 5.68 **19.144** 3.9×10^{-9} μg Pb^{2+}/100 mL blood **19.146** No NaCl will precipitate. **19.147**(a) A and D (b) pH_A = 4.35; pH_B = 8.67; pH_C = 2.67; pH_D = 4.57 (c) C, A, D, B (d) B

Chapter 20

Answer to Boxed Reading Problem: B20.2 −12.6 kJ/mol

• **20.2** A spontaneous process occurs by itself, whereas a nonspontaneous process requires a continuous input of energy to make it happen. It is possible to cause a nonspontaneous process to occur, but the process stops once the energy source is removed. A reaction that is nonspontaneous under one set of conditions may be spontaneous under a different set of conditions. **20.5** The transition from liquid to gas involves a greater increase in dispersal of energy and freedom of motion than does the transition from solid to liquid. **20.6** In an exothermic reaction, $\Delta S_{surr} > 0$. In an endothermic reaction, $\Delta S_{surr} < 0$. A chemical cold pack for injuries is an example of an application using a spontaneous endothermic process. **20.8** a, b, and c **20.10** a and b **20.12**(a) positive (b) negative (c) negative **20.14**(a) positive (b) positive (c) positive **20.16**(a) negative (b) negative (c) positive **20.18**(a) positive (b) negative (c) positive **20.20**(a) positive (b) negative (c) positive **20.22**(a) Butane. The double bond in 2-butene restricts freedom of rotation. (b) Xe(*g*). It has the greater molar mass. (c) $CH_4(g)$. Gases have greater entropy than liquids. **20.24**(a) $C_2H_5OH(l)$. It is a more complex molecule. (b) $KClO_3(aq)$. Ions in solution have their energy more dispersed than those in a solid. (c) K(*s*). It has a greater molar mass. **20.26**(a) Diamond < graphite < charcoal. Freedom of motion is least in the network solid; more freedom between graphite sheets; most freedom in amorphous solid. (b) Ice < liquid water < water vapor. Entropy increases as a substance changes from solid to liquid to gas. (c) O atoms < O_2 < O_3. Entropy increases with molecular complexity. **20.28**(a) $ClO_4^-(aq) > ClO_3^-(aq) > ClO_2^-(aq)$; decreasing molecular complexity (b) $NO_2(g) > NO(g) > N_2(g)$. N_2 has lower standard molar entropy because it consists of two of the same atoms; the other species have two different types of atoms. NO_2 is more complex than NO. (c) $Fe_3O_4(s) > Fe_2O_3(s) > Al_2O_3(s)$. Fe_3O_4 is more complex and more massive. Fe_2O_3 is more massive than Al_2O_3. **20.31** For a system at equilibrium, $\Delta S_{univ} = \Delta S_{sys} + \Delta S_{surr} = 0$. For a system moving to equilibrium, $\Delta S_{univ} > 0$. **20.32** $S^\circ_{Cl_2O(g)} = 2S^\circ_{HClO(g)} - S^\circ_{H_2O(g)} - \Delta S^\circ_{rxn}$ **20.33**(a) negative; ΔS° = −172.4 J/K (b) positive; ΔS° = 141.6 J/K (c) negative; ΔS° = −837 J/K **20.35** ΔS° = 93.1 J/K; yes, the positive sign of ΔS is expected because there is a net increase in the number of gas molecules. **20.37** ΔS° = −311 J/K; yes, the negative entropy change matches the decrease in moles of gas. **20.39** −75.6 J/K **20.41** −242 J/K **20.44** −97.2 J/K **20.46** A spontaneous proces has $\Delta S_{univ} > 0$. Since the absolute temperature is always posi tive, ΔG_{sys} must be negative ($\Delta G_{sys} < 0$) for a spontaneous pro cess. **20.48** ΔH° is positive and ΔS° is positive. Melting is an example. **20.49** The entropy changes little within a phase. As long as the substance does not change phase, the value of ΔS° relatively unaffected by temperature. **20.50**(a) −1138.0 kJ (b) −1379.4 kJ (c) −224 kJ **20.52**(a) −1138 kJ (b) −1379 kJ (c) −226 kJ **20.54**(a) Entropy decreases (ΔS° is negative) because the number of moles of gas decreases. The combustion of CO releases energy (ΔH° is negative). (b) −257.2 kJ or −257.3 kJ, depending on the method **20.56**(a) −0.409 kJ/mol·K (b) −197 kJ/mol **20.58**(a) ΔH°_{rxn} = 90.7 kJ; ΔS°_{rxn} = 221 J/K (b) At 28°C, ΔG° = 24.3 kJ; at 128°C, ΔG° = 2.2 kJ; at 228°C, ΔG° = −19.9 kJ (c) For the substances in their standard states, the reaction is nonspontaneou at 28°C, near equilibrium at 128°C, and spontaneous at 228° **20.60** ΔH° = 30910 J, ΔS° = 93.15 J/K, *T* = 331.8 K **20.62**(a) ΔH°_{rxn} = −241.826 kJ, ΔS°_{rxn} = −44.4 J/K, ΔG°_{rxn} = −228.60 kJ (b) Yes. The reaction will become nonspontaneous at higher temperatures. (c) The reaction is spontaneous below 5.45×10^3 K. **20.64**(a) ΔG° is a relatively large positiv value. (b) *K* >> 1. *Q* depends on initial conditions, not eq librium conditions. **20.67** The standard free energy change, ΔG°, applies when all components of the system are in thei standard states; $\Delta G^\circ = \Delta G$ when all concentrations equal 1 and all partial pressures equal 1 atm. **20.68**(a) 1.7×10^6 (b) 3.89×10^{-34} (c) 1.26×10^{48} **20.70**(a) 6.57×10^{173} (b) 4.46×10^{-15} (c) 3.46×10^4 **20.72** 4.89×10^{-51} **20.74** 3.36×10^5 **20.76** 2.7×10^4 J/mol; no **20.78**(a) 2.9×10^4 J/mol (b) The reverse direction, formation of reactants, is spontaneous, so the reaction proceeds to the left. (c) 7.0×

J/mol; the reaction proceeds to the left to reach equilibrium. **20.80**(a) no T (b) 163 kJ (c) 1×10^2 kJ/mol **20.83**(a) spontaneous (b) + (c) + (d) − (e) −, not spontaneous (f) − **20.87**(a) 2.3×10^2 (b) The treatment is to administer oxygen-rich air; increasing the concentration of oxygen shifts the equilibrium to the left, in the direction of $Hb\cdot O_2$. **20.89** −370. kJ **20.91**(a) $2N_2O_5(g) + 6F_2(g) \longrightarrow 4NF_3(g) + 5O_2(g)$ (b) $\Delta G^\circ_{rxn} = -569$ kJ (c) $\Delta G_{rxn} = -5.60\times10^2$ kJ/mol **20.93** $\Delta H^\circ_{rxn} = -137.14$ kJ; $\Delta S^\circ_{rxn} = -120.3$ J/K; $\Delta G^\circ_{rxn} = -101.25$ kJ **20.101**(a) 1.67×10^3 J/mol (b) 7.37×10^3 J/mol (c) -4.04×10^3 J/mol (d) 0.19 **20.105**(a) 465 K (b) 6.59×10^{-4} (c) The reaction rate is higher at the higher temperature. The shorter time required (kinetics) overshadows the lower yield (thermodynamics).

Chapter 24

Answers to Boxed Reading Problems: B24.1 In the *s*-process, a nucleus captures a neutron sometime over a long period of time. Then the nucleus emits a beta particle to form another element. The stable isotopes of most heavy elements up to ^{209}Bi form by the *s*-process. The *r*-process very quickly forms less stable isotopes and those with A greater than 230 by multiple neutron captures, followed by multiple beta decays. **B24.3** The simultaneous fusion of three nuclei is a termolecular process. Termolecular processes have a very low probability of occurring. The bimolecular fusion of ^{8}Be with ^{4}He is more likely. **B24.4** $^{210}_{83}Bi \longrightarrow {}^{0}_{-1}\beta + {}^{210}_{84}Po$ (nuclide A); $^{210}_{84}Po \longrightarrow {}^{4}_{2}\alpha + {}^{206}_{82}Pb$ (nuclide B); $^{206}_{82}Pb + 3{}^{1}_{0}n \longrightarrow {}^{209}_{82}Pb$ (nuclide C); $^{209}_{82}Pb \longrightarrow {}^{0}_{-1}\beta + {}^{210}_{83}Bi$ (nuclide D)

• **24.1**(a) Chemical reactions are accompanied by relatively small changes in energy; nuclear reactions are accompanied by relatively large changes in energy. (b) Increasing temperature increases the rate of a chemical reaction but has no effect on a nuclear reaction. (c) Both chemical and nuclear reaction rates increase with higher reactant concentrations. (d) If the reactant is limiting in a chemical reaction, then more reactant produces more product and the yield increases. The presence of more radioactive reactant results in more decay product, so a higher reactant concentration increases the yield. **24.2**(a) 95.02% (b) The atomic mass is larger than the isotopic mass of ^{32}S. Sulfur-32 is the lightest isotope. **24.4**(a) Z down by 2, N down by 2 (b) Z up by 1, N down by 1 (c) no change in Z or N (d) Z down by 1, N up by 1 (e) Z down by 1, N up by 1 A different element is produced in all cases except c. **24.6** A neutron-rich nuclide decays by beta (minus) decay. A neutron-poor nuclide undergoes positron decay or electron capture. **24.8**(a) $^{234}_{92}U \longrightarrow {}^{4}_{2}\alpha + {}^{230}_{90}Th$ (b) $^{232}_{93}Np + {}^{0}_{-1}e \longrightarrow {}^{232}_{92}U$ (c) $^{12}_{7}N \longrightarrow {}^{0}_{1}\beta + {}^{12}_{6}C$ **24.10**(a) $^{27}_{12}Mg \longrightarrow {}^{0}_{-1}\beta + {}^{27}_{13}Al$ (b) $^{23}_{12}Mg \longrightarrow {}^{0}_{1}\beta + {}^{23}_{11}Na$ (c) $^{103}_{46}Pd + {}^{0}_{-1}e \longrightarrow {}^{103}_{45}Rh$ **24.12**(a) $^{48}_{23}V \longrightarrow {}^{48}_{22}Ti + {}^{0}_{1}\beta$ (b) $^{107}_{48}Cd + {}^{0}_{-1}e \longrightarrow {}^{107}_{47}Ag$ (c) $^{210}_{86}Rn \longrightarrow {}^{206}_{84}Po + {}^{4}_{2}\alpha$ **24.14**(a) $^{186}_{78}Pt + {}^{0}_{-1}e \longrightarrow {}^{186}_{77}Ir$ (b) $^{225}_{89}Ac \longrightarrow {}^{221}_{87}Fr + {}^{4}_{2}\alpha$ (c) $^{129}_{52}Te \longrightarrow {}^{129}_{53}I + {}^{0}_{-1}\beta$ **24.16**(a) Appears stable because its N and Z values are both magic numbers, but its N/Z ratio (1.50) is too high; it is unstable. (b) Appears unstable because its Z value is an odd number, but its N/Z ratio (1.19) is in the band of stability, so it is stable. (c) Unstable because its N/Z ratio is too high. **24.18**(a) The N/Z ratio for ^{127}I is 1.4; it is stable. (b) The N/Z ratio for ^{106}Sn is 1.1; it is unstable because this ratio is too low. (c) The N/Z ratio is 1.1 for ^{68}As. The ratio is within the range of stability, but the nuclide is most likely unstable because there are odd numbers of both protons and neutrons. **24.20**(a) alpha decay (b) positron decay or electron capture (c) positron decay or electron capture **24.22**(a) beta (minus) decay (b) positron decay or electron capture (c) alpha decay **24.24** Stability results from a favorable N/Z ratio, even numbered N and/or Z, and the occurrence of magic numbers. The N/Z ratio of ^{52}Cr is 1.17, which is within the band of stability. The fact that Z is even does not account for the variation in stability because all isotopes of chromium have the same Z. However, ^{52}Cr has 28 neutrons, so N is both an even number and a magic number for this isotope only. **24.28** seven α emissions and four β^- emissions **24.31** No, it is not valid to conclude that $t_{1/2}$ equals 1 min because the number of nuclei is so small. Decay rate is an average rate and is only meaningful when the sample is macroscopic and contains a large number of nuclei. For the sample containing 6×10^{12} nuclei, the conclusion is valid. **24.33** 2.56×10^{-2} Ci/g **24.35** 1.4×10^8 Bq/g **24.37** 1×10^{-12} day^{-1} **24.39** 2.31×10^{-7} yr^{-1} **24.41** 1.49 mg **24.43** 2.2×10^9 yr **24.45** 30 dpm **24.47** 1.0×10^6 yr **24.50** Neither γ radiation nor neutron beams have charge, so neither is deflected by a magnetic or electric field. Neutron beams differ from γ radiation in that a neutron has a mass approximately equal to that of a proton. It was observed that a neutron beam induces the emission of protons from a substance; γ radiation does not cause such emission. **24.52** Protons are repelled from the target nuclei due to interaction with like (positive) charges. Higher energy is required to overcome the repulsion. **24.53**(a) $^{10}_{5}B + {}^{4}_{2}\alpha \longrightarrow {}^{1}_{0}n + {}^{13}_{7}N$ (b) $^{28}_{14}Si + {}^{2}_{1}H \longrightarrow {}^{1}_{0}n + {}^{29}_{15}P$ (c) $^{242}_{96}Cm + {}^{4}_{2}\alpha \longrightarrow 2{}^{1}_{0}n + {}^{244}_{98}Cf$ **24.58** Ionizing radiation is more dangerous to children because their rapidly dividing cells are more susceptible to radiation than adults' slowly dividing cells. **24.60**(a) 5.4×10^{-7} rad (b) 5.4×10^{-9} Gy **24.62**(a) 7.5×10^{-10} Gy (b) 7.5×10^{-5} mrem (c) 7.5×10^{-10} Sv **24.65** 1.86×10^{-3} rad **24.67** NAA does not destroy the sample, while chemical analyses do. Neutrons bombard a nonradioactive sample, inducing some atoms within the sample to be radioactive. The radioisotopes decay by emitting radiation characteristic of each isotope. **24.73** Energy is released when a nucleus forms from nucleons. The nuclear binding energy is the quantity of energy holding 1 mol of nuclei together. This energy must be absorbed to break up the nucleus into nucleons and is released when nucleons come together. **24.75**(a) 1.861×10^4 eV (b) 2.981×10^{-15} J **24.77** 7.6×10^{11} J **24.79**(a) 7.976 MeV/nucleon (b) 127.6 MeV/atom (c) 1.231×10^{10} kJ/mol **24.81**(a) 8.768 MeV/nucleon (b) 517.3 MeV/atom (c) 4.99×10^{10} kJ/mol **24.85** Radioactive decay is a spontaneous process in which unstable nuclei emit radioactive particles and energy. Fission occurs as the result of high-energy bombardment of nuclei with small particles that cause the nuclei to break into smaller nuclides, radioactive particles, and energy. All fission events are not the same. The nuclei split in a number of ways to produce several different products. **24.88** The water serves to slow the neutrons so that they are better able to cause a fission reaction. Heavy water is a better moderator because it does not absorb neutrons as well as light water does; thus, more neutrons are available to initiate the fission process. However, D_2O does not occur naturally in great abundance, so its production adds to the cost of a heavy-water reactor. **24.93**(a) 1.1×10^{-29} kg (b) 9.9×10^{-13} J (c) 5.9×10^8 kJ/mol; this is approximately 1 million times larger than a typical enthalpy of reaction. **24.95** 8.0×10^3 yr **24.98** 1.35×10^{-5} M **24.100** 6.2×10^{-2} **24.102**(a) 5.99 h (b) 21% **24.104**(a) 0.999 (b) 0.298 (c) 5.58×10^{-6} (d) Radiocarbon dating is more reliable for the fraction in part (b) because a significant amount of ^{14}C has decayed and a significant amount remains. Therefore, a change in the amount of ^{14}C will be noticeable. For the fraction in part (a), very little ^{14}C has decayed, and for (c) very little ^{14}C remains. In either case, it will be more difficult to measure the change, so the error will be relatively large. **24.106** 6.58 h **24.110** 4.904×10^{-9} L/h **24.113** 81 yr **24.115**(a) 0.15 Bq/L (b) 0.27 Bq/L (c) 3.3 d; a total of 12.8 d **24.118** 7.4 s **24.121** 1926

24.124 6.27×10^5 eV/reaction, 6.05×10^7 kJ/mol reaction **24.127**(a) 2.07×10^{-17} J (b) 1.45×10^7 H atoms (c) 1.4960×10^{-5} J (d) 1.4959×10^{-5} J (e) No, the captain should continue using the current technology. **24.130**(a) 0.043 MeV, 2.9×10^{-11} m (b) 4.713 MeV **24.134**(a) 3.26×10^3 d (b) 3.2×10^{-3} s (c) 2.78×10^{11} yr **24.136**(a) 1.80×10^{17} J (b) 6.15×10^{16} kJ (c) The procedure in part (b) produces more energy per kilogram of antihydrogen. **24.137** 9.316×10^2 MeV **24.141** 7.81 d

Numbers in parentheses refer to the page(s) on which a term is introduced and/or discussed.

A

absolute scale (also *Kelvin scale*) The preferred temperature scale in scientific work, which has absolute zero (0 K, or −273.15°C) as the lowest temperature. (23) [See also *kelvin (K)*.]

absorption spectrum The spectrum produced when atoms absorb specific wavelengths of incoming light and become excited from lower to higher energy levels. (273)

abundance The amount of an element in a particular region of the natural world. (905)

accuracy The closeness of a measurement to the actual value. (29)

acid In common laboratory terms, any species that produces H^+ ions when dissolved in water. (145) [See also *Arrhenius, Brønsted-Lowry,* and *Lewis acid-base definitions.*]

acid anhydride A compound, usually formed by a dehydration-condensation reaction of an oxoacid, that yields two molecules of the acid when it reacts with water. (600)

acid-base buffer (also *buffer*) A solution that resists changes in pH when a small amount of either strong acid or strong base is added. (765)

acid-base indicator An organic molecule whose color is different in acid and in base and is used to monitor the equivalence point of a titration or the pH of a solution. (728)

acid-base reaction Any reaction between an acid and a base. (145) (See also *neutralization reaction.*)

acid-base titration curve A plot of the pH of a solution of acid (or base) versus the volume of base (or acid) added to the solution. (774)

acid-dissociation (acid-ionization) constant (K_a) An equilibrium constant for the dissociation of an acid (HA) in H_2O to yield the conjugate base (A^-) and H_3O^+:

$$K_a = \frac{[H_3O^+][A^-]}{[HA]} \qquad (722)$$

actinides The Period 7 elements that constitute the second inner transition series (5*f* block), which includes thorium (Th; $Z = 90$) through lawrencium (Lr; $Z = 103$). (306, 952)

activated complex (See *transition state.*)

activation energy (E_a) The minimum energy with which molecules must collide to react. (649)

active site The region of an enzyme formed by specific amino acid side chains at which catalysis occurs. (662)

activity ($\mathcal{A}$) (also *decay rate*) The change in number of nuclei ($\mathcal{N}$) of a radioactive sample divided by the change in time (t). (988)

activity series of the metals A listing of metals arranged in order of decreasing strength of the metal as a reducing agent in aqueous reactions. (165)

actual yield The amount of product actually obtained in a chemical reaction. (112)

addition polymer (also *chain-reaction,* or *chain-growth, polymer*) A polymer formed when monomers (usually containing C=C) combine through an addition reaction. (604)

addition reaction A type of organic reaction in which atoms linked by a multiple bond become bonded to more atoms. (588)

adduct The product of a Lewis acid-base reaction characterized by the formation of a new covalent bond. (751)

adenosine triphosphate (ATP) A high-energy molecule that serves most commonly as a store and source of energy in organisms. (836)

alcohol An organic compound (ending, *-ol*) that contains a $-\overset{|}{\underset{|}{\mathrm{C}}}-\underset{..}{\ddot{\mathrm{O}}}-\mathrm{H}$ functional group. (591)

aldehyde An organic compound (ending, *-al*) that contains the carbonyl functional group ($\mathrm{C}{=}\underset{..}{\ddot{\mathrm{O}}}$) in which the carbonyl C is also bonded to H. (597)

alkane A hydrocarbon that contains only single bonds and no rings (general formula, C_nH_{2n+2}). (576)

alkene A hydrocarbon that contains at least one C=C bond (general formula, C_nH_{2n}). (582)

alkyl group A saturated hydrocarbon chain with one bond available. (588)

alkyl halide (See *haloalkane.*)

alkyne A hydrocarbon that contains at least one C≡C bond (general formula, C_nH_{2n-2}). (583)

allotrope One of two or more crystalline or molecular forms of an element. In general, one allotrope is more stable than another at a particular pressure and temperature. (539)

alloy A mixture with metallic properties that consists of solid phases of two or more pure elements, a solid-solid solution, or distinct intermediate phases. (354, 482, 921)

alpha (α) decay A radioactive process in which an alpha particle is emitted from a nucleus. (981)

alpha particle (α or $^4_2He^{2+}$) A positively charged particle, identical to a helium-4 nucleus, that is one of the common types of radioactive emissions. (979)

amide An organic compound that contains the $-\overset{\overset{:\mathrm{O}:}{\|}}{\mathrm{C}}-\underset{..}{\overset{|}{\mathrm{N}}}-$ functional group. (599)

amine An organic compound (general formula, $-\overset{|}{\underset{|}{\mathrm{C}}}-\underset{|}{\ddot{\mathrm{N}}}-$) derived structurally by replacing one or more H atoms of ammonia with organic groups; a weak organic base. (594, 754)

amino acid An organic compound [general formula, H_2N—CH(R)—COOH] with at least one carboxyl and one amine group on the same molecule; the monomer unit of a protein. (483, 608)

amorphous solid A solid that has a poorly defined shape because it lacks extensive molecular-level ordering of its particles. (441)

ampere (A) The SI unit of electric current; 1 ampere of current results when 1 coulomb flows through a conductor in 1 second. (890)

amphoteric Able to act as either an acid or a base. (316)

amplitude The height of the crest (or depth of the trough) of a wave; related to the intensity of the energy (brightness of the light). (262)

angular momentum quantum number (l) An integer from 0 to $n - 1$ that is related to the shape of an atomic orbital. (281)

anion A negatively charged ion. (55)

anode The electrode at which oxidation occurs in an electrochemical cell. Electrons are given up by the reducing agent and leave the cell at the anode. (856)

antibonding MO A molecular orbital formed when wave functions are subtracted from each other, which decreases electron density between the nuclei and leaves a node. Electrons occupying such an orbital destabilize the molecule. (406)

apatite A compound of general formula $Ca_5(PO_4)_3X$, where X is generally F, Cl, or OH; a source of phosphorus. (914)

aqueous solution A solution in which water is the solvent. (70)

aromatic hydrocarbon A compound of C and H with one or more rings of C atoms (often drawn with alternating C—C and C=C bonds), in which there is extensive delocalization of π electrons. (584)

Arrhenius acid-base definition A model of acid-base behavior in which an acid is a substance that has H in its formula and dissociates in water to yield H_3O^+, and a base is a substance that has OH in its formula and produces OH^- in water. (720)

Arrhenius equation An equation that expresses the exponential relationship between temperature and the rate constant: $k = Ae^{-E_a/RT}$. (649)

atmosphere The mixture of gases that extends from a planet's surface and eventually merges with outer space; the gaseous portion of Earth's crust. (212, 908) (For the unit, see *standard atmosphere.*)

atom The smallest particle of an element that retains the chemical nature of the element. A neutral, spherical entity composed of a positively charged central nucleus surrounded by one or more negatively charged electrons. (43)

atomic mass (also *atomic weight*) The average of the masses of the naturally occurring isotopes of an element weighted according to their abundances. (50)

atomic mass unit (amu) (also *dalton, Da*) A mass exactly equal to $\frac{1}{12}$ the mass of a carbon-12 atom. (50)

atomic number (*Z*) The unique number of protons in the nucleus of each atom of an element (equal to the number of electrons in the neutral atom). An integer that expresses the positive charge of a nucleus or subatomic particle in multiples of the electronic charge. (48)

atomic orbital (also *wave function*) A mathematical expression that describes the motion of the electron's matter-wave in terms of time and position in the region of the nucleus. The term is used qualitatively to mean the region of space in which there is a high probability of finding the electron. (279)

atomic solid A solid consisting of individual atoms held together by dispersion forces; the frozen noble gases are the only examples. (449)

atomic symbol (also *element symbol*) A one- or two-letter abbreviation for the English, Latin, or Greek name of an element. (49)

atomic weight (See *atomic mass.*)

aufbau principle The conceptual approach for building up atoms by adding one proton at a time to the nucleus and one electron around it to obtain the ground-state electron configurations of the elements. (299)

autoionization (also *self-ionization*) A reaction in which two molecules of a substance react to give ions. The most important example is for water:

$$2H_2O(l) \rightleftharpoons H_3O^+(aq) + OH^-(aq) \qquad (724)$$

average rate The change in concentration of reactants (or products) divided by a finite time period. (630)

Avogadro's law The gas law stating that, at fixed temperature and pressure, equal volumes of any ideal gas contain equal numbers of particles, and, therefore, the volume of a gas is directly proportional to its amount (mol): $V \propto n$. (190)

Avogadro's number A number (6.022×10^{23} to four significant figures) equal to the number of atoms in exactly 12 g of carbon-12; the number of atoms, molecules, or formula units in one mole of an element or compound. (83)

axial group An atom (or group) that lies above or below the trigonal plane of a trigonal bipyramidal molecule, or a similar structural feature in a molecule. (377)

B

background radiation Natural ionizing radiation, the most important form of which is cosmic radiation. (997)

balancing coefficient (also *stoichiometric coefficient*) A numerical multiplier of all the atoms in the formula immediately following it in a balanced chemical equation. (99)

band of stability The band of stable nuclides that appears on a plot of number of neutrons versus number of protons for all nuclides. (983)

band theory An extension of molecular orbital (MO) theory that explains many properties of metals and other solids, in particular, the differences in electrical conductivity of conductors, semiconductors, and insulators. (452)

barometer A device used to measure atmospheric pressure. Most commonly, a tube open at one end, which is filled with mercury and inverted into a dish of mercury. (183)

base In common laboratory terms, any species that produces OH^- ions when dissolved in water. (146) [See also *Arrhenius, Brønsted-Lowry,* and *Lewis acid-base definitions.*]

base-dissociation (base-ionization) constant (K_b) An equilibrium constant for the reaction of a base (B) with H_2O to yield the conjugate acid (BH^+) and OH^-:

$$K_b = \frac{[BH^+][OH^-]}{[B]} \qquad (740)$$

base pair Two complementary mononucleotide bases that are H bonded to each other; guanine (G) always pairs with cytosine (C), and adenine (A) always pairs with thymine (T) (or uracil, U). (613)

base unit (also *fundamental unit*) A unit that defines the standard for one of the seven physical quantities in the International System of Units (SI). (17)

basic-oxygen process The method used to convert pig iron to steel, in which O_2 is blown over and through molten pig iron to oxidize impurities and decrease the content of carbon. (925)

battery A group of voltaic cells arranged in series; primary and secondary types are self-contained, but flow batteries are not. (878)

becquerel (Bq) The SI unit of radioactivity; 1 Bq = 1 d/s (disintegration per second). (988)

bent shape (also *V shape*) A molecular shape that arises when a central atom is bonded to two other atoms and has one or two lone pairs; occurs as the AX_2E shape class (bond angle $< 120°$) in the trigonal planar arrangement and as the AX_2E_2 shape class (bond angle $< 109.5°$) in the tetrahedral arrangement. (375)

beta (β) decay A radioactive change that encompasses any of three specific processes— β^- decay, β^+ emission, and e^- capture. (981)

beta (β^-) decay A radioactive process in which a beta particle is emitted from a nucleus. (981)

beta particle (β, β^-, or ${}^{0}_{-1}\beta$) A negatively charged particle, identified as a high-speed electron, that is one of the common types of radioactive emissions. (979)

bimolecular reaction An elementary reaction involving the collision of two reactant species. (655)

binary covalent compound A compound that consists of atoms of two elements in which bonding occurs primarily through electron sharing. (65)

binary ionic compound A compound that consists of the oppositely charged ions of two elements. (55)

biomass conversion The process of applying chemical and biological methods to convert plant or animal matter into fuels. (249)

biosphere The living systems that inhabit Earth. (908)

blast furnace A tower-shaped furnace made of brick material in which intense heat and blasts of air are used to convert iron ore and coke to iron metal and carbon dioxide. (924)

body-centered cubic unit cell A unit cell in which a particle lies at each corner and in the center of a cube. (442)

boiling point (bp or T_b) The temperature at which the vapor pressure of a gas equals the external (atmospheric) pressure. (428)

boiling point elevation (ΔT_b) The increase in the boiling point of a solvent caused by the presence of dissolved solute. (501)

bond angle The angle formed by the nuclei of two surrounding atoms with the nucleus of the central atom at the vertex. (374)

bond energy (BE) (also *bond enthalpy* or *bond strength*) The enthalpy change (always >0) accompanying the breakage of a given bond in 1 mol of gaseous molecules. (339)

bond length The distance between the nuclei of two bonded atoms. (340)

bond order The number of electron pairs shared by two bonded atoms. (339)

bonding MO A molecular orbital formed when wave functions are added to each other, which increases electron density between the nuclei. Electrons occupying such an orbital stabilize the molecule. (406)

bonding pair (also *shared pair*) An electron pair shared by two nuclei; the mutual attraction between the nuclei and the electron pair forms a covalent bond. (339)

Born-Haber cycle A series of hypothetical steps and their enthalpy changes that convert elements to an ionic compound; it is used to calculate the lattice energy. (333)

Boyle's law The gas law stating that, at constant temperature and amount of gas, the volume occupied by a gas is inversely proportional to the applied (external) pressure: $V \propto 1/P$. (187)

branch A side chain appended to a polymer backbone or longest sequence of atoms in an organic compound. (465)

bridge bond (also *three-center, two-electron bond*) A covalent bond in which three atoms are held together by two electrons. (536)

Brønsted-Lowry acid-base definition A model of acid-base behavior based on proton transfer, in which an acid and a base are defined, respectively, as species that donate and accept a proton. (729)

buffer (See *acid-base buffer.*)

buffer capacity A measure of the ability of a buffer to resist a change in pH; related to the total concentrations and relative proportions of buffer components. (770)

buffer range The pH range over which a buffer acts effectively. (771)

C

calibration The process of correcting for systematic error of a measuring device by comparing it to a known standard. (29)

calorie (cal) A unit of energy defined as exactly 4.184 joules; originally defined as the heat needed to raise the temperature of 1 g of water 1°C (from 14.5°C to 15.5°C). (233)

calorimeter A device used to measure the heat released or absorbed by a physical or chemical process taking place within it. (239)

capillarity (or *capillary action*) A property that results in a liquid rising through a narrow space against the pull of gravity. (438)

carbon steel The steel that is produced by the basic-oxygen process, contains about 1% to 1.5% C and other impurities, and is alloyed with metals that prevent corrosion and increase strength. (925)

carbonyl group The C═O grouping of atoms. (597)

carboxylic acid An organic compound (ending, *-oic acid*) that contains the —C(═O)—ÖH group. (599)

catalyst A substance or mixture that increases the rate of a reaction without being used up in the process. (660)

catenation The process by which atoms of an element bond to each other in chains; most common with carbon in organic compounds but also occurs with boron, silicon, sulfur, and several other elements. (572)

cathode The electrode at which reduction occurs in an electrochemical cell. Electrons enter the cell and are acquired by the oxidizing agent at the cathode. (856)

cathode ray The ray of light emitted by the cathode (negative electrode) in a gas discharge tube; travels in straight lines, unless deflected by magnetic or electric fields. (45)

cation A positively charged ion. (55)

cell potential (E_{cell}) (also *electromotive force,* or *emf; cell voltage*) The potential difference between the electrodes of an electrochemical cell when no current flows. (861)

Celsius scale (formerly *centigrade scale*) A temperature scale in which the freezing and boiling points of water are defined as 0°C and 100°C, respectively. (23)

ceramic A nonmetallic, nonpolymeric solid that is hardened by heating it to high temperatures and, in most cases, consists of silicate microcrystals suspended in a glassy cementing medium. (459)

chain reaction In nuclear fission, a self-sustaining process in which neutrons released by splitting of one nucleus cause other nuclei to split, which releases more neutrons, and so on. (1006)

change in enthalpy (ΔH) The change in internal energy plus the product of the constant pressure and the change in volume: $\Delta H = \Delta E + P\Delta V$; the heat lost or gained at constant pressure: $\Delta H = q_P$. (235)

charge density The ratio of the charge of an ion to its volume. (489)

Charles's law The gas law stating that at constant pressure, the volume occupied by a fixed amount of gas is directly proportional to its absolute temperature: $V \propto T$. (188)

chelate A complex ion in which the metal ion is bonded to a bidentate or polydentate ligand. (955)

chemical bond The force that holds two atoms together in a molecule (or formula unit). (55)
chemical change (also *chemical reaction*) A change in which one or more substances are converted into one or more substances with different composition and properties. (4)
chemical equation A statement that uses chemical formulas to express the identities and quantities of the substances involved in a chemical or physical change. (98)
chemical formula A notation of atomic symbols and numerical subscripts that shows the type and number of each atom in a molecule or formula unit of a substance. (59)
chemical kinetics The study of the rates and mechanisms of reactions. (627)
chemical property A characteristic of a substance that appears as it interacts with, or transforms into, other substances. (4)
chemical reaction (See *chemical change.*)
chemistry The scientific study of matter and its properties, the changes it undergoes, and the energy associated with those changes. (4)
chiral molecule One that is not superimposable on its mirror image; an optically active molecule. In organic compounds, a chiral molecule typically contains a C atom bonded to four different groups (asymmetric C). (580)
chlor-alkali process An industrial method that electrolyzes concentrated aqueous NaCl and produces Cl_2, H_2, and NaOH. (936)
chromatography A separation technique in which a mixture is dissolved in a fluid (gas or liquid), and the components are separated through differences in adsorption to (or solubility in) a solid surface (or viscous liquid). (72)
***cis-trans* isomers** (See *geometric isomers.*)
Clausius-Clapeyron equation An equation that expresses the linear relationship between vapor pressure P of a liquid and temperature T; in two-point form, it is

$$\ln \frac{P_2}{P_1} = \frac{-\Delta H_{\text{vap}}}{R}\left(\frac{1}{T_2} - \frac{1}{T_1}\right) \quad (427)$$

coal gasification An industrial process for altering the large molecules in coal to sulfur-free gaseous fuels. (249)
colligative property A property of a solution that depends on the number, not the identity, of solute particles. (499) (See also *boiling point elevation, freezing point depression, osmotic pressure,* and *vapor pressure lowering.*)
collision frequency The average number of collisions per second that a particle undergoes. (211)
collision theory A model that explains reaction rate as based on the number, energy, and orientation of colliding particles. (648)
colloid A heterogeneous mixture in which a solute-like phase is dispersed throughout a solvent-like phase. (508)
combustion The process of burning in air, often with release of heat and light. (10)
combustion analysis A method for determining the formula of a compound from the amounts of its combustion products; used commonly for organic compounds. (95)
common-ion effect The shift in the position of an ionic equilibrium away from an ion involved in the process that is caused by the addition or presence of that ion. (766)
complex (See *coordination compound.*)
complex ion An ion consisting of a central metal ion bonded covalently to molecules and/or anions called ligands (792, 953)
composition The types and amounts of simpler substances that make up a sample of matter. (4)
compound A substance composed of two or more elements that are chemically combined in fixed proportions. (38)
concentration A measure of the quantity of solute dissolved in a given quantity of solution (or solvent). (114)
concentration cell A voltaic cell in which both compartments contain the same components but at different concentrations. (874)
condensation The process of a gas changing into a liquid. (420)
condensation polymer A polymer formed by monomers with two functional groups that are linked together in a dehydration-condensation reaction. (606)
conduction band In band theory, the empty, higher energy portion of the band of molecular orbitals into which electrons move when conducting heat and electricity. (453)
conductor A substance (usually a metal) that conducts an electric current well. (453)
conjugate acid-base pair Two species related to each other through the gain or loss of a proton; the acid has one more proton than its conjugate base. (729)
constitutional isomers (also *structural isomers*) Compounds with the same molecular formula but different arrangements of atoms. (579, 957)
contact process An industrial process for the manufacture of sulfuric acid based on the catalyzed oxidation of SO_2. (934)
controlled experiment An experiment that measures the effect of one variable at a time by keeping other variables constant. (12)
conversion factor A ratio of equivalent quantities that is equal to 1 and used to convert the units of a quantity. (13)
coordinate covalent bond A covalent bond formed when one atom donates both electrons to provide the shared pair and, once formed, is identical to any covalent single bond. (961)
coordination compound (also *complex*) A substance containing at least one complex ion and counter ion(s). (953)
coordination isomers Two or more coordination compounds with the same composition in which the complex ions have different ligand arrangements. (957)
coordination number In a crystal, the number of nearest neighbors surrounding a particle. (442) In a complex, the number of ligand atoms bonded to the central metal ion. (953)
copolymer A polymer that consists of two or more types of monomer. (465)
core The dense, innermost region of Earth. (906)
core electrons (See *inner electrons.*)
corrosion The natural redox process that results in unwanted oxidation of a metal. (882)
coulomb (C) The SI unit of electric charge. One coulomb is the charge of 6.242×10^{18} electrons; one electron possesses a charge of 1.602×10^{-19} C. (862)
Coulomb's law A law stating that the electrostatic energy between particles A and B is directly proportional to the product of their charges and inversely proportional to the distance between them:

$$\text{electrostatic energy} \propto \frac{\text{charge A} \times \text{charge B}}{\text{distance}} \quad (335)$$

counter ion A simple ion associated with a complex ion in a coordination compound. (953)

coupling of reactions The pairing of reactions of which one releases enough free energy for the other to occur. (834)

covalent bond A type of bond in which atoms are bonded through the sharing of electrons; the mutual attraction of the nuclei and an electron pair that holds atoms together in a molecule. (58, 338)

covalent bonding The idealized bonding type that is based on localized electron-pair sharing between two atoms with little difference in their tendencies to lose or gain electrons (most commonly nonmetals). (330)

covalent compound A compound that consists of atoms bonded together by shared electron pairs. (55)

covalent radius One-half the shortest distance between nuclei of identical covalently bonded atoms. (308)

critical mass The minimum mass needed to achieve a chain reaction. (1007)

critical point The point on a phase diagram above which the vapor cannot be condensed to a liquid; the end of the liquid-gas curve. (429)

crosslink A branch that covalently joins one polymer chain to another. (465)

crust The thin, light, heterogeneous outer layer of Earth, which consists of gasous, liquid, and solid regions. (906)

crystal defect Any of a variety of disruptions in the regularity of a crystal structure. (455)

crystal field splitting energy (Δ) The difference in energy between two sets of metal-ion *d* orbitals that results from electrostatic interactions with the surrounding ligands. (964)

crystal field theory A model that explains the color and magnetism of coordination compounds based on the effects of ligands on metal-ion *d*-orbital energies. (962)

crystalline solid Solid with a well-defined shape because of the orderly arrangement of the atoms, molecules, or ions. (441)

crystallization A technique used to separate and purify the components of a mixture through differences in solubility in which a component comes out of solution as crystals. (72)

cubic closest packing A crystal structure based on the face-centered cubic unit cell in which the layers have an *abcabc* . . . pattern. (444)

cubic meter (m^3) The SI-derived unit of volume. (18)

curie (Ci) The most common unit of radioactivity, defined as the number of nuclei disintegrating each second in 1 g of radium-226; 1 Ci = 3.70×10^{10} d/s (disintegrations per second). (988)

cyclic hydrocarbon A hydrocarbon with one or more rings in its structure. (578)

D

***d* orbital** An atomic orbital with $l = 2$. (286)

dalton (Da) A unit of mass identical to *atomic mass unit.* (50)

Dalton's law of partial pressures A gas law stating that, in a mixture of unreacting gases, the total pressure is the sum of the partial pressures of the individual gases: $P_{total} = P_1 + P_2 + \cdots$. (199)

data Pieces of quantitative information obtained by observation. (12)

de Broglie wavelength The wavelength of a moving particle obtained from the de Broglie equation: $\lambda = h/mu$. (276)

decay constant The rate constant *k* for radioactive decay. (988)

decay series (also *disintegration series*) The succession of steps a parent nucleus undergoes as it decays into a stable daughter nucleus. (986)

degree of polymerization (*n*) The number of monomer repeat units in a polymer chain. (461)

dehydration-condensation reaction A reaction in which an H_2O molecule is lost for every pair of OH groups that join. (550)

delocalization (See *electron-pair delocalization.*)

density (*d*) An intensive physical property of a substance at a given temperature and pressure, defined as the ratio of the mass to the volume: $d = m/V$. (22)

deposition The process of changing directly from gas to solid. (421)

derived unit Any of various combinations of the seven SI base units. (17)

desalination A process used to remove large amounts of ions from seawater, usually by reverse osmosis. (511)

deuterons Nuclei of the stable hydrogen isotope deuterium, ^2H. (993)

diagonal relationship Physical and chemical similarities between a Period 2 element and one located diagonally down and to the right in Period 3. (533)

diamagnetism The tendency of a species not to be attracted (or to be slightly repelled) by a magnetic field as a result of its electrons being paired. (319)

diastereomers (See *geometric isomers.*)

differentiation The geochemical process of forming regions in Earth based on differences in composition and density. (906)

diffraction The phenomenon in which a wave striking the edge of an object bends around it. A wave passing through a slit as wide as its wavelength forms a circular wave. (264)

diffusion The movement of one fluid through another. (210)

dimensional analysis (also *factor-label method*) A calculation method in which arithmetic steps are accompanied by canceling units that represent physical dimensions. (15)

dipole-dipole force The intermolecular attraction between oppositely charged poles of nearby polar molecules. (432)

dipole–induced dipole force The intermolecular attraction between a polar molecule and the oppositely charged pole it induces in a nearby molecule. (478)

dipole moment (μ) A measure of molecular polarity; the magnitude of the partial charges on the ends of a molecule (in coulombs) times the distance between them (in meters). (383)

disaccharide An organic compound formed by a dehydration-condensation reaction between two simple sugars (monosaccharides). (607)

disintegration series (See *decay series.*)

dispersion force (also *London force*) The intermolecular attraction between all particles as a result of instantaneous polarizations of their electron clouds; the intermolecular force primarily responsible for the condensed states of nonpolar substances. (435)

disproportionation A reaction in which a given substance is both oxidized and reduced. (547)

distillation A separation technique in which a more volatile component of a mixture vaporizes and condenses separately from the less volatile components. (72)

donor atom An atom that donates a lone pair of electrons to form a covalent bond, usually from ligand to metal ion in a complex. (954)

doping Adding small amounts of other elements into the crystal structure of a semiconductor to enhance a specific property, usually conductivity. (455)

double bond A covalent bond that consists of two bonding pairs; two atoms sharing four electrons in the form of one σ and one π bond. (339)
double helix The two intertwined polynucleotide strands held together by H bonds that form the structure of DNA (deoxyribonucleic acid). (487, 612)
Downs cell An industrial apparatus that electrolyzes molten NaCl to produce sodium and chlorine. (923)
dynamic equilibrium The condition at which the forward and reverse reactions are taking place at the same rate, so there is no net change in the amounts of reactants or products. (167)

E

e_g orbitals The set of orbitals (composed of $d_{x^2-y^2}$ and d_{z^2}) that results when the energies of the metal-ion *d* orbitals are split by a ligand field. This set is higher in energy than the other (t_{2g}) set in an octahedral field of ligands and lower in energy in a tetrahedral field. (964)
effective collision A collision in which the particles meet with sufficient energy and an orientation that allows them to react. (651)
effective nuclear charge (Z_{eff}) The nuclear charge an electron actually experiences as a result of shielding effects due to the presence of other electrons. (297)
effusion The process by which a gas escapes from its container through a tiny hole into an evacuated space. (209)
elastomer A polymeric material that can be stretched and springs back to its original shape when released. (465)
electrochemical cell A system that incorporates a redox reaction to produce or use electrical energy. (851)
electrochemistry The study of the relationship between chemical change and electrical work. (851)
electrode The part of an electrochemical cell that conducts the electricity between the cell and the surroundings. (855)
electrolysis The nonspontaneous lysing (splitting) of a substance, often to its component elements, by supplying electrical energy. (886)
electrolyte A substance that conducts a current when it dissolves in water. (137, 499) A mixture of ions, in which the electrodes of an electrochemical cell are immersed, that conducts a current. (855)
electrolytic cell An electrochemical system that uses electrical energy to drive a nonspontaneous chemical reaction ($\Delta G > 0$). (855)
electromagnetic radiation (also *electromagnetic energy* or *radiant energy*) Oscillating, perpendicular electric and magnetic fields moving simultaneously through space as waves and manifested as visible light, x-rays, microwaves, radio waves, and so on. (261)
electromagnetic spectrum The continuum of wavelengths of radiant energy. (262)
electromotive force (emf) (See *cell potential.*)
electron (e^-) A subatomic particle that possesses a unit negative charge (-1.60218×10^{-19} C) and occupies the space around the atomic nucleus. (48)
electron affinity (EA) The energy change (in kJ) accompanying the addition of one mole of electrons to one mole of gaseous atoms or ions. (314)
electron capture (EC) A type of radioactive decay in which a nucleus draws in an orbital electron, usually one from the lowest energy level, and releases energy. (981)
electron cloud depiction An imaginary representation of an electron's rapidly changing position around the nucleus over time. (280)
electron configuration The distribution of electrons within the orbitals of the atoms of an element; also the notation for such a distribution. (295)
electron deficient Referring to a bonded atom, such as Be or B, that has fewer than eight valence electrons. (369)
electron density diagram (also *electron probability density diagram*) The pictorial representation for a given energy sublevel of the quantity ψ^2 (the probability density of the electron lying within a particular tiny volume) as a function of *r* (distance from the nucleus). (280)
electron-pair delocalization (also *delocalization*) The process by which electron density is spread over several atoms rather than remaining between two. (367)
electron-sea model A qualitative description of metallic bonding proposing that metal atoms pool their valence electrons into a delocalized "sea" of electrons in which the metal cores (metal ions) are submerged in an orderly array. (354)
electron volt (eV) The energy (in joules, J) that an electron acquires when it moves through a potential difference of 1 volt; 1 eV = 1.602×10^{-19} J. (1004)
electronegativity (EN) The relative ability of a bonded atom to attract shared electrons. (349)
electronegativity difference (ΔEN) The difference in electronegativities between the atoms in a bond. (351)
electrorefining An industrial, electrolytic purification process in which a sample of impure metal acts as the anode and a sample of the pure metal acts as the cathode. (921)
element The simplest type of substance with unique physical and chemical properties. An element consists of only one kind of atom, so it cannot be broken down into simpler substances. (38)
element symbol (See *atomic symbol.*)
elementary reaction (also *elementary step*) A simple reaction that describes a single molecular event in a proposed reaction mechanism. (655)
elimination reaction A type of organic reaction in which C atoms are bonded to fewer atoms in the product than in the reactant, which leads to multiple bonding. (589)
emission spectrum The line spectrum produced when excited atoms return to lower energy levels and emit photons characteristic of the element. (273)
empirical formula A chemical formula that shows the lowest relative number of atoms of each element in a compound. (92)
enantiomers (See *optical isomers.*)
end point The point in a titration at which the indicator changes color. (152, 776)
endothermic process A process that occurs with an absorption of heat from the surroundings and therefore an increase in the enthalpy of the system ($\Delta H > 0$). (237)
energy The capacity to do work, that is, to move matter. (8) [See also *kinetic energy* (E_k) and *potential energy* (E_p).]
enthalpy (*H*) A thermodynamic quantity that is the sum of the internal energy plus the product of the pressure and volume. (235)
enthalpy diagram A graphic depiction of the enthalpy change of a system. (237)

enthalpy of formation (ΔH_f) (also *heat of formation*) The enthalpy change occurring when 1 mol of a compound forms from its elements. When all components are in their standard states, this is called the *standard enthalpy of formation* (ΔH_f°). (246)
enthalpy of fusion (See *heat of fusion.*)
enthalpy of hydration (See *heat of hydration.*)
enthalpy of reaction (ΔH_{rxn}) (also *heat of reaction*) The enthalpy change that occurs during a reaction. When all components are in their standard states, this is called the *standard enthalpy of reaction* (ΔH°_{rxn}). (246)
enthalpy of solution (See *heat of solution.*)
enthalpy of sublimation (See *heat of sublimation.*)
enthalpy of vaporization (See *heat of vaporization.*)
entropy (S) A thermodynamic quantity related to the number of ways the energy of a system can be dispersed through the motions of its particles. (490, 814)
environmental cycle The physical, chemical, and biological paths through which the atoms of an element move within Earth's crust. (911)
enzyme A biological macromolecule (usually a protein) that acts as a catalyst. (662)
enzyme-substrate complex (ES) The intermediate in an enzyme-catalyzed reaction, which consists of enzyme and substrate(s) and whose concentration determines the rate of product formation. (663)
equatorial group An atom (or group) that lies in the trigonal plane of a trigonal bipyramidal molecule, or a similar structural feature in a molecule. (377)
equilibrium constant (K) The value obtained when equilibrium concentrations are substituted into the reaction quotient. (679)
equilibrium vapor pressure (See *vapor pressure.*)
equivalence point The point in a titration when the number of moles of the added species is stoichiometrically equivalent to the original number of moles of the other species. (152, 775)
ester An organic compound that contains the 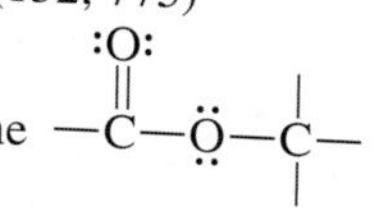 group. (599)
exact number A quantity, usually obtained by counting or based on a unit definition, that has no uncertainty associated with it and, therefore, contains as many significant figures as a calculation requires. (28)
exchange reaction (See *metathesis reaction.*)
excited state Any electron configuration of an atom or molecule other than the lowest energy (ground) state. (269)
exclusion principle A principle developed by Wolfgang Pauli stating that no two electrons in an atom can have the same set of four quantum numbers. The principle arises from the fact that an orbital has a maximum occupancy of two electrons and their spins are paired. (297)
exothermic process A process that occurs with a release of heat to the surroundings and therefore a decrease in the enthalpy of the system ($\Delta H < 0$). (236)
expanded valence shell A valence level that can accommodate more than eight electrons by using available *d* orbitals; occurs only with central nonmetal atoms from Period 3 or higher. (370)
experiment A set of procedural steps that tests a hypothesis. (12)
extensive property A property, such as mass, that depends on the quantity of substance present. (25)

F

face-centered cubic unit cell A unit cell in which a particle occurs at each corner and in the center of each face of a cube. (442)
Faraday constant (F) The physical constant representing the charge of 1 mol of electrons: $F = 96{,}485$ C/mol e^-. (870)
fatty acid A carboxylic acid that has a long hydrocarbon chain and is derived from a natural source. (599)
filtration A method of separating the components of a mixture on the basis of differences in particle size. (72)
first law of thermodynamics (See *law of conservation of energy.*)
fission The process by which a heavier nucleus splits into lighter nuclei with the release of energy. (1003)
fixation A chemical/biochemical process that converts a gaseous substance in the environment into a condensed form that can be used by organisms. (911)
flame test A procedure for identifying the presence of metal ions in which a granule of a compound or a drop of its solution is placed in a flame to observe a characteristic color. (273)
flotation A metallurgical process in which oil and detergent are mixed with pulverized ore in water to create a slurry that separates the mineral from the gangue. (917)
formal charge The hypothetical charge on an atom in a molecule or ion, equal to the number of valence electrons minus the sum of all the unshared and half the shared valence electrons. (368)
formation constant (K_f) An equilibrium constant for the formation of a complex ion from the hydrated metal ion and ligands. (794)
formation equation An equation in which 1 mole of a compound forms from its elements. (246)
formula mass The sum (in amu) of the atomic masses of a formula unit of a (usually ionic) compound. (66)
formula unit The chemical unit of a compound that contains the relative numbers of the types of atoms or ions expressed in the chemical formula. (60)
fossil fuel Any fuel, including coal, petroleum, and natural gas, derived from the products of the decay of dead organisms. (249)
fraction by mass (also *mass fraction*) The portion of a compound's mass contributed by an element; the mass of an element in a compound divided by the mass of the compound. (41)
fractional distillation A physical process involving numerous vaporization-condensation steps used to separate two or more volatile components. (505)
free energy (G) A thermodynamic quantity that is the difference between the enthalpy and the product of the absolute temperature and the entropy: $G = H - TS$. (827)
free energy change (ΔG) The change in free energy that occurs during a reaction. (827)
free radical A molecular or atomic species with one or more unpaired electrons, which typically make it very reactive. (370, 996)
freezing The process of cooling a liquid until it solidifies. (420)
freezing point depression (ΔT_f) The lowering of the freezing point of a solvent caused by the presence of dissolved solute particles. (502)
frequency (ν) The number of cycles a wave undergoes per second, expressed in units of 1/second, or s^{-1} [also called *hertz* (Hz)]; related inversely to wavelength. (261)

frequency factor (A) The product of the collision frequency Z and an orientation probability factor p that is specific for a reaction. (651)
fuel cell (also *flow battery*) A battery that is not self-contained and in which electricity is generated by the controlled oxidation of a fuel. (881)
functional group A specific combination of atoms, typically containing a carbon-carbon multiple bond and/or carbon-heteroatom bond, that reacts in a characteristic way no matter what molecule it occurs in. (573)
fundamental unit (See *base unit.*)
fusion (See *melting.*)
fusion (nuclear) The process by which light nuclei combine to form a heavier nucleus with the release of energy. (1003)

G

galvanic cell (See *voltaic cell.*)
gamma emission The type of radioactive decay in which gamma rays are emitted from an excited nucleus. (981)
gamma (γ) ray A very high-energy photon. (979)
gangue In an ore, the debris, such as sand, rock, and clay, attached to the mineral. (917)
gas One of the three states of matter. A gas fills its container regardless of the shape because its particles are far apart. (6)
Geiger-Müller counter An ionization counter that detects radioactive emissions through their ionization of gas atoms within the instrument. (987)
genetic code The set of three-base sequences that is translated into specific amino acids during the process of protein synthesis. (613)
geometric isomers (also *cis-trans isomers* or *diastereomers*) Stereoisomers in which the molecules have the same connections between atoms but differ in the spatial arrangements of the atoms. The *cis* isomer has similar groups on the same side of a double bond; the *trans* isomer has them on opposite sides. (582, 958)
Graham's law of effusion A gas law stating that the rate of effusion of a gas is inversely proportional to the square root of its density (or molar mass):

$$\text{rate} \propto \frac{1}{\sqrt{\mathcal{M}}} \qquad (209)$$

gray (Gy) The SI unit of absorbed radiation dose; 1 Gy = 1 J/kg tissue. (996)
green chemistry Field that is focused on developing methods to synthesize compounds efficiently and reduce or prevent the release of harmful products into the environment. (113)
ground state The electron configuration of an atom or ion that is lowest in energy. (269)
group A vertical column in the periodic table; elements in a group usually have the same outer electron configuration and, thus, similar chemical behavior. (53)

H

H bond (See *hydrogen bond.*)
Haber process An industrial process used to form ammonia from its elements. (706)
half-cell A portion of an electrochemical cell in which a half-reaction takes place. (857)
half-life ($t_{1/2}$) In chemical processes, the time required for half the initial reactant concentration to be consumed. (644) In nuclear processes, the time required for half the initial number of nuclei in a sample to decay. (988)
half-reaction method A method of balancing redox reactions by treating the oxidation and reduction half-reactions separately. (852)
haloalkane (also *alkyl halide*) A hydrocarbon with one or more halogen atoms (X) in place of H; contains a $-\overset{|}{\underset{|}{C}}-\ddot{\underset{\cdot\cdot}{X}}\!:$ group. (593)
hard water Water that contains large amounts of divalent cations, especially Ca^{2+} and Mg^{2+}. (510)
heat (q) (also *thermal energy*) The energy transferred between objects because of a difference in their temperatures only. (23, 230)
heat capacity The quantity of heat required to change the temperature of an object by 1 K. (238)
heat of formation (See *enthalpy of formation.*)
heat of fusion (ΔH_{fus}) (also *enthalpy of fusion*) The enthalpy change occurring when 1 mol of a solid substance melts; designated ΔH°_{fus} at the standard state. (421)
heat of hydration (ΔH_{hydr}) (also *enthalpy of hydration*) The enthalpy change occurring when 1 mol of a gaseous species (often an ion) is hydrated. The sum of the enthalpies from separating water molecules and mixing the gaseous species with them; designated ΔH°_{hydr} at the standard state. (489)
heat of reaction (ΔH_{rxn}) (See *enthalpy of reaction.*)
heat of solution (ΔH_{soln}) (also *enthalpy of solution*) The enthalpy change occurring when a solution forms from solute and solvent. The sum of the enthalpies from separating solute and solvent substances and mixing them; designated ΔH°_{soln} at the standard state. (488)
heat of sublimation (ΔH_{subl}) (also *enthalpy of sublimation*) The enthalpy change occurring when 1 mol of a solid substance changes directly to a gas. The sum of the heats of fusion and vaporization; designated ΔH°_{subl} at the standard state. (421)
heat of vaporization (ΔH_{vap}) (also *enthalpy of vaporization*) The enthalpy change occurring when 1 mol of a liquid substance vaporizes; designated ΔH°_{vap} at the standard state. (421)
heating-cooling curve A plot of temperature vs. time for a substance when heat is absorbed or released by the system at a constant rate. (422)
Henderson-Hasselbalch equation An equation for calculating the pH of a buffer system:

$$\text{pH} = \text{p}K_a + \log\left(\frac{[\text{base}]}{[\text{acid}]}\right) \qquad (770)$$

Henry's law A law stating that the solubility of a gas in a liquid is directly proportional to the partial pressure of the gas above the liquid: $S_{gas} = k_H \times P_{gas}$. (494)
Hess's law A law stating that the enthalpy change of an overall process is the sum of the enthalpy changes of the individual steps. (244)
heteroatom Any atom in an organic compound other than C or H. (573)
heterogeneous catalyst A catalyst that occurs in a different phase from the reactants, usually a solid interacting with gaseous or liquid reactants. (661)
heterogeneous mixture A mixture that has one or more visible boundaries among its components. (70)

hexagonal closest packing A crystal structure based on the hexagonal unit cell in which the layers have an *abab* . . . pattern. (444)
high-spin complex Complex ion that has the same number of unpaired electrons as in the isolated metal ion; contains weak-field ligands. (966)
homogeneous catalyst A catalyst (gas, liquid, or soluble solid) that exists in the same phase as the reactants. (660)
homogeneous mixture (also *solution*) A mixture that has no visible boundaries among its components. (70)
homologous series A series of organic compounds in which each member differs from the next by a $—CH_2—$ (methylene) group. (576)
homonuclear diatomic molecule A molecule composed of two identical atoms. (408)
Hund's rule A principle stating that when orbitals of equal energy are available, the electron configuration of lowest energy has the maximum number of unpaired electrons with parallel spins. (300)
hybrid orbital An atomic orbital postulated to form during bonding by the mathematical mixing of specific combinations of nonequivalent orbitals in a given atom. (396)
hybridization A postulated process of orbital mixing to form hybrid orbitals. (396)
hydrate A compound in which a specific number of water molecules are associated with each formula unit. (63)
hydration Solvation in water. (489)
hydration shell The oriented cluster of water molecules that surrounds an ion in aqueous solution. (478)
hydrocarbon An organic compound that contains only H and C atoms. (574)
hydrogen bond (H bond) A type of dipole-dipole force that arises between molecules that have an H atom bonded to a small, highly electronegative atom with lone pairs, usually N, O, or F. (432)
hydrogenation The addition of hydrogen to a carbon-carbon multiple bond to form a carbon-carbon single bond. (662)
hydrolysis Cleaving a molecule by reaction with water, in which one part of the molecule bonds to the water —OH and the other to the water H. (600)
hydronium ion (H_3O^+) A proton covalently bonded to a water molecule. (720)
hydrosphere The liquid portion of Earth's crust. (908)
hypothesis A testable proposal made to explain an observation. If inconsistent with experimental results, a hypothesis is revised or discarded. (12)

I

ideal gas A hypothetical gas that exhibits linear relationships among volume, pressure, temperature, and amount (mol) at all conditions; approximated by simple gases at ordinary conditions. (186)
ideal gas law (also *ideal gas equation*) An equation that expresses the relationships among volume, pressure, temperature, and amount (mol) of an ideal gas: $PV = nRT$. (191)
ideal solution A solution whose vapor pressure equals the mole fraction of the solvent times the vapor pressure of the pure solvent; approximated only by very dilute solutions. (500) (See also *Raoult's law*.)
indicator (See *acid-base indicator*.)
induced-fit model A model of enzyme action that pictures the binding of the substrate as inducing the active site to change its shape and become catalytically active. (663)
infrared (IR) The region of the electromagnetic spectrum between the microwave and visible regions. (262)
infrared (IR) spectroscopy An instrumental technique for determining the types of bonds in a covalent molecule by measuring the absorption of IR radiation. (343)
initial rate The instantaneous rate occurring as soon as the reactants are mixed, that is, at $t = 0$. (631)
inner electrons (also *core electrons*) Electrons that fill all the energy levels of an atom except the valence level; electrons also present in atoms of the previous noble gas and any completed transition series. (306)
inner transition elements The elements of the periodic table in which f orbitals are being filled; the lanthanides and actinides. (306, 952)
instantaneous rate The reaction rate at a particular time, given by the slope of a tangent to a plot of reactant concentration vs. time. (631)
insulator A substance (usually a nonmetal) that does not conduct an electric current. (453)
integrated rate law A mathematical expression for reactant concentration as a function of time. (642)
intensive property A property, such as density, that does not depend on the quantity of substance present. (25)
interhalogen compound A compound consisting entirely of halogens. (558)
intermolecular forces (also *interparticle forces*) The attractive and repulsive forces among the particles—molecules, atoms, or ions—in a sample of matter. (419)
internal energy (*E*) The sum of the kinetic and potential energies of all the particles in a system. (230)
ion A charged particle that forms from an atom (or covalently bonded group of atoms) when it gains or loses one or more electrons. (55)
ion-dipole force The intermolecular attractive force between an ion and a polar molecule (dipole). (432)
ion exchange A process of softening water by exchanging one type of ion (usually Ca^{2+}) for another (usually Na^+) by binding the ions on a specially designed resin. (511)
ion–induced dipole force The attractive force between an ion and the dipole it induces in the electron cloud of a nearby nonpolar molecule. (478)
ion pair A pair of ions that form a gaseous ionic molecule; sometimes formed when a salt boils. (337)
ion-product constant for water (K_w) The equilibrium constant for the autoionization of water; equal to 1.0×10^{-14} at 298 K.

$$K_w = [H_3O^+][OH^-] \qquad (724)$$

ionic atmosphere A cluster of ions of net opposite charge surrounding a given ion in solution. (506)
ionic bonding The idealized type of bonding based on the attraction of oppositely charged ions that arise through electron transfer between atoms with large differences in their tendencies to lose or gain electrons (typically metals and nonmetals). (330)
ionic compound A compound that consists of oppositely charged ions. (55)
ionic radius The size of an ion as measured by the distance between the nuclei of adjacent ions in a crystalline ionic compound. (320)

ionic solid A solid whose unit cell contains cations and anions. (449)

ionization In nuclear chemistry, the process by which a substance absorbs energy from high-energy radioactive particles and loses an electron to become ionized. (995)

ionization energy (IE) The energy (in kJ) required to remove completely one mole of electrons from one mole of gaseous atoms or ions. (311)

ionizing radiation The high-energy radiation from natural and artificial sources that forms ions in a substance by causing electron loss. (995)

isoelectronic Having the same number and configuration of electrons as another species. (317)

isomer One of two or more compounds with the same molecular formula but different properties, often as a result of different arrangements of atoms. (97, 579, 957)

isotopes Atoms of a given atomic number (that is, of a specific element) that have different numbers of neutrons and therefore different mass numbers. (49, 978)

isotopic mass The mass (in amu) of an isotope relative to the mass of carbon-12. (50)

J

joule (J) The SI unit of energy; $1\ \mathrm{J} = 1\ \mathrm{kg{\cdot}m^2/s^2}$. (233)

K

kelvin (K) The SI base unit of temperature. The kelvin is the same size as the Celsius degree. (23)

Kelvin scale (See *absolute scale.*)

ketone An organic compound (ending, *-one*) that contains a carbonyl group bonded to two other C atoms, 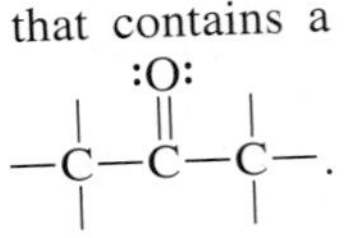. (597)

kilogram (kg) The SI base unit of mass. (20)

kinetic energy (E_k) The energy an object has because of its motion. (8)

kinetic-molecular theory The model that explains gas behavior in terms of particles in random motion whose volumes and interactions are negligible. (204)

L

lanthanide contraction The additional decrease in atomic and ionic size, beyond the expected trend, caused by the poor shielding of the increasing nuclear charge by *f* electrons in the elements following the lanthanides. (949)

lanthanides (also *rare earths*) The Period 6 (4*f*) series of inner transition elements, which includes cerium (Ce; Z = 58) through lutetium (Lu; Z = 71). (306, 952)

lattice The three-dimensional arrangement of points created by choosing each point to be at the same location within each particle of a crystal; thus, the lattice consists of all points with identical surroundings. (442)

lattice energy ($\Delta H^\circ_{\mathrm{lattice}}$) The enthalpy change (always positive) that accompanies the separation of 1 mol of a solid ionic compound into gaseous ions. (333)

law (See *natural law.*)

law of chemical equilibrium (also *law of mass action*) The law stating that when a system reaches equilibrium at a given temperature, the ratio of quantities that make up the reaction quotient has a constant numerical value. (680)

law of conservation of energy (also *first law of thermodynamics*) A basic observation that the total energy of the universe is constant; thus, $\Delta E_{\mathrm{universe}} = \Delta E_{\mathrm{system}} + \Delta E_{\mathrm{surroundings}} = 0$. (233)

law of definite (or constant) composition A mass law stating that, no matter what its source, a particular compound is composed of the same elements in the same parts (fractions) by mass. (41)

law of mass action (See *law of chemical equilibrium.*)

law of mass conservation A mass law stating that the total mass of substances does not change during a chemical reaction. (40)

law of multiple proportions A mass law stating that if elements A and B react to form two or more compounds, the different masses of B that combine with a fixed mass of A can be expressed as a ratio of small whole numbers. (42)

Le Châtelier's principle A principle stating that if a system in a state of equilibrium is disturbed, it will undergo a change that shifts its equilibrium position in a direction that reduces the effect of the disturbance. (698)

leaching A hydrometallurgical process that extracts a metal selectively, usually through formation of a complex ion. (918)

level (also *shell*) A specific energy state of an atom given by the principal quantum number *n*. (282)

leveling effect The inability of a solvent to distinguish the strength of an acid (or base) that is stronger than the conjugate acid (or conjugate base) of the solvent. (750)

Lewis acid-base definition A model of acid-base behavior in which acids and bases are defined, respectively, as species that accept and donate an electron pair. (751)

Lewis electron-dot symbol A notation in which the element symbol represents the nucleus and inner electrons, and surrounding dots represent the valence electrons. (331)

Lewis structure (also *Lewis formula*) A structural formula consisting of electron-dot symbols, with lines as bonding pairs and dots as lone pairs. (363)

ligand A molecule or anion bonded to a central metal ion in a complex ion. (792, 953)

like-dissolves-like rule An empirical observation stating that substances having similar kinds of intermolecular forces dissolve in each other. (478)

limiting reactant (also *limiting reagent*) The reactant that is consumed when a reaction occurs and, therefore, the one that determines the maximum amount of product that can form. (107)

line spectrum A series of separated lines of different colors representing photons whose wavelengths are characteristic of an element. (267) (See also *emission spectrum.*)

linear arrangement The geometric arrangement obtained when two electron groups maximize their separation around a central atom. (374)

linear shape A molecular shape formed by three atoms lying in a straight line, with a bond angle of 180° (shape class AX_2 or AX_2E_3). (374)

linkage isomers Coordination compounds with the same composition but with different ligand donor atoms linked to the central metal ion. (957)

lipid Any of a class of biomolecules, including fats, that are soluble in nonpolar solvents and not soluble in water. (600)

lipid bilayer An extended sheetlike double layer of phospholipid molecules that forms in water and has the charged heads of the molecules on the surfaces of the bilayer and the nonpolar tails within the interior. (485)

liquid One of the three states of matter. A liquid fills a container to the extent of its own volume and thus forms a surface. (5)
liquid crystal A substance that flows like a liquid but packs like a crystalline solid at the molecular level. (456)
liter (L) A non-SI unit of volume equivalent to 1 cubic decimeter (0.001 m^3). (18)
lithosphere The solid portion of Earth's crust. (908)
lock-and-key model A model of enzyme function that pictures the enzyme active site and the substrate as rigid shapes that fit together as a lock and key, respectively. (663)
London force (See *dispersion force.*)
lone pair (also *unshared pair*) An electron pair that is part of an atom's valence level but not involved in covalent bonding. (339)
low-spin complex Complex ion that has fewer unpaired electrons than in the free metal ion because of the presence of strong-field ligands. (966)

M

macromolecule (See *polymer.*)
magnetic quantum number (m_l) An integer from $-l$ through 0 to $+l$ that specifies the orientation of an atomic orbital in the three-dimensional space about the nucleus. (281)
manometer A device used to measure the pressure of a gas in a laboratory experiment. (184)
mantle A thick homogeneous layer of Earth's internal structure that lies between the core and the crust. (906)
mass The quantity of matter an object contains. Balances are designed to measure mass. (20)
mass-action expression (See *reaction quotient.*)
mass fraction (See *fraction by mass.*)
mass number (A) The total number of protons and neutrons in the nucleus of an atom. (49)
mass percent (also *mass %* or *percent by mass*) The fraction by mass expressed as a percentage. (41) A concentration term [% (w/w)] expressed as the mass of solute dissolved in 100. parts by mass of solution. (496)
mass spectrometry An instrumental method for measuring the relative masses of particles in a sample by creating charged particles and separating them according to their mass-charge ratio. (50)
matter Anything that possesses mass and occupies volume. (4)
mean free path The average distance a molecule travels between collisions at a given temperature and pressure. (211)
melting (also *fusion*) The change of a substance from a solid to a liquid. (420)
melting point (mp or T_f) The temperature at which the solid and liquid forms of a substance are at equilibrium. (429)
metabolic pathway A biochemical reaction sequence that flows in one direction and has each reaction enzyme catalyzed. (708)
metal A substance or mixture that is relatively shiny and malleable and is a good conductor of heat and electricity. In reactions, metals tend to transfer electrons to nonmetals and form ionic compounds. (54)
metallic bonding An idealized type of bonding based on the attraction between metal ions and their delocalized valence electrons. (331) (See also *electron-sea model.*)
metallic radius One-half the shortest distance between the nuclei of adjacent individual atoms in a crystal of an element. (308)
metallic solid A solid whose individual atoms are held together by metallic bonding. (451)
metalloid (also *semimetal*) An element with properties between those of metals and nonmetals. (54)
metallurgy The branch of materials science concerned with the extraction and utilization of metals. (917)
metathesis reaction (also *double-displacement reaction*) A reaction in which atoms or ions of two compounds exchange bonding partners. (143)
meter (m) The SI base unit of length. The distance light travels in a vacuum in 1/299,792,458 second. (18)
methanogenesis The process of producing methane by anaerobic biodegradation of plant and animal waste. (249)
milliliter (mL) A volume (0.001 L) equivalent to 1 cm^3. (18)
millimeter of mercury (mmHg) A unit of pressure based on the difference in the heights of mercury in a barometer or manometer. Renamed the *torr* in honor of Torricelli. (185)
mineral The portion of an ore that contains the element of interest, a mineral is a naturally occurring, homogeneous, crystalline inorganic solid, with a well-defined composition. (917)
miscible Soluble in any proportion. (478)
mixture A group of two or more elements and/or compounds that are physically intermingled. (39)
MO bond order One-half the difference between the number of electrons in bonding and antibonding MOs. (407)
model (also *theory*) A simplified conceptual picture based on experiment that explains how a natural phenomenon occurs. (12)
molality (m) A concentration term expressed as number of moles of solute dissolved in 1000 g (1 kg) of solvent. (495)
molar heat capacity (C) The quantity of heat required to change the temperature of 1 mol of a substance by 1 K. (238)
molar mass ($\mathcal{M}$) The mass of 1 mol of entities (atoms, molecules, or formula units) of a substance, in units of g/mol. (84)
molarity (M) A concentration term expressed as the moles of solute dissolved in 1 L of solution. (114)
mole (mol) The SI base unit for amount of a substance. The amount that contains a number of objects equal to the number of atoms in exactly 12 g of carbon-12 (which is 6.022×10^{23}). (83)
mole fraction (X) A concentration term expressed as the ratio of moles of one component of a mixture to the total moles present. (200, 496)
molecular equation A chemical equation showing a reaction in solution in which reactants and products appear as intact, undissociated compounds. (140)
molecular formula A formula that shows the actual number of atoms of each element in a molecule of a compound. (68, 92)
molecular mass (also *molecular weight*) The sum (in amu) of the atomic masses of the elements in a molecule (or formula unit) of a compound. (66)
molecular orbital (MO) An orbital of given energy and shape that extends over a molecule and can be occupied by no more than two paired electrons. (405)
molecular orbital (MO) diagram A depiction of the relative energy and number of electrons in each MO, as well as the atomic orbitals from which the MOs form. (406)
molecular orbital (MO) theory A model that describes a molecule as a collection of nuclei and electrons in which the electrons occupy orbitals that extend over the entire molecule. (405)
molecular polarity The overall distribution of electronic charge in a molecule, determined by its shape and bond polarities. (383)

molecular shape The three-dimensional structure defined by the relative positions of the atomic nuclei in a molecule. (373)
molecular solid A solid held together by intermolecular forces between individual molecules. (449)
molecular weight (See *molecular mass.*)
molecularity The number of reactant particles involved in an elementary step. (655)
molecule A structure consisting of two or more atoms that are bound chemically and behave as an independent unit. (38)
monatomic ion An ion derived from a single atom. (55)
monomer A small molecule, linked covalently to others of the same or similar type to form a polymer; the repeat unit of the polymer. (461)
mononucleotide A monomer unit of a nucleic acid, consisting of an N-containing base, a sugar, and a phosphate group. (487, 611)
monosaccharide A simple sugar; a polyhydroxy ketone or aldehyde with three to nine C atoms. (607)

N

nanotechnology The science and engineering of nanoscale (1–100 nm) systems. (466)
natural law (also *law*) A summary, often in mathematical form, of a universal observation. (12)
Nernst equation An equation stating that the voltage of an electrochemical cell under any conditions depends on the standard cell voltage and the concentrations of the cell components:

$$E_{cell} = E^{\circ}_{cell} - \frac{RT}{nF} \ln Q \qquad (872)$$

net ionic equation A chemical equation of a reaction in solution in which spectator ions have been eliminated to show the actual chemical change. (141)
network covalent solid A solid in which all the atoms are bonded covalently so that individual molecules are not present. (451)
neutralization Process that occurs when an H^+ ion from an acid combines with an OH^- ion from a base to form H_2O. (720)
neutralization reaction An acid-base reaction that yields water and a solution of a salt; when the H^+ ions of a strong acid react with an equivalent amount of the OH^- ions of a strong base, the solution is neutral. (145)
neutron (n^0) An uncharged subatomic particle found in the nucleus, with a mass slightly greater than that of a proton. (48)
nitrile An organic compound containing the —C≡N: group. (603)
node A region of an orbital where the probability of finding the electron is zero. (285)
nonbonding MO A molecular orbital that is not involved in bonding. (412)
nonelectrolyte A substance whose aqueous solution does not conduct an electric current. (139, 499)
nonmetal An element that lacks metallic properties. In reactions, nonmetals tend to share electrons with each other to form covalent compounds or accept electrons from metals to form ionic compounds. (54)
nonpolar covalent bond A covalent bond between identical atoms such that the bonding pair is shared equally. (351)
nuclear binding energy The energy required to break 1 mole of nuclei of an element into individual nucleons. (1004)
nuclear magnetic resonance (NMR) spectroscopy An instrumental technique used to determine the molecular environment of a given type of nucleus, most often ^1H, from its absorption of radio waves in a magnetic field. (586)
nuclear transmutation The induced conversion of one nucleus into another by bombardment with a particle. (992)
nucleic acid An unbranched polymer consisting of mononucleotides that occurs as two types, DNA and RNA (deoxyribonucleic and ribonucleic acids), which differ chemically in the nature of the sugar portion of the mononucleotides. (487, 611)
nucleon A subatomic particle found in the nucleus; a proton or neutron. (978)
nucleus The tiny central region of the atom that contains all the positive charge and essentially all the mass. (47)
nuclide A nuclear species with specified numbers of protons and neutrons. (978)

O

observation A fact obtained with the senses, often with the aid of instruments. Quantitative observations provide data that can be compared. (12)
occurrence (also *source*) The form(s) in which an element exists in nature. (909)
octahedral arrangement The geometric arrangement obtained when six electron groups maximize their space around a central atom; when all six groups are bonding groups, the molecular shape is octahedral (AX_6; ideal bond angle = 90°). (378)
octet rule The observation that when atoms bond, they often lose, gain, or share electrons to attain a filled outer level of eight electrons (or two for H and Li). (331)
optical isomers (also *enantiomers*) A pair of stereoisomers consisting of a molecule and its mirror image that cannot be superimposed on each other. (580, 959)
optically active Able to rotate the plane of polarized light. (581)
orbital diagram A depiction of orbital occupancy in terms of electron number and spin shown by means of arrows in a series of small boxes, lines, or circles. (299)
ore A naturally occurring compound or mixture of compounds from which an element can be profitably extracted. (909)
organic compound A compound in which carbon is nearly always bonded to itself and to hydrogen, and often to other elements. (571)
organometallic compound An organic compound in which carbon has a polar covalent bond to a metal atom. (598)
osmosis The process by which solvent flows through a semipermeable membrane from a dilute to a concentrated solution. (503)
osmotic pressure (Π) The pressure that results from the ability of solvent, but not solute, particles to cross a semipermeable membrane. The pressure required to prevent the net movement of solvent across the membrane. (503)
outer electrons Electrons that occupy the highest energy level (highest *n* value) and are, on average, farthest from the nucleus. (306)
overall (net) equation A chemical equation that is the sum of two or more balanced sequential equations in which a product of one becomes a reactant for the next. (106)
overvoltage The additional voltage, usually associated with gaseous products forming at an electrode, that is required above the standard cell voltage to accomplish electrolysis. (888)
oxidation The loss of electrons by a species, accompanied by an increase in oxidation number. (154)

oxidation number (O.N.) (also *oxidation state*) A number equal to the magnitude of the charge an atom would have if its shared electrons were held completely by the atom that attracts them more strongly. (155)

oxidation number method A method for balancing redox reactions in which the change in oxidation numbers is used to determine balancing coefficients. (158)

oxidation-reduction reaction (also *redox reaction*) A process in which there is a net movement of electrons from one reactant (reducing agent) to another (oxidizing agent). (153)

oxidation state (See *oxidation number.*)

oxidizing agent The substance that accepts electrons in a reaction and undergoes a decrease in oxidation number. (154)

oxoanion An anion in which an element is bonded to one or more oxygen atoms. (63)

P

***p* orbital** An atomic orbital with $l = 1$. (285)

packing efficiency The percentage of the available volume occupied by atoms, ions, or molecules in a unit cell. (444)

paramagnetism The tendency of a species with unpaired electrons to be attracted by an external magnetic field. (319)

partial ionic character An estimate of the actual charge separation in a bond (caused by the electronegativity difference of the bonded atoms) relative to complete separation. (351)

partial pressure The portion of the total pressure contributed by a gas in a mixture of gases. (199)

particle accelerator A device used to impart high kinetic energies to nuclear particles. (993)

pascal (Pa) The SI unit of pressure; $1\ \text{Pa} = 1\ \text{N/m}^2$. (185)

penetration The process by which an outer electron moves through the region occupied by the core electrons to spend part of its time closer to the nucleus; penetration increases the average effective nuclear charge for that electron. (298)

percent by mass (mass %) (See *mass percent.*)

percent yield (% yield) The actual yield of a reaction expressed as a percentage of the theoretical yield. (112)

period A horizontal row of the periodic table. (53)

periodic law A law stating that when the elements are arranged by atomic number, they exhibit a periodic recurrence of properties. (295)

periodic table of the elements A table in which the elements are arranged by atomic number into columns (groups) and rows (periods). (53)

pH The negative common logarithm of $[H_3O^+]$. (726)

phase A physically distinct and homogeneous part of a system. (419)

phase change A physical change from one phase to another, usually referring to a change in physical state. (420)

phase diagram A diagram used to describe the stable phases and phase changes of a substance as a function of temperature and pressure. (429)

photoelectric effect The observation that when monochromatic light of sufficient frequency shines on a metal, an electric current is produced. (266)

photon A quantum of electromagnetic radiation. (266)

photovoltaic cell A device capable of converting light directly into electricity. (251)

physical change A change in which the physical form (or state) of a substance, but not its composition, is altered. (4)

physical property A characteristic shown by a substance itself, without interacting with or changing into other substances. (4)

pi (π) bond A covalent bond formed by sideways overlap of two atomic orbitals that has two regions of electron density, one above and one below the internuclear axis. (403)

pi (π) MO A molecular orbital formed by combination of two atomic (usually *p*) orbitals whose orientations are perpendicular to the internuclear axis. (408)

Planck's constant (*h*) A proportionality constant relating the energy and frequency of a photon, equal to $6.626\times10^{-34}\ \text{J·s}$. (266)

plastic A material that, when deformed, retains its new shape. (465)

polar covalent bond A covalent bond in which the electron pair is shared unequally, so the bond has partially negative and partially positive poles. (351)

polar molecule A molecule with an unequal distribution of charge as a result of its polar bonds and shape. (136)

polarimeter A device used to measure the rotation of plane-polarized light by an optically active compound. (581)

polarizability The ease with which a particle's electron cloud can be distorted. (434)

polyatomic ion An ion in which two or more atoms are bonded covalently. (59)

polymer (also *macromolecule*) An extremely large molecule that results from the covalent linking of many simpler molecular units (monomers). (461)

polyprotic acid An acid with more than one ionizable proton. (737)

polysaccharide A macromolecule composed of many simple sugars linked covalently. (607)

positron (β^+) The antiparticle of an electron. (981)

positron emission A type of radioactive decay in which a positron is emitted from a nucleus. (981)

potential energy (E_p) The energy an object has as a result of its position relative to other objects or because of its composition. (8)

precipitate The insoluble product of a precipitation reaction. (141)

precipitation reaction A reaction in which two soluble ionic compounds form an insoluble product, a precipitate. (141)

precision (also *reproducibility*) The closeness of a measurement to other measurements of the same phenomenon in a series of experiments. (28)

pressure (*P*) The force exerted per unit of surface area. (183)

pressure-volume work (*PV* work) A type of work in which a volume change occurs against an external pressure. (235)

principal quantum number (*n*) A positive integer that specifies the energy and relative size of an atomic orbital; a number that specifies an energy level in an atom. (281)

probability contour A shape that defines the volume around an atomic nucleus within which an electron spends a given percentage of its time. (281)

product A substance formed in a chemical reaction. (99)

property A characteristic that gives a substance its unique identity. (4)

protein A natural, linear polymer composed of any of about 20 types of amino acid monomers linked together by peptide bonds. (483, 608)

proton (p^+) A subatomic particle found in the nucleus that has a unit positive charge (1.60218×10^{-19} C). (48)
proton acceptor A substance that accepts an H^+ ion; a Brønsted-Lowry base. (729)
proton donor A substance that donates an H^+ ion; a Brønsted-Lowry acid. (729)
pseudo–noble gas configuration The $(n-1)d^{10}$ configuration of a *p*-block metal ion that has an empty outer energy level. (317)

Q

quantum A packet of energy equal to $h\nu$. The smallest quantity of energy that can be emitted or absorbed. (266)
quantum mechanics The branch of physics that examines the wave motion of objects on the atomic scale. (279)
quantum number A number that specifies a property of an orbital or an electron. (266)

R

rad (*r*adiation-*a*bsorbed *d*ose) The quantity of radiation that results in 0.01 J of energy being absorbed per kilogram of tissue; 1 rad = 0.01 J/kg tissue = 10^{-2} Gy. (996)
radial probability distribution plot The graphic depiction of the total probability distribution (sum of ψ^2) of an electron in the region near the nucleus. (280)
radioactivity The emissions resulting from the spontaneous disintegration of an unstable nucleus. (977)
radioisotope An isotope with an unstable nucleus that decays through radioactive emissions. (990)
radioisotopic dating A method for determining the age of an object based on the rate of decay of a particular radioactive nuclide relative to a stable nuclide. (990)
radius of gyration (R_g) A measure of the size of a coiled polymer chain, expressed as the average distance from the center of mass of the chain to its outside edge. (463)
random coil The shape adopted by most polymer chains and caused by random rotation about the bonds joining the repeat units. (462)
random error Error that occurs in all measurements (with its size depending on the measurer's skill and the instrument's precision) and results in values *both* higher and lower than the actual value. (29)
Raoult's law A law stating that the vapor pressure of solvent above a solution equals the mole fraction of solvent times the vapor pressure of pure solvent: $P_{solvent} = X_{solvent} \times P^\circ_{solvent}$. (500)
rare earths (See *lanthanides.*)
rate constant (*k*) The proportionality constant that relates reaction rate to reactant (and product) concentrations. (634)
rate-determining step (also *rate-limiting step*) The slowest step in a reaction mechanism and therefore the step that limits the overall rate. (656)
rate law (also *rate equation*) An equation that expresses the rate of a reaction as a function of reactant (and product) concentrations. (634)
reactant A starting substance in a chemical reaction. (99)
reaction energy diagram A graph that shows the potential energy of a reacting system as it progresses from reactants to products. (652)
reaction intermediate A substance that is formed and used up during the overall reaction and therefore does not appear in the overall equation. (657)
reaction mechanism A series of elementary steps that sum to the overall reaction and is consistent with the rate law. (655)
reaction order The exponent of a reactant concentration in a rate law that shows how the rate is affected by changes in that concentration. (634)
reaction quotient (*Q*) (also *mass-action expression*) A ratio of terms for a given reaction consisting of product concentrations multiplied together and divided by reactant concentrations multiplied together, each raised to the power of their balancing coefficient. The value of *Q* changes until the system reaches equilibrium, at which point it equals *K*. (680)
reaction rate The change in the concentrations of reactants (or products) with time. (627)
reactor core The part of a nuclear reactor that contains the fuel rods and generates heat from fission. (1008)
redox reaction (See *oxidation-reduction reaction.*)
reducing agent The substance that donates electrons in a redox reaction and undergoes an increase in oxidation number. (154)
reduction The gain of electrons by a species, accompanied by a decrease in oxidation number. (154)
refraction A phenomenon in which a wave changes its speed and therefore its direction as it passes through a phase boundary into a different medium. (263)
rem (*r*oentgen *e*quivalent for *m*an) The unit of radiation dosage for a human based on the product of the number of rads and a factor related to the biological tissue; 1 rem = 10^{-2} Sv. (996)
reproducibility (See *precision.*)
resonance hybrid The weighted average of the resonance structures of a molecule. (367)
resonance structure (also *resonance form*) One of two or more Lewis structures for a molecule that cannot be adequately depicted by a single structure. Resonance structures differ only in the position of bonding and lone electron pairs. (367)
reverse osmosis A process for preparing drinkable water that uses an applied pressure greater than the osmotic pressure to remove ions from an aqueous solution, typically seawater. (511)
rms (root-mean-square) speed (u_{rms}) The speed of a molecule having the average kinetic energy; very close to the most probable speed. (209)
roasting A pyrometallurgical process in which metal sulfides are converted to oxides. (918)
round off The process of removing digits based on a series of rules to obtain an answer with the proper number of significant figures (or decimal places). (27)

S

***s* orbital** An atomic orbital with $l = 0$. (284)
salt An ionic compound that results from an Arrhenius acid-base reaction after solvent is removed. (148)
salt bridge An inverted U tube containing a solution of a nonreacting electrolyte that connects the compartments of a voltaic cell and maintains neutrality by allowing ions to flow between compartments. (859)
saturated hydrocarbon A hydrocarbon in which each C is bonded to four other atoms. (576)
saturated solution A solution that contains the maximum amount of dissolved solute at a given temperature (prepared with undissolved solute present). (492)

scanning tunneling microscopy An instrumental technique that uses electrons moving across a minute gap to observe the topography of a surface on the atomic scale. (447)

Schrödinger equation An equation that describes how the electron matter-wave changes in space around the nucleus. Solutions of the equation provide allowable energy levels of the atom. (279)

scientific method A process of creative thinking and testing aimed at objective, verifiable discoveries of the causes of natural events. (12)

scintillation counter A device used to measure radioactivity through its excitation of atoms and their subsequent emission of light. (987)

screening (See *shielding.*)

second (s) The SI base unit of time. (25)

second law of thermodynamics A law stating that a process occurs spontaneously in the direction that increases the entropy of the universe. (817)

seesaw shape A molecular shape caused by the presence of one equatorial lone pair in a trigonal bipyramidal arrangement (AX_4E). (377)

selective precipitation The process of separating ions through differences in the solubility of their compounds with a given precipitating ion. (791)

self-ionization (See *autoionization.*)

semiconductor A substance whose electrical conductivity is poor at room temperature but increases significantly with rising temperature. (453)

semimetal (See *metalloid.*)

semipermeable membrane A membrane that allows solvent, but not solute, to pass through. (503)

shared pair (See *bonding pair.*)

shell (See *level.*)

shielding (also *screening*) The ability of other electrons, especially those occupying inner orbitals, to lessen the nuclear attraction for an outer electron. (297)

SI unit A unit composed of one or more of the base units of the Système International d'Unités, a revised metric system. (17)

side reaction An undesired chemical reaction that consumes some of the reactant and reduces the overall yield of the desired product. (112)

sievert (Sv) The SI unit of human radiation dosage; 1 Sv = 100 rem. (996)

sigma (σ) bond A type of covalent bond that arises through end-to-end orbital overlap and has most of its electron density along an imaginary line joining the nuclei. (403)

sigma (σ) MO A molecular orbital that is cylindrically symmetrical about an imaginary line that runs through the nuclei of the component atoms. (406)

significant figures The digits obtained in a measurement. The greater the number of significant figures, the greater the certainty of the measurement. (25)

silicate A type of compound found throughout rocks and soil and consisting of repeating —Si—O groupings and, in most cases, metal cations. (542)

silicone A type of synthetic polymer containing —Si—O repeat units, with organic groups and crosslinks. (542)

simple cubic unit cell A unit cell in which a particle occupies each corner of a cube. (442)

single bond A bond that consists of one electron pair. (339)

slag A molten waste product formed in a blast furnace by the reaction of acidic silica with a basic metal oxide. (925)

smelting Heating a mineral with a reducing agent, such as coke, to obtain a metal. (919)

soap The salt formed in a reaction between a fatty acid and a strong base, usually a Group 1A(1) or 2A(2) hydroxide. (485)

solid One of the three states of matter. A solid has a fixed shape that does not conform to the container shape. (5)

solubility (*S*) The maximum amount of solute that dissolves in a fixed quantity of a particular solvent at a specified temperature. (478)

solubility-product constant (K_{sp}) An equilibrium constant for a slightly soluble ionic compound dissolving in water. (783)

solute The substance that dissolves in the solvent. (114, 478)

solution (See *homogeneous mixture.*)

solvated Surrounded closely by solvent molecules. (136)

solvation The process of surrounding a solute particle with solvent particles. (489)

solvent The substance in which the solute(s) dissolve. (114, 478)

source (See *occurrence.*)

***sp* hybrid orbital** An orbital formed by the mixing of one *s* and one *p* orbital of a central atom. (396)

sp^2 hybrid orbital An orbital formed by the mixing of one *s* and two *p* orbitals of a central atom. (398)

sp^3 hybrid orbital An orbital formed by the mixing of one *s* and three *p* orbitals of a central atom. (398)

sp^3d hybrid orbital An orbital formed by the mixing of one *s*, three *p*, and one *d* orbital of a central atom. (399)

sp^3d^2 hybrid orbital An orbital formed by the mixing of one *s*, three *p*, and two *d* orbitals of a central atom. (400)

specific heat capacity (*c*) The quantity of heat required to change the temperature of 1 gram of a material by 1 K. (238)

spectator ion An ion that is present as part of a reactant but is not involved in the chemical change. (141)

spectrochemical series A ranking of ligands in terms of their ability to split *d*-orbital energies. (965)

spectrometry Any instrumental technique that uses a portion of the electromagnetic spectrum to measure the atomic and molecular energy levels of a substance. (273)

speed of light (*c*) A fundamental constant giving the speed at which electromagnetic radiation travels in a vacuum: $c = 2.99792458 \times 10^8$ m/s. (262)

spin quantum number (m_s) A number, either $+\frac{1}{2}$ or $-\frac{1}{2}$, that indicates the direction of electron spin. (296)

spontaneous change A change that occurs by itself, that is, without an ongoing input of external energy. (811)

square planar shape A molecular shape (AX_4E_2) caused by the presence of two lone pairs at opposite vertices in an octahedral arrangement. (378)

square pyramidal shape A molecular shape (AX_5E) caused by the presence of one lone pair in an octahedral arrangement. (378)

standard atmosphere (atm) The average atmospheric pressure measured at sea level and 0°C, defined as 1.01325×10^5 Pa. (185)

standard cell potential (E°_{cell}) The potential of a cell measured with all components in their standard states and no current flowing. (862)

standard electrode potential ($E^\circ_{\text{half-cell}}$) (also *standard half-cell potential*) The standard potential of a half-cell, with the half-reaction written as a reduction. (862)
standard enthalpy of formation (ΔH°_f) (also *standard heat of formation*) The enthalpy change occurring when 1 mol of a compound forms from its elements with all components in their standard states. (246)
standard enthalpy of reaction ($\Delta H^\circ_{\text{rxn}}$) (also *standard heat of reaction*) The enthalpy change that occurs during a reaction when all components are in their standard states. (246)
standard entropy of reaction ($\Delta S^\circ_{\text{rxn}}$) The entropy change that occurs when all components are in their standard states. (822)
standard free energy change (ΔG°) The free energy change that occurs when all components are in their standard states. (828)
standard free energy of formation (ΔG°_f) The standard free energy change that occurs when 1 mol of a compound is made from its elements with all components in their standard states. (829)
standard half-cell potential (See *standard electrode potential.*)
standard heat of formation (See *standard enthalpy of formation.*)
standard heat of reaction (See *standard enthalpy of reaction.*)
standard hydrogen electrode (See *standard reference half-cell.*)
standard molar entropy (S°) The entropy of 1 mol of a substance in its standard state. (817)
standard molar volume The volume of 1 mol of an ideal gas at standard temperature and pressure: 22.4141 L. (190)
standard reference half-cell (also *standard hydrogen electrode*) A specially prepared platinum electrode immersed in 1 *M* $H^+(aq)$ through which H_2 gas at 1 atm is bubbled. $E^\circ_{\text{half-cell}}$ is defined as 0 V. (863)
standard state A set of specifications used to compare thermodynamic data: 1 atm for gases behaving ideally, 1 *M* for dissolved species, or the pure substance for liquids and solids. (246)
standard temperature and pressure (STP) The reference conditions for a gas:

$$0^\circ C\ (273.15\ K)\ \text{and}\ 1\ \text{atm}\ (760\ \text{torr}) \qquad (190)$$

state function A property of the system determined by its current state, regardless of how it arrived at that state. (234)
state of matter One of the three physical forms of matter: solid, liquid, or gas. (5)
stationary state In the Bohr model, one of the allowable energy levels of the atom in which it does not release or absorb energy. (269)
steel An alloy of iron with small amounts of carbon and usually other metals. (924)
stellar nucleosynthesis The process by which elements are formed in the stars through nuclear fusion. (1012)
stereoisomers Molecules with the same connections of atoms but different orientations of groups in space. (580, 958) (See also *geometric isomers* and *optical isomers.*)
stoichiometric coefficient (See *balancing coefficient.*)
stoichiometry The study of the mass-mole-number relationships of chemical formulas and reactions. (83)
strong-field ligand A ligand that causes larger crystal field splitting energy and therefore is part of a low-spin complex. (964)
strong force An attractive force that exists between all nucleons and is many times stronger than the electrostatic repulsive force. (984)
structural formula A formula that shows the actual number of atoms, their relative placement, and the bonds between them. (68, 92)
structural isomers (See *constitutional isomers.*)
sublevel (also *subshell*) An energy substate of an atom within a level. Given by the *n* and *l* values, the sublevel designates the size and shape of the atomic orbitals. (282)
sublimation The process by which a solid changes directly into a gas. (421)
substance A type of matter, either an element or a compound, that has a fixed composition. (38)
substitution reaction An organic reaction that occurs when an atom (or group) from one reactant substitutes for one in another reactant. (589)
substrate A reactant that binds to the active site in an enzyme-catalyzed reaction. (662)
superconductivity The ability to conduct a current with no loss of energy to resistive heating. (454)
supersaturated solution An unstable solution in which more solute is dissolved than in a saturated solution. (492)
surface tension The energy required to increase the surface area of a liquid by a given amount. (437)
surroundings All parts of the universe other than the system being considered. (230)
suspension A heterogeneous mixture containing particles that are distinct from the surrounding medium. (508)
synthetic natural gas (SNG) A gaseous fuel mixture, mostly methane, formed from coal. (249)
system The defined part of the universe under study. (230)
systematic error A type of error producing values that are all either higher or lower than the actual value, often caused by faulty equipment or a consistent flaw in technique. (29)

T

t_{2g} orbitals The set of orbitals (composed of d_{xy}, d_{yz}, and d_{xz}) that results when the energies of the metal-ion *d* orbitals are split by a ligand field. This set is lower in energy than the other (e_g) set in an octahedral field and higher in energy in a tetrahedral field. (964)
T shape A molecular shape caused by the presence of two equatorial lone pairs in a trigonal bipyramidal arrangement (AX_3E_2). (377)
temperature (*T*) A measure of how hot or cold a substance is relative to another substance. (23) A measure of the average kinetic energy of the particles in a sample. (208)
tetrahedral arrangement The geometric arrangement formed when four electron groups maximize their separation around a central atom; when all four groups are bonding groups, the molecular shape is tetrahedral (AX_4; ideal bond angle 109.5°). (375)
theoretical yield The amount of product predicted by the stoichiometrically equivalent molar ratio in the balanced equation. (112)
theory (See *model.*)
thermochemical equation A chemical equation that shows the heat involved for the amounts of substances specified. (242)
thermochemistry The branch of thermodynamics that focuses on the heat involved in chemical and physical change. (229)
thermodynamics The study of heat (thermal energy) and its interconversions. (229)
thermometer A device for measuring temperature that contains a fluid that expands or contracts within a graduated tube. (23)
third law of thermodynamics A law stating that the entropy of a perfect crystal is zero at 0 K. (817)

titration A method of determining the concentration of a solution by monitoring relative amounts during its reaction with a solution of known concentration. (152)
torr A unit of pressure identical to 1 mmHg. (185)
total ionic equation An equation for an aqueous reaction that shows all the soluble ionic substances dissociated into ions. (141)
tracer A radioisotope that signals the presence of the species of interest by radioactive emissions. (1000)
transcription The process of producing messenger RNA from DNA. (614)
transition element An element that occupies the *d* block of the periodic table; one whose *d* orbitals are being filled. (303, 945)
transition state (also *activated complex*) An unstable species formed in an effective collision of reactants that exists momentarily when the system is highest in energy and that can either form products or re-form reactants. (652)
transition state theory A model that explains how the energy of reactant collisions is used to form a high-energy transitional species that can change to reactant or product. (652)
translation The process by which messenger RNA specifies the sequence of amino acids and synthesizes proteins. (614)
transuranium element An element with atomic number higher than that of uranium ($Z = 92$). (994)
trigonal bipyramidal arrangement The geometric arrangement formed when five electron groups maximize their separation around a central atom. When all five groups are bonding groups, the molecular shape is trigonal bipyramidal (AX_5; ideal bond angles, axial-center-equatorial 90° and equatorial-center-equatorial 120°). (376)
trigonal planar arrangement The geometric arrangement formed when three electron groups maximize their separation around a central atom. When all three groups are bonding groups, the molecular shape is trigonal planar (AX_3; ideal bond angle 120°). (374)
trigonal pyramidal shape A molecular shape (AX_3E) caused by the presence of one lone pair in a tetrahedral arrangement. (376)
triple bond A covalent bond that consists of three bonding pairs, two atoms sharing six electrons; one σ and two π bonds. (339)
triple point The pressure and temperature at which three phases of a substance are in equilibrium. In a phase diagram, the point at which three phase-transition curves meet. (429)
Tyndall effect The scattering of light by a colloid. (509)

U

ultraviolet (UV) Radiation in the region of the electromagnetic spectrum between the visible and the x-ray regions. (262)
uncertainty A characteristic of every measurement that results from the inexactness of the measuring device and the need to estimate when taking a reading. (25)
uncertainty principle The principle stated by Werner Heisenberg that it is impossible to know simultaneously the exact position and velocity of a particle; the principle becomes important only for particles of very small mass. (278)
unimolecular reaction An elementary reaction that involves the decomposition or rearrangement of a single particle. (655)
unit cell The smallest portion of a crystal that, if repeated in all three directions, gives the crystal. (442)
universal gas constant (*R*) A proportionality constant that relates the energy, amount of substance, and temperature of a system; $R = 0.0820578$ atm·L/mol·K = 8.31447 J/mol·K. (191)
unsaturated hydrocarbon A hydrocarbon with at least one carbon-carbon multiple bond; one in which at least two C atoms are bonded to fewer than four atoms. (582)
unsaturated solution A solution in which more solute can be dissolved at a given temperature. (492)
unshared pair (See *lone pair.*)

V

V shape (See *bent shape.*)
valence band In band theory, the lower energy portion of the band of molecular orbitals, which is filled with valence electrons. (453)
valence bond (VB) theory A model that attempts to reconcile the shapes of molecules with those of atomic orbitals through the concepts of orbital overlap and hybridization. (395)
valence electrons The electrons involved in compound formation; in main-group elements, the electrons in the valence (outer) level. (306)
valence-shell electron-pair repulsion (VSEPR) theory A model explaining that the shapes of molecules and ions result from minimizing electron-pair repulsions around a central atom. (373)
van der Waals constants Experimentally determined positive numbers used in the van der Waals equation to account for the intermolecular attractions and molecular volume of real gases. (216)
van der Waals equation An equation that accounts for the behavior of real gases. (216)
van der Waals radius One-half of the shortest distance between the nuclei of identical nonbonded atoms. (431)
vapor pressure (also *equilibrium vapor pressure*) The pressure exerted by a vapor at equilibrium with its liquid in a closed system. (426)
vapor pressure lowering (ΔP) The lowering of the vapor pressure of a solvent caused by the presence of dissolved solute particles. (499)
vaporization The process of changing from a liquid to a gas. (420)
variable A quantity that can have more than a single value. (12) (See also *controlled experiment.*)
viscosity A measure of the resistance of a liquid to flow. (439)
volatility The tendency of a substance to become a gas. (72)
volt (V) The SI unit of electric potential: 1 V = 1 J/C. (862)
voltage (See *cell potential.*)
voltaic cell (also *galvanic cell*) An electrochemical cell that uses a spontaneous redox reaction to generate electric energy. (855)
volume (*V*) The space occupied by a sample of matter. (18)
volume percent [% (v/v)] A concentration term defined as the volume of solute in 100. volumes of solution. (496)

W

wastewater Used water, usually containing industrial and/or residential waste, that is treated before being returned to the environment. (511)
water softening The process of replacing the hard-water ions Ca^{2+} and Mg^{2+} with Na^+ ions. (510)

wave function (See *atomic orbital.*)
wave-particle duality The principle stating that both matter and energy have wavelike and particle-like properties. (277)
wavelength (λ) The distance between any point on a wave and the corresponding point on the next wave, that is, the distance a wave travels during one cycle. (262)
weak-field ligand A ligand that causes smaller crystal field splitting energy and therefore is part of a high-spin complex. (964)
weight The force exerted by a gravitational field on an object that is directly proportional to its mass. (20)
work (w) The energy transferred when an object is moved by a force. (231)

X

x-ray diffraction analysis An instrumental technique used to determine dimensions of a crystal structure by measuring the diffraction patterns caused by x-rays impinging on the crystal. (447)

Z

zone refining A process used to purify metals and metalloids in which impurities are removed from a bar of the element by concentrating them in a thin molten zone. (921)

Chapter 1

Opener: © The McGraw-Hill Companies, Inc./John Thoeming Photographer; 1.1A: © Paul Morrell/Stone/Getty Images; 1.1B: © The McGraw-Hill Companies, Inc./Stephen Frisch Photographer; Table 1.1A: © The McGraw-Hill Companies, Inc./Stephen Frisch Photographer; Table 1.1B: © Ruth Melnick; Table 1.1C-E: © The McGraw-Hill Companies, Inc./Stephen Frisch Photographer; p. 7: Gallileo Project, SSI, University of Arizona; 1.4: © SSPL/The Image Works; 1.5A: © George Haling/Photo Researchers, Inc.; 1.5B: © Javier Soriano/AFP/Getty Images; 1.5C: © Kiselev Andrey Velerevich/Shutterstock.com; 1.5D: © ayazad/Shutterstock.com; 1.8A: © The McGraw-Hill Companies, Inc./Stephen Frisch Photographer; 1.8B: © BrandTech Scientific, Inc.; 1.13A-B: © The McGraw-Hill Companies, Inc./Stephen Frisch Photographer.

Chapter 2

Opener: © Mark Schneider/Visuals Unlimited; Table 2.1(all), 2.2A-B: © The McGraw-Hill Companies, Inc./Stephen Frisch Photographer; 2.3(top): © Punchstock RF; 2.3(bottom): © Alexander Cherednichenko/Shutterstock.com; p. 45: © Roman Crochuk/Shutterstock.com; 2.10(all), 2.11A(both), 2.11E: © The McGraw-Hill Companies, Inc./Stephen Frisch Photographer; 2.16: © Mark Schneider/Visuals Unlimited; 2.19A-B: © The McGraw-Hill Companies, Inc./Stephen Frisch Photographer.

Chapter 3

Opener: © Stepan Jezek/Shutterstock.com; 3.1, 3.7(all): © The McGraw-Hill Companies, Inc./Charles Winters Photographer; p. 104: © The McGraw-Hill Companies, Inc./Stephen Frisch Photographer; p. 105: © Richard Megna/Fundamental Photographs, NYC; 3.14A-D, 3.15(both): © The McGraw-Hill Companies, Inc./Stephen Frisch Photographer.

Chapter 4

Opener: © Paul Avis/Stone Getty Images; 4.3A-C, 4.4(both): © The McGraw-Hill Companies, Inc./Stephen Frisch Photographer; 4.5: © The McGraw-Hill Companies, Inc./Richard Megna, Photographer; 4.6, 4.8A-B: © The McGraw-Hill Companies, Inc./Stephen Frisch Photographer; 4.10: © The McGraw-Hill Companies, Inc./Charles Winters Photographer; 4.11A-C, p. 158, 4.14(both), 4.15(all), 4.16(all), 4.17(all), 4.18, 4.19(both): © The McGraw-Hill Companies, Inc./Stephen Frisch Photographer.

Chapter 5

Opener: © The McGraw-Hill Companies, Inc./John Thoeming Photographer; 5.1A-C, 5.2A-B: © The McGraw-Hill Companies, Inc./Stephen Frisch Photographer; 5.10: © The McGraw-Hill Companies, Inc./Charles Winters Photographer; p. 198: © Charles F. McCarthy/Shutterstock.com; p. 203: © The McGraw-Hill Companies, Inc./Stephen Frisch Photographer.

Chapter 6

Opener: © The McGraw-Hill Companies, Inc./Charles Winters Photographer; 6.1: © The McGraw-Hill Companies, Inc./Stephen Frisch Photographer.

Chapter 7

Opener: © Orla/Shutterstock.com; p. 264: © Anthony McAulay/Shutterstock.com; 7.5A: © Richard Megna/Fundamental Photographs, NYC; 7.6A: © Ravi/Shutterstock.com; 7.6B: © The McGraw-Hill Companies, Inc./Charles Winters Photographer; 7.6C: © Feng Yu/Shutterstock.com; B7.1A(both): © The McGraw-Hill Companies, Inc./Stephen Frisch Photographer; B7.1B: Washington DC Convention & Visitors Association; 7.13A-B: PSSC Physics © 1965, Education Development Center, Inc.; D.C. Heath & Company/Education Development Center, Inc.; 7.14: © Dennis Kunkel/Phototake.com.

Chapter 8

CO8: © bbostjan/Shutterstock.com; 8.9A-B, 8.21(all), 8.23: © The McGraw-Hill Companies, Inc./Stephen Frisch Photographer.

Chapter 9

Opener(crystal): © E. R. Degginger/Photo Researchers, Inc.; Opener(candle): © Dolgisch/Shutterstock.com; Opener(copper): © The McGraw-Hill Companies, Inc./Stephen Frisch Photographer; 9.6A-B, 9.9A, 9.10(all), 9.15, 9.26, 9.29: © The McGraw-Hill Companies, Inc./Stephen Frisch Photographer; p. 355: © Diane Hirsch/Fundamental Photographs, NYC.

Chapter 10

Opener: © Jill Braaten; 10.2A(all), 10.6(both): © The McGraw-Hill Companies, Inc./Stephen Frisch Photographer.

Chapter 11

11.23: © The McGraw-Hill Companies, Inc./Charles Winters Photographer.

Chapter 12

Opener: © Cathleen Howland/Shutterstock.com; p. 420: © Christopher Meder Photography/Shutterstock.com; 12.1A: © dinadesign/Shutterstock.com; 12.1B: © Jill Birschbach Photo Services; 12.9: © The McGraw-Hill Companies, Inc./Richard Megna Photographer; p. 438(strider): © Nuridsany & Perennou /Photo Researchers, Inc.; p. 438(dew): © Rod Planck/Photo Researchers, Inc.; 12.21A-B: © The McGraw-Hill Companies, Inc./Stephen Frisch Photographer; 12.23B: © Scott Camazine/Photo Researchers, Inc.; 12.25A: © Jeffrey A. Scovil Photography (Wayne Thompson Minerals); 12.25B: © Mark Schneider/Visuals Unlimited; 12.25C: © Jeffrey A. Scovil Photography; 12.25D: © Jeffrey A. Scovil Photography (Francis Benjamin Collection); Page 444: © Bryan Busovicki/Shutterstock.com; B12.3: Courtesy National Institute of Standards and Technology; 12.43A: © J. R. Factor/Photo Researchers, Inc.; 12.43B: © James Dennis/Phototake.com; p. 465: © Ingram Publishing/Alamy; 12.49: Courtesy of Benoit Dubertret; 12.50: © & by permission from Ferrotec (USA) Corporation. May not be reproduced without written permission; 12.51: T. Sasaki/Rice University (Image courtesy of Rice University Office of Media Relations and Information).

Chapter 13

Opener: © CNRI/Photo Researchers, Inc.; 13.4A: © Ruth Melnick; 13.4B: © Ingram Publishing/AGE Fotostock RF; 13.18A-C: © The McGraw-Hill Companies, Inc./Stephen Frisch Photographer; 13.20: © Photodisc/Getty RF; p. 494: © Peter Scoones/Photo Researchers, Inc.; 13.22A-C: © The McGraw-Hill Companies, Inc./Stephen Frisch Photographer; 13.29A-C: © David M. Phillips/Photo Researchers, Inc.; 13.30A: © Ed Degginger/Color-Pic; 13.30B: © Corbis RF; 13.31: © Earth Satellite Corporation/SPL/Photo Researchers, Inc.; B13.3A: © Robert Essel/Corbis.

Chapter 14

Opener(left): © Joseph T. & Suzanne L. Collins/Photo Researchers, Inc.; Opener(right): © Joel Sartore/National Geographic Stock; Table 14.1, p. 529,

530(top & bottom), 532, 534, 536, 538: © The McGraw-Hill Companies, Inc./Stephen Frisch Photographer; 14.10A: © Gordon Vrdoljak, UC Berkeley Electron Microscope Lab; 14.11A-B: © The McGraw-Hill Companies, Inc./Stephen Frisch Photographer; 14.15 © Gontar/Shutterstock.com; Page 544: © The McGraw-Hill Companies, Inc./Stephen Frisch Photographer; p. 547: © Daniel Stein/iStockphoto.com; p. 551, 14.21: © The McGraw-Hill Companies, Inc./Stephen Frisch Photographer; p. 555(right): © Steve Cole/Getty RF; p. 556, 14.23B, p. 562: © The McGraw-Hill Companies, Inc./Stephen Frisch Photographer; 14.26: © Ed Degginger/Color-Pic.

Chapter 15

Opener: © Georgy Markov/Shutterstock.com; 15.8: © Martin Bough/Fundamental Photographs, NYC; B15.4A: © Zephyr/Photo Researchers, Inc.; 15.14A-B: © The McGraw-Hill Companies, Inc./Richard Megna Photographer; p. 600: © Jill Braaten; 15.28: © The McGraw-Hill Companies, Inc./Charles Winters Photographer; Page 608: © The McGraw-Hill Companies, Inc./Pat Watson Photographer; 15.32A: © J. Gross/SPL/Photo Researchers, Inc.; 15.32B: © Ed Degginger/Color-Pic; B15.7: © Courtesy of Orchid Cellmark.

Chapter 16

Opener: © avatra images/Alamy; 16.2(explosion): © Crown Copyright/Health & Safety Lab./Photo Researchers, Inc.; 16.2(fruit, baby): © Ruth Melnick; 16.2(landscape): © Publiphoto/Photo Researchers, Inc.; 16.3A-B: © The McGraw-Hill Companies, Inc./Stephen Frisch Photographer; Page 629: © Roberta Schmidt/AFP/Getty Images; p. 649: © Sipa via AP Images; 16.24A-B: © 2009 Richard Megna, Fundamental Photographs, NYC; B16.1: NASA.

Chapter 17

Opener: © Richard Megna, Fundamental Photographs, NYC; 17.1A-D: © The McGraw-Hill Companies, Inc./Stephen Frisch Photographer; Page 698: © AfriPics.com/Alamy.

Chapter 18

Opener: © Jill Braaten; Table 18.1(acids, bases), 18.2, 18.6A-B: © The McGraw-Hill Companies, Inc./Stephen Frisch Photographer.

Chapter 19

Opener: © Michael J. Thompson/Shutterstock.com; 19.1A-B, 19.2A-B, 19.6: © The McGraw-Hill Companies, Inc./Stephen Frisch Photographer; 19.11: © Jackie Lewin, Royal Free Hospital/Photo Researchers, Inc.; p. 785: © Jeffrey A. Scovil Photography; 19.12A-B: © The McGraw-Hill Companies, Inc./Stephen Frisch Photographer; p. 787: © CNRI/Science Source/Photo Researchers, Inc.; 19.13: © The McGraw-Hill Companies, Inc./Stephen Frisch Photographer; 19.14: © Ruth Melnick; p. 790: © The McGraw-Hill Companies, Inc./Stephen Frisch Photographer; p. 797: © Phil Degginger/Color-Pic; 19.17: © The McGraw-Hill Companies, Inc./Stephen Frisch Photographer.

Chapter 20

Opener: © Ian Clark/Image State/Photolibrary.com; 20.1A-B: © The McGraw-Hill Companies, Inc./Stephen Frisch Photographer; 20.12: © Vanderbilt University-Clinical Nutrition Research; p. 828: © PhotoDisc RF.

Chapter 21

Opener: © ifong/Shutterstock.com; 21.1, 21.2, 21.3, 21.4B: © The McGraw-Hill Companies, Inc./Stephen Frisch Photographer; 21.6: © Richard Megna/Fundamental Photographs, NYC; 21.8: © The McGraw-Hill Companies, Inc./Stephen Frisch Photographer; 21.14: Photo © F. W. Goro; 21.15: © Jill Braaten; 21.16: © The McGraw-Hill Companies, Inc./Pat Watson Photographer; 21.17: Courtesy of the Guidant Corporation; 21.19: © The McGraw-Hill Companies, Inc./Stephen Frisch Photographer; 21.20: © AP/Wide World Photos; 21.22A: © Alfred Dias/Photo Researchers, Inc.; 21.23: © David Weintraub/Photo Researchers, Inc.; 21.27: © Jill Braaten; 21.28, p. 889: © The McGraw-Hill Companies, Inc./Stephen Frisch Photographer.

Chapter 22

Opener: © Cooper-Hewitt, National Design Museum, Smithsonian Institution/Art Resource, NY; 22.3A: © Doug Sherman/Geofile; 22.3B: © University of Cambridge, Department of Earth Sciences; p. 908: © Ruth Melnick; p. 909: © Robert Holmes/Corbis; p. 917: © Patrick W. Grace/Photo Researchers, Inc.; 22.12: © Richard Megna/Fundamental Photographs, NYC; p. 922: © Christine L. Case/Visuals Unlimited; p. 924: © Remi Benali; 22.18: Courtesy Bethlehem Steel Corporation; p. 926: © Lee Prince/Shutterstock.com; 22.19: © Tom Hollyman/Photo Researchers, Inc.; p. 927: © James L. Amos/Peter Arnold, Inc./Photolibrary.com; p. 929: © Hank Morgan/Rainbow; p. 931: © Ken Whitmore/Getty Images; 22.23c: © Nathan Benn/Woodfin Camp & Associates.

Chapter 23

Opener: © VanHart/Shutterstock.com; 23.2, 23.5A-B, 23.6: © The McGraw-Hill Companies, Inc./Stephen Frisch Photographer; 23.8: © Richard Megna/Fundamental Photographs, NYC; p. 963: © Pete Turner/The Image Bank/Getty Images; 23.19A: © The McGraw-Hill Companies, Inc./Pat Watson Photographer; 23.20A-B: © The McGraw-Hill Companies, Inc./Stephen Frisch Photographer.

Chapter 24

Opener(bananas): © Goncharuk/Shutterstock.com; Opener(pellet): © Mitsubishi Nuclear Fuel Co., Ltd.; 24.4: © Hank Morgan/Rainbow; 24.5: © Meridian Biotechnologies Ltd.; p. 991: © Copyright 1978 by Vernon Miller. For use by permission for Business Wire via Getty Images; p. 993: © Hulton Archive/Getty Images; p. 994: © Maximilien Brice/CERN; 24.13A: © Scott Camazine/Photo Researchers, Inc.; 24.13B: © T. Youssef/Custom Medical Stock Photo; 24.14: © Dr. Robert Friedland/SPL/Photo Researchers, Inc.; 24.15: © Dr. Dennis Olson/Meat Lab, Iowa State University, Ames, IA; 24.20: © Albert Copley/Visuals Unlimited; 24.21: © Dietmar Krause/Princeton Plasma Physics Lab.

Page numbers followed by *f* indicate figures; *mn,* marginal notes; *n,* footnotes; and *t,* tables. Page numbers preceded by "A-" indicate pages in the *Appendix*. Page numbers preceded by "G-" indicate pages in the *Glossary.*

A

B

E

J

K

L

P

Q

R

S

Fundamental Physical Constants (six significant figures)

Avogadro's number	N_A	$= 6.02214\times10^{23}$/mol
atomic mass unit	amu	$= 1.66054\times10^{-27}$ kg
charge of the electron (or proton)	e	$= 1.60218\times10^{-19}$ C
Faraday constant	F	$= 9.64853\times10^{4}$ C/mol
mass of the electron	m_e	$= 9.10939\times10^{-31}$ kg
mass of the neutron	m_n	$= 1.67493\times10^{-27}$ kg
mass of the proton	m_p	$= 1.67262\times10^{-27}$ kg
Planck's constant	h	$= 6.62607\times10^{-34}$ J·s
speed of light in a vacuum	c	$= 2.99792\times10^{8}$ m/s
standard acceleration of gravity	g	$= 9.80665$ m/s^2
universal gas constant	R	$= 8.31447$ J/(mol·K)
		$= 8.20578\times10^{-2}$ (atm·L)/(mol·K)

SI Unit Prefixes

p	n	μ	m	c	d	k	M	G
pico-	nano-	micro-	milli-	centi-	deci-	kilo-	mega-	giga-
10^{-12}	10^{-9}	10^{-6}	10^{-3}	10^{-2}	10^{-1}	10^{3}	10^{6}	10^{9}

Conversions and Relationships

Length

SI unit: meter, m

1 km = 1000 m
= 0.62 mile (mi)
1 inch (in) = 2.54 cm
1 m = 1.094 yards (yd)
1 pm = 10^{-12} m = 0.01 Å

Volume

SI unit: cubic meter, m^3

1 dm^3 = 10^{-3} m^3
= 1 liter (L)
= 1.057 quarts (qt)
1 cm^3 = 1 mL
1 m^3 = 35.3 ft^3

Pressure

SI unit: pascal, Pa

1 Pa = 1 N/m^2
= 1 kg/m·s^2
1 atm = 1.01325×10^5 Pa
= 760 torr
1 bar = 1×10^5 Pa

Mass

SI unit: kilogram, kg

1 kg = 10^3 g
= 2.205 lb
1 metric ton (t) = 10^3 kg

Energy

SI unit: joule, J

1 J = 1 kg·m^2/s^2
= 1 coulomb·volt (1 C·V)
1 cal = 4.184 J
1 eV = 1.602×10^{-19} J

Math relationships

$\pi = 3.1416$
volume of sphere $= \frac{4}{3}\pi r^3$
volume of cylinder $= \pi r^2 h$

Temperature

SI unit: kelvin, K

0 K = −273.15°C
mp of H_2O = 0°C (273.15 K)
bp of H_2O = 100°C (373.15 K)
T (K) = T (°C) + 273.15
T (°C) = [T (°F) − 32]$\frac{5}{9}$
T (°F) = $\frac{9}{5}T$ (°C) + 32

Useful Data and Information

Atomic and Molecular Properties

Atomic radii	Figure 8.13, p. 309
Bond energies	Table 9.2, p. 340
Bond lengths	Table 9.2, p. 340
Ground-state electron configurations	Figure 8.10, p. 305
Electronegativity values	Figure 9.21, p. 349
Ionic radii	Figure 8.29, p. 321
First ionization energies	Figure 8.16, p. 312
Molecular shapes	Figure 10.10, p. 379

Equilibrium Constants and Thermodynamic Data

K_a of hydrated metal ions	Appendix C, p. A-12
K_a of selected acids	Appendix C, pp. A-8 to A-10
Strengths of conjugate acid-base pairs	Figure 18.8, p. 731
K_b of amine bases	Appendix C, p. A-11
K_f of complex ions	Table 19.4, p. 796, and Appendix C, p. A-12
K_{sp} of slightly soluble ionic compounds	Appendix C, p. A-13
Standard electrode potentials, $E^\circ_{\text{half-cell}}$	Appendix D, p. A-14
Standard free energies of formation, ΔG°_f	Appendix B, pp. A-5 to A-7
Standard heats of formation, ΔH°_f	Appendix B, pp. A-5 to A-7
Standard molar entropies, S°	Appendix B, pp. A-5 to A-7

Names and Formulas

Ligands	Table 23.7, p. 956
Metals in complex anions	Table 23.8, p. 956
Metals with more than one monatomic ion	Table 2.4, p. 62
Monatomic ions	Table 2.3, p. 60
Organic functional groups	Table 15.5, p. 592
Polyatomic ions	Table 2.5, p. 62

Properties of the Elements

Group 1A(1): Alkali metals	p. 529
Group 2A(2): Alkaline earth metals	p. 532
Group 3A(13): Boron family	p. 534
Group 4A(14): Carbon family	p. 538
Group 5A(15): Nitrogen family	p. 544
Group 6A(16): Oxygen family	p. 551
Group 7A(17): Halogens	p. 556
Group 8A(18): Noble gases	p. 562
Period 4 transition metals, atomic properties	Figure 23.3, p. 948
Period 4 transition metals, oxidation states	Table 23.2, p. 950

Miscellaneous

Rules for assigning an oxidation number	Table 4.3, p. 155
SI-English equivalent quantities	Table 1.4, p. 18
Solubility rules for ionic compounds in water	Table 4.1, p. 143
Vapor pressure of water	Table 5.2, p. 200